The Geology of North America
Volume H

The Caribbean Region

Edited by

Gabriel Dengo
Centro de Estudios Geológicos de América Central
Apartado 468
Guatemala City, Guatemala

J. E. Case
U.S. Geological Survey
345 Middlefield Road
Menlo Park, California 94025

1990

Acknowledgment

Publication of this volume, one of the synthesis volumes of *The Decade of North American Geology Project* series, has been made possible by members and friends of The Geological Society of America, corporations, and government agencies through contributions to the Decade of North American Geology fund of the Geological Society of America Foundation.

Following is a list of individuals, corporations, and government agencies giving and/or pledging more than $50,000 in support of the DNAG Project:

Amoco Production Company
ARCO Exploration Company
Chevron Corporation
Cities Service Oil and Gas Company
Diamond Shamrock Exploration
  Corporation
Exxon Production Research Company
Getty Oil Company
Gulf Oil Exploration and Production
  Company
Paul V. Hoovler
Kennecott Minerals Company
Kerr McGee Corporation
Marathon Oil Company
Maxus Energy Corporation
McMoRan Oil and Gas Company
Mobil Oil Corporation
Occidental Petroleum Corporation

Pennzoil Exploration and
  Production Company
Phillips Petroleum Company
Shell Oil Company
Caswell Silver
Standard Oil Production Company
Oryx Energy Company (formerly
  Sun Exploration and Production
  Company)
Superior Oil Company
Tenneco Oil Company
Texaco, Inc.
Union Oil Company of California
Union Pacific Corporation and
  its operating companies:
    Union Pacific Resources Company
    Union Pacific Railroad Company
    Upland Industries Corporation
U.S. Department of Energy

Published by The Geological Society of America, Inc.
3300 Penrose Place, P.O. Box 9140, Boulder, Colorado 80301

Printed in U.S.A.

Library of Congress Cataloging-in-Publication Data

The Caribbean region / edited by Gabriel Dengo, J. E. Case.
    p.   cm. — (The Geology of North America ; v. H)
    Includes bibliographical references and index.
    ISBN 0-8137-5212-4
    1. Geology—Caribbean Area. I. Dengo, Gabriel. II. Case, James
  E., 1933–   . III. Series.
QE71.G48   1986   vol. H
[QE220]
557 s—dc20
[557.29]   90-40295
                                            CIP

Front cover: Part of the "Geological Map of Part of Guatemala and El Salvador" surveyed in 1865-1866 by Auguste Dollfus and Eugene de Montserrat. This is the oldest geological map of part of Central America and one of the first geological maps produced in the Western Hemisphere.

10   9   8   7   6   5   4   3   2

Contents

iii

REGIONAL GEOPHYSICS AND GEOCHEMISTRY

GEOLOGICAL EVOLUTION AND RESOURCES

Plates
(in accompanying slipcase)

Preface

The Geology of North America series has been prepared to mark the Centennial of The Geological Society of America. It represents the cooperative efforts of more than 1,000 individuals from academia, state and federal agencies of many countries, and industry to prepare syntheses that are as current and authoritative as possible about the geology of the North American continent and adjacent oceanic regions.

This series is part of the Decade of North American Geology (DNAG) Project, which also includes eight wall maps at a scale of 1:5,000,000 that summarize the geology, tectonics, magnetic and gravity anomaly patterns, regional stress fields, thermal aspects, seismicity, and neotectonics of North America and its surroundings. Together, the synthesis volumes and maps are the first coordinated effort to integrate all available knowledge about the geology and geophysics of a crustal plate on a regional scale.

The products of the DNAG Project present the state of knowledge of the geology and geophysics of North America in the 1980s, and they point the way toward work to be done in the decades ahead.

This book has been a major international effort involving authors and organizations from 13 countries. In addition to the contributions from organizations and individuals acknowledged at the front of this book, major support has been provided to one of the editors (Case) by the U.S. Geological Survey.

A. R. Palmer
General Editor for the volumes
published by The Geological Society
of America

J. O. Wheeler
General Editor for the volumes
published by the Geological
Survey of Canada

Foreword

It is a pleasure to present to the geological community this volume, Geology of the Caribbean region, for the Decade of North American Geology (DNAG). The volume is truly international in scope, with respect to both geography (Plate 1) and contributions from scientists of many nations. Dozens of dedicated geologists and geophysicists devoted months and years in preparing the 19 chapters and 14 plates that make up the volume. Government agencies, academic institutions, and industry organizations have provided outstanding support for the effort. Diligent reviewers spent much time with the manuscripts and maps, and found the task to be difficult because so many of the initial manuscripts exceeded space limitations. Some manuscripts required several rounds of review because of problems with style or scientific content. In addition to formal DNAG reviewers, most authors sought colleague reviews prior to submittal. We thank all of the authors for their patience with editors and reviewers.

The Caribbean region represents one of the most geologically exciting parts of the world. As stated by Draper and Dengo (this volume): "In the two hundred years since the birth of modern geology, many prominent figures have worked in the Caribbean region, and their experiences there were seminal in the formation of hypotheses central to the development of the science." The chapters and plates in the volume represent a summary of the data and conclusions of literally thousands of geologists and geophysicists in the region.

Preparation of the volume was complex logistically because many authors reside in countries where mail service is very slow, including the United States. Telephone bills were large. For some chapters, the author and reviewers had divergent views, and these had to be reconciled in amicable fashion. All of the authors had other work commitments, and about ten of the senior authors had serious illnesses during the years of preparation.

We deeply regret the untimely death of Denis Westercamp, a key author of the chapter on the Lesser Antilles.

Selection of authors was a traumatic process for us. For all chapters, we had a wide choice from which to select a principal author. We sought authors who are knowledgeable, write fluently, and are objective. Once the senior authors had been selected, they chose the other authors; in some cases, we suggested co-authors. For several chapters, senior authorship changed by decision of the original authors. As far as we know, we "lost" only a few authors because of job commitments or internal incompatibility, but we "stretched" many friendships during the editorial process.

The focus of the volume is on regional geology and geophysics, magmatic processes, energy and metallic resources, marine geology, and tectonic processes and evolution. Originally, another volume aimed at stratigraphic-paleontologic aspects was planned, but the Geological Society of America abandoned the volume because of cost with respect to the whole DNAG series. We regret this decision. However, the plates in the volume compiled by Maurrasse and others showing many old and new stratigraphic-lithologic columns for the region represent an invaluable contribution to the scientific community.

Readers will find that some chapters are controversial, as expected for a region where so many geologists have worked and thought and written about its geologic evolution. Students and others unfamiliar with the region should remember that virtually every chapter would have a different set of interpretive conclusions if a different set of authors had been selected. It has been said that a new model for the tectonic evolution of the region has been formulated by each new worker in the region. At scientific meetings, we have a game that we play after presentation of the latest conceptual model—"That's number 1,023." Two chapters are devoted to conceptual models for the tectonic evolution of the region: the first, by Pindell and Barrett, is a modern plate-tectonics interpretation; the second, by Morris and others, is a presentation of a new hypothesis of mantle surge tectonics, which is an alternative to the plate-tectonics hypothesis and which utilizes some data from seismic tomography. Three models for the tectonic evolution that have not received adequate attention are those based on the "eugeosyncline-miogeosyncline (tectogene)" concept, those based on phase changes (basification), and those based on more recent concepts of suspect or tectonostratigraphic terranes.

For the whole region, there has been much controversy regarding stratigraphic names, correlations of units, and ages. Many isotopic ages are suspect because the samples perhaps were weathered or hydrothermally altered, or were collected from sites that were not covered by detailed geologic maps. Some paleomagnetic interpretations were reported in the literature where site locations were not specified by latitude and longitude; problems of weathering, alteration, and detailed geologic maps plague evaluation of some data.

In many ways, we believe that the most valuable part of this volume is the comprehensive bibliography that is included with most chapters. We note that the emphasis has been on the post-1960 literature. These references, in turn, will lead the readers back to the pre-1960 literature. Synthesis volumes by Nairn and Stehli (1975), Butterlin (1977), Zeil (1979), Weyl (1980), Bonini and others (1984), and Mascle and others (1985) are exceptionally useful, as well as transactions volumes of the Caribbean, Central America, and Latin American Geological Conferences and Congresses listed in the chapter by Draper and Dengo.

We thank the dozens (hundreds?) of typists, secretaries, and draftspersons who provided essential support for preparation of this volume. Working with A. R. ("Pete") Palmer, Jean Davis, the publications staff of the Geological Society of America, and contractors while preparing this complex volume has been a pleasure.

REFERENCES CITED

Bonini, W. E., Hargraves, R. B., and Shagam, R., eds., 1984, The Caribbean–South American plate boundary and regional tectonics: Geological Society of America Memoir 162, 421 p.

Butterlin, J., 1977, Géologie structurale de la région des Caraïbes (Mexique–Amérique Centrale–Antilles–Cordillère Caraïbe): Paris, Masson, 259 p.

Mascle, A., ed., 1985, Caribbean Geodynamics Symposium, Paris, February 5-8, 1985: Paris, Editions Technip, 565 p.

Nairn, A.E.M., and Stehli, F. G., eds., 1975, The ocean basins and margins; V. 3, The Gulf of Mexico and the Caribbean: New York, Plenum Press, 706 p.

Weyl, R., 1980, Geology of Central America, 2nd ed.: Berlin, Gebrüder Borntraeger, 371 p.

Zeil, W., 1979, The Andes; A geological review: Berlin, Gebrüder Borntraeger, 260 p.

J. E. Case
Gabriel Dengo
September, 1989

The Geology of North America
Vol. H, The Caribbean Region
The Geological Society of America, 1990

Chapter 1

History of geological investigation
in the Caribbean region

Grenville Draper
Department of Geology, Florida International University, Miami, Florida 33199
Gabriel Dengo
Centro de Estudios Geológicos de América Central, Apartado 468, Guatemala City, Guatemala

INTRODUCTION

For a region that is still not completely explored geologically, the Caribbean has an extraordinarily rich history of geological investigation. In the two hundred years since the birth of modern geology, many prominent figures have worked in the Caribbean, and their experiences there were seminal in the formation of hypotheses central to the development of the science. Even earlier, the fruits of geological exploitation of precious metals had an important influence in the economic and political history of post-Renaissance Europe.

In tracing the history of geological investigation in the Caribbean region, it becomes apparent that certain periods were characterized by particular modes or climates of inquiry, some imposed by the science of geology, others imposed by society. In the following account, the history of geological investigation is divided into five such periods. In the description of the earlier periods, attention is drawn to a number of books and papers important to the development of geology in the region. In the discussion of later periods, such specific references have been avoided, mainly because they are too numerous to mention individually and because reference to them will be found in the other chapters of this volume. Further references can be found in the bibliography compiled by the Franklin Research Institute Laboratories (1972). The historical portrait presented here has, of necessity, been painted with a broad brush, and apologies are made beforehand for the omission of any favorite geological heroes.

PRE-NINETEENTH CENTURY: PRE-COLUMBIAN TIMES TO THE BEGINNING OF MODERN GEOLOGY

The beginning of geological knowledge of the circum-Caribbean region can be traced to pre-Columbian times; it is evident that the different indigenous groups had an advanced, if utilitarian, knowledge of different rocks and minerals. Alluvial gold, silver, and occasionally native copper were used for orna-ments in Central and South America and Hispaniola. In addition, carved ornaments and artifacts were fashioned from jade in Central America and from serpentinite in northern South America. Obsidian and flint were shaped for arrowheads and axes, important items of trade. At Palenque, in southern Mexico, fossil fish and shark teeth have been found among Mayan artifacts. The Indian stonemasons of Central America had considerable knowledge of the many different types of stone that were used in the construction of the numerous temples and monuments of the area.

The arrival of the conquistadors began a new wave of prospecting in order to satisfy the Spanish desire for precious metals. Ornaments worn by the inhabitants of the Bahamas, Cuba, and Hispaniola had indicated the presence of gold to Columbus and his followers on their first voyage. They first discovered virgin gold in January 1493, when the expedition filled their water barrels in the Río Yaque del Norte, which drains the Cibao Valley of northern Hispaniola (Morison, 1942, p. 309). Flecks of alluvial gold adhered to the hoops of the barrels, and alerted the explorers to the presence of gold on the island. After five centuries of exploitation, gold is still panned in the streams draining the southern flanks of the Cibao Valley. Dissatisfied with the amount of gold available from the alluvial deposits known to the Indians in Hispaniola and other parts of the Caribbean, the Spanish soldiers of fortune established many mines, some of which are still sporadically operated. The largest gold mine in the Western Hemisphere, the Pueblo Viejo Mine in central Hispaniola, is around the site of old Spanish workings.

Petroleum, later to play a more important role than gold and silver in the development of Caribbean geology, was also discovered by the early Spanish explorers. The first description of an oil seep in the New World was made by Juan de Castellanos (1589) in his account of the island of Cubagua, which lies off the coast of Venezuela.

Draper, G., and Dengo, G., 1990, History of geological investigation in the Caribbean region, *in* Dengo, G., and Case, J. E., eds., The Caribbean region: Boulder, Colorado, Geological Society of America, The Geology of North America, v. H.

NINETEENTH CENTURY: PIONEER GEOLOGICAL INVESTIGATIONS

By the late eighteenth century, new types of conquistadors began arriving in the Caribbean. These explorers were the geographers and natural historians who made the first scientific observations and descriptions of the region.

At this time, France was a leader in geological thought, and so it is not surprising that the first account of the geology of the Caribbean is of the French colony of Saint Domingue (now Haiti) in western Hispaniola (Dupuget, 1796).

Between 1799 and 1804, Alexander von Humboldt (Fig. 1) made his epic journeys with Aimée Bonpland through what is now Venezuela, Colombia, and Ecuador and collected a wealth of information about natural history, including the rocks of the region (see Humboldt, 1852). Humboldt's work is of twofold significance. He was the first explorer to bring back rocks and fossils from the New World. Thus, Europe's first exposure to New World geology in any detail was through Humboldt's observations and collections. Secondly, Humboldt's first-hand observations of the volcanoes of the southwestern Caribbean converted him to the Plutonian theory of igneous rocks, and he was later able to use his enormous influence to discredit the Neptunian hypothesis, which then prevailed in Europe.

Although not as influential as Humboldt, a number of other naturalists made observations of the Caribbean region in the early nineteenth century. Francisco José de Caldas, the "patriarch of Colombian naturalists" (Botero-Arango, 1978), made numerous observations and maps of mineral and fossil occurrences in Colombia and Ecuador. Caldas was also one of the first naturalists in the region to attempt to infer changes in climate from observations of vertebrate fossils. Some preliminary observations of the geology of the Antilles were also made during the early nineteenth century, including those of Maclure (1817), who is better known for his work in North America. These contributions were not systematic, however, and lacked the impact of Humboldt's work.

Perhaps the most significant contribution to the geology of the Antilles in this period was made early in the career of the great British geologist, Henry Thomas de la Beche (Fig. 2). De la Beche was descended from Jamaican planters and bureaucrats, and between 1823 and 1825 he visited his family's estate on the island. His excursions around the island resulted in an account of the geology of eastern Jamaica. This account (de la Beche, 1827) is notable because it contained a colored map of eastern Jamaica, which is probably the first geological map of any part of the Western Hemisphere. Unlike other maps of the Americas produced before this time, de la Beche's followed the example of William Smith, and attempted to represent the geology by formations with ascribed ages rather than simply according to rock type. De la Beche later went on to become founder and director of the world's first geological survey, that of Britain.

Significant though they were, the work of Humboldt, de la Beche, and others provided only enticing morsels of information

Figure 1. Alexander von Humboldt (1769–1859). The pioneer scientific explorer of northern South America, von Humboldt travelled extensively in Venezuela, Colombia, and Ecuador, and made extensive reports on the geography and natural history of those regions.

about the region. They created an interest in Caribbean rocks and fossils, however, which later bore fruit as a result of geological advances in Europe and an increasing fascination with the Americas during the late nineteenth century. Charles Lyell's work had shown that travel was a necessary part of the study of the new science of geology. Curious about the contrast between the New World and the old, many investigators from Europe and North America travelled extensively in the Caribbean and reported their findings back to Europe.

The Danish scientist Oersted (1852), although more famous for his investigations of geomagnetism, reported the geological findings of his Central American travels. The spectacular manifestations of seismicity and volcanism in the region also attracted the attention of other scientists (Montessus de Ballore, 1880), but von Seebach was the first to publish a well-documented and illustrated account of the Central American volcanic chain (Seebach, 1892).

Less scientific reasons drew many to Central America in the middle part of the nineteenth century. In the years of the Califor-

Figure 2. Henry Thomas de la Beche (1796–1855). De la Beche was the author of the first description of the geology of Jamaica, and compiler of what is possibly the first geological map of a region of the new world.

Figure 3. Karl Sapper (1866–1945) in 1924. In a long and productive career, Sapper made extensive field studies of the geology and natural history of Central America.

nia gold rush, two routes from the eastern United States to the Pacific coast were across Central America, and some of those who undertook the arduous journey made interesting geological observations. One of them, William Wells, was diverted to a small gold find in the Río Guayape in Honduras; he described in detail the mining operations and other geological aspects (Wells, 1857).

More extensive and systematic regional geological investigations of Central America took place in the later nineteenth century. The French geologists Dollfus and Montserrat (1868), laid the foundations for most of our present-day knowledge of Guatemala and El Salvador, including the first accounts of the stratigraphy and the first geological map of these areas. In 1873 and 1874, the North American geologist and paleontologist, William Gabb, explored and described the geology of the Talamanca Mountains in Costa Rica (Gabb, 1874a, 1874b, 1875); his geological map of the region, however, was never published. British geologists also made important contributions to the geology of Costa Rica (Atwood, 1882), as well as Nicaragua. Belt (1874)

had written on some aspects of Nicaragua's geology, including comments on mineralization and the origin of granite. As a result of his studies, Belt may have been one of the first to propose the idea of granitization, although he never used that term. After Belt, Crawford (1892) made the first systematic surveys of the geology of Nicaragua.

At the close of the nineteenth century the great German geologist and naturalist, Karl Sapper (Fig. 3), undertook extensive investigations in Belize, Guatemala, southern Mexico, Honduras, and (later) in the Central American isthmus (see, for example, Sapper, 1899, 1901). His publications are too numerous to cite completely, but a later book summarized many of his Central American investigations (Sapper, 1937), and this has now become a classic in the geological literature of the region. This later period was also distinguished by the work of the U.S. Geological Survey geologist Robert T. Hill on the geology of Panamá and Costa Rica (Hill, 1898b).

The middle and later parts of the nineteenth century witnessed continued investigations of northern South America, particularly by German geologists inspired by von Humboldt's pioneering work. Outstanding early contributions to the stratigraphy of northern South America were made by Hermann Karsten, who arrived in Venezuela with a doctorate from the University of Berlin and a letter of introduction from Humboldt. As Hedberg (1974) pointed out, Karsten's contribution is all the more remarkable when it is realized that he was primarily a botanist. His botanical interests soon gave way to geology, however, and in his 12 years in South America he published about 20 papers on the geology of Venezuela, Colombia, and Ecuador. An early paper on northern Venezuela (Karsten, 1850) is especially valuable because it included a colored map of the Caribbean Mountains showing the distribution of igneous and metamorphic rocks and Cretaceous and Tertiary strata. This paper even contains the suggestion of a Cretaceous age for the metamorphic rocks—a concept that did not find widespread acceptance until more than 100 years later. After his return to Europe in 1856, Karsten summarized all his work in South America in a map, with a short description, that unfortunately was not published until 30 years later (Karsten, 1886).

Karsten's work was followed by more detailed investigations in particular areas, such as those by the German geographer Alfred Hettner, who described the geology around Bogotá (Hettner, 1892). Many other geologists and prospectors were active in Colombia during this period, and the strong interest in geology and mineral resources led to the establishment of the Escuela de Minas de Medellín in 1887. This institution, later incorporated into the Universidad Nacional, is the oldest center for geological education in the Caribbean region.

The Venezuelan Andes, especially the Cordillera de Mérida and Sierra de Perijá, where the subject of investigation by Wilhelm Seivers during the years 1885–1886. The publications that resulted from the investigations (Seivers, 1888a, b) are still considered to be the most detailed on this region of Venezuela (Schubert, 1977). Seivers also made reconnaissance journeys into the Caribbean Mountains of northern Venezuela and recognized the tectonic origin of many of its features, including the Yaracuy and Valencia basins, which are now interpreted as pull-aparts in a right-lateral strike-slip fault zone.

In addition to the activities of the more academically minded naturalists, the second part of the late nineteenth century also saw the first government-sponsored systematic geological surveys. The first of these was in the then-British island of Trinidad. G. P. Wall and J. G. Sawkins conducted a survey that was published in 1860 (Wall and Sawkins, 1860). This work was followed by further paleontological and stratigraphic work by R. J. Lechmere Guppy (1867, and many subsequent publications). The eponymous Guppy's wider claim to fame is with the small tropical fish that bears his name.

The Lesser Antilles, north of Trinidad, also received the attention of a number of British geologists during this period. The most systematic studies were those of A. J. Jukes-Brown and J. B. Harrison (1891, 1892) on Barbados, whose contributions are of special interest, as they were among the first to describe and recognize pelagic sedimentary rocks on land. They named the Oceanic Formation of Barbados because it is lithologically identical to sediments dredged from the deep ocean by the original *Challenger* expedition. The volcanic islands northwest of Barbados were also sporadically investigated at the end of the nineteenth century, but were not the subject of systematic studies until the twentieth century.

Jamaica, having received geological attention in the early nineteenth century, was also the subject of the second of the attempts at systematic surveys by the British government. J. G. Sawkins, on completing the survey of Trinidad with Wall, went to Jamaica to join Lucas Barrett, a young disciple of Cambridge's Adam Sedgwick. The enthusiastic and talented Barrett attempted fieldwork using the newly developed, but unreliable, diving suit and unfortunately, he met an untimely end in Kingston Harbour. Sawkins completed the survey after Barrett's premature demise, and produced a lengthy report (Sawkins, 1869) and manuscript maps on an unpredecented large scale of about 1:50,000.

In comparison to Jamaica, the other islands of the Greater Antilles received little attention until the early twentieth century. Manuel Fernandez de Castro produced the first account of the geology of Cuba with a geological map of the island (Fernandez de Castro, 1884), the result of extensive field work between 1869 and 1883. At about the same time, the indefatigable William Gabb conducted a reconnaissance survey of Hispaniola (Gabb, 1873), which revealed an enticing geological portrait of the island that was not improved upon until the surveys of the 1920s. In the Virgin Islands, a few limited observations of the rocks had been made earlier in the century, but it was the Danish geologist, Per Teodor Cleve, who made the major contribution (Cleve, 1871). Cleve probably has the distinction of being the first to appreciate that the core of the Greater Antilles is composed of deformed Cretaceous volcanic rocks. Other Danes added to Cleve's work, especially in petrography and mineralization (Högbom, 1905; Böggild, 1907).

Perhaps the most influential student of the rocks of the northern Caribbean in the late nineteenth century was Robert T. Hill (Fig. 4), justifiably called the "father of Antillian Geology" (Schuchert, 1935). His talent lay in synthesizing previous piecemeal observations and combining them with his own to produce accounts of the geology of the islands—particularly Cuba, Jamaica, and Puerto Rico—that were more systematic than anything produced previously (Hill, 1894, 1895, 1898a and b, 1899).

EARLY TWENTIETH CENTURY (1900–1945): MAJOR OIL EXPLORATION, PRELIMINARY GEOPHYSICAL INVESTIGATIONS, AND THE FIRST UNIVERSITY STUDIES

Shortly after the beginning of the twentieth century, geological investigation in the Caribbean region took on a different character and greatly increased in momentum. The cause was the world's rapidly increasing demand for petroleum. The vanguard of this activity was in the southeast Caribbean. Wells were drilled

Figure 4. Robert T. Hill (1858–1941). The "father of Antillean geology." Hill compiled the first systematic descriptions of the geology of Cuba, Jamaica, and Puerto Rico.

1918–1949, when it was second only to that of the United States in world production (Sawyer, 1975).

The principal areas of petroleum exploration in the interwar period were Venezuela, Trinidad, and, to a lesser extent, Colombia and Cuba, the areas where petroleum production was already established. Nevertheless, numerous oil companies undertook extensive, and often arduous, exploration programs in parts of Central America and the Greater Antilles. It is beyond the scope of this chapter to discuss the details of these endeavors, but an exhaustive account of the exploration geologists' adventures and accomplishments can be found in Sawyer's history.

Much of the work done by oil company geologists during this period has never been published. However, Liddle (1928) published a book on the geology of Venezuela based on his work and that of other oil company geologists between 1920 and 1925. Lewis (1932) outlined the results obtained from early exploration work in Cuba. The results of some other unpublished oil company reports emerged after World War II, in a number of academic publications and in compilations by government agencies.

Many new exploration techniques were initiated by oil company personnel in the early twentieth century. The first electric log in the Western Hemisphere was run in 1929 by Schlumberger in a Shell well in the Lake Maracaibo area. Geophysical surveying techniques were used for the first time in this region, beginning with a seismic refraction and magnetic survey in the Brighton region of Trinidad, and followed by gravity, magnetic, and seismic studies in many concessions throughout the Caribbean. The introduction of aerial photography revolutionized surface geological work, especially in the less accessible areas.

The extensive use of foraminifera in stratigraphic correlation, a technique pioneered by Joseph Cushman and subsequently used worldwide, was first developed for the Caribbean by the Swiss geologist, Hans Kugler, and coworkers in the laboratories of Trinidad Leaseholds (later Texaco). In Venezuela, Hollis Hedberg (Fig. 5) combined both foraminiferal and heavy mineral observations in published studies. Kugler's and Hedberg's laboratories influenced a generation of stratigraphers and petroleum geologists (Saunders and Bolli, 1985). Kugler began first with benthonic foraminifera, but later he and his associates developed the use of planktonic species. In his long and productive career, Kugler is credited not only with promoting the use of planktonic foraminifera in stratigraphic correlation, but also with realizing the significance of reworking of microfauna in clastic sequences, and recognizing the importance of stratigraphic traps in petroleum accumulation. Hedberg (1937) was the first to produce conclusive identification of the organic-rich, Cretaceous La Luna Formation as the source of much of the Venezuelan oil.

It would be erroneous to give the impression that the only work done in the early part of the twentieth century was that of oil geologists. Many important contributions were made by geologists examining other resources (for example, Emile Grosse's [1926] work on the Tertiary coal deposits of Colombia). Other significant scientific advances were also made by geologists attached to various government and academic institutions.

in Trinidad as early as 1857, although the first producing well was not in operation until 1902 (Frampton and Birchwood, 1979). Wells were also drilled in Barbados as early as 1896 (Eva, 1985). Interest in oil prospects in Trinidad increased rapidly, resulting in several reports (mainly unpublished) by E. H. Cunningham-Craig, the government geologist.

The vast reserves of oil in Venezuela were not investigated until about 1911, when the situation changed dramatically. Despite the difficult terrain, many surveys were undertaken, and drilling began in 1913 (Arnold and others, 1960).

Expansion of exploration and development stalled during the years around World War I, but following the cessation of hostilities, the insatiable thirst of the internal combustion engine soon created more demand for petroleum, especially during the economic boom of the 1920s, when gasoline-powered autos became a vital part of modern life. Old fields were developed further, and there was extensive exploration for new fields. The importance of the Caribbean–Latin American area in the post World War I petroleum industry was demonstrated in the period

Figure 5. Hollis Dow Hedberg (1903–1988). A Penrose medalist, Hedberg had a distinguished career that included nearly 20 years of active work on the petroleum geology of Venezuela.

Figure 6. Thomas Wayland Vaughn (1870–1952). A prolific geologist, Vaughn worked extensively on stratigraphic problems throughout the Caribbean region.

The interoceanic canal between the Atlantic and Pacific oceans was a great impetus to geological investigations in Central America in the early twentieth century (in fact, they had begun in the late nineteenth century). Two routes were identified. One was through Nicaragua and took advantage of the country's navigable lakes and rivers; the other was through the Isthmus of Panama. Both routes were the subject of thorough geological investigation (see Hayes, 1899, on Nicaragua, and MacDonald, 1918, on Panama). Ironically, it was a geological event in the eastern Caribbean, the eruption of Mt. Pelée, that was the decisive factor in finally choosing the Panama route (see below).

On May 8, 1902, Mt. Pelée on Martinique exploded in one of the most famous, and most disastrous, eruptions in history. French, British, and North American geologists rushed to the scene. The subsequent reports, especially those of Alfred Lacroix (1904, 1908), which contain the first use of the term "nuée ardente," and of Anderson and Flett (1903, 1908), effectively created the new science of volcanology, and established the Car-

ibbean as its birthplace. The eruption was also of importance in selecting the site of the Panama Canal, as it took place just before the U.S. Congress met to choose between the Panamanian and Nicaraguan alternatives. Aware that the Nicaraguan route passed near to active volcanoes, and alarmed by the Mt. Pelée disaster, Congress decided to build the interoceanic canal through the isthmus.

The eruption of Mt. Pelée came to the notice of the engineer-businessman Frank Perret who, on hearing of the disaster, decided to devote his life to volcanology. The decision was of great importance for the new science, because he was later a resident in St. Pierre (where his statue still stands) during the eruptions of 1929–1932. His subsequent memoir (Perret, 1937) has become a classic on the eruption mechanisms of nuées ardentes.

Despite the drama of Perret's exploits, the foremost scholars of Caribbean geology in this period were probably Thomas Wayland Vaughan (Fig. 6) and Wendell P. Woodring. Vaughan's

Figure 7. Harry Hammond Hess (1906–1969). Shown here in his Princeton office during the mid-1960s, Hess participated in some of the first geophysical investigations in the Caribbean, and later directed many geological investigations in the Greater Antilles and Venezuela. (Photograph courtesy of archives of Department of Geology, Princeton University.)

interest in the Caribbean began when he performed some paleontological work on specimens collected by R. T. Hill, and was reinforced by his participation in a geological reconnaissance of Cuba made during the U.S. military occupation of that country (Hayes and others, 1899). Vaughan made many contributions to the stratigraphy and paleontology of the northeast Caribbean and Central America during the first part of the twentieth century, and established his reputation as an expert on the geology of the region. As a result, Vaughan was asked by the U.S. government to organize a geological reconnaissance of Hispaniola, at that time only poorly known geologically. Vaughan's team, including the young Woodring, went into the field in 1919. The survey produced two outstanding volumes on the geology of Hispaniola (Vaughan and others, 1921; Woodring and others, 1924) that were not substantially improved upon for another thirty years. After their return to the Smithsonian Institution, they continued to produce many works on Caribbean geology and paleontology.

Vaughan and Woodring were not the only American scholars with an interest in the Caribbean. In the early years of the twentieth century, the New York Academy of Sciences organized a scientific survey of "Porto Rico" and adjacent areas. The expeditions of the survey investigated many aspects of the island's natural history, including its geology. As a result, Charles P. Berkey (1915) was able to build on R. T. Hill's earlier work to present the first complete outline of the island's geology. H. A. Meyerhoff, who had worked with the scientific survey, continued these investigations while teaching at the University of Puerto Rico and acting as a consultant to the government. Numerous

publications resulted, including a book summarizing the major results (Meyerhoff, 1933).

The early twentieth century saw the first marine geophysical investigations; some of the earliest and most significant of these took place in the Caribbean. In 1926, F. A. Vening-Meinesz mounted his recently developed pendulum gravimeter in a Dutch submarine and made a series of gravity measurements in the northeastern Caribbean. He returned in 1928, this time using a U.S. submarine. These two expeditions were the first to detect the strong negative gravity anomaly over the Puerto Rico Trench. In a more ambitious expedition, Vening-Meinesz discovered and mapped the 8000-km-long negative anomaly over the Java Trench in the East Indies, but then returned to the Caribbean in 1932. Richard Field of Princeton University had organized an expedition with two U.S. Navy submarines and invited Vening-Meinesz along as chief scientist. A young graduate student, Harry Hess (Fig. 7), was recruited by Field to be Vening-Meinesz' assistant. These early geophysical investigations (Hess, 1933) were the beginning of Hess' long and fruitful work in the Caribbean region.

The first attempt to compile existing geological knowledge of the Caribbean was also made in the early 1930s by another academic, Charles Schuchert of Yale University. Schuchert's (1935) book, *Historical geology of the Caribbean-Antillian region,* is still very readable and gives a fascinating picture of the state of geological knowledge of the Caribbean at that time. Strangely, Schuchert only wrote about the Caribbean, and never actually visited the region.

North Americans did not have a monopoly on Caribbean research; during the 1920s and 1930s, the Dutch geologist L.M.R. Rutten of the University of Utrecht led several expeditions to investigate the geology of the Netherlands Antilles and, later, of extensive areas in Cuba. One of the students who accompanied Rutten on his expeditions was H. J. MacGillavry, who was later to continue Rutten's tradition in post-war investigations in the Netherlands Antilles and elsewhere.

The German geologist Richard Weyl (Fig. 8) also began his investigations in the Caribbean in the 1930s; he initially worked in the central Dominican Republic, and later published many papers on the structure and tectonic character of the Antilles and Central America. Weyl's early work is of note in that it heralded a shift in interest from stratigraphy to the tectonic problems of the region.

LATER TWENTIETH CENTURY (1945–1969): OIL AND MINERALS, GEOPHYSICAL SURVEYS, UNIVERSITY PROJECTS, AND REGIONAL CONFERENCES

The twenty years or so following the World War II saw a rapid blooming of Caribbean geological investigation. Academic, industrial, and government geologists all participated in this increased activity. Post-war increases in prosperity in Europe and North America created a demand for oil and minerals, and the relatively unexplored Caribbean on North America's doorstep seemed to be the obvious place to look. Countries of the Caribbean, part of the emerging Third World, were eager to participate in the post-war boom by exploiting their mineral resources. Ministries and bureaus of mines were established to deal with problems of mining legislation, and to do geological work to monitor and encourage exploration by commercial concerns. The resulting geological surveys and mining bureaus, having demonstrated their importance, have subsequently diversified their activities into other geological arenas such as industrial minerals, water resources, and engineering geology. Government institutions thus joined the universities and the oil and mineral companies as important agencies of geological investigation in the region.

Petroleum was even more important in the post-war period than it was before, and Venezuela and Trinidad still dominated production and exploration. The post-war period also saw a dramatic increase in activity related to metalliferous resources. This work had begun during the years of World War II, when U.S. Geological Survey personnel had examined areas in the Caribbean, and particularly Central America, for their strategic mineral potential (Roberts and Irving, 1957). Further post-war exploration resulted in exploitation of many metalliferous deposits in the region, notably base metals and gold and silver in Honduras, Nicaragua, and the Dominican Republic; aluminum in Jamaica, and later in Haiti and the Dominican Republic; and ferro-nickel in Cuba, the Dominican Republic, Guatemala, Venezuela, and Colombia. The island-arc origin of many parts of the Caribbean, and hence their copper potential, excited many mining companies; a great deal of exploration for porphyry copper deposits took

Figure 8. Richard Weyl (1915–1988). After years of experience in the region, particularly in the Dominican Republic, El Salvador, and Costa Rica, he compiled one book on the geology of the Antilles and two on the geology of Central America.

place in the late 1950s and early 1960s. Unfortunately, falling copper prices have meant that none of the deposits, such as those in Puerto Rico and Panamá, have been exploited as of 1986.

A new development in the post-war period was the increasing importance of university research programs. These programs not only gathered more basic geological information about the Caribbean region, but were formulated to test the latest principles of geological thought. In other words, the aim was not simply data collection, but advancement of the science of geology.

The Princeton Caribbean Project, conceived by Harry Hess (Fig. 6), was outstanding in the impact that it had on the study of the geology of the region, and ultimately for the science of geology. Hess' interest in the Caribbean grew from his doctoral studies on serpentinites and his conviction that they were integral parts of orogenic belts. He toyed with the idea that ultramafic rocks were some of the earliest rocks formed in orogenic zones, and that island arcs were precursors to orogeny. Hence, by looking at the role of ultramafic rocks in island-arc settings, clues should be found to the early development of orogenic zones. Hess realized that the many occurrences of ultramafic rocks around the Caribbean made the region an ideal place to test these ideas. The original concept was later abandoned, mainly as a result of the Caribbean Project's findings, but the new information gathered greatly influenced Hess' thinking about the mobility of the Earth's crust and the nature of the sea floor, and culminated in his seminal work on sea-floor spreading (Hess, 1962).

The inspiration for the working methods of the Caribbean Project came from Rutten's Cuban expeditions. Following Rutten's example, Hess' graduate students mapped various areas of the Caribbean from Venezuela to Puerto Rico, many of which contain ultramafic and related rocks. In many cases, the areas investigated were previously unmapped, or at best only superficially mapped, so the gain in stratigraphic and structural knowledge of the region was spectacular. The first thesis was completed in 1946, and by 1972, 36 dissertations had been completed under Hess' supervision. Many of the Princeton team, both Caribbean natives and North Americans, have continued to be active in investigations of the region and have directed and influenced a second generation of students.

Princeton, however, did not have a monopoly on academic research in the Caribbean. In the early 1950s, after a visit to Venezuela, Walter Bucher (1952) of Columbia University compiled a geological map of the country accompanied by explanatory notes. Other institutions, including the Universities of Texas, Pittsburg, Rice, and Dartmouth, all made crucial contributions to the geology of the region, particularly Central America. Howell Williams, of the University of California at Berkeley, saw the possibilities of Central America as a natural laboratory for the investigation of volcanic phenomena. He and his colleagues and students produced many papers on the volcanic geology of El Salvador, Costa Rica, Guatemala, Nicaragua, and Honduras (Williams, 1960). In addition to dealing with Quaternary volcanism, his group also pioneered studies on the extensive Neogene ignimbrites in Central America. These studies were particularly appropriate because the first description of an ignimbrite was probably that of samples from Costa Rica (Romanes, 1912).

European universities also continued to play an essential role in Caribbean geological studies. MacGillavry and his colleagues and students at the University of Amsterdam made extensive investigations in geology and paleontology throughout the Caribbean, but especially in the Netherlands Antilles.

The University of Oxford began a decade-long study of the volcanically active islands of the Lesser Antilles in 1960. The project resulted in several doctoral dissertations and dramatically increased knowledge of the mineralogy, petrology, and geochemistry of these islands.

French geologists also were active in the Lesser Antilles in the post-war period, and were particularly concerned with seismic and volcanological studies on Martinique and Guadeloupe. In the Greater Antilles, Jacques Butterlin worked for several years on the geology of Haiti (Butterlin, 1956, 1960), and was responsible for reviving interest in the geology of the country, and also for inspiring a generation of native Haitian geologists.

The German universities were also active—particularly in Central America—continuing a century long tradition. Richard Weyl's books on the region (Weyl, 1961, 1980) had international influence during this period, as did his book on the Antilles (Weyl, 1966).

As important as the on-land studies were, the initiation of marine studies in this period is of special significance, and is one in which the universities played a vital part. In fact, the Caribbean area can be regarded as the womb of marine geophysics. The pre-war gravity field measurements of Vening-Meinesz and Hess were followed by the first of Maurice Ewing's seismic refraction profiles. These profiles were recorded off St. Thomas during World War II, while he was investigating underwater acoustics for the U.S. Navy. Ewing and his colleagues at the Lamont-Doherty Geological Observatory began marine geological and geophysical surveys in the Caribbean in the early 1950s, and were later joined by investigators from Woods Hole Oceanographic Institution, Duke University, Texas A & M University, Scripps Institute of Oceanography, the University of Miami, and several other North American and European institutions. The Caribbean region became a convenient laboratory in which many of the techniques of marine geology (e.g., seismic refraction, heat flow, piston coring) were perfected. By the end of the 1960s the application of these techniques had established the basic structure of the Caribbean crust, including the Yucatan, Venezuelan, and Colombian basins, the Nicaraguan Rise, Aves and Beata ridges, and Cayman Trough. The nature of the sedimentary deposits was also established, as was the presence of the widespread and enigmatic A'' and B'' seismic reflectors. The way was paved for later detailed studies, including the Deep Sea Drilling Project.

Although the universities of North America and Europe were performing vital research in the region, they could not provide the trained personnel required by the rapidly developing oil, mining, and government interests in the region. The economic and cultural development of the region demanded that it be able to produce its own professional geologists. Similar pressures were felt in other areas of education and universities were established to fulfill these urgent needs. Earth science departments were created at the universities in Puerto Rico, the West Indies in Jamaica and Trinidad, Costa Rica, Venezuela, Colombia, Cuba, and later in Haiti and the Dominican Republic. These institutions continue to provide the geologists needed by industries and governments of the region; as they have scientifically advanced, they are active in both pure and applied research.

Another significant feature of the post-war period was the improvement in communications between the region's investigators, which had begun with the First Venezuelan Geological Congress held in 1937. The Caribbean Geological Conferences, established in 1955, continued to provide an important international forum for government, industry, and university geologists from institutions both within and outside the region to meet, exchange ideas, and develop an appreciation of the Caribbean as a single geological entity. This volume is in many ways heir to the Caribbean Conferences.

The first Caribbean Conference was held in Antigua, and was originally meant to be a gathering of geologists of the British-ruled territories. Just prior to the meeting, delegates from Puerto Rico and French Guiana were added, along with Harry Hess of Princeton. The conference was small—only 37 delegates were present—but nevertheless, it was a great success. One of the delegates, John Weaver of the University of Puerto Rico, worked hard to organize a second, much larger meeting which was held in Mayagüez, Puerto Rico, in 1959. The conferences have subsequently met every three years at different locations (see Table 1).

The Caribbean Conferences also inspired other regional conference series. The Instituto Centroamericana de Investigación y Technología Industrial (ICAITI) was the major force behind the establishment of the Central American Geological Conferences, which began in 1965 and have been held almost every three years (Table 1). Although concerned with a somewhat larger area than the Caribbean, the Latin American Geological Congresses (Table 1) have included many papers on Caribbean topics and have been a valuable forum for the exchange of geological information on the region.

MODERN ERA (1969 TO PRESENT): DEEP-SEA DRILLING AND PLATE TECTONICS

The modern era in Caribbean geology can be considered to have begun in 1969. That was the year of the first deep-sea drilling operations in the Caribbean, and it was also when the impact of the new continental drift and plate tectonics hypotheses began to be felt. Geological thinking about the Caribbean, like that of other regions, has not been the same since.

The world's first marine drilling for entirely stratigraphic purposes was done in 1963 by the vessel *Submarex* on the Nicaraguan Rise (Emiliani, 1982). The hole was drilled partly as a feasibility study for what was later to become the Deep Sea Drilling Project. Again, the Caribbean was a proving ground for a major advance in the earth sciences.

The first Caribbean site of the Deep Sea Drilling Project (DSDP) was in the Venezuelan Basin and was drilled on Leg 4 of the DSDP (Bader and others, 1970). Site 29 firmly established that seismic reflection horizon A″ of the geophysicists was composed of Eocene cherts. The nature of the beds beneath A″ and of the B″ reflector was not determined until the leg 15 expedition of 1970–71 (Edgar and others, 1973). Eight sites were drilled on Leg 15, and in some holes the drillers were able to penetrate the sub A″ layers and sample the B″ layer, which was found to consist of Cretaceous diabase. As will be apparent in other chapters of this volume, the significance of B″ continues to be debated. Despite the advances made by Leg 15, it raised as many questions as it answered, and in the future we should see further deep sea drilling expeditions to the central Caribbean.

The first speculation on the effect of continental drift in the Caribbean seems to have been that of Matley (1926), who suggested that this mechanism could explain his conjecture that the Cayman Islands had separated from Jamaica. In the 1960s, continental drift became part of the larger concept of plate tectonics, and when this new paradigm was applied to the Caribbean, the major effect was probably one of unification. Much of the Caribbean south of the Cayman Trough was a single plate; it really was a single geological, as well as geographical, entity. However, it

TABLE 1. DATES AND LOCATIONS OF REGIONAL CONFERENCES

Conference No.	Year Held	Location
Caribbean Geological Conferences		
1	1955	Antigua
2	1959	Mayaguez, Puerto Rico
3	1962	Kingston, Jamaica
4	1965	Port of Spain, Trinidad
5	1968	St. John, Virgin Islands
6	1971	Isla de Margarita, Venezuela
7	1974	Guadeloupe
8	1977	Curacao
9	1980	Santo Domingo, Dominican Republic
10	1983	Cartagena, Colombia
11	1986	Barbados
Central American Geological Conferences		
1	1965	San Jose, Costa Rica
2	1966	Guatemala City, Guatemala
3	1971	San Jose, Costa Rica
4	1974	Tegucigalpa, Honduras
5	1977	Managua, Nicaragua
6	1984	Managua, Nicaragua
Latin American Geological Conferences		
1	1970	Lima, Peru
2	1973	Caracas, Venezuela
3	1976	Acapulco, Mexico
4	1979	Port-of-Spain, Trinidad
5	1982	Buenos Aires, Argentina
6	1985	Bogota, Colombia

quickly became apparent that the problems of its geological evolution would not be clarified overnight. Certainly, the Caribbean was no "simple" plate. Subduction was occurring on the eastern and western margins of the plate, and right-lateral and left-lateral strike slip was occurring on the southern and northern margins (Molnar and Sykes, 1969). The northern margin, it was later discovered, contained a short spreading segment within it. Moreover, the marine investigations of the late 1960s showed that the southern Caribbean basins, which are underlain by the B″ layer, have a crustal thickness somewhat greater than that of normal ocean floor. Nevertheless, the new and dynamic concept of plate kinematics imparted an unprecedented confidence that structural and tectonic phenomena in the region could be interpreted, and gave an important impetus to the study of these topics.

The evolution of the region through Mesozoic and Cenozoic time, although perhaps less confounding in the plate tectonic paradigm, is nevertheless as complicated as in any previous conceptual framework. Although most modern workers embrace the precepts of plate tectonics, the tectonic evolution of the Caribbean is still among the least understood of any of the world's regions, and is hotly debated in the following chapters.

The present phase of the history of geological investigation is still continuing, and the many ramifications of recent geological investigations will be discussed at length in this volume. A pleasing aspect of this continuing investigation is its international nature. Cooperating with the geologists from the Caribbean region are colleagues from Bulgaria, Canada, France, Germany, Great Britain, Italy, Japan, the Netherlands, Norway, Poland, the Soviet Union, Sweden, and the United States. This cosmopolitan flavor is something of a tradition in Caribbean geology, but it also reflects the importance of the Caribbean as a testing ground for modern geological hypotheses. For instance, in the next few years the Caribbean will be the focus of attempts to measure plate movements directly, using satellite-based precision ranging techniques. The geology of the Caribbean has stimulated the intellectual and exploratory instincts of several generations of geologists, and, as the science develops, the Caribbean region will continue to present new challenges and new inspiration for the earth sciences.

APPENDIX: SUMMARY OF TRANSACTIONS OF THE CARIBBEAN GEOLOGICAL CONFERENCES

Compiled by T. W. Donnelly* and G. Draper

FIRST CARIBBEAN GEOLOGICAL CONFERENCE

Date: 5-8 December 1955
Place: Antigua
Organizing Committee Chairman or Coordinator:
P.H.A. Martin-Kaye
Transactions
Date: 1958
Editor: not given
Publisher: not given
Pages: 70
Available from: no longer available

SECOND CARIBBEAN GEOLOGICAL CONFERENCE

Date: 4-9 January, 1959
Place: Mayaguez, Puerto Rico
Organizing Committee Chairman or Coordinator:
J. Weaver
Transactions
Date: 1962
Editor: J. Weaver
Publisher: University of Puerto Rico
Pages: 176
Available from: University of Puerto Rico,
Mayaguez, Puerto Rico 00708

*T. W. Donnelly's address is Department of Geological Sciences, State University of New York at Binghampton, Binghampton, New York 13901.

THIRD CARIBBEAN GEOLOGICAL CONFERENCE

Date: 2-11 April 1962
Place: Kingston, Jamaica
Organizing Committee Chairman or Coordinator:
E. Robinson
Transactions
Date: 1966
Editor: E. Robinson
Publisher: Geological Survey Department, Jamaica
Pages: 187
Available from: Geolocical Survey Department
Ministry of Mines and Natural Resources
Hope Gardens
Kingston 6, Jamaica

FOURTH CARIBBEAN GEOLOGICAL CONFERENCE

Date: 28 March-12 April 1965
Place: Port of Spain, Trinidad and Tobago
Organizing Committee Chairman or Coordinator:
John B. Saunders
Transactions
Date: 1968
Editor: J. B. Saunders
Publisher: not given
Pages: 457
Available from: Ministry of Petroleum and Mines
Salvatori Building
Port of Spain, Trinidad and Tobago
(Note: may no longer be available)

FIFTH CARIBBEAN GEOLOGICAL CONFERENCE

Date: 1-5 July 1971
Place: Margarita Island, Venezuela
Organizing Committee Chairman or Coordinator:
T. W. Donnelly
Transactions
Date: 1971
Editor: P. Mattson
Publisher: Queens College, City University of New York
Pages: 256
Available from: Bookstore
Queens College
City University of New York
New York, NY 11367
(Note: may no longer be available. Also, ten papers were published in Donnelly, T. W., ed., 1971, Caribbean geophysical, tectonic and petrologic studies: Geological Society of America Memoir 130, 224 p.)

SIXTH CARIBBEAN GEOLOGICAL CONFERENCE

Date: 6-14 July 1971
Place: Margarita Island, Venezuela
Organizing Committee Chairman or Coordinator:
C. Gonzalez de Juana
Transactions
Date: 1972
Editor: C. Petzall
Publisher: not given
Pages: 493
Available from: Escuela de Geologia y Minas
Universidad Central de Venezuela
Apartado 50296
Caracas 105, Venezuela

SEVENTH CARIBBEAN GEOLOGICAL CONFERENCE

Date: 30 June-12 July 1974
Place: Guadeloupe
Organizing Committee Chairman or Coordinator:
    R. Causse
Transactions
    Date: 1976
    Editor: R. Cauusse
    Publisher: Bureau de Recherches Geologiques et
            Minieres (Publication no. 1524)
    Pages: 614
    Available from: Editions du B.R.G.M., B.P. 6009
                45060 Orleans Cedex, France
                        or
                Geoscience Resources
                2990 Anthony Road
                Burlington, NC 27215

EIGHTH CARIBBEAN GEOLOGICAL CONFERENCE

Date: 9-12 July 1977
Place: Willemstad, Curacao
Organizing Committee Chairman or Coordinator:
    H. J. MacGillavry
Transactions
    Date: 1978
    Editor: H. J. MacGillavry and D. Beets
    Publisher: Geologie en Minjnbouw, v. 57, p. 97-384
    Pages: 286
    Available from: Koninklijk Nederlands Geolisch
                Mijnbouwkundig Genootschap
                Mijnbouwstraat 120
                Delft, Netherlands
(Note: Several papers were published in Bulletin Volcanologique,
1980.)

NINTH CARIBBEAN GEOLOGICAL CONFERENCE

Date: 16-20 August 1980
Place: Santo Domingo, Dominican Republic
Organizing Committee Chairman or Coordinator:
    W. Snow
Transactions
    Date: late 1982 (some authors cite 1983)
    Editors: W. Snow, N. gil, R. Llinas, R.
            Rodriguez-Torres, M. Seaward, I. Tavares
    Publisher: not given
    Pages: 716 (2 volumes)
    Available from: 9a Conferencia Geologica del Caribe
                Apartado 2719
                Santo Domingo, Dominican Republic

TENTH CARIBBEAN GEOLOGICAL CONFERENCE

Date: 14-20 August 1983
Place: Cartagena Colombia
Organizing Committee Chairman or Coordinator:
    H. Duque-Caro
Transactions
    Date: 1987
    Editor: H. Duque-Caro
    Publisher: INGEOMINAS, Bogota
    Pages: 497
    Available from: INGEOMINAS
                Diagonal 53 no. 34-53
                Bogota, Colombia

ELEVENTH CARIBBEAN GEOLOGICAL CONFERENCE

Date: July 20-26, 1986
Place: Dover Beach, Barbados

Organizing Committee Chairman or Coordinator:
    L. Barker
Transactions
    Date: 1988
    Editor: L. Barker
    Publisher: not given
    Pages: 518
Available from:
    Energy and Natural Resources Division
    National Petroleum Corporation Building
    Wildey, St. Michael
    Barbados

REFERENCES CITED

Acosta, J., 1590, Historia natural y moral de las Indias: Sevilla, 1846.

Anderson, T., and Flett, J. S., 1903, Report on the eruption of the Soufrière in St. Vincent, in 1902: Royal Society of London Philosophical Transactions, part 1, ser. A, v. 200, p. 353–533.

—— , 1908, A visit to Montagne Pelée, in Martinique: Royal Society of London Philosophical Transactions, part 2, ser. A, v. 208, p. 275–332.

Arnold, R. G., Macready, G. A., and Barrington, T., 1960, The first big oil hunt—Venezuela, 1911–1916: New York, Vantage Press, 353 p.

Atwood, G., 1882, On the geology of a part of Costa Rica, with an appendix (on the igneous rocks) by W. H. Hudleston: Quarterly Journal of the Geological Society, v. 38, p. 328–340.

Bader, R. G., and others, 1970, Initial Reports of the Deep Sea Drilling Project, Volume 4: Washington, D.C., U.S. Government Printing Office, 753 p.

Belt, T., 1874, The naturalist in Nicaragua; A narrative of residence at the gold mines of Chontales; journeys in the savannahs and forest: London, J. M. Dent and sons, 267 p.

Berkey, C. P., 1915, Geological reconnaissance of Porto Rico: New York Academy of Sciences Annals, v. 26, p. 1–70.

Böggild, O. B., 1907, Om Dansk–Vestindiens Geologi: Geografisk Tidsskrift, Koninklik Dansks Geographisk Selskab, v. 19, p. 6–11.

Botero-Arango, G., 1978, Apuntes para una historia de las investigaciones geológicas en Colombia: Ciencia y technología en Colombia: Bogotá, Insitituto Colombiano de Cultura, Editorial Escala, p. 147–169.

Bucher, W. H., 1952, Geologic structure and orogenic history of Venezuela: Geological Society of America Memoir 49, 113 p.

Butterlin, J., 1956, La constitution géologique et la structure de Antilles: Paris, Centre Nationale de la Recherche Scientifique, 453 p.

—— , 1960, Géologié générale et régionale de la Republique d'Haiti: Universite de Paris, Travaux et Memoires de l'Institut des Hautes Etudies de l'Amérique Latine, 194 p.

Castellanos, J., 1589, Elegias de varones illustres de Indias (second edition): Madrid, 1850, 565 p.

Cleve, Per Teodor, 1871, On the geology of the northeastern West India Islands: Svenska Vetenskapsakademiens Handlingar, no. 12, p. 1–48.

Crawford, J., 1892, The geology of Nicaragua: Proceedings of the American Association for the Advancement of Science, v. 40, p. 261–270.

De la Beche, H. T., 1827, Remarks on the geology of Jamaica: Geological Society of London Transactions, ser. 2, v. 2, p. 143–194 (Accompanying map is dated 1823).

Dollfus, A., and Montserrat, E., 1868, Voyage géologique dans les Républiques de Guatemala et de Salvador: Paris, Mission Scientifique au Mexique et dans l'Amerique Central, 539 p.

Dupuget, 1796, Extrait d'un memoire du citoyen Dupuget, intitulé: Coupe d'oeil rapide sur la physique generale et la mineralogie des Antilles: Journal des Mines, v. 3, p. 43–60.

Edgar, N. T., Saunders, J. B., and others, 1973, Initial reports of the Deep Sea Drilling Project, volume 15: Washington, D.C., U.S. Government Printing Office, 1137 p.

Emiliani, C., 1982, A new global geology, *in* Emiliani, C., ed., The oceanic lithosphere: New York, John Wiley and Sons, p. 1687–1728.

Eva, A. N., 1985, The development of petroleum resources on Barbados; A historical review: Transactions of the 4th Latin American Geological Congress, Port of Spain, 1979, p. 345–350.

Fernandez de Castro, M., 1884, Pruebas paleontologicas de que la Isla de Cuba ha estado unida al continente americano y breve idea de su constitucíon geológica: Academia de Ciencias de Habana, Anales, v. 21, p. 146–165.

Frampton, F., and Birchwood, K. M., 1979, Historical and geological tour of the Trinidad oil industry, *in* Field Guide to Trinidad, Tobago, and Barbados: Transactions of the 4th Latin American Geological Congress, Port of Spain, Trinidad and Tobago, 1979, p. 49–58.

Franklin Institute Research Laboratories, 1972, Cooperative Investigations in the Caribbean and adjacent regions (CICAR), volume 3; Bibliography on marine geology and geophysics: Rockville, Maryland, National Oceanic and Atmospheric Administration, 187 p.

Gabb, W. M., 1873, Topography and geology of Santo Domingo: Transactions of the American Philosophical Society, new series, v. 15, p. 49–259.

——, 1874a, Note on the geology of Costa Rica: American Journal of Science, v. 7, p. 438–439.

——, 1874b, Notes on the geology of Costa Rica: American Journal of Science, v. 8, p. 388–390.

——, 1875, Notes on the geology of Costa Rica: American Journal of Science, v. 9, p. 198–204.

Grosse, E., 1926, Geologische Untersuchung des Kohlenführenden Tertiars Antioquias im Westlichen Tiel der Zentralkodillere Kolumbiens zwichen Rio Arma und Sacaojal, Ausgeführt in den Jahren 1920–1923 im Auftrage der Regierung des Departements Antioqua (Ferrocarril de Antioquia): Berlin, Verlag von Dietrich Reimer (Ernst Vohsen), 361 p.

Guppy, R.J.L., 1867, On the Tertiary fossils of the West Indies with especial reference to the classification of the Kainozoic rocks of Trinidad (Proceedings of the Science Association of Trinidad, v. 1, p. 145–176): Bulletin of American Paleontology, v. 8, p. 172–204 (1921 reprint).

Hayes, C. W., 1899, Physiography and geology of regions adjacent to the Nicaragua canal route: Geological Society of America Bulletin, v. 10, p. 285–348.

Hayes, C. W., Vaughn, T. S., and Scott, A. C., 1901, Report on a geological reconnaissance of Cuba, made under the direction of General Leonard Wood: *in* Civil report of Brigadier-General Wood, Military Governor of Cuba for the period from January 1 to December 31, 1901, v. 1, p. 1–23.

Hedberg, H. D., 1931, Cretaceous limestone as petroleum source rock in northwestern Venezuela: American Association of Petroleum Geologists Bulletin, v. 15, p. 229–244.

——, 1937, Stratigraphy of the Rio Queracal section of northeastern Venezuela: Geological Society of America Bulletin, v. 48, p. 1971–2024.

——, 1974, Hermann Karsten; Pioneer geologist in northern South America, 1844–1856: Basel, Verhandlungen der Naturforschungen Gesellschaft, v. 84, p. 32–44.

Hess, H. H., 1933, Interpretation of geological and geophysical observations; Navy–Princeton gravity expedition, West Indies, 1932: U.S. Hydrographic Office, p. 27–54.

——, 1962, History of the ocean basins, *in* Engel, A.G.J., and others, eds., Petrological studies: A volume in honor of A. F. Buddington: New York, Geological Society of America, p. 599–620.

Hettner, A., 1892, Die Kordillere von Bogotá: Petermanns Mitteilungen Goethe, p. 131.

Hill, R. T., 1894, Notes on the Tertiary and later history of Cuba: American Journal of Science, v. 48, p. 196–212.

——, 1895, Notes on the geology of the island of Cuba: Bulletin of the Museum of Comparative Zoology, v. 16, p. 243–288.

——, 1898a, Cuba and Porto Rico: New York, Century, 429 p.

——, 1898b, The geological history of the Isthmus of Panama and portions of Costa Rica: Bulletin of the Museum of Comparative Zoology, v. 28, p. 151–285.

——, 1899, The geology and physiography of Jamaica; Study of a type of Antillean development: Bulletin of the Museum of Comparative Zoology, v. 34, p. 1–226.

Högbom, A. G., 1905, Zür Petrographie der kleinen Antillen: Bulletin of the Geological Institute of the University of Upsala, v. 6, p. 214–232.

Humboldt, A. von, 1852, Personal narrative of travels to the equinoctal regions of the Americas (English translation and edition by Thomasina Ross): London, New York, Routledge, v. 1, 505 p., v. 2, 521 p., v. 3, 442 p. (Reprinted 1971, New York, Blom.)

Jukes-Brown, A. J., and Harrison, J. B., 1891, The geology of Barabados; Part I, The coral rocks of Barbados and other West Indian Islands: Geological Society of London Quarterly Journal, v. 47, p. 197–243.

——, 1892, The geology of Barbados; Part II, The oceanic deposits: Geological Society of London Quarterly Journal, v. 48, p. 170–226.

Karsten, H., 1850, Beitrag zur Kentniss der Gesteine des nordlichen Venezuela: Zeitschrift der Deutschen Geologischen Gessellschaft (Verhandlungen), v. 2, p. 345–361.

——, 1856, La situación Geonostica de la Nueva Granada: republished, 1947, *in* Revista de la Academia Colombiana de Ciencias Exactas, Físicas y Naturales, v. 7, p. 361–381.

——, 1886, Geologie de l'ancienne Colombie bolivarienne, Venezuela, Nouvelle Grenade et Ecuador: Berlin, Friedlinder, 62 p.

Lacroix, A., 1904, La Montagne Pelée et se eruptions: Paris, Masson et Cie, 622 p.

——, 1908, La Montagne Pelée apres ses eruptions: Paris, Masson et Cie, 136 p.

Lewis, J. W., 1932, Geology of Cuba: American Association of Petroleum Geologists Bulletin, v. 16, p. 533–555.

Liddle, R. A., 1928, The geology of Venezuela and Trinidad: Fort Worth, MacGowan, 552 p.

Maclure, W. F., 1817, Observations on the geology of the West Indian islands from Barbados to Santa Cruz: Philadelphia, Journal of the Academy of Natural Sciences, v. 1, p. 134–139.

MacDonald, D. F., 1918, Contributions to the geology and paleontology of the Panama Canal Zone and geologically related areas in the West Indies: U.S. National Museum Bulletin, v. 103, p. 525–545.

Matley, C. A., 1926, The geology of the Cayman Islands, British West Indies, and their relationship to the Bartlett Trough: Geological Society of London Quarterly Journal, v. 82, p. 352–387.

Meyerhoff, H. A., 1933, Geology of Puerto Rico: University of Puerto Rico Monograph, ser. B, no. 1, 306 p.

Molnar, P., and Sykes, L. R., 1969, Tectonics of the Caribbean and Middle America regions from focal mechanisms and seismicity: Geological Society of America Bulletin, v. 80, p. 1639–1664.

Montessus de Ballore, F., 1888, Tremblements de terre et éruptions volcaniques au Centro–Amérique: Dijon, Academie des Sciences et Societé Savante de Saône-et-Loire, 293 p.

Morison, S. E., 1942, Admiral of the Ocean Sea: Boston, Little, Brown, and Co., 680 p.

Oersted, A. S., 1852, La partie central de Costa Rica: Royal Geographic Society Geographic Journal, v. 22, p. 96–99.

Perret, F. A., 1937, The eruption of Mt. Pelée 1929–32: Publications of the Carnegie Institution of Washington, no. 458, 126 p.

Roberts, R. J., and Irving, E. M., 1957, Mineral deposits of Central America: U.S. Geological Survey Bulletin 1034, 205 p.

Romanes, J., 1912, Geology of a part of Costa Rica: Geological Society of London Quarterly Journal, v. 68, p. 103–139.

Sapper, K., 1899, Ueber Gebirgsbau und Boden des nördlichen Mittelamerika: Petermanns Mitteilung, v. 27, no. 127, Goethe, 119 p.

——, 1901, Die Alta Verapaz (Guatemala): Geologischen Gesellschaft Hamburg, Bd. 17, p. 78–214.

——, 1937, Mittelamerika; Handbuch der Regionalen Geologie: Heidelberg, Steinmann and Wikkens, 160 p.

Saunders, J. B., and Bolli, H. M., 1985, Trinidad's contribution to world biostratigraphy: Transactions of the 4th Latin American Geological Congress, Port of Spain, 1979, p. 781–795.

Sawkins, J. G., 1869, Reports on the geology of Jamaica, with contributions from G. P. Wall, L. Barrett, A. Lennox, and C. B. Brown: London, Longmans, 339 p.

Sawyer, J. H., 1975, Latin America after 1920, *in* Owen, E. V., The trek of the oil finders; A history of exploration for petroleum: American Association of Petroleum Geologists Memoir 6, p. 960–1251.

Schubert, C., 1977, Investigaciones geológicas en los Andes de Venezuela: Ibero–Americanisches Archiv, v. 3, p. 295–309.

Schuchert, C., 1935, Historical geology of the Antillean–Caribbean region: New York, Hafner, 811 p. (Facsimile edition reprinted 1968.)

Seebach, K. von, 1892, Über Vulkane Zentralamerikas: Göttingen, Dieterische Verlags–Buchhandlung, 252 p.

Seivers, W., 1888a, Die Cordillere von Merida nebst Bemerkungen über das Karibische Gebirge: Geolgische Abhandlungen (Penck), v. 3, no. 1, 238 p.

—— , 1888b, Die Sierra Nevada de Santa Marta and Sierra de Perija: Berlin, Zeitschrift der Gesellschaft für Erdkunde, v. 23, p. 1–158.

Vaughan, T. W., Cooke, C. W., and Woodring, W. P., and others, 1921, A geological reconnaissance of the Dominican Republic: Dominican Republic Geological Survey Memoir, 268 p., 1 map.

Wall, G. P., and Sawkins, J. G., 1860, Report on the geology of Trinidad: London, Geological Survey Memoir, 211 p.

Wells, W. B., 1857, Explorations and adventures in Honduras, comprising sketches of travel in the gold regions of Olancho, and a review of the history and general resources of Central America: New York, Harper and Brothers, 545 p.

Weyl, R., 1961, Die Geologie Mittelamerikas: Berlin, Gebrüder Borntraeger, 226 p.

—— , 1966, Geologie der Antillen: Berlin, Gebrüder Borntraeger, 410 p.

—— , 1980, Geology of Central America: Berlin, Gebrüder Borntraeger, 371 p.

Williams, H., 1960, Volcanic history of the Guatemala highlands: University of California Publications in Geology, v. 38, p. 1–86.

Woodring, W. P., Brown, J. S., and Burbank, W. S., 1924, Geology of the Republic of Haiti: Port-au-Prince, Department of Public Works, 611 p., and geological map.

Manuscript Accepted by the Society December 18, 1986

ACKNOWLEDGMENTS

We are grateful for hints, tips, leads, anecdotes, photographs, corrections, and comments (both informative and amusing) from W. Bonini, T. W. Donnelly, W. D. MacDonald, F.J-M.R. Maurrasse, F. Nagle, E. Robinson, and C. Schubert, and for their comments on an earlier manuscript. We are also grateful to the astute reviews and suggested additions of H. Hedberg, W. Bonini, and especially J. E. Case. National Science Foundation Grants EAR 8306148 and EAR 8509452 partly supported Draper during the research and writing of this paper. Our greatest thanks go to the pioneers of Caribbean geology, and to their disciples, who were our inspiration.

NOTE ADDED IN PROOF:

TWELFTH CARIBBEAN GEOLOGICAL CONFERENCE

Date: 7–11 August 1989
Place: St. Croix
Organizing committee Chairman and Coordinator:
   F. Nagle
Transactions:
   Date: 1990
   Editors: D. K. Larue and G. Draper
   Publisher: Miami Geological Society
   Pages: 525
   Available from: Miami Geological Society
               P.O. Box 144333
               Coral Gables, FL 33114

The Geology of North America
Vol. H, The Caribbean Region
The Geological Society of America, 1990

Chapter 2

Caribbean crustal provinces; Seismic and gravity evidence

J. E. Case
U.S. Geological Survey, 345 Middlefield Road, Menlo Park, California 94025
William D. MacDonald
Department of Geological Sciences, State University of New York, Binghamton, New York 13901
Paul J. Fox
Graduate School of Oceanography, University of Rhode Island, Narragansett, Rhode Island 02282

INTRODUCTION

Numerous geoscientists have proposed and evaluated many conceptually distinct models for the evolution of the Caribbean region since 1930 (Fig. 1). From these, seven predominant interpretations of Caribbean crustal generation and modification have emerged: (1) sea-floor spreading, involving mid-ocean rifting, tectonic convergence, subduction, and back-arc spreading (for examples, see Pindell and Barrett, this volume); (2) basification of continental crust (Škvor, 1969); (3) lateral shear and transverse extension with attenuation, a variation on plate-tectonic theory (Ball and Harrison, 1969); (4) in situ orthogeosynclinal crustal evolution (Khudoley and Meyerhoff, 1971; Meyerhoff and Meyerhoff, 1972), a process classically associated with the tectogene hypothesis; (5) magmatic crustal thickening, related to magmatic-arc emplacement near subduction zones, to "hot-spot" magmatism (Officer and others, 1957; Duncan and Hargraves, 1984), to basaltic intrusion (Burke and others, 1984), and to flood-plateau basaltic volcanism (Donnelly, 1973; Donnelly and others, this volume); (6) tectonic crustal thickening and crustal accretion: processes in which tectonites are formed, assembled, or reassembled at convergent plate margins into masses reaching continental thickness (MacDonald, 1972a, b); (7) another process, involving thermal contraction and attendant mantle surges, is described by Morris, Meyerhoff, and others in this volume.

Most of these processes lead to three genetically distinct types of crust (Ewing and Press, 1955; this paper): (1) oceanic, (2) continental, and (3) accretionary. Physical and genetic aspects of these crustal types are discussed below. Crust that cannot be readily assigned to one of these classes is, temporarily at least, categorized as indeterminate.

Knowledge of Caribbean crustal evolution has emerged from studies of exposed rocks, dredges, and deep drill holes, and from geophysical observations in marine and land environments. Fundamental geophysical information has come from seismic refraction and reflection studies, including local earthquake data, and from analyses of regional gravity and magnetic anomalies. The earliest geophysical investigations emphasized marine gravity techniques (Vening-Meinesz and Wright, 1930; Hess, 1938; Worzel and Ewing, 1954; Worzel, 1965). Later on, marine seismic methods, initiated by Maurice and John Ewing and their colleagues (M. Ewing and others, 1954; J. Ewing and others, 1957), became the dominant geophysical technique for studies of Caribbean crustal structure. In this brief review, we summarize some of the principal seismic and gravity results to provide a three-dimensional model of crustal types and to provide a frame of reference for other chapters of this volume.

A basic synthesis of the refraction data for the interior Caribbean marine region was provided by Edgar and others (1971), and for the gravity field of marine and land areas by Bowin (1976). A synthesis of the seismic and gravity data for the Lesser Antillean region is found in the folio by Speed and others (1984). Numerous crustal profiles, emphasizing shallower structure, were compiled by Mascle and others (1985). Many sets of seismic and gravity data and crustal interpretations are provided here as profiles on Plate 2. Derivative contour maps and schematic geologic crustal cross sections, prepared for this chapter, are shown on Plate 3. Summaries of velocities, densities, and thicknesses for the principal geologic provinces are given in Table 1. Interpretations of the offshore stratigraphy and structure of the shallow upper crust, involving undeformed to highly deformed sedimentary and igneous sequences, are summarized in the chapters by Holcombe and others (this volume). Place names are shown on the base maps for Plate 3 or on the bathymetric map by Holcombe and others (Plate 1, this volume).

Physical characteristics of the crust and mantle

To arrive at satisfactory models of crustal evolution, some knowledge of crustal age, composition, and thickness are re-

Case, J. E., MacDonald, W. D., and Fox, P. J., 1990, Caribbean crustal provinces; Seismic and gravity evidence, *in* Dengo, G., and Case, J. E., eds., The Caribbean Region: Boulder, Colorado, Geological Society of America, The Geology of North America, v. H.

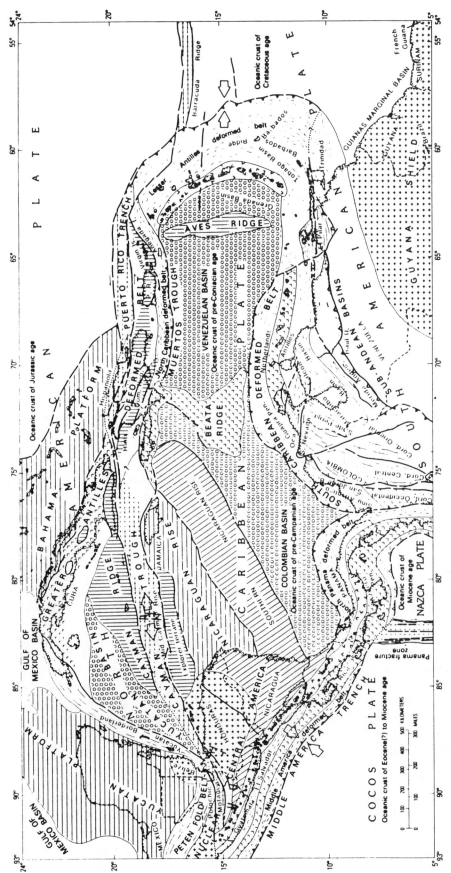

Figure 1. Schematic map of Caribbean region, showing exposed and inferred tectonostratigraphic superterranes, compiled by J. E. Case. Plus pattern, Precambrian and Paleozoic cratonic areas. Horizontal rule pattern, Mesozoic and Cenozoic moderately deformed carbonate platforms (includes local clastic and evaporite deposits). Long dashed pattern, "Laramide" deformed belts involving Cretaceous and Paleogene strata and various older sedimentary and crystalline rocks. Upright-V pattern, areas of oceanic crust, upper mantle(?), and primitive island arcs, mainly of late Mesozoic and Paleogene age, deformed in "Laramide" but also in Neogene time. Lazy-S pattern, Mesozoic metamorphic belts. Vertical rule pattern, Late Cretaceous and Paleogene volcanic complexes, mainly calc-alkalic. Open dot pattern, moderately deformed sub-Andean basins that contain thick Cretaceous and Tertiary marine and continental strata and varying thicknesses of pre-Cretaceous strata. Open circles, deep interior Caribbean basin, relatively undeformed where pelagic hemipelagic, and turbidite strata overlie oceanic crust. Short dashed pattern, Neogene deformed belts that may also involve Cretaceous and Paleogene rocks and deformational events. Diagonal pattern, complex multiterrane including carbonate banks, clastic strata, pelagic strata, and local volcanic and intrusive rocks resting on oceanic, transitional, and continental crust. Random V and large black dot pattern (Holocene volcanoes), Neogene volcanic belts. Crosshatch pattern, complex transform systems; some are "leaky" and constructional, others are transtensional and form graben. Unpatterned areas within the Caribbean region are undefined terranes at present. Unpatterned areas outside the Caribbean region are deep ocean basins covered by varying thicknesses of pelagic, turbidite, and deep-sea fan deposits. Note that any individual terrane may include elements of adjacent terranes and that many terranes actually overlap in their times of deformation. Phanerozoic plutons (not shown) occur in many deformed belts. From Case and Dengo (1982).

TABLE 1. SUMMARY OF CRUSTAL PROPERTIES IN THE CARIBBEAN REGION

Area or Province	Principle Data Source (R = refraction; G = gravity*)	Thickness, Exclusive of Water (km)	Sub-M Velocities (km/sec)	Lower Crustal Velocities (km/sec)	Assumed Densities Across M (g/cm3)	Isostatic State	Inferred Crustal Type	Selected References*	Remarks
Western Cuba	R, G	22 - 32	8.0 - 8.7?	5.9 - 6.7	2.9 - 3.3 / 3.0 - 3.4	@ in mass balance	Accretionary, continental oceanic?	Shcherbavoka and others, 1978, 1980; Soloviev and others, 1964; Shein and others, 1978	Assumption of Vm = 8.1 km/sec
Eastern Cuba	R, G	12 - 25	8.0 - 8.1	5.8 - 6.7	2.9 - 3.3 / 3.0 - 3.4	Large excess mass	Accretionary, oceanic	Bovenko and others, 1980; Soloviev and others, 1964; Shein and others, 1978	Assumption of Vm = 8.1 km/sec
Hispaniola	G, R	20 - 30+	—	—	3.0 - 3.4	Excess mass in eastern Hispaniola	Accretionary, oceanic	Bowin, 1976; Reblin, 1973; McCann and Sykes, 1984	
Jamaica	G, R	20+?	—	—	—	Excess mass	Accretionary, oceanic	Andrew, 1969; Bowin, 1976	
Puerto Rico	G, R	20 - 30	—	—	3.0 - 3.4	Excess mass	Accretionary, oceanic	Talwani and others, 1959; Bunce and Fahlquist, 1962	
Lesser Antilles	R, G	20 - 35	8.0	6.4 - 6.9	3.16 - 3.42 / 2.9 - 3.3	Excess mass	Accretionary, mixed oceanic and continental?	Westbrook, 1975; Bowin, 1976; Speed and others, 1984	
Leeward Antilles	G, R	20 - 25	—	—	3.0 - 3.45	Excess mass	Accretionary, oceanic	Silver and others, 1975; Lagaay, 1969; Folinsbee, 1972	
Northern Venezuela	G, R	20 - 35	—	—	2.9 - 3.1 / 2.9 - 3.3 / 2.95 - 3.1 / 2.7 - 3.3	@ in mass balance	Accretionary, mixed oceanic and continental	Bonini and others, 1977a, b; Bonini, 1978; Folinsbee, 1972; Bowin, 1976	
Guayana Shield and adjacent basins	G	30 - 43	—	—	2.95 - 3.1 / 2.7 - 3.3	@ in mass balance except in eastern Venezuela Basin	Continental	Bonini and others, 1977a, 1977b; Bonini, 1978; Bowin, 1976; Folinsbee, 1972	
Cordillera de Mérida-Cordillera Oriental	G	35 - 40	—	—	2.9 - 3.1 / 2.9 - 3.2 / 2.67 - 3.3	@ in mass balance except in Lake Maracaibo	Continental	Folinsbee, 1972; Kellogg and Bonini, 1982; Hospers and van Wijnen, 1959	
Santa Marta-Guajira	G	20 - 30	—	—	2.9 - 3.2	Excess mass	Accretionary to continental	Case and MacDonald, 1973; Kellogg and Bonini, 1982	
Cordillera Central	R, G	35 - 45	8.0	6.5	2.9 - 3.3	@ in mass balance	Mainly continental	Flüh and others, 1981; Case and others, 1971; Kellogg and others, 1986	Assumption of Vm = 8.0 km/sec

TABLE 1. SUMMARY OF CRUSTAL PROPERTIES IN THE CARIBBEAN REGION (continued)

Area or Province	Principle Data Source (R = refraction; G = gravity)	Thickness, Exclusive of Water (km)	Sub-M Velocities (km/sec)	Lower Crustal Velocities (km/sec)	Assumed Densities Across M (g/cm3)	Isostatic State	Inferred Crustal Type	Selected References*	Remarks
Cordillera Occidental-Serrania de Baudo	R, G	22 - 30	8.0	6.6 - 6.8	2.9 - 3.3	Large excess mass	Accretionary, oceanic	Fluh and others, 1981; Case and others, 1971; Kellogg and others, 1986	Assumption of Vm = 8.0 km/sec
Panama-Costa Rica	G, R	25 - 40+	7.9	6.5	3.1 - 3.3 / 3.1 - 3.4	Excess mass	Accretionary, oceanic	Case, 1974a; Briceno-Guarupe, 1978; Matumoto and others, 1976; Matumoto and others, 1977; Matumoto and Latham, 1977	
Nicauagua-Honduras-Guatemala (Chortis block)	R, G	25 - 46	8.0	6.8	3.0 - 3.36	@ in mass balance	Continental, oceanic, accretionary	Couch and Woodcock, 1981; Kim and others, 1982; Case and Donnelly, 1976; Case, 1980; Victor, 1976	Assumption of Vm = 8.0 km/sec
Maya block	G, R	20 - 25+	7.9 - 8.2?	6.8 - 7.1?	2.8 - 3.3	@ in mass balance	Continental to accretionary	Dillon and others, 1972; Buffler and others, 1980; Couch and Woodcock, 1981	
Yucatan Basin	R, G	9 - 20	8.1	6.1	2.9 - 3.3	@ in mass balance	Oceanic	Dillon and others, 1982; Dillon and Vedder, 1973; Ewing and others, 1960; Uchupi, 1973	
Cayman Ridge	R, G	>20	---	6.5 - 7.2+	2.8 - 3.3	@ in mass balance	Oceanic? magmatic belt	Bowin, 1976; Dillon and others, 1972	
Cayman Trough	R, G	4 - 17	8.1 - 8.3	6.2 - 7.6?	2.8 - 3.3	@ in mass balance	Oceanic, possibly continental in west	Bowin, 1976; Dillon and others, 1972; Dowling and Fahlquist, 1986; J. D. Dowling, pers. comm., 1986; Ewing and others, 1960; Holcombe and others, this volume	
Northern Nicaraguan Rise	R, G	19 - 25	---	6.1 - 7.6?	2.8 - 3.3	@ in mass balance	Continental? in west; oceanic? in east	Ewing and others, 1960	Scant refraction data
Southern Nicaraguan Rise	R, G	19 - 22	7.8 - 8.2	6.1 - 6.7	3.0 - 3.3	@ in mass balance	Oceanic; continental? in west	Edgar and others, 1971; Ewing and others, 1960; Edgar and others, 1973	Scant refraction data in west
Colombian Basin and north Panama deformed belt	R, G	12 - 20	7.8 - 8.2	7.3 - 7.0	3.1 - 3.4 / 2.9 - 3.2	@ in mass balance	Oceanic	Edgar and others, 1971; Ewing and others, 1960; Briceno-Garupe, 1978; Kellogg and Bonini, 1982; Ludwig and others, 1975	
Beata Ridge	R, G	15 - 21	8.0 - 8.5	6.3 - 6.8	---	@ in mass balance	Oceanic	Edgar and others, 1971; Fox and Heezen, 1975; Ewing and others, 1960	
South Caribbean deformed belt	R, G	15 - 25	8.1	6.6 - 7.3?	3.0 - 3.45 / 2.7 - 3.3	Mass deficiency	Accretionary. Mainly oceanic	Edgar and others, 1971; Ladd and Watkins, 1979; Silver and others, 1975; Talwani and others, 1977; Folinsbee, 1972	Scant refraction data
Venezuelan Basin and north Caribbean deformed belt	R, G	7 - 20	7.8 - 8.3	5.8 - 7.6	3.0 - 3.45	@ in mass balance	Oceanic; accretionary in north	Edgar and others, 1971; Diebold and others, 1981; Edgar and others, 1973	

TABLE 1. SUMMARY OF CRUSTAL PROPERTIES IN THE CARIBBEAN REGION (continued)

Area or Province	Principle Data Source (R = refraction; G = gravity)	Thickness, Exclusive of Water (km)	Sub-M Velocities (km/sec)	Lower Crustal Velocities (km/sec)	Assumed Densities Across M (g/cm3)	Isostatic State	Inferred Crustal Type	Selected References*	Remarks
Aves Ridge	R, G	25 - 35	8.2?	7.4?	3.16 - 3.42 / 3.05 - 3.3	@ in mass balance	Accretionary (magmatic belt?)	Boynton and others, 1979; Bowin 1976; Kearey, 1976; Speed and others, 1984	
Grenada Basin	R, G	18 - 25	8.2	7.4	3.16 - 3.42 / 3.05 - 3.3	@ in mass balance	Oceanic? (in south)	Boynton and others, 1979; Bowin 1976; Kearey, 1976; Speed and others, 1984	
Lesser Antilles deformed belt	R, G	14 - 25	8.0 - 8.3	6.7	3.1 - 3.42 / 2.9 - 3.3	Large mass deficiency	Accretionary	Westbrook, 1975; Bowin, 1976; Boynton and others, 1979; Speed and others, 1984	
South American oceanic plate	R, G	8 - 10	8.0 - 8.3	6.7	2.95 - 3.42 / 2.9 - 3.3 / 2.8 - 3.1	@ in mass balance	Oceanic	Bowin, 1976; Westbrook, 1975; Speed and others, 1984; Birch, 1970	
Nares Province	R, G	4 - 9	8.0 - 8.4	6.9 - 7.1	2.85 - 3.3	@ in mass balance	Oceanic	Talwani and others, 1959; Bunce and Fahlquist, 1962; Officer and others, 1957, 1959	
Puerto Rico Trench	R, G	9 - 15	7.9 - 8.4	6.3 - 6.8 / 6.6 - 7.4	3.0 - 3.4 / 3.0 - 3.3	mass deficiency	Accretionary (oceanic)	Talwani and others, 1959; Bunce and Fahlquist, 1962; Bowin, 1976; Officer and others, 1957, 1959	
Bahama Platform	G	15 - 25	—	—	2.67 - 3.35	@ in mass balance	Oceanic? in southeast; continental? in northwest	Uchupi and others, 1971; Shein and others, 1978	
Nazca plate	G	6? - 16	7.6? - 8.0	6.6?	2.9 - 3.28	@ in mass balance	Oceanic	Briceno-Guarupe, 1978; Barday, 1974; Flüh and others, 1981; van Andel and others, 1971	
Cocos plate	R, G	5 - 10	7.8	6.8	2.9 - 3.32	@ in mass balance	Oceanic	Victor, 1976; Couch and Woodcock, 1981; Shor and Fisher, 1961	
Middle America Trench and borderland	R	10 - 20	8.0 - 8.2	6.5 - 6.9	2.9 - 3.32 / 2.9 - 3.36	@ in mass balance	Accretionary oceanic-continental	Ibrahim and others, 1979; Auboin and others, 1981; Shor and Fisher, 1961; von Huene and others, 1980	Scant refraction data

*Many classic papers are cited in the more recent references listed here.

quired. Composition and density are related, and both influence seismic velocities and regional gravity variations (Plate 2). The crustal cross sections of Plate 2 provide many examples of measured depth-velocity and assumed velocity-density relations. Most investigators have used the empirical velocity-density curves of J. E. Nafe and C. L. Drake (cited by Talwani and others, 1959) or subsequent modifications by Ludwig and others (1970; Fig. 2). Many definitions of crustal types have been proposed. For the Caribbean region, the following physical definitions of continental and oceanic crust are used. *Continental crust* is of low average density, 2.7 to 2.9 g/cm³, has an intermediate to silicic bulk composition, at least in its upper part; it contains a high proportion of pre-Mesozoic and especially of Precambrian metamorphic and igneous rocks, and it is typically 20 to 45 km thick, as determined from limited refraction data and gravity models. P-wave velocities commonly range from 5.5 to 7.0 km/sec, with much variation. *Oceanic crust* is mafic in composition, is of high density, 2.85 to 3.0 g/cm³, typically is 6 to 10 km thick, and has depths to the Mohorovičić discontinuity (M or Moho) of 10 to 15 km below sea level. Velocities commonly range from 6.0 to 7.0 km/sec (or more). In the Caribbean region, ages of crustal formation range from pre–Late Jurassic to Holocene. *Mantle* rocks are considered to be ultramafic, having densities of about 3.1 to 3.4 g/cm³, and commonly having velocities of 7.8 to 8.3 km/sec or more. The boundary between crust and mantle is defined by a major velocity increase, typically from about 6.7 to 7.0 km/sec in the lower crust to about 8.1 km/sec in the upper mantle.

We emphasize that P-wave velocities of rocks overlap for oceanic crust and lower continental crust, so that velocities alone cannot be used to distinguish crustal types. As our definition of accretionary crust includes genetic as well as physical criteria, it is discussed later.

A summary of the range in velocity structure of the Caribbean region is shown in Figure 3.

DATA FROM SEISMIC REFRACTION AND REFLECTION

Soon after World War II, Maurice Ewing and his colleagues began a long series of pioneering marine seismic refraction surveys (Worzel and Ewing, 1948; Officer and others, 1957, 1959; J. Ewing and others, 1957, 1960; Talwani and others, 1959; Edgar and others, 1971). Subsequent refraction (and reflection) studies have generally substantiated the principal results of earlier investigations.

These early experiments were successful in outlining the crustal thickness and velocity structure of the major physiographic provinces of the Caribbean region (Plates 2 and 3). The results established that the major basins of the Caribbean have essentially oceanic affinities, with two important differences: Caribbean crust appeared to be somewhat thicker than the "typical" oceanic crust of the major ocean basins, and in places it appeared to be overlain by unusually thick sequences of low-velocity stratified material. Shallow platforms, ridges, and mar-

gins of the Caribbean were found to be characterized by thick crustal assemblages, exceeding 20 km.

The early seismic refraction experiments, carried out mainly before 1960, were followed by single-channel seismic reflection investigations that utilized relatively small sound sources. These single-channel systems were unable to resolve many deeper boundaries, but were very successful in defining the acoustic stratigraphy of material overlying the crystalline basement (J. Ewing

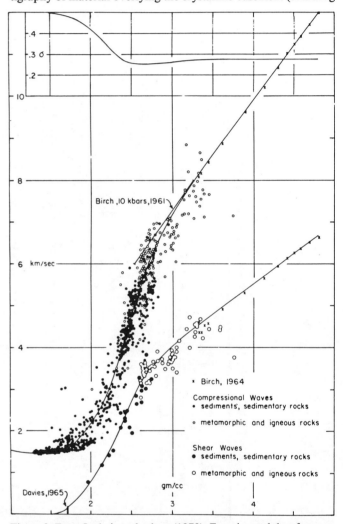

Figure 2. From Ludwig and others (1970). Experimental data for compressional velocity, V_p, and shear velocity, V_s, in unconsolidated sediments, sedimentary, metamorphic, and igneous rocks plotted against the observed densities. The curves drawn through the measured points are joined smoothly at the high-velocity end to the solution II of Birch (1964) for the mantle. The compressional velocity curve is compared over the range 6 to 8 km/sec with the Birch (1961) least-square solution, $V_p = -0.98 + 2/76\rho$ to observations on velocities and densities of rocks at 10 kbars with mean atomic weight less than 24. The velocity-density curves should not be regarded as functional relationships between velocity and density. They are indicative only of the general trend for commonly occurring rocks. Effects of the low-velocity layer in the mantle between densities of about 3.3 and 3.6 gm/cm³ are shown only in the points of the solution II of Birch (1961). The curve of Poisson's ratio, σ, (inset, upper right corner) was drawn from the smooth curves of V_p and V_s. Sources for the figure data are provided in the original article.

and others, 1967; Edgar and others, 1971). Holcombe and others (this volume) provide a summary of data and interpretations derived from seismic reflection.

In a very general way, the early refraction data indicated that the crust below the sedimentary sequence comprises one or two layers having velocities greater than about 5 km/sec (Plate 2; Edgar and others, 1971). Land-refraction data in Cuba (Bovenko and others, 1980, 1982; Scherbakova and others, 1977, 1978, 1980) and Central America (Matumoto and Latham, 1977, Matumoto and others, 1977; Kim and others, 1982) suggest three or more crustal layers (velocities greater than 5.0 km/sec) or many layers having gradual increases in velocity with depth. Similarly, a many-layered crust, including possible low-velocity layers, has been found in the Cordillera Occidental and Cordillera Central of Colombia (Mooney and others, 1979; Flüh and others, 1981; Meissner and others, 1976).

The velocity structure and acoustic stratigraphy of the interior Caribbean area were increasingly refined during the interval from 1970 to 1985 with the use of sonobuoy wide-angle reflection and refraction lines (Ludwig and others, 1975; Houtz and Ludwig, 1977) and multichannel seismic reflection techniques (Ladd and others, 1977; Ladd and Watkins, 1978, 1980; Talwani and others, 1977; Biju-Duval and others, 1978, 1983; Stoffa and others, 1981; Diebold and others, 1981). These studies indicated that crustal thicknesses and velocity structures of the Colombian and Venezuelan Basins are more variable than previously thought, but that the seismic velocities of the basement fall within the range of values associated with the major ocean basins. The apparent thickened crust (20 km) recorded along some of the early refraction lines in the Colombian Basin resulted from the location of these experiments along buried basement ridges (Houtz and Ludwig, 1977).

Major Basins and Troughs

Yucatán Basin. The Yucatán Basin, located south and west of Cuba (Plate 2: b, i, j, k), represents the least studied physiographic province of the Caribbean. Only one unreversed, end-to-end refraction profile has been published (J. Ewing and others, 1960). Mantle velocities were recorded at depths of about 13 km; the crust here has a thickness of 8.5 km (Plate 3), typical of oceanic crust. Apparent acoustic basement of the Yucatán Basin is rough, as indicated by single-channel reflection surveys, and is overlain by as much as 2 seconds (more than 2 km) of stratified material (Dillon and others, 1972; Uchupi, 1973).

Cayman Trough. The Cayman Trough, an anomalous 5- to 6-km-deep east-west cleft between the North American and Caribbean plates, is the result of sea-floor spreading along a short, 100-km extensional ridge zone that links the Oriente transform in the north to the Swan transform in the south (Holcombe and others, 1973, this volume). A number of reversed and unreversed refraction profiles, as well as a gravity model (Bowin, 1968; Plate 2: i, j, k), reveal that the solid crust here is anomalously thin, 5 km, even when compared with that of the major ocean basins (Ewing

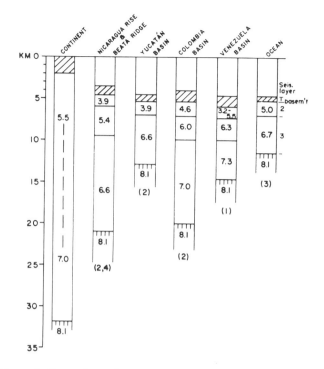

Figure 3. Comparison of velocity structure of Caribbean basins and ridges with those of continents and ocean basins. From Edgar and others, 1971, Figure 9. Seismic velocities in km/sec. Published with permission of the authors and The American Association of Petroleum Geologists.

and others, 1960). A thin blanket, 0.5 to 1.0 km, of 2.0 km/sec sediment overlies a 2.0- to 2.5-km layer of low velocity, 3.3 to 4.7 km/sec, which in turn is underlain by a thin (3.0 km) main crustal layer having a 6.6 km/sec velocity. Velocities typical of upper mantle, 8.2 to 8.3 km/sec, are recorded throughout the Cayman Trough. Submersible sampling on the rift-valley walls of the Mid-Cayman Rise recovered gabbroic and serpentinized ultramafic rocks from scarps, also suggesting that the crust created along this short extensional segment is anomalously thin (CAY-TROUGH, 1979; Stroup and Fox, 1981). Dredges of materials from the walls of the trough include samples of carbonate and clastic rocks and volcanic material (Perfit and Heezen, 1978; Holcombe and others, this volume).

Colombian Basin. The velocity structure of the Colombian Basin has been determined by many widely separated refraction profiles (Officer and others, 1959; J. Ewing and others, 1960; Edgar and others, 1971; Ludwig and others, 1975; Houtz and Ludwig, 1977). The crust of the Colombian Basin has clear oceanic affinities but exhibits variable thickness from 10 to 22 km (Plate 2: e, i, l, m, n, r), which seems related partly to the presence of buried basement ridges (Houtz and Ludwig, 1977). A thick assemblage of sedimentary material, which may or may not contain intrusives in the form of sills (seismic reflector B″), is found throughout much of the Colombian Basin (Plate 2: l, m, n). Sedimentary thicknesses approach 4 km in basement depressions and thin to 1 km over basement highs (see discussion by Holcombe and others, this volume).

Underlying the sedimentary assemblage, crustal velocities range from 4.0 km/sec at shallow levels to 8.0 km/sec, or more, at the crust-mantle boundary. Extrusive and shallow intrusive rocks probably dominate at shallow levels in the velocity range 4.0 to 6.0 km/sec, whereas mafic plutonic rocks or their metamorphic equivalents dominate in the velocity range of 6.4 to 7.3 km/sec at deeper crustal levels. The thickness of this lower crustal layer ranges from 8 km beneath the depressions to 14 km beneath the basement ridges (Plates 2 and 3).

Venezuelan Basin. The Venezuelan Basin has received more attention in terms of seismic surveys than any other Caribbean physiographic province (Plate 2: l, r, s, aa). Officer and colleagues (Officer and others, 1957; Officer and others, 1959) inferred an oceanic character for this basin and demonstrated that, on average, this crust is thicker (depth to M of 15–20 km) than crust of the main ocean basins. The crustal complexity (Plate 2) has been revealed by velocity-depth profiles from sonobuoy and multichannel seismic experiments (Ludwig and others, 1975; Hopkins, 1973; Stoffa and others, 1981; Talwani and others, 1977; Ladd and others, 1977; Biju-Duval and others, 1978; Diebold and others, 1981).

Ludwig and others (1975, p. 115) proposed that " . . . the Venezuela basin has normal oceanic crust that has been depressed about 3 km by the addition of flood basalts, and that the velocity structure of 'typical' Caribbean crust (6.2 on 7.3 km/sec material) does not exist in the Colombia and Venezuela Basins, except as arbitrary divisions in a scattering of crustal and basement velocities that range between 4.0 and 7.5 km/sec, as they do in other ocean basins." Houtz and Ludwig (1977) considered the Colombian Basin to have an oceanic crust that is deeper than normal because of the addition of more than 3 km of sedimentary material. Holcombe and others (this volume) discuss complexities of the shallow crustal character in more detail, including the nature of sub-B″ reflectors and smooth versus rough acoustic basement in the Venezuelan Basin, and interpretations of magnetic anomalies.

Grenada Basin. The Grenada Basin is an elongate and somewhat shallow marine basin, with depths mainly less than 3,000 m, separating the Aves Ridge from the Lesser Antilles island arc. It possibly originated by early Tertiary back-arc spreading as the Lesser Antilles subduction zone migrated eastward away from the Aves Ridge (Westbrook, 1975; Pinet and others, 1985; see also discussion by Morris and others, this volume).

Early studies (Officer and others, 1959) measured a minimum crustal thickness of about 15 km for the central southern Grenada Basin. Subsequent refraction measurements (Boynton and others, 1979) found an average crustal thickness of 18 km for the same area, with mantle velocities near 8.1 km/sec. Seismic refraction studies farther south (Edgar and others, 1971) and in the north (Officer and others, 1959) did not record waves refracted from the M-discontinuity.

The crustal thickness of this basin is somewhat greater than that of typical Atlantic oceanic crust (Plate 3). Grenada Basin crust resembles that of Pacific back-arc basins, with which it presumably shares a similar origin (Westbrook, 1975). The northern half of the Grenada Basin has rougher morphology, shallower water depths, and thinner sedimentary layers, possibly indicative of a history different from that of the southern half (Pinet and others, 1985; Holcombe and others, this volume; see also Rial, 1976).

Major ridges and rises

A variety of mainly submarine ridges and rises are found in the Caribbean region; only the major ridges are treated here. The Mid-Cayman Ridge, a small ridge trending north-south near 082°W, is the only known active ridge of ocean-floor spreading in the Caribbean region (Holcombe and others, 1973; Macdonald and Holcombe, 1978). It is described in more detail by Holcombe and others (this volume).

The elongate Cayman Ridge separates the Yucatán Basin and Cayman Trough. Seismic refraction studies (J. Ewing and others, 1960) suggest a minimum crustal thickness of 17 km over the crest of the Cayman Ridge, although a refraction at M was not clearly identified. Bowin (1968) and Dillon and others (1972) derived a maximum crustal thickness across this ridge of 18 to 20 km by gravity modelling. An origin related to transform faulting is suggested by the active Oriente transform fault that parallels the south limit of the east half of the ridge (Holcombe and others, 1973), and the ridge may also represent a segment of an inactive magmatic arc (Perfit and Heezen, 1978).

Crustal thicknesses are poorly controlled under the Nicaraguan Rise, a major bathymetric high that separates the Colombian Basin from the Cayman Trough. This rise is subdivided into a shallow northern part, the upper rise, and a deeper southern part, the lower rise, by the Pedro Bank fault zone. Two perpendicular reversed refraction lines over the upper rise, and a reversed line over the lower rise, failed to reveal depth to the mantle (J. Ewing and others, 1960). Only at the eastern end of the rise, southwest of Haiti, were J. Ewing and others (1960) successful at sounding depth to M. Their reversed line and an overlapping reversed line (Edgar and others, 1971) indicate crustal thickness in the range of 20 to 23 km. Papazachos (1964) noted that along a travel path between Colombia and Cuba, which crosses the Nicaraguan Rise, surface waves suggest continental crust. The Nicaraguan Rise has several geologic components, the origins of which are mainly unknown as yet. The rise appears to include calc-alkalic magmatic complexes along its northern margin, and continues westward into continental crust of the Chortis block (Plate 3). The southern part has a seismic stratigraphy with affinities to the Colombian Basin (Holcombe and others, this volume).

Both longitudinal and transverse refraction surveys were made across Beata Ridge (J. Ewing and others, 1960; Edgar and others, 1971). An unreversed refraction profile along the ridge trend suggested a maximum crustal thickness of about 17 km near 15°N. Crossing this, a reversed profile showed an average thickness of 23 km. Underlying apparent mantle velocities are high, 8.5 km/sec, along both refraction lines. Normal faults are abundant along the Beata Ridge, especially along its flanks (Case and Holcombe, 1980). Volcanic loading, isostatic(?) uplift, transform faulting (Christofferson, 1973), and block faulting (Fox and Heezen, 1975) have all been proposed as origins for the ridge. Burke and others (1978) have proposed that the ridge was produced by faulting associated with north-south compression of a buoyant Caribbean plate.

Three tectonically related, north-south–trending ridges dominate the eastern Caribbean. From west to east, these are the Aves Ridge, the Lesser Antilles island arc (see Maury and others, this volume), and the Barbados Ridge.

Along the Aves Ridge, numerous seismic investigations have failed to determine the depth to the M-discontinuity (Officer and others, 1957, 1959; Edgar and others, 1971; Boynton and others, 1979). The crustal thickness of this presumed remnant arc (Westbrook, 1975; Pinet and others, 1985) has been estimated at 28 to 31 km by combining seismic data with data from gravity models (Boynton and others, 1979; Kearey, 1974).

According to Rial (1976, p. 1917–1918), "High attenuation of short-period body waves and extremely low surface-wave group velocities have been found for seismic paths that traverse the crust and upper mantle beneath the concave side of the Lesser Antilles island arc (eastern Caribbean). The observations can be explained in terms of . . . models of lithospheric plate subduction at other island arcs, . . . a characteristic of which is the existence of an abnormally low Q zone and upper mantle above the downgoing slab. . . . The Aves swell is probably not related tectonically to the low-Q zone, or to the subduction process, at least presently."

Deformed ridges (see Holcombe and others, this volume)

The crustal structure beneath the Lesser Antilles island arc, which began to evolve in early Tertiary time, has been the subject of many marine geophysical studies (Tolstoy and others, 1953; J. Ewing and others, 1957; Officer and others, 1957, 1959; Edgar and others, 1971; Westbrook, 1975; Boynton and others, 1979; summarized by Speed and others, 1984; see Maury and others, this volume, for additional references). Only one of these studies recorded refracted waves from the Moho beneath the arc. The crustal thickness under the arc is estimated at 30 to 35 km by modelling of gravity data, which is controlled laterally by seismic refraction data (Westbrook, 1975; Boynton and others, 1979).

The Barbados Ridge is a narrow ridge trending south from Barbados Island. This ridge marks the bathymetric high of the Barbados accretionary prism. That thick wedge of deformed sediment has been accumulating since the early Tertiary along the convergence axis of the Lesser Antilles subduction zone. Numerous seismic refraction investigations have been made of this accretionary prism (J. Ewing and others, 1957; Officer and others, 1957, 1959; Edgar and others, 1971; Westbrook, 1975; Boynton and others, 1979). Near Barbados, J. Ewing and others (1957) showed that the minimum thickness of this prism is 10 km. From

analysis of seismic, gravity, and magnetic data, Westbrook (1975) concluded that the accretionary prism above the oceanic igneous layers attains a thickness of about 20 km near Barbados. Northward the prism thins. At 18°N, the total crustal thickness, including the oceanic igneous layers, was found to be 14 km above mantle of velocity 8.35 to 8.64 km/sec (Officer and others, 1959). Refraction experiments at the south end of the prism did not detect the M-discontinuity (Edgar and others, 1971; Speed and others, 1984).

The Curaçao Ridge, an eastward prolongation of the south Caribbean deformed belt, is another bathymetric high associated with an accretionary complex. Its seismic characteristics have been investigated by many groups, including Edgar and others (1971), Silver and others (1975), Talwani and others (1977), and Ladd and others (1984). The thickness of deformed strata above igneous layers of the subducting Caribbean crust exceeds 14 km under the axis of the Curaçao Ridge (Edgar and others, 1971). A comparable thickness, 12 km, of deformed strata in the accretionary wedge was derived by Silver and others (1975) by modelling a gravity profile across the ridge.

Talwani and others (1977) noted a progressive southward decrease in upper-mantle velocities in the Caribbean plate in seismic reflection records approaching the Curaçao Ridge. This observation indicates that a systematic regional investigation of upper-mantle velocity and velocity anisotropy could lead to a better understanding of many major Caribbean crustal structures.

Margins and land areas

Only a few determinations of crustal thickness have been made for land areas in this region (Plates 2 and 3). Refraction studies in Cuba (Plate 2: x) employed high-energy sources in quarries or lakes that were detected by variably spaced seismometer arrays (Shcherbakova and others, 1978, 1980; Bovenko and others, 1980, 1982). High-energy sources, both on land and offshore, have also been used to study the continental margin transition in northwestern South America (Plate 2g, 2h; Meissner and others, 1976; Meyer and others, 1976; Flüh and others, 1981, Flüh, 1983). In Central America, seismic studies have utilized both artificial and earthquake sources in analyses of crustal structure (Plate 2d; Matumoto and Latham, 1977; Matumoto and others, 1976, 1977; Kim and others, 1982).

Shcherbakova and others (1980) defined a three-layer crust in western Cuba: an upper layer having velocities of 2.0 to 4.6 km/sec, associated with volcanic metasedimentary and carbonate metaclasite formations; a middle layer having average velocities of 6.2 km/sec; and a lower crustal layer having average velocities of 7.2 km/sec. The crust ranges from 21 to 33 km in thickness. In eastern Cuba, Bovenko and others (1980, 1982) recognized an upper layer having velocities of 4.0 to 5.8 km/sec and a second layer having velocities of 6.9 to 7.8 km/sec; a mantle velocity of 8.1 km/sec was assumed in their calculations. A great variation in crustal thickness—from about 12 to 34 km—was found in their study (Plate 2: x; see also Iturralde and others, 1986).

In northern Central America, Kim and others (1982) identified three main layers: an upper layer, about 9 km thick, having a velocity of about 5.9 km/sec, which was correlated with Tertiary volcanic rocks and possibly older sedimentary rocks beneath; a second layer, about 15 km thick, having an average velocity of about 6.1 km/sec, possibly the crystalline basement of late Paleozoic or older rocks; and a third layer, about 13 km thick, probably a mafic complex. A mantle velocity of 8.0 km/sec was assumed for their computations.

From analysis of small earthquakes, Matumoto and others (1977) determined a crustal thickness of about 44 km in Costa Rica; they identified two main crustal layers: an upper layer, about 8 km thick, having a velocity of about 5.1 km/sec, and a lower layer, about 36 km thick, in which the velocity increases from 6.1 to 6.6 km/sec (Plate 2: d). Mantle velocity is about 7.9 km/sec. Offshore, near the Nicoya Peninsula, 7 km of material having velocities of 5.0 km/sec or lower, overlies 13 km of 5.9 km/sec material, which in turn, overlies material having velocities of about 6.4 km/sec (lower crust?); mantle velocities were not detected (Buffler and others, 1985).

In northwestern Colombia, Flüh and others (1981; and E. R. Flüh, personal communication, 1987) interpreted the crustal structure from east to west (Plate 2: g) as follows: Cordillera Central (continental crust), about 20 km of 6.1 km/sec material (upper crust) above 21 to 26 km of 6.5 km/sec material (lower crust); Cordillera Occidental (oceanic crust), about 32 km of complex crust having velocities of 5.7 to 6.9 km/sec, including a low-velocity zone; Serrania de Baudó, about 8 to 10 km of 5.7 to 6.7 km/sec material above 20 km of material having velocities of 6.7 to 6.9 km/sec; crustal structure of the Panamá Basin is normal oceanic. Mantle velocities of 8.0 and 7.8 km/sec were assumed.

GRAVITY EVIDENCE BEARING ON CARIBBEAN CRUSTAL STRUCTURE

Gravity data are useful for estimating crustal thickness and density, especially when tied to refraction profiles. Although gravity anomaly models yield nonunique solutions, limits are provided by the known ranges of rock densities and through use of such empirical velocity-density curves as those by Ludwig and others (1970; Fig. 2).

The most comprehensive report of gravity anomalies of the Caribbean region was prepared by Bowin (1976). His compilation and interpretation of free-air and simple Bouguer anomaly maps were based on land and offshore data collected by many different groups. An updated gravity anomaly map has been compiled by Westbrook and others (Plate 7). Many gravitationally derived crustal models are shown on Plate 2; the following discussion is keyed to the gravity anomaly map and Plate 2.

Isostatic anomalies provide valuable insight into active structures and the tectonic processes that produce them. Isostatic anomalies are computed from free-air anomalies using corrections for topography, for water depth, and for changes in assumed depth to a compensating level (an arbitrary depth above which Archimedean mass-balance is assumed) as a function of elevation, according to such models as those of Airy, Pratt, or Heiskanen. From comparison of topography, free-air, and Bouguer anomalies, and computed isostatic anomalies, subjective interpretations can be made of the extent of regional isostatic balance. Isostatic anomalies that average about zero over large areas suggest that columns are in approximate mass balance. Negative isostatic anomalies may indicate mass deficiencies, as compared with "standard" columns, and such areas should tend to rise. Positive anomalies indicate mass excess and should tend to sink. Where the mass excesses or deficiencies are sustained, horizontal forces are overriding vertical forces. Many negative or positive isostatic anomalies have intracrustal sources, as determined from steep gradients; thick, low-density sedimentary basins may produce lows, or thick sequences of mafic volcanic rocks, for example, may produce highs. With additional input from seismicity (McCann and Pennington, this volume) and neotectonic data (Mann and others, this volume), some inferences about the Neogene state of stress can be drawn.

Isostatic anomalies have been calculated for the Lesser Antilles by Andrew and others (1970), for the eastern Caribbean by Bush and Bush (1969), for the Netherlands Antilles by Lagaay (1969), for northern South America by Hospers and van Wijnen (1959), for the Venezuelan borderland by O. Snellius (cited by Worzel, 1965), and for Costa Rica, including an isostatic residual anomaly map, by Ponce and Case (1986, 1987). Anomalies for a few other areas were cited by Bowin (1976). Notably lacking are isostatic anomaly maps for most of Central America and for much of the marine region of the Caribbean.

Quantitative estimates of the mass in a crustal column down to some level below the crust-mantle interface can be made and compared with "standard" oceanic or continental crustal columns. Columns having greater than standard masses are regarded as having excess mass. Such comparisons were made by Edgar and others (1971) who computed the mass per unit area to a depth of 32 km at each refraction receiving station that recorded mantle velocities. Velocities were converted to densities using the Nafe-Drake velocity-density curves. A "standard" oceanic mass of 93.1×10^5 gm/cm^2 was computed by similar methods using an assumed density of 3.4 g/cm^3. The mass per unit area of an average Venezuela Basin velocity section is 91.59×10^5 g/cm^2, which is slightly lower than, but very similar to the "standard" oceanic mass. Similar computations also have been made for gravity models by Bowin (1976), Talwani and others (1959), Silver and others (1975), Kellogg and Bonini (1982); and others, briefly discussed below.

Offshore areas
(see Plate 7)

Caribbean Sea. The Yucatán Basin appears to be in approximate isostatic equilibrium, with free-air anomalies near zero (Plate 2; see Bowin, 1976). Negative anomalies in areas south of

Cuba and along the Yucatán borderland probably reflect thick, low-density sedimentary deposits. These areas are virtually aseismic.

Gravity anomalies (Plate 2: j, k) along the Cayman Trough generally reflect the topography. This region is in apparent isostatic equilibrium except for the bathymetric deeps at the edges of the trough and bordering highs (Bowin, 1968, 1976). The Cayman Trough has a low to moderate level of seismicity, consistent with low spreading rates at the Mid-Cayman Ridge (Holcombe and others; McCann and Pennington, this volume).

Free-air anomalies over both the northern and southern Nicaraguan Rise average near zero, indicating approximate isostatic equilibrium. Scattered hypocenters, graben structures, and isolated volcanic bodies may indicate slow extension within the rise.

In the Colombian and Venezuelan basins, free-air anomalies are near zero, indicating approximate isostatic equilibrium. Local lows over Beata Ridge are superimposed on a general high, and local highs occur over Aves Ridge, both areas of relatively thickened crust. Larger negative anomalies occur over the accretionary prism of the north Caribbean deformed belt, south of Puerto Rico (Plate 2: z); over the south Caribbean deformed belt, north of Colombia and Venezuela (Plate 2: t, u, k); and over the north Panamá deformed belt (Plate 2: e). These lows are attributable to thick prisms of deformed, low-density mainly Tertiary sedimentary strata, thickened by Neogene convergence along the respective north and south Caribbean plate boundaries.

Atlantic. East of the main Caribbean basins, the Puerto Rico Trench partly coincides with the northern part of the famed "negative strip" (Hess, 1938; Vening-Meinesz and Wright, 1930). The large negative free-air anomaly (–350 mGals) over the trench has been analyzed by Talwani and others (1959) and Talwani (1964), using refraction data for control (Plate 2: z). They found that the anomaly can be produced by contrasts involving the great water depth (up to 8 km), low-density sediment layers (about 3 km of material of density 2.0–2.4 g/cm^3), and a two-layer, relatively thick crust (depth to M = 17 to 22 km, densities 2.7 and 3.0 g/cm^3) as compared with adjacent Atlantic crust (M = 10–13 km). Their model still resulted in a net mass deficiency over the trench as compared with a standard oceanic column, and they concluded that the trench is out of local mass balance, as indicated by Airy isostatic anomalies of –250 to –350 mGals. Farther southeast, the negative free-air anomaly corresponds to great thicknesses (20+ km) of deformed Tertiary deposits of low density (about 2.0 to 2.5 g/cm^3) in the accretionary prism fronting the Lesser Antilles (Plate 2: bb, cc; see Bowin, 1976; Westbrook, 1975; Westbrook, 1982). Bowin found a net mass deficiency over the deformed complex. Pratt-Hayford isostatic anomalies range from about –100 to –150 mGals (Bush and Bush, 1969).

Pacific. West of the Caribbean region, a major negative free-air anomaly overlies the Middle America Trench (Plate 2: a, b, c) and filled segments of the Colombian Trench (Plate 2: e, see Couch and Woodcock, 1981; Victor, 1976; Briceño-Guarupe, 1978).

Land areas

Greater Antilles. Western Cuba appears to be in local mass equilibrium, to judge by negative Bouguer anomalies (Soloviev and others, 1964). The gravity and refraction data of central Cuba are less determinate, but probably the crust is in mass balance there too. Eastern Cuba shows very large positive Bouguer anomalies (+100 to +150 mGals), even over some high elevations, and thus points to large mass imbalance. The excess mass beneath eastern Cuba indicates a shallow fragment of upper mantle or oceanic crust, as shown by the many exposed mafic and ultramafic bodies. We suggest that a dense, wedgelike(?) block is present, possibly resulting from convergence (Paleogene?) between the North American and Caribbean plates along the Cayman boundary or between eastern Cuba and the Bahamas block along the Old Bahamas Passage boundary. The low level of seismic activity suggests that this excess mass presently is being supported by flow rather than by fracture.

Over Jamaica, Bouguer anomalies range from about zero to as much as +100 mGals over the Blue Mountains (Plate 7), and excess mass and positive isostatic anomalies were indicated by Andrew (1969; cited by Bowin, 1976). Seismicity and positive Bouguer anomalies here suggest uplift associated with faults of the adjacent Cayman transform system, as do uplifted terraces (Mann and others, this volume).

Bouguer anomalies over Hispaniola are generally positive, and range from zero to +100 mGals (Bowin, 1976). They indicate a lack of mass balance and suggest positive isostatic anomalies. Values as low as –100 mGals for the major basins indicate thick, low-density Tertiary sedimentary fill (Plate 2: o). Large positive Bouguer anomalies and high seismicity in eastern Hispaniola may be related to incipient subduction of the Bahamas platform or other elements of the North America plate (McCann and Sykes, 1984; McCann and Pennington, this volume).

Bouguer anomalies in excess of +100 mGals are found over Puerto Rico, locally at high elevations. Talwani and others (1959) computed isostatic anomalies of +55 to +84 mGal (T = 32 km) for the island (Plate 2: z); Talwani (1964) also computed a net excess mass for the island as compared with a "standard" oceanic column. This positive belt extends eastward through the Virgin Islands, paralleling the negative anomaly zone to the north.

Lesser Antilles. In the eastern Caribbean region a major positive gravity anomaly belt occurs parallel to and east of the northern Lesser Antilles. Southward, this belt follows the trend of the islands in the southern Lesser Antilles. The free-air high, which ranges from +100 to +200 mGals, continues southwest to Margarita Island. Many isostatic anomalies, computed for the Lesser Antilles by Andrew and others (1970), exceed +100 mGals. These positive anomalies indicate that the Lesser Antilles are not in mass balance with respect to standard oceanic columns, and that considerable excess mass is present (Plate 2: bb, and cc).

Comparatively high seismic velocities at shallow depths (Officer and others, 1959; Westbrook and Ladd, 1984) are consistent with the thick and dense crust beneath the Lesser Antilles (see models by Bowin, 1976; and Westbrook, 1975). These data may be explained by (1) multiple stacking of obducted oceanic crust during the earlier stages of convergence between the ancestral Caribbean and North American plates, or (2) from loading by early mafic volcanism along the magmatic arc. Active seismicity indicates that the Lesser Antilles and northeastern Venezuela-Trinidad regions are presently in a high state of stress related to tectonic convergence (McCann and Pennington, this volume).

South America. Major negative free-air and Bouguer anomalies over the eastern Venezuela Basin indicate mass deficiencies of the thick sedimentary fill and, in the east, low-density intracrustal masses (Plate 2: w, dd; see Bowin, 1976; Bonini, 1978). A southwestward extension of the Lesser Antilles accretionary zone might be suggested by the continuity of the negative Bouguer anomaly across the margin of northeastern South America. If so, the zone crosses the El Pilar fault zone, widely assumed to be part of the boundary between the South American and Caribbean plates (see discussions by Bowin, 1976; Bonini, 1978; Pérez and Aggarwal, 1981). Crustal thicknesses of 25 to 47 km have been computed from gravity anomalies (Bowin, 1976; Bonini, 1978).

In western Venezuela, regional isostatic anomalies over the Maracaibo Basin are as low as –60 mGals. Negative gravity anomalies of this basin are consistent with the great thickness of low-density sedimentary rocks (4–8 km; Plate 2: v). By contrast, the adjacent Merida Andes, a zone of moderate seismicity, has regional isostatic anomalies from +10 to +20 mGals (Bouguer anomalies from –40 to –60 mGals; Hospers and van Wijnen, 1959).

Positive free-air and Bouguer anomalies of more than +100 mGals along most of the Netherlands and Venezuelan Antilles indicate mass imbalance with excess mass (Plate 2: t, u). Lagaay (1969) showed that isostatic anomalies range from +50 mGals to +100 mGals over the Netherlands Antilles where Cretaceous mafic submarine volcanic rocks are abundant. The uplifted dense mass may be sustained by rather slow tectonic convergence across the South Caribbean deformed belt, consistent with the low level of seismicity.

In northwestern Colombia, where the Guajira Peninsula and Sierra Nevada de Santa Marta are characterized by Precambrian basement gneisses, Bouguer anomalies range from +100 to more than +125 mGals. The positive anomalies over the Sierra Nevada persist up to 2,000 m. According to Case and MacDonald (1973), Bouguer anomalies attain values exceeding +130 mGals in the northwest corner of the Santa Marta massif, and would be greater if local topographic corrections were taken into account. These strongly positive values may be due in part to relatively dense metamorphic rocks. But more significantly, they indicate thin continental crust and that the area is out of isostatic equilibrium. Bonini and others (1980) modelled a two-layer crust having densities of 2.7 and 2.8 g/cm^3, extending to a depth of about 25 km (Plate 2: v). As in the Netherlands Antilles region,

uplift of this crustal block is associated with slow tectonic convergence between the Caribbean and South American plates. The massif shows low historic seismic activity, in spite of the youthful character of the bordering faults (Mann and others, this volume).

Farther southwest along the Colombian coast, Bouguer anomalies are slightly negative (0 to –50 mGals), consistent with the thickness (as much as 10 km) of low-density Tertiary deposits (Plate 3, cross section).

Continental crust, up to 45 km thick, underlies the Central and Oriental Cordilleras of northern Colombia (Plate 2: f, g, h; Plate 3, cross section). Bouguer anomalies are negative, ranging from –120 to –180 mGals. Neogene to Holocene uplift is indicated here.

The Colombian Cordillera Occidental, Serrania de Baudó, and eastern Panamá, characterized by abundant Cretaceous mafic volcanic rocks, have strong positive Bouguer anomalies, ranging up to +100 mGals. Refraction data in western Colombia indicate crustal thicknesses up to 30 km (Plate 2: f, g, h). The area is out of isostatic equilibrium with an excess of mass, probably sustained by convergence between the Nazca and South American plates. Generally speaking, a high level of seismicity characterizes this northwest corner of South America, in the general vicinity of the triple junction along which the Caribbean–South America and Caribbean-Nazca convergence zones unite.

Central America. Western Panamá and Costa Rica have Bouguer anomalies ranging from zero to –100 mGals. The area is probably in mass balance, except on the Azuero and Nicoya Peninsulas where large positive isostatic residual anomalies of more than +100 mGals occur (Ponce and Case, 1986, 1987). From exposures of basalt and pelagic strata, deformed oceanic crust is inferred to extend in an accretionary zone under parts of the Chorotega block (Escalante, this volume) in the isthmus linking the Chortis block to South America (Plate 2: d). Near San Jose, Costa Rica, a large negative Bouguer anomaly (Plate 7) coextensive with Neogene volcanic rocks, suggests the presence of an included "continental" block within the accretionary zone where the crustal thickness is more than 40 km.

To the northwest in Nicaragua, Honduras, El Salvador, Guatemala, and southern Mexico, Bouguer anomalies are generally negative (0 to –125 mGals). The Chortis and Maya blocks are underlain by continental crust (Plate 3, cross section), except for accretionary slivers of oceanic materials caught up in the Motagua fault zone and in the accretionary prism associated with the Middle America trench (Case and others, 1984). This region appears to be in isostatic equilibrium for the most part (Plate 2: a, b). A high level of seismicity characterizes the triple junction where the Middle America convergence zone is apparently intersected by the Motagua-Polochic fault system of the western Cayman Trough transform zone.

The low-lying Yucatán Peninsula is in virtual mass equilibrium, having free-air and Bouguer anomalies of ±50 mGals. At the northeast margin, however, anomalies locally exceed +100 mGals, indicating a dense mass, probably intracrustal because gradients on the flank of the anomaly are steep.

CRUSTAL THICKNESS AND DEPTH TO THE M–DISCONTINUITY

Contour maps of crustal thickness and depth to M have been prepared from the available geophysical data (Plate 3).

The base of the crust is presumed to be a compositional boundary or a phase change that is not directly observable. Its location can be approximated by the M-velocity discontinuity, below which upper-mantle velocities are commonly 7.8 km/sec or greater. Such velocities have been measured in eclogite and in ultramafic rocks like peridotite, dunite, and pyroxenite (Christensen, 1982), and thus are consistent with materials inferred to represent the upper mantle.

The velocity contrast defined as M may represent different phenomena at various localities under continental and oceanic crust. Under oceanic crust, at least three different interpretations have been offered for M: (1) The boundary between ultramafic cumulates and ultramafic mantle tectonites (see Coleman, 1977; Hopson and others, 1981), but whether these rocks have greatly different velocities is unclear. (2) The contact between gabbro and cumulate dunite in oceanic crustal cumulates ("seismic moho" of Gass and Smewing, 1973). (3) The base of hydrated serpentinized mantle under ocean basins; that is, a hydration "front" (Hess, 1962).

The usual assumption in interpreting depth to M is that it represents the lowest plagioclase-bearing level in the oceanic section of crustal cumulates. In areas of continental crust, structural and intrusive complexities lead to additional interpretations for M: (4) A structural contact across a low-angle detachment fault, as in the case of listric extensional faulting to the base of the crust or as in delamination (Lister and others, 1986; Bird, 1979). (5) An intrusive contact, such as the base of a large body intruded at the base of the crust, and with or without differentiation and metamorphism (Furlong and Fountain, 1986; Lister and others, 1986; Fyfe, 1978). (6) Phase changes, such as gabbro-eclogite (Lovering, 1958; Green and Ringwood, 1967), or mafic granulite-eclogite transitions, may represent M under both oceanic and continental realms. Because such phase changes may be thermally sensitive (Griffin and O'Reilly, 1987), anomalous depths to M may reflect elevated geotherms, especially in regions of recent igneous activity.

Any assumption, especially in contouring depths or thicknesses, is not without its risks, as the preceding list of alternative interpretive possibilities makes clear.

Errors in the contours can result from many different causes. For example, the control points for estimates of thickness of solid crust and depth to M (Plate 3: b, c) are very irregularly distributed. Better seismic control over marine areas than over land areas leads to more reliable contours over most marine areas. Also, the different geophysical methods—seismic reflection, seismic refraction, and gravity—have different resolving powers. Depths could be in error by 5 km, or even more, where smoothed estimates from graivty models have been used for control. Thus, contour maps should be regarded as approximations until much more seismic refraction and deep-crustal reflection data become available.

Depth to the M-discontinuity varies greatly in the region. In areas of continental crust, such as Central America and the Guayana Shield, depth to M varies from about 25 to 45 km (Plate 3). In areas of oceanic crust, the depth varies from about 10 to 20 km. In zones of accreted crust, the depth ranges from 15 to 30 km. Thickness of the solid crust (excluding water layer) ranges from 5 to 45 km (Plate 3).

The configuration of the base of accretionary crust is probably more complex than shown. Highly variable depths to M are suggested for Cuba, where refraction data are most complete (Bovenko and others, 1980, 1982; Shcherbakova and others, 1978, 1980). This irregularity may be typical for analogous accretionary crustal areas elsewhere around the Caribbean.

CRUSTAL PROVINCES

Basic crustal types

As noted earlier, the three major crustal types are oceanic, continental, and accretionary (Fig. 4).

Oceanic crust is formed mainly at mid-oceanic ridges and hotspots, and to a lesser extent at leaky transform faults and by spreading in back-arc basins.

Continental crust, consisting of masses 25 to 45 km thick, was formed by primitive mantle differentiation and multiple episodes of magmatism, sedimentation, and metamorphism. It is typically old crystalline rock, predominantly Precambrian but also incorporating Paleozoic metamorphic terranes.

Accretionary crust consists of tectonites of diverse origins: igneous, sedimentary, and metamorphic. The principal process operating to collect and reshape rocks into accretionary masses is plate convergence in a subduction or obduction mode. The locus of accretion, as used here, is along former or active convergent plate margins.

Assignment of pre-Mesozoic crystalline rocks to continental crust and of Mesozoic and younger metamorphic assemblages to accretionary crust is a somewhat arbitrary convention. The major part of continental crust may have evolved by processes of tectonic accretion and subsequent modification throughout Precambrian and Phanerozoic time (MacDonald, 1972a; Reymer and Schubert, 1983). Some authors use the term accretionary in referring to new crust which, by magmatism, forms at the trailing edges of diverging plates. Such a process is undoubtedly one of accretion. The resulting crust is, however, widely recognized by common consensus as oceanic. From this point of view, the term *tectonitic crust* (MacDonald, 1972a) might be preferable to accretionary crust. However, prevailing usage favors the latter.

Indeterminate crust results where geologic events have obscured the crustal genesis. Sedimentation or volcanism may simultaneously thicken oceanic crust, while also "masking," perhaps through burial or through burial metamorphism, the original magnetic "stripping" (area 6, Fig. 4). Similarly, continental crust

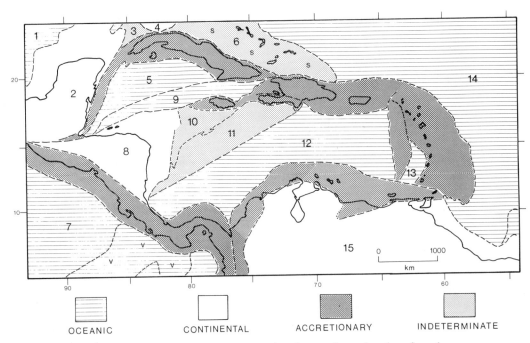

Figure 4. Crustal types in the Caribbean region. See text for explanation of numbers.

OCEANIC   CONTINENTAL   ACCRETIONARY   INDETERMINATE

might be thinned in places by extension, and subsequently covered by a thick sedimentary veneer. Distinguishing the genetic origin of some crust, therefore, may not be possible.

Modifications of the basic crustal types

Igneous, sedimentary, and tectonic processes of diverse kinds mask or alter the essential character of the crust. For example, thick veneers of sedimentary or volcanic strata obscure the underlying crustal foundation, as noted above. Formation of magmatic arcs associated with subduction adds large amounts of new materials as extensive sheets of volcanic strata, massive batholithic intrusions, and reworked materials (Plate 3, cross sections). Hot-spot magmatism is believed to increase crustal thickness in oceanic areas by producing linear aseismic ridges of mafic materials, both extrusive and intrusive (Cocos Ridge, for example). In continental areas, hot-spot magmatism may result in a net thinning of the crust, as a consequence of partial melting and explosive caldera eruption (Suppe and others, 1975).

Tectonic movements are also important. Lateral shear, caused by oblique convergence or transform faulting, imprints cataclastic metamorphic effects while also tectonically mixing crustal components. Imbricate underthrusting and overthrusting (obduction; Oxburgh, 1972) during plate convergence likewise displaces crustal layers into new configurations, while increasing crustal thickness (Plate 3, cross sections). Sedimentary and volcanic strata may be folded into or underplated onto the adjacent crust in these environments (Watkins and others, 1981). Also, crustal collision of allochthonous blocks may juxtapose crustal masses of very different origins (in northwestern Colombia, for example).

Finally, crustal thickness may be reduced by tectonic erosion along trenches, a process that recycles crustal materials into the mantle, along with other subducted oceanic crustal materials (Rutland, 1971; Scholl and others, 1980; Hussong and Wipperman, 1981). Complicating the interpretation of crustal events in many areas of former subduction zones are the effects of metamorphism, partial fusion, and metasomatism, all of which give older crustal materials a new mineralogic, textural, and structural identity.

With the above processes in mind, the crustal provinces of the Caribbean are reviewed. The genetic origins of some of these provinces are unknown as a result of the complications noted above. Nevertheless, common characteristics of thickness, relief, elevation, age, lithology, structure, and so forth serve to define the provinces. Because of the voluminous geological literature, we mention only a few references; many additional references are in the report by Case and others (1984) and elsewhere in this volume.

Oceanic crustal provinces. Oceanic crust in the Caribbean region is of many different but often imprecisely known ages. In order of increasing apparent age, the major provinces including associated ridges, are:

a. Cayman Trough (area 9, Fig. 4): Miocene or older(?) to Holocene (Holcombe and others, this volume; Perfit and Heezen, 1978; Rosencrantz and others, 1988); this is the only area having identified paired sea-floor spreading magnetic anomalies as identified by Macdonald and Holcombe (1978).

b. Cocos/Nazca crust (area 7, Fig. 4): Eocene(?) to Holocene (Lonsdale and Klitgord, 1978; van Andel and others, 1971; Couch and Woodcock, 1981).

c. Grenada back-arc basin (area 13, Fig. 4): Age unknown,

possibly Paleogene(?) (Biju-Duval and others, 1978; Pinet and others, 1985).

d. Yucatán Basin (area 5, Fig. 4): Age unknown, possibly Cretaceous(?) to Paleogene(?) (Dillon and others, 1972; Uchupi, 1973; Hall and Yeung, 1980).

e. Colombian and Venezuelan Basins (area 12, Fig. 4): Cretaceous or older (Edgar and others, 1971; Holcombe and others, this volume; Ghosh and others, 1984); perhaps Jurassic (Diebold and others, 1981).

f. Atlantic (area 14, Fig. 4): Jurassic to Cretaceous near the Caribbean region (Vogt and Tucholke, 1986; Sheridan and Grow, 1988).

Gulf of Mexico (1): Mid-Mesozoic age (?) (Antoine and Ewing, 1963; Buffler and others, 1980, 1981; Ibrahim and others, 1981; see also Salvador, 1990 and Sawyer and Buffler, 1990).

Continental crust: The principal blocks. Broad expanses of lower density crust, in thicknesses of 25 to 45 km, characterize the continental crust of the region. The oldest known rocks are in the 3-billion-year-old Imataca complex of the Guayana Shield in Venezuela. The principal blocks of continental crust are:

a. South American continent (area 15, Fig. 4), including the Guayana Shield and its lateral equivalents exposed in the Merida Andes, Central and Eastern Cordilleras of Colombia, Sierra Nevada de Santa Marta, and Guajira peninsular ranges (Martín-Bellizzia, 1974; Martín, 1978; Gibbs and Baron, 1983; Onstott and Hargraves, 1982; Case and others, this volume).

b. Chortis block of Central America (area 8, Fig. 4) (Dengo, 1973; Horne and others, 1976a, 1976b, this volume; Weyl, 1980).

c. Maya block of Central America (area 2, Fig. 4) (Dengo, 1973; López Ramos, 1981; Donnelly and López-Ramos, this volume).

d. North American continent (area 4, Fig. 4) represented by the south tip of the Florida Peninsula, possibly attenuated continental crust (see also Barnett, 1975; Klitgord and others, 1984; and Salvador, 1990).

Zones of accretionary crust. Five major, geologically distinct zones of accretionary crust can be distinguished in the Caribbean region (shaded unnumbered areas of Fig. 4). These zones form a discontinuous loop around the Caribbean. The age of accumulation ranges from Jurassic to Recent. Over most of the area, there were two principal accretionary episodes: Cretaceous to Paleogene, and Eocene to Holocene. The major accretionary zones are:

a. Central American accretionary complex (Seely, 1979; von Huene and others, 1980; Woodcock, 1975; Couch and Woodcock, 1981; Ladd and others, this volume; Aubouin and others, 1981, 1982).

b. North Panamá deformed belt (Case and Holcombe, 1980; Lu and others, 1983).

c. South Caribbean–northern South America accretionary complexes (Holcombe and others, this volume; Silver and others, 1975; Edgar and others, 1971; Talwani and others, 1977; Ladd

and Watkins, 1979; Bellizzia and Dengo, this volume; Case and others, 1984).

d. Lesser Antilles accretionary complex (Speed and others, 1984; Westbrook, 1975; Holcombe and others, this volume; Maury and others, this volume; Westbrook and McCann, 1986).

d. Greater Antilles accretionary complex (Lewis and others, this volume; Khudoley and Meyerhoff, 1971; Ladd and others, this volume; Ladd and Watkins, 1978; Biju-Duval and others, 1983).

Most of the accretionary complexes probably result from normal or somewhat oblique tectonic convergence. Segments of some complexes, however, may have been emplaced at their present sites after great lateral displacements from original sites of formation, as indicated by data from paleomagnetic investigations.

Unknowns in the genesis of Caribbean crust

Some of the uncertainties in the age, origin, and intrinsic nature of the Caribbean crust follow.

Oceanic crust. Except for a small area with symmetric magnetic anomalies spanning the Mid-Cayman Ridge (and some scientists question the age assignments), neither the age nor the spreading fabric of any other part of the Caribbean oceanic crust is known with certainty (see magnetic map compiled by Hall and Westbrook, this volume).

The oldest crust is probably in the Gulf of Mexico, where a widespread Jurassic evaporite layer indicates a Mesozoic age (see Salvador, 1989). The overlying Mesozoic and Cenozoic deposits here exceed 10 km in thickness, and make the underlying crustal floor difficult to reach with drilling technology of the 1980s.

The Yucatán Basin (area 5, Fig. 4) may be of back-arc or fore-arc origin, but sphenochasmic rifting has also been proposed (Dillon and others, 1972). Hall and Yeung (1980) attributed northeast-trending magnetic anomalies there to spreading of Late Cretaceous through Early Cenozoic time. A pattern of ridges and valleys radiates from the southwest corner of the basin, but an orthogonal ridge and transform morphology characteristic of oceanic crust is not apparent.

A back-arc spreading origin has also been postulated for the Grenada Basin (area 13, Fig. 4), associated with a Cretaceous to Paleogene eastward migration of the Lesser Antilles subduction zone (Biju-Duval and others, 1978; Pinet and others, 1985). Pinet and others also considered the possibility that the Grenada Basin crust may be a fragment of older oceanic crust isolated by a Paleogene subduction-zone jump toward the east.

As noted previously, the Colombian and Venezuelan Basins (area 12, Fig. 4) have been shown by wide-angle reflection and vertical reflection studies (Houtz and Ludwig, 1977; Diebold and others, 1981) to be closer in thickness to normal oceanic crust than was suggested by earlier refraction work (J. Ewing and others, 1957, 1960). Greater crustal thickness in the Venezuelan Basin has been attributed to loading by flood basalts and in the

Colombian Basin to loading by sedimentary deposits (Houtz and Ludwig, 1977; Ludwig and others, 1975). The age, orientation of oceanic ocean-floor spreading fabric (if any), and ultimate locus of origin of these basins are still mysteries to most geologists. The Deep Sea Drilling Project (DSDP) drilling penetrated Turonian, Campanian, and younger strata, and deeper seismic reflectors are therefore Turonian or older (see Holcombe and others, this volume). The water depth is anomalously shallow for crust of Cretaceous age. Burke and others (1978) have explored explanations for an unusual apparent buoyancy of the crust. A possible Late Cretaceous plateau flood-basalt eruption has been postulated for these basins (Donnelly, 1973; Donnelly and others, this volume) and may mask the original spreading fabric and magnetic patterns. Discussions of magnetic patterns have been summarized by Holcombe and others (this volume).

Continental crust. The extent of Precambrian continental crust in the Caribbean region is still imprecisely known. Many areas require further mapping and radiometric dating to resolve the distribution and age of crystalline terranes. Deep drilling to the continental basement is also needed. In South America, widely spaced data suggest that the northern limit of Precambrian crust extends from the central Guajira Peninsula through the central Sierra Nevada de Santa Marta to the west flank of the Cordillera Central (area 15, Fig. 4; Plate 3, cross section). This limit is covered by thick Tertiary sedimentary sequences over broad areas in northern Colombia (San Jorge Basin, Rancheria Basin) and northern Venezuela (Falcón Basin).

In Central America, Precambrian rocks are exposed in the southern Maya block and possibly in the northern Chortis block (area 8, Fig. 4). In the Chortis block, possible Precambrian metamorphic rocks are known only in northern Honduras (Horne and others, 1976a, and this volume), although metamorphic rocks of unknown age are much more widely distributed. The metamorphic rocks appear to extend southward beneath the volcanic apron of central Honduras into Nicaragua and eastward in the Nicaraguan Rise.

Precambrian rocks exposed along the south edge of the Maya block (area 2, Fig. 4; López Ramos, 1981; Gomberg and others, 1968; and Donnelly and others, this volume) are presumed also to underlie much of the Maya block. Much of the Maya block is covered by thick Mesozoic and Cenozoic strata. Pennsylvanian and Permian strata are exposed in the Maya Mountains of Belize (Donnelly and others, this volume).

The age of the deep crust under south Florida is similarly unclear (area 4, Fig. 4). Deep wells in central Florida have yielded Paleozoic fossils. The continental crust of Florida thins southward, where the oldest rocks drilled under south Florida are Jurassic volcanic rocks. The foundation for these is unknown (Klitgord and others, 1984; Sawyer and Buffler, 1990).

Accretionary zones. The contact between the Precambrian and Paleozoic continental crust of South America and the accretionary terranes of the south Caribbean margin is basically the landward limit of metamorphosed Cretaceous rocks of oceanic facies. This boundary presumably is the eroded edge of upthrust Mesozoic metamorphosed tectonites that once lay deeply buried in an accretionary prism. Southward of this limit, scattered remnants of late Paleozoic metamorphic rocks are found (MacDonald, 1972b), probably from a much older cycle of accretion. North of this limit, the accretionary zone now stretching across northern South America (Fig. 4) is a dual zone. The southern part was uplifted and exposed at the end of the Late Cretaceous to early Tertiary accretionary cycle. The northern, mainly submerged part, represents an Eocene to Holocene accretionary cycle, and is actively growing today.

Another dual zone of accretionary crust with, however, a significant magmatic arc component, is found in the eastern Caribbean area. The western zone, the Aves Ridge region, is interpreted to have a Cretaceous to Paleogene accumulation age (Fox and Heezen, 1975). The eastern Lesser Antilles zone is mainly post-Eocene to Holocene but includes older rocks such as the late Mesozoic rocks of La Desirade (Bouysse and others, 1983).

The Greater Antilles accretionary zone incorporates rocks as old as Jurassic in Puerto Rico (Mattson and Pessagno, 1979) and Jurassic and possibly older in Cuba (Khudoley and Meyerhoff, 1971; Morris and others, this volume), but the accretionary episode in the Greater Antilles occurred mainly in the Cretaceous to Paleogene interval, with significant magmatic-arc activity (Lewis and others, this volume). Precambrian isotopic ages (910–945 Ma) have been reported from northern Cuba by Somin and Millán (1977). Paleozoic(?) ages have also been reported from Cuba. If these ages are correct, such rocks might represent the upwarped edge of the North American continent, as an extension of the Florida basement. Alternatively, an included Precambrian allochthonous collisional terrane might be indicated.

Metamorphic rocks dredged from along the Yucatán borderland (Pyle and others, 1973) are similar to metamorphic rocks of Cuba and suggest the continuation of the Greater Antilles accretionary zone along the Yucatán margin (shaded area between provinces 2 and 5, Fig. 4).

That portion of the accretionary crust linking the southern peninsula of Haiti to Jamaica may be more continuous than shown (north provinces 8, 10, and 11, Fig. 4). The Bay of Islands area north of Honduras includes possible ophiolites and metamorphic rocks (McBirney and Bass, 1969) of a probable Cretaceous accretionary episode. Also, a zone of Jurassic, Early Cretaceous, and Late Cretaceous age marks one or more former magmatic arcs in the Chortis block (Horne and others, 1976b; this volume). These observations suggest the continuation of the Haiti-Jamaica segment of the Greater Antilles accretionary crustal zone across the north side of the Nicaraguan Rise as far as the west end of the Cayman Trough, but a continuation into Cuba is not precluded by available data (see discussion by Lewis and others, this volume).

On the Pacific side of Central America, a series of mafic and ultramafic-cored peninsulas are uplifted along the Central America accretionary zone. These are the Santa Elena, Nicoya, Osa, Burica, and Azuero Peninsulas of Costa Rica and Panamá. Gravity and seismic evidence indicate that similar masses occur along the continental shelf to the northwest. Uplift of some of these peninsulas is probably related to subduction of the aseismic Cocos and Coiba Ridges beneath the Middle America Trench (Schmidt-Effing, 1979; Galli-Olivier, 1979; Lundberg, 1982). At its southeast limit, the Central America accretionary zone appears to merge with the accretionary zone along the Pacific margin of eastern Panamá and the Serrania de Baudó of Colombia. The accretionary zone north of the Chorotega block appears to be colliding with the South Caribbean accretionary zone near the Golfo de Urabá. The eastern contact of the Central America accretionary zone with the Chortis continental crust is masked by a thick cover of volcanic rocks across Honduras and Nicaragua. That contact has therefore been approximated by the eastern flank of the volcano-tectonic depression.

Indeterminate crust. Quite perplexing, and holding little hope for early resolution, are the genetic origins of the areas of indeterminate crust in the Bahamas region and in the Nicaraguan Rise. A vast expanse of thick crust of uniform sea-level elevation characterizes the Bahama Platform. The shallow-water limestones extend downward in age into the Cretaceous and attain a total thickness of at least 6 km. The nature of the foundation for this platform is unknown. The minimum age of the foundation for the carbonates is probably Jurassic (Klitgord and others, 1984; Watkins and others, 1986; see Sheridan and Grow, 1988).

The northern part of the Nicaraguan Rise (area 10, Fig. 4) may consist partly of an accretionary zone, as suggested earlier. The thickness of this province, about 20 to 25 km, could be explained by attenuation of continental crust, perhaps during Mesozoic separation of North and South America. The southern part of the rise (area 11, Fig. 4) is thinner still, and underlies correspondingly deeper waters. Holcombe and others (this volume) postulate that the southern part may be underlain by crust similar to the Colombian Basin. A possible clue to the origin of this zone is found at its northeast limit, where it abuts the Greater Antilles accretionary zone. In the southern peninsula of Haiti, Cretaceous to early Cenozoic deep-marine sedimentary rocks and basalts (Butterlin, 1960; Maurrasse, 1980a, 1980b; Maurrasse and others, 1979, 1982; Lewis and others, this volume) have been interpreted as an exposed uplifted deformed edge of this unusual "Colombian Basin" province. These rocks are very different from the magmatic arc rocks north of the peninsula in central and northern Hispaniola.

CONCLUSIONS

Except for the Cayman Trough, an ocean-floor spreading fabric is not known with certainty for any of the main Caribbean basins. The ultimate age, structure, and evolution of the Caribbean oceanic regions are as yet unclear. Speculatively, the relative

crustal ages of the basins seem likely to increase in the following order: Cayman Trough, Grenada Basin, Yucatán Basin, and Colombian-Venezuelan Basins.

The structure and history of the exposed continental and accretionary crustal areas are better understood than those of the marine areas. The Precambrian and Paleozoic continental crystalline terranes of northern South America are better known than those of Central America. Precambrian or Paleozoic crustal remnants in the Greater Antilles are suspect. Late Mesozoic to earliest Cenozoic accretion produced significant volumes of crust in the Greater Antilles and in northern South America, and probably also in the Aves Ridge area near the Lesser Antilles. Accretionary crust of this age is known in Central America but is well studied only in the Nicoya Peninsula of Costa Rica. A younger episode of crustal accretion, still in progress, has produced significant volumes of tectonites in the Lesser Antilles deformed belt, along the margins of Puerto Rico and Hispaniola, in northern South America, and along the Pacific margin of Central America.

Solutions to some of the problems of crustal evolution must await technical advances, but a few problems are within reach of technology of the late 1980s. Land topography and marine bathymetry available in digital form in 1988 allow the computation of terrain corrections, complete Bouguer anomaly maps, and isostatic and isostatic-residual anomaly maps for the entire region. Such maps are useful for a broad spectrum of geologic problems (see Simpson and others, 1986; Jachens and Griscom, 1985). At sea, deep drilling sites in the Yucatán Basin, Grenada Basin, Venezuelan Basin (to date sub-B" layers), and on the Nicaraguan Rise stand out as important objectives to help resolve the age and genesis of these crustal provinces. On land, improved mapping, radiometric dating, refraction, and deep drilling are needed in the older terranes of Cuba, the Chortis block, and northern Andean regions.

With slight improvement in deep-sea drilling technology, the thinner areas of Caribbean crust, such as in the Cayman Trough, might provide opportunities for drilling to M, an objective of global interest. But even with deep drilling, the origin and evolutionary chronology of the deep Caribbean basins are likely to remain elusive for many years to come.

ACKNOWLEDGMENTS

We thank our colleagues C. O. Bowin, T. W. Donnelly, R. C. Jachens, W. J. Ludwig, W. D. Mooney, Frederick Nagle, and J. S. Watkins, who provided constructive reviews of earlier versions of the manuscript. E. R. Flüh provided original material for a refraction profile, and R. T. Buffler provided original material for a refraction profile in Costa Rica. A. R. Palmer and Gabriel Dengo provided editorial guidance throughout preparation of this chapter.

REFERENCES

Andrew, E. M., 1969, Gravity surveys in Jamaica: Great Britain Institute of Geological Sciences Geophysical Report no. GP/0/40, 32 p.

Andrew, E. M., Masson Smith, D., and Robson, G. R., 1970, Gravity anomalies in the Lesser Antilles: Great Britain Institute of Geological Sciences Geophysical Paper no. 5, 21 p.

Antoine, J. W., and Ewing, J. I., 1963, Seismic refraction measurements on the margins of the Gulf of Mexico: Journal of Geophysical Research, v. 68, p. 1975–1996.

Arden, D. D., Jr., 1975, Geology of Jamaica and the Nicaragua Rise, *in* Nairn, A.E.M., and Stehli, F. G., eds., The ocean basins and margins; v. 3, The Gulf of Mexico and the Caribbean: New York, Plenum Press, p. 617–661.

Aubouin, J., von Huene, R., and others, 1981, Summary of Deep Sea Drilling Project Leg 67; Shipboard results from the Mid-America trench transect off Guatemala, *in* Colloquium on the Geology of Continental Margins, Proceedings, 26th International Geological Congress, Paris, July 7–17, 1980: Oceanologica Acta, supplement to v. 4, p. 225–232.

Aubouin, J., von Huene, R., and others, 1982, Initial reports of the Deep Sea Drilling Project: Washington, D.C. U.S. Government Printing Office, v. 67, 799 p.

Ball, M. M., and Harrison, C.G.A., 1969, Origin of the Gulf and Caribbean and implications regarding ocean ridge extension, migration, and shear: Gulf Coast Association of Geological Societies Transactions, v. 19, p. 287–294.

Barday, R. J., 1974, Structure of the Panamá Basin from marine gravity data [M.S. thesis]: Corvallis, Oregon State University, 99 p.

Barnett, R. S., 1975, Basement structure of Florida and its tectonic implications: Gulf Coast Association of Geological Societies Transactions, v. 25, p. 122–142.

Biju-Duval, B., Mascle, A., Montadert, L., and Wanneson, J., 1978, Seismic investigations in the Colombia, Venezuela, and Grenada Basins, and on the Barbados Ridge for future IPOD drilling: Geologie en Mijnbouw, v. 57, no. 2, p. 105–116.

Biju-Duval, B., Bizon, G., Mascle, A., and Muller, C., 1983, Active margin processes; Field observations in southern Hispaniola, *in* Watkins, J. S., and Drake, E. L., eds., Studies in continental margin geology: American Association of Petroleum Geologists Memoir 34, p. 325–344.

Birch, F. S., 1970, The Barracuda fault zone in the western North Atlantic: Deep-Sea Research, v. 17, p. 847–859.

Bird, P., 1979, Continental delamination and the Colorado Plateau: Journal of Geophysical Research, v. 84, no. B13, p. 7561–7571.

Bonini, W. E., 1978, Anomalous crust in the eastern Venezuela Basin and the Bouguer gravity anomaly field of northern Venezuela and the Caribbean borderland: Geologie en Mijnbouw, v. 57, no. 2, p. 117–122.

Bonini, W. E., Acker, C., and Buzan, G., 1977a, Gravity studies across the western Caribbean Mountains, Venezuela, *in* Memoria, Congreso Latino-americano de Geología, IV, Caracas, 1977: Venezuela Ministerio de Minas e Hidrocarburos, Boletín de Geología, Publicación Especial no. 7, v. 4, p. 2300–2323.

Bonini, W., Pimstein de Gaete, C., and Graterol, V., compilers, 1977b, Mapa de anomalías de Bouguer de la parte norte de Venezuela y areas vecinas: Venezuela Ministerio de Energía y Minas, scale 1:1,000,000.

Bonini, W. E., Garing, J. D., and Kellogg, J. N., 1980, Late Cenozoic uplifts of the Maracaibo–Santa Marta block, slow subduction of the Caribbean plate, and results from a gravity study: Santo Domingo, Dominican Republic, Transactions of the 9th Caribbean Geological Conference, p. 99–105.

Bouysse, P., Schmidt-Effing, R., and Westercamp, D., 1983, La Dèsirade Island (Lesser Antilles) revisited; Lower Cretaceous radiolarian cherts and arguments against an ophiolitic origin for the basal complex: Geology, v. 11, p. 244.

Bovenko, V. G., Shcherbakova, B. E., and Hernández, H., 1980, 1982, Novyye geofizicheskiye dannyye o glubinnour stroyenii vostochnoy kuby (New geophysical data on the deep structure of eastern Cuba): Sovetskaya Geologiya,

no. 9, p. 101–109; translation *in* International Geology Review, v. 24, no. 10, p. 1155–1162.

Bowin, C. O., 1968, Geophysical study of the Cayman Trough: Journal of Geophysical Research, v. 73, p. 5159–5173.

—— , 1976, Caribbean gravity field and plate tectonics: Geological Society of America Special Paper 169, 79 p.

Boynton, C. H., Westbrook, G. K., Bott, M.H.P., and Long, R. E., 1979, A seismic refraction investigation of crustal structure beneath the Lesser Antilles island arc: Geophysical Journal of the Royal Astronomical Society, v. 58, p. 371–393.

Briceño-Guarupe, L. A., 1978, The crustal structure and tectonic framework of the Gulf of Panamá [M.S. thesis]: Corvallis, Oregon State University, 71 p.

Buffler, R. T., Watkins, J. S., Shaub, F. J., and Worzel, J. L., 1980, Structure and early geologic history of the deep central Gulf of Mexico Basin, *in* Pilger, R. H., Jr., ed., The origin of the Gulf of Mexico and the early opening of the Central North Atlantic Ocean; Proceedings of a symposium, March 3–5, 1980, Baton Rouge, Louisiana: Baton Rouge, Louisiana State University School of Geoscience, 103 p.

Buffler, R. T., Shaub, F. J., Huerta, R., Ibrahim, A.B.K., and Watkins, J. S., 1981, A model for the early evolution of the Gulf of Mexico Basin, *in* Colloquium on the Geology of Continental Margins, Proceedings, 26th International Geological Congress, Paris, July 7–17, 1980: Oceanologica Acta, supplement to v. 4, p. 129–136.

Buffler, R. T., Matsumoto, T., and Crowe, J. C., 1985, Costa Rica [cross section], *in* Ladd, J. W., and Buffler, R. T., eds., Middle America Trench off western Central America, Atlas 7, Ocean Margin Drilling Program, Regional Atlas Series: Woods Hole, Massachusetts, Marine Science International, sheet 13.

Bunce, E. T., and Fahlquist, D. A., 1962, Geophysical investigation of the Puerto Rico Trench and outer ridge: Journal of Geophysical Research, v. 67, p. 3955–3972.

Bunce, E. T., and Hersey, J. B., 1966, Continuous seismic profiles of the outer ridge and Nares Basin north of Puerto Rico: Geological Society of America Bulletin, v. 77, p. 803–811.

Burbach, V.N.G., Frohlich, C., Pennington, W. D., and Matumoto, T., 1984, Seismicity and tectonics of the subducted Cocos Plate: Journal of Geophysical Research, v. 89, no. B9, p. 7719–7735.

Burke, K., Cooper, C., Dewey, J. F., Mann, P., and Pindell, J. L., 1984, Caribbean tectonics and relative plate motions, *in* Bonini, W. E., Hargraves, R. B., and Shagam, R., eds., The Caribbean–South American plate boundary and regional tectonics; Geological Society of America Memoir 162, p. 31–63.

Burke, K. P., Fox, P. J., and Şengör, A.M.C., 1978, Buoyant ocean floor and the evolution of the Caribbean: Journal of Geophysical Research, v. 83, no. B8, p. 3949–3954.

Bush, S. A., and Bush, P. A., 1969, Isostatic gravity map of the eastern Caribbean region: Gulf Coast Association of Geological Societies Transactions, v. 19, p. 281–285.

Butterlin, J., 1960, Géologie géneral et regional de la République d'Haiti: Paris, Travaux et Mémoires de l'Institut des Hautes Etudes de l'Amerique Latine, v. 6, University of Paris, 194 p.

Case, J. E., 1974a, Oceanic crust forms basement of eastern Panamá: Geological Society of America Bulletin, v. 85, p. 645–652.

—— , 1974b, Major basins along the continental margin of southern South America, *in* Burk, C. A., and Drake, C. L., eds., The geology of continental margins: New York, Springer-Verlag, p. 733–742.

—— , 1975, Geophysical studies in the Caribbean Sea, *in* Nairn, A.E.M., and Stehli, F. G., eds., The ocean basins and margins; v. 3, The Gulf of Mexico and Caribbean: New York, Plenum Press, p. 107–108.

—— , 1980, Crustal setting of mafic and ultramafic rocks and associated ore deposits of the Caribbean region: U.S. Geological Survey Open-File Report 80-304, 94 p., and 6 plates.

Case, J. E., and Dengo, G., 1982, The Caribbean Region, *in* Palmer, A. R., ed.,

Perspectives in regional geological synthesis; Planning for The Geology of North America: Boulder, Colorado, Geological Society of America D-NAG Special Publication 1, p. 163–170.

Case, J. E., and Donnelly, T. W., 1976, Gravitational evidence for crustal structure in central Guatemala [abs.]: EOS American Geophysical Union Transactions, v. 57, no. 12, p. 948–949.

Case, J. E., and Holcombe, T. L., 1980, Geologic-tectonic map of the Caribbean region: U.S. Geological Survey Miscellaneous Investigations Map I-1100, scale 1:2,500,000.

Case, J. E., and MacDonald, W. D., 1973, Regional gravity anomalies and crustal structure in northern Colombia: Geological Society of America Bulletin, v. 84, p. 2905–2916.

Case, J. E., Durán, L. G., López, R. A., and Moore, W. R., 1971, Tectonic investigations in western Colombia and eastern Panamá: Geological Society of America Bulletin, v. 82, p. 2685–2712.

Case, J. E., Holcombe, T. L., and Martin, R. G., 1984, Map of geologic provinces in the Caribbean region, *in* Bonini, W. E., Hargraves, R. B., and Shagam, R., eds., The Caribbean–South American plate boundary and regional tectonics: Geological Society of America Memoir 162, p. 1–30; map, scale 1:5,000,000.

CAYTROUGH, 1979, Geological and geophysical investigation of the Mid-Cayman Rise spreading center; Initial results and observations, *in* Talwani, M., Harrison, C. G., and Hayes, D. E., eds., Deep drilling results in the Atlantic Ocean: American Geophysical Union Maurice Ewing Series 2, p. 66–93.

Christensen, N. I., 1982, Seismic velocities, *in* Carmichael, R. S., ed., Handbook of physical properties of rocks, v. 2: Boca Raton, Florida, CRC Press, Incorporated, p. 1–228.

Christofferson, E., 1973, Linear magnetic anomalies in the Colombia basin, Central Caribbean Sea: Geological Society of America Bulletin, v. 84, p. 3217–3230.

Coleman, R. G., 1977, Ophiolites: New York, Springer-Verlag, 229 p.

Couch, R., and Woodcock, S., 1981, Gravity and structure of the continental margins of southwestern Mexico and northwestern Guatemala: Journal of Geophysical Research, v. 86, no. B3, p. 1829–1840.

Dengo, G., 1973, Estructura geológica, historia tectónica y morfología de America Central: Instituto Centroamericano de Investigación Tecnología Industrial, 2nd ed., p. 1–52.

Dickinson, W. R., and Seely, D. R., 1979, Structure and stratigraphy of forearc regions: American Association of Petroleum Geologists Bulletin, v. 63, p. 2–31.

Diebold, J. B., Stoffa, P. L., Buhl, P., and Truchan, M., 1981, Venezuela Basin crustal structure: Journal of Geophysical Research, v. 86, no. B9, p. 7901–7923.

Dillon, W. P., and Vedder, J. G., 1973, Structure and development of the continental margin of British Honduras: Geological Society of America Bulletin, v. 84, no. 8, p. 2713–2732.

Dillon, W. P., Vedder, J. G., and Graf, R. J., 1972, Structural profile of the northwestern Caribbean: Earth and Planetary Science Letters, v. 17, p. 175–180.

Donnelly, T. W., 1973, Late Cretaceous basalts from the Caribbean; A possible flood basalt province of vast size [abs.]: EOS American Geophysical Union Transactions, v. 54, p. 1004.

Dowling, J. J., and Fahlquist, D. A., 1967, Seismic refraction profiles in the vicinity of the Cayman Trough: EOS American Geophysical Union Transactions, v. 48, no. 1, p. 27–28.

Duncan, R. A., and Hargraves, R. B., 1984, Plate tectonic evolution of the Caribbean region in the mantle reference frame, *in* Bonini, W. E., Hargraves, R. B., and Shagam, R., eds., The Caribbean–South American plate boundary and regional tectonics: Geological Society of America Memoir 162, p. 81–93.

Edgar, N. T., Ewing, J. I., and Hennion, J., 1971, Seismic refraction and reflection in the Caribbean Sea: American Association of Petroleum Geologists Bulletin, v. 55, p. 833–870.

Ewing, J. I., and Heezen, B. C., 1955, Puerto Rico Trench topographic and geophysical data, *in* Poldervaart, A., ed., Crust of the Earth (A symposium): Geological Society of American Special Paper 62, p. 255–267.

Ewing, J. I., Officer, C. B., Johnson, H. R., and Edwards, R. S., 1957, Geophysical investigations in the eastern Caribbean; Trinidad shelf, Tobago Trough, Barbados Ridge, Atlantic Ocean: Geological Society of America Bulletin, v. 68, p. 897–912.

Ewing, J. I., Antoine, J., and Ewing, M., 1960, Geophysical measurements in the western Caribbean Sea and in the Gulf of Mexico: Journal of Geophysical Research, v. 65, p. 4087–4126.

Ewing, J. I., Talwani, M., Ewing, M., and Edgar, T., 1967, Sediments of the Caribbean: Miami University, Studies in Tropical Oceanography, v. 5, p. 88–102.

Ewing, M., and Press, F., 1955, Geophysical contrasts between continents and ocean basins, *in* Poldervaart, A., ed., Crust of the Earth (A symposium): Geological Society of America Special Paper 62, p. 1–16.

Ewing, M., and Worzel, J. L., 1954, Gravity anomalies and structure of the West Indies, pt. I: Geological Society of America Bulletin, v. 65, p. 165–173.

Ewing, M., Sutton, G. H., and Officer, C. B., Jr., 1954, Seismic refraction measurements in the Atlantic Ocean; Part 6, Typical deep stations, North America Basin: Seismological Society of America Bulletin, v. 44, p. 21–38.

Flüh, E. R., 1983, The basic igneous complex; Trace of an ancient Galapagos hot spot aseismic ridge?: Zentralblatt für Geologie und Paläontologie, Teil 1, Allgemeine, angewandte, regionale und historisch Geologie, Heft 3/4, p. 291–303.

Flüh, H. E., Milkereit, B., Meissner, R., Meyer, R. P., Ramírez, J. E., Quintero, J. de C., and Udias, J., 1981, Seismic refraction observations in northwestern Colombia at latitude 5.5°N: Zentralblatt für Geologie und Paläontologie, Teil 1, Allgemeine, angewandte, regionale und historisch Geologie, Heft 3/4, p. 231–342.

Folinsbee, R. A., 1972, The gravity field and plate boundaries in Venezuela [Ph.D. thesis]: Cambridge, Massachusetts Institute of Technology and Woods Hole Oceanographic Institution, 160 p.

Fox, P. J., and Heezen, B. C., 1975, Geology of the Caribbean crust, *in* Nairn, A.E.M., and Stehli, F. G., eds., The ocean basins and margins; v. 3, The Gulf of Mexico and the Caribbean: New York, Plenum Press, p. 421–466.

Furlong, K. P., and Fountain, D. M., 1986, Continental crustal underplating; Thermal considerations and seismic-petrological consequences: Journal of Geophysical Research, v. 91, no. B8, p. 8285–8294.

Fyfe, W. S., 1978, The evolution of the Earth's crust; Modern plate tectonics to ancient hot spot tectonics: Chemical Geology, v. 23, p. 89–114.

Galli-Olivier, C., 1979, Ophiolite and island arc volcanism in Costa Rica: Geological Society of America Bulletin, v. 90, p. 444–452.

Gass, I. G., and Smewing, J. D., 1973, Intrusion, extrusion, and metamorphism of constructive margins; Evidence from the Troodos massif, Cyprus: Nature, v. 242, p. 26–29.

Gettrust, J. F., Iwatake, B. T., Hussong, D. M., Bellizzia, A., and Gajardo, E., 1978, Crust and upper mantle structure of the northern Venezuela–southern Caribbean Sea transition zone [abs.]: EOS American Geophysical Union Transactions, v. 59, no. 12, p. 1132.

Ghosh, N., Hall, S. A., and Casey, J. F., 1984, Seafloor spreading magnetic anomalies in the Venezuelan Basin, *in* Bonini, W. E., Hargraves, R. B., and Shagam, R., eds., The Caribbean–South American plate boundary and regional tectonics: Geological Society of America Memoir 162, p. 65–80.

Gibbs, A. K., and Barron, C. N., 1983, The Guiana Shield reviewed: Episodes, v. 1983, no. 2, p. 7–14.a

Gomberg, D. N., Banks, P. D., and McBirney, A. R., 1968, Guatemala; Preliminary zircon ages from the central Cordillera: Science, v. 162, p. 121–122.

Green, D. H., and Ringwood, A. E., 1967, An experimental investigation of the gabbro to eclogite transformation and its petrological applications: Geochimica et Cosmochimica Acta, v. 31, p. 767–833.

Griffin, W. H., and O'Reilly, S. Y., 1987, Is the continental Moho the crust-mantle boundary?: Geology, v. 15, p. 241–244.

Hall, S. A., and Yeung, T., 1980, A study of magnetic anomalies in the Yucatán

Basin: Transactions, 9th Caribbean Geological Conference, Santo Domingo, Dominican Republic, p. 519–526.

Hersey, J. B., Officer, C. B., Johnson, H. R., and Bergstrom, S., 1952, Seismic refraction observations north of the Brownson deep: Seismological Society of America Bulletin, v. 42, no. 4, p. 291–306.

Hess, H. H., 1938, Gravity anomalies and island arc structure with particular reference to the West Indies: American Philosophical Society Proceedings, v. 79, p. 71–96.

——, 1962, Evolution of ocean basins, *in* Engel, A. J., James, H. L., and Leonard, B. F., eds., Petrologic studies; A volume in honor of A. F. Buddington: Geological Society of America, p. 599–620.

Holcombe, T. L., Vogt, P. R., Matthews, J. E., and Murchison, R. R., 1973, Evidence for sea-floor spreading in the Cayman Trough: Earth and Planetary Science Letters, v. 20, p. 357–371.

Hopkins, H. R., 1973, Geology of the Aruba Gap abyssal plain near DSDP site 153, *in* Edgar, N. T., Saunders, J. B., and others, eds., Initial reports of the Deep Sea Drilling Project: Washington, D.C., U.S. Government Printing Office, v. 15, p. 1029–1050.

Horne, G. S., Clark, G. S., and Pushkar, P., 1976a, Pre-Cretaceous rocks in northwestern Honduras; Basement terrane in Sierra de Omoa: American Association of Petroleum Geologists Bulletin, v. 60, p. 566–583.

Horne, G. S., Pushkar, P., and Shafiqullah, M., 1976b, Laramide plutons on the landward continuation of the Bonacca Ridge, northern Honduras: Instituto Centroamericano de Investigacion y Tecnologia Industrial (Guatemala), Publicaciones Geológicas, v. 5, p. 84–90.

Hopson, C. H., Coleman, R. G., Gregory, R. T., Pallister, J. S., and Bailey, E. H., 1981, Geologic section through the Samail ophiolite and associated rocks along a Muscat–Ibra transect, southeastern Oman Mountains: Journal of Geophysical Research, v. 86, p. 2527–2544.

Hospers, J., and van Wijnen, 1959, The gravity field of the Venezuelan Andes and adjacent basins: Verhandlingen der Koninklije Nederlandse Akademie van Wetenschappen, Afdeeling Natuurkunde, Eerste Reeks, Deel 23, no. 2, 95 p.

Houtz, R. E., and Ludwig, W. J., 1977, Structure of Colombia Basin, Caribbean Sea, from profiler-sonobuoy measurements: Journal of Geophysical Research, v. 82, p. 4861–4867.

Hussong, D. M., and Wipperman, L. K., 1981, Vertical movement and tectonic erosion of the continental wall of the Peru–Chile trench near 11°30′S latitude, *in* Kulm, L. D., Dymond, J., and others, eds., Nazca Plate; Crustal formation and Andean convergence: Geological Society of America Memoir 154, p. 509–524.

Ibrahim, A. K., Latham, G. V., and Ladd, J., 1979, Seismic refraction and reflection measurements in the Middle America Trench offshore Guatemala: Journal of Geophysical Research, v. 84, no. B10, p. 5643–5649.

Ibrahim, A. K., Carye, J., Latham, G., and Buffler, R. T., 1981, Crustal structure in Gulf of Mexico from OBS refraction and multichannel reflection data: American Association of Petroleum Geologists Bulletin, v. 65, no. 7, p. 1207–1229.

Iturralde, M. A., Hartwich, R., and others, 1986, Ofiolitas de Camagüey: Naturaleza, posición tectónica y sedimentos derivados: Revista Tecnologica, v. 16, Serie, Geología, no. 2, p. 29–32.

Jachens, R. C., and Griscom, A., 1985, An isostatic residual gravity anomaly map of California; A residual map for interpretation of anomalies from intracrustal sources, *in* Hinze, W. J., ed., The utility of regional gravity and magnetic anomaly maps: Society of Exploration Geophysicists, p. 347–360.

Kearey, P., 1974, Gravity and seismic reflection investigations into the crustal structure of the Aves Ridge, eastern Caribbean: Geophysical Journal of the Royal Astronomical Society, v. 38, p. 435–448.

——, 1976, Gravity and seismic reflection investigation into the crustal structure of the Aves Ridge, eastern Caribbean: Transactions, 7th Caribbean Geological Conference, Guadaloupe, 1974, p. 311–320.

Kellogg, J. N., and Bonini, W. E., 1982, Subduction of the Caribbean plate and basement uplifts in the overriding South American plate: Tectonics, v. 1, p. 251–276.

Kellogg, J. N., Ouijiofor, I. J., and Kansakar, D. R., 1986, Cenozoic tectonics of

the Panamá and North Andes blocks, *in* Valdiri Wagner, J., ed., Memoirs of the 6th Latin American Geological Congress, Bogota, Colombia, Oct. 1985: Bogota, INGEOMINAS, p. 41–59.

Khudoley, K. M., and Meyerhoff, A. A., 1971, Paleogeography and geological history of Greater Antilles: Geological Society of America Memoir 129, 199 p.

Klitgord, K. D., Popenoe, P., and Schouten, H., 1984, Florida; A Jurassic transform plate boundary: Journal of Geophysical Research, v. B9, p. 7753–7772.

Kim, J. J., Matumoto, T., and Latham, G. V., 1982, A crustal section of northern Central America as inferred from wide-angle reflections from shallow earthquakes: Seismological Society of America Bulletin, v. 72, p. 925–940.

Ladd, J. W., and Watkins, J. S., 1978, Active margin structures within the north slope of the Muertos Trench: Geologie en Mijnbouw, v. 57, no. 2, p. 255–260.

——, 1979, Tectonic development of trench-arc complexes on the northern and southern margins of the Venezuela Basin, *in* Watkins, J. S., Montadert, L., and Dickerson, P. W., eds., Geological and geophysical investigations of continental margins: American Association of Petroleum Geologists Memoir 29, p. 363–371.

——, 1980, Seismic stratigraphy of the western Venezuela Basin: Marine Geology, v. 35, p. 21–41.

Ladd, J. W., Worzel, J. L., and Watkins, J. S., 1977, Multifold seismic reflection records from the northern Venezuela Basin and the north slope of the Muertas Trench, *in* Talwani, M., and Pittman, W. C., III, eds., Island arc trenches and back-arc basins: American Geophysical Union, Maurice Ewing Series, p. 41–56.

Ladd, J. W., Truchan, M., Talwani, M., Stoffa, P. L., Buhl, P., Houtz, R., Mauffret, A., and Westbrook, G., 1984, Seismic reflection profiles across the southern margin of the Caribbean *in* Bonini, W. E., Hargraves, R. B., and Shagam, R., eds., The Caribbean–South American plate boundary and regional tectonics: Geological Society of America Memoir 162, p. 153–160.

Lagaay, R. A., 1969, Geophysical investigations of the Netherlands Leeward Antilles: Verhandlingen der Koninklije Nederlandse Akademie van Wetenschappen, Afdeeling Natuurkunde, Eerste Reeks, Deel 25, no. 2, North-Holland Publishing Company, 86 p.

Lister, G. S., Etheridge, M. A., and Symonds, P. A., 1986, Detachment faulting and the evolution of passive continental margins: Geology, v. 14, p. 246–250.

Lonsdale, P., and Klitgord, K. D., 1978, Structure and tectonic history of the eastern Panamá Basin: Geological Society of America Bulletin, v. 89, p. 981–999.

López Ramos, E., 1981, Geología de México, v. 3 [2nd ed.]: Mexico City, Privately printed, 446 p.

Lovering, J. F., 1958, The nature of the Mohorovičić discontinuity: EOS American Geophysical Union Transactions, v. 39, p. 947–955.

Lu, R. S., McMillen, K. J., and Phillips, J. D., 1983, Multichannel seismic survey of the Colombia Basin and adjacent margin, *in* Watkins, J. S., and Drake, C. L., eds., Studies in continental margin geology: American Association of Petroleum Geologists Memoir 34, p. 359–410.

Ludwig, W. J., Nafe, J. E., and Drake, C. L., 1970, Seismic refraction, *in* Maxwell, A. E., ed., The sea, v. 4, pt. 1: New York, Wiley Interscience, p. 53–84.

Ludwig, W. J., Houtz, R. E., and Ewing, J. I., 1975, Profiler-sonobuoy measurements in Colombia and Venezuela Basins, Caribbean Sea: American Association of Petroleum Geologists Bulletin, v. 59, p. 115–121.

Lundberg, N. M., 1982, Evolution of the slope landward of the Middle America Trench, Nicoya Peninsula, Costa Rica, *in* Leggett, J. K., ed., Trench-forearc geology, sedimentation, and tectonics on modern and active plate margins: Geological Society of London Special Publication 10, Oxford, Blackwell, p. 131–147.

Macdonald, K. C., and Holcombe, T. L., 1978, Inversion of magnetic anomalies and sea-floor spreading in the Cayman Trough: Earth and Planetary Science Letters, v. 40, p. 407–414.

MacDonald, W. D., 1972a, Continental crust, crustal evolution, and the Caribbean, *in* Shagam, R., Hargraves, R. B., and others, eds., Studies in Earth and space sciences; A memoir in honor of Harry Hammond Hess: Geological Society of America Memoir 132, p. 351–362.

——, 1972b, Late Paleozoic tectonics of northern South America: Anais Academia Brasileira Ciencias, v. 44, supplement, p. 197–208.

Martín F. C., 1978, Mapa tectónico, Norte de America del Sur: Venezuela Ministerio de Energía y Minas, scale 1:2,500,000.

Martín-Bellizzia, C., 1974, Paleotectónica del Escudo de Guayana, *in* Memoria, Conferencia Geológica Inter-Guayanas, IX, Ciudad Guayana, 1973: Venezuela Ministerio de Minas e Hidrocarburos Boletin de Geología, Publicación Especial, no. 6, p. 251–305.

Martin, R. G., and Case, J. E., 1975, Geophysical studies in the Gulf of Mexico, *in* Nairn, A.E.M., and Stehli, F. G., eds., The ocean basins and margins; v. 3, The Gulf of Mexico and the Caribbean: New York, Plenum Press, p. 65–106.

Mascle, A., Cazes, M., and Le Quellec, P., 1985, Structure des marges et bassins Caraïbes; Une revue, *in* Mascle, A., ed., Caribbean geodynamics, Symposium, Paris, February 5–8, 1985: Paris, Éditions Technip, p. 1–20.

Mattson, P. H., and Pessagno, E. A., 1979, Jurassic and early Cretaceous radiolarians in Puerto Rican ophiolite; Tectonic implications: Geology, v. 7, p. 440–444.

Matumoto, T., and Latham, G., 1977, Refraction profile in the vicinity of Nicoya Peninsula, Costa Rica [abs.]: EOS Transactions American Geophysical Union, v. 58, no. 12, p. 1150.

Matumoto, T., Latham, G., Ohtake, M., and Umana, J., 1976, Seismic studies in northern Costa Rica [abs.]: EOS Transactions American Geophysical Union, v. 57, no. 4, p. 290.

Matumoto, T., Ohtake, M., Latham, G., and Umana, J., 1977, Crustal structure in southern Central America: Seismological Society of America Bulletin, v. 67, no. 1, p. 121–135.

Maurrasse, F., 1980a, New data on the stratigraphy of the Southern Peninsula of Haiti: Transactions du 1er Colloque sur de Géologie D'Haïti, Port-au-Prince, Haïti, 1980, p. 184–199.

——, 1980b, Les marges continentales d'Haïti, Port-au-Prince, Haïti, 1980, p. 200–206.

Maurrasse, F., Husler, J., Georges, G., Schmitt, R., and Damond, P., 1979, Upraised Caribbean sea floor below acoustic reflector B″ at the Southern Peninsula of Haiti: Geologie en Mijnbouw, v. 58, no. 1, p. 71–83.

Maurrasse, F. J-M. R., Pierre-Louis, F., and Rigaud, J.-G., 1982, Cenozoic facies distribution in the Southern Peninsula of Haiti and the Barahona: Transactions, 9th Caribbean Geological Conference, Santo Domingo, Dominican Republic, 1980, v. 1, p. 161–174.

McBirney, A. R., and Bass, M. N., 1969, Geology of Bay Islands, Gulf of Honduras, *in* McBirney, A. R., ed., Tectonic relations of northern Central America and the western Caribbean: American Association of Petroleum Geologists Memoir 11, p. 229–243.

McCann, W. R., and Sykes, L. R., 1984, Subduction of aseismic ridges beneath the Caribbean plate; Implications for the tectonics and seismic potential of the northeastern Caribbean: Journal of Geophysical Research, v. 89, no. B6, p. 4493–4519.

Meissner, R. O., Flüh, E. R., Stibane, F., and Berg, E., 1976, Dynamics of the active plate boundary in southwest Colombia according to recent geophysical measurements: Tectonophysics, v. 35, p. 115–136.

Meyer, R. P., and 7 others, 1976, Project Nariño III; Refraction observation across a leading edge, Malpelo Island to the Colombian Cordillera Occidental, *in* Sutton, G. H., Manghnani, M. H., Moberly, R., and McAfee, E. V., eds., The geophysics of the Pacific Ocean Basin and its margin: American Geophysical Union Monograph 19, p. 105–132.

Meyerhoff, A. A., and Meyerhoff, H. A., 1972, Continental drift; 4, The Caribbean "plate": Journal of Geology, v. 80, p. 34–60.

Mooney, W. D., Meyer, R. P., Laurence, J. P., Meyer, H., and Ramírez, J. E., 1979, Seismic refraction studies in the Western Cordillera, Colombia: Seismological Society of America Bulletin, v. 69, p. 1745–1761.

Officer, C. B., Jr., Ewing, J. I., Edwards, R. S., and Johnson, H. R., 1957,

Geophysical investigations in the eastern Caribbean; Venezuelan basin, Antilles island arc, and Puerto Rico trench: Geological Society of America Bulletin, v. 68, p. 359–378.

Officer, C. B., Ewing, J. I., Hennion, J. F., Harkrider, D. G., and Miller, D. E., 1959, Geophysical investigations in the eastern Caribbean; Summary of 1955 and 1956 cruises, *in* Ahrens, L. H., Press, F., Rankama, K., and Runcorn, S. K., eds., Physics and chemistry of the Earth: London, Pergamon Press, v. 3, p. 17–109.

Onstott, T. C., and Hargraves, R. B., 1982, Paleomagnetic data and the Proterozoic apparent polar wander curve for the Venezuelan Guayana Shield: Transactions, 9th Caribbean Geological Conference, Santo Domingo, Dominican Republic, p. 475–508.

Oxburgh, E. R., 1972, Flake tectonics and continental collision: Nature, v. 239, p. 202–204.

Papazachos, B. C., 1964, Dispersion of Rayleigh waves in the Gulf of Mexico and Caribbean Sea: Seismological Society of America, v. 54, p. 909–926.

Perfit, M. R., and Heezen, B. C., 1978, The geology and evolution of the Cayman Trench: Geological Society of America Bulletin, v. 89, p. 1155–1174.

Pérez, O. J., and Aggarwal, Y. P., 1981, Present-day tectonics of the southeastern Caribbean and northeastern Venezuela: Journal of Geophysical Research, v. 86, p. 10791–10804.

Pinet, B., Lajat, D., LeQuellec, P., and Bouysse, P., 1985, Structure of Aves Ridge and Grenada Basin from multichannel seismic data, *in* Mascle, A., ed., Geodynamique des Caraïbes: Paris, Éditions Technip, p. 53–64.

Ponce, D. A., and Case, J. E., 1986, Crustal structure of Costa Rica inferred from gravity data [abs.]: EOS American Geophysical Union Transactions, v. 67, no. 44, p. 1212.

——, 1987, Geophysical interpretation of Costa Rica, *in* Mineral resource assessment of the Republic of Costa Rica: U.S. Geological Survey Miscellaneous Investigations Map I-1865, p. 8–17, scale 1:500,000.

Pyle, T. E., Meyerhoff, A. A., Fahlquist, D. A., Antoine, J. W., McCrevey, J. A., and Jones, P. C., 1973, Metamorphic rocks from northwestern Caribbean Sea: Earth and Planetary Science Letters, v. 18, p. 339–344.

Reblin, M. T., 1973, Regional gravity survey of the Dominican Republic [M.S. thesis]: Salt Lake City, University of Utah, 122 p.

Reymer, A., and Schubert, G., 1984, Phanerozoic addition rates to the continental crust and crustal growth: Tectonics, v. 3, p. 63–77.

Rial, J. A., 1976, Seismic-wave transmission across the Caribbean plate; High attenuation on concave side of Lesser Antilles Island arc: Seismological Society of America Bulletin, v. 66, p. 1905–1920.

Rosencrantz, E., Ross, M. I., and Sclater, J. G., 1988, Age and spreading history of the Cayman Trough as determined from depth, heat flow, and magnetic anomalies: Journal of Geophysical Research, v. 93, no. B3, p. 2141–2157.

Rutland, R.W.R., 1971, Andean orogeny and ocean floor spreading: Nature, v. 233, p. 252–255.

Salvador, A., ed., 1990, The Gulf of Mexico region: Boulder, Colorado, Geological Society of America, The Geology of North America, v. J, (in press).

Sawyer, D. S., and Buffler, 1990, Crust and Mantle of the Gulf of Mexico region, *in* Salvador, A., ed., The Gulf of Mexico region: Boulder, Colorado, The Geological Society of America, The Geology of North America, v. J, (in press).

Schmidt-Effing, R., 1979, Alter und Genese des Nicoya–Komplexes, einer ozeanischen Paläokruste (Oberjura bis Eozän) in südlichen Zentralamerika: Geologischen Rundschau, v. 68, no. 2, p. 457–494.

Scholl, D. W., von Huene, R., Vallier, T. L., and Howell, D. G., 1980, Sedimentary masses and concepts about tectonic processes at underthrust ocean margins: Geology, v. 8, p. 564–568.

Seely, D. R., 1979, The evolution of structural highs bordering major forearc basins, *in* Watkins, J. S., Montadert, L., and Dickerson, P. W., eds., Geological and geophysical investigations of continental margins: American Association of Petroleum Geologists Memoir 29, p. 245–260.

Shcherbakova, B. E., Bovenko, V. G., and Hernández, H., 1977, Structure of the crust beneath western Cuba: Sovetskaya Geologya, no. 8, p. 138–143. (in Russian).

——— , 1978, 1980: Relief on the Mohorovičić surface in the western part of Cuba: Doklady Akademii Nauk SSSR, v. 238, no. 3, p. 561–564; translation *in* Doklady Earth Science Section, v. 238, no. 1, p. 7–9.

Shein, V. S., Ivanov, S. S., Kleschev, K. A., Khain, V. Ye., Marrero, M., and Socorro, R., 1978, Tectonics of Cuba and the surrounding shelf: Sovetskaya Geologya, no. 2, p. 104–119 (in Russian).

Sheridan, R. E., and Grow, J. A., 1988, eds., The Atlantic continental margin, U.S.: Boulder, Colorado, The Geological Society of America, The Geology of North America, v. I-2, 610 p.

Shor, G. G., Jr., and Fisher, R. L., 1961, Middle America Trench; Seismic-refraction studies: Geological Society of America Bulletin, v. 72, no. 5, p. 721–730.

Silver, E. A., Case, J. E., and MacGillavry, H. J., 1975, Geophysical study of the Venezuelan Borderland: Geological Society of America Bulletin, v. 86, p. 213–226.

Simpson, R. W., Jachens, R. C., Blakely, R. J., and Saltus, R. W., 1986, A new isostatic regional gravity map of the conterminous United States with a discussion on the significance of isostatic residual anomalies: Journal of Geophysical Research, v. 91, no. B8, p. 8348–8372.

Škvor, V., 1969, The Caribbean area; A case of destruction and regeneration of continent: Geological Society of America Bulletin, v. 80, p. 961–968.

Soloviev, O. N., Skidan, S. A., Skidan, I. K., Pankratov, A. P., and Judoley, C. M., 1964, Comentarios sobre el mapa gravimétrico de la Isla de Cuba: Cuba, La Habana, Ministerio de Industrias, Revista Tecnológica, v. 2, no. 2, p. 8–19.

Somin, M. L., and Millán, G., 1977, Sobre la edad de las rocas metamórficas de Cuba: Informe científico-técnico no. 2, Academia de Ciencias de Cuba, Instituto de Geología y Paleontología, p. 3–11.

Speed, R. C., 8 others, 1984, Lesser Antilles arc and adjacent terranes: Ocean Margin Drilling Program Atlas Series, Atlas 10: Woods Hole, Massachusetts Marine Science International, 27 sheets.

Stroup, J. B., and Fox, P. J., 1981, Geologic investigations in the Cayman Trough; Evidence for thin oceanic crust along the Mid-Cayman Rise: Journal of Geology, v. 89, p. 395–420.

Stoffa, P. L., Mauffret, A., Truchan, M., and Buhl, P., 1981, Sub-B″ layering in the southern Caribbean; The Aruba Gap and Venezuela Basin: Earth and Planetary Science Letters, v. 53, p. 131–146.

Suppe, J., Powell, C., and Berry, R., 1975, Regional topography, seismicity, Quaternary volcanism, and the present-day tectonics of the western United States: American Journal of Science, v. 275A, p. 397–436.

Talwani, M., 1964, A review of marine geophysics: Marine Geology, v. 2, p. 29–80.

Talwani, M., Sutton, G. H., and Worzel, J. L., 1959, A crustal section across the Puerto Rico Trench: Journal of Geophysical Research, v. 64, p. 1545–1555.

Talwani, M., Windisch, C. C., Stoffa, P. L., Buhl, P., and Houtz, R. E., 1977, Multichannel seismic study in the Venezuelan Basin and Curaçao Ridge *in* Talwani, M., and Pitman, W. C., III, eds., Island arcs, deep sea trenches, and back-arc basins: American Geophysical Union, Maurice Ewing Series, v. 1, p. 83–98.

Tolstoy, I., Edwards, R. S., and Ewing, M., 1953, Seismic refraction measurements in the Atlantic Ocean (Part 3): Seismological Society of America Bulletin, v. 43, p. 35–48.

Uchupi, E., 1973, Eastern Yucatan continental margin and western Caribbean tectonics: American Association of Petroleum Geologists Bulletin, v. 57, no. 6, p. 1075–1085.

Uchupi, E., Milliman, J. D., Luyendyk, B. P., Bowin, C. O., and Emery, K. O., 1971, Structure and origin of southern Bahamas: American Association of Petroleum Geologists Bulletin, v. 55, no. 5, p. 687–704.

van Andel, Tj. H., Heath, G. R., Malfait, B. T., Heinrichs, D. F., and Ewing, J. I., 1971, Tectonics of the Panamá Basin, eastern equatorial Pacific: Geological Society of America Bulletin, v. 82, p. 1489–1508.

Veining-Meinesz, F. A., and Wright, F. E., 1930, The gravity measuring cruise of the U.S. Submarine S–21: U.S. Naval Observatory Publication 13, Appendix I, 94 p.

Victor, L., 1976, Structures of the continental margin of Central America from northern Nicaragua to northern Panamá [M.S. thesis]: Corvallis, Oregon State University, 76 p.

Vogt, P. R., and Tucholke, B. E., eds., 1986, The western North Atlantic region: Boulder, Colorado, The Geological Society of America, The Geology of North America, v. M, 696 p.

von Huene, R., Aubouin, J., and others, 1980, Leg 67: The Deep Sea Drilling Project Mid-America Trench transect off Guatemala: Geological Society of America Bulletin, v. 91, part 1, p. 421–432.

Watkins, J. S., Moore, J. C., and others, 1981, Accretion, underplating, subduction, and tectonic evolution, southern Mexico, *in* Colloquium on the Geology of Continental Margins, Proceedings 26th International Geological Congress, Paris, July 7–17, 1980: Oceanologica Acta, supplement to v. 4, p. 213–224.

Watkins, J. S., Pytte, A. M., and Houtz, R. E., 1986, Exploration history and future prospects of the U.S. Atlantic margin, *in* Halbouty, M. T., ed., Future petroleum provinces of the world: American Association of Petroleum Geologists Memoir 40, p. 269–290.

Westbrook, G. K., 1975, The structure of the crust and upper mantle in the region of Barbados and the Lesser Antilles: Geophysical Journal of the Royal Astronomical Society, v. 43, p. 201–242.

——— , 1982, The Barbados Ridge complex; Tectonics of a mature forearc system: Geological Society of London Special Publication 8, p. 275–290.

Westbrook, G. K., and Ladd, J. W., 1984, Seismic refraction velocity structure, *in* Speed, R. C., and 8 others, eds., Lesser Antilles arc and adjacent terranes Atlas 10, Ocean Margin Drilling Program, Regional Atlas Series: Woods Hole, Massachusetts Marine Science International, sheet 6.

Westbrook, G. K., and McCann, W. R., 1986, Subduction of Atlantic lithosphere beneath the Caribbean, *in* Vogt, P. R., and Tucholke, B. E., eds., The western North Atlantic region: Boulder, Colorado, The Geological Society of America, The Geology of North America, v. M, p. 341–350.

Weyl, R., 1980, Geology of Central America [2nd ed.]: Berlin, Gebrüder Borntraeger, 371 p.

Woodcock, S. F., 1975, Crustal structure of the Tehuantepec Ridge and adjacent continental margins of southwestern Mexico and western Guatemala [M.S. thesis]: Corvallis, Oregon State University, 52 p.

Worzel, J. L., 1965, Pendulum gravity measurements at sea, 1936–1959: New York, John Wiley & Sons, Incorporated, 422 p.

Worzel, J. L., and Ewing, M., 1948, Explosion sounds in shallow water, *in* Worzel, J. L., Ewing, M., and Pekeris, C. L., eds., Propagation of sound in water: Geological Society of America Memoir 27, p. 1–53.

——— , 1954, Gravity anomalies and structure of the West Indies, pt. 2: Geological Society of America Bulletin, v. 65, p. 195–199.

MANUSCRIPT ACCEPTED BY THE SOCIETY JULY 12, 1988

Chapter 3

Northern Central America; The Maya and Chortis blocks

Thomas W. Donnelly
Department of Geological Sciences, State University of New York at Binghamton, Binghamton, New York 13901
Gregory S. Horne
Department of Earth and Environmental Sciences, Wesleyan University, Middletown, Connecticut 06457
Richard C. Finch
Department of Earth Sciences, Tennessee Technological University, Cookeville, Tennessee 38505
Ernesto López-Ramos
Instituto de Geología, Apartado Postal 70-296, Ciudad Universitaria, 04510 México D.F., México

INTRODUCTION

Northern (nuclear) Central America is conveniently divided into the Maya (sometimes called Yucatán) and Chortis blocks (Fig. 1). The division between the two blocks is the Motagua suture zone, which follows the Motagua River in east and central Guatemala, but whose western extension is buried beneath Tertiary volcanic cover in western Guatemala. The Maya block includes Guatemala north of the Motagua suture zone, Belize, the Yucatán Peninsula, and Mexico west to the Isthmus of Tehuantepec. The Chortis block consists of southern Guatemala, El Salvador, Honduras, an indeterminate part of northern Nicaragua, and the water-covered Nicaraguan Rise. The boundary between these blocks along the Motagua suture zone of central Guatemala marks the locus of interblock suturing in latest Cretaceous time.

This chapter emphasizes the older geologic history of northern Central America. Certain geologic topics relevant to this area will appear in other chapters of this volume, especially seismicity, neotectonics, magmatism, volcanism, paleomagnetism, mineral deposits, and energy.

Our discussion of the Maya block is limited to Belize and Guatemala north of the Motagua Valley; adjacent Mexican portions will be described in volumes of the Geology of North America covering Mexico and the Gulf of Mexico. Some Mexican rock occurrences which are especially pertinent to the interpretation of Guatemalan units are, however, included here. The Motagua suture zone between the Maya and Chortis blocks is discussed in this subchapter.

The Chortis block subchapter emphasizes the geology of Honduras, where most of the older rocks of this block occur. The Nicaraguan Rise is discussed by Holcombe and others, and Case and others (this volume).

The Maya and Chortis blocks are especially important for Caribbean geology because of their extensive pre-Cretaceous stratigraphy and their metamorphic basements of pre-late Paleozoic age. These basement terranes are lithologically different in the two blocks. Although there are stratigraphic parallels for the suprabasement sedimentary series, the pre-Tertiary sediments of each block are not directly correlative to coeval strata on the other. Both blocks are "exotic terranes" of uncertain origin, but the Maya block is generally believed to originate in the present Gulf of Mexico, and the Chortis block appears to have been derived from the Pacific coast of Mexico. Definitive lithologic or stratigraphic evidence for their original locations, however, has not yet been advanced.

THE MAYA BLOCK AND MOTAGUA SUTURE ZONE

T. W. Donnelly and E. López-Ramos

INTRODUCTION

The Maya block has a well-exposed metamorphic basement along its southern boundary; however, the pre-late Paleozoic history can only be conjectured. Pennsylvanian to Cenozoic history includes: thick marine sedimentation in a late Paleozoic trough; continental sedimentation during the Jurassic and possibly Early Cretaceous; deposition of a thick, reef-bounded carbonate basin with extensive evaporites during the Early Cretaceous; deposition of platform limestones during the Late Cretaceous; deformation and accompanying thick clastic sedimentation along the southern border during a Late Cretaceous and early Tertiary suturing event, accompanied by emplacement by overthrust and sliding of an ophiolite complex; and deposition in a variety of dominantly continental sedimentary environments during the later Tertiary

Donnelly, T. W., Horne, G. S., Finch, R. C., and López-Ramos, E., 1990, Northern Central America; the Maya and Chortis blocks, *in* Dengo, G., and Case, J. E., eds., The Caribbean region: Boulder, Colorado, Geological Society of America, The Geology of North America, v. H.

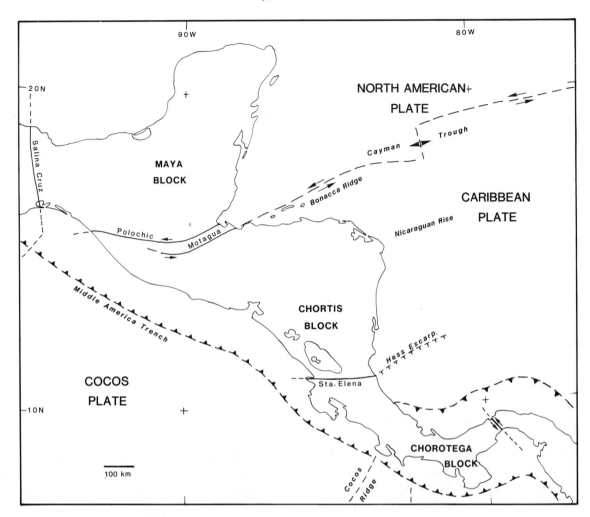

Figure 1. Index map of northern Central America showing regional tectonic features. International boundaries shown in Plate 1.

(Plates 4 and 5b). Transcurrent faulting has affected the southern border during the Neogene; earlier movements on this plate-boundary fault system are controversial.

Although several pioneering works appeared during the nineteenth century, the first comprehensive study of the area was by Sapper (1899), whose major findings have stood the test of nearly a century of subsequent work. Sapper's final publication (1937) provided a complete summary of geological knowledge prior to World War II. Shortly thereafter, geological studies expanded, originally in connection with the quest for mineral deposits during the war (Roberts and Irving, 1957). During the sixties, geological studies were spurred by a new series of excellent topographic maps and improved road systems that marked the recent economic growth of the Central American republics. The earliest of these more detailed studies, which emphasized making of large-scale geological maps, were those by McBirney (1963) and Walper (1960). Two decades of vigorous geological research produced numerous doctoral dissertations and masters theses (the

results of which are mainly unpublished) by students from Rice University, Louisiana State University, University of Texas at Austin, the State University of New York at Binghamton, Dartmouth University, University of Texas at Arlington, Texas A & M University, and University of Pittsburgh. These studies were based on detailed quadrangle geologic maps and associated structural, paleontological, stratigraphic, and petrological studies.

Belize has been the object of papers by Bateson and Hall (1971; 1977). The Louisiana State University, University of Idaho, the Colorado School of Mines, and the State University of New York at Binghamton have contributed studies on the Paleozoic inlier of the Maya Mountains of Belize. The remainder of the country has been investigated mainly during exploratory oil-well drilling, the results of which are mainly unpublished (Rao, 1982).

Several additional studies and summaries have been contributed by Dengo (1967, 1968, 1969) and Dengo and Bohnenberger (1969). A field project of the German Geological Mission to Guatemala ended abruptly in 1970, and very few of the results of this apparently fruitful study are available. Several petrological studies relating to the ophiolitic complex have been published by Bertrand and coworkers (1975–1980) from the Universite de Genève.

The most comprehensive sources for geological information on this area are the excellent earlier German and later English summaries by Weyl (1961, 1980) in the series "Beiträge zur Regionalen Geologie der Erde." Some material that appeared in the earlier edition has been omitted in the later, so reference to both editions is essential.

MORPHOTECTONIC UNITS OF THE MAYA BLOCK OF GUATEMALA AND BELIZE

The southern boundary of the Maya block is the Motagua Valley and its buried westward extension in western Guatemala (Fig. 2). Immediately north of this southern boundary is an east-trending range that reaches 3000 m in elevation in several places. The range is underlain by (?)Paleozoic metamorphic rocks and consists of the Sierra de Chuacús to the west, the Sierra de las Minas to the east, and farther east, the more subdued Montañas del Mico, which are underlain mainly by Permian limestones and other sedimentary rocks.

Ophiolitic rocks, including locally extensive eclogites and amphibolites, occur within and adjacent to the Motagua zone along the southern border of the block, and also a few tens of kilometers north of this zone. Especially extensive occurrences are found in the vicinity of Morazán and Los Amates, and a large occurrence is found on the northern edge of the Chortis block in the vicinity of Sanarate. Major allochthonous bodies of this rock comprise the Sierra de Santa Cruz north of the Polochic River, and a similarly large, east-trending elongate massif between Salamá and Tactic and south of this river.

The curvilinearity of the Motagua valley has led to the speculation that it marks a major transcurrent fault. Certain smaller tributary valleys (Río Guastatoya, Río Managuá) do, in fact, occur along the line of the fault that moved during the 1976 earthquake. However, in general this line does not coincide with prominent topographic lineations within or on the fringes of the valley. Within the lower Motagua valley, between Quiriguá and Morales, is the Bananeras depression, a 30 by 10 km rift basin completely filled with late Cenozoic sediment.

About 25 km north of the Motagua valley, and extending westward into Mexico, is a series of three river valleys with east-trending reaches that form a single linear trend. From east to west these are the Polochic, Chixoy, and Cuilco rivers; their trend marks the Polochic fault. At the east end of this valley is the rift depression of Lago Izabal, a 40 by 20 km depression similar to the Bananeras depression. The major transcurrent fault probably follows the south side of this lake and merges with the Motagua fault zone near Morales. The north side of the lake is marked by an important normal fault (Fig. 4).

The entire highland unit north of the Polochic fault zone is underlain by open folds oriented approximately east–west. The dominant bedrock unit is composed of Cretaceous limestones and dolomites and smaller exposures of Paleozoic sedimentary rocks, Jurassic red beds, and Late Cretaceous–early Tertiary wackes. From east to west the named morphological units are: Sierra de Santa Cruz (underlain by an ophiolite); the Sierra de Chamá, a series of gentle east-west elongate hills; and the Cordillera de Cuchumatanes, a prominent carbonate upland more than 3000 m high.

The Maya Mountains of Belize are an elevated terrane (90 by 50 km) underlain by Paleozoic sedimentary rocks and an older granitic pluton. These are intruded by several younger plutons.

North of the Sierra de Chamá and west of the Maya Mountains, the main part of northern Guatemala (Dept. El Petén, northern Alta Verapaz, and northern El Quiche) is a relatively flat, elevated (100 to 200 m) southern extension of the Yucatán platform. A minor east-trending swell in the center of the Petén is expressed as a series of limestone hills with extensive karst development (Sierra del Lacandón; Libertad arch).

Within the Maya block there are very few post-Triassic igneous rocks, except for ophiolitic allochthons emplaced at the end of the Cretaceous and minor igneous bodies in the Cordillera de Cuchumatanes. Neither are there the characteristic northeast-southwest en-echelon young rift valleys characteristic of the northern margin of the Chortis block. Proposed extensions of the geology or morphology of the Maya block eastward to correlate with the Cayman Rise (Kesler and others, 1974) do not exist. Instead, the Yucatán Basin margin is a typically rifted passive margin (Dillon and Vedder, 1973) of apparent, but not established, late Mesozoic age.

PRECAMBRIAN AND PALEOZOIC METAMORPHIC ROCKS

The older metamorphic rocks of the Maya block crop out along the southern boundary of the block and as basement in several wells in northern Guatemala, the Yucatán Peninsula of Mexico, and northern Belize (Plates 4 and 5b). They constitute the Chuacús Series (McBirney, 1963) (Fig. 3), which forms a nearly continuous band just north of the Motagua suture zone for a distance of about 350 km. In the east, this series has been studied by Bosc (1971), van den Boom (1972), Newcomb (1975), Johnson (1984), and Roper (1976, 1978). McBirney's original Chuacús Series included amphibolites, many of which are now attributed to the allochthonous El Tambor Formation, which is a Cretaceous ophiolite. The remaining Chuacús is dominantly mica schist and gneiss, and minor mappable marble units and thin, scattered quartzite and metavolcanic layers.

Van den Boom (1972) summarized the Chuacús Series in the Salamá area, including within it some rocks here included with the late Paleozoic Santa Rosa Group. He concluded that these rocks represented a Barrovian series of increasingly metamorphosed rocks, grading from a chloritic schist into a granitized rock of igneous aspect. The present view is that his "chloritic

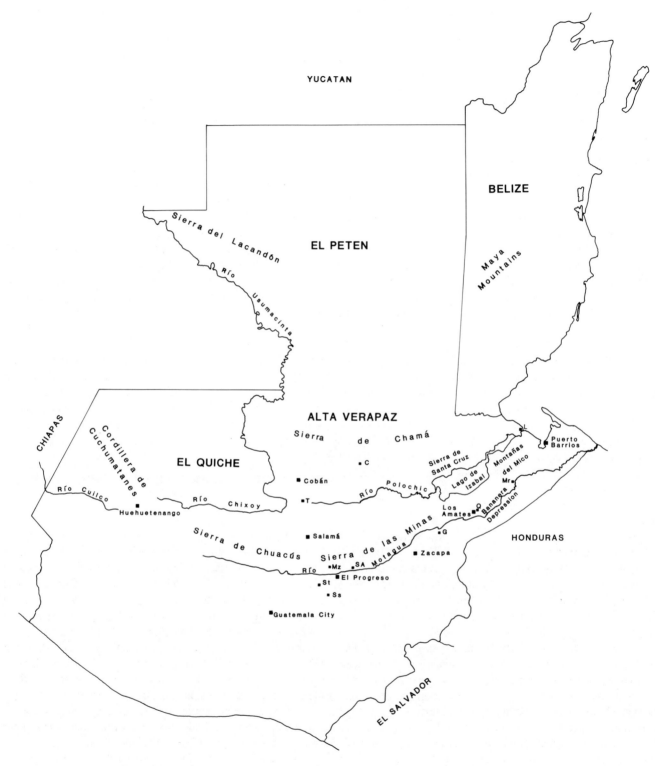

Figure 2. Map of Guatemala and Belize showing major rivers, mountain ranges, and other important geological features.   Smaller towns are abbreviated as follows: C = Cahabón; G = Gualán; L = Livingston; Mr = Morales; Mz = Morazán; Q = Quiriguá; St = Sanarate; Ss = Sansare; SA = San Agustín Acasaguastlán; T = Tactic.

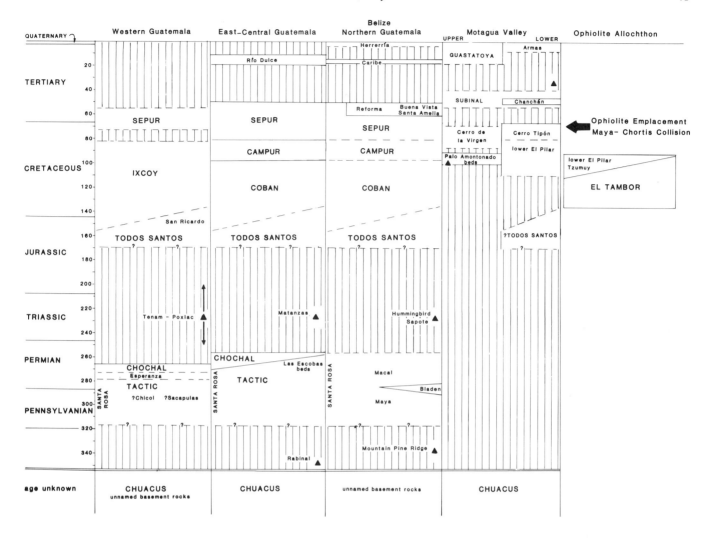

Figure 3. Stratigraphic sections for western Guatemala, east-central Guatemala, northern Guatemala and Belize, and Motagua Valley; Ophiolite allochthon is also indicated. Note that dashed lines indicate uncertainty about age limits. Solid triangles are granitic intrusions, keyed according to their ages. Las Escobas Beds and Palo Amontonado Beds are informal names.

schist" is lightly metamorphosed Pennsylvanian–Permian shale of the Tactic Formation' the granitized rock is the intrusive Rabinal granite; and that metamorphic isograds within the Chuacús proper cannot be established in this highly faulted terrane.

In the eastern area (San Agustín to Los Amates) the Chuacús Series is less metamorphosed than in the Salamá area, where McBirney originally described it. Here there are two widely recognized and easily separable units. The San Agustín Formation (Bosc, 1971) is a mylonitized metagranitoid, which is generally an augen gneiss. At its highest levels of deformation the feldspar augen have been stretched into nearly unrecognizable long, thin, pale streaks. The formation is compositionally divided into metagranitoids of homogeneous composition and migmatites with more variable compositions. The mylonitization is believed to

have resulted from the Late Cretaceous suturing event. An earlier history can be seen in isoclinal folding, but the later overprint has virtually destroyed all usable earlier structural elements.

The Jones Formation (Newcomb, 1975) is dominantly mica schist. Within this formation occurs the San Lorenzo marble, which is generally nearly pure calcite with a very low magnesium content. It is not distinguishable mineralogically and chemically from other thin marble layers within the Jones Formation. However, farther east in the Gualán area, Johnson (1984) found dolomite within this marble. The Jones Formation is more sodic than is typical for clastic sediments (including graywackes), and this unit of schist, marble, and minor quartzite evidently includes a high proportion of original volcanic material. A greenstone unit consists of schist of basaltic composition, the relatively low TiO_2

and high K_2O values of which led Newcomb to interpret them as orogenic basalts and andesites.

Newcomb (1975) suggested that the Chuacús Series of McBirney (1963) and the San Agustín, Jones, and San Lorenzo Formations might not be completely correlative. The higher grade of metamorphism in McBirney's area around Salamá and the extensive Late Cretaceous thrust faulting of the metamorphic belt make such correlations tenuous, although the lithologies are similar.

The petrography of the eastern Chuacús Series has been most thoroughly described by McBirney (1963), van der Boom (1972), Bosc (1971), Newcomb (1975, 1978) and Johnson (1984). The metasediments consist dominantly of schists, including quartzite and calcareous layers, metamorphosed originally (age unknown) to grades as high as lower amphibolite, and subsequently deformed and retrogressively metamorphosed during the Late Cretaceous. The metasedimentary rocks are dominantly quartz-muscovite-albite-chlorite schists with sporadic biotite and/or garnet and local chloritoid, sillimanite (Río Hondo area only; Newcomb, 1975), staurolite (Salamá area only, McBirney, 1963), and kyanite. There is abundant petrographic and structural evidence for multiple events, but only the later (Late Cretaceous) can be dated. The migmatitic part of the San Agustín Formation may represent an especially large remnant of an earlier metamoprhic event.

Late Cretaceous deformation produced a widespread retrogressive metamorphism and pervasive deformation; lineations and foliations show that the deformation was a north–south compressive event (Bosc, 1971; Newcomb, 1975; Johnson, 1984). Cataclastic rocks, some of which texturally approach ultramylonite, are found extensively along the southernmost exposures of the Chuacús Series, and more sporadically throughout the Sierra de Chuacús and Sierra de las Minas. Kyanite in the El Chol quadrangle (some of which are sufficiently large to have been proposed for exploitation), may relate to this event.

In western Guatemala, similar metamorphic rocks have been described by Anderson (1969), Kesler and others (1970), and C. Dengo (1982). Kesler and others (1970) correlated these rocks with the Chuacús Series, and their descriptions seem to fit the metasedimentary part of that group. The Pucal Marble appears to occupy a position analogous to that of the San Lorenzo Formation to the east, but the graphitic schists found in this formation are not found in the east. From descriptions it is not clear that there is a westward equivalent of the metagranitoid San Agustín Formation. C. Dengo (1982) cautioned that the textures of the rocks in the western area show a strong overprint of later deformation, including very young shearing associated with the Polochic fault zone.

The protolith of the Chucacús Group is bipartite. The metagranitoids are of unknown age, and there is no way at present to correlate them with any of the pre-Cretaceous plutonic rocks known from elsewhere in the Maya block. The metasedimentary rocks are similarly undistinctive. The possibility exists that all or part of this subunit may be equivalent to the thick Pennsylvani-an–Permian Santa Rosa Group. However, the metabasalts within the Jones Formation are not similar to the rhyolites of the Bladen volcanics or the greenstones and dacites of the Providencia Sequence, the only well-known volcanic units within that group. Furthermore, the high sodium content of the Jones Formation suggests a significant volcanic component throughout. However, the locally dolomitic San Lorenzo Formation bears some resemblance to the limestones of the Permian Chochal Formation, including the observation that in many places they are distinctly fetid.

SUBSURFACE METAMORPHIC BASEMENT

Metamorphic basement has been encountered in four wells in Yucatán and Belize. Yucatán 1 (López-Ramos, 1975) encountered a varicolored crystalloblastic quartz chlorite schist intruded (questionably) by a rhyolite, beneath the Todos Santos Formation. Different radiometric ages have been given for the metaigneous rocks (Dengo, 1969; Viniegra, 1971). Neither of these dates has been documented. In Yucatán 4 (López Ramos, 1975) a lightly metamorphosed quartzite was found beneath the Todos Santos Formation. In Basil Jones 1 (Fig. 4), schist, phyllite, and shale were found beneath a thick Cretaceous limestone and shale sequence. In Pachacán 1 (Fig. 4) unspecified metamorphic rocks were found beneath the Todos Santos Formation. In the case of the latter two wells, these metamorphic rocks may be in contact with metamorphosed Paleozoic sedimentary rocks that surround the northern Belize subsurface granite body. The correlations of these metamorphic rocks are uncertain.

PALEOZOIC, MESOZOIC, AND CENOZOIC GRANITIC ROCKS AND ASSOCIATED MINERALIZATION

Scattered granitic bodies of the Maya block fall into two age categories, but the available information is not substantial and must be viewed cautiously. Some of the published radiometric data were originally calculated using older decay constants. In other cases the radiometric interpretations appear to be more complex than originally thought.

Pre-Cretaceous granitic rocks

The Rabinal granite has been dated by the lead-uranium method from extracted zircons (Gomberg and others, 1968). The extrapolated isotopic ratio trend intersects the concordia line at 1,075 and 345 Ma. The earlier age could be the age of inherited zircons, and the latter the age of magmatism and emplacement. McBirney (1963), has described this granite as a stage of a migmatitic, anatectic series; van den Boom (1972) concluded that this granite is the nonmagmatic product of the granitization of an arkose. In the western Cuchumatanes Mountains, Marcus (1974) has described the "old granite," which is very similar to and may be correlative with the Rabinal granite.

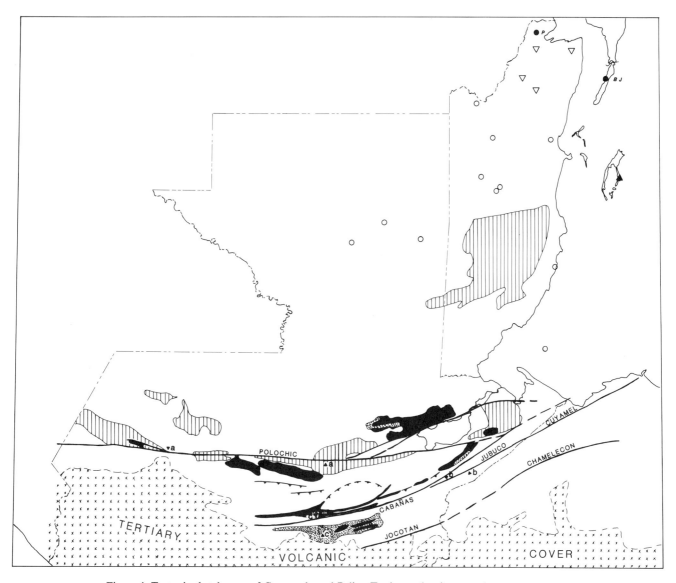

Figure 4. Tectonic sketch map of Guatemala and Belize. Tertiary volcanic cover shown as x pattern. Main occurrences of Paleozoic rocks are shown as vertical lined pattern. Black shapes are serpentine allochthons; stipple pattern shows major occurrences of other ophiolitic lithologies. Major Neogene strike-slip faults are named; solid triangles show matching lithologies as follows: a = 131 km sinistral offset of Polochic fault system based on Permian anticlinoria and offset river drainages (Burkart, 1978); b = maximum 20 km sinistral offset of Jubuco fault based on Río Morjá on south side and El Rico alluvial fan on north side (Muller, 1979; Johnson, 1984); c: very small offset of Motagua fault system based on north-dipping amphibolite with minor eclogite (Lawrence, 1975; McBirney and others, 1967; Donnelly, unpublished). Some major thrust and reverse faults shown with toothed pattern. Virtually all serpentine bodies occur along faults of this variety. Wells encountering metamorphic rocks shown as solid circles (P = Pachacán; B J = Basil Jones). Wells encountering granite shown as open inverted triangles. Turneffe Cay well encountering ophiolite shown as solid triangle. Wells encountering Paleozoic sediments shown as open circles.

An early Carboniferous age is implied for both the Rabinal Granite and the Mountain Pine Ridge pluton of Belize. In the latter, seven whole-rock samples of Bateson and Hall (1977) fall on a good isochron of about 336 Ma. Although this granite has been assumed to intrude late Paleozoic sedimentary rocks, there is no contact aureole (Dawe, 1984), and stream-sediment samples lack the chiastolite and andalusite found around other, clearly younger granitic bodies in the Maya Mountains.

Triassic magmatism is inferred for the Hummingbird and Sapote granites of Belize and the Matanzas granite of eastern

Guatemala. The Belize granites are surrounded by chiastolitic shales of the Macal Series of Paleozoic age. Four K/Ar ages of extracted biotites given by Bateson and Hall and an unpublished fifth date cluster between 226 and 237 Ma, or early Late Triassic. Similar ages are seen in two of three whole-rock K/Ar ages in the Mountain Pine Ridge granite, which has a considerably older Rb/Sr age. The lack of a contact aureole and the presence of a broad zone of hydrothermal alteration (Dawe, 1984) in both the granite and surrounding Paleozoic sedimentary rocks (resulting in widespread formation of tourmaline and sericite) indicate that the younger age here represents reheating and alteration coeval with the younger granites.

The Matanzas granite of eastern Guatemala has yielded a Rb/Sr age of 227 Ma based on whole rock, microcline, and plagioclase separates; however, muscovite and biotite give discrepant results (P. Pushkar, unpub. data). J. Sutter (personal communication, 1984) found younger ages for the biotite (161 Ma) and muscovite (212 Ma, 213 Ma) by the Ar 39/40 method. Apparently the granite has undergone later thermal modification, and it is doubtfully included here with the Belize granites. Another indication of a thermal event of Triassic age is Sutter's (unpublished) age of 238 Ma (Ar 39/40 on hornblende) from an amphibolite within the Chuacús Series.

These few pre-Cretaceous radiometric data cluster into Triassic (Ladinian–Carnian) and Mississippian (Visean) intervals. These ages have no relation to known radiometric ages from the Chortis block (Horne and others, this volume).

In western Guatemala several poorly exposed granite bodies, the largest of which is exposed along 14 km of a river course, are presumed to be post-Paleozoic, pre-Jurassic (Anderson and others, 1973). Small bodies of granite near the Polochic fault zone are post-Paleozoic and pre-Tertiary (Anderson, 1969).

Marcus (1974) has described several granitic and other intrusive rocks of apparent pre-Cretaceous age in the western Cuchumatanes Mountains. The Tenam-Poxlac granites are deformed and considered to be post-Paleozoic and pre-Jurassic. Litke (1975) reported a single K/Ar age of 196 Ma for this granite. Undeformed micrographic granites are of unknown age but in part appear to intrude the Tenam-Poxlac granites. A small complex of high-Ti alkalic gabbros and syenites similarly intrude Paleozoic rocks.

Motagua Valley Granitic Rocks

A series of granitic plutons within the Motagua Valley is found from immediately north of Guatemala City eastward nearly to Zacapa. These plutons intrude metamorphic rocks. Ritchie and McDowell (1979) reported K/Ar ages of 95 and 104 Ma on the westernmost pluton.

Clemons and Long (1971) attempted to date the Chiquimula pluton, but did not find a single age. Some granites are evidently Paleozoic in age and may correspond to granitoids intrusive into the Las Ovejas metamorphic series of the northern Chortis block. Less siliceous granitoids lie on a 50-Ma Rb/Sr isochron.

Several smaller plutons occur near El Progreso, Zacapa (probably part of the Chiquimula pluton), and southeast of Los Amates. The latter pluton (Buena Vista) has somewhat alkalic affinities (Muller, 1979). J. Sutter (personal communication, 1984) obtained Ar 39/40 dates for three of these small bodies and found a remarkable agreement among them: 34.7, 34.9, and 35.0 Ma. A granitic body at San Pedro Sula, Honduras, lies along the trend formed by these three bodies; it has been dated by Horne and others (1976b) at 35.9 Ma.

Post-Early Cretaceous Mineralization

Several occurrences of mineralization along the southern Maya block imply that magmatic activity may be more widespread than occurrences of igneous rocks. Kesler and Ascarrunz-K. (1973) summarized occurrences of lead-zinc mineralization in a 160-km belt stretching from the Cuchumatanes Mountains to Cobán. These deposits occur in replacements of both the Permian and Early Cretaceous carbonates, and several occur very near the Polochic fault zone. Collins and Kesler (1969) described a tungsten-antimony deposit in Permian rocks close to this fault zone.

LATE PALEOZOIC SEDIMENTARY ROCKS

There are two main sedimentary rock units of late Paleozoic age in the Maya block (Fig. 3): a lower clastic unit, called the Santa Rosa Group, and an upper limestone called the Chochal Limestone.

The late Paleozoic clastic sedimentary rocks of the Maya block are generally known as the Santa Rosa Group. The nomenclature of this series has been controversial. Dollfus and de Montserrat (1868) introduced the term for what they considered to be the oldest sedimentary rocks overlying the metamorphic rocks of central Guatemala. In the original sense, the term included three rock series: an older clastic sequence, limestones, and younger sandstones and conglomerates. Dolfuss and de Montserrat thought the age of these three units was Triassic on the basis of a supposed lithological resemblance to European rocks, but the Paleozoic age of the lower part of the sequence was recognized by Sapper (1899), who divided the Paleozoic part of the sequence into an underlying clastic "Santa Rosa Schichten" and an overlying "Karbonkalke." As summarized by Bohnenberger (1966), later workers generally used the term "Santa Rosa" for the lower clastic sequence, which are overlain by the Permian Chochal Limestone and the Jurassic to Cretaceous Todos Santos Formation. This is the usage followed in this chapter.

A differing usage was presented in a recent paper (Clemons and others, 1974), which suggests that the Chochal Limestone and a lithologically intermediate unit, the Esperanza Formation, should be included in the Santa Rosa Group. This usage was prompted by a northward facies change in the Chochal Limestone to shale, locally removing the lithologic contrast with the underlying Tactic Shale. However, the Chochal is in most places a limestone; also, an angular unconformity separating the Chochal Limestone and underlying clastic deposits in eastern Guatemala reinforces the desirability of excluding it from the Santa Rosa Group.

A part of the nomenclatural problem of the term Santa Rosa was the unfortunate location of the type locality on a formation now recognized to be Mesozoic (Finca Santa Rosa in Baja Verapaz). Vinson (1962) made the unusual suggestion that another place in western Guatemala also named "Santa Rosa" would provide a less ambiguous type locality, because it was located on the Paleozoic series. This suggestion has not been followed. The present usage refers to a clastic sequence occurring in part a few kilometers north of the original locality; no type section is recognized.

Santa Rosa Group

The most extensive areas of outcrop of this group are (1) in western Guatemala and adjacent Chiapas, extending eastward in an increasingly narrow belt to the Caribbean coast of Guatemala, and (2) in the Maya Mountains of Belize, including subsurface occurrences in exploratory oil wells of Belize and northern Guatemala (Fig. 4). There are two major lithologic series in this group: sandstones and conglomerates in the lower part, grading to shales in the upper. Carbonaceous material occurs in minor amounts, and some beds in the upper shales are calcareous. Volcanic units are locally thick in Belize and also occur in western Guatemala.

In the Cordillera de Cuchumatanes and Polochic fault zone of western Guatemala the Santa Rosa Group has been divided into three units. The lowest part of the sequence consists of dominantly conglomeratic units: the Chicol Conglomerate (Anderson, 1969), the Sacapulas Formation (Bohnenberger, 1966; Forth, 1971) and Cantel and Providencia Sequences (Litke, 1975). The overlying Tactic Shale grades upward into the Permian (Wolfcampian) Esperanza Formation, which in turn grades into the overlying Chochal Limestone (Anderson and others, 1973). The Esperanza Formation is lithologically intermediate between the Tactic Formation and Chochal Limestone and is not recognized in eastern Guatemala, where the contact between these formations is much more abrupt.

Older Santa Rosa Group units

The Chicol Formation (800 to 1200 m) is a poorly exposed, highly deformed sandstone and conglomerate sequence. The finer grained beds are varicolored, ranging from red to gray and black. The conglomerates contain a colorful array of limestone and quartzite clasts. Parts of the section are calcareous, but the limestones have yielded only crinoid columnals. Anderson (1969) reported that the poorly exposed upper part of the section contains "several tens or perhaps a few hundreds of meters" of volcanic units, which consist of plagioclase-bearing tuffaceous beds.

The Sacapulas Formation (800 to 1200 m) was described most thoroughly by Forth (1971) from outcrops about 40 km east of the Chicol beds. It is lithologically very similar to the Chicol but contains limestone units near its top. The unit also contains highly altered tuffaceous beds.

The Providencia sequence (thickness unknown; Litke, 1975) occurs near Barillas and consists of altered greenstones and siliceous volcanic rocks overlain by coarse conglomerates, which in turn are overlain by Tactic Shale. The Cantel sequence (more than 100 m; Litke, 1975) also occurs in the Barillas quadrangle and consists of 100 m of conglomerates, sandstones, shales, and thin-bedded radiolarian siltstones. This sequence also contains some volcanic glass. These older coarse clastic units are poorly exposed and lack stratigraphically useful fossils.

The pre-Tactic ages of the Providencia and Cantel sequences are established by superposition and by occurrences of Cantel debris within the Tactic Shales. On the other hand, the Chicol and Sacapulas Formations are fault bounded and lack direct criteria for an age assignment.

Near Senahú in eastern Guatemala, Bonis (1967) found small occurrences of red beds and conglomerates, some apparently interlayered with carbonate rocks, which he assigned to the older Santa Rosa.

Tactic Shale

In eastern Guatemala (Cobán area), the Paleozoic section consists of 500 m of Tactic Shale underlying 700 m of Chochal Limestone; there is a fairly sharp transition between the two (Walper, 1960). Near Huehuetenango it is at least 800 m thick. It is a featureless dark shale unit with some calcareous beds near the top. The name was introduced by Walper (1960), who rejected the existing term "Santa Rosa" for any part of the sequence. The shale is generally unfossiliferous, but calcareous interbeds near Cobán have yielded foraminifera (see below).

In the Maya Mountains of Belize, the entire Paleozoic section was divided by Dixon (1956) into the underlying Maya Series of coarse clastics and the overlying Macal Series of shales and with local limestones. Dixon considered the Maya more deformed than the Macal, and concluded that an important unconformity separated them. Thorough studies of this area by Kesler and others (1971) and by Bateson and Hall (1977) showed that the two units are conformable and were simultaneously deformed. However, some confusion remains, and the existence of metamorphosed shales has led several workers to differentiate between a Paleozoic metamorphic series and the Santa Rosa series (Bonis and others, 1970). The metamorphism, however, results from contact effects around Triassic granitic plutons.

The most thorough study of these sedimentary rocks is that by Nelson (1984), who showed that the two series in the northwestern Maya Mountains are each about 3,000 m thick. The lower part (Dixon's "Maya") is sandy with conspicuous quartzite-clast conglomerates, and the upper part ("Macal") is dominantly shale; thin limestone beds are found near the lower boundary.

Nelson reported several traces of paleocurrent direction. The included ripple cross lamination, large-scale cross stratification, asymmetrical ripple marks, scour marks, and parting-step lineations. When corrected for dip and fold plunge, Nelson found that paleocurrents were generally toward the west-northwest. The inferred environment of deposition was a continental rise with prograding submarine fans. The provenance is inferred to be an older metamorphic terrane; there is no evidence of a volcanic arc. The thin limestones, however, have plagioclase grains, indicative of magmatic activity.

A poorly exposed limestone unit in the center of the Maya Mountains was described by Bateson and Hall (1977). These limestones are several hundred meters thick and contain crinoids; fusulinids indicate a Permian age. Shale interbeds suggest that this unit is stratigraphically part of the upper Macal.

In eastern Guatemala a limited but significant section of sandstones containing minor limestone and local carbonaceous debris occurs beneath the Chochal Limestone near Puerto Barrios. These beds, which have not been previously described, are called informally the Las Escobas beds, from their exposure in the river of that name. They are perhaps a few hundred meters thick and contain abundant brachiopods, carbonized wood, and fenestellid bryozoans. Thin limestone beds contain few fusulinids but a wealth of other foraminifera. An angular unconformity of about 30° separates this unit from the overlying Chochal Limestone. Lithologically, this section is very similar to facies seen in Belize and quite unlike Tactic lithologies seen farther west in Guatemala. The angular unconformity shows an Early Permian deformational event.

In the southern Maya Mountains, a thick volcanic series named the Bladen Formation was most recently described by Druecker (1978). This sequence is 1,500 to 1,800 m thick and consists of thick rhyolitic and dacitic flows, ash-flow tuffs, and tuff breccias. The unit is moderately deformed on a large scale, but highly deformed on a small scale, with local isoclinal folding.

The age of the Santa Rosa Group is established convincingly from a combination of paleontological and radiometric data from Belize. Rb/Sr data from the Bladen volcanics (Bateson and Hall, 1977) show four points tightly aligned along an isochron at 285 Ma (Pennsylvanian-Permian boundary), with a fifth point aberrant. Brachiopod data from the lower Macal are suggestive of a Pennsylvanian age. Fusulinids, possibly from slightly higher in the section, are Permian (Leonardian; Ross, 1962). Still higher in the section the goniatite *Perrinites hilli* of Leonardian age has been found.

In the northwestern Maya Mountains, rhyolitic tuffs, which are evidently correlative with the Bladen volcanic rocks, occur at about the same level as the brachiopod-bearing beds. Thus the Macal Series is dominantly Permian, possibly Pennsylvanian at its base, and the underlying Maya Series is undated. Because the sedimentary rocks in the Mountain Pine Ridge area were evidently deposited subsequent to the emplacement of the large granitic pluton with a Rb/Sr age of about 340 Ma, the Maya is bracketed within the Pennsylvanian.

In eastern Guatemala, the Las Escobas beds have yielded fusulinids (*Schubertella* and *Eoverbeekina*) and other foraminifera (*Hemigordius, Globivalvulina, Ammodiscus,* and *Tetrataxis*) which indicate an Early Permian (Wolfcampian) age (M. Nestell, det.).

In the vicinity of Cobán, the Tactic Shale contains Leonardian fusulinids in its upper part (Kling, 1960; Ross, 1979).

In Chiapas, the Santa Rosa Group occurs in two series (López-Ramos, 1981). The lower unit is more metamorphosed and consists of phyllite, shale, and marl. A single find of a Pennsylvanian fossil establishes the age, although Hernández García (1973) believed its higher metamorphic grade indicated an older age. The upper Santa Rosa consists of sand and shale and interlayered limestone. The same Early Permian fusulinid (*Eoverbeekina americana*) is found in the Mexican sections as well as the Tactic Shale near Cobán (Kling, 1960). Another Chiapas unit, the Grupera Formation, is possibly equivalent to the transitional Esperanza Formation of Guatemala.

Chochal Limestone

The Chochal Limestone was named by Roberts and Irving (1957), who described a section in western Guatemala about 200 m thick and estimated the total thickness at about 600 m. Sapper (1899) had earlier called this unit the "Karbonkalke."

Walper (1960) reported at least 640 m of Chochal Limestone near Purulhá, in east-central Guatemala. The lithology is almost exclusively fetid limestone and dolomite and minor shale beds. The contact near Cobán with the underlying Tactic is sharp, although to the west it is more gradational (intervening Esperanza Formation). Kling (1960) and Walper (1960) evidently measured the same section at about the same time; however, their descriptions and thickness estimates differ. Chochal facies have been described as back reef by Kling. Bonis (1967) described similar rocks near Senahú, about 20 km east of the section studied by Kling and by Walper.

In western Guatemala, Anderson and others (1973) described between 500 and 1,000 m of Chochal Limestone and series of interlayered siltstone, sandstone, limestone, and dolomite (the Tuilán Member) in the upper part of the section. The occurrence of the goniatite *Perrinites* cf *hilli* suggests a correlation with the upper part of the Macal of Belize.

In easternmost Guatemala the Chochal Limestone is widespread but little studied; it forms a large part of the Montánas del Mico.

The age of the Chochal has been given by Kling as Wolfcampian to Leonardian in western Guatemala and Leonardian to possible Guadalupian in eastern Guatemala. Ross (1979) placed the Cobán occurrences of Chochal in the latest Leonardian to Guadalupian. The Mexican lithological equivalents are the Vainilla and the Paso Hondo (also mistakenly written Paseo Hondo) Limestones of Chiapas, which are in excess of 660 m thick (López-Ramos, 1981). These limestones span the late Wolfcampian to Leonardian.

MIDDLE MESOZOIC CLASTIC SEDIMENTARY ROCKS

The stratigraphic history between the mid-Permian and Jurassic is unknown for the Maya block because most of the area was probably emergent during this time. The Mexican and Gulf of Mexico salt basins (Viniegra, 1971) probably came into existence during the Triassic, but there are no recorded sedimentary rocks of this age from the Maya block. Beginning in the Late Jurassic, a red bed sequence (Todos Santos Formation) accumulated. It is conglomeratic near the base, but consists dominantly of red beds and, especially toward the top, includes gray and green shales, limestones, and gypsum. The lower contact, where exposed, is invariably a sharp unconformity. Where the upper units are carbonates, the contact with overlying carbonates is commonly gradational.

Sapper (1899) named this unit the "Todos Santos-Schichten" but failed to designate a type section. Richards (1963) described a type section near Todos Santos Cuchumatanes in western Guatemala, and delineated a younger unit, the San Ricardo Formation, which contained a distinctive limestone subunit. This younger unit is lithologically variable and cannot be mapped over a broad area; consequently the name is not widely used in Guatemala. Current stratigraphic practice is to use the name "Todos Santos" for all clastic units between the Permian limestones and Cretaceous dolomites.

The thickness of the Todos Santos Formation is highly variable. The type section of Richards, (including his San Ricardo) is about 1,250 m thick; comparable thicknesses are seen to the northwest (Chiapas) and to the southeast (near Cobán). In the northern area (El Petén, the Yucatán, Belize), thicknesses are commonly a few meters to tens of meters (locally 100 m or more). However, the thickness does not diminish northward and northeastward in a simple fashion; in northwestern Guatemala the thickness diminishes to virtually zero on the Poxlac uplift northeast of Todos Santos, and thickens to several hundred meters still farther northeast (Anderson and others, 1973).

Limestones and evaporites occur sporadically near the top of the formation in Guatemala. The La Ventosa limestone member of the San Ricardo Formation (Richards, 1963) is nearly 50 m thick but lacks stratigraphically useful fossils. Gypsum is commonly associated with outcrops of the Todos Santos in northwestern Guatemala (Forth, 1971). In the subsurface of the Petén region and Belize, anhydrite has been found. According to Viniegra (1971), the Todos Santos of Guatemala fringes a vast salt basin located primarily in Mexico; the extension of salt to Guatemalan territory, however, is limited to the northwestern fringe of that country. Viniegra also showed an intervening belt of anhydrite between the salt and red beds on the eastern edge of the salt basin.

The age of the Todos Santos is known mainly from paleontological information from marine interbeds in Mexico; the beds have yielded Jurassic ammonites, and an Early Cretaceous fauna has been found near the top (Viniegra, 1971). Blair (1981) reported an Early Cretaceous (Berriasian) palynomorph flora in Chiapas.

The deposition of the Todos Santos unit reflects the development of horsts and grabens during the Jurassic separation of North and South America. The thick and coarse facies in western Guatemala suggest that the southern edge of the Maya block may have been close to a zone of major faulting, whereas the thinner, finer grained facies in northern Guatemala indicate deposition of alluvial sediments as a series of coalescing fan deposits on a relatively mature surface.

The Honduras Group clastic deposits (Horne and others, this chapter) of southern Guatemala and throughout Honduras contrast in appearance with those of the Todos Santos of central Guatemala, which are commonly very arkosic; the western Chortis block sandstones are red-cemented, clean quartz sands that occur in at least two localities immediately beneath Albian fossil localities. Similar sandstones in southeastern Guatemala are interbedded with Aptian limestones, suggesting a younger age there for the Honduras Group.

CRETACEOUS LIMESTONES AND DOLOMITES

In 1899 Sapper mapped two carbonate units in the Department of Alta Verapaz (Fig. 2), naming them (without defining type sections) the "Cobankalke" and "Rudistenkalke." Vinson (1962) designated a type section for the Cobán Formation and defined the Campur Formation. Sapper's and Vinson's division of the Cretaceous section into thick dolomite overlain by thin limestone has prevailed in eastern and northern Guatemala and in Belize. However, in western Guatemala the lithological distinction is commonly more difficult. For this reason, Termer (1932) introduced the name Ixcoy Formation for a carbonate section in western Guatemala whose relationship to Sapper's two units was uncertain. Anderson and others (1973) continued Termer's usage in western Guatemala.

Other recent usage of these names has varied. Walper (1960) applied the name Ixcoy to the lower part of the carbonate section near the town of Cobán, and restricted the name Cobán to the upper part, with a "distinctive" thin-bedded unit separating the two. Walper's Ixcoy is dominantly dolomite and his overlying Cobán dominantly limestone. This use of the Ixcoy is not acceptable; Termer had intended the term to include the entire carbonate section. Vinson (1962), who worked at the same time with Walper but who seems not to have communicated with him, approached these rocks differently. He relegated the lower, dolomitic section to the Cobán Formation, and called the upper limestone the Campur Limestone. However, he did not discuss the contact between the two units other than to call it gradational.

The most recent study of this interval in Guatemala is that of Paulsen and Koch (1980) in southern Alta Verapaz. Their results reinforce the apparent lithologic contrast between the two units, but their stratigraphy is not in accord with either that of Vinson or other contemporary workers. Their Cobán is divided into a lower (dominantly dolomite) unit and an upper (dominantly thin-bedded limestone with minor dolomite) unit. They take as their definition of the base of the Campur the lowest point at which rudist debris is first noted. This break is not easily recognized, and the formational boundary of Paulsen and Koch is erratic. Vinson had placed the boundary at a major lithological break, which is preferable to the more recent Paulsen and Koch boundary. We refer Paulsen and Koch's "Lower Cobán" to the Cobán and their "Upper Cobán" to the Campur, recognizing that the contact between the two units is variably gradational.

Dengo (1983) used the term Ixcoy Group to include both the Cobán and Campur Formations along the Mexican-Guatemalan frontier. Dengo's usage of the Ixcoy as a group name for the combined Cobán and Campus is a practical continuation of Termer's name where the two formations cannot be distinguished.

Although in places the Cobán was deposited directly on basement rock or on the Permian section, more commonly it overlies the Todos Santos. The facies change from dominantly continental sands and conglomerates to mainly dolomitic carbonates is gradational and corresponds to an evaporitic interval. The basal contact is probably diachronous, transgressing from the northwest to the southeast. Bishop (1980) presented an extended discussion of this transition. In Chiapas, López-Ramos (1981) indicated a hiatus at the base of the Mexican correlative to the Cobán.

The Cobán Formation is a dominantly dolomitic, highly recrystallized massive limestone, as seen in outcrop along the southern margin of the Maya block. Intraformational breccias are common; these are dominantly dolomitic but contain siliceous limestones, and sparse shales and siltstones. Sections of thin-bedded limestone tens of meters thick with sparse dolomite occur near the top of the Cobán. Evaporite solution breccias are common (Blount and Moore, 1969), and there are several occurrences of secondary gypsum in the vicinity of the outcrops of this unit. Anhydrite is found in drilled sections and becomes increasingly common to the north. Salt has been encountered in drilled sections, but its stratigraphic age might be Jurassic or older.

The Campur Formation is a fine-grained limestone with locally abundant rudist debris. Other lithologies (dolomite, shale, siltstone, limestone breccia, conglomerate) are minor. The lower boundary is the lithological break between dominantly massive dolomites below, and thin-bedded, fine-grained limestones above. In drilled sections in the Petén district, some anhydrite is found in this unit, but far less than in the Cobán.

Most of the thickness of the Cretaceous carbonate section in Guatemala is within the Cobán. Thicknesses are difficult to estimate for several reasons: (1) in many sections the base is not seen; (2) the Cobán-Campur boundary is often indistinct; (3) the Cobán is dominantly a monotonous, highly recrystallized dolomite with few paleontological marker zones; and (4) local structural complications (even the angle of dip) are commonly not apparent. Where the thickness can be estimated, the Cobán varies from about 1,500 to about 2,000 m thick in outcrop. Subsurface thicknesses vary from a few hundred meters in central

Belize to about 3 km in the northern Petén. In the subsurface, anhydrite is common, and in the thickest sections, which occur in the western Petén district of Guatemala, salt (possibly Jurassic) occurs. The Campur formation is 800 m thick at its type area but thins to the south.

Stratigraphically useful fossils are very rare within the Cobán. An *Orbitolina* horizon of Albian age is recognized in many drilled sections and has been found in outcrop (Walper, 1960); it has not been established whether it is correlative with the prominent *Orbitolina* horizon seen at the base of the Atima Limestone of the Chortis block.

The Campur was dated originally by Vinson as Coniacian to Campanian. Wilson (1974) pointed out that the occurrence of *Globotruncana calcarata,* a characteristic Campanian form, suggests that this formation has a dominantly younger rather than older age. Paulsen and Koch (1980) extended the range from Cenomanian to Maastrichtian; most of their ages fall into the older part (Cenomanian–Turonian) of this interval.

Correlatives of the Cobán and Campur Formations are widespread in southern Mexico, and biostratigraphic information from outcrop and subsurface occurrences in Chiapas are superior to those from Guatemala. Beds of this age are especially important in southern Mexico as reservoir horizons for some of this hemisphere's most productive oil wells. The Cobán-correlative section in Mexico has been divided into lower (Chinameca) and upper (Sierra Madre) formations. The Tithonian to Neocomian Chinameca, however, can be correlated in part with locally prominent calcareous units found at the top of the San Ricardo, leaving the Sierra Madre as a close equivalent to the Cobán plus Campur. López-Ramos (1981) further divided this carbonate unit in Chiapas into the Sierra Madre Limestone, which he considered Albian and Cenomanian, and an overlying unnamed limestone of Turonian to Santonian age. He set the lower age limit for the Sierra Madre in the early Albian and showed that the Albian–Cenomanian boundary corresponds to a lithological change from massive dolomite to mixed carbonate lithologies. The upper unit is probably correlative with the Campur Limestone. Steele (1982) and Waite (1983) studied in detail a 2,500-m-thick section of these carbonates near Ocozocuautla, Chiapas. The lower 1,000 m is dolomite that contains sparse microfossils. The upper 1,500 m is dominantly limestone of Cenomanian to early Santonian age and has a range of shallow, open-water facies. They extended the name Sierra Madre to the top of this section, contrary to López-Ramos' usage.

In northern Guatemala and Belize, the Cobán is a thick dolomite grading into a thick (up to 3 km) anhydrite northward and westward (into Mexico). The subsurface evaporate basin has been considered to have restricted salt in its central part (Viniegra, 1971); however, such an inference is difficult to sustain because of the known occurrence of secondarily intrusive salt. In southern Mexico the evaporite-dolomite basin is bordered on the northwest (Tabasco–Campeche coast) by the "Reforma Trend," a major oil reservoir. There is no comparable reefal trend known on the southern (central Guatemala) border. The favored explanation is that it never existed (Bishop, 1980), but the destruction of textual evidence for such deposits or their removal during the Late Cretaceous suturing event cannot be ruled out.

The Albian–Cenomanian boundary marks a change from dolomite to a mixed limestone and minor dolomite facies. The Campur limestones are thinner bedded than the Cobán and have only very limited occurrences of dolomite or anhydrite. Their first appearance marks the end of restricted circulation conditions that prevailed to the end of the Albian.

Correlations of the Cobán-Campur interval with other Caribbean units are not clear. In the Chortis block, the corresponding carbonate interval begins with thin-bedded, dark, ammonite-bearing Aptian limestones, passes upward through a locally thick reefal Albian–Cenomanian limestone, and upward into thinner Cenomanian limestones interbedded with red sandstones. Except for the similarity of some fossil zones (such as the *Orbitolina* beds mentioned above), there is little resemblance between the Cobán-Campur sequence and the Chortis-block units. Highly tectonized sedimentary and volcanic rocks of this age have been found within the Motagua suture zone. These are not considered to represent units correlative to the Cobán-Campur.

CRETACEOUS OPHIOLITIC ASSEMBLAGE OF THE MOTAGUA SUTURE ZONE

A dismembered ophiolitic assemblage, called the El Tambor Group, is widespread and conspicuous in central Guatemala. Most occurrences are within the Motagua suture zone, but large allochthonous bodies are also located about 20 km to the south and 50 km to the north of the zone. The dominant lithology is serpentinite, but wacke is abundant and pillow basalts and diabase dike fragments are widespread. Gabbros, plagiogranites, and slightly serpentinized peridotites occur locally. Chert and rare pelagic limestone are interbedded with basalt. Metamorphosed equivalents, which are dominantly amphibolites but include scarce eclogite enveloped in serpentinite, form large outcrop areas adjacent to the Motagua suture zone. Associated sedimentary materials include thick wackes (some of which are volcaniclastic) which are at least in part interbedded with basaltic flows. In general the metamorphic grade is slightly higher in the lowermost exposures. Measured sections in the Sanarate area show about one-quarter metavolcanics and three-quarters metasediments. The basalts and most of the amphibolites have the composition of low-K, oceanic basalts (Lawrence, 1975). The phyllites and schists are metagraywackes, some of which are graphitic. Some sections of interbedded chert and wacke have been tectonically transformed into pseudoconglomerates. The distinction in the field between El Tambor phyllites and the older San Diego phyllites (Horne and others, this volume) is a challenging task, especially where they have been faulted together.

Jadeites and albitites (Foshag, 1954; Silva, 1970) from the central Motagua Valley are not included in this group but are considered to be metamorphosed and metasomatized inclusions of Chuacús Series metamorphic rocks within some serpentinites in the Motagua Valley.

Sapper (1899) first recognized the Motagua and Polochic valley serpentinites and established a Cretaceous age of emplacement. Dengo (1968, 1969, 1972) emphasized their location along major fault zones between plates. McBirney (1963) emphasized the unknown age of the serpentinites and implied that they might be older than the Chuacús Series. McBirney (1963), Williams and others (1964), and McBirney and Bass (1969a) described graywackes, cherts, and metabasalts of what was first called the El Tambor Formation (McBirney and Bass, 1969a), noting the association of serpentinite with these rocks but not explicitly including it in the formation. They concluded that the assemblage was probably but not certainly Paleozoic in age—a view that persisted until the mid 1970s. Bosc (1971) restricted the definition of the El Tambor Formation, removing from it a distinctly older and more highly metamorphosed series of gneisses which he named the Las Ovejas metamorphic series and which is the widespread basement unit of the northern Chortis Block. Meyerhoff and Meyerhoff (1972) stated that this assemblage was Cretaceous, but their evidence has never been specified. Wilson (1974) described the same sequence as the "Jalapa Basinal Melange." He included within this sequence the "Sanarate Limestone" and the "El Sesteadero conglomerates," both of which are now excluded from the sequence (see below).

Lawrence (1975) described in the Sanarate quadrangle the most extensive exposures of the El Tambor Group, giving its total thickness as between 3,000 and 9,000 m. His thicknesses are very problematical; thrust faulting is pervasive, and the assumption of an orderly stratigraphic sequence is doubtful. Lawrence's lowest unit, the Sansare amphibolite, which is about 3,000 m thick, is here excluded from the normal stratigraphic sequence and considered a fault slice of originally similar materials with an uncertain stratigraphic relationship. It is lithologically identical to extensive amphibolites within serpentinite near Morazán, north of the Motagua Valley, and to smaller bodies near Cahabón, north of the Polochic Valley (Rosenfeld, 1981).

Lawrence's (1975) El Tambor Group passes upward from wackes with metavolcanic interbeds to shales and sandstones which are locally calcareous (Agua Salobrega Phyllite, 500 m). The uppermost Cerro de la Virgen Limestone, which Wilson (1974) named the "Sanarate Limestone" and in which he found a rudist of the subfamily Sauvagesiinae, is a highly deformed and marmorized limestone with few phyllitic interbeds. The lower contact of the Cerro de la Virgen Limestone is a thrust fault, and the stratigraphic continuity of the limestone with the Agua Salobrega Phyllite is uncertain. Future work might show that the limestone, and perhaps also the phyllite unit, should be separated from the El Tambor Group.

Muller (1979) described an assemblage in the vicinity of Los Amates containing mafic igneous rocks (Juan de Paz ophiolites) and associated sedimentary rocks (lower El Pilar Group) which, though highly faulted and poorly exposed, are virtually unmetamorphosed. Muller also described The La Pita amphibolite-marble assemblage, which occurs at the base of the ophiolite on top of the Chuacús metamorphic rocks near Los Amates. This assemblage is highly deformed, contains amphiboles of higher pressure composition (in contrast with higher temperature amphiboles of the Sansare amphibolite), and represents a high-pressure facies formed at the base of the ophiolite during emplacement by thrusting.

Within the Motagua Valley and including some disjunct bodies outside of this valley, the El Tambor Group is further represented by scattered, more or less metamorphosed serpentinites, dunites, amphibolites, eclogites, and basalts (McBirney and others, 1967; Bosc, 1971; Bertrand and Sarp, 1976; Bertrand and Vuagnat, 1975, 1976, 1977; Bertrand and others, 1980). Although some units are metasomatized (Puente Plátanos complex; Lawrence, 1975; also several eclogites and amphibolites), most have chemical compositions of peridotites or oceanic basalts. Bertrand and others (1980) inferred a K/Ar age of 58.5 Ma for the assemblage. This age seems too young both because of several microfossil occurrences and because the age of tectonism of the entire rock assemblage of the Motagua Valley is closer to 68 Ma (see below).

An extensive serpentinite occurrence (80 × 10 km) with a central body of slightly serpentinized peridotite occurs between Salamá and Tactic. McBirney (1963) interpreted this unit as a faulted slab, but Nicolaus (1971) showed it as a funnel-shaped intrusion in cross section. McBirney's interpretation, which is also similar to the mapped relationships of the Sierra de Santa Cruz ophiolite, is preferred here.

In western Guatemala, smaller bodies of serpentine occur in the vicinity of the Polochic fault. The largest of these is about 10 km long; no other mafic lithologies have been recorded in this region.

In the Sierra de Santa Cruz, north of Lago de Izabal, Petersen and Zantop (1980) and Rosenfeld (1981) described an ophiolitic assemblage essentially identical to the less-metamorphosed rocks near Los Amates, 60 km to the southeast. The Sierra de Santa Cruz ophiolite contains fresh, though tectonized, gabbros which are very similar to those of much younger age described from the walls of the Cayman Trough (Malcolm, 1980; Ito and Anderson, 1983). This assemblage also includes minor amphibolite of the Sansare type and extensive metasedimentary units, including an apparent trench-filling hemipelagic sequence called the Jolomax Formation. Two microfossil occurrences from interbeds within the basalt of the Sierra de Santa Cruz sequence yielded late Valanginian to Aptian, and early Cenomanian ages.

Within the Sierra de Santa Cruz ophiolite Rosenfeld (1981) described a small synclinal sequence of volcaniclastic wackes and siliceous beds named the Tzumúy Formation (515 to 600 m thick). This formation is dominantly fine grained near the base and coarsens upward to volcaniclastic wackes. Conglomeratic beds contain andesite and dacite fragments. Chert in the lower part carries radiolarians with an Aptian–Albian age. This sequence was evidently deposited on the upper pillow basalts of the ophiolite and contains some basalt in its lower part, possibly as a slump block.

Muller (1979) described a highly faulted series of mud-stones, wackes, pelagic marls, and olistostromes found in the vicinity of Los Amates and Quiriguá as the El Pilar Group; he estimated a total thickness of 1,500 to 2,000 m. The group is divisible into lower and upper sequences; the upper sequence is named the Cerro Tipón Formation and is discussed below. A thin basal unit of poorly exposed quartzose and red to tan sandstones was included by Muller within this group; however, its similarity to the Todos Santos Formation and its striking lithologic contrast with the remaining part of the section suggests that these beds should be omitted from the El Pilar Group. The remaining lower El Pilar Group consists of volcaniclastic wackes and mudstones with minor siliceous tuffite, chert, and radiolarian mudstone. The cherts are invariably associated with pillow basalts, but poor exposures have prevented confirmation that they are interbedded with these basalts. This sequence is inferred to be a distal hemipelagic to pelagic sedimentary series deposited on and adjacent to the basalt. A radiolarian chert has yielded similar taxa to those found in the Tzumúy beds and an age of Hauterivian–Aptian has been assigned.

The available age information for the El Tambor Group and associated lower El Pilar Group and Tzumúy Formation sediments from the Los Amates and Cahabón areas (Muller, 1979; Rosenfeld, 1981) suggests an Early Cretaceous to Cenomanian age for the basalt and an Aptian–Albian age for the surrounding and partly overlying clastic sedimentary units.

Not discussed here are several sedimentary units that occur north of Guatemala City and were discussed by Wilson (1974). Some of these may belong to the oceanic rock sequence discussed here as part of the ophiolite; others are probably northern outliers of the Yojoa Group of the Chortis block; still others are of uncertain placement.

All exposures of the El Tambor Group are in fault contact with older or underlying rocks. The large body in the Sierra de Santa Cruz was shown to be in thrust-fault contact with the underlying Sepur wackes by Wilson (1974). Bosc (1971), Lawrence (1975), and Muller (1979), all established thrust-fault relations with underlying rocks. Rosenfeld (1981) interpreted the Sierra de Santa Cruz body as a major gravity slide and found late Campanian microfossils in the underlying autochthonous rocks.

The ophiolite is the host rock for two major ore deposits, both in the Sierra de Santa Cruz. Near Cahabón, a Cyprus-type copper deposit (Petersen and Zantop, 1980; Rosenfeld, 1981) produced chalcopyrite until the recent unfavorable economic climate forced the closing of the mine. Near El Estor a major nickel laterite deposit has now closed for similar reasons.

LATE CRETACEOUS–EARLY TERTIARY CLASTIC SEDIMENTARY ROCKS

The change from stable platform limestone to mobile belt wacke is recorded as a disconformable or abruptly conformable lithologic transition throughout central Guatemala from stable platform carbonates to immature wackes. The wacke sequence was called the "Sepur-Schichten" by Sapper (1899); here they are called the Sepur Group, following Dengo (1983). Recent descriptions include those by Bonis (1967), Cepek (1975), Paulsen and Koch (1980), and Rosenfeld (1981).

It is not surprising that the nomenclatural history of this unit has been complex: the facies are highly variable laterally and only slightly less so vertically; exotic, olistostromal lithologies are widespread and fossils are scarce. A prejudice for confining the name "Sepur" to Cretaceous units and introducing new names for lower Tertiary units was introduced by Vinson (1962). In light of several recent studies, such a division at the era boundary is not supportable. Thus, the term "Sepur Group" as used here includes both Vinson's "Verapaz" and "Petén" Groups, which should not be confused with the Petén Formation of Honduras. The formations merged into this group are the Sepur, Chemal, Cambio, and Toledo (all wackes), Lacandón (detrital limestone), Reforma (clay shales), Santa Amelia (limestone, dolomite, and marl), and Buena Vista (gypsiferous calcareous sediments). Some of these units, especially the calcareous ones, should probably be retained because of their potential mappability; others, mainly the wacke units, should be evaluated carefully with the view of discarding most, especially those originally defined by chronostratigraphic level.

The Sepur Group contains abundant ophiolitic debris ranging from serpentine grains to ophiolitic slide masses many kilometers wide, which record the tectonic emplacement of these ophiolitic rocks, beginning in the Late Cretaceous. It is dominantly a shale-sandstone flysch unit of turbidites that represents a submarine fan complex. It can be divided into a lower and upper unit; the Santa Cruz ophiolitic allochthon occurs at the boundary between the two.

Rosenfeld (1981) has described the various lithological components of the lower portion of the Sepur in central-eastern Guatemala, which is close to the depocenter of the unit. His reference section is given as 2,640 m thick, but this thickness is uncertain because of lithologic monotony, a poorly defined base, and locally disrupted structure. The lower unit consists dominantly of sandy and shaly flysch and minor interbedded polymictic conglomerate beds up to 20 m thick, some of which contain blocks of limestone and calc-alkaline volcanic and plutonic clasts up to 25 cm in length. The exotic limestone blocks do not appear to be derived from the underlying Campur Limestone, but instead resemble Campanian-age limestone units found within the Motagua Valley. The calc-alkaline volcanic and plutonic cobbles do not resemble any rocks found in Guatemala of Campanian or older age. Similarly, there is no identifiable source in northern Honduras, although our knowledge of such lithologies there is more limited.

Within this section and several other more limited sections are beds of calcirudite with identifiable larger foraminifera, as well as *Inoceramus* and radiolitid rudist fragments, all of which have been placed in the Campanian. A pelagic calcilutite bed immediately beneath the ophiolitic allochthon contains a late Campanian fauna.

The lower part of the Sepur contains limited identifiable

ophiolitic debris (mainly detrital serpentine); the conspicuous polymictic conglomerates that occur in channels cut into the turbidite fan, however, do not also carry ophiolitic debris. The upper Sepur elsewhere has more abundant ophiolitic debris.

Rosenfeld (1981) determined that the Sepur sedimentary debris was derived from the south, where the southern basinal boundary was a rising mass with fringing carbonate deposits and locally exposed ophiolite. In detail, however, many of the sedimentary features show east- or west-directed transport on the turbidite fan.

Elsewhere in Alta Verapaz and southern Belize (Toledo Formation), the Sepur Group contains Paleocene and lower Eocene fossils, showing that the fan persisted well into the Tertiary. In the Petén district, a facies boundary separates dominantly clastic (south) from carbonate-bearing (north) units. From south to north, these are the Cambio Formation (20 to 100 m of locally conglomeratic wacke) and the Santa Amelia Formation (1300 m of carbonates), overlain by the Buena Vista Formation (200 m of gypsiferous carbonates). These rock units show that during the Tertiary the advancing clastic wedge was sufficiently uplifted to restrict oceanic circulation against an elevated northern basement platform.

CRETACEOUS CLASTIC AND CARBONATE UNITS IN THE MOTAGUA VALLEY

Several more-or-less tectonized carbonate units are found within the Motagua Valley. Although these bear some resemblance to the autochthonous Campur Limestone north of the valley, they are sufficiently distinctive to merit a separate discussion. These include the Cerro de la Virgen Limestone (discussed above), the Cerro Tipón Formation, which occurs near Los Amates and Quiriguá, and abundant limestone clasts of unknown origin within the Subinal Formation (see below).

The Cerro Tipón Formation was named by Muller (1979) for a small mountain near Los Amates with a conspicuous outcrop of an especially large (more than 2 km) limestone slide block within a volcaniclastic wacke-pelagic marl sequence. The coarse clastic deposits range in grain size up to coarse, clast-supported conglomerates. The clastic deposits have a conspicuous volcanic content, and near the base of the unit a 1 by 2 km, evidently allochthonous, block of dark porphyritic basaltic andesite is found within the sequence. Although some of the igneous fragments within this unit may be derived from the ophiolite, many may have been derived from calc-alkaline assemblages.

The remainder of the Cerro Tipón section consists of pelagic marls, generally with poorly preserved pelagic foraminifera and coccoliths, and allodapic calcarenites and calcirudites. These beds are especially conspicuous toward the top of the section and are interstratified with limestone olistostromes containing large blocks with abundant reef-type organisms (rudists, corals, gastropods). The limestones are clastic and coarser grained than those typical of the Campur Limestone and are apparently not correlated with this unit. At the top of the section, pelagic mudstones grade upward into red mudstones, which carry coccoliths and serpentinite fragments, attesting to marine deposition of variably weathered terrigenous clastics.

The interbedding of pelagic units with coarse clastic deposits has no clear counterpart elsewhere in Guatemala except, on a less-dramatic scale, within the Sepur Formation in which beds of pelagic limestone are found locally within turbiditic sands. The pelagic fraction of the Cerro Tipón Formation is much higher than that of the Sepur Formation, and the olistoliths range to far greater sizes. The age of this unit ranges from Campanian–early Maastrichtian in the lower part to Maastrichtian in the upper part. It is evidently a proximal equivalent to the Sepur Formation and may represent sedimentation along a topographically rugged, emergent coastline. The Cerro de la Virgen Limestone is a possible equivalent to the thick limestone part of the Cerro Tipon Formation, but its intense internal deformation will probably defy attempts to confirm this correlation.

A limited exposure of reddish sandstones and intercalated limestone found near the Motagua River north of El Progreso is here informally named the "Palo Amontonado" beds. These beds were noted by Hirschmann (1963) and Reeves (1967), who considered them to be part of the Subinal Formation. They were also mentioned by Wilson (1976). The unit lies conformably beneath the lower Subinal Formation and consists of a few hundred meters of dominantly red sandstone and conglomerate, with a high content of andesite and basalt clasts. At least two intercalated limestones have been identified, a thin (less than a meter) limestone with Cenomanian benthic foraminifera (*Rhipidolina, Cuneolina, Dicyclina*; J. A. Broekman and P. Marks, det.), and a coarser, thicker bed with rudists (*Plagiotchyus*; J. Ward, det.), an echinoid (*Goniopygus* aff *zitteli*; T. Phelan det., Reeves, 1967), and other molluscs. These beds have no correlative on the Maya block, but the age and coincidence of red clastics and limestones strongly suggest a correlation with widespread units of this age (Esquias and Jaitique Formations; Horne and others, this volume) in central Honduras.

MIDDLE TO LATE TERTIARY SEDIMENTARY UNITS

Following the deposition of the thick Sepur Group clastic wedge in the Late Cretaceous to Eocene, the Guatemala–Belize portion of the Maya block became almost completely emergent; subsequent sedimentation is largely limited to terrestrial facies. There are no recent summary studies on later Tertiary stratigraphy, and much of the knowledge of these units is still unpublished, including data from exploratory wells. The Late Cretaceous suturing event (see below) produced uplift, followed by local development of extensive grabens in which local, dominantly clastic units were deposited. Neogene clastic units locally contain high contents of volcanic rock derived from early to middle Miocene ignimbrites on the Chortis block and later Pacific-margin calc-alkaline explosive volcanic centers.

Tertiary Units of El Petén and the Caribbean Coast

Vinson (1962) described several stratigraphic units in El Petén, including the undated Desempeño Conglomerate, a local unit which reaches a maximum thickness of 200 m. The Caribe Formation is an 800-m-thick Middle Miocene (van den Bold, 1969) deltaic to terrestrial sandstone-shale sequence. The Lacantún Conglomerate underlies the Caribe Formation; it contains many red beds and its thickness varies locally from 300 to 500 m.

Along the Caribbean coast in eastern Guatemala the Río Dulce Formation occurs in an anticline cut through by the Río Dulce. This richly fossiliferous limestone was dated as early to middle Miocene by van den Bold (1969). Its outcrop thickness is about 1000 m.

The coast of Guatemala and southern Belize, continuing westward around most of the shoreline of Lago de Izabal, is the locus of a nearly continuous belt of varicolored claystones, subordinate marl and sandstone, and scattered lignite beds. It is evidently Pliocene, has a reported thickness of 240 m, and was named the Herrería Formation by Vinson (1962).

The Subinal Formation

The Subinal Formation (Hirschmann, 1963) is the most extensive of several Tertiary formations that occur within the Motagua Valley; its extensive exposures along major highways are especially conspicuous in eastern Guatemala. We divide it into lower and upper units; only the upper is well exposed and well known.

The lower unit is poorly understood and might be found to consist of separate units whose only relationship to each other is their relative stratigraphic position beneath the upper. In the upper Motagua Valley the lower part consists of thick beds of white to tan quartz-pebble conglomerates, and a minor pebble component of metamorphic and plutonic rocks. Farther east, in the Los Amates area, Muller (1979) described a section of nearly pure serpentinite sandstone and conglomerates containing thin beds of dolomite, which are evidently secondary after the serpentinite. The exposed section at Cerros Chinos is a few hundred meters thick, and grades downward into dirty quartzose sandstones that contain obscure plant fossils.

The Chanchán Member of the Subinal Formation occurs near the base of the upper unit (Newcomb, 1975; Muller, 1979). It is a highly distinctive, pale-brownish-gray micaceous mudstone to siltstone with beds of brecciated black limestone locally rich in ostracods. Newcomb found a thin bed crowded with *Lagunitis,* a high-spired Eocene brackish-water gastropod, which provides the only biostratigraphic information for this formation. Similar gastropods were later found within the upper Subinal (Johnson, 1984).

The upper Subinal is a series of dominantly red sandstones and conglomerates displaying point bars, channel fills, and floodplain sequences typical of riverine fluvial sequences. Near Gualán there is a substantial fraction of greenish, fine-grained beds.

Hirschmann (1963) measured two sections in the type area, the thicker being about 900 m. Near Gualán, Johnson (1984) estimated a thickness of about 1,500 m. The pebble lithologies of the Subinal Formation are dominantly quartz and fine-grained metamorphic rocks. Plutonic pebbles are minor but widespread; volcanic pebbles are rare. A recurring lithology in the western exposures is limestone pebble and cobble conglomerates. These limestones are crowded with pelagic foraminifera, nearly all of which are of Maastrichtian age (Bosc, 1971). Although there are Maastrichtian fossils reported from the Campur Limestone (Paulsen and Koch, 1980), these are minor, and reported taxa are different from those within the Subinal clasts. The Cerro Tipón limestones described by Muller contain abundant molluscan and coralline debris. Evidently the limestone source beds for the Subinal conglomerates have been removed by erosion. Hirschmann's report of older limestones may refer instead to those of the Palo Amontonado beds, which he included in the Subinal.

Although the volcanic-pebble content of the Subinal is low, there are rhyolitic-tuff beds up to 15 cm thick found sparingly throughout its outcrop extent in the Motagua Valley.

South of the Motagua Vally, on the Chortis block, the Subinal has been studied by Burkart (1965) near Quezaltepeque and Esquipulas. In this area it has a higher content of volcanic debris and locally has intercalated andesite flows. Deaton and Burkart (1984b) reported a K/Ar date of 42 Ma from one of these cobbles.

Near Sanarate, Lawrence (1975) found a thick (3,000 m) section of red conglomerates and sandstones in a graben within the El Tambor Formation. On the basis of similar lithologies, especially with the volcanic-bearing section described by Burkart, Lawrence correlated these with the Subinal Formation. Wilson (1974) named them the El Sesteadero Conglomerates of the Jalapa basinal melange, but they clearly have no relationship to the latter unit.

Younger Clastic Sedimentary Units of the Motagua Valley

The Guastatoya Formation was described by Reeves (1967) and Bosc (1971) from exposures on the south side of the Motagua River in the vicinity of El Progreso. Lawrence (1975) described similar sedimentary rocks from the Sanarate quadrangle, about 15 km south of the Motagua River. The Guastatoya Formation has a maximum thickness of 265 m. The dominant lithology of this unit is thick beds of conglomerates. Clast assemblages are locally dominated either by marble, granitic debris, metamorphic rocks, or serpentinite cobbles. The second-most-abundant lithology is volcaniclastic sandstone. Minor lithologies include lignitic shales with plant leaves and a fossil bird (Donnelly, unpublished), and dark, ostracod-bearing limestones. Another lithology possibly associated with this formation is thin-bedded diatomite, which is found at several places just east of Guatemala City. Ignimbrites are widespread, and one basalt flow was seen. The age is unknown but presumably within the Late Miocene–Qua-

ternary period of active calc-alkaline volcanism of the northwestern Chortis block.

The complete extent of this unit is not known. Nearly continuous exposures occur from near Petacá, just northeast of Guatemala City, to Río Hondo, 75 km to the east. Elsewhere in the Motagua Valley, limited exposures of well-lithified cobble and boulder conglomerates that may be correlative with this unit are found, but many finer grained conglomerates may prove to belong to the lower Subinal.

Muller (1979) described the Junquillo Formation, a 200-m-thick (minimum) clastic unit near Los Amates. This unit, which contains several rhyolitic ignimbrite beds and abundant tuffaceous debris, was correlated tentatively with the upper Padre Miguel Group of the Chortis block. The age is unknown.

A general correlation among the Gustatoya and Junquillo Formations and the San Jacinto Formation of the Padre Miguel Group (Horne and others, this volume) has been suggested, at least in part, by several authors. In favor of such a general correlation is the pre-Pleistocene and post-Subinal age of these units, and their high content of volcanic debris. Against such a correlation is a paucity of fossil or other age information and striking lithologic variety.

In the lower Motagua Valley, the Armas Formation, whose thickness may reach 2,500 to 3,000 m (Vinson, 1962), fills the Bananeras depression and is also found along the margins of the valley east of this depression. The lower part, occurring in the subsurface only, consists mainly of red beds. The upper part consists of red beds interbedded to the east with deltaic claystone, siltstone, and sandstone. The age is probably Pliocene, and the formation may be found to grade into the Herrerría Formation.

Late Cenozoic volcanic deposits

Volcanic deposits of late Cenozoic age are found along the Pacific margin of Guatemala. These include the Late Miocene Colotenango Conglomerates (Anderson, 1969; Deaton, 1982; Deaton and Burkart, 1984a), which are discussed below in relation to movements on the Polochic fault.

STRUCTURAL GEOLOGY AND TECTONIC HISTORY OF THE MAYA BLOCK AND MOTAGUA SUTURE ZONE

Compressive structures of the Late Cretaceous

Although there is widespread evidence of pre-Cretaceous structures within the Chuacús metamorphic series (Newcomb, 1975, 1978; Roper, 1976; Johnson, 1984), most of the structure seen in this unit, as well as in the Paleozoic Santa Rosa Group, and the Todos Santos, Cobán, and Campur Formations, is Late Cretaceous to early Tertiary in age. The undated earlier metamorphism of this unit is largely obscured by a later retrogressive event (Newcomb, 1975; Johnson, 1984) that effectively masks the history of deformation and metamorphism in almost all areas.

The supposed pre-Pennsylvanian structures described by Kesler (1971) are almost certainly much younger.

The valley of the Río Motagua is the site of the Motagua suture zone between the Maya and Chortis blocks. The abrupt mountain front on the north side of the valley coincides with several reverse faults displacing units of the Chuacús metamorphic series (Fig. 4); lineations indicate transport to the north. These faults are slightly en echelon to the valley, and several faults trend northeastward into the mountain range; their frontal positions are occupied by structurally higher faults. Only a few of these faults are named; for example, the San Agustín fault of Bosc (1971), which has been mistakenly shown as a strike-slip fault. In the frontal zone, as well as in detached hills within the valley, most of the bedrock lithologies are variably cataclastized San Agustín gneiss. Most of the faults are marked by continuous serpentinite bands. Several workers in the Motagua Valley (beginning with Bosc, 1971) have suggested that these are thrust faults. Their present high-angle dip is largely the result of late Cenozoic rotation accompanying the young uplift of the Sierras along the southern margin of the Maya block.

Within the Las Ovejas metamorphic series and El Tambor Group on the south side of the Motagua valley is a series of thrust faults, most of which are marked by serpentinite. Although these do not mark the geomorphic boundary of the valley, some of these faults mark other geomorphically prominent features such as the Cerro de la Virgen limestone belt in the mountain of that name. Minor structural features show that transport was to the south.

Farther to the north, several high-angle reverse faults are located between major stratigraphic units. McBirney mapped such faults in the Salamá area; the southernmost separates the overlying Chuacús metamorphics from the underlying Paleozoic Santa Rosa Group shales. This contact is marked with highly deformed, locally mylonitized rocks, and the conclusion of Nicolaus (1971) and van dem Boom (1972) that this boundary is a Barrovian isograd flies in the face of overwhelming evidence in favor of McBirney's interpretation of a major fault.

The pattern of folds of southern El Petén and northern Alta Verapaz (Bonis and others, 1970) shows that this major portion of the Maya block consists of folded and locally reverse-faulted Cretaceous sediments with apparent overturning to the north. The possibility that this fold sequence is bottomed by highly deformed anhydrite or even salt is suggested by the fold geometry.

In the vicinity of Tactic and Cobán, Nicolaus (1971) showed numerous thrust faults, oriented east–west and dipping south, separating various Permian and Cretaceous units. Although some of these faults may be confused with later strike-slip faults, the pattern indicates north–south compressions. Farther west, Dengo (1983) has shown that a similar folding pattern occurs where the southern margin of the block extends into Chiapas.

The compressive deformation that pervasively deformed the southern Maya block resulted from the collision of the Chortis block with the Maya block. Mid-Cretaceous oceanic crust that had formed between these blocks was obducted as ophiolite onto both blocks during the suturing event. The widespread retrogressive metamorphism and thrust faulting of the Chuacus metamorphic series is presumed to reflect the same collisional event. This deformation was dated directly by Sutter (1979, and unpublished) by use of Ar 39/40 technique on hornblende, muscovite, and biotite from retrogressively metamorphosed Chuacús metamorphic rocks. Nine of thirteen samples are dated between 66 and 70 Ma and four others range from 63 to 78 Ma. A 66–70 Ma age is consistent with the biostratigraphically determined age for the Sierra de Santa Cruz ophiolite slide, which immediately overlies pelagic late Campanian fossils. The presumption is very strong that an early Maastrichtian compressive event resulted in both the retrograde metamorphism and the emplacement of the ophiolite. A further indication of this deformation is a hiatus in Campanian sedimentation in western Guatemala and Chiapas (López-Ramos, 1981; Dengo, 1983). Minor younger movements within the Motagua Valley might be the result of flower structures associated with strike-slip faulting.

Structure of the Maya Mountains

As summarized by Bateson and Hall (1971), the Maya Mountains of Belize consist of a synclinorium of Santa Rosa Group sediments bounded on north and south by fault systems. Their summary map suggests that the northern fault system is a group of fairly minor faults, which Dawe (1984) and Nelson (1984) suggest might be reverse faults. The southern fault system is poorly exposed and possibly minor. Well data (unpublished) just north and west of the Maya Mountains show (from thinned stratigraphic sections) that this area was elevated during much of the Mesozoic.

Late Cenozoic strike-slip faulting

Figure 1 shows two through-going, approximately east–west river systems in Guatemala: the Motagua on the south and the Polochic, Chixoy, and Cuilco (east to west) on the north. Sapper (1899) recognized the fault control of these valleys. The linearity of these systems has suggested to several workers extensive transcurrent motion. The presence or absence of such motions has formed one of the most bitterly contested geologic questions in the entire Caribbean area. One school of thought is that these faults are the extension of the southern boundary fault of the Cayman Trench (Taber, 1922), and have a collective Cenozoic offset of 1,000 km or more (Hess and Maxwell, 1953; Burke and others, 1984; Wadge and Burke, 1983).

Most field geologists working in Guatemala have minimized the total Cenozoic offset on the major fault systems (Fig. 4). The Polochic fault has received the most attention: Burkart (1978, 1983), Burkart and Moreno (1983), and Burkart and Self (1985) have all argued persuasively for about 130 km total offset. Anderson and others (1985) challenged these estimates; they prefer a total offset of only "several kilometers." C. Dengo (1982) analyzed in detail a part of the Polochic fault zone and the related Taluca fault zone in western Guatemala. He estimated about 20 km offset on the older Taluca fault before the Polochic fault developed, but he did not estimate a total offset for the system. Most workers favor the Burkart interpretation, and none favors a larger offset.

Deaton (1982) and Deaton and Burkart (1984a) used the occurrence of distinctive serpentine debris and radiometrically dated volcanic clasts in the Colotenango beds of western Guatemala to establish the inception of movement of this fault at about 10 Ma, and suggested that most of the movement could have occurred during about 3.7 m.y.

The Motagua fault system has received extensive attention since the disastrous earthquake of 1976, which produced up to 2 m of instantaneous sinistral offset and about the same amount in post-quake creep (Bucknam and others, 1978). As Schwartz and others (1979) showed, numerous young sinistral offsets in the tens of meters are found along this fault. The fault trace of the 1976 earthquake (named the Cabañas fault by Bosc, 1971) is topographically obscure and cuts the Eocene Subinal Formation near El Progreso with little apparent offset of sedimentary facies. The correspondence on opposite sides (Fig. 4) of the Motagua Valley (Morazan to Sansare) of extensive, lithologically identical amphibolites, with a distinctive gravity signature (unpublished), and widespread eclogites (McBirney and others, 1967; Lawrence, 1975; unpublished) argues for very limited Cenozoic offset. McBirney (1963) suggested a 20 km sinistral offset of young volcanics slightly west of this area.

The Jubuco fault on the south side of the Motagua Valley (Muller, 1979; Johnson, 1984), which extends northeastward into Honduras as the Cuyamel fault (Horne and others, 1976a), is one of the most interesting of the entire east–west fault sets. As Muller and Johnson have shown, alluvial fans identifiable with specific river systems have been offset sinistrally for up to 20 km (Fig. 3). However, offsets decrease westward and disappear near Gualán.

In addition to these major systems, parallel but subordinate systems have been recognized. The southernmost was called the Jocotán fault system by Crane (1965). It has subsequently been shown to align with the Chamelecón fault of western Honduras. Donnelly and others (1968) suggested that it had considerable dip-slip movement during Cretaceous limestone accumulation. It shows no signs of transcurrent offset.

Several lines of evidence point to 130 km of offset on the Polochic fault system and perhaps no more than a few tens of kilometers on the Motagua system. The problem of the accommodation of about 1,000 km sinistral Cenozoic offset in the Cayman Trough remains unresolved.

Tectonic history of the Maya block of Guatemala and Belize

The basement of the Maya block consists of schists and gneisses that cannot presently be correlated with basement rocks of other areas. The contrast between these basement rocks and the Las Ovejas metamorphic rocks found directly across the Motagua suture zone was noted by Bosc (1971) and several later workers. The Late Pennsylvanian–Permian sediments deposited on this basement have been related faunally to the Midcontinent-Andean realm (southern United States, Mexico, northern South America) by Ross (1979). Pindell and Dewey (1982) have located this block in the present Gulf of Mexico prior to the Mesozoic fragmentation of western Gondwanaland. The Early Permian unconformity and Pennsylvanian–Permian volcanic rocks, however, have no clear counterpart in either North America or South America.

The mainly Jurassic Todos Santos redbeds are the middle America counterpart of the Newark Series of eastern North America and the La Quinta Formation of northern South America: a taphrogeosynclinal accumulation accompanying the fragmentation of the Americas.

The dolomites and evaporites of the Early Cretaceous Cobán Formation have their closest counterparts in the southern Bahamas and northern Cuba. The nature of the southern boundary of this immense evaporite basin is unknown because of subsequent deformation. The transition to more open-water limestone accumulation corresponds closely with the Albian-Cenomanian boundary.

The ophiolites of the El Tambor have their counterparts throughout the entire Caribbean (chapter on magmatic history, this volume) and extending south to Ecuador. The youngest age recorded in Guatemala is Cenomanian. This ophiolite was obducted in latest Campanian or Maastrichtian, an age remarkably close to similar episodes elsewhere in the northern Caribbean.

The compressive suturing of the gap between the Maya and Chortis block initiated the Sepur clastic wedge, which continued at least until the Eocene.

Throughout the period of compressive deformation and the subsequent period of tectonic relaxation, igneous activity was not recorded on the Maya block, except cryptically in the form of very small hydrothermal ore deposits. Pacific-margin volcanic activity occurred in the latest Cenozoic.

The middle and late Cenozoic of the Maya block was a period of emergence and local accumulation of thick terrestrial deposits, especially along the Motagua Valley suture zone. Marine deposits are seen only along the Caribbean coast and in northern Guatemala, adjacent to Yucatán.

During the late Cenozoic, strike-slip motions were distributed among the two major strike-slip fault systems; the bulk of the offset was apparently along the Polochic system, and there was minor, very young offset in the Motagua system.

THE CHORTIS BLOCK

G. S. Horne, R. C. Finch, and T. W. Donnelly

The Chortis block is clearly and sharply defined on the northwest by the Motagua fault zone and on the southwest by the

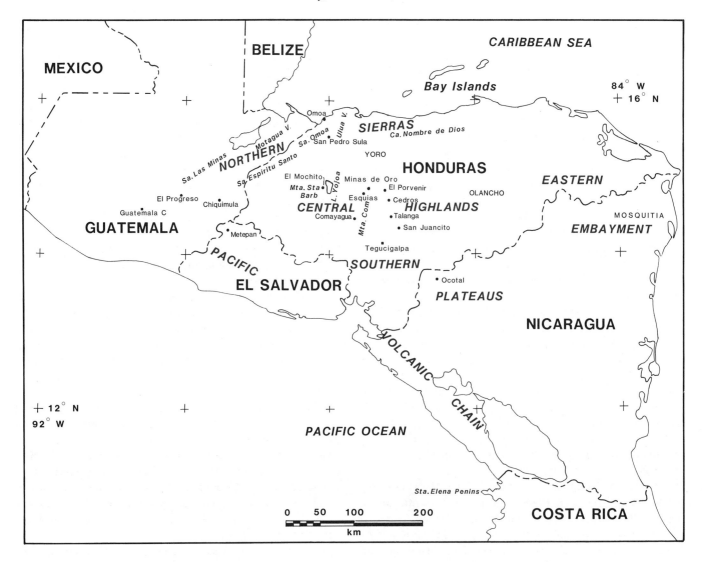

Figure 5. Geographic map of Chortis block showing locations of places cited in text.

Middle America Trench boundary with the Cocos Plate (Fig. 1; Plates 4 and 5b). The southern limits of the Chortis basement have been covered by Cenozoic volcanics, but probably extend as far as the Santa Elena peninsula in northernmost Costa Rica and the Hess Escarpment offshore to the east, together interpreted as a crustal suture (de Boer, 1979; Dengo, 1985). The eastern margin of the Chortis block is problematic; it is not separated from the Nicaraguan Rise by any obvious discontinuity. Yet Jamaica, on the eastern end of the Nicaraguan Rise, is distinctly different from the Chortis block. Geophysical data indicate the Nicaraguan Rise is underlain by younger (?) and thinner crust (Edgar and others, 1971) of indeterminate origin which somehow connects to the continental crust of the Chortis block (Arden, 1975, p. 632). Thus, the Chortis block includes southeastern Guatemala, all of El Salvador and Honduras, and probably most of Nicaragua.

The Chortis block has been tectonically active almost continuously since the Early Cretaceous. Its rugged physiography is a direct reflection of this tectonic history, and it may be subdivided into distinct morphotectonic regions: northern sierras, central highlands, eastern embayment, southern plateaus, and the Pacific volcanic chain (Fig. 5). These have been cut and partly delineated by characteristic sets of major faults that reflect both past and neotectonic instability. The northern sierras are high mountain ranges that extend through southeastern Guatemala and along northern Honduras. They consist mainly of metamorphic basement rocks intruded by numerous plutons of wide-ranging ages. These ranges are bounded to the south by major faults in valleys parallel to the Motagua fault zone and Caribbean Plate boundary: the Jocotán, Chamelecón, Ceiba, and Aguán faults (Fig. 6). South of these the central highlands of Honduras consist of scat-

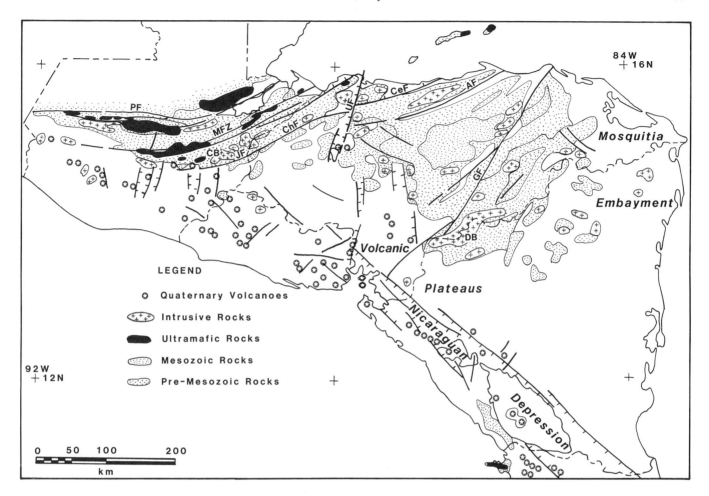

Figure 6. Tectonic sketch map of Chortis block: AF = Aguán fault, CB = Chiquimula batholith, CeF = Ceiba fault, ChF = Chamelecón fault, DB = Dipilto batholith, GF = Guayape fault, JF = Jocotán fault, MFZ = Motogua fault zone, PF = Polochic fault, UF = Ulua fault.

tered basement uplifts mantled and separated by a folded and block-faulted sequence of Mesozoic sedimentary strata. These successions thicken somewhat to the east across the Guayape fault into the Mosquitía Embayment, a vast jungle lowland in eastern Honduras and Nicaragua developed on a Mesozoic–Cenozoic marine basin that continues eastward under the Nicaraguan Rise.

South of the central highlands, and extending discontinuously northward onto the central highlands as surmounting caps, a thick edifice of Neogene effusives, dominantly rhyolitic ignimbrites, form the high plateaus of El Salvador, southern Guatemala, southern Honduras, and Nicaragua. These have been locally block faulted into rhombic horsts and grabens, as have the highlands to the north. Capping the Neogene volcanic edifice along the Pacific coast is a chain of active Quaternary stratovolcanoes that extends from southwestern Guatemala to Costa Rica. Some of these volcanoes are aligned along faults at a high angle to the coast and many others are concentrated along the margins of

the Nicaraguan Depression (McBirney and Williams, 1965), a major elongate graben subparallel to the coast and the trend of the Middle America Trench. The Honduras Depression is another hypothesized extensional feature that is postulated to transect the Chortis block in several offset north–south segments (Muehlberger and Ritchie, 1975; Burkart and Self, 1985); however, the evidence for such a feature is ambiguous and not compelling (Zúniga, 1975; Horne and others, 1976b).

BASEMENT OF THE CHORTIS BLOCK

The Chortis block contains extensive and widespread exposures of metamorphic rocks and the only known pre-Mesozoic rocks on the Caribbean Plate. Basic mapping since 1970 has shown that early ideas of the simplicity of the Chortis basement were erroneous. The metamorphic rocks exposed in different areas are far more diverse than the monotonous low-grade phyllites once attributed to the region; they reflect complex histories and they may not be correlative throughout the block. The Chortis block itself may be a collage of smaller crustal fragments of diverse origin.

The metamorphic rocks on the Chortis block are exposed in three principal regions and will be discussed in that order: (1) a basement ridge along the northern margin of the block; (2) a group of basement horsts uplifted above the Mesozoic central highlands of Honduras; and (3) a vast, poorly exposed, and remote eastern terrane.

Northern Marginal Complex

The northern margin of the Chortis block consists of a ridge of metamorphic and plutonic rocks that extends from just northeast of Guatemala City east-northeast along the north coast of Honduras (Fig. 6). Basement rocks are widely exposed along this ridge in the mountains south of the Motagua Valley in Guatemala; this ridge continues into Honduras as the Sierras de Espírito Santo and de Omoa. The ridge is interrupted in northern Honduras by the north-trending Ulúa Valley, but it apparently continues eastward again in the Cordillera Nombre de Dios and perhaps in the Bay Islands.

This basement ridge is bounded to the north by the Motagua fault zone in Guatemala and by the Cayman Trough just north of the Bonacca Ridge off northern Honduras. Although the crustal boundary between the North America and Caribbean plates is expressed in the western Caribbean by the Cayman Trough (Molnar and Sykes, 1969; Holcombe and others, 1973), in Guatemala that boundary is diffuse and may be shared by the Motagua zone and the Polochic fault (Kesler, 1971; Muehlberger and Ritchie, 1975; Burkart, 1978, 1983) to the north of and subparallel to the Motagua zone. This suggests that the Sierra Las Minas, situated between the Polochic and Motagua faults and containing extensive exposures of the Chuacús Group of Maya block basement, may be a crustal remnant of the Maya block on the Caribbean plate that has been sliced off the North American plate after having been sutured to the Chortis block. This would indicate that the two fault zones may not be related genetically, and probably have experienced different and compound kinematic histories.

The southern boundary of the basement ridge also is defined by major fault zones: the Jocotán-Chamelecón through eastern Guatemala and northwestern Honduras, and the Aguán across northern Honduras (Fig. 6). These fault zones generally juxtapose pre-Mesozoic basement rocks and a Mesozoic ophiolite sequence and collisional complex to the north (Lawrence, 1975), against an extensive Mesozoic cratonic sedimentary sequence to the south which rests unconformably upon other metamorphic rocks. Stratigraphic and structural evidence (Donnelly and others, 1968; Horne and others, 1976a) indicates that the northern marginal complex was uplifted along these fault zones in the Cretaceous, thus exposing probably the deepest crustal levels that crop out on the Chortis block.

Southern Border of the Motagua Valley

Two sequences of metamorphic rocks are exposed in eastern Guatemala along the southern border of the Motagua Valley (Fig. 5). An older sequence of high-grade rocks is generally north of a younger sequence of low-grade rocks. The older sequence is bounded to the north by the Motagua fault zone and is structurally beneath metamorphosed mafic rocks of the Cretaceous El Tambor Group (McBirney and Bass, 1969a; Wilson, 1974; Lawrence, 1976). The younger sequence is bounded to the south by the Jocotán fault zone and is in fault contact with the older sequence to the north; structural and metamorphic differences indicate they are separated by a major unconformity (Donnelly and others, 1968). Both sequences have been intruded by calc-alkaline plutons of probable Cretaceous age (Williams and others, 1964; Clemons, 1966; Clemons and Long, 1971; Ritchie and McDowell, 1979).

The older high-grade sequence was named the Las Ovejas Complex (Bosc, 1971; Schwartz, 1976) and consists dominantly of quartzofeldspathic gneiss and two-mica schist and subordinate marble and amphibolite, cut by foliated granitoid plutons (Schwartz, 1976; Muller, 1979). Sillimanite is widespread, andalusite is common in eastern exposures, garnet and K-feldspar are less common, and staurolite is confined to Al- and Fe-rich metasedimentary strata. An older structural fabric of ductile isoclinal folds was overprinted by more brittle structures, such as flexural open folds and kink bands, as well as retrograde metamorphism.

The younger low-grade sequence is called the San Diego phyllite (Lawrence, 1975, 1976), which was originally correlated with the Santa Rosa Group exposed to the north of the Motagua fault zone (Burkart and others, 1973). It consists of a monotonous sequence of quartzomicaceous and graphitic phyllites and locally conspicuous thin quartzite layers; pyrite cubes are common, and heavy mineral separates universally contain distinctive yellow tourmalines. Foliations are steeply dipping and strike subparallel with the Motagua fault zone.

The Chiquimula batholith (Fig. 6) is one of a series of large, probably composite plutons that intruded both metamorphic sequences in the Cretaceous and early Tertiary (Clemons and Long, 1971). Some of what was mapped as Chiquimula probably consists of granites and adamellites of the Las Ovejas Complex. Volumetrically more important gabbro and granodiorite give a well-defined Rb-Sr isochron of 50 Ma. A similar pluton at the western end of the basement ridge has been dated by K-Ar as about 94–104 Ma (Ritchie and McDowell, 1979).

Sierras del Espírito Santo and Omoa

The Sierras de Espírito Santo and de Omoa in northwestern Honduras represent the northeastward continuation of the same basement terrane that is exposed along the southern border of the Motagua Valley in Guatemala. Similar metamorphic, plutonic, and ophiolitic rocks crop out in both areas, but the age relationships of the basement are better constrained in Honduras.

Rocks described by Horne and others (1976a, p. 573) as probably being part of an ophiolite assemblage crop out in the northernmost part of the Sierras east of Omoa (Fig. 5). This low-grade metavolcanic sequence includes greenstone, metadacite, metatuff, and metagraywacke that contains lenses of talc schist and steatitized serpentinite. It probably is correlative with the Cretaceous El Tambor Group in Guatemala (McBirney and Bass, 1969a; Wilson, 1974; Lawrence, 1976), and should not be included as part of the pre-Mesozoic basement sequence of the Chortis block.

The pre-Mesozoic metamorphic rocks that crop out within the Sierras were divided (Horne and others, 1976a) into an older sequence of almandine-amphibolite facies that is unconformably overlain by and infolded with a younger sequence of low greenschist facies metasedimentary strata. Where present close to the trace of the Chamelecón fault, both sequences have been altered dynamically to cataclasites, submylonites, and phyllonites.

The older sequence crops out principally in the higher central part of the Sierras, but is is also intricately infolded with the younger sequence to the southwest, adjacent to the Chamelecón fault. The rocks within the older sequence have a wide range of textures and compositions, including garnet two-mica schist, garnetiferous quartzofeldspathic gneiss, staurolite schist, amphibolite, calcic hornblende gneiss, and minor micaceous marble. Three generations of penetrative structural fabric have been identified in these rocks (Horne and others, 1976a). Early structures consist of tightly appressed isoclinal folds with only a relict axial planar foliation. Later similar folds have a strong axial-planar foliation that probably was initially north trending and east dipping; fold axes are coincident with hornblende lineations and plunged northeastward prior to still-later flexural deformation. The latest deformation consisted of flexing of the earlier foliation into conical east-trending folds and crenulations with incipient strain-slip cleavage; this last fabric is most prominently developed along the south flank of the Sierras in proximity to the Chamelecón fault.

The younger sequence generally mantles the older sequence along the south flank of the Sierras. Its unconformable relationship upon the older sequence is nowhere directly exposed, but is demonstrable on the basis of localized contrasts in texture, metamorphic grade, and structural fabric where the two have been folded together. The rocks in the younger sequence are aluminous and pelitic, and consist of a well-layered succession of calcareous phyllite, sericite schist, graphitic schist, slate, and characteristic but thin and irregularly distributed beds of finely crystalline marble and quartzite. These metasedimentary strata have been penetratively deformed by only one generation of structures, which are similar in style and geometry to the latest structural fabric in the older sequence (Horne and others, 1976a). The strata have a slaty cleavage that dips steeply north-northwest; mesoscopic similar folds plunge gently east-northeast, roughly parallel to the trace of the Chamelecón fault.

The minimum ages of the metamorphic sequences exposed in the Sierras de Espírito Santo and de Omoa have been determined by Rb-Sr whole-rock dating of plutons that have intruded the sequences (Horne and others, 1976a). A metaigneous complex of granodiorite gneiss and tonalite granofels exposed in the central core of the Omoas has yielded a very poor isochron that could be late Precambrian to early Paleozoic; these rocks clearly demand more attention and better age resolution. On the other hand, foliated metatonalite and adamellite gneiss that have intruded the older metamorphic sequence in the Omoas north of San Pedro Sula have yielded a well-defined whole-rock isochron age of 305 ±12 Ma; thus, the older metamorphic sequence is pre-Pennsylvanian and probably was metamorphosed coincident with plutonic intrusion in the Early Pennsylvanian. The younger sequence of metasedimentary strata is undated and crosscut by several undeformed batholiths that probably are Mesozoic to early Tertiary, and it is unconformably overlain locally by Early Cretaceous limestone (Horne and others, 1976a, 1976b).

Cordillera Nombre de Dios—Bay Islands

The northern marginal basement complex of the Chortis block continues east of the Ulúa Valley along the north coast of Honduras in the Cordillera Nombre de Dios (Fig. 3), and perhaps also offshore to the north in the Bay Islands. Knowledge of the geology of these areas has advanced little since the early part of this century and the initial explorations by Sapper (1905) and Powers (1918).

Foye (1918) described a suite of metamorphic and plutonic rocks from the Cordillera Nombre de Dios and other areas that were collected by Powers (1918) in a traverse along the northern coastal railway of Honduras. These included a wide variety of rock types and, although no bedrock mapping was attempted, Powers and Foye generalized the following succession:

1. A metamorphic basement complex composed the main mass of the Cordillera and consists of mica schists, slates, quartzites, and abundant and diverse mafic orthogneisses.

2. This complex was widely intruded by massive plutons of principally tonalitic composition along the central and higher portion of the Cordillera.

3. The north flank of the Cordillera was subsequently mantled by various volcanic rocks of felsic to mafic composition. Although Williams and McBirney (1969) suggested that the plutonic rocks probably were Paleozoic, more recent studies (Horne and others, 1976b) indicate that many of them are Cretaceous.

Reconnaissance mapping of the Bay Islands (McBirney and Bass, 1969b) revealed a metamorphic sequence of schists, amphibolite, marble cut by sodic granite, dacite, gabbro, uralitized pyroxene hornblendite, and serpentinite. Although the metamorphic rocks could be equivalent with similar rocks exposed within the basement sequence in the Cordillera Nombre de Dios to the south or the Sierra de Omoa to the southwest, it is possible that the mafic and ultramafic rocks are El Tambor equivalents (Donnelly and López-Ramos, this volume) and may reflect Late Cretaceous or early Tertiary ophiolite obduction. McBirney and Bass

(1969b) described mudstones, chert, and graywacke in progressive metamorphic states grading into the main metamorphic sequence; therefore, the entire metamorphic assemblage on the Bay Islands could also be the result of crustal suturing rather than being part of the Chortis basement.

Central horsts

Pre-Jurassic metamorphic rocks are exposed in scattered mountain ranges that have been uplifted along faulted margins as basement horsts that poke through the surrounding terrain of Mesozoic sedimentary strata in the central highlands of Honduras. Although some workers have attempted to relate these uplifts to a linear belt of so-called "Laramide" and later deformations across the Chortis block (Everett, 1970; Fakundiny, 1970; Emmet, 1983), the widespread distribution of the basement horsts does not lend itself to obvious trend analysis. Moreover, stratigraphic evidence indicates that at least some of the blocks were uplifted by the mid-Mesozoic and largely controlled the pattern of Cretaceous deposition. Metamorphic rocks in only three of these uplifts have been studied in any detail. Most previous workers have assumed that they are all correlative and equivalent with part of the metamorphic succession exposed in the northern marginal complex. Considering the widely separated distribution of the basement uplifts and the demarcation of the northern marginal complex by a major fault zone, this simple assumption may be unjustified and misleading.

San Juancito Uplift

Metasedimentary strata are exposed in the faulted core of the San Juancito uplift, some 20 km northeast of Tegucigalpa (Fig. 5). Carpenter (1954) named these rocks the Petén Formation. They consist of pyritiferous graphitic schist, quartzose sericite schist, massive quartzite, and other psammitic beds. The foliation in these strata parallels compositional layering and trends north-northeast, nearly normal to the trend of the basement block; it has been flexed into gently west-northwest–plunging conical folds together with layering in unmetamorphosed strata of the El Plan Formation exposed nearby. The minimum age of the Petén Formation may be constrained by the assumption that the problematic El Plan Formation, which probably is Jurassic, rests unconformably on the Petén; but such a relationship has not been seen or documented.

Montaña de Comayagua

The Montaña de Comayagua is a large basement massif that rises above the Tertiary volcanic ranges and plateaus of central Honduras about 50 km northwest of Tegucigalpa (Fig. 5). Fakundiny (1970; Fakundiny and Everett, 1976) named the Cacaguapa Schist for the metamorphic succession that crops out on the western flank of the Montaña and subdivided it into the Humuya and Las Marías Members. The Humuya Member is only well exposed in the gorge of the Río Humuya; it consists of sheared metaconglomerate of quartz pebbles to igneous and metamorphic boulders, interlayered with schistose blastomylonite with quartz augen, and mylonitized felsitic metaigneous layers. Fakundiny (1970, p. 27–31) described schistosites in metaconglomerate boulders oriented askew to the regional foliation in the metaconglomerate matrix and adjacent strata as evidence of derivation from an older metamorphic terrane. The more widespread Las Marías Member consists of muscovite-quartz schist, phyllite, minor chlorite and graphite schists, and prominent beds of siliceous marble and quartzite; mineral assemblages are typical of greenschist facies, perhaps locally attaining the lower grades of amphibolite facies. The contact between the Humuya and Las Marías Members has not been observed and the relation between them is unknown, although Fakundiny (1970, p. 36) suggested that the Humuya was in a lower structural position. The foliation in the Las Marías has been folded by two distinct deformational episodes; early southwest-plunging crenulations with mineral lineations parallel to the intersection of strain-slip cleavage with schistosity, and later, upright, northerly-trending open flexures. Both members are demonstrably overlain unconformably by unmetamorphosed terrigenous strata of the Honduras Group, which sets the age limit for the Cacaguapa Schist as pre-Jurassic.

El Porvenir Horst

Another large massif of metamorphic rocks is the El Porvenir horst about 70 km northeast of Tegucigalpa (Fig. 5). Simonson (1977) tentatively correlated these rocks with the Cacaguapa Schist and subdivided them into two metasedimentary and two metaigneous units. The oldest unit is a mylonitic schist with potassic augen, thought to represent an early metamorphosed granitic pluton. This is unconformably succeeded by garnet-bearing pelitic schist in the epidote-amphibolite facies, and minor marble, quartzite, and basic schist beds. Simonson (1977) thought these were gradational into an adjacent belt of low greenschist facies, strongly sheared sericitic phyllite that contains quartz layers and blebs and minor marble, quartzite, and mafic phyllite beds. Both metasedimentary units contain the same deformational fabric, consisting of an older northwest-dipping foliation parallel to compositional layering, cut by a later strain-slip foliation that is axial planar to crenulations in the early foliation; intersections of the two sets of foliation are parallel to fold axes in the early foliation and plunge gently to the northwest. Mylonitic tonalitic gneiss has intruded both metasedimentary units, and a mylonitic granitic gneiss containing xenoliths of marble cross cuts the lower grade phyllitic unit. The higher grade sequence has also been intruded by an undeformed adamellite with a K-Ar minimum age of 114 Ma (Horne and others, 1976c). The metasedimentary sequence is unconformably overlain by unmetamorphosed strata of the Honduras Group of Jurassic age (King, 1972; Delevoryas and Srivastava, 1981).

Terra Incognita

Some of the earliest studied but least understood metamorphic rocks on the Chortis block are exposed in northwestern Nicaragua and adjacent parts of Honduras (Fig. 6). Zoppis Bracci (1957) described a low greenschist facies succession of phyllite and schists that contain minor quartzite and marble beds, which he called the Palacagüina Formation. Structures in these strata have a prominent east-northeast trend; foliations are gently inclined to the south and fold vergence is northerly. Engles (1964) described another low greenschist facies metavolcanic assemblage of tuffs, pillow basalts, and diabase in northern Nicaragua, which he implied was younger than the Palacagüina. Rocks similar to each of these assemblages are widely exposed in the remote regions of northern Nicaragua and southeastern Honduras (Zoppis Bracci and del Giudice, 1958; Mills and Hugh, 1974).

The Dipilto batholith is a calc-alkaline adamellite to tonalite that has intruded the Palacagüina in its type area near Ocotal, Nicaragua (Fig. 2). Similar plutons seem distributed in an east-northeast trend through northwestern Nicaragua from the Pacific to the Caribbean (McBirney and Williams, 1965). Various attempts to date the Dipilto have yielded mineral dates that range from 80 to 115 Ma (Zoppis Bracci and del Giudice, 1961; Pushkar and others, 1972; Garayer and Viramonte, 1971); Horne and Clark (unpub.) have obtained an excellent 4-point whole-rock Rb-Sr isochron age of 140 ±15 Ma. Thus, the Palacagüina must be pre-Cretaceous, but the metavolcanic assemblages described by Engles (1964) could be of Cretaceous age, as suggested by Mills and Hugh (1974).

Metasedimentary rocks similar to the Palacagüina, the Petén, and the Cacaguapa are poorly exposed but widespread across northern and eastern Honduras, principally in the departments of Yoro and Olancho (Elvir, 1974). These have only been briefly described from reconnaissance traverses along major rivers in the Mosquitia (Mills and Hugh, 1974) and the few roads through the remote region (Williams and McBirney, 1969; the authors, unpublished information). Most of the metamorphic exposures are of mica schist and phyllite, and minor amounts of quartzite, marble, and amphibolite.

Correlations

Although many early workers assumed that most of the metamorphic sequences exposed on the Chortis block are correlative, more detailed studies of the basement in various separated areas have indicated that significant differences exist among the sequences. It seems reasonable to correlate the Las Ovejas in the Motagua Valley with the old, high-grade sequence exposed along strike in the Sierras de Espírito Santo and de Omoa, and with similar rocks in the Cordillera Nombre de Dios, however, rocks similar to these have not been described south of the Jocotán-Chamelecón-Aguán fault zone. The higher grade sequence at El Porvenir, which seems similar, is thought to be gradational to and equivalent with the adjacent lower grade pelitic sequence. Moreover, nothing like the Humuya Member of the Cacaguapa Schist in the Montaña de Comayagua area has been described elsewhere on the Chortis block. However, nearly every exposed sequence of higher grade metamorphic rocks on the Chortis block has suffered a high degree of pervasive internal deformation; penetrative cataclastic and mylonitic fabrics are ubiquitous and indicate at least one widespread episode of dynamic metamorphism. The significance of this is not known.

Low-grade greenschist facies pelitic sequences of schist and phyllite are generally similar everywhere and very difficult to differentiate or correlate. Obvious similarities do exist among the San Diego Phyllite in the Motagua Valley, the upper sequence of schist in the Sierras de Espírito Santo and de Omoa, the Petén Formation at San Juancito, the Las Marías Member of the Cacaguapa Schist at Comayagua, the low-grade succession at El Porvenir, and the Palacagüina Formation at Ocotál (Fig. 7). All are predominantly pelitic sequences in the low greenschist facies, and most have minor associated quartzite and/or marble beds. Some workers have suggested that they are correlative with the Carboniferous Santa Rosa Group widely exposed on the Maya block (Clemons, 1966; Horne and others, 1976a), but age equivalence is not known or even indicated. Moreover, the paleogeographic relationship between the two blocks in the late Paleozoic is conjectoral at best.

MESOZOIC STRATIGRAPHY

The state of stratigraphic understanding of the Chortis block still is very unsettled and partly confused (e.g., Wilson and others, 1978). Early studies of the region were of a reconnaissance nature and for the most part were not based on detailed mapping. From these early reconnaissances, many basic assumptions and simplifying generalizations were made, and these have pervaded much of the subsequent literature; unfortunately, many have been shown by more recent detailed mapping to have been oversimplified or erroneous.

To review, the early studies recognized the existence of a lower red bed sequence, an intervening Cretaceous limestone, upper red beds, and a succeeding sequence of Tertiary volcanic rocks. As studies continued, the following interpretations evolved into a widely accepted stratigraphic framework:

1. The lower red beds seemed similar to and were correlated with the Todos Santos Formation in western Guatemala (Mills and others, 1967; Burkart and others, 1973).

2. Massive Cretaceous carbonate units exposed throughout the Chortis block were assumed to be equivalent or closely related, and were placed together in one sequence called the Yojoa Group (Mills and others, 1967; Williams and McBirney, 1969).

3. Red beds overlying limestones were all correlated with the well-known sequence exposed near Tegucigalpa called the Valle de Angeles Formation (Carpenter, 1954; Mills and others, 1967; Williams and McBirney, 1969).

4. Volcanic rocks in general came to be regarded as exclusively Cenozoic and were divided by composition into an early sequence of andesitic rocks called the Matagalpa Formation and a younger pile of dominantly ignimbritic felsic effusives named the Padre Miguel Group (Williams and McBirney, 1969; Burkart and others, 1973).

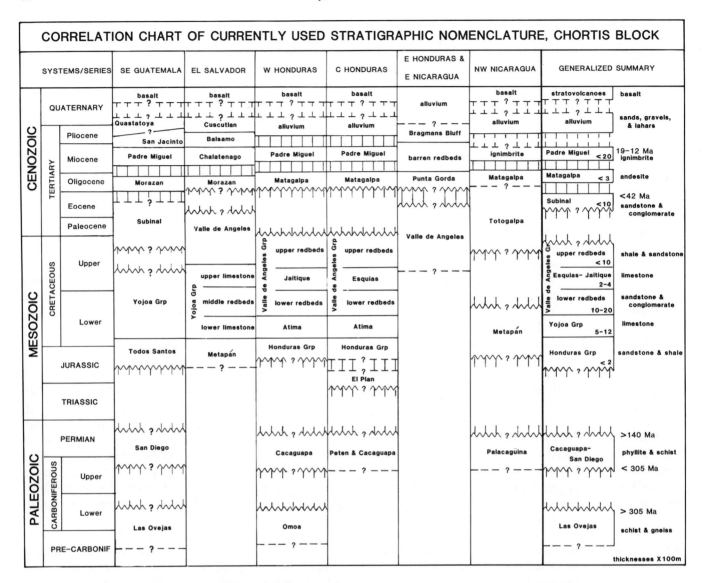

Figure 7. Correlation chart of stratigraphic nomenclature currently used in various parts of Chortis block; generalized summary section is compiled at right.

Earlier stratigraphic terminology applied by Fritzgartner (1891), Sapper (1899, 1905, 1937) and Weaver (1942)—such as Tegucigalpa, Metapán, and Esquías—fell into disuse or was abandoned.

Detailed mapping in the San Juancito area (Fig. 5) of central Honduras by Carpenter (1954) revealed a stratigraphic succession that did not conform very well with these ideas and, consequently, it was often discounted or the area was considered anomalous. Since about 1970 a basic quadrangle mapping program of the Mesozoic sequences widely exposed in the central highlands of Honduras has slowly revealed that the San Juancito succession is neither totally unique nor incorrect, and that many of the early generalizations were incorrect. For example: (1) The basal sequence that rests on the basement does not consist of dominantly red clastics, and is at least in part marine. (2) At least two massive Cretaceous carbonate units, separated by a thick sequence of coarse redbeds, are widely exposed across the Chortis block, inevitably leading to "jump correlations" and some of the early oversimplifications. (3) Red beds exist in two distinct sequences, each overlying one of the major limestone units. (4) Volcanic rocks have been found in various parts of the Mesozoic succession and do not have age-distinctive compositions. The Mesozoic stratigraphic succession on the Chortis block has been found to be quite variable.

Basal Sequence

The greatest confusion and misunderstanding concerning the Mesozoic stratigraphy of the Chortis block has centered on the nature and significance of the basal part of the sequence, herein named the Honduras Group. This is largely because most units that underlie limestones were considered part of the basal sequence, even if they could not be shown to rest on the basement. These rocks usually have been called Todos Santos or Metapán and it therefore seems advisable to briefly review the origin and application of those terms.

Todos Santos–Metapán problem. The Todos Santos Formation was defined as a red clastic sequence in northwestern Guatemala (Sapper, 1894); it was later extended into southeastern Mexico (Sapper, 1937) and across much of Guatemala (McBirney, 1963; Anderson and others, 1973). The name was also applied to lower red beds in southeastern Guatemala (Burkart and others, 1973) and was widely used throughout Honduras (Mills and others, 1967), thus extending the Todos Santos Formation across a plate boundary from the Maya block to the Chortis block. Considering that the paleogeographic relationship between the two blocks is unknown and conjectural, it now seems unwise to continue this practice.

Sapper (1899) described a sequence of terrigenous clastic rocks that are overlain by Cretaceous limestone in northwestern El Salvador (Fig. 5) that he called the "Metapán strata." Sapper (1937) and many later workers thought the "Metapán strata" were equivalent with the Todos Santos and believed they were probably Jurassic. Later workers in El Salvador (Stirton and Gealey, 1949; Dürr and Stober, 1956; Mayer, 1967) expanded the application of "Metapán strata" to ultimately include the entire sedimentary succession in the Metapán area (see Weber, 1979, for review and discussion). The term has also been applied widely across the Chortis block to a variety of successions (Schuchert, 1935; Weaver, 1942; Roberts and Irving, 1957; Zoppis Bracci and del Giudice, 1958), further confusing its meaning. Following recent detailed mapping in the Metapán area, Weber (1979) has redefined the succession of "Metapán strata" and wisely recommended that the term be used only informally in the Metapán area, and not applied elsewhere.

Usage of the term Todos Santos should also be abandoned on the Chortis block for two reasons. First, as noted above and by Finch (1981, p. 1323), the Todos Santos was defined in a terrane with unknown paleogeographic relation to the Chortis block (Gose and Swartz, 1977), and it probably was not lithologically continuous onto that block. Second, most of what has been called Todos Santos on the Chortis block (Mills and others, 1967; Williams and McBirney, 1969; Everett, 1970; Fakundiny, 1970) probably is not even in the same relative stratigraphic position as the Todos Santos, and was miscorrelated because it was beneath limestone assumed to be part of the Lower Cretaceous Yojoa Group. As will be discussed later, many of these sequences have subsequently been shown to be lower Valle de Angeles red beds overlain by Cenomanian limestone (Atwood, 1972; Finch, 1972, 1981; Horne and others, 1974; Fakundiny and Everett, 1976).

El Plan Formation. The El Plan Formation is the least understood and most problematic stratigraphic unit on the Chortis block. Its areal distribution, environment of deposition, age

relation, contacts with other units, relative stratigraphic position, and paleogeographic significance have all been subject to continuing controversy. Carpenter (1954) defined the El Plan Formation in the San Juancito area of central Honduras (Fig. 5) as consisting of about 900 m of alternations of shale-siltstone units and sandstone-grit-siltstone units, each in well-bedded packages 30 m or more thick. Similar strata also have been described elsewhere from scattered localities throughout Honduras (Carpenter, 1954; Mills and others, 1967; UNDP, 1972; Mills and Hugh, 1974; Ritchie and Finch, 1985); however, it is not known whether they are all correlative.

Carpenter (1954) described plant-bearing beds, rare pebble-conglomerate lenses, and marly beds in the El Plan which he felt indicated flood-plain to shallow-marine depositional conditions. Wilson (1974) interpreted these strata as intermontane lacustrine deposits. The authors and others have noted flyschlike attributes in the succession, including rhythmic alternations of graded sandstone having sharp scoured bases, gradational upward into mudstones that have contorted laminations, suggesting deposition by turbidity currents. Perhaps all these observations are not incompatible with deposition in a terrigenous shelf environment.

Newberry (1888) described 14 species of cycads and related plants from the El Plan at San Juancito which he believed to be of Rhaetian age; others, however, thought they could be Jurassic (Knowlton, 1918; Müllerried, 1942a, 1942b). Unfortunately, Newberry's collection is missing, and additional plant specimens from nearby localities have been identified as Jurassic (Ritchie and Finch, 1985). Carpenter (1954) described another exposure of siltstone and sandstone near San Juancito that contains a diverse marine fauna of Middle Jurassic age; he thought this was younger than the El Plan, but the two are not visibly in unfaulted contact.

Part of the problem with the El Plan Formation is that no one has ever reported seeing it in direct, unfaulted contact with any other stratigraphic unit. Because it is the oldest known sedimentary rock unit on the Chortis block, it is assumed that it unconformably overlies the metamorphic Petén Formation (Carpenter, 1954; Mills and others, 1967; Wilson, 1974). Carpenter (1954) also assumed that his "undefined Jurassic" strata described above rested conformably on the El Plan, but he could not describe the unexposed contact. It is not known with certainty what relationship the El Plan Formation has with the Honduras Group or the younger Yojoa Group. It seems reasonable to assume that the El Plan is equivalent with at least part of the Honduras Group.

Honduras Group. Basal siliciclastic strata that rest unconformably upon the metamorphic basement and/or are conformably overlain by massive limestone of probably Early Cretaceous age have been mapped discontinuously across much of the Chortis block. Usually these strata have been correlated with either the Todos Santos Formation of western Guatemala or the Metapán Formation of northwestern El Salvador, a practice which should be discontinued, as explained earlier. Because the basal sequences vary somewhat from area to area, and because some areas may have more than one mappable sequence between the basement and the Lower Cretaceous Yojoa Group, we propose collecting the various basal siliciclastic sequences into a group of unnamed formations. These sequences are widely exposed across Honduras; therefore, we propose naming this the Honduras Group.

The Honduras Group is hereby designated as predominantly siliciclastic strata of Jurassic to Early Cretaceous age that rest on the basement and are overlain by Yojoa limestones of known Aptian–Albian age. The group could include or be partly equivalent with the El Plan Formation described above. However, the numerous described sequences of terrigenous red beds that underlie limestones thought to be Yojoa-like are ambiguous and are not included in the group until their stratigraphic positions can be demonstrated unequivocally by faunal or physical means. Many of these sequences may in fact be part of the Upper Cretaceous Valle de Angeles Group, as indicated in the introduction to this section.

Mapped sequences of strata that unequivocally may be assigned to the Honduras Group are relatively few and rather different from the numerous successions of red beds formerly referred to the Todos Santos Formation. Unambiguous examples are exposed in three areas of Honduras: in the cores of several faulted or anticlinal uplifts to the north of Tegucigalpa, around the western margin of the Comayagua basement massif, and in western Honduras near Lake Yojoa (Fig. 5).

In the San Juancito area, northeast of Tegucigalpa, Carpenter (1954) described a 30-m-thick section of siltstone and sandstone containing Jurassic bivalves that he believed was above the El Plan Formation. To the northwest of San Juancito—near the villages of Talanga, Cedros, Minas de Oro, and El Porvenir (Fig. 5)—several workers (Atwood, 1972; King, 1972; Simonson, 1977) have described various sections of shale and quartzose sandstone with minor pebble conglomerate that rest unconformably on the basement and in most places are gradationally overlain by the Lower Cretaceous Atima limestone. None of these have been described as red bed sequences; although plant fossils were found at several localities, undated marine faunas of bivalves and gastropods were also found, and all sections are less than a few hundred meters thick. King (1972) inferred that at least part of the succession was equivalent with the El Plan Formation.

On the west flank of the Comayagua basement massif, Everett (1970) and Fakundiny (1970) reported extensive exposures of red beds that they correlated with the Todos Santos, but most of these strata were later reassigned to the Valle de Angeles Group (Fakundiny and Everett, 1976). The only strata that subsequently could be included in the Honduras Group are a sequence of quartz- and metamorphic-pebble conglomerate, sandstone, and tuff, that locally may exceed 50 m in thickness, can be shown to lie directly on the basement, and are overlain by *Orbitolina*-bearing Atima limestone (Fakundiny and Everett, 1976).

Just west of Lake Yojoa in western Honduras, up to 35 m of shale, limey shale, and quartzose sandstone have been drilled below known Atima limestone in the El Mochito Mine (R. C. Finch, personal communication). A little farther west, on the west side of Montaña Santa Bárbara, Finch mapped a 75-m section of sandstone, quartz-pebble conglomerate, siltstone, shale, and associated calcareous beds in the upper part apparently gradational up into the overlying Atima Formation. Just southeast of Lake Yojoa (Curran, 1980) a similar sequence of gray-green sandstone, mudstone, metamorphic-pebble conglomerate, and associated sandy limestone and shale directly underlies the Atima limestone; the basement is not exposed.

Unambiguous exposures of the Honduras Group are rarely known elsewhere, but the group is probably widely exposed across the Chortis block (Ritchie and Finch, 1985). Weber (1979) redescribed a section in the Mepatán area of northwestern El Salvador that probably conforms closely to Sapper's (1899) original "Metapán strata." This section consists of at least 200 m of variegated sandstone, conglomerate, siltstone, and shale, and intercalations of andesite and basalt up to 20 m thick. A similar succession is exposed nearby in southeastern Guatemala (Burkart and others, 1973). Although the basement is not exposed in those areas, these strata are conformably overlain by dated Atima limestone of Albian age, and they have been called the Todos Santos Formation, after Sapper's (1937) correlation; they should be included in the Honduras Group. Red beds in the Metapán area that underlie Cenomanian limestone (Wilson, 1974; Weber, 1979), and most of what has been called Todos Santos red beds elsewhere on the Chortis block, may be red equivalents of the Honduras Group, or part of the Valle de Angeles Group.

In summary, the Honduras Group is now known: (1) to rest unconformably upon the basement and grade upward into the Lower Cretaceous Atima Formation (Fig. 7); (2) to consist dominantly of siliciclastic sequences of shale and siltstone, and sandstone, locally important pebble conglomerate, and minor calcareous beds (in most areas these are not red bed sequences); (3) to be of variable thickness, from a few to many hundreds of meters thick, and widely distributed from southeastern Guatemala to easternmost Honduras; and (4) to contain both plant fossils and marine faunas, some of which have been dated as Jurassic (Delevoryas and Srivastava, 1981; Ritchie and Finch, 1985).

Yojoa Group

Mills and others (1967) defined the Yojoa Group as consisting of four formations that crop out near Lake Yojoa in western Honduras: (1) the lower Cantarranas Formation, a shaly limestone of Neocomian–Aptian age; (2) the middle Atima Formation, a massive fossiliferous carbonate unit of Aptian–Albian age; (3) the upper Guare Formation, a thin-bedded petroliferous and argillaceous limestone of Cenomanian age; and (4) the Ilama Formation, a limestone breccia-conglomerate unit locally present above or below the Atima Formation.

Although the Cantarranas Formation was the original carbonate unit that Mills and others (1967) expanded into the Yojoa

Group, its age and relative stratigraphic position in the type area (Carpenter, 1954) are in question, and the unit needs to be studied further and redefined. The Atima Formation is the most widely recognized and least controversial stratigraphic unit that crops out on the Chortis block; nevertheless, younger massive limestones commonly have been confused with the Atima. However, the Guare Formation has been found (Finch, 1972; Wilson, 1974; Curran, 1980) to be separated from the rest of the Yojoa Group by a thick sequence of red beds, and it was therefore reduced to a member of the Jaitique Formation in the Upper Cretaceous Valle de Angeles Group (Finch, 1981). Because the Ilama Formation is not in a consistent stratigraphic position and is easily mistaken for younger limestone-pebble conglomerates that occur variously through the Valle de Angeles Group, Finch (1981) recommended that the term be abandoned.

Cantarranas Formation. The Cantarranas Formation was originally defined by Carpenter (1954), in the San Juancito area of central Honduras, as consisting of three members: a lower massive limestone, a middle unit of calcareous shale and sandstone, and an upper massive limestone, all totaling about 180 m thickness. Mills and others (1967) correlated the upper massive member with their Atima Formation and restricted application of Cantarranas to the lower two of the original three members. Mills and others (1967) recognized their revised Cantarranas—varying considerably in lithology and in thickness (up to 200 m)—in many stratigraphic sections across Honduras; they interpreted it as having been deposited in a restricted backreef environment.

There are many inherent problems with the Cantarranas Formation, and most recent workers have not found it to be a useful mappable unit. Even Carpenter (1954) had difficulty determining its stratigraphic position, and no one has been able to satisfactorily resolve its age. Mills and others (1967) cited evidence of Neocomian to Albian ages in sections they correlated with the Cantarranas, and at the type section they attributed a probable Albian–possible Late Cretaceous age to the upper member (Atima?). However, Wilson (1974) believed the type Cantarranas at San Juancito is Cenomanian, raising the possibility that it could be equivalent to other Cenomanian limestones reported from the Valle de Angeles Group (Horne and others, 1974; Finch, 1981), considerably above the Yojoa Group. Thus, only the Atima Formation seems to remain in the Yojoa Group as a useful stratigraphic unit.

Atima Formation. The Atima Formation was recognized by Mills and others (1967) as the most widespread and distinctive unit in the Yojoa Group; it consists of dark-gray, massive biomicrite, and locally has shaly partings and stringers of bedded chert; orbitolinid coquina beds and rudistid bioherms are common associations. The formation has been mapped widely across the Chortis block from southeastern Guatemala (Burkart and others, 1973) and northwestern El Salvador (Weber, 1979), across Honduras (Fakundiny and Everett, 1976; Finch, 1981), at least as far as northern Nicaragua (Zoppis Bracci and del Giudice, 1958).

The thickness of the Atima varies from as thin as 100 m or so around the flanks of old basement highs (Fakundiny, 1970;

Simonson, 1977) to 1,200 m or more in depocenters in western (Finch, 1981) and northeastern Honduras (Mills and others, 1967). The lithofacies of the Atima is also variable; it is usually described as representing a shallow carbonate bank environment with scattered skeletal-sand shoals and rudistid patch reefs. However, in the El Mochito Mine in western Honduras (Fig. 5), the Atima is divided by a 115-m-thick green mudstone into upper and lower massive limestones, each about 500 m thick and seemingly representing shoaling-upward, shallow-water bank facies (Finch, 1981). Similar shoaling-upward sequences have also been described in the Atima from central Honduras (Emmet, 1983).

Deepwater facies of the Yojoa have been reported in central Honduras (Wilson, 1974, "Talanga limestone") and southeastern Guatemala (Crane, 1965; Burkart and others, 1973). In the latter area, remarkable thickness and facies contrasts exist across the Jocotán fault (Fig. 6), where Crane (1965) described 1,300 m of Albian thin-bedded deepwater limestone to the south of the fault (correlated by Clemons [1969] to the Canterranas Formation), overlain by 400 m of massive, shallow-marine limestone (correlated with the Atima) having a thick basal limestone breccia-fanglomerate. Farther south, Burkart (1965) reported the lower section to be of dark, shaly, thin-bedded limestone containing Aptian ammonites; no breccia zone separates the overlying massive Albian limestone. To the north, across the Jocotán fault, Clemons (1969) found only 300 m of Atima-like massive limestone resting directly on the basement of the northern marginal complex. This contrast prompted Donnelly and others (1968) to suggest that up-to-the-north dip-slip motion occurred on the Jocotán fault in the Early Cretaceous; similar relationships have been described along trend to the northeast across the Chamelecón fault in northwestern Honduras (Horne and others, 1976a).

Contacts between the Atima Formation or other basal Yojoa Group strata and the underlying clastic strata of the Honduras Group are conformable wherever exposed and are commonly gradational. Contacts with the overlying red beds of the Valle de Angeles Group have been described as conformable wherever mapped, but Wilson (1974) felt that the lithic contrasts between the two demanded a tectonic disturbance and unconformity. Mills and others (1967) believed the Atima was dominantly of Albian age. Finch (1981) indicated that the lower Atima in the El Mochito Mine was latest Neocomian through late Aptian and that the upper Atima was latest Aptian through late Albian.

It should be noted that in El Salvador (Weber, 1979; Baxter, 1984) the Yojoa Group includes not only a basal massive limestone, probably equivalent to the Atima Formation, but also overlying red beds and an upper limestone that in Honduras are considered to be part of the succeeding Valle de Angeles Group (Fig. 7).

Valle de Angeles Group

Carpenter (1954) named the Valle de Angeles Formation for the thick sequence of reddish clastic rocks that crop out between Tegucigalpa and San Juancito, Honduras. These strata had been previously called the Tegucigalpa Formation (Fritzgartner, 1891), which was later expanded to include the much older strata which ultimately became known as the El Plan Formation (Sapper, 1905). Carpenter (1954) thought the Valle de Angeles clastics were deposited in a terrestrial intermontane area immediately adjacent to highland sources. Because they were believed to overlie the Cretaceous Cantarranas Formation, he thought the Valle de Angeles strata were probably Late Cretaceous to early Tertiary.

The Valle de Angeles was raised to group status (Mills and others, 1967) by including all sedimentary rocks above the Lower Cretaceous Yojoa Group and beneath mid-Tertiary volcanic formations. A limestone unit named the Esquías Formation (Weaver, 1942) was included in the group as the only named formation (Mills and others, 1967); this served to subdivide the group into lower and upper red bed sequences.

The problem of red beds

Prior to 1968 and the inception of detailed quadrangle mapping in the Mesozoic highlands of central Honduras, as many as four red bed sequences had been recognized on the Chortis block: (1) red beds beneath massive Cretaceous limestone, usually referred to the Todos Santos Formation: (2) red beds above massive Cretaceous limestone, usually referred to the Valle de Angeles Formation; (3) red beds above the Esquías marly limestone, rarely described but relegated to the upper part of the Valle de Angeles Group; and (4) red beds that demonstrably rest unconformably upon folded Mesozoic strata, correlated to the Tertiary Subinal Formation of Guatemala (Hirschmann, 1963).

Red siliciclastic strata, unfortunately, are not unique, and without some type of distinguishing feature, each of these four units could easily be mistaken for another. For example, stratigraphic correlation of red bed units relative to massive Cretaceous limestone was obviated by the recognition that the Esquías and other limestones in the Valle de Angeles were also massive and similar to the Yojoa Group (Horne and others, 1974; Finch, 1981). Williams and McBirney (1969) believed that the Valle de Angeles was prevolcanic, and that the presence of volcanic strata or debris in red beds indicated at most mid-Tertiary age and probable equivalence with the Subinal; however, volcanic strata and debris have subsequently been found throughout the Mesozoic succession on the Chortis block. The Subinal equivalents have been recognized in a few places where they rest with marked unconformity on folded Mesozoic strata, including the Valle de Angeles (Horne and others, 1974), but they are very difficult to recognize where basal discordance is not evident (Williams and McBirney, 1969), or where the Valle de Angeles may not be present (Burkart and others, 1973). Although brown and reddish hues have been described in the pre-Yojoa Honduras Group, they are not common and the group is not dominantly a red bed sequence.

Since about 1970, a generalized succession for the Valle de

Angeles Group has evolved following the recognition of widespread mid-Cretaceous limestones (Horne and others, 1974; Fakundiny and Everett, 1976; Finch, 1981) that effectively divide the group into three major units: (1) lower coarse-grained red beds and conglomerates that rest conformably upon Lower Cretaceous carbonate rocks of the Yojoa Group, informally designated as the lower Valle de Angeles Group; (2) middle carbonate sequences of Cenomanian age that are gradational with both underlying and overlying red bed sequences, called the Esquías Formation in central Honduras and the Jaitique Formation in west-central Honduras; and (3) upper fine-grained red beds that are locally gypsiferous and that are overlain with marked angular unconformity by Tertiary volcanic strata; these are informally called the upper Valle de Angeles Group.

Lower red beds. The lower red bed sequence of the Valle de Angeles Group has been described widely throughout the Chortis block, across Honduras (Mills and others, 1967; Williams and McBirney, 1969; Horne and others, 1974; Fakundiny and Everett, 1976; Finch, 1981) to the Caribbean coast of eastern Honduras and Nicaragua (Mills and Hugh, 1974). The red bed sequence that separates the two limestones of the so-called "Yojoa Group" in El Salvador (Weber, 1979; Baxter, 1984) is also here considered equivalent to the lower red beds of the Valle de Angeles Group (Fig. 7). The following is a generalized description of these red bed sequences.

The lower red beds are distinctly coarser grained, more conglomeratic, and more variable in color, texture, and composition than the upper red beds in the Valle de Angeles Group. They often have been misidentified as the basal siliciclastic sequence and have been miscorrelated with the Todos Santos Formation. Typical exposures are dominated by well-bedded variegated sandstone and massive, poorly bedded quartz-pebble conglomerate in red sandy matrix. Red siltstone and maroon claystone commonly are more abundant but are less resistant and less well exposed. The sandstones vary locally in composition from quartzose, to feldspathic, to lithic with pelitic grains; primary sedimentary structures suggest fluvial conditions. Conglomerates compose anywhere from 10 to 25 percent of the section. Clasts most commonly are vein quartz, but volcanic or metamorphic pebbles may be abundant locally; clast fabric and internal structures suggest braided stream or alluvial fan deposition. Intercalations of minor volcaniclastic beds, volcanic flows, thin limestones, and oligomictic limestone-pebble conglomerate have been reported in various parts of the section.

The thickness of the lower red bed sequence is quite variable locally, but usually is about 1,000 m or so. It has been found to thin from as much as 2,000 m (Horne and others, 1974) to absence (Simonson, 1977) over a distance of only 40 km in central Honduras, as if it had been deposited into an intermontane trough or graben. Where the lower contact with the underlying Yojoa carbonate rocks is exposed, it is usually described as conformable, even gradational. An increase in the prevalence of thin limestones and marlstones toward the top of the sequence suggests transitions up into the overlying carbonate rocks. The only fossil reported from the lower red beds is the femur of a Cretaceous ornithopod found close to the top of the section near the type area of the overlying Esquías Formation (Horne and others, 1974).

Middle carbonate rocks. The recognition of a major sequence of carbonate rocks within the Valle de Angeles Group was critical in defining and attempting to resolve the red bed problem on the Chortis block. Although Mills and others (1967) had suggested that a relatively unimportant marly limestone divided the Valle de Angeles into upper and lower red beds, they did not consider it to be widespread or similar to the Atima limestones. Subsequent workers have abundantly documented the fact that mid-Cretaceous carbonate rocks are well developed and widespread across much of the Chortis block, and that in many places they had been confused with limestones in the Yojoa Group (Atwood, 1972; Finch, 1972, 1981; King, 1972; Horne and others, 1974; Wilson, 1974; Fakundiny and Everett, 1976; Simonson, 1977; Curran, 1980). These carbonate sequences have been variously called the Esquías, Guare, and Jaitique Formations.

The Esquías Formation (Weaver, 1942) was restudied in its type are (Atwood, 1972) and found to consist of over 400 m of dominantly argillaceous carbonate rocks that ultimately were traced discontinuously over a large area in central Honduras (King, 1972; Fakundiny and Everett, 1976). Thus, the Esquías was redefined (Horne and others, 1974) as a major carbonate sequence, in part very similar to the Atima but of probably Cenomanian age, that is conformably contained within the predominantly red bed sequence of the Valle de Angeles Group. The biofabric and sedimentary structures in the Esquías and both subjacent and superjacent strata are indicative of a marine transgression to a shallow protected nearshore environment, followed by regression or progradation of terrigenous facies.

The Jaitique Formation (Finch, 1981) was defined as a sequence of Cenomanian carbonate rocks up to 200 m thick within the Valle de Angeles red beds; it is widely exposed to the west (Finch, 1972) and southwest (Curran, 1980) of Lake Yojoa (Fig. 5). The Jaitique typically consists of a lower member, 100 m or more thick, of massive biomicrite, and a thin upper member of shaly thin-bedded limestone that had been called the Guare Formation, previously included within the Yojoa Group (Mills and others, 1967). Finch (1981) redesignated the Guare as a member of the Jaitique and suggested that it indicated a regressive transition from open-shelf carbonate conditions to hypersaline lagoonal or intertidal mudflat conditions. The Jaitique and Esquías Formations seem to occupy similar stratigraphic positions within the Valle de Angeles Group, and they are of generally equivalent age (Fig. 7). Although the Jaitique is only half as thick or less than the Esquías, and the lithofacies of the two are somewhat different, both reflect similar histories and environmental conditions.

Very similar sequences of mid-Cretaceous limestones overlie redbeds in El Salvador (Weber, 1979) and Guatemala (Bosc, 1971), and they are thought to be equivalents of the Esquías-

Jaitique Formations. In El Salvador these are included in the upper part of the so-called "Yojoa Group" (Baxter, 1984).

Upper red beds. The upper red bed sequence of the Valle de Angeles Group is generally finer grained and more uniformly red than the lower sequence. It typically consists of brick-red, brownish to maroon fine sandstone, siltstone, shale, and claystone, and locally has beds of rounded-limestone–pebble-cobble conglomerate in red quartzose sandy matrix. Volcanic detritus is common in parts of the sequence, and disseminated or nodular gypsum is locally present in the lower part. These lithosomes and their contained primary sedimentary structures have indicated floodplain, sabkha, deltaic, and shallow-marine environmental conditions to many workers (Williams and McBirney, 1969; Horne and others, 1974; Fakundiny and Everett, 1976; Finch, 1981).

The lower contact with underlying carbonate rocks has been described as conformable (Horne and others, 1974) to gradational (Finch, 1981). The upper contact is a marked angular unconformity with overlying volcanic strata of the middle Tertiary Matagalpa Formation or late Tertiary Padre Miguel Group, and buries a surface with pronounced erosional relief. The thickness of the upper redbeds varies according to the amount of erosion expressed at this surface; it has been measured from 0 to 1,000 m. The age is limited by the Cenomanian age of the underlying carbonate rocks and the probable Oligocene age of the oldest overlying volcanic rocks.

Other units. Other stratigraphic units that may be correlative with parts of the Valle de Angeles Group have been described from various areas on the Chortis block. For example, the Totogalpa Formation (del Giudice, 1960) is a thick sequence of conglomeratic red beds that rests unconformably upon the Palacagüina Schist and Dipilto batholith in northern Nicaragua (Fig. 7). The Totogalpa was thought to be Tertiary because it contained volcanic detritus (McBirney and Williams, 1965), and the Dipilto was believed to be Late Cretaceous (Zoppis Bracci and del Giudice, 1961). However, volcanic rocks and detritus have been described from throughout the Mesozoic section on the Chortis block, and the Dipilto batholith has been dated as Late Jurassic (see section on the basement of Terra Incognita). Thus, it is possible that the Totogalpa could be equivalent with very similar red beds in the Valle de Angeles Group. Alternatively, it could correlate with the lower Tertiary Subinal Formation in southeastern Guatemala (Burkart and others, 1973); it is also possible that some of what has been mapped as Subinal could be equivalent with the Valle de Angeles exposed nearby in both western Honduras (UNDP, 1972) and northwestern El Salvador (Weber, 1979).

In the San Juancito area of central Honduras, Carpenter (1954) described a terrestrial volcanic sequence that rests with discontinuity on the El Plan Formation and is unconformably overlain by the late Tertiary felsic volcanic edifice. This sequence includes the Colonia andesitic tuffs and breccias, the Crucero tuffaceous dacite flows, and the Plancitos Formation of bedded, reworked andesitic debris, all totaling about 2,000 m in thickness.

Carpenter (1954) thought that all of these were Cretaceous, but he could not resolve their stratigraphic position relative to either the Cantarranas or Valle de Angeles Formations. Wilson (1974) thought that the Plancitos dips under the Cantarranas, which he believed was correlative with the Esquías Formation. Thus, these three units seem to represent a localized volcanic facies of the lower Valle de Angeles Group and/or the Yojoa Group.

A similar succession of volcanic rocks succeeded by limestone was also mapped to the north of San Juancito on the northern flank of the El Porvenir basement uplift (Fig. 5). Simonson (1977) described about 1,000 m of andesite porphyry breccia and tuff that overlies and intertongues with the upper part of the Yojoa Group carbonate sequence. These were called the Naranjal volcanic deposits and were found to contain assorted clasts, slabs, lenses, and intercalations of carbonate rocks. The Naranjal is conformably overlain by basinal carbonates of the Guatemalita beds, thinly bedded argillaceous and tuffaceous limestones that contain a pelagic microfauna and exhibit evidence of deep-water turbidite deposition. This succession is unconformably blanketed by the late Tertiary volcanic pile; no red beds of the Valle de Angeles Group have been recognized in the area. Simonson (1977) suggested that the Guatemalita beds were possibly correlative with Cenomanian limestones elsewhere, allowing the Naranjal volcanics to be another localized volcanic facies of the lower Valle de Angeles and upper Yojoa Groups.

CENOZOIC STRATIGRAPHY

The Cenozoic stratigraphy of the Chortis block consists of thick shallow marine to coarse terrestrial deposits in an eastern basin, and Paleogene terrigenous clastics overlain by middle and upper Cenozoic volcanics over the rest of the region. One prominent formation, the Valle de Angeles, has already been discussed in the section on Mesozoic stratigraphy; however, it may extend into the Paleogene.

The Mosquitía region of eastern Honduras and Nicaragua has at least 4,500 m of Cenozoic sedimentary rocks in a basin with a shallow medial ridge (Coco River Ridge, Fig. 6). The formations seen in test wells are, from bottom to top (Fig. 7), the Valle de Angeles, Punta Gorda, barren red beds, and Bragman's Bluff Formations (Mills and Hugh, 1974). The Valle de Angeles Formation is at least 800 m thick and consists dominantly of red silty, sandy, and limey shale and minor conglomerates, evaporites, and thin limestones. The Oligocene–Miocene Punta Gorda Formation is up to 1,600 m thick and consists of marine shale, with minor limestones. The barren red beds are up to 1,100 m thick and consist of alternating red and gray shales, sandstones, and minor limestones. The Pliocene–Pleistocene Bragman's Bluff Formation is about 850 m thick and consists of sandstones and gravels and minor limestones and local interbedded shales.

Subinal Formation

The Subinal Formation was named by Hirschmann (1963) for exposures of red beds in the Motagua Valley of Guatemala. It is widespread in southeastern Guatemala (Burkart, 1965; Burkart and others, 1973) and northern El Salvador (Weber, 1979), where it was called "Valle de Angeles." Similar red beds in northern Nicaragua (Zoppis Bracci and del Guidice, 1960) were named the Totogalpa Formation (Fig. 7), and were tentatively correlated with the Subinal Formation (McBirney and Williams, 1965). The Subinal may be equivalent to part or all of the upper Valle de Angeles Group of Honduras. The formation is dominantly terrestrial and variable in facies from place to place; thus, its correlation across the western Chortis block is tentative.

In the type area of the Motogua Valley, the Subinal consists of fluvial red sandstones and conglomerates; conspicuous channels cut into thin-bedded floodplain deposits. A lower, highly variable section consists of local thick serpentinite sandstones, massive quartz-pebble conglomerates, and limestone-cobble conglomerates. An estuarine facies contains Eocene gastropods (Newcomb, 1975).

In southeastern Guatemala the Subinal is similar and contains scattered tuff beds throughout, and a few andesitic flows; Deaton and Burkart (1984b) obtained an age of 42 Ma (K/Ar) for an andesitic clast in a conglomerate. There are gypsiferous beds near Chiquimula (Clemons, 1966). Burkart (1965) estimated the maximum thickness as 1,000 m, thinning to less than 100 m near the margins of the larger basins.

Volcanic Stratigraphy

The volcanic stratigraphy of the Chortis block has been reviewed most thoroughly by Reynolds (1977, 1980). This stratigraphy is complex and consists of primary volcanic and epiclastic volcanic units of generally local extent, with minor biogenic units (lignites, fresh-water limestones, diatomites). These strata rest with angular discordance and profound erosional relief directly upon all older rock units. Reconstructions of geological history of the western Chortis block (Dupré, 1970) emphasize that contemporaneous land surfaces were more subdued in the early Tertiary, which resulted in more widespread stratigraphic units during that time.

The (?)Oligocene to Recent stratigraphy of southwestern Central America is dominated by explosive volcanism; this continues now as a series of active stratovolcanoes along the "volcanic front" from western Guatemala through Nicaragua to central Panamá. The stratigraphy is divisible into three general units: (1) an undated and poorly studied lower sequence of andesitic lavas, tuffs, and breccias correlated with the Matagalpa Formation; (2) a lower–middle Miocene thick sequence of siliceous ignimbrites, referred to as the Padre Miguel Group; and (3) post-ignimbrite volcanic and terrigenous sediments with no generally applied stratigraphic name. In addition, small late Quaternary basalt fields are present near Lake Yojoa and Tegucigalpa in Honduras.

Pre-Ignimbrite Units. The Matagalpa Formation of northern Nicaragua and Honduras (McBirney and Williams, 1965) is a widespread but poorly defined volcanogenic formation that occurs over a broad area beneath the Miocene ignimbrite blanket, which covers most of Central America. In most of its occurrences, primary volcanic materials (dominantly andesite) are more abundant than epiclastic volcanic detritus. The Matagalpa Formation reaches a maximum thickness of 300 m in western Honduras, but remains essentially unstudied. In many areas it has been hydrothermally altered.

Wiesemann (1975) gave the name Morazán Formation to older (i.e., preignimbrite) andesitic lavas, tuffs, and breccias in El Salvador (Fig. 7). Reynolds (1980) extended this name into southern Guatemala. Older, unnamed siliceous and intermediate tuffaceous units have been mapped close to Guatemala City, and there is doubtless several hundred meters of similar material widely distributed in southeastern Guatemala. The application of a stratigraphic name to such a poorly understood and essentially undated sequence of volcanic rocks is premature, and we recommend simply using the designation "possible Matagalpa equivalent" for occurrences of the pre-ignimbrite volcanics.

Miocene ignimbrites. The Miocene ignimbrites of the western Chortis block cover most of southern Guatemala, western Honduras, northern El Salvador, and central Nicaragua, an area of at least 10,000 km^2. The erupted volume is on the order of thousands of cubic kilometers, and the maximum thicknesses recorded locally are about 2,000 m (Williams and McBirney, 1969). The ignimbrites erupted on a nearly flat surface of older metamorphic rocks, Mesozoic strata, Matagalpa volcanics, and Subinal red beds. Stratigraphic studies by Burkart (1965; and Burkart and others, 1973) defined and described the Padre Miguel Group of southeastern Guatemala; the name has subsequently been extended through most of the Honduras sequence and remains perhaps the only widely used name for the entire sequence. One nomenclatural problem, however, is the original inclusion within the Padre Miguel Group of the overlying San Jacinto Formation. As Reynolds (1977, 1980) pointed out, this latter unit is probably distinctly younger. Therefore, the continued use of the name Padre Miguel should probably be restricted to the ignimbritic portion of the sequence. Studies by Dupré (1970) and Curran (1980) in Honduras have produced detailed local stratigraphic and petrographic data; however, their stratigraphic subdivisions have not been applied over a broad area.

The Padre Miguel Group at the type area in southeastern Guatemala is of variable thickness up to about 700 m. It consists of thick ignimbrite packages in the lower part of the section, grading upward into a mixture of ignimbrites, laharic deposits, air-fall ash, sandstones, conglomerates, and capping basalt flows. The age of the sequence is best known from radiometric data of F. McDowell (personal communication, 1984; see chapter on the history of Caribbean magmatism, this volume) which show that the ignimbrites erupted first at 19 Ma and continued in volume to about 14 Ma, with activity divided approximately into an earlier and later period. Some of the capping basalts, which were originally considered to be Quaternary on the basis of the excellent preservation of the eruptive morphology, are about 12 to 13 Ma;

others bury Indian archeological sites and must be Holocene (Williams and McBirney, 1969).

Wiesemann (1975) introduced the Chalatanango Formation for the El Salvadoran equivalents of this ignimbrite sequence (Fig. 7). Reynolds (1980) suggested a middle or upper Miocene age for this unit, but the more extensive data of F. McDowell (personal communication, 1984) suggest that this is probably unreasonably young for the unit. We suggest that the Chalatenango Formation is equivalent to the older and middle Miocene ignimbrites of Honduras and Guatemala. The Guacamayas dacitic tuff at San Juancito in Honduras (Carpenter, 1954), is probably also in part equivalent to the ignimbrites.

Post-ignimbrite units. The ignimbritic units of the western Chortis block are overlain by a highly variable sequence of fluvial, lacustrine, and volcanic sedimentary units of sands and gravels, laharic deposits, ash beds, basalt flows, and minor lignites, fresh-water limestones, and diatomite beds. There is virtually no reliable age information for these units, and they have been assigned various names (Fig. 7).

Williams (1960) summarized postignimbrite units in the Guatemala highlands as heterogeneous, but dominantly volcanic; diatomites near Guatemala City were considered Pliocene in some places and Miocene in others. Reeves (1967) described a variable sequence of polymictic conglomerates up to 45 m thick in the vicinity of El Progreso as the Guastatoya Formation. Bosc (1971) described a similar, but thicker (264 m) and more variable section of dominantly sandstone and conglomerate, with a high proportion of rhyolitic tuff and tuff breccia, and also dark shales with plant fossils, dark fresh-water limestones, and interbedded lignite.

In El Salvador, Wiesemann (1975) named thick andesitic lavas, tuffs, and breccias the Bálsamo Formation; the overlying Cuscatlán Formation contains rhyolitic tuff, volcanic sandstones, and basalt lava. Reynolds (1977, 1980) noted widespread basalt and andesite accumulations in Guatemala, which he correlated with the Bálsamo Formation. Crane (1965) and Burkart and others (1973) also described the San Jacinto Formation in southeastern Guatemala; it consists of up to 500 m of predominantly fluvial sandstone, with abundant interbedded basaltic and rhyolitic pyroclastic debris and basalt flows. A single radiometric date of 4 Ma suggests a Pliocene age for at least part of this unit and possible equivalence with the Cuscatlán Formation (Reynolds, 1980).

A Pleistocene–Recent series of spectacular stratovolcanoes dominates the landscape of the Pacific margin of Central America. Small Quaternary cinder cones are found scattered behind the volcanic front and range eastward into distinctly alkalic varieties. These are discussed in the chapter on neotectonics and volcanism in Middle America, elsewhere in this volume.

In summary, the Cenozoic stratigraphy of the Chortis block is not well known. Early units are poorly exposed and generally unfossiliferous. Later units tend to be locally variable, volcanogenic, and also relatively unfossiliferous. The radiometric age range of the ignimbrite event and its capping basalts has been established as early to middle Miocene, but the remainder of the Cenozoic section is essentially undated.

TECTONIC HISTORY OF THE CHORTIS BLOCK

The early history of the Chortis block is exceedingly difficult to reconstruct because of the palinspastic problem of restoring the block to its pre-Mesozoic paleogeographic position. For more than a quarter century the block has been recognized by many as having originated elsewhere and having been tectonically moved to its present position; i.e., what is today popularly known as a suspect terrane.

There is no hard evidence that documents the pre-Mesozoic position of the Chortis block, and very little data exist that even constrain possibilities (Gose, 1985). Unfortunately, many of the speculations that have been proposed have ignored the small amount of geologic data that are known from the Chortis block; these speculations usually have been simple geometric models based mainly on major plate trajectories since the Mesozoic. This is illustrated by the wide variety of palinspastic models that have been proposed for the early Mesozoic position of the Chortis block. For example: (1) in the central Gulf of Mexico (Carey, 1958; Freeland and Dietz, 1971; Helwig, 1975); (2) against the Yucatán Peninsula in the Gulf of Honduras (Walper and Rowett, 1972; Dillon and Vedder, 1973; Uchupi, 1973); (3) in its present position (Meyerhoff and Meyerhoff, 1972; Wilson, 1974; Iturralde-Vinent, 1975); (4) along the southwest coast of Mexico (Malfait and Dinkelman, 1972; Pindell and Dewey, 1982; Anderson and Schmidt, 1983; Dengo, 1985; Pindell and Barrett, this volume); (5) off the northwest coast of South America (Van der Voo and others, 1976; Ross, 1979); and (6) in the Pacific Ocean (Gose and Swartz, 1977; Sykes and others, 1982).

Of these, the only models that have seriously considered the nature of the basement and subsequent Mesozoic stratigraphy of the Chortis block are those by Anderson and Schmidt (1983) and by Dengo (1985), both of which place the block adjacent to southwestern Mexico. Although correlations are equivocal, clear affinities exist between the basements of the Chortis and Oaxaca blocks (Ortega-Gutiérrez, 1978; Dengo, 1985). As Dengo pointed out, the Mesozoic succession in the Morelos-Guerrero basin of southwestern Mexico has stronger similarities with the Mesozoic of the Chortis block than with the presently adjacent Maya block.

Pre-Mesozoic History

The oldest rocks known on the present Caribbean Plate are exposed in the basement ridge along the northern margin of the Chortis block. These include a metaigneous complex that is early Paleozoic to late Precambrian in age, which could be equivalent with either Grenvillian gneisses in the Oaxaca complex (Ortega-Gutiérrez and Anderson, 1977) or the younger Acatlán complex (Rodríguez, 1970; Ortega-Gutiérrez, 1978). This complex was nonconformably buried by a sedimentary sequence of domi-

nantly terrigenous strata with minor volcanic and carbonate rocks in the early–mid Paleozoic. This sedimentary sequence was penetratively deformed, regionally metamorphosed to the amphibolite facies, and intruded by batholiths of intermediate composition during a major orogenic episode of probable Pennsylvanian age. That event could also have been coeval with the metamorphism of the Acatlán complex, but it seems not to be obviously correlative with any major orogenic episode elsewhere in North America.

The older basement sequence was unconformably succeeded by a thick marine sequence that transgressed across the entire Chortis block in the late Paleozoic. It consisted predominantly of mudstones, probably derived from the subjacent basement complex, but it also contained notable quartz arenite and limestone members. This younger pelitic sequence was regionally metamorphosed to greenschist facies and exposed to a prolonged period of erosion in the pre-Jurassic. It is very difficult to precisely date this later metamorphic episode or to relate it to other known orogenic events on North America.

If the Chortis block was displaced from southwestern Mexico, it probably had been involved earlier in the Cordilleran evolution of western North America. Considering the collage of suspect terranes that were assembled by accretion onto the western Cordillera, it is unwise at this point to attempt correlations between the early history of the Chortis block and pre-Mesozoic events on North America.

Mesozoic History

At the beginning of the Mesozoic the Chortis block, regardless of its paleogeographic position, probably was an emergent lowland of rolling to moderate relief that had been subjected to a long period of denudation. By the end of the Mesozoic the Chortis block had been sutured to the Maya block along a westward extension of the paleo-Motagua fault zone by convergence or translation, or some combination of the two. During the intervening excursion, tectonic unrest and magmatic activity were sporadic and widespread. Plutonic rocks, volcanic strata, and volcanogenic detritus of Jurassic, Early Cretaceous, and Late Cretaceous age attest to a long interval of magmatism that may be correlative with Nevadan activity in the western Cordillera and could also indicate affinities with western Mexico. Late Cretaceous and early Tertiary brittle deformation and isostatic uplift affected the entire block and have long been considered to be coeval and analogous with Laramide events to the north in Mexico and the eastern Cordillera.

Preservation of the stratigraphic record commenced in the Late Triassic to Early Jurassic with El Plan deposition under either marine or lacustrine conditions in localized low-lying areas; elsewhere, hiatus continued. By Middle Jurassic time the Chortis block was undergoing general marine transgression coincident with epeirogenic instability. Low-lying areas were buried by terrigenous sequences of detritus eroded from nearby uplifting source areas of deeply weathered metamorphic rocks. The resulting Honduras Group records this gradual evolution to general marine conditions and ultimate burial of the Chortis basement; it is probably a discontinuous record with numerous diastems of variable duration and extent.

In the Early Cretaceous, most, if not all, of the Chortis block was being inundated by the Yojoa epeiric sea, and terrigenous source areas were no longer influencing depositional regimes. A biogenic carbonate substrate prograded across the Chortis block. Prolific benthic communities built carbonate bank deposits; localized rudistid patch reefs developed along the advancing edges of the banks. Deeper basinal facies accumulated in local troughs or in front of the advancing platform. Two cycles of carbonate aggradation, separated by a period of terrigenous mud deposition, are evident in some parts of the Chortis block, and they probably represent eustatic fluctuations or epeirogenic readjustments. Scattered volcanic activity and plutonic intrusion locally interrupted the otherwise calm Yojoa marine conditions and probably attest to subduction along some margin of the Chortis block during the excursion to its rendezvous with the Maya block.

By the late Albian, tectonic instability was widespread and general isostatic uplift of the Chortis block had forced the rapid regression of the Yojoa sea. A taphrogenic episode of block faulting produced a basin-and-range physiography of uplifting horsts that contributed coarse detritus to adjacent basins. A complex mosaic of alluvial fan, piedmont plain, floodplain, and perhaps lacustrine or lagoonal-marine lithotopes produced a molasse sequence of Valle de Angeles redbeds. As the Chortis block was again reduced by erosion, the lithosomes became finer grained and locally intercalated with calcareous strata deposited in developing marine embayments.

During the Cenomanian, carbonate platform deposits redeveloped following renewed transgression that probably resulted from a eustatic rise affecting most of North America and much of the Caribbean region. The Esquías and Jaitique limestones accumulated in shallow embayments that encroached across the mellowing terrestrial physiography that had been previously disrupted by block faulting. These carbonate deposits shoaled by aggradation through intertidal to supratidal algal mudflat and sabkha conditions, ultimately leading to the restoration of terrigenous red bed deposition.

The Late Cretaceous history of the Chortis block is obscured by an inadequate and incomplete record. The upper Valle de Angeles red beds are of unknown age range and are only of local distribution, due either to lack of deposition or to subsequent removal by post-Cretaceous erosion. Where present, they seem to indicate relative quiescence on the Chortis block; floodplain, lacustrine, and deltaic environments receive fine detritus from remnant basement highlands, residual carbonate bank prominances, and scattered centers of volcanic activity.

The El Tambor Group (McBirney and Bass, 1969a) in the Motagua Valley of Guatemala is now recognized as Cretaceous (Wilson, 1974), and is thought to represent an ophiolitic sequence (Lawrence, 1976) that accumulated offshore to the north (present orientation) of the Chortis block before its collision

with the Maya block. Presumably the El Tambor and related ultramafic complexes were either obducted or extruded along the suture between and onto both the Maya and Chortis blocks during plate-margin interactions in the latest Cretaceous and ensuing Tertiary (see discussion of the Maya block).

Late Cretaceous–Early Tertiary Tectonism

The Mesozoic record on the Chortis block ended with major and widespread plutonic activity accompanied with or followed by extensive brittle deformation that affected the entire block. Sapper (1899) first recognized the significance of Late Cretaceous to early Tertiary deformation in northern Central America; the evidence for this was later elaborated by Dengo and Bohnenberger (1969). In addition to the abundance of plutons that were intruded during this interval (Williams and McBirney, 1969; Horne and others, 1976b, 1976c), the foremost evidence is the widely recognized marked angular unconformity between the Upper Cretaceous Valle de Angeles Group and the mid-Tertiary Matagalpa Formation of andesitic volcanic rocks. Many have referred to this regional deformational episode as a Laramide event, inferring continuity with the Rocky Mountain belt of North America. Although the age and style of deformation are comparable, the tectonic setting of the two regions clearly was not analogous, not is it likely that the causes of orogenesis in the two regions were directly related. Moreover, plutonism and brittle deformation continued on the Chortis block throughout the Tertiary, and it is difficult to ascribe most structures to a specific age. Additional unconformities exist within the Tertiary and the entire Tertiary volcanic sequence has also been extensively faulted, tilted, and somewhat warped.

Regional dip on the Chortis block is southerly; there is a general gradient from basement rocks exposed to the north, through the central Mesozoic highlands, to the Tertiary volcanic ranges in the south (Fig. 6). This gradient may have been initially established in the Late Cretaceous, as indicated by the structural evidence along the northern margin of the block. If the later extensional structures which affected the Tertiary volcanic sequence as well as the Mesozoic succession are discounted, it becomes clear that the Late Cretaceous–early Tertiary deformational event produced brittle structures in the Mesozoic cover by regional compression. These include large, east-trending flexural folds that typically are asymmetric to the south and vary from broad open structures to tight folds with overturned southerly limbs. The folds are cut by steep dip-slip faults in a variety of orientations, many of which do not affect the overlying volcanic sequence. South vergence of deformation is further supported by the presence of high-angle reverse faults thrust southerly along the south limbs of some major anticlines. Northwest-trending, dextral strike-slip faults have also been mapped locally, which would fit the general strain pattern for the Late Cretaceous–early Tertiary deformational event, but the age of displacement on these faults is not known.

Everett (1970) and Fakundiny (1970) hypothesized that a

major belt of deformation extended N60W through central Honduras and was produced by a major wrench fault in the basement, with the Mesozoic cover responding to transcurrent shear (Fig. 6). Emmet (1983) speculated that this feature was rejuvenated in the Tertiary as a dextral shear zone produced by east–west plate extension. However, the same style and intensity of structures is widespread on the Chortis block and it not restricted only to a northwest-trending belt through the earlier mapped areas. The same strain pattern that pervades the Mesozoic succession on the Chortis block could also be produced simply by regional north–south crustal compression as a result of plate motion at a large angle to the Motagua suture zone.

Cenozoic History

After the crustal collision and initial suturing of the Chortis and Maya blocks in the Late Cretaceous–early Tertiary, the Cenozoic history of the region has been dominated by the interaction of the western margin of the Caribbean Plate with both the adjacent North American and Cocos plates (Molnar and Sykes, 1969). In the first instance, sinistral transform motion between the North American and Caribbean plates has resulted in strike-slip displacements along the Polochic-Motagua fault zones (Muehlberger and Ritchie, 1975; Plafker, 1976). However, evidence of past displacements is ambiguous and the kinematic history of these faults is very controversial (Burkart, 1983; Anderson and others, 1985). In the second instance, oblique convergence with the Cocos Plate has resulted in the Quaternary development of an Andean-type volcanic front along the Pacific margin of the Chortis block–Caribbean Plate (Stoiber and Carr, 1973; Carr, 1984), and crustal extension with internal block rotation within the Chortis block (Burkart and Self, 1985). Aspects of all of these topics are discussed in greater detail in several other chapters of this volume (e.g., Carr and Stoiber; Donnelly and others; and Pindell and Barrett).

REFERENCES CITED

Anderson, T. H., 1969, Geology of the San Sebastian Huehuetenango quadrangle, Guatemala, Central America [Ph.D. thesis]: Austin, University of Texas, 217 p.
Anderson, T. H., and Schmidt, V. A., 1983, The evolution of Middle America and the Gulf of Mexico-Caribbean Sea during Mesozoic time: Geological Society of America Bulletin, v. 94, p. 941–966.
Anderson, T. H., Burkart, B., Clemons, R. E., Bohnenberger, O. H., and Blount, D. N., 1973, Geology of the western Altos Cuchumatanes, northwestern Guatemala: Geological Society of America Bulletin, v. 84, p. 805–826.
Anderson, T. H., Erdlac, R. J., and Sandstrom, M. A., 1985, Late Cretaceous allochthons and post-Cretaceous strike-slip displacement along the Cuilco–Chixoy–Polochic fault, Guatemala: Tectonics, v. 5, p. 453–475.
Arden, D. D., Jr., 1975, Geology of Jamaica and Nicaragua Rise, in Nairn, A.E.M., and Stehli, F. G., eds., The ocean basins and margins, Volume 3: New York, Plenum Press, p. 617–661.
Atwood, M. G., 1972, Geology of the Minas de Oro quadrangle, Honduras, Central America [M.A. thesis]: Middletown, Connecticut, Wesleyan University, 88 p.
Bateson, J. H., and Hall, I.H.S., 1971, Revised geologic nomenclature for pre-Cretaceous rocks of British Honduras: American Association of Petroleum Geologists Bulletin, v. 55, p. 529–530.
—— , 1977, The geology of the Maya Mountains, Belize: Institute of Geological Sciences, Overseas Memoir 3, 43 p.
Baxter, S., 1984, Léxico Estratigráfico de El Salvador: San Salvador, Superintendencia de Energía, CEL, 108 p.
Bertrand, J., and Sarp, H., 1976, Sur la présence de vuagnatite dans un gabbro ophiolitique du Guatémala: Bulletin Suisse de Minéralogie et Pétrographie, v. 56, p. 540–544.
Bertrand, J., and Vuagnat, M., 1975, Sur la présence de basaltes en coussins dans la zone ophiolitique méridionale del la Cordillère centrale du Guatémala: Bulletin Suisse de Minéralogie et Pétrographie, v. 55, p. 136–142.
—— , 1976, Etude pétrographique de diverses ultrabasites ophiolitiques du Guatémala et leur inclusions: Bulletin Suisse de Minéralogie et Pétrographie, v. 56, p. 527–540.
—— , 1977, Données chimiques diverses sur des ophiolites du Guatémala: Bulletin Suisse de Minéralogie et Pétrographie, v. 57, p. 466–483.
—— , 1980, Inclusions in the serpentine melange of the Motagua fault zone, Guatemala: Archives de Science (Genève), v. 33, p. 321–335.
Bertrand, J., Delaloye, M., Fontignie, D., and Vuagnat, M., 1980, Ages (K–Ar) sur diverses ophiolites et roches associées de la Cordillére Centrale du Guatémala: Bulletin Suisse de Minéralogie et Pétrographie, v. 60, p. 405–412.
Bishop, W. F., 1980, Petroleum geology of northern Central America: Journal of Petroleum Geology, v. 3, p. 3–59.
Blair, T. C., 1981, Alluvial fan deposits of the Todos Santos Formation of central Chiapas, Mexico [M.S. thesis]: Arlington, University of Texas at Arlington, 134 p.
Blount, D. N., and Moore, C. H., Jr., 1969, Depositional and non-depositional carbonate breccias, Chiantla quadrangle, Guatemala: Geological Society of America Bulletin, v. 80, p. 429–442.
Bohnenberger, O. H., 1966, Nomenclatura de las capas Santa rosa en Guatemala: Publicaciones Geológicas del ICAITI (Guatemala) no. 1, p. 47–51.
Bonis, S. B., 1967, Geologic reconnaissance of the Alta Verapaz fold belt, Guatemala [Ph.D. dissertation]: Baton Rouge, Louisiana State University, 146 p.
Bonis, S., Bohnenberger, O., and Dengo, G., 1970, Mapa geológico de la Repúplica de Guatemala: Instituto Geográfico Nacional, Guatemala, four sheets, scale 1:500,000.
Bosc, E., 1971, Geology of the San Agustín Acasaguastlán quadrangle and northeastern part of the El Progreso quadrangle [Ph.D. thesis]: Houston, Texas, Rice University, 131 p.
Bucknam, R. C., Plafker, G., and Sharp, R. V., 1978, Fault movement (afterslip) following the Guatemala earthquake of February 4, 1976: Geology, v. 6, p. 170–173.
Burkart, B., 1965, Geology of the Esquipulas, Chanmagua, and Cerro Montecristo quadrangles, southeastern Guatemala [Ph.D. thesis]: Houston, Texas, Rice University, 121 p.
—— , 1978, Offset across the Polochic fault of Guatemala and Chiapas, Mexico: Geology, v. 6, p. 328–332.
—— , 1983, Neogene North American-Caribbean plate boundary across northern Central America: Offset along the Polochic fault: Tectonophysics, v. 99, p. 251–270.
Burkart, B., and Moreno, G., 1983, North American-Caribbean plate boundary in southern Chiapas, Mexico: Further evidence of Neogene activity [abs.]: Programa Conferencia Geológica del Caribe (Cartagena), 10th, p. 28.
Burkart, B., and Self, B., 1985, Extension and rotation of crustal blocks in northern Central America and its effect upon the volcanic arc: Geology, v. 13,

p. 22–26.

Burkart, B., Clemons, R. E., and Crane, D. C., 1973, Mesozoic and Cenozoic stratigraphy of southeastern Guatemala: American Association of Petroleum Geologists Bulletin, v. 57, p. 63–73.

Burke, K., Cooper, C., Dewey, J. F., Mann, P., and Pindell, J. L., 1984, Caribbean tectonics and relative plate motions: Geological Society of America Memoir 162, p. 31–63.

Carey, S. W., editor, 1958, Continental Drift—A symposium: Hobart, Australia, University of Tasmania, 375 p.

Carpenter, R. H., 1954, Geology and ore deposits of the Rosario mining district and San Juancito Mountains, Honduras, Central America: Geological Society America Bulletin, v. 65, p. 23–38.

Carr, M. J., 1984, Symmetrical and segmented variation of physical and geochemical characteristcs of the Central American volcanic front: Journal of Volcanology and Geothermal Research, v. 20, p. 231–252.

Cepek, P., 1975, Die Kreide-Coccolithen aus der Referenz-Lokalitat der Sepur-Folge bei Lanquin in Guatemala: Geologisch Jahrbuch, v. 14, p. 87–109.

Clemons, R. E., 1966, Geology of the Chiquimula quadrangle, Guatemala Central America [Ph.D. thesis]: Austin, University of Texas, 123 p.

——, 1969, Geologic history of the Chiquimula region, Guatemala: Publicaciones Geológicas del ICAITI, no. 2, p. 72–75.

Clemons, R. E., Anderson, T. H. Bohnenberger, O. H., and Burkart, B., 1974, Stratigraphic nomenclature of recognized Paleozoic and Mesozoic rocks of western Guatemala: American Association of Petroleum Geologists Bulletin, v. 58, p. 313–320.

Clemons, R. E., and Long, L. E., 1971, Petrologic and Rb-Sr isotopic study of the Chiquimula pluton, southeastern Guatemala: Geological Society of America Bulletin, v. 82, p. 2729–2740.

Collins, E. M., and Kesler, S. E., 1969, High temperature tungsten-antimony mineralization, Guatemala: Mineralium Deposita, v. 4, p. 65–71.

Crane, D. C., 1965, Geology of the Jocotán and Timushán quadrangles, southeastern Guatemala [Ph.D. thesis]: Houston, Texas, Rice University, 85 p.

Curran, D. W., 1980, Geology of the Siguatepeque quadrangle, Honduras, Central America [M.S. thesis]: Binghamton, State University of New York at Binghamton, 194 p.

Dawe, S. E., 1984, The geology of the Mountain Pine Ridge area and the relation of the Mountain Pine Ridge granite to the late Paleozoic and early Mesozoic geological history, Belize, Central America [M.S. thesis]: Binghamton, State University of New York, 52 p.

Deaton, B. C., 1982, Relationship of the Colotenango Conglomerate of Guatemala to the motion of the Polochic fault during the Tertiary [M.S. thesis]: Arlington, University of Texas, 97 p.

Deaton, B. C., and Burkart, B., 1984a, Time of sinistral slip along the Polochic fault of Guatemala: Tectonophysics, v. 102, p. 297–313.

——, 1984b, K-Ar ages of samples from the Subinal Formation and Colotenango beds, Guatemala: Isochron/West, no. 39, p. 19–20.

de Boer, J., 1979, The outer arc of the Costa Rican orogen, (oceanic basement complexes of the Nicoya and Santa Elena Peninsulas): Tectonophysics, v. 56, p. 221–259.

Delevoryas, T., and Srivastava, S. C., 1981, Jurassic plants from the Department of Francisco Morazán, central Honduras: Review of Palaeobotany and Palynology, v. 34, p. 345–357.

del Guidice, D., 1960, Apuntes sobre la geología del Departamento de Nueva Segovia: Managua, Nicaragua, Boletín del Servicio Geológico Nacional, no. 4, p. 17–37.

Dengo, C., 1982, Structural analysis of the Polochic fault zone in western Guatemala, Central America [Ph.D. thesis]: College Station, Texas A & M University, 295 p.

Dengo, G., 1967, Geological structure of Central America: Studies in tropical oceanography, no. 5 (Proceedings, International Conference on Tropical Oceanography): University of Miami, Florida, p. 56–73.

——, 1968, Relación de las serpentinitas con la tectónica de América Central: Simposio Panamericano del Manto Superior (Mexico), group 2: p. 23–28.

——, 1969, Problems of tectonic relations between Central America and the Caribbean: Transactions of the Gulf Coast Association of Geological Societies, v. 29, p. 311–320.

——, 1972, Review of Caribbean serpentinites and their tectonic implications: Geological Society of America Memoir 132, p. 303–312.

——, 1983, Informe preliminar de la geología regional de la cuenca media del Río Usumacinta, Guatemala y México: República de Guatemala, Instituto Nacional de Electrificación (INDE), 48 p.

——, 1985, Mid America; tectonic setting for the Pacific margin from southern Mexico to northwestern Colombia, in Nairn, A.E.M., and Stehli, F. G., eds., The ocean basins and margins, Volume 7: New York, Plenum Press, p. 123–180.

Dengo, G., and Bohnenberger, O. H., 1969, Structural development of northern Central America: American Association of Petroleum Geologists Memoir 11, p. 203–220.

Dillon, W. P., and Vedder, J. G., 1973, Structure and development of the continental margin of British Honduras: Geological Society of America Bulletin, v. 84, p. 2713–2732.

Dixon, C. G., 1956 (given also as 1955 or 1957), Geology of southern British Honduras, with notes on adjacent areas: Belize, Government Printing Office, 85 p.

Dollfus, A., and de Montserrat, E., 1868, Voyage géologique dans les Republiques de Guatémala et de Salvador: Paris, Mission Scientifique au Mexique et dans l'Amérique Centrale, 539 p.

Donnelly, T. W., Crane, D., and Burkart, B., 1968, Geologic history of the landward extension of the Bartlett Trough—Preliminary notes: Transactions, 4th Caribbean Geological Conference (Trinidad), p. 225–228.

Druecker, M. D., 1978, The geology of the Bladen Volcanic Series, southern Maya Mountains, Belize, Central America [M.S. thesis]: Golden, Colorado School of Mines, 73 p.

Dupré, E. R., 1970, Geology of the Zambrano quadrangle, Honduras [M.S. thesis]: Austin, University of Texas, 128 p.

Dürr, F., and Stober, G., 1956, Sucesión normal de los Estratos de Metapán: Anales del Servicio Geológico Nacional de El Salvador, Boletín 2, p. 44–54.

Edgar, N. T., Ewing, J. I., and Hennion, J., 1971, Seismic refraction and reflection in the Caribbean Sea: American Association of Petroleum Geologists Bulletin, v. 55, p. 833–970.

Elvir, R., 1974, Mapa geológico de la República de Honduras 1:500,000: Insituto Geográfico Nacional, Tegucigalpa, Honduras, two sheets.

Emmet, P. A., 1983, Geology of the Agalteca quadrangle, Honduras, Central America [M.S. thesis]: Austin, University of Texas, 201 p.

Engels, B., 1964, Geologische problematik und strukturanalyse Nikaraguas: Geologischen Rundschau, bd. 54, p. 758–795.

Everett, J. R., 1970, Geology of the Comayagua quadrangle, Honduras, Central America [Ph.D. thesis]: Austin, University of Texas, 152 p.

Fakundiny, R. H., 1970, Geology of the El Rosario quadrangle, Honduras, Central America [Ph.D. thesis]: Austin, University of Texas, 234 p.

Fakundiny, R. H., and Everett, J. R., 1976, Re-examination of the stratigraphy of the El Rosario and Comayagua quadrangles, Honduras: Publicaciones Geológicas del ICAITI, Guatemala, no. 5, p. 31–42.

Finch, R. C., 1972, Geology of the San Pedro Zacapa quadrangle, Honduras [Ph.D. thesis]: Austin, University of Texas, 238 p.

——, 1981, Mesozoic stratigraphy of central Honduras: American Association of Petroleum Geologists Bulletin, v. 65, p. 1320–1333.

Forth, D. R., 1971, Structure and stratigraphy of the Sacapulas quadrangle, Guatemala, with particular emphasis on Paleozoic rocks [M.S. thesis]: Baton Rouge, Louisiana State University, 113 p.

Foshag, W. F., 1954, Estudios mineralógicos sobre el jade de Guatemala: Antropología e Historia de Guatemala (Publicación de IDAEH, Guatemala), v. 6, no. 1, p. 1–47.

Foye, W. G., 1918, Notes on a collection of rocks from Honduras, central America: Journal of Geology, v. 26, p. 524–531.

Freeland, G., and Dietz, R., 1971, Plate tectonic evolution of the Caribbean-Gulf of Mexico region: Nature, v. 232, p. 20–23.

Fritzgartner, R., 1891, Kaleidoscopic views of Honduras: Tegucigalpa, Honduras

Mining Journal, nos. 6–8.

Garayar, J., and Viramonte, J., 1971, Sobre el hallazgo de peridotitas en Nicaragua: Resumenes de III Reunión de Geólogos de America Central, San José, Costa Rica, p. 24–25.

Gomberg, D. M., Banks, P. O., and McBirney, A. R., 1968, Guatemala: Preliminary zircon ages from central cordillera: Science, v. 162, p. 121–122.

Gose, W. A., 1985, Caribbean tectonics from a paleomagnetic perspective, *in* Stehli, F. G., and Webb, S. D., eds., The great American biotic interchange: New York, Plenum Press, p. 285–301.

Gose, W. A., and Swartz, D. K., 1977, Paleomagnetic results from Cretaceous sediments in Honduras: Tectonic implications: Geology, v. 5, p. 505–508.

Helwig, J., 1975, Tectonic evolution of the southern continental margin of North America from a Paleozoic perspective, *in* Nairn, A.E.M., and Stehli, F. G., eds., The Gulf of Mexico and Caribbean, v. 3: New York, Plenum Press, p. 243–255.

Hernández García, R., 1973, Paleografía del Paleozóico de Chiapas, Mexico: Boletín Asociación Mexicana de Geólogos Petroleros, v. 25, p. 79–113.

Hess, H. H., and Maxwell, J. C., 1953, Caribbean research project: Geological Society of America Bulletin, v. 64, p. 1–6.

Hirschmann, T. S., 1963, Reconnaissance geology and stratigraphy of the Subinal Formation (Tertiary) of the El Progreso area, Guatemala, C.A. [M.S. thesis]: Bloomington, Indiana University, 66 p.

Holcombe, T. L., Vogt, P. R., Matthews, J. E., and Murchison, R. R., 1973, Evidence for sea-floor spreading in the Cayman Trough: Earth and Planetary Science Letters, v. 20, p. 357–371.

Horne, G. S., Atwood, M. G., and King, A. P., 1974, Stratigraphy, sedimentology, and paleoenvironment of Esquias Formation of Honduras: American Association of Petroleum Geologists Bulletin, v. 60, p. 176–188.

Horne, G. S., Clark, G. S., and Pushkar, P., 1976a, Pre-Cretaceous rocks of northwestern Honduras: Basement terrane in Sierra de Omoa: American Association of Petroleum Geologists Bulletin, v. 60, p. 566–583.

Horne, G. S., Pushkar, P., and Shafiqullah, M., 1976b, Laramide plutons on the landward continuation of the Bonacca ridge, northern Honduras: Transactions, 7th Conférence Géologique des Caraïbes, Guadeloupe, p. 383–588.

—— , 1976c, Preliminary K-Ar dates from the Laramide series of central Honduras: Publicaciones Geológicas del ICAITI, no. 5, p. 91–98.

Ito, E., and Anderson, A. T., Jr., 1983, Submarine metamorphism of gabbros from the mid-Cayman Rise: Petrographic and mineralogic constraints on hydrothermal processes at slow-spreading ridges: Contributions to Mineralogy and Petrology, v. 82, p. 371–388.

Iturralde-Vinent, M. A., 1975, Problems in application of modern tectonic hypotheses to Cuba and adjacent region: American Association of Petroleum Geologists Bulletin, v. 59, p. 838–855.

Johnson, K. R., 1984, Geology of the Gualán and southern Sierra de las Minas quadrangles, Guatemala [Ph.D. thesis]: Binghamton, State University of New York at Binghamton, 300 p.

Kesler, S. E., 1971, Nature of ancestral orogenic zone in nuclear Central America: American Association of Petroleum Geologists Bulletin, v. 55, p. 2116–2129.

Kesler, S. E., and Ascarrunz-K., R., 1973, Lead-zinc mineralization in carbonate rocks, central Guatemala: Economic Geology, v. 68, p. 1263–1274.

Kesler, S. E., Bateson, J. H., Josey, W. L., Cramer, G. H., and Simmons, W. A., 1971, Mesoscopic structural homogeneity of Maya Series and Macal Series, Mountain Pine Ridge, British Honduras: American Association of Petroleum Geologists Bulletin, v. 55, p. 97–103.

Kesler, S. E., Josey, W. L., and Collins, E. M., 1970, Basement rocks of western nuclear Central America: The western Chuacús Group, Guatemala: Geological society of America Bulletin, v. 81, p. 3307–3322.

Kesler, S. E., Kienle, C. F., and Bateson, J. H., 1974, Tectonic significance of intrusive rocks in the Maya Mountains, British Honduras: Geological Society of America Bulletin, v. 85, p. 549–552.

King, A. P., 1972, Geology of the Talanga and Cedros quadrangles, Honduras, Central America: Tegucigalpa, Departamento de Geología e Hidrografía, Instituto Geográfico Nacional de Honduras, Open-File Report, 68 p.

Kling, S. A., 1960, Permian fusilinids from Guatemala: Journal of Paleontology,

v. 34, p. 637–655.

Knowlton, F. W., 1918, Relations between the Mesozoic floras of North and South America: Geological Society of America Bulletin, v. 29, p. 607–614.

Lawrence, D. P., 1975, Petrology and structural geology of the Sanarate–El Progreso area, Guatemala [Ph.D. thesis]: Binghamton, State University of New York at Binghamton, 255 p.

—— , 1976, Tectonic implications of the geochemistry and petrology of the El Tambor Formation: Probable oceanic crust in central Guatemala: Geological Society of America Abstracts with Programs, v. 8, p. 973–974.

Litke, G. R., 1975, The stratigraphy and sedimentation of the Barillas quadrangle, Department of Huehuetenango, Guatemala, C.A. [M.S. thesis]: Arlington, University of Texas, 196 p.

López-Ramos, E., 1975, Geological summary of the Yucatan Peninsula, *in* Nairn, A.E.M., and Stehli, F. G., eds., The Ocean Basins and Margins, v. 3: New York, Plenum Press, p. 257–282.

López-Ramos, E., 1981, Geología de México: Volume III: Mexico City, 446 p. (published privately).

Malcolm, F. L., 1980, Microstructures of the Cayman Trough gabbros: Journal of Geology, v. 89, p. 657–688.

Malfait, B. T., and Dinkelman, M. G., 1972, Circum-Caribbean tectonic and igneous activity and evolution of the Caribbean plate: Geological Society of America Bulletin, v. 83, p. 251–272.

Marcus, D. L., 1974, Igneous and metamorphic petrology of Barillas quadrangle, northwestern Guatemala [M.S. thesis]: Arlington, University of Texas, 117 p.

McBirney, A. R., 1963, Geology of a part of the central Guatemalan Cordillera: University of California Publications in Geological Sciences, v. 38, p. 177–242.

McBirney, A. R., and Bass, M. N., 1969a, Structural relations of pre-Mesozoic rocks of northern Central America: American Associaton of Petroleum Geologists Memoir 11, p. 269–280.

—— , 1969b, Geology of Bay Islands, Gulf of Honduras: American Association of Petroleum Geologists Memoir 11, p. 229–243.

McBirney, A. R., and Williams, H., 1965, Volcanic geology of Nicaragua: University of California Publications in Geological Sciences, v. 55, 65 p.

McBirney, A. R., Aoki, K. I., and Bass, M., 1967, Eclogite and jadeite from the Motagua fault zone, Guatemala: American Mineralogist, v. 52, p. 908–918.

Meyer, J. D., 1967, Geology of the Ahuachapán area, western El Salvador, Central America: New Orleans, Tulane University, Tulane Studies in Geology, v. 5, p. 195–215.

Meyerhoff, A. A., and Meyerhoff, H. A., 1972, Continental drift; IV: The Caribbean "Plate": Journal of Geology, v. 80, p. 34–60.

Mills, R. A., and Hugh, K. E., 1974, Reconnaissance geologic map of Mosquitía region, Honduras and Nicaragua Caribbean coasts: American Association of Petroleum Geologists Bulletin, v. 58, p. 189–207.

Mills, R. A., Hugh, K. E., Feray, D. E., and Swolfs, H. C., 1967, Mesozoic stratigraphy of Honduras: American Association of Petroleum Geologists Bulletin, v. 51, p. 1711–1786.

Molnar, P., and Sykes, L. R., 1969, Tectonics of the Caribbean and Middle America regions from focal mechanisms and seismicity: Geological Society of America Bulletin, v. 80, p. 1639–1684.

Muehlberger, W. R., and Ritchie, A. W., 1975, Caribbean-American plate boundary in Guatemala and southern Mexico as seen on Skylab IV orbital photography: Geology, v. 3, p. 232–235.

Muller, P. D., 1979, Geology of the Los Amates quadrangle and vicinity, Guatemala, Central America [Ph.D. thesis]: Binghamton, State University of New York at Binghamton, 326 p.

Mullerreid, F.K.G., 1942a, The Mesozoic of Mexico and Central America: Proceedings of 8th American Science Congress, Geological Sciences, v. 4, p. 125–147.

—— , 1942b, Contribution to the geology of northwestern Central America: Proceedings of 8th American Science Congress, Geological Sciences, v. 4, p. 469–482.

Nelson, J. R., 1984, Sedimentology and stratigraphy of the late Paleozoic rocks of the Mountain Pine Ridge, Belize [Masters project]: Binghamton, State University of New York at Binghamton, 52 p.

Newberry, J. S., 1888, Rhaetic plants from Honduras: American Journal of Science, v. 36, p. 342–351.

Newcomb, W. E., 1975, Geology, structure, and metamorphism of the Chuacús Group, Río Hondo quadrangle and vicinity, Guatemala [Ph.D. thesis]: Binghamton, State University of New York, 115 p.

—— , 1978, Retrograde cataclastic gneiss north of Motagua fault zone, east-central Guatemala: Geologie en Mijnbouw, v. 57, p. 271–276.

Nicolaus, H. J., 1971, Geologische Übersichtskarte, 1,125,000; Baja Verapaz und Südteil der Alta Verapaz (Guatemala): Hannover, Bundesanstalt für Bodenforschung.

Ortega-Gutiérrez, F., 1978, Estratigrafia del complejo de Acatlán en las Mixteca Baja, Estados de Pueblo y Oaxaca: Universidad Nacional Autónoma de México, Instituto Geológico Revista, v. 2, p. 112–131.

Ortega-Gutiérrez, F., and Anderson, T. H., 1977, Lithologies and geochronology of the Precambrian craton of southern Mexico: Geological Society of America Abstracts with Programs, v. 9, p. 1121–1122.

Paulsen, S., and Koch, W., 1980, Die marine Kreide in Teilen der Alta Verapaz und der Baja Verapaz, Guatemala: Geologischen Jahrbuch, ser. B, v. 38, p. 3–87.

Petersen, E. U., and Zantop, M., 1980, The Oxec deposit, Guatemala: An ophiolite copper occurrence: Economic Geology, v. 75, p. 1053–1065.

Pindell, J., and Dewey, J. P., 1982, Permo–Triassic reconstruction of western Pangea and the evolution of the Gulf of Mexico/Caribbean region: Tectonics, v. 1, p. 179–211.

Plafker, G., 1976, Tectonic aspects of the Guatemalan earthquake of 4 February 1976: Science, v. 193, p. 1201–1208.

Powers, S., 1918, Notes on the geology of eastern Guatemala and northwestern Spanish Honduras: Journal of Geology, v. 26, p. 507–523.

Pushkar, P., McBirney, A. R., and Kudo, A. M., 1972, The isotopic composition of strontium in Central American ignimbrites: Bulletin Volcanologique, v. 35, p. 265–294.

Rao, R. P., 1982, Exploration in Belize gains momentum: Oil and Gas Journal, 27 September, p. 308–318.

Reeves, T. K., 1967, Geology of the southern half of the El Progreso quadrangle, El Progreso, Guatemala [M.S. thesis]: Houston, Texas, Rice University, 87 p.

Reynolds, J. H., 1977, Tertiary volcanic stratigraphy of northern Central America [M.S. thesis]: Hanover, New Hampshire, Dartmouth College, 88 p.

—— , 1980, Late Tertiary volcanic stratigraphy of northern Central America: Bulletin Volcanologique, v. 43, p. 601–608.

Richards, H. G., 1963, Stratigraphy of earliest Mesozoic sediments in southeastern Mexico and western Guatemala: American Association of Petroleum Geologists Bulletin, v. 47, p. 1861–1870.

Ritchie, A. W., and Finch, R. C., 1985, Widespread Jurassic strata on the Chortis block of the Caribbean plate: Geological Society of America Abstracts with Programs, v. 17, p. 700–701.

Ritchie, A. W., and McDowell, F. W., 1979, K–Ar ages of plutonic and volcanic rocks from the volcanic highlands of Guatemala northwest of Guatemala City: Isochron/West, no. 25, p. 3–4.

Roberts, R. J., and Irving, E. M., 1957, Mineral deposits of Central America: U.S. Geological Survey Bulletin 1034, 205 p.

Rodríguez, T. R., 1970, Geología metamórfica del area de Acatalán, Estado de Puebla: Sociedad Geológica Mexicana, Libra Guía de Excursión México–Oaxaca, p. 51–54.

Roper, P. J., 1976, Lithologic subdivisions of the Chuacús Group and their structural significance in the southwestern end of the Sierras las Minas Range, Guatemala: Transactions, Conférence Géologique des Caraïbes, Guadeloupe, p. 589–594.

—— , 1978, Stratigraphy of the Chuacús Group on the south side of the Sierra las Minas Range, Guatemala: Geologie en Mijnbouw, v. 57, p. 309–313.

Rosenfeld, J. H., 1981, Geology of the western Sierra de Santa Cruz, Guatemala, Central America: An ophiolite sequence [Ph.D. thesis]: Binghamton, State University of New York at Binghamton, 315 p.

Ross, C. A., 1962, Permian foraminifera from British Honduras: Paleontology,

v. 5, p. 297–306.

—— , 1979, Late Paleozoic collision of North and South America: Geology, v. 7, p. 41–44.

Sapper, K. T., 1894, Grundzuge del physikalischen geographie von Guatemaka: Petermann's Mitteilungen, Erg., v. 24, 59 p.

—— , 1899, Über Gebirgsbau und Boden des nördlichen Mittelamerika: Peter-manns Mitteilungen, Gotha, v. 27, 119 p.

—— , 1905, Über Gebirgsbau und Boden des Südlichen Mittelamerika: Peter-mann's Mitteilungen, Erg., v. 32, 82 p.

—— , 1937, Mittelamerika: Handbuch der Regionalen Geologie: Heidelberg, Steinman und Wilckens, v. 8, 4a, 160 p.

Schuchert, C., 1935, Historical geology of the Antillean–Caribbean region: New York, John Wiley, 811 p.

Schwartz, D. P., 1976, Geology of the Zacapa quadrangle and vicinity, Guatemala [Ph.D. thesis]: Binghamton, State University of New York at Binghamton, 179 p.

Schwartz, D. P., Cluft, L., and Donnelly, T. W., 1979, Quaternary faulting along the Caribbean–North American plate boundary in Central America: Tectonophysics, v. 52, p. 431–445.

Silva, Z.C.G., 1970, Origin of albitites from eastern Guatemala: Boletim dos Servicos de Geologia e Minas, Brazil, no. 22, p. 23–32.

Simonson, B. M., 1977, Geology of the El Porvenir quadrangle, Honduras, Central America: Tegucigalpa, Instituto Geográfico Nacional, Departamento de Geología e Hidrografía, Open-File Report, 84 p.

Steele, D. R., 1982, Physical stratigraphy and petrology of the Cretaceous Sierra Madre Limestone, west-central Chiapas, Mexico [M.S. thesis]: Arlington, University of Texas, 174 p.

Stirton, R. A., and Gealey, W. K., 1949, Reconnaissance of the geology and vertebrate paleontology of El Salvador, Central America: Geological Society of America Bulletin, v. 60, p. 1731–1753.

Stoiber, R. E., and Carr, M. J., 1973, Quaternary volcanic and tectonic segmentation of Central America: Bulletin Volcanologique, v. 37, p. 304–325.

Sutter, J. F., 1979, Late Cretaceous collisional tectonics along the Motagua fault zone, Guatemala: Geological Society of America Abstracts with Programs, v. 11, p. 525–526.

Sykes, L. R., McCann, W. R., and Kafka, A. L., 1982, Motion of Caribbean plate during last 7 million years and implications for earlier movements: Journal of Geophysical Research, v. 87, p. 10656–10676.

Taber, S., 1922, The great fault troughs of the Antilles: Journal of Geology, v. 30, p. 89–114.

Termer, F., 1932, Geologie von Nordwestguatemala: Berlin, Zeitschrift Gesselschaft Erdkunde, no. 7–8, p. 240–248.

Uchupi, E., 1972, Eastern Yucatan continental margin and western Caribbean tectonics: American Association of Petroleum Geologists Bulletin, v. 57, p. 1075–1085.

UNDP, 1972, Investigación de los recursos minerales en áreas seleccionadas, Honduras: Geología de la región noroeste de Honduras: New York, United Nations Development Program, Informe Tecnico DP/SF/UN/96, 28 p.

van den Bold, W. A., 1969, Estado de nuestro conocimiento de los ostracodos fosiles de América Central: Publicaciones Geológicas del ICAITI (Guatemala), no. 2, p. 51–53.

van den Boom, G., 1972, Petrofazielle Gliederung des metamorphen Grundgebirges in der Sierra de Chuacus, Guatemala: Geologischen Jahrbuch, Bieheft 122, p. 5–49.

Van der Voo, R., Mauk, F. J., and French, R. B., 1976, Permian–Triassic continental configurations and the origin of the Gulf of Mexico: Geology, v. 4, p. 177–180.

Viniegra, O. F., 1971, Age and evolution of salt basins of southeastern Mexico: American Association of Petroleum Geologists Bulletin, v. 55, p. 478–494.

Vinson, G. L., 1962, Upper Cretaceous and Tertiary stratigraphy of Guatemala: American Association of Petroleum Geologists Bulletin, v. 46, p. 425–456.

Wadge, G., and Burke, K., 1983, Neogene Caribbean plate rotation and associated Central American tectonic evolution: Tectonics, v. 2, p. 633–643.

Waite, L. E., 1983, Biostratigraphy and paleoenvironmental analysis of the Sierra

Madre Limestone (Cretaceous), Chiapas, southern Mexico [M.S. thesis]: Arlington, University of Texas, 192 p.

Walper, J. L., 1960, Geology of the Cobán-Purulhá area, Alta Verapaz, Guatemala: American Association of Petroleum Geologists Bulletin, v. 44, p. 1273–1315.

Walper, J. L., and Rowett, C. L., 1972, Plate tectonics and the origin of the Caribbean Sea and Gulf of Mexico: Transactions of the Gulf Coast Association of Geological Societies, v. 22, p. 105–116.

Weaver, C. E., 1942, A general summary of the Mesozoic of South America and Central America: Proceedings, 8th American Scientific Congress, Geological Sciences, v. 4, p. 179–180.

Weber, H. S., 1979, On the lithology and stratigraphy of the "Estratos de Metapán" in the Republic of El Salvador, Central America: Geologischen Jahrbuch, v. 37, p. 31–54.

Weyl, R., 1961, Die Geologie Mittelamerikas: Berlin, Gebrüder Borntraeger, 226 p.

—— , 1980, Geology of Central America: Berlin, Gebrüder Borntraeger, 371 p.

Wiesemann, G., 1975, Remarks on the geologic structure of the Republic of El Salvador: University of Hamburg, Mitteilungen Geologischen und Palaeontologischen Institut, v. 44, p. 557–574.

Williams, H., 1960, Volcanic history of the Guatemala Highlands: University of California Publications in Geological Sciences, v. 38, p. 1–86.

Williams, H., and McBirney, A. R., 1969, Volcanic history of Honduras: University of California Publications in Geological Sciences, v. 85, 101 p.

Williams, H., McBirney, A. R., and Dengo, G., 1964, Geologic reconnaissance of southeastern Guatemala: University of California Publications in Geological Sciences, v. 50, 56 p.

Wilson, H. H., 1974, Cretaceous sedimentation and orogeny in nuclear Central America: American Association of Petroleum Geologists Bulletin, v. 58, p. 1348–1396.

—— , 1976, Guidebook for AAPG 1976 post-convention field trip to Guatemala, May 27th to 31st: New Orleans Geological Society, v. 5, p. 4.

Wilson, H. H., Meyerhoff, A. A., MacDonald, W. D., and Gose, W. A., 1978,

Comments and reply *on* "Paleomagnetic results from Cretaceous sediments in Honduras: Tectonic implications": Geology, v. 6, p. 440–447.

Zoppis Bracci, L., 1957, Estudio geológico de la región de Palacagüina y su depósito de antimonio: Managua, Boletín del Servicio Geológico Nacional de Nicaragua, no. 1, p. 29–34.

Zoppis Bracci, L., and del Guidice, D., 1958, Un reconocimiento geológico del Río Bocay y parte del Río Coco: Managua, Boletín del Servicio Geológico Nacional de Nicaragua, no. 2, p. 81–112.

—— , 1960, Reconocimiento geológico del Valle de Punta Gorda: Managua, Boletín del Servicio Geológico Nacional de Nicaragua, no. 4, p. 61–83.

—— , 1961, Estudio preliminar de las mineralizaciones de túngsteno y molíbdeno de Marvelizo, Departamento de Nueva Segovia: Managua, Boletín del Servicio Geológico Nacional de Nicaragua, no. 5, p. 31–61.

Zúniga Izagirre, M. A., 1975, Gravity and magnetic survey of the Sula Valley, Honduras, Central America [Ph.D. thesis]: Austin, University of Texas, 155 p.

MANUSCRIPT ACCEPTED BY THE SOCIETY DECEMBER 19, 1986

ACKNOWLEDGMENTS

The assistance of several people who provided valuable unpublished information is gratefully acknowledged. Josh Rosenfeld, Jim Pindell, and R. P. Rao provided well information. Emile Pessagno, W. Woodring, Merlynd Nestell, H. J. MacGillavry, J. E. van Hinte, J. A. Broekman, and P. Marks provided valuable biostratigraphic information. John Sutter and Paul Pushkar provided unpublished radiometric data. T. Donnelly is grateful to all of his former students and present colleagues who have provided so many stimulating discussions of Guatemala and Belize geology. Geological investigations in Guatemala have been supported by the Instituto Geográfico Nacional, whose chief geologist, Oscar Salazar, has provided extensive support. The National Science Foundation has supported most of these studies. We also thank W. Muehlburger and B. Burkart for extended comments on an earlier version of this manuscript.

NOTE ADDED IN PROOF

A further examination of microfossils of the Las Escobas beds of Permian age of eastern Guatemala by M. Nestell has added the foraminiferal genera *Stafella* (a fusuline) and *Glomospira* to the brief faunal list. Most significantly, Nestell (personal communication, 1989) now believes the age of the beds to be Leonardian or younger. This age is very close to that of the overlying Chochal limestone, which has been dated elsewhere in eastern Guatemala as Leonardian to Guadalupian, and in western Guatemala as Wolfcampian to Leonardian. The angular unconformity between the Las Escobas beds indicates a significant deformation whose age is now closely constrained.

There remains no satisfactory distant correlative of these beds. A. Pszczolkowski has shown me photographs of microfossils of Permian age found in pebbles within the San Cayetano Formation of Cuba. However, these appear to me to represent a different facies and fauna. Although they may eventually be shown to be related, such a correlation is not now apparent. Neither is there an obvious correlation with the Palmarito Formation of the Venezuelan Andes, although the gross lithologic resemblances are striking. McKee and others (1988) have described the lithic and stratigraphic evidence for a compressive deformation in northeastern Mexico extending from the late Carboniferous through the latest Guadalupian. The angular unconformity above the Las Ecobas beds appears to belong to the same orogenic event.

REFERENCE

McKee, J. W., Jones, N. W., and Anderson, T. H., 1988, Las Delicias basin; A record of late Paleozoic arc volcanism in northeastern Mexico: Geology, v. 16, p. 37–40.

The Geology of North America
Vol. H, The Caribbean region
The Geological Society of America, 1990

Chapter 4

*Geology and tectonic evolution of the northern Caribbean margin**

John F. Lewis
Geology Department, George Washington University, Washington, D.C. 20052
Grenville Draper
Geology Department, Florida International University, Miami, Florida 33199

INTRODUCTION

The northern Caribbean plate margin is a complex orogen that has developed since at least Jurassic time as a result of convergent and transcurrent tectonics. Early convergence produced an island-arc structure that was modified by Tertiary strike-slip movements. Many hypotheses have been proposed to explain the tectonic evolution of the region, but as our knowledge of the area has progressed, few have survived rigorous testing. Even today, the models based on modern theories of plate tectonics are still vigorously debated, and no single hypothesis has met with widespread acceptance.

In broad terms, the northern Caribbean margin is an east-west–trending, dissected and segmented ridge structure that separates the Caribbean basin from the American plate to the north. The modern margin is tectonically active and is characterized by intermediate crustal thicknesses, high seismicity, large Bouguer gravity and magnetic anomalies, late Cenozoic volcanic activity on central Hispaniola, and active oceanic volcanism in the Cayman trough spreading center.

Principal geographic features of the northern margin are shown on Plate 1. The ridge structure of the Greater Antilles rises above sea level as the four large islands of the Greater Antilles, namely Cuba, Hispaniola, Puerto Rico, and Jamaica. The Virgin Islands archipelago of about 100 islands forms the eastern extremity of the Greater Antilles, and is terminated to the east by the Anegada fault, which is a comparatively young feature (probably early Tertiary). Many consider that the eastern Greater An-

tilles formerly continued as a curved arc to the southeast, at least as far as Guadeloupe. For the purposes of this description, however, the islands southeast of St. Croix are considered to be part of the Lesser Antilles (Maury and others, this volume).

A deep depression, the Puerto Rico Trench, occurs north of Puerto Rico along the northeastern part of the Caribbean plate. This feature continues west to become the Bahama Channel, which separates Hispaniola and the northwest part of Cuba from the Bahama Platform.

The Cayman Trough forms the northwestern section of the present-day active-margin zone and separates the Nicaraguan Rise and Jamaica from the Cayman Ridge and Cuba. Most of Cuba is located well within the stable North American plate, but the southeastern extremity of Cuba is continuous with the Cayman Ridge and can therefore be considered a part of the active plate-boundary zone. Northwestern Cuba lies south of the Gulf of Mexico and the Bahama Platform and is separated from the Cayman Ridge and Cayman Trough by the Yucatan Basin. The Nicaraguan Rise is a very large structure forming the southern boundary to the Cayman Trough and connects the Greater Antilles to Central America. Jamaica is located at its northeast extremity and is connected by a broad ridge to the Southern Peninsula of Haiti.

The rocks of the northern margin of the Caribbean region were formed as a result of Mesozoic and Cenozoic tectonic activity. The sedimentary rocks were deposited in small and discontinuous basins of active tectonic zones and represent a wide range of depositional environments. The volcanic rocks are dominantly calc-alkaline, but the earlier stages of volcanism produced large volumes of spilite and keratophyre of the primitive island-arc series of Donnelly and Rogers (1978). Later in the evolution of the Greater Antilles, granitoid intrusions were emplaced when the volcanic-sedimentary rocks had accumulated to a considerable thickness. Restricted zones of Cretaceous volcanic-sedimen-

---

*With contributions by:
C. Bourdon, Département de Géotectonique, L'Université Pièrre et Marie Curie, Paris, France
C. Bowin, Department of Geology and Geophysics, Woods Hole Oceanographic Institution, Woods Hole, Massachusetts 02543
P. Mattson, Geology Department, Queens College, Flushing, New York 11367
F. Maurrasse, Geology Department, Florida International University, Miami, Florida 33199
F. Nagle, Geology Department, University of Miami, Miami, Florida 33124
G. Pardo, 906 Amberson Avenue, Pittsburgh, Pennsylvania 15232

Lewis, J. F., and Draper, G., 1990, Geology and tectonic evolution of the northern Caribbean margin, *in* Dengo, G., and Case, J. E., eds., The Caribbean region: Boulder, Colorado, Geological Society of America, The Geology of North America, v. H.

tary rocks were metamorphosed, producing metamorphic belts of dominantly greenstones, greenschists, and amphibolites, with some small areas of quartzofeldspathic schists. Subduction of oceanic floor created belts of blueschist and associated rocks. Ophiolites, representing latest Jurassic and Cretaceous oceanic crust, were emplaced at various localities from mid-Cretaceous to Paleogene time (Wadge and others, 1984). Subduction-related processes essentially ceased in the early Tertiary. Most of the Cenozoic (at least since post–middle Eocene) was a time of relative tectonic quiescence in many parts of the northern Caribbean, which allowed the accumulation of thick sequences of limestones that now rest unconformably over the Cretaceous and early Tertiary rocks.

Marine and seismic evidence indicates that present motion along the northern Caribbean plate is left-lateral strike-slip, which field evidence suggests has been the dominant movement since the middle Tertiary. Such large-scale movement was even postulated before the era of plate tectonics by Hess and Maxwell (1953), who based their hypothesis on the distribution of metamorphic rocks. Marine surveys and calculations of plate motion have led to estimates of as much as 1,400 km of east-west translation along the Cayman Trough, which suggests an average rate of movement between the Caribbean and North American plates of about 3 cm/yr since the early middle Eocene. A number of recent models have suggested that the overall displacement across the northern Caribbean was accommodated by movement on the boundary faults of individual elements (terranes?) within the plate-boundary zone.

Most of our present knowledge of the tectonic evolution of the northern plate-boundary zone of the Caribbean comes from studies of the geology of the islands. Although important similarities exist among the islands, each has its own unique geology and tectonic history. For this reason, the following description of the northern margin is described in terms of the geology of individual island segments. The final section of this chapter attempts to summarize present ideas of the tectonic history of the entire margin. Stratigraphic details have been kept to a minimum. Plate 5A gives summary stratigraphic charts for each island in the Greater Antilles.

CUBA

John F. Lewis

INTRODUCTION AND REGIONAL SETTING

Cuba is a Jurassic–Cretaceous–early Tertiary orogen whose constitution and evolution differs in many ways from the other islands of the Greater Antilles. Most of our knowledge of the geology of western, northern, and central Cuba stems from the work of oil company geologists during the early and mid-1950s. Much of this work remains unpublished, but several review papers published in the 1960s and early 1970s present good

summaries of the work accomplished up to that time (Furrazola-Bermúdez and others, 1964; Pushcharovskiy, 1967; Meyerhoff and Hatten, 1968; Khudoley, 1967a and b; Khudoley and Meyerhoff, 1971; Pardo, 1975; Mattson, 1974a). Since the 1960s, Cuban, Polish, and other Eastern European geologists have added significant contributions, particularly with respect to the stratigraphy, metamorphism, and structural and tectonic evolution of the island. New geologic and tectonic maps (Cuba, 1985a and b) at a scale of 1:500,000 have been published, and recent reviews of the geology of Cuba have been made by Cobiella (1984) and Iturralde-Vinent (1988). This section attempts to review and interpret the published information in light of modern tectonics and the regional geology of the Greater Antilles. Although Cuba now lies within the North American plate, the interpretation of its geology is vital to an understanding of the evolution of the northwestern part of the Caribbean plate.

Cuba essentially consists of two broad structural provinces that follow the elongation of the island and reflect its earlier pre–early Tertiary development (Figs. 1 and 2). In central Cuba, the northern province forms a zone along the southern margin of the Florida-Bahama platform and the northern coastal area of Cuba. This is the miogeosynclinal sedimentary province of many previous workers. The sedimentary rocks were deposited in environments ranging from a shallow-water continental platform in the north to a deep-marine (oceanic) environment in the south. The central/southern province, the eugeosyncline of many previous workers, consists essentially of a northern oceanic belt of ultramafic-mafic rocks (ophiolite associations) juxtaposed against a southern area of thick sequences of Cretaceous volcanic-arc rocks and sedimentary rocks intruded by granitoid rocks. Areas of complexly deformed metamorphic rocks are also exposed in the southern province. Volcanic rocks of Paleogene age occur in the southeast (Oriente province), and granitoid rocks of Paleocene age intrude these volcanic sequences.

GEOPHYSICAL FEATURES

Regional seismic profiles. The crustal structure of Cuba has been determined from regional seismic profiling by Scherbakova and others (1977, 1978, 1980) and Bovenko and others (1980, 1982). The thickness of crust beneath the Bahama platform in the north is about 30 to 36 km. A crustal profile across Cuba is included in Plate 3.

Gravity. Regional gravity anomaly maps of Cuba have been compiled by Soloviev and others, (1964), Ipatenko and Sashina (1971), Pardo (1975), Bowin (1976), and Case (1980). These data are included in the regional gravity anomaly map (Plate 7). The anomaly pattern follows the structural trend of the island and is generally positive; anomalies range from about –25 mgals to +50 mgals, with positive anomalies dominating.

Aeromagnetic anomaly maps of Cuba have been presented and discussed by Soloviev and others (1964) and Pardo (1975). A simplified compilation prepared by Case (1980) has been incorporated into the regional aeromagnetic map (Plate 6).

STRUCTURAL FEATURES AND STRATIGRAPHY

Figures 1 and 2 show most of the principal geologic and structural/tectonic features of Cuba. The geological and structural/tectonic maps of Cuba at a scale of 1:500,000 (Cuba, 1985a and b; Anon., 1978; Shein and others, 1984) allow an interpretation of the tectonic features and history of the region. Three principal structural/tectonic zones are distinguished on the tectonic map and represent the nature of both the basement rocks and the allochthonous cover (Fig. 3b). The crustal profiles in Figure 3 show the contrasting interpretations as to the deeper crustal structures below Cuba.

Most major faults in Cuba (Fig. 2; Cuba, 1985a) seem to be high angle, and some exhibit a strike-slip component. The faults separating the morphotectonic zones are assumed to be major thrust faults but appear to be relatively steep at the near surface, e.g., the Las Villas fault (Fig. 2), which dips either vertically or steeply southward.

Thrust and nappe structures, a characteristic feature of Cuban geology, were first demonstrated during the extensive oil exploration in the 1940s and 1950s, and recent investigations by Cuban, Russian, and particularly Polish geologists working in western and northern Cuba have added to the understanding of the nature of these thrust structures (Mossakovskiy and Albear, 1978). Mapping in the Sierra de los Organos and Sierra del Rosario, and detailed studies of drill cores from the Habana-Matanzas area, have shown a repeated alternation of thrust sheets composed essentially of ultramafic rocks (commonly including mélange units), volcanic rock sequences of Early Cretaceous age or older, and units of Campanian-Maastrichtian age termed "molasse." These thrust sheets tectonically overlie the "miogeosynclinal" Cretaceous carbonate sequences and, in places, Paleocene to middle Eocene clay-carbonate rocks.

Much of the basic Cuban stratigraphy as presently accepted was originally outlined by oil company geologists working in the 1940s and 1950s. Summaries of these studies are contained in Furrazola-Bermúdez and others (1964), Meyerhoff and Hatten (1968), Khudoley and Meyerhoff (1971), and Pardo (1975). More recent revisions are included in the detailed summaries of the presently accepted stratigraphy (Kusnetzov and others, 1977). The essential features of Cuban stratigraphy are summarized on Plate 5A.

STRUCTURAL/TECTONIC SEGMENTS AND ZONES

Based on its present-day topography, and geological and geophysical information, Cuba can be divided ideally into six areas or segments, each one having its own stratigraphic and structural character (Figs. 1 and 2; Pardo, 1975). These areas are structural highs or uplifted blocks and largely represent deformed pre–middle Eocene rocks surrounded by relatively thin and undisturbed deposits that range in age from late Eocene to Pleistocene.

For the purposes of this description, Cuba is divided into three major blocks (Fig. 2) following Meyerhoff and Hatten (1968): (1) the western block—the Pinar del Río province, including the Guaniguanico structural zone; (2) the central block, which occupies three-fourths of the island and is separated from the western block by the Pinar del Río fault; and (3) the eastern block—the Oriente province east of the Cauto fault.

WESTERN CUBA: PINAR DEL RIÓ BELT AND GUANIGUANICO FACIES STRUCTURAL ZONE

Most authorities now consider the Pinar del Rió belt in western Cuba to be a separate morphotectonic unit distinct from central Cuba (Figs. 1 and 2). The main area referred to in the belt is the Cordillera de Guaniguanico (Guaniguanico facies structural zone of Pszczolkowski, 1978). Although there are similarities between the rock sequences of the Cordillera Guaniguanico and other zones of central Cuba, there are many important differences. Some of the most controversial arguments in the geology of the Greater Antilles have centered on this area (e.g., Khudoley and Meyerhoff, 1971). The Cordillera includes two main mountain ranges, the Sierra de los Organos to the southwest and the Sierra del Rosario in the northeast (Figs. 1 and 2). The geology of the Sierra de los Organos is better known.

Extensive studies of the Pinar del Río area were carried out by oil companies in the 1950s, which led to many advances in the understanding of the area stratigraphy, largely as a result of the recognition of thrust sheets (nappes) in the Sierra de los Organos (Hatten, 1957, 1967; Rigassi, 1963). Geologists from the Polish Academy of Sciences have added to this picture by their descriptions of the complicated structures in the Sierra del Rosario (Pszczolkowski, 1976a and b, 1982) and in the Sierra de los Organos (Piotrowska, 1975, 1976, 1978). The following description is taken from the review by Mossakovskiy and Albear (1978), which is based on the work of Pszczolkowski (1976a and b), who distinguished four stratigraphic/structural sequences or units in the Sierra del Rosario region (Fig. 4).

In the northernmost area of the mountains, the *Bahía Honda structural unit* (Fig. 4) is allochthonous and consists of ophiolitic rocks and "eugeosynclinal" complexes. The unit occupies the highest structural position. The upper layers or sheets are composed of ultramafic rocks and mafic lavas and gabbros. The lower sheets are composed of mafic tuffs interstratified with mafic and intermediate lavas, siliceous slates, and laminated limestones. The Bahía Honda unit, therefore, seems to represent an overturned oceanic sequence. Deposits of lower Eocene clays, siltstones, polymict gravelly sandstones, and pebble conglomerates, specific to the superimposed molasse basins, are contained in the structurally highest sheet. The thrust sheets dip northward and overlie the Quiñones structural unit along gently dipping tectonic contacts.

The *Quiñones structural unit* itself consists mainly of carbonate rocks of Jurassic to Maastrichtian age. It has a northward-dipping structure and forms the northern limb of the

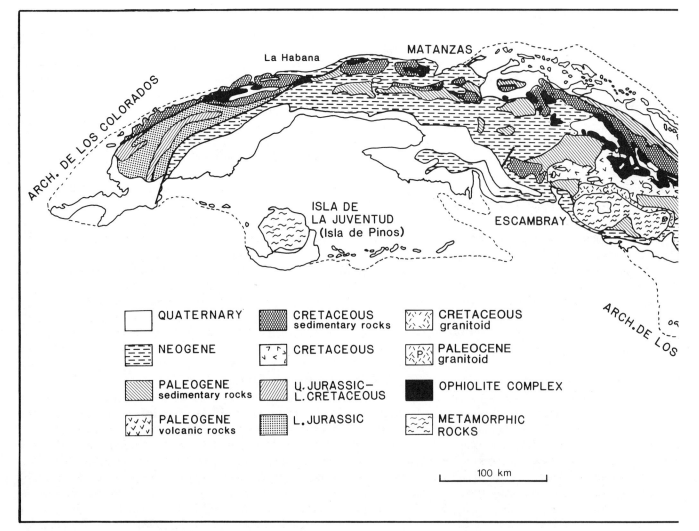

Figure 1. Generalized geological map of Cuba. Compiled mainly from Cuba (1985a), Butterlin (1977), and Case (1980). The separate ophiolite complexes reflect the structural segmentation of the pre-Eocene rocks.

main Sierra del Rosario antiform. The unit contains at least three thrust sheets, each associated with an olistostrome unit.

The *Cinco Pesos unit,* composed of a packet of thrust sheets, mainly consists of limestones of Jurassic to Late Cretaceous age together with some diabase members. The unit includes the San Cayetano Formation, described below. The rocks dip southward and form the southern limb of the Sierra del Rosario antiform.

The unnamed lowermost structural unit is exposed in the core of the antiform as a series of windows within the Cinco Pesos unit. This unit is autochthonous and consists of a sequence of sedimentary rocks ranging from Tithonian to Maastrichtian in age, which in many respects, is similar to that of the Placetas zone of Furrazola-Bermúdez and others (1964; see also our discussion on central Cuba). The section is capped by a 400-m-thick olistostrome sequence.

The Pinar del Río area is important in that it contains the largest exposure of rocks of Jurassic age in Cuba. The rocks of the San Cayetano Formation, exposed in the Sierra del Rosario and Sierra de los Organos, are of Late to Middle Jurassic age and are, thus, the oldest paleontologically dated rocks exposed in Cuba and the Greater Antilles. The rocks consist of white to grayish quartzose sandstones and siltstones, mica-rich gray shales, carbonaceous shales, and friable arkoses (Haczewski, 1976) and are reddish weathering. In parts the sequences have been described as flysch-like and in places the rocks are slightly metamorphosed to phyllites and semi-quartzites. Minor volcanic rocks have been recognized in the basal part of the San Cayetano Formation (Piotrowska, 1976).

In the Sierra de los Organos, the San Cayetano is overlain by the Jagua Formation, which consists of about 300 m of crystalline limestones containing a late Oxfordian fauna. The Jagua Formation is in turn overlain by the Viñales Formation, which is composed of a calcareous breccia at its base, followed by 1,000 m of thick-bedded gray limestones and dolomites. The ammonitic fauna in the Viñales Formation indicate a Kimmeridgian to early Tithonian age. There has been considerable controversy in the

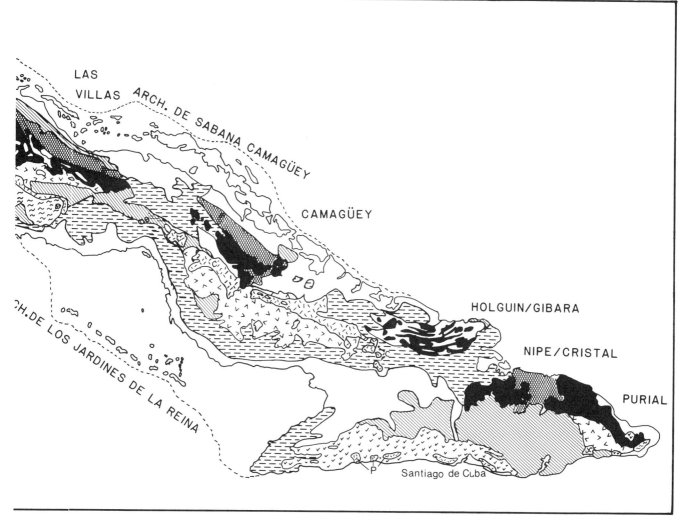

literature concerning the relations between the Jagua and Viñales Formations (see Butterlin, 1977; Kusnetzov and others, 1977; and Pszczolkowski, 1978, for summary).

The Jurassic rocks of Cuba have been correlated with Jurassic continental or shelf red beds in nuclear Central America and the Jurassic evaporites and marine limestone sequences in the Gulf of Mexico, but these correlations have been controversial (Khudoley and Meyerhoff, 1971).

Early sedimentation in the Sierra de los Organos was essentially deltaic, with a possible continental Central American or North American source (Khudoley and Meyerhoff, 1971). By middle Oxfordian time, little continental terrigenous material was being deposited, and shallow-water carbonate deposits accumulated. This gave way in the Tithonian to a deepening of the basin and to widespread, but thin, pelagic carbonate deposition. Pszczolkowski (1978) proposed that the pelagic deposits of Late Jurassic–Cretaceous age in the Sierra de los Organos were probably deposited on a submarine plateau rather than in an oceanic trough, as originally suggested by Iturralde-Vinent (1975). The Cretaceous and Jurassic-Cretaceous siliceous and clay sequences in the Sierra del Rosario accumulated in these deeper basins,

which would have separated the area of pelagic deposition from the influx of terrigeneous and volcanic matter.

By late Cenomanian and Turonian time, the northern sequence of the Sierra del Rosario was, in part, influenced by volcanic activity. Pelagic limestones formed during the Coniacian to Santonian in the Sierra de las Organos (upper part of Pons Formation) and persisted into Campanian-Maastrichtian time. Pelagic deposits of this age are poorly represented in the Sierra del Rosario, where the Campanian to Maastrichtian strata are clastic deposits of mainly limestone breccias (Buenavista and Cascarajicara Formations of Pszczolkowski, 1978). There has been considerable discussion as to the age and origin of these clastic deposits. Mossakovskiy and Albear (1978) have pointed out that, although there are remains of Campanian-Maastrichtian rudistids and orbitoids in the clasts, there are indications of the occurrence of Paleogene foraminifera in the matrix (Khudoley and Meyerhoff, 1971, p. 122; Pszczolkowsky, 1978, p. 46), perhaps making these chaotic deposits equivalent in age to other major olistostrome units of definite late Eocene age (discussed below).

The presence of shallow-water carbonate clasts suggests

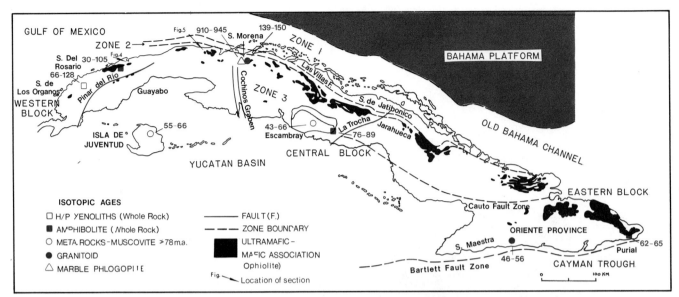

Figure 2. General map of Cuba showing morphotectonic zones, structural blocks, major faults, distribution of ophiolites and metamorphic complexes, and age determinations in millions of years. W.R. = whole-rock determinations. H/P = high-pressure metamorphism

that, at the time of their deposition, the Sierra del Rosario area must have been close to the Bahama Platform (Meyerhoff and Hatten, 1968), perhaps as early as Maastrichtian time, or that the clasts originated from the crushing of a sedimentary wedge that lay to the east of the Yucatán, as suggested by Gealey (1980). The absence of pre-Campanian and Campanian sediments in the Sierra del Rosario presumably resulted from tectonic movements in the late Late Cretaceous.

Pelagic limestones and cherts were still accumulating in the Sierra de los Organos area during the early Paleocene, but only a limited area of these late early Paleocene rocks is preserved.

The important rocks of late Paleocene age in the Sierra del Organos area olistostrome-like breccias intercalated with pelagic micritic limestones (Ancón Formation). These deposits, which are partly slump deposits, accumulated in deep submarine depressions, presumably resulting from differential uplift of blocks. The disconformity at the base of these late Paleocene deposits might mark the initiation of the movements and possibly thrusting.

Pelagic and clastic deposits of the upper Paleocene Pica Pica Formation (Pszczolkowski, 1978) were replaced by terrigenous (mainly volcanic sediments) in the early Eocene. The Pica Pica Formation supersedes the Manacas and Vieja Formations of former workers. The sediments are largely flysch deposits according to Pszczolkowski (1978), but include the chaotic units or olistostromes of Mossakovskiy and Albear (1978). The general view is that these deposits were formed in front of a moving thrust sheet prior to the crustal collision and folding in the middle Eocene.

CENTRAL CUBA

Central Cuba can be divided into several facies/structural zones or tectonostratigraphic belts, reflecting depressions and pos-

itive areas and geologic structure. Pardo (1952, 1975) was the first to describe the stratigraphy and structure in terms of belts or zones in central Cuba. The framework for a detailed stratigraphy of the Late Jurassic and Cretaceous strata in central Cuba was established by Bronnimann (1953, unpublished report *in* Furrazola-Bermudez and others, 1964) using planktonic foraminifera and nannoplankton. The scheme used by Gulf Oil Company geologists at that time was published by Bronnimann and Pardo (1956). The terminology has been used in different ways (e.g., Khudoley and Meyerhoff, 1971), and a summary is given in Table 1. In this chapter, the scheme published by Ducloz and Vaugnat (1962) has been adopted and simplified (Fig. 2). Following Mattson (1974a), the northern zones have been grouped into one.

Zone 1. Zone 1 is the miogeosyncline of Khudoley (1967a) and represents the well-documented dolomite and anhydrite-limestone sequences of the southern edge of the Bahama-Florida Platform and northern Cuba (Fig. 3). The zone can be subdivided into a series of narrow linear belts, each characterized by a diagnostic stratigraphy and tectonic style. The detailed subzonal divisions used are, from north to south, the Bahama Platform, the Bahama Channel, and the Cayo Coco–Remedios zones (Ducloz and Vaugnat, 1962; Furrazola-Bermudez and others, 1964).

The northernmost part of Zone 1 is situated over the southern margin of the Bahama Platform. Drill cores and magnetic and seismic data indicate that this area consists of at least 11 km of flat-lying sedimentary rock overlying the "magnetic basement." Little is known of the rocks underlying the Old Bahama Channel between Cuba and the Bahama Platform, but rocks of Zone 1 are known in some detail through drill cores in the Cayo Coco zone along the north coast.

As noted by Pardo (1975), the Cayo Coco section measures

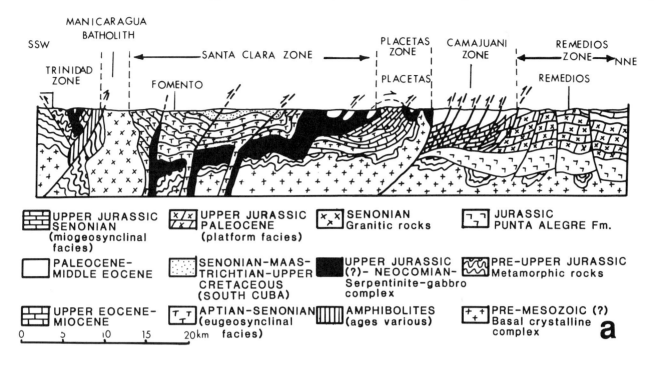

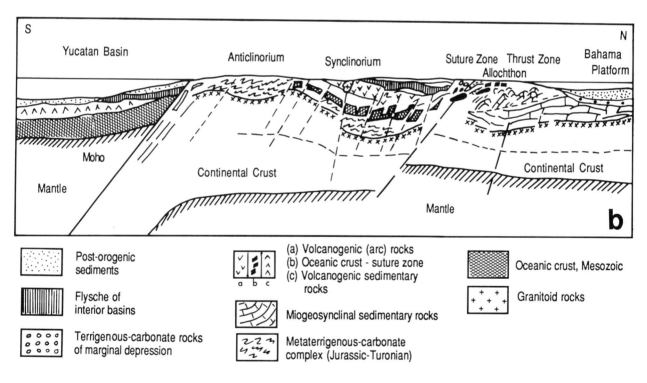

Figure 3. Interpretive crustal profiles across central Cuba: (a) after Meyerhoff and Hatten (1968) showing the deep root structures; (b) from the tectonic map of Cuba (1985b) showing the allochthonous nature of surface rocks.

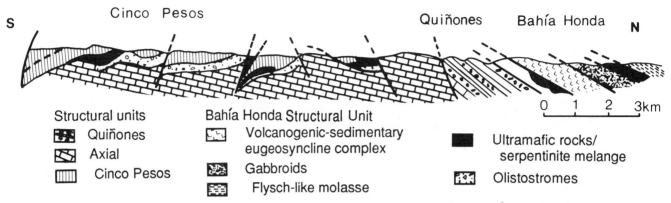

Figure 4. Cross section of the Sierra del Rosario (after Mossakovskiy and Albear, 1978). Location of section shown on Figure 2.

about 5,000 m, but the base is not known. The oldest rocks penetrated are interbedded dolomites and anhydrites of the Upper Jurassic Punta Alegre Formation. This formation crops out only as blocks in salt domes in Camagüey and in northwestern Matanzas. The thickness of the Punta Alegre Formation is unknown, but could be on the order of 600 to 1,700 m. Khudoley and Meyerhoff (1971) stated that the Punta Alegre and San Cayetano Formations are not necessarily equivalent, as assumed by Furrazola-Bermúdez and others (1964). The drill core section is continuous upward into the Cretaceous, and a complete Cretaceous to lower Eocene section is present. The Lower Cretaceous consists of more than 600 m of massive, secondary-dolomite, shallow-water, miliolid limestones ranging in age from Neocomian through Aptian, followed by 1,000 m of pelagic limestones and marls with chert nodules of Albian through Coniacian age. Limestones of Maastrichtian age are fragmental and in places coarsely conglomeratic. The Maastrichtian limestones are conformably overlain by several hundred meters of marls, limestones, and fragmental limestones of Paleocene to middle Eocene age. Although no physical break in the section is apparent at the base of the Tertiary, earlier paleontological studies did not find fossils diagnostic of the Paleocene, and this stage was considered to be missing. However, diagnostic fossils have now been recorded (Kusnetzov and others, 1977).

Pardo (1975) noted that Upper Cretaceous pelagic shales and marls, present in the Cayo Coco belt, are equivalent in age to shallow-water platform carbonates to the south. He suggested, therefore, that there must have existed a situation similar to the present-day Bahama Banks, in which shallow-water platforms were separated by deeper-water tongues.

Zone 2. Zone 2 includes the Placetas and Camajuaní zones of Ducloz and Vaugnat (1962) and Meyerhoff and Hatten (1968) and is essentially equivalent to the Las Villas zone (the intrageosynclinal welt of Khudoley, 1967a). The area of the zone, as known in central Cuba, extends from northern Habana Province (subsurface at Guanabo) to central Camagüey Province (Loma Camajuán; Figs. 1 and 2) and occupies windows in the allochthonous ophiolite sequence. The zone is essentially the deep-

water-facies extension to the south of Zone 1, but the thickness of the deposits is only one-fifth that of the time-equivalent shallow-water carbonates of the Cayo Coco–Remedios zones. The southern part of the zone was considered to be a structural high or median welt by previous workers, and was thought to have formed a barrier between the miogeosyncline (Zone 1) to the north and the eugeosyncline (Zone 3) to the south (see Furrazola-Bermúdez and others, 1964, Figs. 88 and 89). The rocks of Zone 2 span a time range of Tithonian to Maastrichtian and include pelagic limestones, calcareous turbidites, and radiolarian cherts with lesser amounts of sandstones, marls, and tuffs.

Pardo (1975) described the lower part of the sequence in the southern part of Zone 2 (Placetas belt of Pardo, 1975) as consisting of brown pelagic limestones, containing abundant nannoplankton and radiolaria interbedded with dark shales of Neocomian age. The Neocomian limestones and a basal quartz-Neocomian limestone clast conglomerate lie unconformably over "basement" rocks at three localities: La Rana, Sierra Morena, and Tres Guanos (Pardo, 1975; personal communication, 1986). Above this lie brown sandy limestones and calcareous quartz sandstones interbedded with tan shales. These beds are overlain by fragmental limestones, dense argillaceous limestones, thin-bedded brown cherts, brownish-gray noncalcareous shales, and occasional quartz sandstone of Albian through Turonian age. Parts of the Coniacian and Santonian appear to be missing, and Campanian to Maastrichtian limestones lie discordantly on erosion surfaces on older rocks. This hiatus was the basis of the postulated mid-Cretaceous orogeny of Meyerhoff and Hatten (1968).

Structurally, Zone 2 rocks are folded into tight anticlinoria, and deformation becomes more intense in the southern part of the zone.

Zone 3. Zone 3 is the eugeosynclinal belt of previous workers, and essentially the Zaza zone of Meyerhoff and Hatten (1968), also termed the Santa Clara zone in central Cuba by Ducloz and Vaugnat (1962). This zone covers most of south-central Cuba south of Zone 2 and is limited to the northwest by the Pinar del Río fault, and in the southeast partly by the Cauto

TABLE 1. ZONATION SCHEMES FOR STRUCTURAL FACIES OF CENTRAL CUBA

AUTHORS	STRUCTURAL - FACIES ZONES								
MEYERHOFF and HATTEN* (1968)	Zaza		Las Villas		Zulueta		Remedios	Cayo Coco	
DUCLOZ and VAUGNAT (1962)	Santa Clara		Placetas		Camajuani		Remedios		
PARDO** (1975)	Cabaiguan	Domingo	Cifuentes	Placetas	Las Villas	Jatibonico	Sagua la Chica	Yaguajay	Coastal Belt
KHUDOLEY (1967)	Zaza		Las Villas		Remedios			Cayo Coco	Old Bahama Channel
KNIPPER and CABRERA (1974)	Seibabo	Santa Clara	Placetas	San Felipe	Camajuani		Remedios		
MATTSON (1974a) This paper	Zone 3				Zone 2		Zone 1		

*Incorporates work of Hatten and others (1958).
+Incorporates fork of Bronnimann and Pardo (1954).

fault zone (Fig. 2). The rocks in this zone differ completely from those in the northern zones in being composed of a complex of ultramafic-mafic plutonic rocks, mafic and felsic lavas, volcaniclastic deposits, and deep- to shallow-water deposits.

Since the first major descriptions of the rocks of the Santa Clara area (Thiadens, 1937; Rutten, 1936), a number of attempts have been made to define a satisfactory stratigraphy (see reviews by Díaz de Villavilla, 1985; Dilla and García, 1985). In recent years, a distinction has been made between the belt of ultramafic-mafic and associated rocks (the oceanic belt), which corresponds largely with the Domingo belt of Pardo (1975), and the extensive sequences of volcanic-arc rocks and deposits to the south, which correspond with the Cabaiguán belt of Pardo (1975).

Most of the sequences in the oceanic belt (Domingo belt of Pardo, 1975) are strongly disturbed (dismembered) and allochthonous. Wassal (1956) was the first to document a layered serpentinite-gabbro sequence about 1,000 m thick, overlain by spilite, basalt, andesite, and pyroclastic and sedimentary rock about 1,500 m thick (5,000 m thick according to Meyerhoff and Hatten, 1968). The sedimentary rocks are tuffaceous limestones, chert, shale, and sandstones. The fauna is largely pelagic, but the occurrence of tuffaceous sandstones, conglomerates, and rudistid reef facies, particularly in the upper part of the section, indicates a shallowing of the sedimentary environments. The pelagic strata intercalated with the main mafic-ultramafic sequences give ages from pre-Albian to Cenomanian. The ultramafic–mafic complexes, however, are allochthonous, and their actual age is perhaps Late Triassic to Late Jurassic, according to Iturralde-Vinent (1983).

The volcanic-arc rocks (Cabaiguán belt of Pardo, 1975) are of Aptian-Albian to at least Campanian age and are intruded by granitoid rocks of pre-Maastrichtian age. Pardo (1975) described the southern part of the Cabaiguán belt as a thick sequence of rocks north of the Trinidad Mountains whose base is not visible. The oldest beds are in fault contact with the igneous-metamorphic complex of the Trinidad Mountains (see below). The base of the sequence of "older volcanics" consists of probably many thousands of feet of basalt flows and dolerites interbedded with fine- to coarse-grained clastic deposits. The rocks are considered to be Early Cretaceous in age. Next in the sequence are fragmental limestones containing Jurassic reworked oolites and shales of apparent Cenomanian age. The rocks grade into a sequence of tuffaceous sandstones, conglomerates, and rudistid limestones, also of Cenomanian age, which pass into a pelagic sequence of tuffs, sandstones, shales, and limestones of Turonian age. A second period of volcanic activity is of Turonian-Senonian age and is made up of flows of andesite and quartz andesite. Hypersthene basalts formed the last stage of activity in the Maastrichtian. Both the volcanism and sedimentation appear to have been submarine, except during the Maastrichtian.

Cabrera and others (1981) have described the sequence of Cretaceous volcanic and sedimentary rocks intruded by granitoid

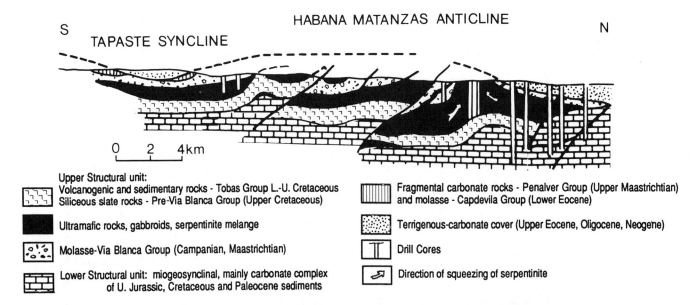

Figure 5. Cross section of the Matanzas–La Habana region in northwest Cuba (after Mossakovskiy and Albear, 1978). Location of section shown on Figure 2.

rocks from the Camagüey-Tumas area. The basal units consist of mafic lavas with isolated beds of sedimentary rocks containing a Turonian fauna overlain by, and interdigitating with, tuffs and volcanogenic deposits of andesitic and basaltic andesite composition and early Coniacian-Campanian in age. An erosional unconformity separates the basal sequence from an overlying Campanian formation, characterized by rhyodacitic ignimbrite flows, tuffs, and epiclastic rocks followed by dacitic epiclastic rocks that become more felsic in the upper part of the sequence. Folding of this whole sequence apparently took place in the Turonian-Campanian interval.

Gealey (1980) has interpreted the rocks of the Domingo belt to be the ophiolite basement of a fore-arc basin and the Cabaiguán belt to be the fore-arc basin volcanic and volcanogenic sedimentary fill.

The morphotectonic zones described above can be traced only in central Cuba in Las Villas, Camagüey, Habana, and Matanzas areas. Elsewhere, the original position of the principal morphotectonic zones has been disturbed tectonically.

Studies in the region of the Habana-Matanzas anticline (Bronnimann and Rigassi, 1963) have shown the region to be overlain by a multiple-nappe structure. Mossakovskiy and Albear (1978) grouped the component tectonic sheets into two main structural units separated by a subhorizontal principal thrust surface. The lower structural unit (para autochthon) unites tectonic sheets of Jurassic-Cretaceous and Paleocene–lower Eocene miogeosynclinal deposits from the north. The upper structural unit (allochthon) consists of essentially three rock assemblages derived from the Cretaceous–middle Eocene rocks of the southern "eugeosynclinal zone" (Fig. 5). The lowermost assemblage is made up of Cretaceous volcanic and volcanogenic sedimentary members of the Tobas Group, including its lower (diabase-basalt) and upper (andesite tuff) members. Fragments of the Cenoma-

nian-Turonian siliceous slate pre-Vía Blanca Group and fragments of terrigenous, tuffaceous, and carbonate members of the Upper Cretaceous "eugeosynclinal" sequence are also present.

The second assemblage consists of superimposed clastic deposits, described as "molasse basins," which include the Campanian-Maastrichtian limestone conglomerates of the Vía Blanca Group, clastic carbonate formations of the Penalver Group, and the lower Eocene flysch-like Universidad Group.

The third assemblage comprises fragments of oceanic crust, namely basalts, diabase, gabbros, and various ultramafic rocks. In places the primary structure of the oceanic layers is preserved in undisturbed, 1- to 2-km-thick sequences. As a rule, the oceanic crustal layer tectonically overlies other thick sheets composed of the Cretaceous Tobas eruptive-tuff group, apparently demonstrating an overturned sequence of oceanic crust and "eugeosynclinal" strata (Fig. 5).

The tectonic sheets have been folded into gentle antiforms and synforms, and broken by reverse and strike-slip faulting into tectonic blocks. These blocks were subjected to further tectonic displacement during late Cenozoic time.

Thrust faulting is also documented in the Camagüey and Gibara/Holguín structures in the eastern part of the central block (Thayer and Guild, 1947; Kozary, 1968; Knipper and Cabrera, 1974). Thayer and Guild (1947) considered the thrusting to be from the north to the south in these structures, but in the Holguín/Gibara area the thin, imbricate, ultramafic/carbonate sheets described by Kozary (1968) are probably accretionary-wedge structures (Wadge and others, 1984).

EASTERN BLOCK: ORIENTE PROVINCE

Igneous, metamorphic, and sedimentary rocks in southeast Cuba, particularly in the Sierra Maestra, contain structural and

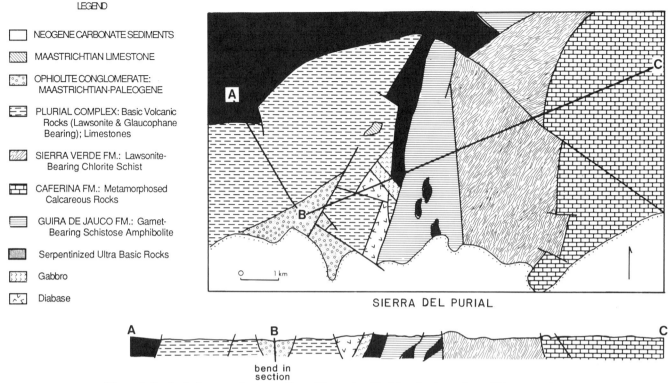

LEGEND

☐ NEOGENE CARBONATE SEDIMENTS

▨ MAASTRICHTIAN LIMESTONE

▨ OPHIOLITE CONGLOMERATE:
   MAASTRICHTIAN-PALEOGENE

▨ PLURIAL COMPLEX: Basic Volcanic
   Rocks (Lawsonite & Glaucophane
   Bearing); Limestones

▨ SIERRA VERDE FM.: Lawsonite-
   Bearing Chlorite Schist

▨ CAFERINA FM.: Metamorphosed
   Calcareous Rocks

▨ GUIRA DE JAUCO FM.: Garnet-
   Bearing Schistose Amphibolite

▨ Serpentinized Ultra Basic Rocks

▨ Gabbro

▨ Diabase

SIERRA DEL PURIAL

bend in
section

Figure 6. Geological map and cross section of the eastern Purial region in southeast Oriente province (after Millán and others, 1985).

compositional features decidedly different from other parts of Cuba, and form a third structural block. The three most significant features of this block are the extensive mafic and felsic volcanism, the early Eocene granitoid plutonic activity, and the distinctive blueschist-amphibolite-ophiolite suite. Moreover, the physiographically east-west–trending Sierra Maestra structure clearly differs from that of the rest of Cuba and is apparently an uplifted part of the Cayman Rise (Taber, 1934; Perfit and Heezen, 1978). The geology of part of the area was first described by Lewis and Straczek (1955). Important later contributions are those of Boiteau and Michard (1976), Cobiella and others (1977, 1984), Millán and others (1985), and a monograph published by the Cuban Academy of Sciences (Anon., 1983). The last includes details of the stratigraphy and structural facies zones.

The oldest rocks in the eastern block are probably the serpentinites and associated metamorphic rocks in the Nipe-Cristal and Purial areas (Fig. 1). Meyerhoff, in Khudoley and Meyerhoff (1971), considered the quartzites and mica schists cropping out in the Sierra de Nipe and Sierra de Cristal to be of Paleozoic age. However, Millán and others (1985) have reported that the protolith of the metamorphic rocks forming the Sierra del Purial in the southeast Oriente province have Jurassic(?) and Late Cretaceous ages, based on microfossil evidence. Several main units have been distinguished by Cobiella and others (1984) and Millán and others (1985). Figure 6 shows the field relations as presented by Millán and others (1985) in the Sierra del Purial. Rocks of the Purial complex, which occupy a large part of the western Sierra

del Purial, are mainly mafic volcanic rocks that have undergone high-P/low-T regional metamorphism. The rocks are highly deformed and display isoclinal folding. However, the degree of metamorphism in the Purial complex is variable, with some rocks containing lawsonite and glaucophane but others having actinolite greenschist assemblages. Foraminifera from intercalated limestones yield a pre-Maastrichtian, late Senonian age.

The Asunción complex (Chafarina and Sierra Verde Formations of Millán and others, 1985) to the east includes dark-banded marbles—graphitic in places—transitional into calcareous schists, together with phyllites, metavolcanic rocks, and radiolarian-bearing metasilicates. Microfossils indicate an age from Late Jurassic to Early Cretaceous.

An area of amphibolites, the Guira de Juaco Formation (Mocambo Amphibolites of Cobiella and others, 1984) lies between, and in fault contact with, the above two complexes. The rocks are metagabbros, and show an affinity with oceanic tholeiites based on major-element chemistry. An age of 75 Ma has been determined by K/Ar methods, which presumably reflects the age of metamorphism.

Study of small-scale structures in the schists and marbles has shown that three phases of deformation affected the Purial metamorphic rocks (Boiteau and Michard, 1976). The amphibolites are polymetamorphic and are probably older than the schistose metavolcanic rocks.

The structural and stratigraphic relations have led Millán and others (1985) to conclude that the volcanic rocks of the

Sierra del Purial were metamorphosed, isoclinally folded, and uplifted over the brief interval between the Campanian and Maastrichtian.

An ophiolitic association, consisting of serpentinites, leucocratic gabbros, and dolerites, crops out in the extreme east of the Sierra del Purial (Fig. 6). A serpentinite conglomerate unit is considered to be of Maastrichtian age. Cobiella and others (1977) considered that emplacement of ophiolite took place in the Paleocene and that the rocks are allochthonous. However, Thayer and Guild (1947) did not consider horizontal movement to be important in the eastern Oriente province, and the contact features drawn on the map by Millán and others (1985), reproduced in Figure 6, indicate vertical uplift. The evidence is discussed by Cobiella (1978, 1984) and Cobiella and others (1984).

A sequence of tuffs with intercalations of andesites, termed the Santo Domingo Formation, occurs to the south of the Sierra Cristal. These rocks are not fossiliferous, but their age is considered to be pre-Maastrichtian, probably Senonian. Other nonmetamorphosed volcanic sequences in the Sierra Maestra are probably correlative. The presence of Upper Cretaceous pyroclastic deposits and lavas in the Sierra Purial indicates that extensive volcanic activity took place throughout Late Cretaceous time.

In the eastern Sierra del Purial, the Santo Domingo Formation is overlain unconformably by a sequence of sandstones, siltstones, and conglomerates, the Micara Formation of Maastrichtian to Paleocene age. At least two other formations of Maastrichtian age are known, namely the La Picota Formation, probably a mélange, and the Canas Formation composed of massive limestones.

The Cretaceous units described above are overlain unconformably by the El Cobre Formation of Paleocene to late Eocene age. The formation occurs over a wide area and is now divided into several subunits. It is made up chiefly of water-lain pyroclastic rocks and attains a total thickness of between 4,500 and 6,000 m in the Sierra Maestra. The pyroclastic rocks are massive to well-bedded tuffs and water-lain breccias. Lava flows consisting of basalts and dacites are common in the lower part of the formation, and tuffaceous limestones in the upper part. Dacites, andesites, diorites, and basalts intrude the El Cobre mainly as stocks and dikes.

The San Ignacio Formation, composed of polymict breccias with intercalated limestones, is of the same age as the uppermost part of the El Cobre, but was deposited in a separate basin. The San Luis Formation of late Eocene age, composed of terrigenous clastic deposits, overlies the El Cobre and San Ignacio Formations with discordance. Cobiella and others (1984) have distinguished three sequences of chaotic deposits of late Eocene–Oligocene age, namely the Capiro, Sabanalamar, and Macquey Formations, which are interpreted as having been deposited in depressions between mountainous areas after the middle Eocene tectonism. Small banks and reefs were developed, represented by the Cabeza de Vaca Formation.

Sedimentary strata of Neogene age (La Cruz and Imias Formations and others) overlie the older units (Jakes, 1983; Co-

biella and others, 1984). The rocks are predominantly marine carbonates of shallow-water origin. Quaternary deposits include prominent alluvial-fan deposits and raised reefs along the eastern coast (Taber, 1934; Horsfield, 1975; Franco, 1983; Brezsnyanszky and others, 1983).

IGNEOUS AND METAMORPHIC ROCKS

Ophiolitic rock associations

Cuba contains the most extensive outcrops of ultramafic-mafic rocks in the Caribbean region. The outcrop area is more than 6,500 km^2, and if Eocene sedimentary rocks were removed, the area would exceed 15,000 km^2 (Kozary, 1968; Khudoley and Meyerhoff, 1971). The most extensive outcrops are those of Las Villas, Camagüey, Gibara/Holguín, Nipe/Cristal, and Purial areas (Fig. 1).

Thayer and Guild (1947) were of the opinion that there are two basic types of serpentinized peridotites in Cuba. Those of the first type are highly tectonized, but essentially stratiform or sheet-like, occurring along major thrust faults. Those of the second type are massive, domical protrusions occurring in the Oriente province. On the other hand, Cobiella and others (1984) concluded that the ultramafic rocks in eastern Cuba do not show substantial differences in their form of emplacement or degree of deformation from those in central Cuba. Although there is no complete published study of recent work by Cuban geologists, Fonseca and others (1984, a and b) and Iturralde-Vinent and others (1984) have pointed out that the Cuban ultramafic-mafic complexes show most, if not all, the features of classical ophiolites: that is, dunite peridotites at the base, cumulate gabbros, diabase dike complexes, and tholeiitic basalts capped by marine sedimentary rocks. Most of these rocks are heavily tectonized with a brecciated fabric and are fractured and foliated. The rocks have been metamorphosed up to amphibolite facies, which is considered to have occurred in Jurassic to early Neocomian time (Millán and Somin, 1982). The ultramafic rocks are composed of dunite, harzburgite, lherzolite, pyroxenite, and wehrlite, but most are now at least 40 percent serpentinized. Cumulates include normal gabbros, olivine gabbros, troctolites, anorthosites, and lherzolites. Past workers have considered that the ophiolites formed the substrata to the Cretaceous arc rocks. An alternative view, widely held today, is that the ophiolites are slices of the oceanic lithosphere that were obducted when Cuba collided with the Bahama Platform (Gealey, 1980; Wadge and others, 1984; Iturralde-Vinent and others, 1984). Chemical analyses of gabbros and diabases show a close similarity to abyssal tholeiites (Somin and Millán, 1981; Millán and Somin, 1982; Fonseca and others, 1984b).

Tectonic blocks of mafic composition occur in the serpentinites, and are found in many localities, particularly in units described as "mélange" zones. Two groups of mafic rocks are present: (1) eclogites and garnet amphibolites, and (2) pumpellyite-, lawsonite-, and glaucophane-bearing schists. Chlorite and muscovite schists, graphite schists, pegmatites, and quartz rocks also occur. Gealey (1980) suggested that these mafic exotic blocks must have formed under high-P/low-T conditions in the subduction zone and were ripped off from this zone along the footwall as the peridotite was brought to the surface along the obduction plane.

Granitoid intrusive rocks

The main belt of granitoid rocks in central Cuba extends for about 90 km from north of the Trinidad Mountains to the western margin of the Cauto Basin (Fig. 1). The rocks are intruded into the Cretaceous volcanogenic-sedimentary complex of the Zaza zone (Zone 3). Meyerhoff and others (1969) considered that the intrusions were emplaced during folding in mid-Cretaceous time (Albian through Turonian). Because fragments of the granitoids are found in Maastrichtian rocks. this gives an upper limit to their age, and Meyerhoff and others (1969) considered the age of intrusion to range from Cenomanian to Maastrichtian. A K/Ar date of 61 Ma on biotite from the Tres Guano quartz monzonite, reported by Meyerhoff and others (1969) and Khudoley and Meyerhoff (1971), was considered by them to be caused by resetting during Campanian-Eocene orogeny.

Judging from the limited petrographic/chemical data available, the granitoid rocks of the central belt are diorites, quartz diorites, granodiorites, and granites similar to many other Greater Antillean granitoids.

A second, narrow, east-west–trending belt of granitoid rocks occurs in the Sierra Maestra of the Oriente zone. The rocks from this belt are described as quartz diorites (Meyerhoff and others, 1969) but also include minor gabbros, diorites, and trondhjemites, according to Pérez and Equipko (1981). These rocks are younger than those of central Cuba; three quartz diorites from the Sierra Maestra belt have yielded whole-rock K/Ar dates ranging from 46 to 58 Ma (Meyerhoff and others, 1969).

Metamorphic rocks

The metamorphic rocks of Cuba can be divided into the following units (Somin and Millán, 1977; Millán and Somin, 1982): (1) carbonate, terrigenous, and metabasic rocks of the Escambray and Isla de Juventud; (2) greenschists and lawsonite-glaucophane schists of the Purial Mountains, Oriente Province; (3) gneisses and marbles of a pre-Mesozoic sialic complex; and (4) tectonic blocks and inclusions in serpentinites. Locations and age determinations are shown on Figure 2.

Type 1. The association termed "carbonate-terrigenous" is by far the most extensive and forms the main rock type in the metamorphic complexes of the Isla de Juventud-Isla de Pinos and Escambray. Metamorphism is of the high-T/medium- to high-P type in the Isla de Juventud, in contrast to the low-T/high-P assemblages in metabasic rocks in the Escambray complex (Somin and Millán, 1976). There has been considerable controversy in the literature over the age of these metamorphic com-

plexes, but fossil evidence by Millán and Myczynski (1978) strongly indicates a Jurassic– Early Cretaceous age for the protolith of the Escambray rocks.

The metamorphic rocks of the Isla de la Juventud have been studied by Millán (1981) and Somin and Millán (1981). Carbonate sequences on the island include various marbles and calc-silicate schists. Typical mineral associations in marble are diopside-calcite and diopside-calcite-mica-tremolite. Terrigenous (quartzofeldspathic to pelitic) rocks in the north Isla de Juventud characteristically contain the assemblage kyanite-almandine-muscovite±biotite. Plagioclase (andesine) is generally present. In the eastern part of the island the characteristic association is kyanite with staurolite and the common assemblage is kyanite-staurolite-muscovite±biotite. A small area of gneisses contain the assemblages quartz-andesine–biotite-orthoclase-garnet-andesine and quartz-andesine-biotite-hornblende. In the eastern border, greissens occur in crystalline schists, and quartz-muscovite rocks with garnet are found. Five stages of superposed folding are recognized, all of which appear to be synmetamorphic.

The Escambray terrane (Fig. 7) is also described as terrigenous carbonate, but the complex contains a considerable amount of mafic (metavolcanic?) and some ultramafic rock. The rocks, which are Jurassic to Cretaceous in age according to fossil evidence, occupy two structural domes or cupulas connected by a narrow bridge beneath a Paleogene cover. The complex has been studied in some detail by Somin and Millán (1981) and Millán and Somin (1981, 1985a).

The dominant lithologies in Escambray are pelitic and psammitic schists, and marbles. Other lithologies include greenschists and amphibolites, and serpentinized peridotite. Lenses and blocks of garnet-glaucophane schist and eclogite occur within serpentinites on the peripheral parts of the complex (Fig. 7). The thinly bedded pure marbles with metabreccias and metagraywackes appear to correspond to the Middle Upper Cretaceous sedimentary units elsewhere in Cuba and, according to Millán and Somin (1984), all the lithologies can be correlated with rocks in eastern Cuba and, in part, with those in the Placetas zone of north-central Cuba.

The metamorphic zoning is inverted and concentric; that is, the lowest grade is in the central parts of the structure of the two domes (Fig. 7). Four superposed phases of folding are recognized in the Escambray complex (Millán and Somin, 1981; Somin and Millán, 1981). A first phase of isoclinal folds with small amplitude is superposed by second and third phases, producing a complex geometry. The fourth phase postdates the main metamorphism and resulted in open concentric folding. Somin (1984) recognized three overthrust structures (nappes) or complexes, each containing a separate sequence formed in different environments and brought together by major horizontal displacement.

The different elements of the Escambray massif are considered to represent an active continental margin situated behind a volcanic arc (Millán and Somin, 1985a). However, no outcrops of a truly pre-Mesozoic crystalline basement appear to occur within the Escambray complex. These authors considered that the inverted metamorphism of the Escambray massif resulted from subduction below a volcanic arc probably situated to the south. The thermal event causing the metamorphism was in the Late Cretaceous, judging from K/Ar determinations on biotites (Fig. 2). An age of 80 Ma on white mica from a pegmatite cutting the Escambray complex apparently gives a minimum date for the metamorphism (Millán and Somin, 1982).

A large mass of amphibolite (the Mabujina amphibolite) lies in fault contact with the main Escambray complex along its northern margin (Fig. 7). Most workers believe that the metamorphism of the amphibolite mass is related to the emplacement of the Manicaragua granitoid batholith to the north, and is probably a younger feature because lenses of quartz diorite and plagioclase granite form extended belts in the amphibolite, whereas granitoid rocks are absent from the Escambray complex proper. The amphibolites give a K/Ar retention age of 89 Ma.

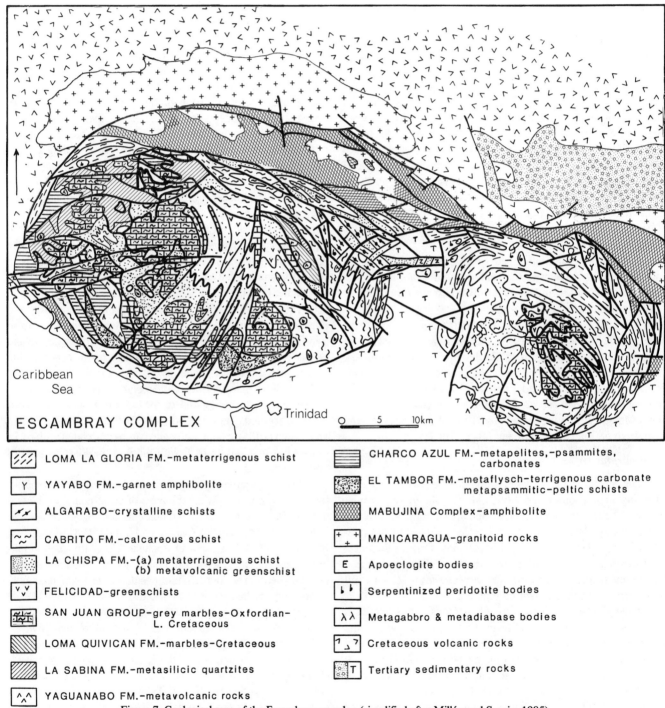

ESCAMBRAY COMPLEX

/// LOMA LA GLORIA FM.-metaterrigenous schist	☰ CHARCO AZUL FM.-metapelites,-psammites, carbonates
Y YAYABO FM.-garnet amphibolite	⋰ EL TAMBOR FM.-metaflysch-terrigenous carbonate metapsammitic-peltic schists
⁄⁄ ALGARABO-crystalline schists	⬡ MABUJINA Complex-amphibolite
~~ CABRITO FM.-calcareous schist	+ + MANICARAGUA-granitoid rocks
⋰ LA CHISPA FM.-(a) metaterrigenous schist (b) metavolcanic greenschist	E Apoeclogite bodies
ᵛᵛ FELICIDAD-greenschists	⌐⌐ Serpentinized peridotite bodies
▦ SAN JUAN GROUP-grey marbles-Oxfordian- L. Cretaceous	λλ Metagabbro & metadiabase bodies
/// LOMA QUIVICAN FM.-marbles-Cretaceous	⌐⌐ Cretaceous volcanic rocks
/// LA SABINA FM.-metasilicic quartzites	T Tertiary sedimentary rocks
^^ YAGUANABO FM.-metavolcanic rocks	

Figure 7. Geological map of the Escambray complex (simplified after Millán and Somin, 1985).

Hatten and others (1989) prefer the conclusion that the protolith of the Mabujina amphibolites and associated gneisses are of Late Jurassic?–Early Cretaceous age and that metamorphism resulted from the intrusion of the Manicaragua pluton, which took place in the Late Cretaceous. Millán and Somin (1985b) favored the hypothesis that the greater part of the protolith of the complex were basalts forming the lower part of the Cretaceous volcanic arc. The amphibolites appear to correspond to oceanic tholeiites, although some analyses show calc-alkaline affinities (Somin and Millán, 1981; Millán and Somin, 1982). However, the complexity of the amphibolite structure, its thickness, and association with granitoids seem to exclude its formation as typical oceanic crust.

Type 2. Greenschists and glaucophane-lawsonite schists occur as an allochthonous? metavolcanic unit in the southeastern extreme of the Purial Mountains in the south Oriente province (Figs. 1, 2, and 6). The association also includes serpentinites and amphibolites, along with marbles and jasper in tectonic contact with the schistose rocks. Amphibolites and eclogites occur as tectonic blocks in the serpentinites. The rocks have been described by Millán and others (1985), Boiteau and Michard (1976), and Cobiella and others (1977, 1984).

The Sierra del Purial consists of a variety of lithologies, mainly metavolcanic rocks ranging from blueschists and greenschists to volcanic rocks with only slight alteration. The metamorphic rock types include chlorite schists, calcareous schists, marbles, and tremolite-actinolite schists, and glaucophane schists.

Zoisite-, clinopyroxene-, and rare garnet-bearing rocks occur with eclogites in a serpentinite mélange in the Sierra del Purial. Isotopic ages for some of these metamorphic xenoliths from different localities range from 83 to 128 Ma, indicating that they were from a terrane of mafic composition and were metamorphosed in the Jurassic and Early Cretaceous.

Milán and others (1985) point out the unique features of the association and that there is no other place in Cuba where volcanic rocks have been metamorphosed by high-P/low-T regional metamorphism to the glaucophane-schist facies.

Type 3. Pre-Mesozoic sialic complex: Two occurrences of exotic blocks of metamorphic rocks have been reported from northwestern Cuba. The first locality, El Guayabo, located northeast of the town of Pinar del Río, is an outcrop of polymict conglomerates from the lower part of the Paleogene sequence. The conglomerates include gneisses with the mineral assemblage quartz-albite-muscovite-biotite-garnet. Such an assemblage has not been reported from elsewhere in Cuba and is believed to have originated from a sialic basement complex. K/Ar determinations on muscovites from the gneisses have given ages of between 55 and 71 Ma, but these ages probably reflect a later thermal event. If it is assumed that much of the Pinar del Río belt is allochthonous and derived from the south, these gneissic sialic blocks are evidence of sialic basement in the southern part of Cuba.

Poor exposures of in situ blocks of phlogopite-, diopside-, and vesuvianite-bearing marbles crop out near the town of Sierra Morena, eastern Matanzas, and lie within the Placetas zone of

Ducloz and Vaugnat (1962). K/Ar determinations on phlogopite crystals have yielded ages of 945 ± 25 and 910 ± 25 Ma, which correspond to the late Proterozoic. Cataclastic granites and pegmatites, which crop out in the same area but separately, have given K/Ar ages between 139 and 150 Ma (Late Jurassic). Structural relations between these rocks and the Cretaceous sedimentary sequence are not understood.

The marbles from the Sierra Morena, which have yielded Precambrian K/Ar dates, and the gneisses from Guayabo presumably represent ancient sialic crust in the northwestern Caribbean region. These marbles are cut by granitic rocks that have yielded dates between 139 and 150 Ma (Late Jurassic).

Blocks of medium-grained schistose gneiss composed of the assemblage quartz-plagioclase-garnet-biotite are found in a gypsum diapir of Late Triassic to Late Jurassic age at Valle Yumurí near Matanzas. Such rocks must be pre–early Mesozoic and are presumably also derived from a sialic basement.

Hatten and others (1958, see Furrazola-Bermúdez and others, 1964; Cobiella, 1984, p. 19) have described the Perea metamorphic complex, which crops out as a window through the Jurassic-Cretaceous cover in the Jarahueca area in central Cuba (Fig. 2). The rocks include hornfels of mafic composition, actinolite-cordierite and hornblende-plagioclase schists, and metagraywackes. The stratigraphic data indicate a pre–Late Jurassic age for the complex, and Hatten and colleagues considered that the metamorphism resulted from the intrusion of the Tres Guanos quartz monzonite and the San Marcos troctolite.

GEOLOGIC AND TECTONIC EVOLUTION OF CUBA

A number of models have been put forward over the past two decades attempting to explain the geologic evolution of Cuba. These include models based on the theory of basification (Furrazola-Bermúdez and others, 1964; Khudoley, 1967a), expansion (Levchenko, 1979; Iturralde-Vinent, 1981, 1983), and contraction (Meyerhoff and Hatten, 1968; Iturralde-Vinent, 1981). Other models and aspects of the geologic history have been described by Khudoley and Meyerhoff (1971) and Pardo (1975). In the following summary, the emphasis will be placed on current plate-tectonic theories.

The recent geophysical and geological work outlined in this description suggests that western and central Cuba is mainly underlain by continental crust. This miogeosynclinal region is interpreted either as an extension to the south of the Bahama platform or, alternatively, as a part of continental Central America. Cuban and Soviet geologists have distinguished the development of the crystalline basement of Cuba as the "pre-Mesozoic" or "pre-Alpine" orogenic cycle (Shein and others, 1984). The Mesozoic eugeosynclinal rocks in Cuba are a superposed allochthonous cover resulting from the Paleogene collision between the Greater Antillean arc and the Bahama Platform. This interpretation is put forward in the tectonic map of Cuba (Anon., 1978; Shein and others, 1978, 1984; Cuba, 1985b) and is essentially the same as that put forward by Gealey (1980). In this model, the ophiolites of western and central Cuba represent the oceanic basement to a fore-arc basin of an island arc that has been thrust onto the passive margin of the Bahama Platform. Thus, the arc rocks are all interpreted to be allochthonous. In contrast, eastern Cuba, south and east of the Cauto Basin, seems to have had a different history, which is more comparable to that of northern Hispaniola. The large thrust faults that characterize western and central Cuba are less well developed in eastern Cuba, and most of the terrane seems to be autochthonous or parautochthonous. Moreover, magmatic rocks are more widespread and are younger than in the rest of Cuba.

The older rocks in Cuba forming the miogeosynclinal basement are essentially a passive continental margin sequence. The origin of these deposits is still controversial and may have been derived either from the Florida-Bahama Platform or Central America. It is possible that western Cuba was close to Guatemala and the Yucatán Peninsula, such that a depositional area of present-day western Cuba received continental sediments similar to those found in Central America.

However, by middle Oxfordian time, little continental terrigenous material was deposited in the Guaniguanico province, indicating that, even if it had been adjacent to Central America, this area must have been separated from it by this time (Pszczolkowsky, 1978). This is earlier than proposed by other authors (Iturralde-Vinent, 1975). By Late Jurassic time, the northern Cuba–Bahamas region was probably part of the large evaporate basin that covered the whole or part of the Gulf of Mexico (Pardo, 1975).

In central Cuba, in the middle Oxfordian, conditions were such that widespread dolomites and oolitic limestones were deposited. In the latest Jurassic (Tithonian), and into the Neocomian, there was uplift and erosion of Jurassic strata followed by a marked deepening of the basement, particularly to the south, and sedimentation of thin beds of limestones and cherts with abundant nannoplankton and radiolaria.

Although the geochemical characteristics of the igneous rocks of the eugeosynclinal allochthon are yet to be investigated, it is apparent that all components, including oceanic ones, of a Cretaceous island-arc system are present. Unfortunately, the timing of initiation of subduction related to this arc, and its polarity, are not clear. If the stratigraphy and dating are correct, then it is apparent that the metamorphosed mafic and ultramafic rocks in eastern Cuba and those in the Escambray area could represent the remnants of an Early Cretaceous subduction episode (Mattson, 1973, 1979; Millán and Somin, 1984). Mattson (1973, 1979) considered this subduction zone to stretch right along the proto–northern Antillean arc, and oceanic crust was subducted to the north. Other investigators are of the opinion that magmatic activity began before the Cretaceous. Meyerhoff (in Khudoley and Meyerhoff, 1971) concluded that the eugeosyncline began to form in the Tithonian and that a Late Jurassic (pre-Tithonian) unconformity separates the volcanic rocks from the Kimmeridgian(?) and older metamorphic rocks in southern Cuba, but that there is no unconformity in northern Cuba.

A second, younger phase of subduction-related magmatism occurred in the later Cretaceous; this seems to have begun in Aptian-Albian time and produced the volcanic rocks of the Zaza zone (Cabaiguán belt) of central and eastern Cuba. Subduction continued until at least mid-Campanian time when a major hiatus apparently marks the end of subduction and magmatism in the Zaza zone.

Folding and uplift of the central volcanic arc occurred during the mid-Campanian, following the cessation of magmatism. Cooling of the Escambray metamorphic rocks also apparently occurred at this time, and some authors have suggested that obduction of ophiolitic rocks in western Cuba began at this time. A separate subduction segment existed in eastern Cuba; there magmatism continued into the Eocene, as it did on the eastern islands.

Tectonic movements that occurred between the Maastrichtian and early Eocene, although locally important, are reflected only by local discordances and disconformities in the stratigraphic record. This is the so-called Laramide orogenic phase of some authors (see review by Khudoley and Meyerhoff, 1971). The most important pulses are considered to have occurred at 66, 64, and 58 to 54 Ma and are recorded as olistostromes, breccias, and conglomerates reflecting major uplift events, which may have been attributed to the advance of thrust sheets at these times (Pszczolkowski and Flores, written communication, 1984). In the middle Eocene, around 47 to 44 Ma, the Cuban Cretaceous arc structure reached the culmination of its collision with the Bahama platform, an event that caused major thrusting in western and central Cuba and coincides with the time of numerous stratigraphic hiatuses (44 to 45 Ma) in the Caribbean Sea (Moore and others, 1978; Pszczolkowski and Flores, 1984).

In plate-tectonic terms, the collision resulted from consumption of Jurassic-Cretaceous crust to the north along a southward-dipping Benioff zone. Gealey (1980) suggested that the western end of the Cuban arc moved along a transform fault at the margin of the Yucatán Peninsula. If the models suggested by Gealey (1980) and Shein and others (1984) are correct, then part of the subduction zone, the fore-arc basin, and the arc itself were obducted over the Bahama platform as an allochthonous sheet. The crustal shortening implied by these models is probably about 300 km.

Thrusting in eastern Cuba does not seem to be as extensive and dramatic as in western Cuba, possibly because the Sierra Maestra was a separate crustal block attached to northern Hispaniola, which was not deformed so dramatically by the collision event (Wadge and others, 1984). The post–middle Eocene evolution of Cuba, described as the platform stage by Iturralde-Vinent (1977, 1978), is comparatively simple (Meyerhoff and Hatten, 1968; Iturralde-Vinent, 1969). Following the mid-Eocene thrusting event, Cuba developed into a series of uplifted segments or blocks separated by at least eight isolated marine basins. Except for the Cauto Basin, which seems to have been controlled by the Cauto fault zone, the other basins seem to be structural downwarps. In the deeper basins, sedimentation was essentially continuous throughout the late Eocene to at least late Miocene time.

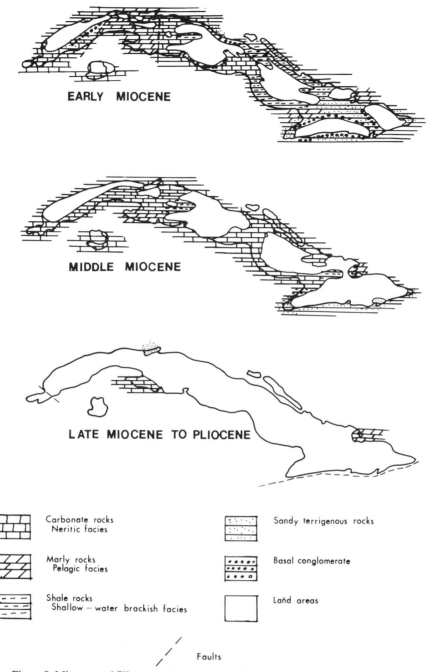

EARLY MIOCENE

MIDDLE MIOCENE

LATE MIOCENE TO PLIOCENE

Carbonate rocks
Neritic facies

Marly rocks
Pelagic facies

Shale rocks
Shallow — water brackish facies

Sandy terrigenous rocks

Basal conglomerate

Land areas

Faults

Figure 8. Miocene and Pliocene paleogeography of Cuba (after Iturralde-Vinent, 1969).

The Cauto Basin contains 2,300 to 2,400 m of middle Eocene–Pliocene rocks in the axial part, and at least 4,000 m of Paleocene through early Miocene sediment was deposited in the Los Palacios Basin in west-central Cuba. Iturralde-Vinent (1969) described the lithofacies and concluded that the Neogene is characterized by atypical transgressive-regressive carbonate sequences.

Throughout the Miocene, the overall history (Fig. 8) is that of gradual emergence of Cuba with changes in facies and gradual restriction in the area of the sedimentary basins. By the end of the middle Miocene, all of the island had emerged except for the Zapata Peninsula of the northernmost Matanzas and part of the Oriente areas. Broad, regional-scale folding of the lower Miocene rocks occurred at this time. Small-scale fold structures resulted from rejuvenated pre-Neogene structures. Diapirs of Jurassic salt, which must have been detached from their source during the Eocene or earlier movements, underwent further migration along the major faults during the mid-Tertiary. According to Meyerhoff and Hatten (1968), the latest diapiric movements were post-Miocene.

HISPANIOLA

J. F. Lewis, G. Draper, C. Bowin, L. Bourdon,
F. Maurrasse, and F. Nagle

GENERAL FEATURES OF THE
PHYSIOGRAPHY AND GEOLOGY

Hispaniola is the second-largest island in the Greater Antilles and is divided politically into two countries. Haiti occupies the western part of the island, and the Dominican Republic the eastern part. The island is situated on the east-west–trending Greater Antilles platform and is separated from Cuba to the northwest by the Windward Passage (4,000 m deep), from Jamaica to the west-southwest by the Jamaica Passage (3,000 m deep), and to the east from Puerto Rico by the Mona Passage (Plate 1). The Old Bahama Channel, which is the westward geomorphic extension of the Puerto Rico Trench, separates Hispaniola from the Bahama Banks to the north.

Five physiographic-structural trends converge in Hispaniola: the main axis of the Greater Antilles, the Cayman Trench, the Nicaraguan rise, the Beata ridge, and the Bahamas-Cuba intersection. Thus, Hispaniola often has been referred to as the "structural knot" of the northern Caribbean (Weaver, 1977).

Hispaniola contains the highest elevations and some of the most rugged topography in the northern Caribbean, and its physiography is characterized by the alternation of three major valleys and four main mountain ranges (Fig. 9). In the central and northwestern part of the country the mountain ranges trend about N40–50°W, oblique to the main axis of the island. As noted by Vaughan and others, (1921), this trend is parallel to the structural grain of central and eastern Cuba. In contrast, the mountains of the Massif de la Hotte and Massif de la Selle of the Southern Peninsula trend east-west, parallel to the axis of the island and the Greater Antilles as a whole.

The geology of Hispaniola (Fig. 10) has recently been summarized by Bowin (1975) and updated by Lewis (1980). Earlier major regional geological studies in the Dominican Republic include those of Vaughan and others (1921), Weyl (1941), many unpublished oil company reports, Bowin (1960, 1966), Palmer (1963, 1979), and Nagle (1966, 1979). In Haiti, early investigations were made by Woodring and others (1924), and Butterlin (1960). The basic stratigraphy in Haiti is contained in the works of Jones (1918), Woodring and others (1924), and Butterlin (1960). In the Dominican Republic the main references are Vaughan and others (1921), Bermúdez (1949), and Bowin (1975). An outline of much of the stratigraphy in Hispaniola as known prior to 1955 is contained in the report by Butterlin and others (1965). This publication contains references to many unpublished reports of the work of oil companies done in the 1940s. The review by Bowin (1975) contains a general summary of the stratigraphy in Hispaniola. Stratigraphic columns compiled for representative morphotectonic zones are on Plate 5A. Regional compilations by the Organization of American States (1966) re-

sulted in geological maps at 1:250,000 of the Dominican Republic (Blesch, 1966) and Haiti (Organization of American States, 1972). Exploration in Haiti by the United Nations has resulted in a geological map compilation at 1:200,000 (United Nations, 1979). A modified version of this map (at 1:1,000,000) has been published by Vila and others (1983). A bibliography of geological literature on Hispaniola was compiled by Pagan (1976). The libraries of the Dirección General de Minería in the Dominican Republic and the Bureau de Mines et Energetiques in Haiti contain unpublished reports of specific regions and projects.

During the past ten years, much new data has become available from programs directed toward exploration for economic resources, and also from academic research. Our understanding of geologic relations has improved markedly, but many basic problems have yet to be resolved.

At this time, a number of new papers on the geology of Hispaniola, not reviewed here, are being assembled for a Geological Society of America Special Paper.

REGIONAL GEOPHYSICAL DATA

Gravity measurements in the Haitian part of Hispaniola have been made by Bowin (1968, unpublished data) and in the Dominican Republic by the Inter-American Geodetic Survey, the Cartographic Institute, Bowin (1968), and Reblin (1973). Free air and Bouguer anomaly maps for Hispaniola were published by Bowin (1975), and the data are included in regional maps (Bowin, 1976) (Plate 7).

Although no on-land seismic-refraction surveys are available for Hispaniola, marine seismic-refraction data are available for the area southeast of Cuba across the Jamaica Passage and the Beata ridge. Some profiles have been reproduced in the contribution by Case and others (Plate 2r).

MAJOR GEOLOGIC AND STRUCTURAL FEATURES
AND MORPHOTECTONIC ZONES

Hispaniola is a complex island-arc structure (Fig. 10) that evolved from at least Early Cretaceous time. Metamorphic rocks occur in belts of mafic greenschists, greenstones, felsic metavolcanic rocks, and serpentinized peridotite in the middle of the island, and blueschists, serpentinites, and associated rocks form a separate zone along the island's north coast. Volcanic and volcaniclastic rocks dominate the Upper Cretaceous sections, and in the center of the island arc intruded by Late Cretaceous–early Tertiary granitoid plutons. Extensive pelagic limestones were deposited over the southwestern part of the island during the Paleocene and Eocene. Strike-slip faulting, which had begun by the mid-Tertiary, resulted in the formation of deep basins in which thick sequences of clastic sediments accumulated.

The island and its surroundings can be divided into physiographic zones, each of which also has distinct geologic characteristics. These morphotectonic zones (Lewis, 1980) or terranes (Case and others, 1984) generally form WNW-ESE–trending

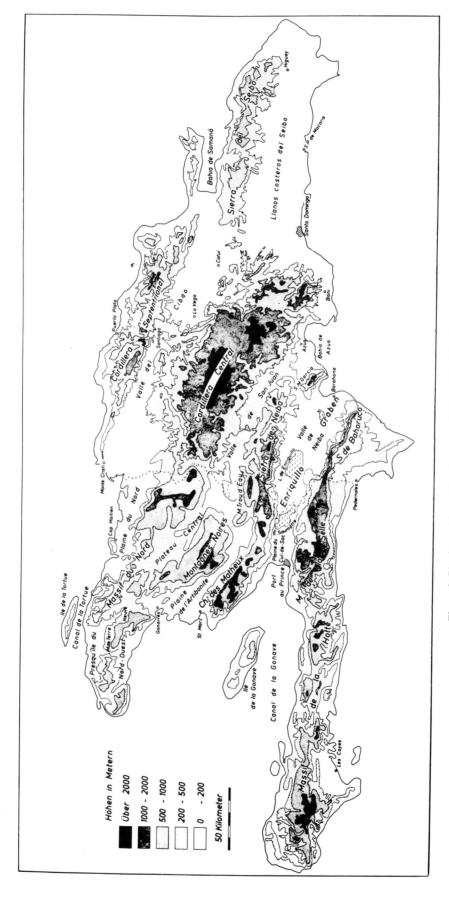

Figure 9. Physiographic and locality map of Hispaniola (after Weyl, 1966).

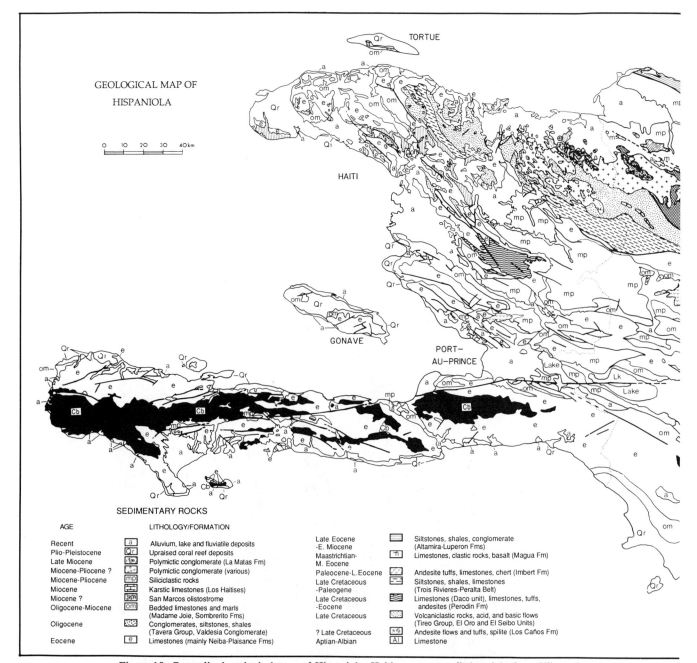

GEOLOGICAL MAP OF
HISPANIOLA

0 10 20 30 40km

TORTUE

HAITI

GONAVE

PORT-
AU-PRINCE

SEDIMENTARY ROCKS

AGE		LITHOLOGY/FORMATION
Recent	a	Alluvium, lake and fluviatile deposits
Plio-Pleistocene	Qr	Upraised coral reef deposits
Late Miocene	Lm	Polymictic conglomerate (La Matas Fm)
Miocene-Pliocene ?		Polymictic conglomerate (various)
Miocene-Pliocene	mp	Siliciclastic rocks
Miocene		Karstic limestones (Los Haitises)
Miocene ?	Sm	San Marcos olistostrome
Oligocene-Miocene	om	Bedded limestones and marls (Madame Joie, Sombrerito Fms)
Oligocene		Conglomerates, siltstones, shales (Tavera Group, Valdesia Conglomerate)
Eocene	e	Limestones (mainly Neiba-Plaisance Fms)

Late Eocene -E. Miocene		Siltstones, shales, conglomerate (Altamira-Luperon Fms)
Maastrichtian- M. Eocene	m	Limestones, clastic rocks, basalt (Magua Fm)
Paleocene-L.Eocene		Andesite tuffs, limestones, chert (Imbert Fm)
Late Cretaceous -Paleogene		Siltstones, shales, limestones (Trois Rivieres-Peralta Belt)
Late Cretaceous -Eocene		Limestones (Daco unit), limestones, tuffs, andesites (Perodin Fm)
Late Cretaceous		Volcaniclastic rocks, acid, and basic flows (Tireo Group, El Oro and El Seibo Units)
? Late Cretaceous		Andesite flows and tuffs, spilite (Los Caños Fm)
Aptian-Albian	Al	Limestone

Figure 10. Generalized geological map of Hispaniola. Haitian part compiled mainly from Vila and others (1983). Dominican part compiled from various sources especially Blesch (1966), Bowin (1975), Eberle and others (1982), Breuner (1985), Bourdon (1985), Mann and others (1986, unpublished compilation maps at 1:100,000), and J. F. Lewis (unpublished data).

belts (Fig. 11). The boundaries between the zones are mainly tectonic and are generally well defined. The zones are as follows:

Zone 1   Old Bahama channel

Zone 2   North Coast belt (Cordillera Septentrional–Peninsula de Samaná)

Zone 3   Valle del Cibao

Zone 4   Cordillera Central (Massif du Nord–Cordillera Central–Presqu'île du Nord-Ouest; Ile de la Tortue)

Zone 5   Northwestern South-central zone (Plateau Central–Valle de San Juan; Llanura de Azúa; Sierra de Ocoa; Montagnes Noires; Chaines des Matheux; Sierra de Neiba–Sierra de Martín García; San Cristóbal–San Pedro Basins; Ile de la Gonave)

Zone 6   Plaine du Cul de Sac–Valle de Enriquillo

Zone 7   Presqu'île du Sud–Peninsula del Sur (Massif de la Selle–Massif de la Hotte–Sierra de Bahoruco)

Zone 8   Peninsula del Este; Sierra del Seibo; Llanos costeros del Seibo

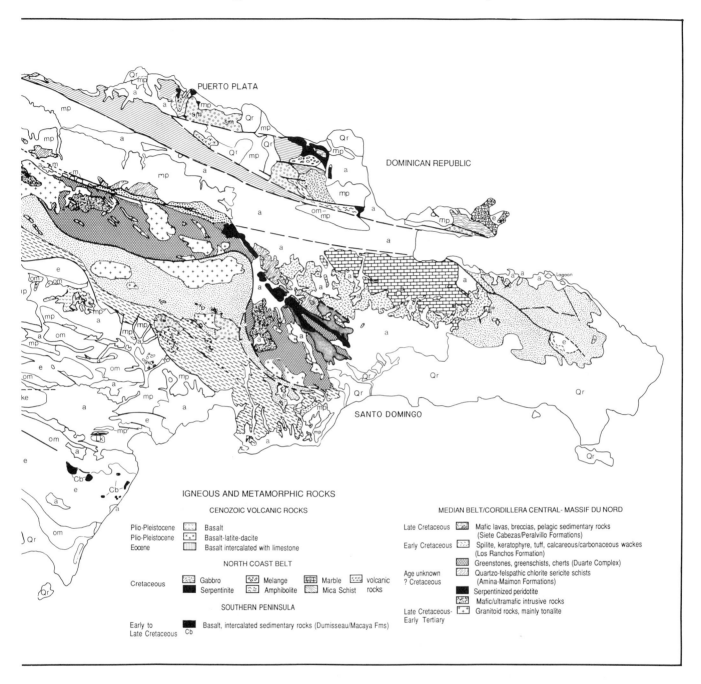

IGNEOUS AND METAMORPHIC ROCKS

CENOZOIC VOLCANIC ROCKS

Plio-Pleistocene		Basalt
Plio-Pleistocene		Basalt-latite-dacite
Eocene		Basalt intercalated with limestone

NORTH COAST BELT

Cretaceous		Gabbro		Melange		Marble		volcanic
		Serpentinite		Amphibolite		Mica Schist		rocks

SOUTHERN PENINSULA

Early to Late Cretaceous	Cb	Basalt, intercalated sedimentary rocks (Dumisseau/Macaya Fms)

MEDIAN BELT/CORDILLERA CENTRAL- MASSIF DU NORD

Late Cretaceous		Mafic lavas, breccias, pelagic sedimentary rocks (Siete Cabezas/Peralvillo Formations)
Early Cretaceous		Spilite, keratophyre, tuff, calcareous/carbonaceous wackes (Los Ranchos Formation)
		Greenstones, greenschists, cherts (Duarte Complex)
Age unknown ? Cretaceous		Quartzo-felspathic chlorite sericite schists (Amina-Maimon Formations)
		Serpentinized peridotite
		Mafic/ultramafic intrusive rocks
Late Cretaceous- Early Tertiary		Granitoid rocks, mainly tonalite

A summary of the features of most of the major faults and lineaments on Hispaniola is given in Figure 11. Although no definitive statement can yet be made about the complex fracture patterns on Hispaniola, recent studies of some of the major faults and lineaments have given a better understanding of these features. For example, Duplan (1974) and others have shown the dominance of a northwest- and a northeast-trending fracture system. The young volcanic centers lie at the intersections of these fractures (OLADE, 1980; Vespucci, 1982).

Studies of the Peninsula del Sur fault zone by Mann and others (1984b) and Calmus (1983) have shown the existence of small pull-apart basins and fault trough structures, which indi-

cates the general transtensional nature of the fault zone. Mann and others (1984a) consider that the Camú and Septentrional faults in the north are transpressional or convergent strike-slip fault systems. They further consider that the dominance of reverse and oblique strike-slip faults in northern and west-central Hispaniola suggests that this part of island constitutes a restraining bend in the east-west–trending plate-boundary zone.

ZONE 1: OLD BAHAMA CHANNEL (TRENCH)

The Old Bahama Channel, which is the westward geomorphic extension of the Puerto Rico Trench, is a major trench-like

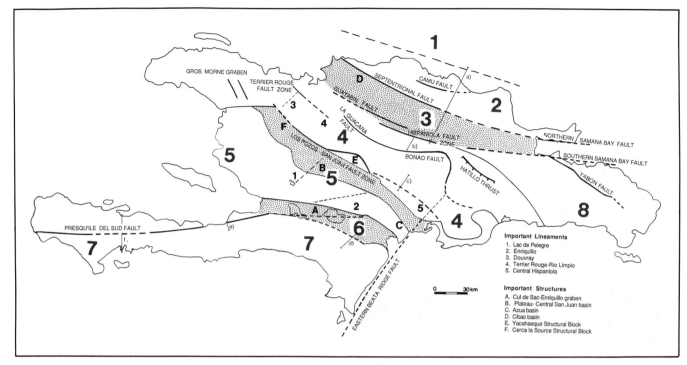

Figure 11. Morphotectonic zones, major faults and lineaments, and major structures in Hispaniola (after Lewis, 1980).

feature situated between the Bahama Platform to the north and the Greater Antillean (Hispaniola) platform to the south. The deepest part of the trench is 4,100 m. Richardson (1977) pointed out that the channel shallows considerably to the west near the Windward Passage, where it bifurcates into the Cayman Trough (south of Cuba) and the western Old Bahama Channel (north of Cuba). The southern slope of the trench is steeper than the northern slope, in agreement with the southern polarity of possible limited subduction, as suggested from the earthquake data. There are more than 400 m of horizontal and southward-dipping calcareous and siliceous turbidites in the trench, disturbed by what appear to be normal faults (Richardson, 1977). Dredge samples from the south wall of the western Puerto Rico Trench include serpentinite, greenschist, and marble, indicating an apparent northern and eastern continuation of the Hispaniolan high-P/low-T metamorphic belt of Zone 2 (Perfit and others, 1980; Nagle, 1974).

ZONE 2: CORDILLERA SEPTENTRIONAL–PENINSULA DE SAMANÁ (NORTH COAST BELT)

This zone forms the most northerly belt of mountains in the Dominican Republic, with an average topographic elevation of about 500 m and some peaks that attain altitudes of 1,000 to 1,400 m. Most of the region is composed of sedimentary rocks of Cenozoic age, but pre-Eocene rocks occur in the Samaná Peninsula, south of Río San Juan and around Puerto Plata (Fig. 12; Plate 5A) (Nagle, 1974). These areas contain igneous and meta-

morphic rocks, including serpentinites, which are of Cretaceous to Paleocene age. Each of these areas of older rock has a distinct character, and is described below.

Samaná Peninsula

The presence of metamorphic rocks in the Samaná Peninsula was first reported by Vaughan and others (1921). Nagle (1974) gave a brief description of the geology and reported the presence of blueschists and eclogites close to the town of Samaná.

Further studies by Joyce (1982, 1983) have revealed that most of the metamorphic rocks in the peninsula form a coherent terrane that can be divided into a unit of mica schists with minor marble bands and a marble unit with minor mica schist bands. These rocks constitute a low-grade zone characterized by the presence of lawsonite and/or pumpellyite, which occurs in schists throughout the peninsula. Blueschists, eclogites, and calc-silicate gneisses are found as layers within mica schists and marbles in a narrow, 1- to 2-km-wide, 10-km-long belt in the southeast portion of the peninsula. Within this zone, a mélange-like body with an altered ultramafic matrix also occurs (Draper and Nagle, 1989). Blocks in the body are composed of eclogite, blueschist, and calcite-rich metasomatites. The eclogites in both the coherent terrane and the mélange-like body are composed of garnet and pale green omphacites, with accessory carbonate, mica, epidote, and rutile. Many eclogite blocks have zoned rinds, or envelopes, of glaucophane schist (Joyce, 1982). Mafic blueschists contain glaucophane, garnet, paragonitic and phengitic mica, pumpellyite, and epidote. Joyce (1982) estimated that prograde recrystallization of blueschist and eclogite assemblages in the coherent terrane took place at 400 to 500°C and 10 Kb. In contrast, Perfit and others (1982) estimated that eclogite blocks in the mélange equilibrated at about 600°C and 20 Kb. Many rocks show evidence of partial metasomatism, and this probably makes estimates of prograde temperatures and pressures unreliable.

Perfit and McCulloch (1982) obtained a Sm-Nd age of 78 ± 30 Ma on a garnet-glaucophane pair in an eclogite from the mélange, whereas a Rb/Sr isochron from co-existing mica-glaucophane gave an age of 90 ± 10 Ma. These ages (about 85 Ma) are consistent with K-Ar ages on glaucophane from the coherent terrane by Joyce and Aronson (1989), who found that K-Ar ages from micas are concordant and in the range of 37 to 40 Ma. Thus, it appears that the high-pressure assemblages equilibrated in Late Cretaceous time, but the blocking temperature of the mica was not reached until the late Eocene.

Structural studies by Joyce (1982) indicate three important deformation phases within the main body of the Samaná terrane. As in the other pre-Neogene inliers, serpentinite is present in the Samaná area, but the Samaná bodies are small and appear to be lenticular bodies associated with fault zones. One of these is in contact with overlying Neogene limestones, and hence its emplacement is probably associated with neotectonic activity.

Río San Juan complex

This complex of igneous and metamorphic rocks lies between Puerto Plata and the Samaná Peninsula (Fig. 12). The first account of this region appears to have been in an unpublished report by Beall (1944). Further information was given by Nagle (1974), but it was not until the report of Eberle and others (1982) that a preliminary map and description of all the major rock units present were available. At the time of this writing (1984–1986) the area was being investigated by G. Draper and F. Nagle, and the description here is based on their results.

There are four major units in the region (Fig. 12). The northern part of the area contains large bodies of tectonized serpentinite that are closely associated with a schist terrane dominated by fine-grained greenschist rocks. A second schist terrane on the southern border of the region is composed of coarse-grained amphibolite-facies rocks. The two schist terranes are separated by a gabbroic intrusive complex.

Eberle and others (1982) and Draper and Nagle (1985, and unpublished data) have shown that the northern schist terrane is composed of four separate units: (1) the Hicotea schists, a fine-grained brecciated schist; (2) the Puerca Gorda schists, mafic schists with minor mica schist bands; (3) the El Guineal schists, mica schists with minor mafic bands; and (4) the Jagua Clara and Arroyo Sabana mélanges, mélange units of blueschist blocks within a metasomatically altered ultramafic matrix.

Although these units generally display greenschist-facies assemblages, fine-grained lawsonite and glaucophane are developed in some samples of the Puerca Gorda and especially the Hicotea schists. Between these two units is the Jagua Clara mélange (the "megabreccia" unit of Eberle and others, 1982) of high-pressure metamorphic blocks in an altered, serpentiniferous matrix. The blocks of the matrix are of several lithologies, but coarse-grained garnet blueschists and greenstones with large (2 to 5 cm) garnets (retrograded eclogites) are the most common. Many blocks have a rind of actinolite and some seem to be composed entirely of coarse-grained actinolite.

The Cuaba amphibolites form a southern schist-gneiss terrane on the southern border of the Río San Juan complex. The rocks are dominantly mafic in composition in the western end of the outcrop, but appear to be intermediate in composition farther

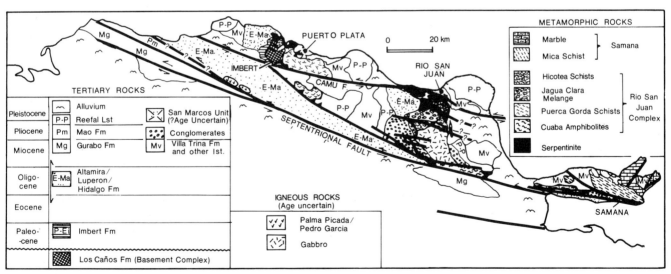

Figure 12. Simplified geological map of the Cordillera Septentrional, Samaná region, Dominican Republic. Compiled from Nagle (1966), Eberle and others (1982), Joyce (1982), and unpublished data of Draper and Nagle.

to the east. In addition to the common hornblende-plagioclase-epidote assemblages, garnet occurs in the central and eastern parts of the outcrop, and may attain diameters of up to 2 cm. The Río Boba intrusive suite, which divides the two schist terranes, is dominantly gabbroic, but ultramafic and dioritic compositions are also present. The gabbros intrude the Cuaba amphibolites, but along the northern boundary of the Río Bobo body the contacts are all faults. Therefore, the two southernmost units are considered to be genetically separate from the northern schists.

The three major serpentinite bodies of the North Coast region are protrusive, brecciated bodies, which contain inclusions of other rocks found in the Río San Juan complex. Rare metamorphic inclusions occur (Weyl, 1941; Nagle, 1974), but the most common inclusions are rounded cobbles of rocks from the intrusive suite. The serpentinites were probably emplaced during Neogene tectonic activity as cold diapiric intrusions into the surrounding Altamira Formation, although some sedimentary serpentinite types may be present.

Puerto Plata, Pedro Garcia, and Palma Picada areas

Pre-Eocene rocks, exposed in three areas in the western part of the Cordillera Septentrional, are distinguished from the Samaná and Río San Juan regions by the presence of volcanic rocks.

The Puerto Plata area has a complicated pre-Paleocene basement composed of serpentinite, gabbro, and volcanic rocks in a complex relationship (Nagle 1966, 1971a, 1974, 1979; Eberle and others, 1982; Pindell, 1985). Massive brecciated serpentinite occurs in four major bodies and several smaller ones. Just north of the Camú fault, blueschists, amphibolite, and black marble occur as tectonic blocks in a brecciated serpentiniferous matrix.

Gabbroic and dioritic blocks are common inclusions in the serpentinite and are often very large. In other places, gabbro appears to intrude serpentinite as dikes that are often converted to rodingite. The volcanic rocks of the Los Caños Formation also seem to be part of this complex (Pindell, 1985), rather than overlying it as originally suggested by Nagle (1966). The Los Caños rocks are mainly andesitic(?) flows and tuffs, but mafic spilites also occur. Pillow lavas and hyaloclastites indicate a submarine origin for these rocks. Overlying the Los Caños Formation is a 1-km-thick deformed sequence of deposits with interbedded dacitic tuffs known as the Imbert Formation (Nagle, 1966; Pindell, 1985). Fossils in cherts and thin limestones indicate a Paleocene–early Eocene age, which is the last dated volcanism in the region.

The Pedro García region, south of Puerto Plata, contains tuffs, mafic amygdaloidal lava flows, and basaltic dikes and is intruded by a small tonalite stock. Lava flows, which are apparently the oldest unit present, contain veins of chalcocite and native copper. Bowin and Nagle (1982) reported a preliminary whole-rock K-Ar date of 72 ± 7 Ma on a mafic flow from this unit.

Eberle and others (1982) also reported a porphyry body of intermediate composition in the Palma Picada area, situated in the southwest portion of the Cordillera Septentrional. No isotopic dates are available for this body, but overlying shales yield a middle Eocene coccolith fauna, thus indicating that the body is early Eocene or older in age.

Eocene and post-Eocene rocks

Sedimentary rocks of Eocene and post-Eocene age rest unconformably on the Cretaceous-Paleocene(?) basement rocks and are the dominant rock type in the Cordillera Central and Samaná Peninsula.

To the west of Puerto Plata, the La Isla limestone (Nagle, 1966, 1979) forms prominent hills and rests unconformably on the basement complex. The age of this shallow-water limestone unit is controversial. Nagle (1966) was unable to find paleontological evidence, but suggested a post–middle Eocene age because he believed it to rest unconformably on the San Marcos "olistostrome" unit (see below). Pindell (1985) suggested that the La Isla limestone rests unconformably upon the Imbert, but beneath the San Marcos olistostrome unit. Early Tertiary(?) fossil fragments (E. Robinson, reported by Pindell, 1985), when combined with the Maastrichtian-Paleocene age reported by Bourgois and others (1982), suggest a Paleocene age for the La Isla; thus, the La Isla may be younger than or equivalent to the Imbert Formation.

Extensive siltstone-shale-sandstone "turbidite" sequences with intercalated conglomerate horizons of apparent late Eocene age are exposed in the central Cordillera Septentrional south of the Camú fault (Fig. 12), and with equivalent-age clastic sediments north of the Camú fault. In the Luperón area these have been mapped as the Altamira and Luperón Formations, respectively (Nagle, 1966, 1979; Eberle and others, 1982; Redmond, 1982a and b; Pindell, 1985). The two units seem to be contemporaneous, but were probably deposited in separate basins, or as different lobes of a submarine fan (Eberle and others, 1982). Although most studies of the microfauna (Bermúdez, 1949; Bourgois and others, 1982; Robinson, 1980, unpublished; Čepec, 1982, unpublished) indicate a late Eocene to Oligocene age for Altamira and Luperón Formations, Baroni-Urbani and Saunders (1982) report the presence of early Miocene microfossils from beds close to the amber-bearing strata in the Altamira Formation. Thus, it is possible that the deposition of the Altamira Formation spanned the late Eocene to early Miocene.

The Dominican Republic is famous for its amber, most of which comes from the upper parts of the Altamira Formation. Besides commercial importance, amber is of interest to paleontologists because it yields a rich arthropod and vertebrate fauna (Sanderson and Farr, 1960; Baroni-Urbani and Saunders, 1982).

The Altamira and Luperón Formations are folded and unconformably overlain by shallowly dipping Neogene conglomerates, marls, and limestones of the Villa Trina Formation. Marls with intercalated bioclastic horizons are found at Pico Isabela de Torres near Puerto Plata and in the central Cordillera Septentrional, east of Puerto Plata. The rocks are well bedded, and certain horizons contain synsedimentary slump-fold structures.

The rocks at Isabela de Torres were dated as early to middle Miocene age by Nagle (1966), but middle to late Miocene age by Bourgois and others (1982). Relatively flat-lying conglomerates to the southwest and southeast of the Río San Juan complex are probably contemporaneous with the marls, although Eberle and others (1982) suggested that some of these could represent Quaternary deposits.

Considerable controversy exists over the structure, age, and origin of the San Marcos olistostrome originally described by Nagle (1966, 1972). This chaotic unit is exposed over a wide area east of Puerto Plata, and contains large blocks, up to several tens of meters across, in a clay matrix. The blocks include lithologies from the other units of the area and have been interpreted by Nagle (1966, 1972) to represent an Eocene submarine-gravity-slide deposit. Bourgois and others (1982) considered the San Marcos unit to be of early to middle Miocene age or later, containing blocks of Cretaceous to mid-Miocene rocks. Pindell (1985) has suggested that the San Marcos unit may overlie all other units in the area and resulted from mud diapirism associated with post–mid-Miocene tectonic movements.

In the Samaná Peninsula, limestone conglomerates and coral-bearing yellow limestones overlie the metamorphic rocks. These limestones have not been the subject of recent investigations, but Vaughan and others (1921) gave an Oligocene-Miocene age based on corals collected from a limestone unit. Miocene-Pliocene lignite, lignitic clays, conglomerates, and limestones occur in the narrow strip on the southwestern shore of the peninsula (Vaughan and others, 1921; Joyce, 1982; Rosario Dominicana, unpublished reports).

Pliocene to Pleistocene reefal limestones form a cap over the Miocene marls in much of the Cordillera Septentrional (Eberle and others, 1982), and possibly also in the Samaná Peninsula. This cap dips very gently to the north and has a well-developed "mogote"-type karst topography.

Structural and tectonic evolution

The presence of 85-m.y.-old blueschist metamorphic and associated rocks in the eastern part of the North Coast belt indicates that at least part of the belt was a subduction zone from Late Cretaceous time (Nagle, 1971a, 1974). Volcanic rocks in the western part of the belt suggest, however, a volcanic-arc setting for Late Cretaceous to early Eocene. Eberle and others (1982) suggested that these two regions represented fragments of an island-arc "paired belt." Bowin and Nagle (1982), on the other hand, explained this same juxtaposition of rocks by suggesting that the pre-Eocene of the North Coast belt represents a zone of tectonic mixing of trench-derived and arc-derived rocks. The concentration of volcanic rocks in the western part of the belt is not explained by any of these authors, however. Structural trends in the metamorphic rocks of the Samaná Peninsula and the Río San Juan complex strike northwest-southeast, and possibly this represents the trend of the Cretaceous island arc. Structures such as the Camú and Septentrional faults, which cut obliquely

through this earlier trend, may thus expose both a portion of the trench terrane and a portion of the arc terrane in the present WNW-ESE–trending belt.

Because Eocene and early Miocene rocks are strongly deformed in the Cordillera Septentrional, this major Neogene deformation probably took place during middle to late Miocene time and thus would seem to be related to Neogene left-lateral shear on the northern Caribbean plate boundary. Nonetheless, it has been difficult to assess the extent of strike-slip displacement on the major faults due to the lack of suitable offset rock units. The only such attempt was that of Eberle and others (1982), who suggested that the ultramafic rocks of the Puerto Plata region, north of the Camú fault, were once connected to those of the Río San Juan complex, south of the eastward extension of the Camú fault. If this is correct, it implies a displacement of some 60 km.

It is apparent that the North Coast belt is still tectonically active because Pleistocene reef terraces and the elevated coastal topography point to continued uplift (Horsfield, 1975).

ZONE 3: VALLE DEL CIBAO (CIBAO BASIN)

The Cibao Basin contains a thick, essentially conformable, marine, siliciclastic carbonate succession of Miocene-Pliocene age. The succession (Yaque Group) is well exposed in the rivers that have dissected the broad peneplain (or piedmont plateau of Antonini, 1968, 1979) in the southern part of the valley. These Neogene deposits are well known for their fossil content, and their paleontology and stratigraphy have been the subject of recent detailed studies (Saunders and others, 1982). Bowin (1960, p. 179) estimated about 9 km of sedimentary fill near Santiago from gravity data, and drilling showed over 4 km of Pliocene sediments without reaching basement. The sedimentary strata are nearly horizontal, and faulting and post-depositional folding is minimal in contrast to those in the San Juan and Enriquillo Basins. The lowermost unit, the Bulla conglomerate of early Miocene age, overlies the Tavera Group clastic succession of Oligocene age with strong unconformity. Such facies presumably resulted from rapid uplift of the Cordillera Central in early Miocene time. The succession was deposited under conditions ranging from shallow shelf to deep water (Evans, 1986). Thin, but distinct areas of piedmont plains deposits overlie the Neogene sediments (Antonini, 1968, 1979).

ZONE 4. CORDILLERA CENTRAL–MASSIF DU NORD–PRESQU'ILE DU NORD-OUEST

The Cordillera Central–Massif du Nord (Fig. 9), which is the main mountain system in Hispaniola, consists of principally Cretaceous volcanic, metamorphic, and plutonic rocks. These major lithologies are contained within fault-bounded parallel belts, which form the main structural grain of the central part of the island (Fig. 10).

For convenience of description and the understanding of relations, the rock units are divided into eight groups (Figs. 10

and 11; largely after Bowin, 1966): (1) the Median belt of meta-morphosed and undated formations, (2) Cretaceous formations northeast of the Median belt, (3) Tertiary rocks of the Hispaniola fault zone, (4) Upper Cretaceous volcanic and volcaniclastic rocks in the central Cordillera Central–Massif du Nord, (5) Presqu'ile du Nord-Ouest d'Haiti, (6) Tortue Island, (7) Upper Cretaceous sedimentary rocks of the southwest Cordillera Central–Massif du Nord, and (8) plutonic rocks of the Cordillera Central–Massif du Nord.

Median belt

Metamorphic units. Two lithologically and structurally distinct metamorphic units of greenschist grade, the Amina-Maimón Schists and the Duarte complex, occur in the Median belt separated by a wide fault zone (the Hispaniola fault zone of Bowin, 1975), within which major bodies of serpentinized peridotite and associated mafic volcanic rock occur.

The Maimón Schists are foliated, regionally metamorphosed rocks that occur in the northeast part of the Median belt (Bowin, 1966). Mapping by geologists from Rosario Dominicana S.A. and Falconbridge Dominicana S.A. have shown that about 90 percent of the Maimón Schists protolith consists of volcanic or volcaniclastic rocks, with the remaining 10 percent consisting of limestone, shale, sandstone, and graphite schists with syngenetic massive sulfides and siliceous iron-formations. Although the larger part of the Maimón Schists are moderately to well foliated, some areas previously mapped as Maimón Schists are composed of massive mafic rock (S. E. Kesler, personal communication, 1986). About one-third or more of the Maimón rocks are silicic (dacite and/or keratophyre) and are characterized by albite-quartz-sericite metamorphic assemblages. The remainder is mafic to intermediate in composition, in which epidote-chlorite-bearing assemblages are common.

Farther to the west, similar rocks are exposed that were mapped as the Amina Schists by Palmer (1963, 1979) and Antonini (1968, 1979). They have been studied in more detail by Draper and Lewis (1982), who showed that the rocks of the Amina Schists are mainly tightly folded, multilayered metasediments consisting of competent leucocratic, quartzo-feldspathic layers alternating with darker green, mafic layers. Other lithologies include laminated schists, quartzites, and metaconglomerates. The protolith of the Amina Schists, therefore, appears to be sedimentary, but of volcanic provenance. The commonly occurring minerals are chlorite, epidote, quartz, and albite, with minor actinolite and muscovite. Several lithologies, such as epidote-chlorite–rich greenschists and the metaconglomerates, are common to both the Amina and Maimón Schists. The lithologic correlations and similarities in structural position and style strongly indicate the equivalence of the Amina and Maimón Formations (Bowin, 1975; Draper and Lewis, 1982). Chemical analyses determined for representative lithologies show that the Amina Schists are essentially bimodal and range from basaltic to quartz keratophyric composition (Draper and Lewis, 1982). All

rocks are characterized by high Fe/Mg ratios and very low K contents. Draper and Lewis (1982) also found that the Amina Schists exhibit an S-tectonite fabric that has been tightly folded with a north-northeast vergence and a later, orthogonal folding episode, which produced open chevron folds.

The Duarte complex (Bowin, 1966; Draper and Lewis, 1989) is composed of mainly massive, and in places schistose, regionally metamorphosed mafic volcanic rocks. The same belt of metabasic rocks probably extends westward into Haiti, where a complex suite of metabasic volcanic rock crops out in the northeastern Massif du Nord (Nicolini, 1977). The greenstones and greenschists of the Duarte complex are mainly metabasalts consisting of varying proportions of actinolite-tremolite, chlorite, epidote, albite, and opaque minerals. High-magnesium types occur as tremolite-chlorite rock. The orientation of the foliation is generally steeply inclined and parallel to the regional structural trends, although locally the structures are complex.

North of Jarabacoa, Palmer (1963, 1979) found the sequence of spilitic lavas, mafic metatuff, intrusive diabase, minor carbonaceous phyllite, cherts, and calcareous shale to be of low-grade subgreenschist facies and that the rocks graded southward into the main greenschist facies of the Duarte Formation. West of Jarabacoa, at El Yujo, Duarte metabasic volcanic rocks are separated from metamorphosed intermediate and felsic rock types by a sequence of carbonaceous shales, cherts, and limestones (Francisco Contreras, personal communication, 1985). There seems to be considerable resemblance between the sedimentary, mafic, and felsic rocks of this area and those of the Siete Cabezas and Maimón units.

Bowin (1975) and Palmer (1979) suggested that the Duarte Formation might be metamorphosed oceanic crust, but this interpretation may be overly simplistic. Geochemical investigations of the metabasaltic rocks suggest that, although the protolith of the Duarte complex has oceanic affinities, it is enriched in large ion lithophile elements that give the Duarte rocks a geochemical signature similar to that of Pacific seamounts. Thus, the Duarte complex may possibly be part of a seamount structure or, alternatively, represents the very earliest volcanic products of the Hispaniolan island arc (Lewis and others, 1983; Draper and Lewis, 1989; Lewis and Jimenez, 1986). Duarte metabasic rocks also show similarities with the Cretaceous basalts of the Southern Peninsula of Haiti (Donnelly and others, this volume).

Undated, unmetamorphosed rocks of the Median belt. Bowin (1966) gave the name Peravillo Formation to the unmetamorphosed volcanic rocks that lie in fault contact between the Loma Caribe peridotite and the Maimón Schists (Prince, 1981, unpublished).

Another belt of volcanic rocks, the Siete Cabezas Formation (Bowin, 1966), underlies the high terrain immediately southwest of the Loma Caribe peridotite and is probably equivalent to the Peravillo Formation. The rocks are predominantly vitric basalt flows, but include minor breccias and subordinate tuffs, wackes, and cherts. The contact with the Duarte complex to the south is mainly a high-angle fault. Cenomanian-Coniacian ages have been reported (Boisseau, 1987) from cherts of the formation, and geo-chemical data indicate a strong similarity between the composition of oceanic basalts and that of the Siete Cabezas' vitric lavas (Donnelly and Rogers, 1978).

Formations northeast of the Median belt

Rocks north of the Hatillo thrust, which is the northeast boundary of the Median belt, are virtually unmetamorphosed. The main rocks exposed in the Hatillo area are the keratophyres, basalts, and clastic deposits of the Los Ranchos Formation of apparent Aptian-Albian age. Russell and others (1980, 1982) and Kesler and others (1981) have divided the Los Ranchos Formation into four members, including: the Zambrana member, a black limestone containing plant remains of Early Cretaceous age; and the Pueblo Viejo member, composed of volcanogenic conglomerate and sandstone, carbonaceous pyritic sedimentary rock, and quartz keratophyre. The latter member hosts the gold-silver orebody of the Puebo Viejo mine. The Los Ranchos Formation is overlain in the south by the Hatillo limestone, which is dated as Aptian-Albian (Bowin, 1966). This establishes the Los Ranchos Formation as the oldest unmetamorphosed rocks on the island. Mapping by the Dirección General de Minería (Brouwer and Brouwer, 1982), and Bourdon (1985) has shown that rocks of the Los Ranchos Formation extend east from Hatillo for 270 km to the Yabón fault (Zone 8).

Other units in the northern region include the Las Cañas limestone of Late Cretaceous age and the unconformably overlying, tuffaceous Loma Caballero Formation of Paleocene–middle Eocene age.

Tertiary rocks of the Hispaniola fault zone

Palmer (1963, 1979) gave the name "Magua Formation" to a narrow fault-bounded belt of indurated conglomerate, sandstone, mudstone, limestone, and volcanic rocks, which are exposed within the San Juan de las Matas graben structure or pull-apart basin along the Hispaniola fault zone. The age of the unit is Maastrichtian to Eocene, possibly middle Eocene.

Mapping by Antonini (1979) and United Nations geologists in the Moncion area, and by C. Monster (unpublished data) farther west, has shown that other isolated exposures of volcano-genic sediments, basalts, and Eocene limestones occur along a narrow northwest-trending belt that lies between outcrops of the Duarte complex and Amina Schists.

It now seems that the Hispaniola fault zone, including the lower Tertiary units within it, extends along a west-northwest trend into Haiti, south of Tortue Island (Fig. 10). It is also possible that some of the rocks of unknown age, occurring within or close to the fault zone, and previously mapped by Palmer (1963) as part of the Duarte Formation, are units of the Magua Formation. All these sequences have the same regional structural position.

Conglomerates and sandstones of the lower to middle Oligocene Tavera Group are also preserved within San Juan de las Matas graben structure (otherwise known as the Tavera basin) in the Hispaniola fault zone. The stratigraphy of the units within the Tavera Group, as set out by Palmer (1963, 1979), has been revised slightly (Reimer, 1978; Groetsch, 1982). The important feature of this revision is that the turbiditic Janico Formation is of late Oligocene age and lies conformably above the Represa conglomerate. The Velazquitos Formation of early to middle Oligocene age is the oldest unit and lies unconformably on the Duarte complex. Groetsch (1982) has shown that the resedimented conglomerates (Represa Formation) and turbidites (Janico Formation) constitute a progradational sequence deposited within a submarine fan complex.

Upper Cretaceous volcanic-volcaniclastic rocks in the central Cordillera Central–Massif du Nord

An extensive belt of volcaniclastic rocks and lavas of Late Cretaceous age extends along the central Cordillera Central and into the Massif du Nord in Haiti. The belt is 35 km wide, perpendicular to strike in the east Cordillera Central, but narrows to the west. The rocks occur in the most rugged terrane in Hispaniola and, hence, little is known of the sequence. Bowin (1966) assigned the name "Tireo Formation" to the tuffs, lapilli tuffs, quartz keratophyres, and rare limestones exposed in the Constanza area. The name "Tireo Formation" has been commonly applied to all the sequence exposed along the belt, at least in the Dominican Republic.

Mesnier (1980) found the sequence in the central part of the Cordillera Central to consist of thickly bedded tuffs, finely bedded crystal and accretionary lapilli tuffs, vitroclastic breccias of mafic to intermediate composition, rhyolites, and "ignimbrites" with intercalated cherts and limestone lenses. The limestones give a Turonian to early Santonian age to the sequence. The upper part is silicified and mineralized in places. The sequences are intruded by dacite porphyries, rhyolite dikes, and small stocks of microdiorite, one of which has been dated at 74 Ma by the K/Ar method.

In the Restauración area, on the border with Haiti, similar volcanic rocks have been mapped by Lewis and others (1982) and by geologists from Rosario Dominicana S.A. The main sequences are: (1) a marine sequence of shales and limestones; (2) finely laminated greenish tuffs and breccias, also of probable marine origin; (3) interbedded red and green tuffs, some with accretionary lapilli; (4) polymict conglomerates, breccias, and interbedded lavas; and (5) felsic lavas, mainly dacites, and volcaniclastic rocks intruded by keratophyric lavas and plugs (the youngest series to the south). Other rocks include chert and limestone. Preliminary $^{40}Ar/^{39}Ar$ dating has given an age of 81.4 ± 0.8 Ma for the dacitic magmatism. Overlying calcareous shales give a Campanian age from foraminifera and a Campanian-Maastrichtian age from nannofossils (determinations by E. Robinson and M. J. Jiang). A brief petrologic description of the Restauración-area rocks is given by Jiménez and Lewis (1989) and Amarante and others (1989).

Similar rocks occur across the border in the Massif du Nord of Haiti. United Nations geologists have distinguished three sequences (Ph. Nicolini, 1977; P. Nicolini 1981). The Perches Series consists of mainly silicic volcaniclastic carbonaceous shales and rhyolites. Correlation of this unit with the Los Ranchos Formation in the Dominican Republic has been suggested, but not proved. The widespread Terrier Rouge Series includes basalts, andesites, andesitic tuffs, agglomerates, and conglomerates and is overlain by a felsic series (Limbe–La Mine Series) composed of dacitic flows and stocks, and volcaniclastic units. The Terrier Rouge and La Mine Series correlate with the Tireo Formation in the Dominican Republic.

Extensive epithermal polymetallic mineralization, including Au-Ag, occurs along the whole belt, associated with the acid rocks (Ph. Nicolini, 1977; P. Nicolini, 1981; Jiménez and others, 1986; Amarante and others, 1989). Descriptions of the deposits are contained in numerous unpublished reports at the Bureau des Mines in Haiti and the Dirección General de Minería.

Presqu'île du Nord-Ouest, Haiti

Small windows through an extensive block-faulted Tertiary cover expose Upper Cretaceous volcanic rocks intruded by granitoid stocks and dikes in the Presqu'île du Nord-Ouest of Haiti (Cheilletz, 1976) (Figs. 9 and 10). In the Limbe area in the western Massif du Nord, Kachrillo (1977) has described a series of weakly metamorphosed, high-titanium basalts apparently overlain by a series of andesitic tuffs with interstratified calcareous lenses of late Campanian age. Both the basalts and andesites are intruded by stocks of diorite, tonalite, and trondjhemite.

The oldest rocks in the Terre Neuve area are the Upper Cretaceous Colombier volcanics, which are overlain unconformably by Upper Cretaceous sediments. These rocks are intruded by a quartz-monzonite stock dated at 66.2 Ma (Kesler, 1971). Whole-rock K/Ar dates on the small quartz diorite (tonalite) intrusives have given an average age of 56 Ma (Cheilletz and others, 1978). Paleocene–middle Eocene limestones unconformably overlie the Cretaceous rocks. Basalts and dolerites, well exposed in the area of Ennery, are interstratified with the middle and upper Eocene limestones. Although the lavas at Ennery have not been dated, an age of 57.1 ± 4.6 Ma was obtained for a basalt sample from flows at the Baie de Henne, northwest Haiti (Bellon and others, 1985).

A detrital series of Oligo-Miocene age (Crete Formation) overlies the Eocene rocks along the margins of the Presqu'île du Nord-Ouest. Extensive block faulting is apparent in this area.

Ile de la Tortue

Extension of the structural boundary trends (Fig. 11) indicate that Tortue Island (l'Ile de la Tortue) north of Haiti lies along the boundary between Zones 3 and 4 (Draper and Lewis, 1982). The main features of the geology of Tortue Island have been summarized by Woodring and others (1924), Butterlin (1960), and Vila and others (1982).

Uplifted wave-cut terraces of Pleistocene reefs form the main exposure of the island. These reef deposits cover a complex of calcareous schists bearing an upper Senonian microfauna, silicic metavolcanic rocks, and greenschists that, in part, is overlain by limestones of Paleocene-Eocene age and a conglomerate unit of possible Neogene age. The conglomerate includes boulders of mafic and intermediate-volcanic rocks, granitoid rocks, and chlorite-bearing greenschists, amphibolites, and rare eclogites.

The in situ metamorphic rocks are well-foliated quartz-albite-epidote chlorite schists (meta-tuff and meta-rhyolites) intercalated with white marble. The Tortue greenschists, therefore, bear a remarkable similarity to the Amina-Maimón rocks, and this supports the assumption that these rocks form the basement to the Cibao Basin (Zone 3). This hypothesis is supported by the recent discovery of a submerged northwest-trending ridge structure northwest of Monte-Cristi (T. Edgar and R. W. Rodríguez, personal communication, 1985), which appears to be an eastern extension of Tortue Island to the mainland.

Upper Cretaceous–lower Tertiary clastic deposits of the south Massif du Nord–Cordillera Central

A prominent belt (up to 15 km wide) of dominantly interbedded shales and sandstones of Late Cretaceous to Paleogene age can be traced along the southern flanks of the Massif du Nord and the Cordillera Central (Fig. 10). In the western Massif du Nord the deposits are known as the Trois Rivières Formation (Butterlin, 1954). Here they consist of folded shales and gray argillites interbedded with massive rudistid limestones with lesser amounts of sandstones and conglomerates, and are of Campanian-Maastrichtian age.

In the southeast Massif du Nord and the western Cordillera Central the rocks are distinctly flysch-like in character, and shales show a well-developed cleavage (Cheilletz and Lewis, 1976). At the base of the section, in Haiti and near Restauración in the Dominican Republic, the rocks have yielded Campanian-Maastrichtian ages that can be correlated with the Trois Rivières Formation (J. F. Lewis, unpublished data, 1982; Boisson, 1987).

The shale-siltstone (turbidite) and limestone sequences in the Sierra de Ocoa in the southeast Cordillera Central lie in the same belt (the Ocoa or Peralta belt), but the rocks are less deformed than in the western part. Lewis and others (1989) and Dolan (1988) have shown that the shale-siltstone-limestone sequences in the Padre las Casas and Sierra de Ocoa areas are reworked and redeposited sediments of middle to late Eocene age. Dolan (1986) considered that the abrupt changes from arc-derived turbidite to platform-derived limestone sequences signify rapid sedimentary responses to changes in sea level.

The El Número section in the southeast Cordillera Central of the area has been examined by Mascle and others (1980) and Heubeck (1988). The western section includes pelagic siliceous limestones of late Paleocene to early Eocene age, and radiolarian cherts and shales with faulted contacts against turbidite deposits. The eastern outcrops are mainly marls and siltstones of late middle Eocene age and include exotic shallow-water limestone blocks (olistoliths) of middle Eocene age (Eva, 1980). This chaotic facies, which also contains conglomerates and was called "Eocene a blocks d'Ocoa" by Bourgois and others (1979a), is interpreted as olistostrome deposits.

Biju-Duval and others (1983) described stratigraphic and structural features of the southeast Cordillera Central and concluded that the sequences represent the uplifted part of the western extension of the accretionary complex and fore-arc basin north of the Muertos trench (Matthews and Holcombe, 1976; Ladd and Watkins, 1978, 1979; Ladd and others, this volume). They postulated that the uplift resulted from collision and partial subduction of the thick Beata ridge crust beneath the Cordillera Central, and inferred that the pelagic slope and trench-derived sediments were accreted in tectonic slices to the inner part of the accretionary wedge complex. An alternative interpretation is that the Upper Cretaceous–Eocene sedimentary section (Peralta–Ocoa–Trois Rivière units) along the southeastern Cordillera Central represents a back-arc rather than a fore-arc sequence (cf. Dickinson and Suczek, 1979; Dolan, 1986, 1988).

Plutonic rocks of the Massif du Nord–Cordillera Central

Ultramafic-mafic and granitoid igneous rocks form a major part of the outcrop in the Massif du Nord–Cordillera Central (Zone 4). Major features were summarized by Lewis (1982a and b).

Serpentinized peridotite, generally known as the Loma Caribe peridotite, forms an almost continuous mass, essentially a linear belt from the northwest of the city of Santo Domingo to La Vega, a distance of 95 km (Bowin, 1966). Aeromagnetic surveys carried out for mining and oil exploration in the southeast Dominican Republic have shown that the Loma Caribe peridotite belt must extend to the southeast beneath the Quaternary and Tertiary limestones east of Santo Domingo. This has been confirmed by Mercedes Company drilling (C. Monster and C. Bowin, personal communication, 1984). The rock is mainly harzburgite (about 70 percent serpentinized), but lherzolite, dunite dikes, and small gabbroic masses are also present (Haldemann and others, 1979). Tectonic inclusions are common and display high-T/low-P metamorphism (rodingites) or no metamorphism, in contrast to the high-P xenoliths in the North Coast peridotites. The peridotite is bounded to the south by the metamafic rocks of the Duarte complex and a parallel belt of unmetamorphosed basalts of the Siete Cabezas Formation, and to the north by the metabasic and quartzo-feldspathic rocks of the Amina-Maimón Formation of probable island-arc affinities. Although the Loma peridotite has many of the features of Alpine-type peridotites, the question of whether the peridotite is part of a dismembered ophiolite has not been clearly answered (Lewis, 1982a). Nickel laterite has been mined from the area since 1970.

Granitoid plutons form a linear belt and are an important part of the outcrop along the Cordillera Central (Lewis, 1982b). Several of the plutons are batholiths, and the rocks intrude the

Duarte greenschists, and also the volcaniclastic and volcanic rocks of the Tireo Formation. The granitoid rocks are mainly hornblende tonalites. Other rock types include diorite, quartz diorite, granodiorites, leucotonalites, trondjhemites, and aplites.

K/Ar and Rb/Sr mineral and whole-rock age determinations have given dates ranging from 92 to 48 Ma for the granitoid rocks (Bowin, 1975; Kesler and Sutter, 1977; Feigenson, 1978a and b; Bellon and others, 1985).

ZONE 5. NORTHWESTERN–SOUTH-CENTRAL ZONE

Zone 5 is the most ill-defined zone in Hispaniola. The zone includes the Plateau Central–San Juan Valley and the mountain ranges of the Chaines des Matheux–Montagnes Noires–Sierra de Neiba–Martín García. The San Cristóbal and San Pedro Basins are also included in this zone. Where observed, the northern boundary to Zone 5 is a major fault zone (in part the Los Pozos–San Juan fault zone) that separates the Cenozoic deposits of the Plaine Central–San Juan–Azúa Basins and the Cretaceous rocks of the Cordillera Central–Massif du Nord.

Because of poor exposure it is not clear whether or not the Montagnes Noires–Neiba Mountains are underlain by basaltic lava of Cretaceous age. Pelagic limestones (*calcaires du Daco*) in the Montagnes Noires are reported to be Late Cretaceous in age (Vila and others, 1983). According to Butterlin (1957, 1960), however, the rocks in this region consist essentially of middle Eocene limestones (with chert) and argillites with intercalated tuffs, andesitic breccias, and rare basalts (Perodin Formation). Andesite dikes and sills, dacites, and quartz-diorites are also reported from the Perodin Formation by Butterlin (1960). Butterlin compared the sequence with the Cobre Formation in the Sierra Maestra of Cuba. Similar rocks have been mapped in the central Sierra de Neiba Mountains (Bourgois and others, 1979b; Breuner, 1985) and are of middle Eocene age. Two samples from the volcanic rocks in the Neiba Mountains north of the town of Sierra de Neiba have been dated at 52.7 and 51.1 Ma, in agreement with their occurrence in rocks of Eocene age (Bellon and others, 1985).

Miogypsina-bearing chalky and siliceous limestones are well represented along the northern flanks of the Montagnes Noires and Sierra de Neiba. This is the late Oligocene–early Miocene Madame Joie Formation in Haiti and the Sombrerito Formation in the Dominican Republic. A small area of downfaulted, lower middle Miocene sedimentary rock showing little deformation is preserved within the southern Sierra de Neiba. These contain basaltic tuffs in the lower section, which have been dated paleontologically as basal middle Miocene, indicating pyroclastic activity around 15 Ma in this area (J. F. Lewis, unpublished data, 1981; Breuner, 1985).

The island of Gonâve (Ile de la Gonâve) is situated in the gulf between the northern and southern peninsulas of Haiti. Its geology was summarized by Butterlin (1960), and a recent study by Mercier de Lepinay and others (1985) supported by satellite imagery gives new structural information. The overall structure of the island consists of a northwest-trending dome exposing a core of Upper Eocene limestones, overlain by a Miocene sequence. Pliocene–Quaternary marine terraces testify to recent uplift.

The Plateau Central–San Juan Valley is essentially a simple synclinal basin structure with more than 7,600 m of Tertiary strata bounded to the south and north by high-angle thrust faults (Woodring and others, 1924; Michael and Lewis, 1980; Lewis and others, 1983; Breuner, 1985; Nemec, 1982).

Volcanic rocks of late Cenozoic (Pliocene-Pleistocene) age are exposed along the northern margins of the San Juan Valley. Those in the northwestern part of the valley are alkali basalts, including basanites and limburgites (MacDonald and Melson, 1969), whereas the volcanic field in the eastern part of the valley, which extends northwest into the Cordillera Central, is a basalt-trachyandesite(latite)-dacite-trachyte suite (Vespucci, 1982, 1987).

Aspects of the stratigraphy, structural evolution, and sedimentary environments of the Plateau Central–San Juan basin have been studied by van den Bold (1974, 1981), Michael (1978), Dubreuihl (1982), and Breuner (1985). The Azua area has recently been studied by Mascle and others (1980), Cooper (1982), and Biju-Duval and others (1983). The nature of the basement rocks underlying the basin is not known. The oldest known sediments are detrital clastics of early Eocene (possibly Paleocene) age (Abuillot Formation) interbedded with limestones that crop out in upthrusted slices north and south of the basin. Clastic sedimentation must have persisted throughout the Eocene in the northeast part, whereas a continuous sequence of open-marine limestone deposition is apparent in the western part from at least early middle Eocene through at least late Oligocene.

Dubreuihl (1982) has shown that in the early stages of development of the sedimentary basin in the east Plateau Central, a ridge of Eocene carbonates separated the basin such that, until Langhanian time (biostratigraphic Zone N11), mainly detrital material accumulated in the northern part, whereas pelagic carbonates were deposited in the southern part of the basin.

An important nondepositional hiatus of about 4 m.y. at the end of the Oligocene is recorded in the Candelon well in the western San Juan Valley, but the extent of this hiatus is not yet well recorded. During early Miocene time, a change to more terrigenous deposition occurred, followed by accumulation of 400 m of relatively shallow-water mudstones and siltstones in the Plateau Central and southwestern San Juan Valley in the middle Miocene. At this time the sea regressed southward, resulting in the deposition of coarse clastic material and shallow-water lagoonal deposits. By late Miocene time, shallowing had occurred over most of the area, but turbidite sedimentation (submarine fan complexes, Breuner, 1985) persisted into the early Pliocene in the eastern San Juan–Azua Valleys. An important uplift event of the Cordillera Central took place 3 to 4 m.y. ago, resulting in an extensive conglomerate facies (Las Matas conglomerate). Further movement resulted in the present topography of the area.

Tertiary sedimentary rocks of the San Cristóbal and San Pedro Basins

Biju-Duval and others (1983) described the Tertiary sedimentary deposits from the Nizao–San Cristóbal area as forming a broad asymmetrical syncline (San Cristóbal Basin), which appears to be the landward extension of the marine San Pedro Basin. They further considered that the San Pedro–San Cristóbal Basins are fore-arc structures. The basin sediments rest on a tectonized wedge of the accretionary prism structure to the south, which is exposed as a thrust belt in the southeast Cordillera Central, as described in Zone 4. In the basal part of the San Cristóbal Basin, massive algal limestones of early Paleocene age unconformably overlie metavolcaniclastic sedimentary rocks derived from the Tireo Formation and Cretaceous tonalite plutons (Dominguez, 1987). A clastic section of shales, sandstones, and conglomerates has been dated as late Eocene by Vila and Feinberg (1982) and is correlated with the "Eocene a blocs d'Ocoa" unit of Bourgois and others (1979a). At Valdesia, upper Eocene turbidites are overlain by a polymictic conglomerate-sandstone-limestone sequence (Valdesia Conglomerate) of early to middle Oligocene age (Mascle and others, 1980). These strata are interpreted to have been deposited as part of an upper-slope apron under conditions of high rates of sedimentation and subsidence.

To the southeast of the Nizao River, Miocene rocks (NN1 to NN6 nannozones) onlap the Oligocene conglomerates. These are mainly a bedded shale facies but include conglomerates, limestones, and bioclastic sandy limestones, indicating both shallow and open-marine conditions.

ZONE 6. CUL DE SAC–VALLE DE ENRIQUILLO

The southernmost major valley in Hispaniola is the fault-bounded depression and sedimentary basin known as the Valle de Cul de Sac in Haiti and the Valle de Enriquillo in the Dominican Republic. Two large lakes and one small lake occur in the valley. Lago Enriquillo in the east is the largest (about 300 km^2): its present level is 40 m below sea level. Cenozoic marine sedimentary deposits, totaling about 6,000 m, including a Pliocene evaporite sequence, fill the Cul de Sac–Enriquillo basin. The basin sedimentary deposits are folded and faulted. Although most of the structural elements trend east-west in the hills southwest of the valley, the low hills in the southeast—composed of the evaporite sediments—curve to the northeast. Reverse faults are a prominent feature along the north and south margins of the basin.

Although fault scarps are difficult to recognize along the valley margins because of rapid erosion and cover by Quaternary alluvial fans, raised terraces are prominent along the north-central part of the valley.

Sedimentary rocks crop out in the central and southern parts of the Enriquillo and Cul de Sac Valleys and are mainly terrigenous-evaporite sequences of late Miocene–Pliocene age. Two main formations have been defined. The Angostura Formation consists of 3 km of black shales, black and red sandstones, and limestones underlain by a thick sequence of gypsum and rock salt. The base grades laterally into the clastic series of the Arroyo Blanco Formation (Dohm, 1942) of late Miocene age. The Las Salinas Formation overlies the Angostura Formation and consists of a thick series of brown to buff calcareous clays, sandy shales, and paper shales interbedded with limestone conglomerates and coquina beds. The lower part of the Las Salinas is dated as late Miocene, the upper part Pliocene. Van den Bold (1975) correlated the Las Salinas with the Morne Delmas Formation of Haiti.

A coral limestone unit (Jimani Formation) of Pleistocene age (van den Bold, 1975) overlies the clastic rocks. This limestone is folded and unconformably overlain by a horizontal Holocene fringing coral reef cropping out at 5 m above sea level around the valley margins (Mann and others, 1984b; Taylor and others, 1985).

ZONE 7. PRESQU'ILE DU SUD (PENINSULA DEL SUR; SOUTHERN PENINSULA)

The Southern Peninsula of Hispaniola is a distinct physiographic province characterized by extremely rugged relief with locally well-developed karst. The peninsula consists of two structural blocks, the western Massif de la Hotte and the eastern Massif de la Selle-Bahoruco, separated by a structural low, the Jacmel-Fauche depression. The rocks exposed in the area range in age from Early Cretaceous to Quaternary and include a section of pelagic sedimentary rocks that span the Cretaceous-Tertiary boundary.

Cretaceous rocks

Cretaceous rocks are exposed along the central axial area of the peninsula. Three formations have been described: the Dumisseau, Macaya, and Río Arriba Formations.

The Dumisseau Formation (Maurrasse and others, 1979) is a complex sequence of igneous and sedimentary rocks. The formation is characterized by a sequence of interbedded pillowed and nonpillowed basalts, dolerites, pelagic limestone, intrabasinal volcanogenic turbidites, varicolored cherts, and siliceous siltstones. The sequence becomes more calcareous toward the top. Although a shallow-water limestone has been reported from one locality north of Jacmel (Reeside, 1947), no shallow-water facies has yet been found at any other locality. From studies of the foraminifera and radiolarian fauna, Maurrasse and others (1979) have concluded that the Dumisseau Formation ranges from the late Early Cretaceous to the Turonian age.

K/Ar age determinations made on two samples of basalt and diabase from the Dumisseau Formation have given ages of 75 ± 1.5 (Sayeed and others, 1978) and 85 Ma (van den Berghe, 1983). Three basalts from the region of Palmes and a flow from near Jacmel have yielded dates of 95.3 to 102.3 Ma. Other samples from higher in the sequence have given dates of 70.5 to 74.2 Ma (Bellon and others, 1985).

Acoustic-reflector "horizon B" in the Venezuelan Basin is composed of tholeiitic basalts and dolerite sills intercalated with and overlain by pelagic sedimentary rocks of Coniacian to Campanian age (Edgar and others, 1973). Because of the similarity of the two sequences, the upper part of the Dumisseau Formation has been correlated with the Caribbean sea-floor section (Maurrasse and others, 1979).

The upper part of the Cretaceous section in the central Massif de la Selle includes a chaotic sequence (Mercier de Lepinay and others, 1979) consisting of blocks of late Albian to upper Coniacian-Santonian radiolarian cherts, siliceous limestones, and dolerites in a volcanic sedimentary matrix of Campanian-late Maastrichtian age (Fig. 13). This unit is overlain by a unit of Coniacian chert beds intercalated with volcaniclastic turbidites. Mercier de Lepinay and others (1979) interpreted both of these units as having been emplaced as a nappe in Maastrichtian time. As pointed out by Biju-Duval and others (1983), most of the reverse-fault contacts affect upper Miocene strata. They concluded that it is equally possible that the chaotic facies could have resulted from sedimentary processes unrelated to thrusting, such as gravity sliding down the slopes of seamounts.

The Macaya Formation (Butterlin, 1954), located in the Massif de la Hotte, comprises a sequence of isoclinally folded, veined, varicolored, recrystallized, and sparsely silicified epipelagic biomicrite. The age of the Macaya Formation at the type locality is Campanian to Maastrichtian, as determined from planktonic foraminiferal and radiolaria assemblages (Butterlin, 1954; Ayala Castañares, 1959). Calmus (1983) has described a 76-m continuous section of the Macaya Formation located near Camp Perrin in the Massif de la Hotte. The section consists of a lower part of well-bedded marly limestones alternating with silicified limestones of Coniacian-Santonian age, overlain by poorly bedded silicified limestones of late Santonian-Campanian age. The upper part of the section is more detrital, consisting of interbedded argillites and radiolarian cherts that yield a Maastrichtian fauna. The Macaya sequence is comparable to similar lithofacies recovered from DSDP sites in the Colombian and Venezuelan Basins (Edgar and others, 1973; Maurrasse, 1973). As noted by Biju-Duval and others (1983), high organic productivity and a high rate of subsidence are necessary to explain the thick radiolarian limestones of the Macaya area.

Calmus (1983) considered that the Macaya Formation has been thrust over rocks of early Paleocene age (Rivière Glace and Baraderes Formations), which in turn lie unconformably on a basement of tholeiitic basalt (Fig. 13). Five samples of these tholeiitic basalts have yielded K/Ar ages of 57 to 69.5 ± 7 Ma (Calmus, 1983). These ages are younger than those from the basalts of the Dumisseau Formation.

At the eastern end of the zone, in the Bahoruco Mountains, sedimentary rocks of Cretaceous age were termed the Río Arriba Formation by Llinás (1972). The rocks are composed of intercalations of cream-colored argillaceous and sandy limestone beds with weathered chert stringers having a thickness of about 530 m. Llinás (1972) concluded that the age of the Río Arriba Formation may range from Albian to Maastrichtian based on the presence of *Calcisphaerula* sp. Mafic igneous rocks exposed in the eastern Bahoruco Mountains are correlated with the Dumisseau basalts.

Paleogene, Cretaceous-Tertiary boundary

Several sequences in deep-sea sedimentary deposits that bridge the Cretaceous-Tertiary boundary, probably unique in the northern Caribbean region, have now been described from the Southern Peninsula. The Beloc Formation, which is composed of sedimentary rocks of upper Maastrichtian to earliest Paleocene age, is exposed in the west central Massif de la Selle (Maurrasse, 1981a).

The base of the Beloc Formation is a basaltic conglomerate that grades into and overlies weathered igneous rocks of the Dumisseau Formation. The overlying sequence consists essentially of homogeneous pelagic limestone, with chalk interbeds as

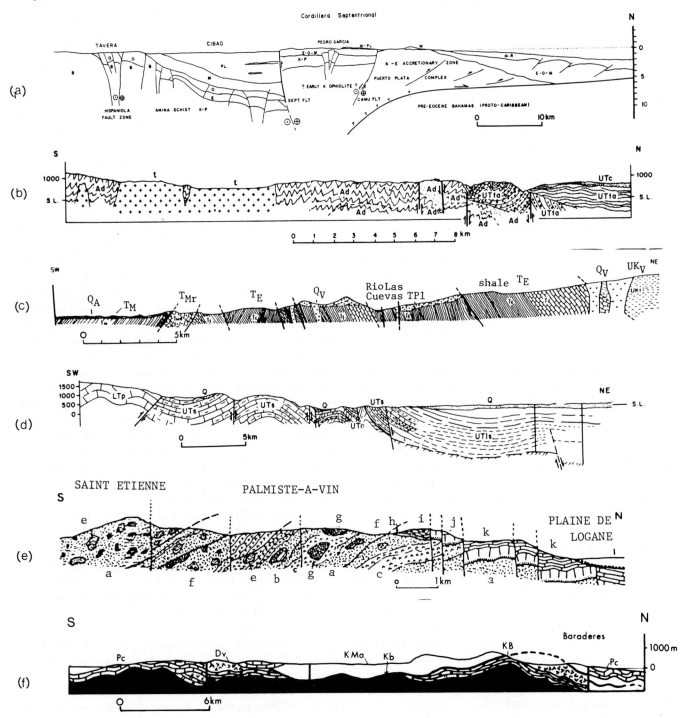

much as 150 m thick. A volcanogenic turbidite bed occurs 40 to 50 m from the base of the formation and marks the approximate biostratigraphic Cretaceous-Tertiary boundary. The boundary is marked by the transition from the *Globotruncana contusa* zone (late Maastrichtian) to the *Globorotalia pseudobulloides* zone (Danian) and (probably) the *Globorotalia trinadadensis* zone (early Paleocene). The absence of typical Danian nannoplankton and the presence of Cretaceous foraminiferal taxa within the assigned Danian remain a puzzle, but presumably are the result of reworking.

Although its lower limit is Late Cretaceous at the type section, outcrops of Campanian and older Maastrichtian rocks immediately north of the village of Beloc suggest that the lower boundary of the Beloc Formation is diachronous. It may, therefore, be older than Maastrichtian in certain areas, or even grade into the uppermost part of the Dumisseau Formation.

The marl above the volcanogenic marker bed at Beloc shows the anomalously high concentration of iridium, which has been found at the Cretaceous-Tertiary boundary elsewhere in the world (Alvarez and others, 1982).

Another sequence of sedimentary rocks that bridge the Cretaceous-Tertiary boundary has been described from the Camp Perrin area in the Massif de la Hotte. It was first described by Butterlin (1950) and was termed the "Rivière Glace Formation" by Calmus (1983). The sequence consists of at least 200 m of bedded clastic sedimentary rocks, rich in organic and volcanic material, which is considered to have been deposited on or at the base of a slope at the end of Maastrichtian to Danian time.

Lower Tertiary rocks

The Marigot Formation (Butterlin, 1954) of Paleocene to early Eocene age is found only in the southern Massif de la Selle, where it overlies the Dumisseau Formation, and includes basaltic conglomerates, sandy shales, calcareous sandstones, and clastic limestones. The upper part of the formation may intergrade with either lower Eocene biocalcarenites and biocalcirudites, or thinly bedded white chalky limestones. The coarser limestone facies are rich in benthic foraminifera, whereas the chalky facies are rich in planktonic foraminifera. Maurrasse (1981a) reported that the Marigot Formation is overlain by limestones similar to the lithofacies described as the Neiba Formation in the Dominican Republic (Dohm *in* Bermúdez, 1949, p. 21), and in other places by limestone with a shallower-water facies.

A continuous Paleocene–lower Eocene section is exposed in the western part of the peninsula. The lower to middle Paleocene section consists of calcareous breccias, sands, and silts, which are in turn, overlain by upper Paleocene polygenetic conglomerates and lower Eocene calcarenites and marls. The faunal assemblage and sedimentary structures indicate a platform environment of deposition. In contrast, the Paleogene section at Port Salut examined by Biju-Duval and others (1983) is composed of chalky and silicified calcareous marls representing a pelagic environment of deposition.

Sequences including rocks of late Eocene to late Oligocene age are found in several areas. Maurrasse (1981a) has described a particular lithology of nannoplanktonic-foraminiferal chalk with very sparse radiolaria as the Jeremie Formation. These chalks occur mainly along the northwest coast of the Presqu'ile du Sud, but also in northwest Haiti. Their age, as determined from planktonic foraminifera, ranges from late middle to early late Oligocene.

In the Massif de la Hotte, of the Marche Leon–Jeremie region, Calmus (1983) has described an almost complete continuous section from middle Eocene to upper Miocene. Limestones and marly limestones of middle to late Eocene age were deposited in a platform environment, which must have existed since the early Paleocene. The Eocene sequence is overlain by thinly bedded, chalky limestones of middle to late Oligocene age, presumably the Jeremie Formation (Maurrasse, 1981a), and grades

Figure 13. Geologic cross sections across Hispaniola. Locations are shown on Figure 11. (a) Generalized and idealized cross section across the Cordillera Septentional and Cibao Valley (Zones 1, 2, and 3 [Fig. 3 of Cooper, 1982]). (b) Cross section across the northern foothills of the Cordillera Central in the region west of La Vega showing the contact relations over the Hispaniola Fault Zone (from Palmer, 1963). Ad = Duarte amphibolite, t = tonalite; UTta = Tertiary Tavera Group; Utc = Upper Tertiary Cercado Formation (siliciclastic rocks). (c) Cross section across the southern foothills of the Cordillera Central near Padre las Casas (Fig. 2 of Lewis and others, 1989; Vespucci, 1987). UKt = Tireo Group; Te = Eocene limestone and shales of the Peralta belt; TM = shales and siltstones late Miocene; TMr = Reefal limestones, Miocene; TP1 - Las Matas Conglomerate; Qv = Volcanic rocks, Quaternary. (d) Cross section showing structural relations across the north Sierra Bahoruco and Enriquillo Valley (from Llinas, 1972). LTp = Plaisance Formation; UTs = Sombrerito Formation, UTa = Angostura Formation; UTls = Las Salinas Formation. (e) Cross section across the northern Massif de la Salle Jacmel road area, Southern Peninsula, showing features of clastic deposits and contact with the Cul de Sac Valley (Fig. 1 from Mercier de Lepinay and others, 1979). a = homogeneous matrix of blocks series, b = bedded zones of the matrix, c = basaltic rocks, e = calcareous and siliceous carbonate blocks, f = basalt rocks, g = blocks of cherty rock, h = graywackes; i = Maastrichtian calcareous marls, j = Palaeocene and Lower Eocene sedimentary rocks, k = Oligo-Miocene sedimentary rocks, q = Quaternary. (f) Cross section across the Massif de la Macaya (Massif de la Hotte), Southern Peninsula showing the contacts between the Macaya Formation and other units (from Calmus, 1983, Fig. 79).

into calcareous yellow marls and sandstones of early Miocene age.

Basic to intermediate lavas with alkaline affinities, associated with sedimentary rocks of upper Paleocene to middle Eocene age, crop out in the area of Baraderes and Nan Raynal in the extreme west of the Southern Peninsula (Calmus, 1983). K/Ar whole-rock ages determined for two samples from Baraderes gave the dates 60.6 and 61 ± 3 Ma, whereas the dates for three samples from Nan Reynal ranged from 45.5 ± 2.3 to 51.6 ± 2.8 Ma (Calmus, 1983; Bellon and others, 1985).

Upper Tertiary rocks

Detailed stratigraphic studies (Maurrasse and others, 1982; van den Berghe, 1983; Calmus, 1983; Bizon and others, 1985) have shown that an almost-complete Miocene section is present in the Southern Peninsula, although a minor hiatus appears to occur in the Burdigalian (NN3-4) interval.

Butterlin (1954) defined two formations in younger Miocene rocks in the Southern Peninsula. The Rivière Grise Formation consists of alternating layers of conglomerates, sandstones, marls, and mudstones. Although originally assigned an Oligocene–early Miocene age by Butterlin, recent studies indicate the formation ranges in age from middle to late Miocene (Maurrasse and others, 1982; van den Berghe, 1983). The Morne Delmas Formation, which either overlies the Rivière Grise Formation, or is a lateral equivalent of its upper part (van den Berghe, 1983), is composed of conglomerates, sandstones, and coarse argillites with occasional limestone beds containing fossil mollusca (Butterlin, 1960).

Upper Miocene deposits of a different facies occur in the small fault-controlled (pull-apart) basins at Camp Perrin and L'Asile. The Camp Perrin Basin contains essentially lacustrine and brackish-water deposits with interstratified black lignites.

The main formation of Pliocene age occurring in the Massif de la Selle-Bahoruco is the Rivière Gauche Formation (Butterlin, 1960). This sequence is well exposed in the Jacmel-Fauche depression and consists of a lower facies of fine-grained detrital sediments overlain by conglomerate made up of dominantly volcanic detritus from a Cretaceous source (van den Berghe, 1983). The base of the formation lies unconformably over Miocene sediments and itself is overlain by Quaternary coral reef and alluvial deposits.

Stratigraphic breaks and history

The recent work in the Southern Peninsula has shown the presence of an almost complete Upper Cretaceous–Tertiary stratigraphic record. Well-defined sedimentary sequences have been established, but the interpretation of unconformities remains controversial. Butterlin (1960) and Mercier de Lepinay and others (1979) concluded that a major unconformity exists between the Cretaceous and Tertiary, as found elsewhere in Hispaniola. On the other hand, several sequences show continuous sedimentation

occurred from the Late Cretaceous to the end of the early Paleocene. The simplest and most satisfactory explanation is that a marine transgression occurred at the time of the Cretaceous-Tertiary boundary, such that sediments of Danian age were derived from an emerging "Laramide edifice" in the northern part of the Southern Peninsula (Calmus, 1983). The occurrence of both calcareous and terrigenous turbidites, chaotic deposits, channeling, and erosional and nondepositional surfaces indicates a complex bathymetry with local listric faulting (Biju-Duval and others, 1983).

A carbonate platform covered the area through late Paleocene time until the end of the early Eocene. The distinct hiatus in sedimentation found between nannoplankton zones NP13 and NP17 (middle Eocene) is interpreted to be due to faulting at this time (van den Berghe, 1983; Bizon and others, 1985). During the late Eocene, a deeper and more open sea environment was established over most of the area. Several facies can be recognized in middle to upper Eocene limestones representing areas of deposition ranging from carbonate platform to pelagic conditions (Maurrasse and others, 1982). Open-marine conditions persisted into the late Oligocene–early Miocene over most of the area with the deposition of chalky limestones. A diastem is reported to occur within the late early Miocene (Burdigalian time), but this is not ubiquitous; there is little doubt that this and other short diastems in the Neogene record resulted from faulting. Small pull-apart basins developed in the early Miocene at Camp Perrin, allowing the rapid accumulation of lacustrine/brackish-water deposits.

As emphasized by Maurrasse and others (1982), a remarkable change occurred during middle Miocene time. The stratigraphy indicates that sedimentation was controlled by differential uplift of fault-controlled blocks, giving rise to rapid changes in facies. Broad deltas developed along the northern regions of the Southern Peninsula, resulting in accumulation of coarse clastic sediments of the upper Miocene (Angostura Formation in the Cul de Sac) to Pliocene (Rivière Gauche Formation in the Jacmel Fauche depression). Eustatic sea-level changes at this time (Vail and others, 1977) may also have controlled the sedimentation (Maurrasse and others, 1982).

Emergence of the whole peninsula and development of the present physiography took place in Pliocene-Pleistocene time.

ZONE 8. PENINSULA DEL ESTE (EASTERN PENINSULA)

Knowledge of the geology of the eastern Dominican Republic is fragmentary partly because of poor exposure. The most definitive work is Bourdon's (1985) thesis of the Hato Mayor–El Seibo–Miches area, which is summarized in Bourdon and others (1985). Bourdon has distinguished three sequences of Cretaceous age: El Seibo unit, El Oro unit, and La Mina slice (Fig. 10).

The El Seibo unit includes the oldest rocks of the eastern Dominican Republic. They are a sequence of low-grade metavolcanics consisting of basalts (including pillow lavas), dacites, rhyolites, andesites, acid tuffs, and volcanic breccias cropping out south and west of Sabana de la Mar, and appear to have the chemical characteristics of the primitive island-arc series as defined by Donnelly and Rogers (1978). A basalt sample has been dated at 112.4 ± 11 Ma by K/Ar (Bellon and others, 1985). The rocks have undergone very low-grade metamorphism, with the development of prehnite pumpellynite, epidote, and chlorite as secondary minerals. The volcanic sequence can be readily traced westward and is correlated with the Los Ranchos Formation (Bowin, 1966; Kesler and others, 1981). This volcanic sequence is overlain by epineritic massive limestones that have yielded an Orbitolina and Rudistid fauna, indicating a late Aptian to early Albian age (Douglas, 1961; Bourdon and others, 1984), and is correlated with the Hatillo Limestone (Bowin, 1966). The upper section includes 10 m of well-bedded limestones with chert nodules containing *Colomiella recta* (Bourdon and others, 1984).

The above sequence is overlain with apparent unconformity by a thick series (>1,000 m) of mostly epiclastic tuffs and breccias with some flows of potassium-rich trachytes (9.97 percent K_2O). One sample of these trachytes has been dated at 65.7 ± 3.3 Ma by K/Ar (analyst: H. Bellon). Bourdon (1985) compared these rocks with the Robles Formation in central Puerto Rico that includes potassium-rich lavas (Jolly, 1971), but recent studies (Lebron and others, 1986) indicate that the lithologies are quite distinct. The upper section is mostly composed of pelagic and turbiditic limestones, which have yielded several Globotruncana faunas indicating Turonian to early Maastrichtian ages.

The Oro unit occupies the northern area. This is a thick series (>1,500 m) of epiclastic sediments (detritus includes volcanic, metamorphic, and ultramafic rocks) with limestone beds and radiolarian cherts. One limestone bed contains well-preserved ammonites (*Peroniceras*) of early Coniacian age (Bourdon and others, 1984). A chert bed has yielded a rich radiolarian fauna indicating a Coniacian age (identified by P. De Wever). The El Oro unit, found only in fault contact with the other units, is highly folded in "chevron" style with associated vertical cleavage.

The La Mina slice, composed of calcareous turbidites, tectonically overlies the El Oro unit. This series of late Senonian age is isoclinally folded with a vergence to the south.

The largest igneous intrusion in the eastern area is the El Valle tonalite. Two samples (a diorite, 54 percent SiO_2; and a granitoid, 70 percent SiO_2) have been dated at 87.3 ± 4.4 and 95 ± 4.8 Ma by K/Ar (Bellon and others, 1985). North of Higuey, De la Fuente and Ellis (1982) have mapped a series of "gabbroic" dikes. Two samples from these dikes have given whole-rock K/Ar dates of 57.8 ± 3 and 68.4 ± 3.4 Ma (Bellon and others, 1985) and appear to have calc-alkaline affinities. The dikes intrude turbidites and epiclastic tuffs of late Senonian age. All these intrusions have experienced low-grade metamorphism as found in the El Seibo unit.

Outcrops of serpentine and gabbro associated with lower Eocene pelagic limestones occur east of El Seibo; they are described by Bourdon (1985) as making up a mélange-like body.

The southern and most eastern part of the Eastern Peninsula is an extensive plain known as the Llanos Costeros del Seibo, which is composed almost entirely of raised coral reef of Pleistocene age. Barrett (1962) recognized eight principal terrace levels around the southeastern coast that appear to be the result of interplay between gradual uplift with marine transgressions during the glacio-eustatic highs in Pleistocene time (Geister, 1982; Schubert and Cowart, 1982).

EVOLUTION OF HISPANIOLA

Considerable controversy exists over the interpretation of the early tectonic evolution of Hispaniola. Most of the questions revolve around the age and origin of the metamorphic and non-metamorphic volcanic rocks in the Median belt, including the Loma Caribe peridotite. Some of the questions being asked include (Lewis, 1982c): Is the Loma Caribe peridotite part of an ophiolite, and is the Hispaniola fault zone a suture? What is the relation of metamorphic rocks of the central Median belt and the North Coast belt? How are the Duarte and Amina Schists juxtaposed in their present positions?

Bowin (1975), followed by Mattson (1979) and Nemec (1982), have discussed a reverse-polarity model for the early tectonic development of the island. They argue that the Loma Caribe fault, along which the peridotite has been emplaced, might have been the site of a former subduction zone consisting of Duarte sea floor dipping to the north. C. O. Bowin (unpublished) considers that northward-dipping subduction continued from pre–middle Aptian to early Maastrichtian time. Polarity reversal then occurred, with southward subduction along the north coast beginning in the late Maastrichtian and ending in the middle Eocene. Mattson (1979), however, suggested that this "flip" took place at about 110 Ma. An alternative model, suggested by Draper and Lewis (1982, 1989), is essentially based on the interpretation that the Maimón-Amina Formations represent the unsubducted portion of an accretionary complex. The Duarte complex, along with the Loma Caribe peridotite, would represent dismembered oceanic crust (ophiolite) that was trapped in the zone between the magmatic arc and the initial trench (arc-trench gap). In this interpretation, the Lower Cretaceous volcanic rocks of the Los Ranchos Formation would represent rocks of a separated volcanic arc to the north. Draper and Lewis (1989) have proposed that a collision event took place between the Duarte terrane and the Los Ranchos arc that resulted in the D_2 folding of the Amina-Maimón Schists, formation of a fabric in the Duarte complex, and initial emplacement of mantle ultramafic rocks along the collision (suture) zone. The collision event must have taken place prior to 127 Ma, which is the K/Ar age of an undeformed hornblendite in the Duarte complex (Bowin, 1966).

Whatever the polarity of the early subduction zone, it is readily accepted that the North Coast belt (Zone 2) of high-pressure metamorphic and ophiolitic rocks is an uplifted subduction complex—a remnant of Late Cretaceous south-verging subduction (Nagle, 1974). Accepting, then, southward-directed subduction in the Late Cretaceous, the resulting magmatic arc is represented by the volcanic rocks of the Tireo Formation and the tonalite granitoids, which would be the exposed roots of this magmatic arc.

The end of the Cretaceous saw a marked change in tectonism in Hispaniola. Although igneous activity continued into the Paleogene (and later), the activity was reduced and restricted. The marked unconformities over the central and northern parts of Hispaniola in the Maastrichtian and at the Cretaceous-Tertiary boundary, the absence of Paleocene sedimentation in northern Haiti, and the turbidite sedimentation throughout the Paleogene in the southern Cordillera Central indicate considerable tectonic activity at this time.

Uplift of the Cordillera Central–Massif du Nord at the end of the Cretaceous was associated with a shift of the axis of sedimentation to the south, and the line of the present Los Pozos–San Juan fault zone must represent the approximate position of the former hinge line in the early Tertiary. Stable open-marine conditions were established over most of the area south of the Cordillera Central–Massif du Nord, resulting in the deposition of pelagic limestone over much of the area. However, clastic terrigenous turbidite sedimentation continued throughout most of Eocene time in the southeastern Cordillera Central.

Subduction ceased at the culmination of the collision of Hispaniola with the Bahama Platform at some time in the Eocene, although the exact timing of this collision has not been determined. Although limited volcanism, and probably some plutonism, occurred in the Eocene, petrogenetic affinities are not clear. The igneous activity that continued at sparse intervals in the late Cenozoic is presumably not directly subduction related. Events in the Eocene that are probably related to the cessation of subduction include the protrusion and extrusion of serpentinite, the thrusting of the Maimón Formation over middle Eocene and Maastrichtian rocks along the Hatillo thrust (Bowin, 1966), and possibly movement on the Bonao fault. Thrusting in the middle Eocene, with a southerly vergence, has been suggested in the Sierra de Neiba (Bourgois and others, 1979b). Thrusting in the southeastern Cordillera Central was a possible cause of the chaotic olistostrome deposits. The apparent hiatus in the middle Eocene in the Southern Peninsula (Calmus, 1983) might also be related to the cessation in subduction.

Uplift and erosion of the North Coast zone took place before the late Eocene (i.e., before the deposition of the Altamira turbidites). Normal rates of erosion would not be fast enough to unroof a subduction complex associated with Eocene subduction (Draper and Bone, 1981), and this early Eocene subduction complex is presumably situated off the north coast (Zone 1).

Major events that occurred during middle to late Oligocene time north of the Cordillera Central included the development of the Tavera basin (a possible pull-apart basin) and the accumulation of sediment within it. The paucity of Oligocene pelagic sediments and the prominence of conglomerates and other clastic sediments over the northern and southeastern areas may reflect a low stand of sea level at this time rather than uplift.

Folding of the Tavera sedimentary rocks and upward movement of the Loma Caribe peridotite, such that it is faulted against the Oligocene Tavera deposits, must have occurred prior to the marked uplift of the Cordillera Central and the marine transgression in the north during the early Miocene. Subsidence of the Cibao Basin occurred, presumably controlled by strike-slip faulting along the Septentrional and Hispaniola fault zones. By the Middle Miocene, the marine transgression was extensive, and shallow seas covered all of the northern area with the development of shelf limestones.

Although gradual uplift had taken place in the southern part of Hispaniola through late Miocene time, the Pliocene-Pleistocene was a time of accelerated uplift and erosion, and resulted in the present physiography. The Cordillera Central must have acted as a rigid block such that the compressional forces generated along the southern transpressional fault systems did not affect the Neogene deposits in the Cibao Basin (Zone 3). Stress from the Neogene oblique subduction along the northern boundary seems to have affected only the North Coast zone (Zone 2).

The regional uplift that was taking place in the south culminated in folding and uplift, followed by volcanism, in the late Pliocene–Pleistocene. The main deformation, which included the main uplift of the Cordillera Central, must have taken place about 3 to 4 Ma, immediately prior to the young volcanism. Uplift of the whole island has continued in Recent time.

Reef limestones deposited in the Pleistocene over the folded basinal sequences are well exposed as uplifted wave-cut terraces in coastal areas (Barrett, 1962; Horsfield, 1975; Geister, 1982; Schubert and Cowart, 1982). Recent uplift of the Cordillera Septentrional, northern Haiti, and Samaná areas seems to have involved tilting to the north as in Puerto Rico. Tectonic instability continues with uplift of the present land area, hot spring activity in the south, and active faulting and abundant seismic activity, particularly to the east and northeast. Fault plane solutions (see McCann and Pennington, this volume) indicate oblique subduction continues along Zone 1.

PUERTO RICO AND THE VIRGIN ISLANDS

P. Mattson, G. Draper, and J. F. Lewis

INTRODUCTION

Puerto Rico and the Virgin Islands are composed of a Mesozoic and lower Tertiary deformed island-arc terrane flanked by middle to upper Tertiary carbonate and clastic deposits. The core contains volcanic, epiclastic, and minor carbonate rocks, all slightly to moderately metamorphosed and intruded by hypabyssal and plutonic igneous rocks.

The geology of Puerto Rico and the Virgin Islands is well mapped through the detailed work of the U.S. Geological Survey (Miscellaneous Investigation Map series) at a scale of 1:20,000 and through several Ph.D. theses. A summary of the

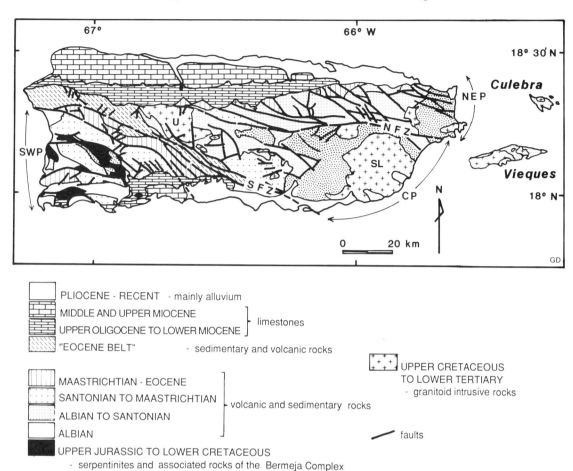

Figure 14. Simplified geologic map of Puerto Rico and the islands of Vieques and Culebra. SWP = Southwestern Igneous province southwest of South fault zone (SFZ) and the Eocene belt. CP = Central Igneous province (includes Vieques) between the South and North fault zones. NEP = Northeastern Igneous province (includes Culebra) north of the North fault zone (NFZ). U and SL = Utuado and San Lorenzo plutons, respectively.

geology and tectonic history of Puerto Rico and the Virgin Islands was made by Khudoley and Meyerhoff (1971) and Mattson (1974b).

GEOPHYSICAL CHARACTERISTICS

Gravity data for Puerto Rico and the Virgin Islands have been presented and discussed by Shurbet and Ewing (1956), Talwani and others (1959), and Bowin (1976). Detailed modeling of the crustal structure across Puerto Rico and the Puerto Rico Trench was carried out by Talwani and others (1959). They derived a crustal thickness of 30 km below Puerto Rico. The regional aeromagnetic map has been interpreted by Griscom and Geddes (1966).

Two lines of evidence indicate that the Puerto Rico–Virgin Islands segment is tectonically active. First, the zone is seismically active; second, seismic-reflection profiles suggest that the area south of the trench has been tilted down to the north, gently deforming Recent sediments in the Puerto Rico Trench and forming the tilted physiographic surface of Puerto Rico.

MORPHOTECTONIC ZONES AND STRATIGRAPHY OF PUERTO RICO

Puerto Rico can be divided into three main morphotectonic zones (Fig. 14): a central area, the Central Igneous zone, underlain by mainly igneous rocks, is flanked by Northern and Southern Carbonate zones, each comprising gently dipping middle Oligocene through middle Miocene marine sedimentary rocks. The rocks of the more extensive northern zone are less faulted and have a better developed karst topography than in the south (Monroe, 1976). Surficial deposits of Miocene to Holocene age cover more than 15 percent of the surface area of Puerto Rico.

The Central Igneous zone or "older complex" of Puerto Rico is composed of lavas and volcanogenic sedimentary rocks, ranging in age from Late Jurassic to late Eocene and intruded by Upper Cretaceous and lower Tertiary granitoid rocks. The central zone can be subdivided into three structural blocks or provinces (Fig. 14), which are separated by major northwest-trending fault zones (Briggs and Akers, 1965; Cox and others, 1977; Barabas,

1977): (1) the Southwestern Igneous province and Eocene belt, (2) the Central Igneous province, and (3) the Northeastern Igneous province.

Left-lateral slip along the bounding faults has made stratigraphic correlation between the provinces difficult, in part because faults and facies boundaries are often parallel. In order to overcome some of the correlation problems, we have adopted the boundaries suggested by Barabas (1977).

OLDER (PRE–UPPER EOCENE) ROCKS OF PUERTO RICO: CENTRAL IGNEOUS ZONE

Southwestern Igneous province and Eocene belt

The Southwestern Igneous province is distinct from the remainder of Puerto Rico in its tectonic style and the unique occurrence of serpentinite with associated chert and amphibolite. This southwestern province, as defined by Barabas (1977), also includes Upper Cretaceous volcanogenic sedimentary deposits with minor volcanic rocks and limestones, and a belt of lower Tertiary volcanic and volcaniclastic rocks (Plate 5A). The lower Tertiary rocks are included because their relation to the underlying Cretaceous rocks is unclear, and at least one author (Krushensky, 1978) has written that there is no stratigraphic break between the two sets of rocks. Two stratigraphic levels can be distinguished in the Southwestern Igneous province: (1) the Bermeja complex of Late Jurassic–Early Cretaceous age and (2) the post-Bermaja volcanic and sedimentary rocks of Late Cretaceous and early Tertiary age.

The Bermeja complex includes several linear belts of serpentinite that occur east and south of Mayaguez. In the southernmost exposure, the serpentinites occur with chert and amphibolite (Mattson, 1960; Tobisch, 1968), which are the oldest isotopically dated rocks in the island. The metamorphic rock of the Bermeja complex is a banded amphibolite of tholeiitic composition (Renz and Verspyck, 1962; Donnelly and others, 1971; Mattson, 1973; Lee and Mattson, 1976). Radiolaria from the cherts have been dated as Tithonian to Aptian (Mattson and Pessagno, 1979), and this agrees with the K/Ar hornblende ages of 126, 110, and 85 Ma on the amphibolite (Tobisch, 1968; Cox and others, 1977). The co-occurrence of chert, metabasalt, amphibolite, and serpentinite prompted Mattson (1973) to label the Bermeja complex an ophiolite, and this view is supported by recent geochemical studies (Lee and Mattson, 1976; Schellekens and others, 1989; Donnelly and others, this volume). The contact relations between the chert and the amphibolite are still a matter of dispute and have been interpreted either as a thrust fault or the sole fault of a gravity slide, with the amphibolites being either contemporaneous or older than the cherts (Mattson and Pessagno, 1979). The other possibility is that the chert-amphibolite contact is an unconformity (R. Krushensky, personal communication in Mattson and Pessagno, 1979). The younger ages given by the amphibolite are thought to be due to thermal resetting by a later intrusive event (Cox and others, 1977; Tobisch, 1968). Mattson (1973) also

suggested that a second nappe movement occurred in Maastrichtian or later time, moving the Campanian-Maastrichtian Parguera limestones northward over the older chert nappe.

Volcanic, volcaniclastic, and carbonate rocks of mainly Late Cretaceous age unconformably overlie the Bermeja complex. The oldest of the overlying rocks seem to be Cenomanian calcareous siltstones, argillaceous limestones, and mudstones of the lower part of the Yauco Formation (Volckman, 1984). By Turonian time, deposits in the Yauco Formation became increasingly volcanic with the deposition of tuffs and volcanic breccias, a pattern that lasted until Maastrichtian time. Contemporaneous with this was deposition of the dominantly volcanic Sabana Grande, Lajas, Cotui (limestone), and Melones Formations. The Parguera limestone was laid down in the southernmost part of the area contemporaneously with the more northerly volcanic formations. The Parguera is principally composed of pelagic limestone and silicified mudstones, but some volcanic flows and conglomerates are present in the section.

Mattson (1966) proposed that a major unconformity occurs at the top of the Cretaceous section, but Kruskensky (1978) disagreed, claiming that lower Tertiary rocks directly overlie and are transitional into the Upper Cretaceous rocks.

The Paleocene to Eocene rocks are similar in their general nature to the underlying Upper Cretaceous rocks and are composed of clastic sedimentary deposits with intercalated volcanic and carbonate horizons, all of which crop out in a long, narrow (less than 10 km) belt, from the northwestern corner of the island to the southeastern coast. The top of the sequence is not exposed because the belt terminates against a major pre–middle Oligocene fault system that separates the Southwest Igneous province from the Central Igneous province.

Central Igneous province

The Central Igneous province is characterized by the presence of large areas of plutonic rocks that have intruded a sequence of Lower to Upper Cretaceous volcanic and volcanically derived rocks.

Layered rocks of Early Cretaceous age are exposed in the Barranquitas and Orocovis Quadrangles (Briggs and Gelabert, 1962; Briggs, 1971) and in a wide area adjacent to the San Lorenzo batholith (Berryhill and Glover, 1960; Berryhill and others, 1960; Rogers, 1979; Rogers and others, 1979; M'Gonigle, 1978). In the earlier stages of mapping of Puerto Rico, these rocks were assigned the name "pre-Robles" rocks (Briggs and Gelabert, 1962; Berryhill and Glover, 1960). Formal formation names were assigned to some of the formations (Briggs, 1969; M'Gonigle, 1978), but other formations are still only indicated with a letter designation.

The Lower Cretaceous rocks are unconformably overlain by rocks of Late Cretaceous age. This sequence includes volcanic flows and breccias intercalated with minor limestones (Berryhill, 1965; Berryhill and Glover, 1960; Briggs, 1969, 1971; Briggs and Gelabert, 1962; Mattson, 1968a and b; Nelson, 1966, 1967a and

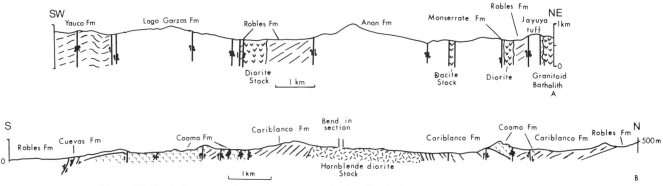

Figure 15. Geologic cross sections across Puerto Rico. Profile A after Mattson (1968a). Profile B after Glover (1961).

b; Nelson and Monroe, 1966; Pease and Briggs, 1960; Glover, 1961, 1971; Rogers, 1979) (Fig. 15).

The Central Igneous province was characterized by volcanism throughout the Cretaceous. The chemistry of the Lower Cretaceous volcanic rocks suggests that they belong to the island-arc tholeiitic or primitive island-arc suites (Donnelly and Rogers, 1980; Donnelly and others, this volume) and probably represent the early stages in the development of an island arc. The Upper Cretaceous volcanic and plutonic rocks all belong to a calc-alkaline suite (Donnelly and others, this volume).

The major intrusions emplaced in the Central igneous province are the Utuado pluton (Weaver, 1958; Chen, 1967, 1969) in the west and the San Lorenzo batholith in the east, with several smaller plutons between them (Fig. 14). The plutons are composite and range in composition from quartz diorite to granodiorite and quartz monzonite. K/Ar ages and field relations show that the major quartz diorite–granodiorite batholiths were emplaced from the Coniacian (88 Ma) to the end of the Paleocene (55 Ma), but the major intrusion probably took place during the Maastrichtian (Cox and others, 1977). Uplift and erosion of the Central Igneous province exposed plutonic rocks as early as Eocene time, as indicated by the presence of granodiorite boulders in the Eocene Cibuco Formation (Nelson, 1967a).

Further intrusive activity took place in the Eocene with the emplacement of small stocks of quartz diorite into rocks of the Eocene belt partly along the southern margins of the Utuado pluton (Fig. 14). K/Ar ages determined on 28 biotite and hornblende samples and 16 fresh rocks showed a range of 46.2 to 34.7 Ma for these stocks, some of which are mineralized (Barabas, 1977, 1982).

The northern part of the Central Igneous province is characterized by volcanic and volcaniclastic rocks of Albian to Maastrichtian age, ranging in composition from predominantly basaltic in the older rocks to mainly felsic in the younger formations. The environment of deposition also changed, from submarine conditions early in the sequence to subaerial later. The volcanic and volcaniclastic rocks can be stratigraphically subdivided into the Río Orocovis Group (Nelson, 1967a) and the Pozas (Berryhill, 1965), Mameyes, and Alonzo Formations (Nelson and Monroe,

1966). The oldest stratigraphic units, the Rio Orocovis Group (Magueyes Member, Perchas Lava, and Avispa Lava) and the Mameyes Formation, contain mainly subaqueous basalt and andesite flows, with associated basaltic volcaniclastic rocks. The overlying Pozas and Alonzo Formations include some marine-deposited lavas in their oldest parts, but contain subaerial pyroclastic deposits in their younger parts that range in composition from dacite to rhyolite (Nelson, 1966).

The geology of Vieques (or Crab) Island is similar to that of the Central Igneous province of Puerto Rico. It consists of a series of undated Cretaceous(?) to Paleocene(?) or Eocene(?) volcanic rocks and granitoid plutons. Undeformed lower Miocene limestone unconformably overlies the igneous rocks (Meyerhoff, 1927; Learned and others, 1973), and thus, the island may have a tectonic history of Cretaceous–lower Tertiary volcanism and pre-Oligocene deformation similar to that of Puerto Rico.

Culebra, although it appears to be structurally part of Puerto Rico, has a Cretaceous to lower Tertiary geologic history similar to that of the U.S. and British Virgin Islands. The island consists of andesitic flows and pyroclastic rocks together with more felsic intrusive rocks, all of uncertain age. By comparison with the Virgin Islands, the rocks are probably of Albian(?) to middle Eocene age with a middle(?) Eocene intrusive event (Banks, 1962).

Northeastern Igneous province

The Northeastern Igneous province contains a sequence of stratified sedimentary and volcanic rocks that range in age from Early Cretaceous to early Tertiary. Three sequences can be distinguished: (1) several thousand meters of dacitic and andesitic lava, tuff, and volcanogenic sedimentary rocks of Early Cretaceous age, conformably overlain by (2) at least 7,500 m of volcanogenic sedimentary deposits and minor amounts of lava of Albian (latest Early Cretaceous) to Campanian (Late Cretaceous) age, which are unconformably overlain by (3) 2,000 m of lower Tertiary shallow-water marine deposits (Pease, 1968; Seiders, 1971). The uppermost Cretaceous unconformity marks a distinct break in sedimentation and is related to the first emergence of a large area in this part of Puerto Rico. The emergent area was the source of the lower Tertiary sediments. The Cretaceous-Tertiary sequence was intruded by a number of small plutons in the Late Cretaceous and by one major stock (Río Blanco stock) in the Eocene (Pease, 1968; Seiders, 1971; Cox and others, 1977; M'Gonigle, 1978; Pease and Monroe, 1977; Briggs and Aguilar-Cortes, 1980). Moreover, the Northeastern Igneous province is characterized by the occurrence of a swarm of possibly early Tertiary-age diabase dikes, striking east-west (Pease, 1968; Seiders, 1971).

LATER (POST–UPPER EOCENE) ROCKS OF PUERTO RICO

Upper Paleogene and Neogene rocks form the surface exposure of the two morphotectonic zones that surround the Central Igneous zone. In both zones, these rocks are essentially all carbonates that lie unconformably on the igneous and clastic sedimentary rocks of the Central Igneous zone. A spectacular tropical karst scenery has developed on these limestones, especially in the Northern Carbonate zone (Monroe, 1976).

Northern Carbonate zone

The sequence of the Northern Carbonate zone ranges in age from mid-Oligocene to late Miocene–Pliocene and extends along almost the whole length of the north coast of the island. The approximate strike of the beds is east-west, with a 4 to 6° dip to the north. Most of the sequence continues offshore, albeit with some facies changes, before being truncated by faults at the edge of the Puerto Rico Trench. The nomenclature used below corresponds to that used by the U.S. Geological Survey (Monroe, 1980). Some workers (e.g., Meyerhoff and others, 1983; Seiglie and Moussa, 1984) have used a slightly different nomenclature.

The oldest rocks in this zone are the mid-Oligocene San Sebastian Formation, which is composed of yellow-brown sandy clays with some conglomerate and lignite beds. These grade into soft fossiliferous limestones at the top of the sequence. In the western part of the island these beds grade laterally and upward into the upper Oligocene Lares Formation. This latter unit is composed of hard, pure, thinly bedded calcarenites with a high coral and algal content.

The conformably overlying Cibao Formation, which also includes the Montebello Limestone Member, is characterized by clastic lenses and horizons, and lateral changes in lithology. It is predominantly calcarenite in the central part of its outcrop, but contains beds of marl sand and gravel in the west and thick lenses of gravel in the east. The upper part of the sequence is probably of early Miocene age (Monroe, 1973).

The overlying Aguada Formation (Los Puetos Limestone in Seiglie and Moussa, 1984, and Meyerhoff and others, 1983) is difficult to distinguish lithologically from the Cibao Formation and seems to be transitional into the middle Miocene Aymamon Formation. The Aymamon Formation is quite distinct, however, and is composed of thickly bedded, locally dolomitic, hard limestone.

An unconformity separates the overlying Quebradillas Formation (= Camuy Formation), which is of late Miocene to Pliocene age (Moussa and others, 1987). The pinkish beds are in distinct color contrast to the underlying rocks, which are very pale brown to light gray. Quartz sand and other terrigenous detritus within the dominant limestones also characterize this formation. According to Moussa and others (1987), the formation has widespread occurrence northward into the Puerto Rico Trench.

Lithological and paleontological evidence indicates that the northern carbonate sequence developed in a shallow-water carbonate-platform environment, although the commonly encountered beds of terrigenous material, especially in the upper part of the sequence, indicate that a source of terrigenous material was exposed in Miocene and possibly Oligocene time. Seiglie and Moussa (1984) have interpreted the changes and depositional environment as a result of eustatic changes in sea level.

Southern Carbonate zone

The Southern Carbonate zone has a smaller area of outcrop and different structure than the Northern Carbonate zone. Characteristically, the bedding dips 12 to 20° to the south, but flattens near the coast. Ages of the rocks range from Oligocene to Pliocene.

The oldest formation of the Southern Carbonate zone is the Juana Diaz Formation, composed of lenticular beds of clastic carbonate gravel, sand, and clay. Frost and others (1983) have interpreted this formation as a series of four cycles of reef development. Most of the deposits are island slope deposits with layers of reefal debris and occasional *Lepidocyclina*-bearing layers. The Oligocene deposits in this formation are clay, but the younger Miocene deposits are marls.

The base of the Ponce Formation is of middle Miocene age and unconformably overlies the Juana Díaz Formation, although there are several minor units between (see Meyerhoff and others, 1983, p. 116). The rest of the formation passes up into late Miocene and Pliocene deposits. The formation consists of hard, light brownish gray calcarenites, which in places contain coralline reef debris.

STRUCTURAL FEATURES OF PUERTO RICO

Puerto Rico shows many manifestations of tectonism, particularly in the older rocks. The principal features are two major fault zones that cross the island in a west-east to west-northwest direction. They have been named the Great North Puerto Rico fault zone and Great South Puerto Rico fault zone (hereafter called North fault zone and South fault zone) by Glover (1971). Although the North fault zone is the clear boundary between the Northeastern Igneous and Central Igneous provinces, the South fault zone is intimately associated with the Eocene belt, and we have assumed the northern limit of this deformed zone to be the boundary between the Central and Southeastern Igneous provinces.

At their northern extremities, both major fault zones are covered unconformably by Oligocene and younger strata, but, near its southern margin, the South fault zone exposes and displaces Oligocene and Miocene rocks in several places (Glover and Mattson, 1973; Krushensky and Monroe, 1975). These fault zones exhibit an overall left-lateral strike-slip, but the amount of slip has not yet been estimated. The lack of lithological and facies correlations across the zones suggests that a large amount of horizontal movement has occurred.

Faults occur within the blocks bordered by the major fault zones, but there is no evidence for major strike-slip movement, and the general pattern seems to be one of normal block faulting.

Low-angle faulting on the island apparently occurs only within and south of the South fault zone. Several units moved northward along gently dipping slide surfaces or thrust faults (Mattson, 1960) during Late Cretaceous and early Tertiary time. Similar gravity slides, mapped in the Río Descalabrado Quadrangle near the east end of the South fault zone (Glover and Mattson, 1973), moved northward in middle Eocene time and were later displaced by left-lateral slip within the fault zone. However, in the Ponce Quadrangle to the west of Río Descalabrado, Krushensky and Monroe (1975) believe southward thrusting preceded lateral slip because of the present-day southward dip of the movement surfaces. Glover and Mattson (1973) disputed this and suggested that uplift of central Puerto Rico since Eocene time has reversed the mapped dip directions.

Large-scale folding in Puerto Rico is restricted to the blocks separated by the two large fault zones. The Central Igneous province contains a generally structurally high region called the Puerto Rico anticlinorium (Berryhill and others, 1960; Kaye, 1956). West of these large folds, the Utuado batholith occupies most of the central structural zone. It is predominantly a structural dome uplifted along a rectangularly shaped network of faults dividing blocks of homoclinal strata.

The Southwestern Igneous province and Eocene belt, south of the South fault zone, is the only part of Puerto Rico where folding is prominent. Folds with anticlinal cores of serpentinite and flanks of Late Cretaceous volcanic and sedimentary rocks have axial planes overturned to the north, and local overturning of Late Cretaceous strata occurs near the top of the ophiolite. Within the Eocene belt, thinly bedded epiclastic deposits are spectacularly folded on both outcrop and regional scale.

As noted by Mattson (1974b), compressional forces must have been active at least in Maastrichtian to middle Eocene time to produce the major fold structures.

The Northern Carbonate zone is essentially undeformed. A few minor faults with less than 30 m of offset have been mapped (Berryhill, 1965). A few flexures disturb the shallow northern dip, but these are of low amplitude and are regionally unimportant.

In contrast to the Northern Carbonate zone, the Southern Carbonate zone is faulted, and dips are steeper. In many places along their northern margin the Tertiary strata are faulted against rocks of the Central Igneous zone. The thickness of the Ponce Formation is unknown because of faulting. Folding, however, is not common.

MORPHOTECTONIC ZONES AND STRATIGRAPHY OF THE VIRGIN ISLANDS

The Virgin Islands can be regarded as two NE zones, trending east-northeast and separated by the similarly trending Anegada Trough. The Northern Virgin Islands zone is an east-northeast extension of Puerto Rico and is composed of two U.S. Virgin Islands (St. Thomas and St. John), and three British Virgin Islands (Tortola, Virgin Gorda, and Anegada), and numerous small cays. The Southern Virgin Islands (or Cruzan) zone includes a submarine ridge running parallel to and south of the Anegada trough, and the island of St. Croix.

The Northern Virgin Islands zone consists of Albian (and possibly earlier) volcanic and plutonic rocks, intruded by minor Upper Cretaceous dikes and plugs. In contrast, the Southern Virgin Islands zone, as exposed on St. Croix, consists of deformed Upper Cretaceous sedimentary rocks intruded by pre–upper Oligocene igneous rocks and unconformably overlain by upper Oligocene to lower Miocene mudstones and limestones.

NORTHERN VIRGIN ISLANDS ZONE

This eastward extension of Puerto Rico island has a volcanic genesis and age range similar to the igneous province of Puerto Rico, but with some differences.

The geology of the U.S. and British Virgin Islands is known in some detail (Fig. 16). The oldest rock unit cropping out in the U.S. Virgin Islands is the Water Island Formation, which is exposed on the islands of St. Thomas and St. John. This formation is almost entirely volcanic, consisting of about 80 percent keratophyre flows, plugs and breccias, and 20 percent spilite flows (Donnelly, 1966). Minor radiolarian tuffs occur throughout the formation and are conspicuous toward its top. Donnelly (1966) tentatively assigned an Albian age to these rocks, which has been proven to be correct based on radiolarian determinations by E. A. Pessagno (personal communication, 1983, to T. W. Donnelly.)

The Virgin Island Group unconformably overlies the Water Island Formation. The rocks of this group occur on St. Thomas and St. John and also in the upper part of the section on Tortola.

The lowermost formation of the Virgin Islands Group is the Louisenhoj Formation, which consists of andesitic pyroclastic material up to 4,000 m thick, overlain by thinly bedded siliceous limestones of the Outer Brass Formation. Pessagno (1976) suggested the age of these formations to be in the range Turonian to early Santonian on the basis of their radiolarian fauna.

Volcanogenic sedimentary rocks overlie the outer Brass Limestones in the northern part of St. Thomas and St. John, and in southern Tortola. The Tutu Formation consists of graywackes and megabreccias composed of debris from the underlying Louisenhoj pyroclastic rocks. A single limestone member, variously

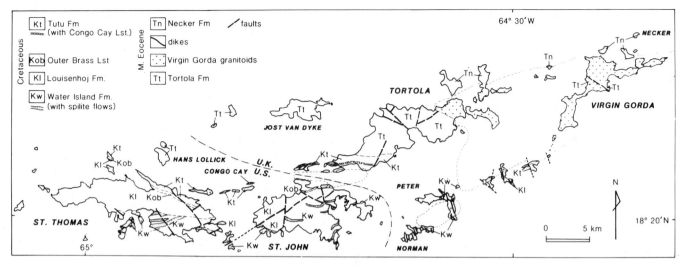

Figure 16. Geologic map of the northern Virgin Islands compiled from Donnelly (1966) and Helsley (1971). Thin dashed lines indicate boundaries of Virgin Gorda granitoid plutons.

known as the Congo Key Member in the U.S. Virgin Islands and the Towers Limestone in Tortola (Martin-Kaye, 1959), is found within this formation.

In the British Virgin Islands, principally Tortola and Virgin Gorda, Cretaceous rocks are only exposed in the southern region, and Tertiary rocks underlie most of the northern part of the island group. The Tertiary Tortola and Necker Formations unconformably overlie the Cretaceous rocks. They include pyroclastic andesites, breccias, and tuffs, as well as several limestones and limestone breccia units. The limestones have yielded foraminifera that indicate a middle Eocene age (Helsley, 1971).

Most of the region of the northeastern British Virgin Islands is underlain by the Virgin Gorda batholith. A smaller pluton underlies the straits between Tortola and St. John. The diorites, tonalites, and granodiorites of the Virgin Gorda batholith were intruded into and metamorphosed the middle Eocene rocks of the Tortola and Necker Formations. However, the uppermost beds in the Necker Formation seem to contain fragments of plutonic rocks from the batholith; thus, Helsley (1971) concluded that intrusion took place in mid- to later Eocene time, and K/Ar dating has confirmed this age (Cox and others, 1977).

Anegada is the most northerly of the Virgin Islands, but the only rocks exposed are Pleistocene to Recent limestones.

The Northern Virgin Islands zone seems to be relatively simple structurally. An extension of the Great Northern fault zone of Puerto Rico probably separates Vieques from the rest of the zone. North of the fault zone, faulting is minor and the main structure is the steep dip of beds that are locally overturned. This deformation affects rocks at a considerable distance from the Virgin Gorda batholith, and so is probably not associated with intrusion. Helsley (1971) reported that the internal structure of the batholith and paleomagnetic evidence indicate that the batholith has been rotated steeply to the north, and hence, intrusion preceded deformation of the area. The Virgin Islands, therefore, probably experienced the same post-Eocene–pre-Oligocene diastrophism as Puerto Rico, although the lack of outcrop of post-Eocene rocks makes it impossible to determine the upper age limit of deformation.

SOUTHERN VIRGIN ISLANDS (CRUZAN) ZONE

St. Croix is an elongate east-west–trending island with elevated eastern and western ends composed of Upper Cretaceous rocks separated by lower-lying Miocene limestone (Fig. 17).

The oldest rocks in St. Crox are the epiclastic mudstones and minor turbidites of the Caledonia Formation, which is exposed on the extreme eastern and western ends of the island (Whetten, 1966). These rocks are at least as old as Campanian, and Speed and others (1979) have suggested, mainly on the basis of isotopic ages of igneous clasts in conglomerate layers, that the age of the lower Caledonia section is Santonian or Cenomanian. At the western end of the island, the Caledonian Formation grades laterally and upward into the tuffaceous Allandale Formation, which in turn is overlain by the Cave Valley Formation, a unit barely distinguishable from the Caledonia Formation. In other words, the turbidites and mudstones of the Caledonia–Cave Valley Formations interfinger with the adjacent tuffaceous sandstones of the Allandale Formation, the turbidites becoming predominant in the upper part of the section.

At the eastern and western ends of the island, the mudstones are overlain by the tuffaceous sandstones of the Judith Fancy Formation. At the western end, these sandstones are intercalated with limestone, conglomerate, and siliceous siltstone members, but in the east, only a single mudstone member breaks the sandstone succession (Whetten, 1966). Whetten (1966) considered the Judith Fancy Formation to be of Campanian age, although the uppermost section may be early Maastrichtian. No upper Maastrichtian or lower Tertiary rocks are exposed on St. Croix.

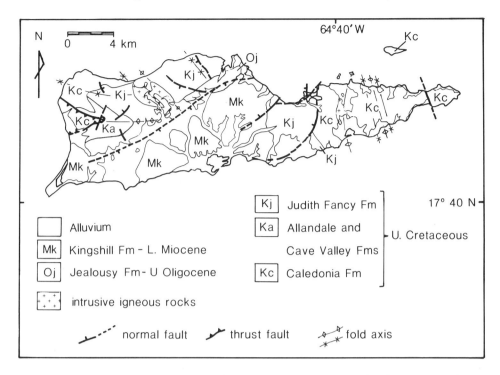

Figure 17. Geologic map of St. Croix (after Whetten, 1966). Thick broken lines indicate buried faults.

Tertiary rocks accumulated in a graben structure between horsts of the Cretaceous rocks at the extreme eastern and western parts of the island. The upper Oligocene Jealousy Formation is mainly composed of mudstones and is mainly a subsurface unit. The Kingshill Formation conformably overlies the Jealousy Formation and is is composed of foraminiferal skeletal micrites, packstone and wackestone, coarse detrital conglomerates, and mudstone (Gerhard and others, 1978). The age of the unit ranges from middle Miocene to early Pliocene (Lidz, 1982).

Structurally, the Cruzan zone is quite distinct from the Northern Virgin Islands zone. Speed (1974) made detailed studies of the structure of the complexly deformed Caledonian, Allandale, and Judith Fancy Formations and recognized three phases of deformation. The earliest phase, at least, took place before the sediments were completely lithified. Because none of these deformations are present in the Jealousy Formation and later rocks, they must be pre–late Oligocene in age. Speed and others (1979) concluded that the first two deformations were probably of Campanian-Maastrichtian age, and that minor intrusives were emplaced after this time but before late Oligocene times.

Crustal extension in an east-west or northwest-southeast direction must have taken place in early Tertiary time to form the graben that is now occupied by the Kingshill and Jealousy Formations.

GEOLOGIC EVOLUTION OF PUERTO RICO AND THE VIRGIN ISLANDS

The oldest unit in Puerto Rico and the Virgin Islands, the Bermeja complex, seems to have originated as Late Jurassic to Early Cretaceous ocean floor (Mattson, 1973). Wadge and others (1984) concluded that it is probably a fragment of proto-Caribbean crust that was obducted northward onto Puerto Rico in Albian or earlier time. The original obduction of the Bermeja complex was presumably associated with subduction, as were the eruption of the thick pyroclastic deposits of the pre–Robles Formations, although it is not clear when the subduction was initiated. The lavas of the Water Island Formation indicate that subduction must have been in progress by at least Aptian-Albian time. The trend and polarity of this early island-arc system, however, have not yet been determined satisfactorily.

Subduction continued throughout Albian to Santonian time, producing pillow lavas, tuffs, and volcanogenic siltstones and sandstones in central and eastern Puerto Rico and the southern Virgin Islands. From Santonian to Eocene time, subduction-related volcanism seems to have shifted slightly to central and northeastern Puerto Rico and to the northern Virgin Islands. Although some unconformities exist within the Maastrichtian and Paleocene deposits of Puerto Rico and, notably, in the Virgin Islands, the type of deposition did not change appreciably. Composition of the volcanism did change a little, however, from andesitic in the Late Cretaceous to more silicic in the Tertiary of both Puerto Rico and the Virgin Islands.

The tectonic style in the Cruzan zone during the Late Cretaceous was quite different from the volcanic province of Puerto Rico and the northern Virgin Islands. Deep-water sedimentation took place at the same time as convergent tectonics, producing syn-sedimentary folding. Crustal convergence was clearly important in producing the island-arc volcanism, and it is likely that this was also the cause of the folding in the sediments of St. Croix. The tectonic environment of the island is not clear, however, and it could represent either a fragment of a Cretaceous subduction complex, deformation of the sedimentary apron of the arc by back-arc thrusting, or deformation of the arc along a strike-slip shear zone. The latter two suggestions seem more likely, as the former would imply subduction to the northeast during Late Cretaceous time, which is the reverse of that inferred from the other islands of the Greater Antilles Ridge.

A fundamental change of tectonic style occurred between middle Eocene and early Oligocene time. Volcanism ceased and was replaced by a major intrusive event in the northern Virgin Islands; middle Eocene and older rocks were tilted, folded, faulted, and uplifted. This deformation was probably associated with the initiation of left-lateral shear on the northern Caribbean plate boundary; certainly, movement on the major strike-slip faults in Puerto Rico took place at this time.

General subsidence and deposition of thick limestone sequences began in the late Eocene and continued until the Pliocene. Birch (1986) suggested that this took place in two stages: the first (mid-Eocene to mid-Oligocene) was in response to extension of hot island-arc crust and sediment loading; the second (mid-Oligocene to Pliocene) was in response to thermal contraction and further sediment loading following the cessation of magmatism. Most of Puerto Rico was probably submerged during the whole of this time, but it is not possible to say if the same was true for the northern Virgin Islands. St. Croix did not share this history with Puerto Rico and the northern Virgin Islands. Minor faulting must have occurred, however, to form the graben in which the Jealousy and Kingshill Formations were deposited.

After the Pliocene (perhaps late Miocene), further tectonism led to anticlinal arching, and subsequent uplift and erosion of Puerto Rico, leaving limestone only in the northern and southern zones. In the northern Virgin Islands, uplift and further northward tilting probably occurred during this period. In the northern part of the Puerto Rico–Virgin Islands Ridge, 3,500 m of rapid subsidence of the trench slope break has occurred (Perfit and others, 1980). The exact cause for all of these movements and their interrelations has not yet been established.

The high seismic activity of the region, particularly along the Puerto Rico Trench, indicates continuing tectonic activity. As noted by Mattson (1974b), regional compressive forces are sufficient to maintain the trench depression and continue northward tilting of the Puerto Rico–Virgin Islands Ridge.

JAMAICA

Grenville Draper

INTRODUCTION

Jamaica is the third largest of the islands of the Greater Antilles, and lies at the eastern extremity of the Nicaraguan Rise.

It is flanked by the Cayman Trough to the north and the Colombian Basin to the south.

The island's rugged topography is most pronounced in the Blue Mountains range, which occupies the eastern third of the island and rises to an elevation of 2,255 m at Blue Mountain Peak. Much of the western two thirds of the island is occupied by spectacular mature karst topography. This topography includes the classic "Cockpit Country," a magnificently developed tropical tower karst (Sweeting, 1958; Day, 1976, 1978). The *terra rossa* covering the limestone of poljes, or interior valleys, and plateaus is the source of bauxite, of which Jamaica is one of the world's leading producers.

Although the heavy vegetation hampers geological investigation, Jamaica is one of the better-known regions in the Greater Antilles. Work began early in the 19th century with a description of the eastern half by Henry Thomass de la Beche (1827). A complete survey of the geology had been made by the late 19th century (Sawkins, 1869). Since then, investigation of the island's varied geology has continued. At this time, 1:50,000-scale geological maps of about three-fourths of the island and a detailed 1:250,000-scale map of the entire island are available from the Geological Survey Department of Jamaica. Recent synopses of the island's geology are available (Robinson and Lewis, 1970; Jackson and others, 1975; Arden, 1975; Meyerhoff and Kreig, 1977b), as is a bibliography of geology from 1827 to 1974 (Kinghorn, 1977).

MORPHOTECTONIC UNITS

Jamaica can be conveniently divided into six morphotectonic units. Three main structural blocks are separated by two northwest-trending graben structures (Fig. 18). From west to east, these are the Hanover block, Montpelier–Newmarket belt, Clarendon block, Wagwater belt, and Blue Mountain block. A sixth, east-west–trending unit, the North Coast belt, abuts against the northern edge of the Clarendon block.

The blocks are composed of Cretaceous volcanic rocks, volcanically derived clastic sedimentary rocks with some minor limestones, and granitoid intrusive rocks that are capped by Tertiary limestones. The Cretaceous rocks are exposed in numerous erosional inliers (Figs. 18 and 19).

The belts separating and flanking the blocks are fault bounded and of Tertiary age. The Wagwater belt is composed of a thick sequence (7,000 m) of clastic sedimentary rocks of Paleocene to middle Eocene age. In contrast, most of the outcrop in the North Coast and the Montpelier-Newmarket belts is Tertiary limestone. However, exploratory boreholes have revealed that lower Tertiary clastic strata underlie the limestone. In the Montpelier-Newmarket belt, more than 1,450 m of sedimentary rocks underlie the limestones (Eva, 1976). Faulting in this latter belt also exposes some of these deposits, as well as the underlying Cretaceous basement.

The structure of Jamaica is dominated by Tertiary faulting, and the larger faults define the boundaries of the morphotectonic

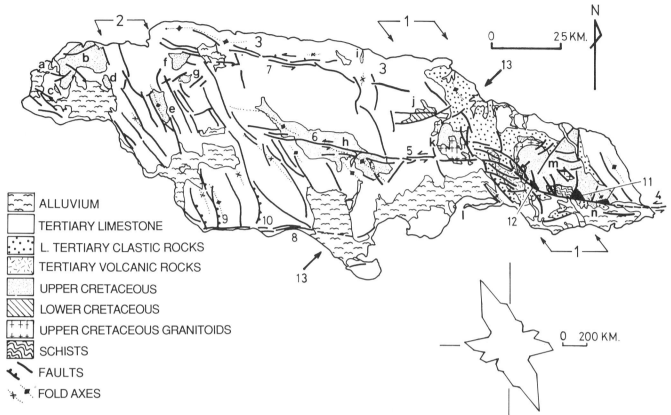

Figure 18. Simplified tectonic map of Jamaica showing the major structural features and tectonically important units (after Draper, 1987). Insert shows the rose diagram of fault traces in the map of McFarlane (1977). Specific features indicated are: 1. Wagwater belt, 2. Newmaket–Montpelier zone, 3. North Coast belt, 4. Plantain Garden fault, 5. Cavaliers fault, 6. Crawle River–Rio Minho fault, 7. Duanvale fault zone, 8. South Coast fault zone, 9. Santa Cruz fault, 10. Spur Tree fault, 11. Bath–Dunrobin ophiolite, 12. Arntully serpentinite, 13. Annotto–Vere lineament (Wadge and Dixon, 1984). The major Cretaceous inliers are also shown: (a) Green Island, (b) Lucea (Hanover), (c) Jerusalem Mt., (d) Grange, (e) Marchmont, (f) Sunderland, (g) Maldon and Calton Hill, (h) Central, (i) St. Ann, (j) Benbow, (k) Above Rocks, (l) Lazaretto (Green Bay), (m) Blue Mountain, (n) Sunning Hill.

units outlined above. The main faults are shown in Figure 18, and the two major fault trends, east-west and northwest-southeast, are obvious. Further analysis (see rose diagram in Fig. 18) indicates that a third northeast-southwest trend is present on land as well as offshore (Burke and others, 1980), although this generally forms shorter fault segments. Much of this faulting is clearly visible on SEASAT side-looking radar imagery (Wadge and Dixon, 1984).

CRUSTAL STRUCTURE AND GEOPHYSICAL CHARACTERISTICS

Knowledge of the crustal structure of Jamaica comes mainly from marine seismic studies of the areas around Jamaica (Edgar and others, 1971; Ewing and others, 1960; see Arden, 1969, 1975, and Holcombe, this volume, for summary). The average crustal thickness of Jamaica and the eastern Nicaraguan rise is about 20 km and reaches a maximum thickness of about 22 km.

The intermediate nature of the crust of the Nicaraguan rise (Plate 3) is also reflected in its gravitational characteristics. Strong positive gravity anomalies occur on the island of Jamaica (Andrews, 1969; Wadge and others, 1982b), but the anomalies decrease westward along the crest of the Nicaraguan Rise (Bowin, 1976), suggesting a thickening of the crust in that direction or a low-density sedimentary section.

An aeromagnetic map of Jamaica, made by the Aero Service Corporation, has been published by Bowin (1976). Although this map shows prominent east-west–trending anomalies, the contours also show a feature trending northwest-southeast, which coincides with the Annotto-Vere lineament visible on SEASAT images of the island (Wadge and Dixon, 1984).

CRETACEOUS ROCKS

A major problem in describing the Cretaceous rocks of Jamaica is the lateral variations in the succession that result from deposition in small basins of the Cretaceous island-arc system. Each inlier, therefore, has a different stratigraphy, and the larger inliers have lateral variations that make correlation across the inlier difficult. Figure 20 and Plate 5A indicate the formations found in the major inliers.

Blue Mountain block

Most of the rocks of the Blue Mountain and Sunning Hill inliers, which occupy the eastern third of the island, are Campanian and Maastrichtian volcanic rocks and volcanogenic sedimentary rocks with major limestone horizons. In addition, the Blue Mountain inlier contains rocks of ophiolitic affinities, granitoid intrusives, and regionally metamorphosed rocks (Fig. 19).

The metamorphic rocks are exposed on the southern flanks of the Blue Mountains and dip northeast under the massif (Wadge and others, 1982a). They consist of mafic blueschists, greenschists, and amphibolite-facies rocks (Kemp, 1971; Draper and others, 1976; Draper, 1978, 1986) that increase in grade westward. Although these rocks were considered much older than any other rocks in Jamaica (Paleozoic by de la Beche, 1827; and pre-Cretaceous by Meyerhoff and Kreig, 1977 a and b), they yielded K/Ar ages of 76.5 ± 2.1 Ma on hornblende separates, and 48.8 ± 1.3 and 52.9 ± 1.4 Ma on mica separates from the amphibolite-facies rocks (Lewis and others, 1973). Draper

(1986) has argued that these ages are cooling ages consistent with the thermal evolution of metamorphic rocks that crystallized in an Early Cretaceous subduction complex, and that the metamorphic rocks may be contemporaneous with Early Cretaceous andesitic volcanic rocks of the Benbow inlier.

The Upper Cretaceous geology of the Blue Mountain inlier has been described by Krijnen and Lee Chin (1978), and the similar geology of the Sunning Hill inlier by Wadge and Eva (1978). Volcanically derived sandstones and conglomerates of Campanian age are found with minor beds of rudistid limestones. These rocks are overlain by a thick sequence of andesitic volcanic rocks in the central and northern Blue Mountains (and Sunning Hill inlier), which in turn are capped by shallow-water limestones of late Campanian to early Maastrichtian age. In contrast, in the southeast Blue Mountains, contemporaneous limestones are pelagic in character and are underlain by a chert-basalt-gabbro ophiolitic complex (Wadge and others, 1982a). Maastrichtian rocks vary laterally. Tuffs and volcanogenic conglomerates with interbedded andesite flows are found to the north of the Blue Mountain inlier, and a thick sequence of turbiditic sandstones and shales, overlain by coarse conglomerate units, occurs in the southern Blue Mountain and Sunning Hill inliers.

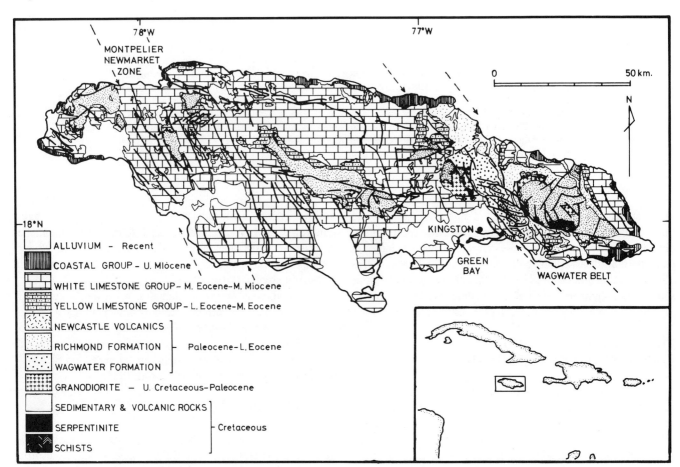

Figure 19. Simplified geological map of Jamaica showing major rock units in the Cretaceous and Tertiary. Insert shows position of Jamaica relative to the other islands in the Greater Antilles (from Draper, 1986).

Granitoid intrusive rocks found in the Blue Mountain inlier intrude Maastrichtian rocks and are overlain by Paleocene limestones, implying a latest Cretaceous age of intrusion. However, Wadge and others (1982a) reported a Santonian (80 ± 5 Ma) K/Ar age from a small stock in the eastern Blue Mountains, indicating a possibility that plutonism may have begun earlier in the Cretaceous.

Clarendon block

The Clarendon block, which forms the central part of the island, contains Cretaceous rocks ranging in age from pre-Barremian to possible latest Maastrichtian age, exposed in five main inliers and several other minor ones. The Cretaceous rocks of the northwestern inliers are dominantly sedimentary in nature, but inliers and wells in the northeastern and southeastern portions of the block contain volcanic rocks. Amphibolites, petrographically identical to those in the Blue Mountain inlier, occur in the Lazaretto inlier of the extreme southeastern part of the block, south of the Annoto-Vere lineament.

The Benbow (previously Guy's Hill) inlier contains the oldest sedimentary rocks in the island and has over 4,000 m of volcanogenic conglomerates, sandstones, volcanic flows, and rudistid limestones (Burke and others, 1968). The oldest rocks are hydrothermally altered andesitic lavas, which are overlain by a bed of Barremian (possibly even pre-Barremian) to Aptian limestones. Furthermore, limestones and intercalated andesite flows are overlain by a sedimentary sequence that includes the Rio Nuevo Formation, now believed to be of Turonian age (Jiang and Robinson, 1987).

The Central inlier is the largest inlier in the Clarendon block and contains Upper Cretaceous igneous rocks and volcaniclastic deposits intercalated with rudistid limestone layers. The oldest rocks are Santonian volcaniclastic conglomerates, which are succeeded by intercalated limestones and shales of Santonian to early Campanian age. Volcanic formations containing epiclastic sandstones and conglomerates interbedded with andesite flows unconformably overlie the shales. Dikes are common in these volcanic formations. Volcanically derived siltstones overlie the volcanic formation and are interbedded with spectacular *Titanosarcolites*-bearing limestones of the Guinea Corn Formation. Previously these were thought to be of Maastrichtian age, but preliminary nannoflora studies (Jiang and Robinson, 1987) indicate a late Campanian to earliest Maastrichtian age. The overlying Summer-

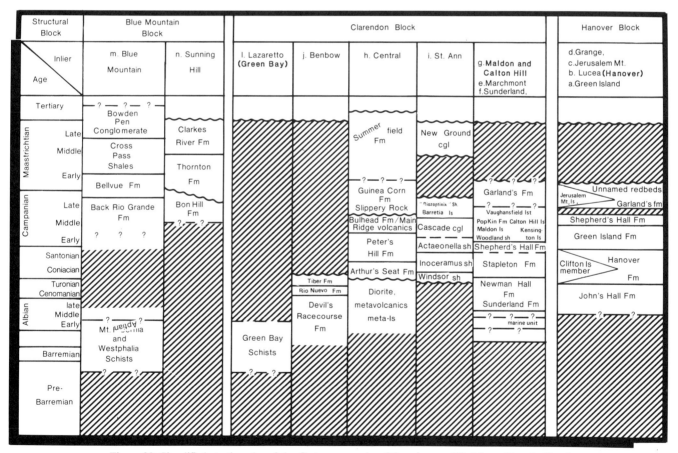

Figure 20. Simplified stratigraphy of the Cretaceous rocks of Jamaica, modified from Meyerhoff and Kreig (1977b), but incorporating data from Krijnen and Lee Chin (1978), Wadge and Eva (1978), Jiang and Robinson (1987), A. N. Eva (personal communication, 1984), and E. Robinson (personal communication, 1984). Locations of columns identified by letters are shown on Figure 18.

field Formation is of interest because it contains red volcanogenic and fluviatile deposits, some containing pumice fragments, in addition to ignimbrite flows (Robinson and Lewis, 1970; Roobol, 1972, 1976).

Volcanogenic rocks of the Central inlier are found in its eastern part, which indicates the location of the Late Cretaceous volcanic centers. A hornfels surrounding the granodiorite stock at Ginger Ridge (Porter, 1970) in the eastern part of the inlier has been determined by K-Ar methods to be about 83 m.y. old (Lewis and others, 1973), which establishes this intrusion as the oldest in the island.

The Above Rocks inlier, east-northeast of the Ginger Ridge area, is dominated by granitoid rocks intruded into undated siliceous sedimentary rocks (Reed, 1966). Isotopic determinations on the granodiorite (Chubb and Burke, 1963) have yielded ages of 63 ± 3 Ma (after adjustment by Harland and others, 1964).

The St. Ann's Great River, Sunderland, Calton Hills, Maldon, and Marchmont inliers in the northern and northwestern parts of the Clarendon block are devoid of the extensive volcanic rocks of the eastern inliers. The St. Ann's Great River inlier contains shales, sandstones, and conglomerates of early Coniacian to late Campanian age that are unconformably overlain by Eocene sediments. The Sunderland, Calton Hill, and Marchmont inliers contain conglomerates and shales of the Sunderland Formation (erroneously called the "Sutherland" Formation by Kashfi, 1983), which are of Santonian to Campanian age (Jiang and Robinson, 1987). In the southern region of these inliers, red Maastrichtian sandstones and conglomerates occur that are similar to those of the Summerfield Formation.

Hanover block

The Hanover block, like the Blue Mountain block, contains only Upper Cretaceous rocks. They are exposed in four inliers: the Lucea (previously, Hanover), Jerusalem Mountain, Green Island, and Grange. The geology of the largest of these, the Lucea inlier, has been recently reevaluated by Grippi (1978, 1980). Two east-west–trending faults divide the area into three blocks.

The central block contains the most complete sequence, with 4,000 m of shales, sandstones, and minor limestones (including the Clifton Limestone Member) ranging from late Santonian to early Campanian in age. These rocks are also notable in that they contain a submarine canyon complex composed of a conglomerate channel fill that cuts across and disturbs the underlying shales and sands (Grippi and Burke, 1980).

The other two structural blocks of the Lucea inlier contain sequences of clastic deposits and minor limestones; the northern block contains Campanian rocks, whereas the southern block contains only channelized sands of Santonian age.

The Green Island, Grange, and Jerusalem Mountain inliers contain lithologies similar to the Lucea inlier, but the rocks are younger. Campanian shales grade upward into a Maastrichtian, arenaceous, red-bed sequence with rudist limestones locally developed at the transition. This sequence is similar to that found in the

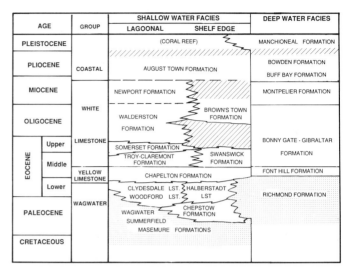

Figure 21. Simplified Tertiary stratigraphy of Jamaica, including facies relationships, adapted from Wright (1976) and Eva and McFarlane (1985). Stippled portions indicate noncarbonate clastic rocks, and diagonally shaded portions indicate periods of nondeposition, or where the rock record has been obliterated.

Sunderland inlier of the Clarendon block. The uppermost unit in the Jerusalem Mountain inlier is the Maastrichtian to Paleocene Masemure Formation, which seems to correlate with the Summerfield Formation and is composed of similar red fluviatile sandstones and conglomerates.

TERTIARY AND QUATERNARY ROCKS

The Tertiary and Quaternary stratigraphy of Jamaica is well known and is shown diagramatically in Figure 21. Carbonate sedimentation has been predominant since the middle Eocene, but thick clastic sequences are found in the Paleocene and lower Eocene. The clastic, largely nonmarine, nature of the Upper Cretaceous and lowermost Tertiary in Jamaica makes it difficult to determine if deposition was continuous in all parts of the island during the Late Cretaceous to Tertiary. In central Jamaica, the Summerfield and Masemure Formations seem to have been deposited from Maastrictian through Early Paleocene time, although there are some indications that the Summerfield may be as young as early Eocene (R. Ahmad, personal communication, 1985). In eastern Jamaica, the Cretaceous-Tertiary transition may fall within the marine Providence-Richmond sequence in the Rio Grande Valley near Port Antonio, and the Cross Pass Shales–Richmond sequence to the northeast of Bath (Jiang and Robinson, 1987), but late Maastrichtian strata have not yet been identified.

Most of the Paleocene rocks in Jamaica are represented by the clastic rocks of the Masemure and Summerfield Formations and the Wagwater Group. The only Paleocene limestone is the Chepstow Formation, which formed on the northern and southern flanks of the Blue Mountains. Eva and McFarlane (1985)

interpreted this unit as back-reef facies because of its molluscan and foraminiferal content. The Chepstow appears to be a platform-carbonate equivalent of the late Paleocene pelagic/turbidite carbonate sequence of the Nonsuch Formation of the John Crow Mountains (Jiang and Robinson, 1987).

The Wagwater Group comprises clastic rocks, volcanic rocks, and minor evaporite and limestones, which range in age from late Paleocene to early Eocene. Green (1977) divided the Wagwater Group into three stratigraphic units. The lower portion, of possible Paleocene age, consists of red conglomerates of the Wagwater Formation. The middle part includes interbedded Wagwater conglomerates and thinly bedded sandstones and shales of the Richmond Formation. The upper part consists almost entirely of Richmond Formation rocks, which overlie the Chepstow Formation in the northern Blue Mountains. Dacitic flows of the Newcastle Volcanics, and minor basalts of the volcanic sequence (Smith and Jackson, 1974; Jackson and Smith, 1979) occur interbedded with the clastic rocks in the middle and upper parts of the sequence. The Halberstadt, Woodford, and Clydesdale Limestones form localized lenses within both the Wagwater and Richmond Formation. Gypsum occurs at several places in the southern Wagwater belt and attains a maximum thickness of 60 m. The total thickness of this whole section in the central Wagwater belt is about 7,000 m.

The paleogeography of the Wagwater belt is very complex, as indicated by the variety of rock types of the Wagwater Group. Westcott and Etheridge (1983) have developed a model in which the Wagwater Formation represents fan-delta and proximal submarine-fan deposits, and the Richmond represents distal submarine-fan deposits. Several fan systems, supplied by erosion of the Cretaceous volcanic rocks, developed at the steep margin of the narrow Wagwater belt basin.

By late early Eocene time, a general marine transgression immersed the entire island, leading to deposition of the thick limestones that now cover two-thirds of the island. Volcanic activity ceased by early middle Eocene times and was followed by a period of relative tectonic quiescence until middle Miocene time. However, the island was not entirely tectonically inactive because the general subsidence, which allowed the accumulation of up to 2,750 m of limestone, was not uniform. The three main blocks of the island remained shallow while the Wagwater, Montpelier–Newmarket, and North Coast belts underwent more rapid subsidence. This pattern is apparent from the various facies developed in the rocks of the Yellow Limestone and White Limestone Groups, as was first recognized by Versey (1957). The environments of the two groups have been determined from a combined study of fauna and lithology. Wright (1976) and Eva and McFarlane (1985) have updated Versey's original scheme with new data to produce a series of paleogeographic maps covering Paleocene to Pliocene time. These reconstructions, shown in Figure 22, indicate that from Paleocene to middle Eocene time, Jamaica experienced an island-wide marine transgression. Deep-water sedimentation began along the eastern north coast region as early as early Eocene, and was well established by early middle Eocene

time. Rapid subsidence of the North Coast, Wagwater, and Montpelier–Newmarket belts and the southern Hanover block produced deep-water environments between the less rapidly subsiding Blue Mountain and Clarendon blocks. This situation seems to have continued until late Miocene to Pliocene time, when emergence took place, subaerially exposing both shallow-water and deep-water limestones. Some of this emergence was probably due to a eustatic sea-level drop (Vail and others, 1977), although much of it may have been due to tectonic causes.

Middle Miocene through Pliocene to Pleistocene sediments in Jamaica form the Coastal Group (Figs. 18 and 21). South and west of the Wagwater and North Coast belts, the Coastal Group is represented by the early Pliocene August Town Formation, which is composed of shallow-water lagoonal and patch-reef sediments with some subaerial to submarine fanglomerates. North and east of the Wagwater fault, Coastal Group sediments are deep-water facies, although they may contain shallow-water fauna derived from adjacent banks. After Aftonian time, most sediments were neritic, and the late Pleistocene geology is expressed mainly as a series of raised marine terraces.

STRUCTURAL AND TECTONIC EVOLUTION

There have been a number of accounts of the tectonic history of Jamaica (Chubb, in Zans and others, 1962; Horsfield and Roobol, 1974; Meyerhoff and Kreig, 1977a and b). Chubb (1960; and in Zans and others, 1962) and Meyerhoff and Kreig (1977a and b) used geosynclinal concepts to characterize the tectonics of the island. This account follows that of Draper (1986, 1987) and, like that of Horsfield and Roobol (1974), attempts to describe the tectonic evolution in terms of plate-tectonic concepts. The tectonic history can be divided into four periods characterized by different geotectonic styles, which are described below.

Cretaceous island-arc phase

The oldest rocks in Jamaica are probably the metamorphic rocks of the Blue Mountains and the Barremian Devils Racecourse Formation. It has been suggested (Draper, 1979, 1986) that the rocks of the Blue Mountains were deposited in the trench region of the early island arc at the same time as the Devils Racecourse rocks were erupted in the accompanying volcanic arc. If this is the case, it would suggest a generally westward-dipping Benioff zone in the Early and possibly middle Cretaceous. The trend of the zone is not obvious, however.

In order to explain the anomalous juxtaposition of the Cretaceous igneous and metamorphic rocks of Jamaica, and their relations to other units, Draper (1986, 1987) has proposed the following tentative model. The Mt. Hibernia and Westphalia Schists were formed within a pre-Campanian fore arc. The exhumation and juxtaposition of the Mt. Hibernia Schists with rocks of the magmatic arc probably took place before or during mid-Campanian time. A mechanism for this has been suggested by Karig (1980), who has argued that oblique convergence may

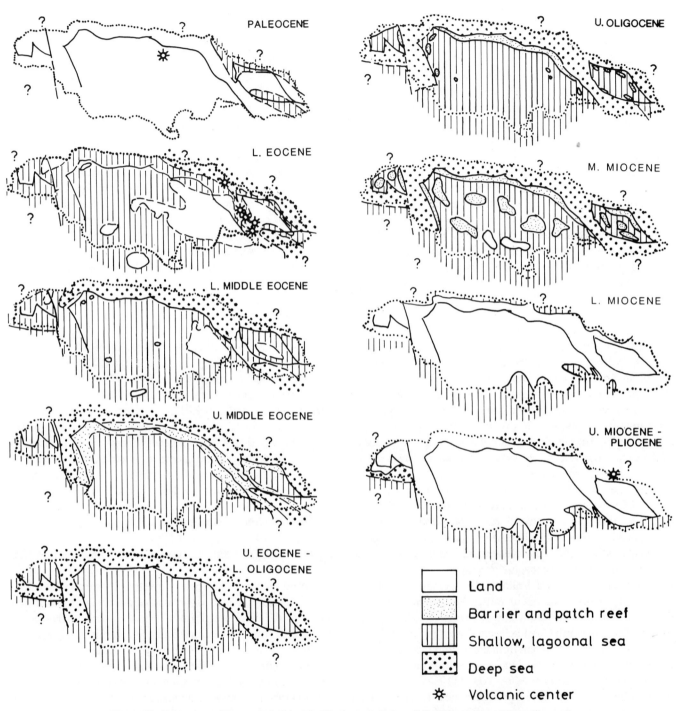

Figure 22. Paleogeographic maps showing the Tertiary evolution of Jamaica (adapted from Eva and McFarlane, 1985). Barrier and patch-reef areas are characterized by coralline and algal bioherms, and reefs; lagoonal areas by thalassia and benthonic foraminifera; and deep-sea areas by pelagic limestones and foraminifera (see Eva and McFarlane, 1985, for details).

cause transcurrent faulting and differential uplift in fore-arc regions. Continued convergence, however, caused the Early Cretaceous volcanism now observable in east-central Jamaica. In Campanian time, adjustment of plate boundaries took place, and the site of subduction in the Jamaica arc system was relocated some 150 km to the southeast of the present island. This tectonic event may have caused the obduction of what is now the Bath-Dunrobin ophiolite, which was emplaced close to the exhumed schist terrane. The shift in the site of subduction also caused a southeast shift in the site of igneous activity to the east of the present island. Thus, a Late Cretaceous magmatic arc was superimposed on the Early Cretaceous accretionary complex and resulted in their present close proximity.

Paleocene to middle Eocene transition

It was during this tectonic phase that the present block-and-graben structure of the island developed. The crust of Jamaica fractured and rifted along the major northwest-southeast trend that is still an important feature of the structure of Jamaica. As the paleogeographic reconstructions in Figure 22 show, rifting was well developed in the Wagwater belt by early Eocene time. Dacitic and minor basaltic volcanism took place contemporaneously with infilling of the basin by Wagwater and Richmond Formation sediments. Geochemical work by Smith and Jackson (1974), Jackson (1977), and Jackson and Smith (1979) has shown that the basalts have within-plate basalt trace-element characteristics, but that the dacites have typical calc-alkaline island-arc characteristics.

Paleogeographic studies also indicate that by middle Eocene time, the northwest-southeast–trending Newmarket-Montpelier and Wagwater grabens and east-west–trending North Coast belt had become established.

Several hypotheses have been put forward to explain these features. Jackson (1977) and Jackson and Smith (1979) suggested that the Wagwater and Newmarket-Montpelier belts developed as back-arc basins in response to southeast-directed subduction in the Paleocene. Mann and Burke (1984 a and b) thought that the Wagwater and Newmarket–Montpelier belts resulted from localized extension as the northern Caribbean plate boundary zone moved eastward past the Yucatan block of Central America. Draper (1979, 1987) suggested that the Wagwater and Newmarket-Montpelier belts may have formed as pull-apart basins in a brief period of right-lateral shear in the Jamaica–Nicaraguan Rise region. None of these hypotheses seem to explain all of the features of early Tertiary rifting in Jamaica, and further research seems to be necessary to explain the causes of this important tectonic event.

Middle Eocene to late Miocene quiescence

This 30-m.y. period was tectonically the quietest in Jamaica's geologic history. Differential subsidence took place, allowing the accumulation of as much as 2,750 m of platform carbonates on the main structural blocks. However, even in this period, some fault movement seems to have controlled sedimentation. The development of deep-water sedimentation in the Montpelier-Newmarket, North Coast, and Wagwater belts suggest that vertical fault movements exceeded sedimentation rates. From late Miocene to Pliocene time an abrupt change in this pattern occurred, and the island rapidly emerged.

Late Miocene to Present left-lateral transcurrent tectonics

Deformation developed during this phase of tectonism overprints the earlier structures and dominates Jamaica's present morphotectonic nature. Structures developed early in this phase include east-west left-lateral transcurrent faults, northeast-southwest–trending normal faults, northwest-southeast reverse faults, and northwest-southeast major and minor folds. Such structures can be developed in a zone of east-west–trending left-lateral shear, and the present situation is one in which deformation is occurring in a 200-km-wide zone on the northern Caribbean plate boundary zone (Burke and others, 1980). The major east-west faults in Jamaica, which were activated or reactivated after this time, show evidence of left-lateral kilometer-scale displacements as well as major vertical movements (Burke and others, 1980; Draper, 1979; Green, 1977; Mann and others, 1985; Wadge and Dixon, 1984). Faults trending northwest-southeast are common in Jamaica. Some of these, such as the Wagwater fault, are early Tertiary normal faults that have been remobilized into reverse-fault structures. Burke and others (1980) proposed that the Santa Cruz and Spur Tree faults, and other major northwest-southeast fault structures, are also reverse faults, but evidence for reverse movement on these faults is not as convincing as for the Wagwater fault. Wadge and Dixon (1984) have also indicated that complex scissor movements have taken place on the northwest-southeast faults, especially in the north-central part of the island.

Considerable oblique folding and tilting of beds accompanies the east-west faults, especially in the region around the Rio Minho–Plantain Garden fault. This has been documented by Wadge and Draper (1978) in the southeastern Blue Mountains, and by Draper (1979), Mann and Burke (1984a), and Mann and others (1985) in the southwestern Blue Mountains and Wagwater belt. This folding has north-south–trending axes. The preliminary structural map of the Clarendon block produced by Wadge and Draper (1977), based on information from the 1:50,000-scale geological maps, also shows a number of open synclinal and anticlinal structures with northwest-southeast–trending axes in the White Limestone of the Clarendon block (see also Fig. 18). The Central inlier itself seems to be a major northwest-southeast anticlinal structure associated with left-lateral deformation. Sedimentological evidence (E. Robinson, personal communication, 1984) indicates that erosional unroofing of the Central inlier began in the middle Miocene, about 9 m.y. ago, probably marking the time of the initiation of major Tertiary deformation throughout Jamaica. This deformation continued to more recent times, as evidenced by steeply dipping, overturned beds in the Pliocene August Town Formation.

TECTONIC EVOLUTION OF
THE GREATER ANTILLES

The fundamental features that emerge from the foregoing descriptions of Greater Antillean geology are that the islands were created as island arcs in the Cretaceous, evolved and were deformed in the Late Cretaceous and early Tertiary, and were further deformed by transcurrent tectonics in the later Cenozoic. Central and western Cuba form an exception to this generalized description because that region is the only one that has true continental crust that is overthrust by oceanic and island-arc rocks and results from collision of part of the Greater Antilles island arc with the Florida-Bahama platform.

Many reviews have been made of the geologic evolution of the northern Caribbean area. Reviews since 1950 include those by Butterlin (1956, 1977), Weyl (1966), MacGillavry (1970), Khudoley and Meyerhoff (1971), Judoley and Furrazola-Bermúdez (1971), Nagle (1971b), and Aubouin and Tardy (1980). Early attempts at synthesizing the tectonic evolution of the northern Caribbean emphasized the paleogeographic factors and geosynclinal theory. For example, Chubb (1960) recognized two Late Cretaceous geosynclines through the Greater Antilles, and similar ideas were expressed by Khudoley and Meyerhoff (1971).

It is now realized that there are wide differences among the stratigraphic sequences in comparing one structural facies zone (morphotectonic zone) with the next, even within any one island. The sedimentary basins must have been relatively small and independent, and the depositional environments changed rapidly in response to tectonic movement and volcanism.

Tectonic models put forward include that of Donnelly (1964), those based on the theory of expansion (Carey, 1963; Levchenko, 1979; Iturralde-Vinent, 1981), those based on contraction (Meyerhoff and Hatten, 1968; Iturralde-Vinent, 1975; Ilich and Meyerhoff, 1980), those based on "oceanization" or "basification" (Bucher, 1947; Eardley, 1954, 1962; Butterlin, 1956; Chubb, 1960; Judoley and Furrazola-Bermúdez, 1971; Škvor, 1969), and those based on mantle-surge tectonics (Morris and others, this volume). More recent models have considered the evolution in terms of plate tectonics (e.g., Bracey and Vogt, 1970; Malfait and Dinkelman, 1972; Iturralde-Vinent, 1975; Ladd, 1976; Mattson, 1979; Maurrasse, 1981b; Walper, 1982; Pindell and Dewey, 1982). In light of our present understanding of the Greater Antilles, the major problems in explaining the tectonic evolution of the northern Caribbean can be expressed as:

1. What is the nature and timing of the Cretaceous to early Tertiary island-arc activity? How many arc systems were there? What was the polarity of the arc(s)?

2. What is the nature and timing of the collision of the Greater Antilles arc(s) with the Florida-Bahama Platform?

3. What is the nature and time of initiation of the Tertiary left-lateral tectonics?

Although all of these questions cannot yet be answered in detail, the broad outlines of the solutions are beginning to be discerned.

Important in any tectonic synthesis is the recognition, dating, and comparison of magmatic, metamorphic, and deformational events, both directly and by their consequences in the sedimentary record. A first attempt at overall correlation for the Caribbean was made by Weyl (1966). In two subsequent reviews, Mattson (1984) and Burke and others (1984) attempted to correlate geologic and deformational features with major plate motions, an approach also taken by Pindell and Barrett (this volume). Compilations of tectonostratigraphic terranes are another possible technique for determining a tectonic synthesis (Case and others, 1984). Although many general features are becoming clear, lack of precise stratigraphic and geochronological information still makes some correlations suspect and open to misinterpretation. However, in order to provide a framework for discussion, Figure 23 is an attempt at a summary chart of various geologic events in the northern Caribbean.

Basement rocks in the central and eastern Greater Antilles are more than 125 m.y. old. The geographic distribution and geochemical characteristics of these early rocks indicate ocean crust to the southwest, with a parallel belt of a more evolved island-arc sequence to the northeast. This geometry suggests subduction of the early Caribbean plate beneath the North American plate, forming a proto-Greater Antilles. This model assumes essentially one single continuous arc for the Greater Antilles. However, the complexities of the geology, particularly in central Hispaniola, have suggested that the single arc model in the early history may be too simplified and that the early evolution could have involved the suturing of two arcs (Draper and Lewis, 1989).

If the Early Cretaceous proto-Greater Antilles arc evolved through subduction from the south, then a polarity reversal must have taken place by the Late Cretaceous. The distribution of ultramafic rocks in Cuba in relation to arc rocks, the uplifted subduction complexes along the north coast of Hispaniola, and relations with the Median metamorphic belt (Nagle, 1974) indicate southward-directed subduction of the North American plate beneath the Caribbean plate. Mattson's (1979) estimate for the timing of this event is about 110 Ma (Albian), but Pindell and Barrett (this volume), who adopt a similar tectonic scheme, suggest that the polarity flip took place at 84 Ma (Santonian-Campanian). The metamorphic ages of blueschists in mélanges in Cuba and Hispaniola, though varied, cluster around 90 Ma, strongly suggesting that they were formed in a single event. Figure 23 also shows that most, but not all of the granitoid plutonic activity in the Greater Antilles took place after 90 Ma. We conclude that it is probable that a change in subduction direction did take place and that it did so at about 85 to 90 Ma. If no subduction polarity reversal took place, there still must have been some major tectonic event at this time.

As Perfit and Heezen (1978) and Wadge and others (1982a) pointed out, most of the reconstructions have ignored the geologic features of the Nicaraguan Rise, Jamaica, southern Cuba,

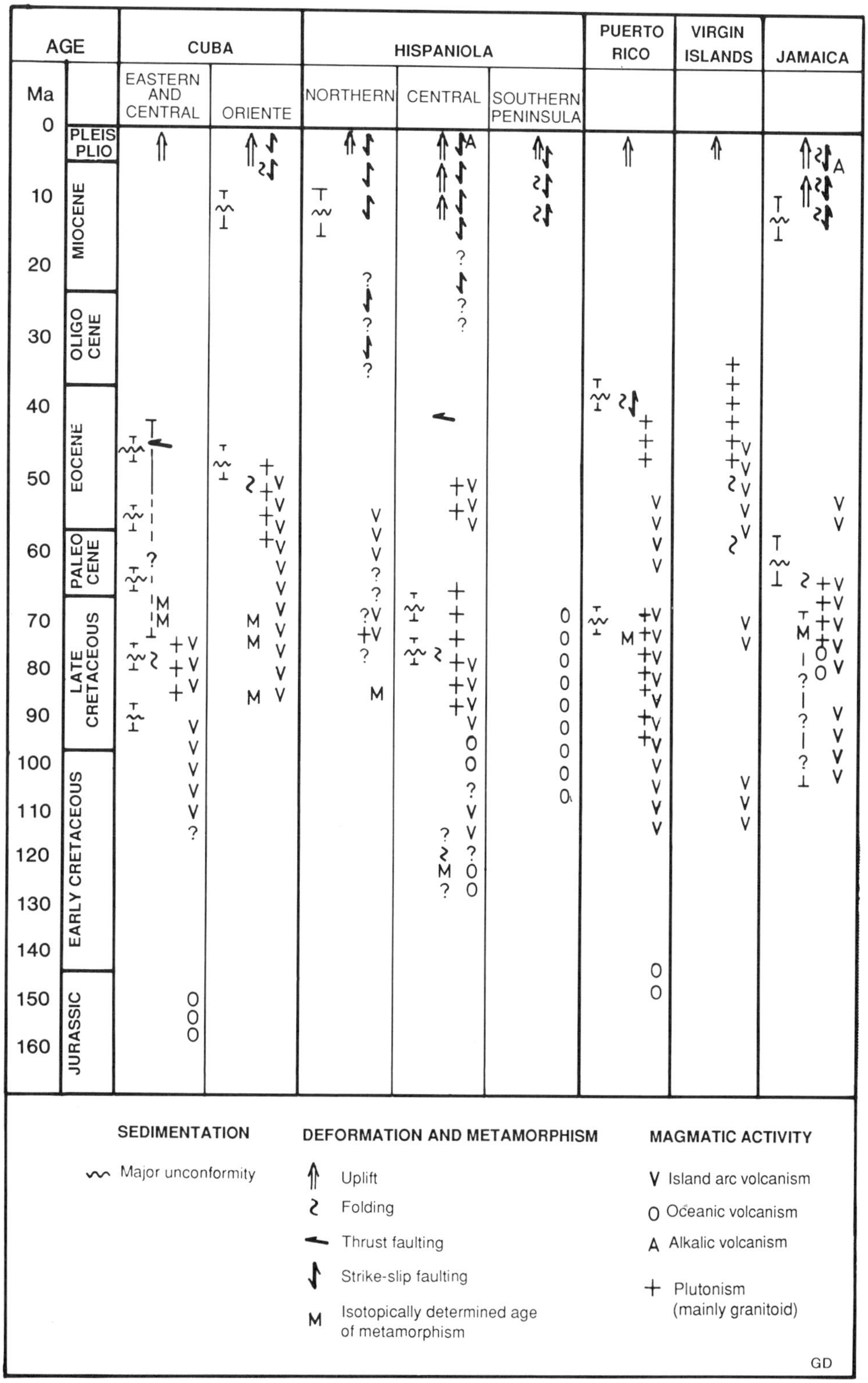

Figure 23. Generalized ages of deformation, metamorphism, magmatism, and major unconformities in the Greater Antilles. Note island-arc magmatism ranges from about 127 Ma (Early Cretaceous) to about 35 Ma (Oligocene), but with further arc magmatism in the late Cenozoic of Hispaniola. Transcurrent tectonics begins in the Oligocene and continues to the present.

and the Yucatan Basin. These authors have suggested that the Oriente province of Cuba was part of a southern arc (i.e., the Nicaraguan Rise), along with Jamaica and Hispaniola, and that a subduction zone dipped south along the present location of the Cayman Trough. In contrast, Draper (1986) has suggested that the subduction zone associated with the Jamaican arc dipped to the north during all of the island's history. Nonetheless, a major tectonic readjustment involving a southward shift in the magmatic axis of the Jamaican–Nicaraguan Rise took place prior to the beginning of the Campanian. This event was probably synchronous with the proposed polarity flip of the main Antillean arc. The most plausible explanation for this activity is that thickened buoyant oceanic crust, formed in the Pacific, forced its way through into the proto-Caribbean area (Pindell and Dewey, 1982; Burke and others, 1978; Pindell and Barrett, this volume). Whatever the cause of the mid-Cretaceouse tectonism, the timing and exact nature of the event are important subjects for further research.

Although the exact timing of the southward-dipping subduction, which lasted through most of the Late Cretaceous, has not been established, it was underway by at least Albian time, as recorded by the volcanic-arc rocks on all the Greater Antillean islands. During Late Cretaceous time, volcanic islands must have existed along the arc-ridge structure. Where exposed, all along the arc from Cuba through Hispaniola to Puerto Rico–Virgin Islands, and in Jamaica, the rocks suggest mainly marine conditions during the interval from late Albian to early Santonian. Considerable subaerial volcanism occurred in central Hispaniola and Puerto Rico during the Senonian, but parts of the central and eastern Greater Antilles were submerged with the accumulation of abundant volcaniclastic sediments.

The cessation of this later phase of subduction and related magmatism does not seem to have been as synchronous as its initiation. In central Cuba, there is apparently no evidence of magmatism beyond the Campanian, but in most of the islands, volcanism and plutonism seem to have persisted until at least the early Eocene. In Jamaica, however, the Eocene volcanism could be related to simple rifting as much as subduction. In the Virgin Islands, arc-related magmatism seems to have lasted as late as middle Oligocene time.

Marked changes in tectonism occurred toward the end of the Cretaceous, as marked by major plutonic intrusion, angular unconformities, and changes in sediment deposition. This is the Laramide Orogeny of Khudoley and Meyerhoff (1971), although an exact correlation with the type area is not implied. Mattson (1984) stressed the importance of a hiatus at 85 ma (that is, at the end of the Santonian as seen in Puerto Rico), which can be correlated with the pre-Campanian unconformity in Cuba. Other important unconformities in the Campanian and Maastrichtian are shown on the correlation diagram. Although the widespread correlation of unconformities has yet to be established, the most marked pulses seem to have occurred within the Campanian and Maastrichtian and at the Maastrichtian-Paleocene boundary.

The tectonic events that occurred in the Late Cretaceous and the cessation of magmatism in the Late Cretaceous and early Tertiary seem to be related to the next important tectonic event, which was the collision of the continental crust of the Florida-Bahama platform with the northward-migrating Greater Antillean arc. This event must have stopped or interrupted subduction, and the structural evidence, like the magmatism, indicates that the collision was diachronous, occurring first in the west and then migrating eastward. As subduction of ocean floor continued in the eastern part of the Greater Antillean arc, convergence continued in the west, resulting in emplacement of ophiolitic rocks by Alpine-style, low-angle thrusting in western and central Cuba. When this collision began is still a subject of controversy. There is some evidence to suggest that thrusting in western Cuba occurred as early as the Late Cretaceous. On the other hand, it is clear that thrusting also occurred in the late Paleocene–Eocene. Although the later date is currently favored in many models (Pindell and Barrett, this volume), the earlier date cannot be discounted.

Although eastern Cuba and Hispaniola may have begun to override the Bahama Platform by Late Paleocene–Eocene time, the plate-boundary kinematics changed from convergence to dominantly left-lateral strike slip, so that large, low-angle thrust structures apparently did not develop in the Greater Antilles east of Cuba.

Estimates of when the left-lateral transcurrent movements began on the northern Caribbean plate boundary vary from Paleocene to Miocene time (see Mann and Burke, 1984a, for review), but the nature of fault-bounded troughs, such as the San José de las Matas graben (Tavera Basin) in northern Hispaniola, would suggest that the initiation was at least early Oligocene (Wadge and Burke, 1983). Sea-floor spreading within the Cayman Trough began in this period, and its initiation and history place important constraints on the amount and rates of fault movement along the northern Caribbean plate boundary. As discussed by Pindell and Barrett (this volume) and Ladd (this volume), spreading in the Cayman Trough suggests that at least 1,050 km of left-lateral strike slip has taken place on the northern Caribbean plate boundary since the Cayman Trough inception. It is apparent that this movement is not accommodated on a single transform fault, but has been distributed through a 200-km-wide North American–Caribbean plate boundary zone (NCPBZ; Burke and others, 1980; Mann and others, this volume). It has also become apparent that major transcurrent movement within this zone has been accommodated by different fault systems at different times. Present-day directions and rates of relative motion have been determined from seismicity and the motion of the larger plates. Mann and Burke (1984b) and Mann and others (this volume) discussed this extrapolation back to the Miocene and earlier, but opinion is still divided on the importance of different fault systems.

Most of the models proposed for the Neogene evolution of the NCPBZ originate from an earlier model by Hess and Maxwell (1953), and involve east-west translation of blocks along major fault zones. As with the original model, most authors define two distinct tectonic provinces: a northern one comprising present-day Cuba, northern Hispaniola, and northern Puerto Rico–Virgin Islands; and a southern one comprising Jamaica and southern Hispaniola. Sykes and others (1982), on the basis of plate motions derived from recent seismicity, further divided the eastern Greater Antilles into three blocks: a southern Hispaniola block (south of the Río San Juan Valley—a feature different from other models), a northern Hispaniola block, and a Puerto Rico–Virgin Islands block. The Southern Peninsula of Haiti and central Hispaniola were suggested to have collided in the Miocene. Pindell and Barrett (this volume) have further developed this model and consider that a minimum of 350 km of offset took place along the Pozos–San Juan fault before the late Miocene. Motion transferred to the Oriente fault in the middle Miocene and resulted in the separation of Cuba from northern Hispaniola.

An alternative scheme, in which major strike-slip movement could have taken place in Oligocene time along the Hispaniola fault zone, was suggested by Mann (1983). The reconstruction involves the positioning of the southeastern Cuban block north of central Hispaniola, and rupture of and movement along the Hispaniola fault zone subparallel to the axis of the former arc.

The last decade has seen many advances in the understanding of Greater Antillean geology, from the point of view of improved field information and also successful application of plate-tectonic theory. As a result, in the decades ahead we can expect to see an increased interest in the Greater Antilles as a natural laboratory for the study of island-arc geology and transcurrent plate boundaries.

REFERENCES CITED

Alvarez, W., and 10 others, 1982, New data on the Cretaceous–Tertiary extinction (abs.): American Association for the Advancement of Science Annual Meeting, Washington, D.C., p. 47.

Andrews, E. M., 1969, Gravity surveys in Jamaica: Institute of Geological Sciences, Geophysical Division Geophysical Report GPO/0/40, 32 p.

Amarante, J. A., Jiménez, J., and Lewis, J. F., 1989, Geology, hydrothermal alteration, and geochemistry of epithermal Au-Ag mineralisation in the Restauración area, Dominican Republic, *in* Transactions, 11th Caribbean Geological Conference, Barbados, 1986: p. 26:1–26:15.

Anon., 1978, Mapa tectónico de Cuba, *in* Altas de Cuba: La Habana, Instituto Cubano de Geodesía y Cartografía, 143 p.

Anon., 1983, Contribución a la geología de Cuba oriental: Instituto de Geología y Paleontología, Academia de Ciencias de Cuba, Editorial Científico-técnica, 273 p.

Antonini, G. A., 1968, Processes and patterns of landscape change in the Línea Noroeste, Dominican Republic [Ph.D. thesis]: New York, Columbia University, 200 p.

——, 1979, Physical geography of northwest Dominican Republic, *in* Lidz, B., and Nagle, F., eds., Hispaniola; Tectonic focal point of the northern Caribbean: Miami Geological Society, p. 69–96.

Arden, D. D., 1969, Geological history of the Nicaragua rise: Transactions of the Gulf Coast Association of Geological Societies, v. 19, p. 245–309.

——, 1975, Geology of Jamaica and the Nicaragua rise, *in*, Nairn, A.E.M. and Stehli, F. G., eds., Ocean basins and margins; Gulf of Mexico and the Caribbean: New York, Plenum Press, v. 3, p. 617–661.

Aubouin, J., and Tardy, M., 1980, L'Amérique alpine; Le domaine caraïbe et ses liaisons avec les cordillères sud-américanies: Congres géologiques international, 26ème, Paris, Colloque C5, p. 14–17.

Ayala Castañares, A., 1959, Estudio de algunos microfósiles planctónicos de las calizas del Cretácico Superior de la República de Haití: Paleontología Mexico, no. 4, 42 p.

Banks, T. H., 1962, Geology of Calebra Island, Puerto Rico [M.S. thesis]: Houston, Texas, Rice University, 75 p.

Barabas, A. H., 1977, Petrologic and geochemical investigations of porphyry copper mineralization in west central Puerto Rico [Ph.D. thesis]: New Haven, Connecticut, Yale University, 466 p.

——, 1982, Potassium-argon dating of magmatic events and hydrothermal activity associated with porphyry copper mineralization in western central Puerto Rico: Economic Geology, v. 77, p. 109–126.

Baroni-Urbani, C., and Saunders, J. R., 1982, The fauna of the Dominican Republic amber; The present status of knowledge, *in* Transactions, 9th Caribbean Geological Conference, Santo Domingo, Dominican Republic, 1980: v. 1, p. 213–224.

Barrett, W., 1962, Emerged and submerged shorelines of the Dominican Republic: Revista Geográphica Instituto Panamericano, Geografia e Historia, v. 30,
p. 51–77.

Beall, R., 1944, The geology of the eastern Cibao Basin, Dominican Republic: Dominican Seaboard Oil Company Report, New York Office no. 35, Santo Domingo (unpublished), 32 p.

Bellon, H., Mercier de Lepinay, B., and Vila, J-M, 1985, Cronologie ^{40}K/^{40}Ar et affinités geochemiques des manifestations magmatiques au Cretace et au Paleogene dans l'île d'Hispaniola (Grandes Antilles), Géodynamiques des Caraïbes, Symposium: Paris, Editions Technip, p. 329–339.

Bermúdez, P. J., 1949, Tertiary smaller foraminifera of the Dominican Republic: Cushman Laboratory for Foraminiferal Research Special Publication 25, 322 p.

Berryhill, H. L., Jr., 1965, Geology of the Ciales Quadrangle, Puerto Rico: U.S. Geological Survey Bulletin 1184, 116 p.

Berryhill, H. L., Jr., and Glover, L., III, 1960, Geologic map of the Cayey Quadrangle, Puerto Rico: U.S. Geological Survey Miscellaneous Geological Investigations Map I-319, scale 1:20,000.

Berryhill, H. L., Jr., Briggs, R. P., Jr., and Glover, L., III, 1960, Stratigraphy, sedimentation, and structure of Late Cretaceous rocks in eastern Puerto Rico; Preliminary report: American Association of Petroleum Geologists Bulletin, v. 44, p. 137–155.

Biju-Duval, B. G., Mascle, A., and Muller, C., 1983, Active margin processes; Field observations in southern Hispaniola, *in* Watkins, J. S., and Drake, C. L., eds., Studies in continental margin geology: American Association of Petroleum Geologists Memoir 34, p. 325–344.

Birch, F. S., 1986, Isostatic, thermal, and flexural models of the subsidence of the north coast of Puerto Rico: Geology, v. 14, p. 427–429.

Bizon, G., Bizon, J. J., Calmus, T., Muller, C., and Van den Berghe, B., 1985, Stratigraphie du Tertiare du sud d'Hispaniola (Grandes Antilles); Influence de la tectonique décrochante sur la paleographie et l'histoire sédimentaire, *in* Mascle, A., ed., Caribbean geodynamics, Symposium, Paris, February 5–8, 1985: Paris, Editions Technip, p. 371–380.

Blesch, R. R., 1966, Mapa geológico preliminar, República Dominicana, *from* Mapas, Vol. II, Reconocimiento y Evaluación de Los Recursos Naturales de la República Dominicana: Washington, D.C., Pan American Union, scale 1:250,000.

Boisseau, M., 1987, Le flanc nord-est de la Cordillère Centrale dominicaine (Hispaniola, Grandes Antilles): Un édifice de Nappes Crétacé polyphase [Doctoral thesis]: Paris, Université Pierre et Marie Curie, 200 p.

Boisson, D., 1987, Etude géologique du Massif du Nord d'Haiti (Hispaniola-Grandes Antilles) [Doctoral thesis]: Paris, Université Pierre et Marie Curie, 215 p.

Boiteau, A., and Michard, A., 1976, Données novelles sur le socle métamorphique de Cuba: Problèmes d'application de la tectonique des plaques, *in* Transactions, 7th Caribbean Geological Conference, Saint-Francois, Guadeloupe, 1974: p. 221–226.

Bourdon, L., 1985, La Cordillère Orientale Dominicaine (Hispaniola, Grandes Antilles): Un arc insulaire Cretace polystructure [Doctoral thesis, 3rd cycle]: Paris, France, Université Pierre et Marie Curie, 203 p.

Bourdon, L., Geyssant, J. R., Mercier de Lepinay, B., and Vila, J. M., 1984, Intérêts paléontologique, chronologique et tectonique de la découverte de *Peroniceras (Ammonoidae Collignoniceratidea)* dans le Coniacien inférieur de la Cordillèra Orientale de la République Dominicaine (Hispaniola, Grandes Antilles): Paris, Comptes Rendus Académie Sciences, v. 298, série II, no. 7, p. 287–292.

Bourdon, L., Mercier de Lepinay, and Vila, J-M., 1985, Etude géologique de la Cordillère Orientale, Dominicaine (Hispaniola, Grandes Antilles), *in* Mascle, A., ed., Caribbean geodynamics, Symposium, Paris, February 5-8, 1985: Paris, Éditions Technip, p. 317–328.

Bourgois, J., Ng R., Tavares, I., and Vila, J-M., 1979a, L'Eocène à blocs d'Ocoa (République Dominicaine, Grandes Antilles); Témoin d'une tectonique tangentielle à vergence Sud dans l'île d'Hispaniola: Societé géologique de France Bulletin, v. 21, no. 6, p. 759–764.

Bourgois, J., Glacon, G., Tavares, I., and Vila, J-M., 1979b, Découverte d'une tectonique tangentielle récente à vergence Sud dans la sierra de Neiba (île d'Hispaniola, République Dominicaine, Grandes Antilles): Paris, Comptes Rendus Academie de Sciences, v. 289, séries D, p. 257–260.

Bourgois, J., Vila, J-M., and Tavares, I., 1982, Datos geológicos neuvos acerca de la región de Puerto Plata (República Dominica), *in* Transactions, 9th Caribbean Geological Conference, Santo Domingo, Dominican Republic, 1980: p. 633–636.

Bovenko, V. G., Shcherbakova, B. E., and Hernández, H., 1980, 1982, Novyye geofizicheskiye dannyye o glubinnour stroyenii vostochnoy kuby (new geophysical data on the deep structure of eastern Cuba): Sovetskaya geologiya, no. 9, p. 101–109: translation *in* International Geology Review, v. 24, no. 10, p. 1155–1162.

Bowin, C., 1960, Geology of central Dominican Republic [Ph.D. thesis]: Princeton, New Jersey, Princeton University, 211 p.

——, 1966, Geology of central Dominican Republic; A case history of part of an island arc, *in* Hess, H. H., ed., Caribbean geological investigations: Geological Society of America Memoir 98, p. 11–84.

——, 1968, Some aspects of the gravity field and tectonics of the northern Caribbean region, *in* Transactions, 5th Caribbean Geological Conference, St. Thomas, Virgin Islands, 1968: New York, Queens College Press, Geological Bulletin 5, p. 1–6.

——, 1975, The geology of Hispaniola, *in* Nairn, A.E.M., and Stehl, F. G., eds., The ocean basins and margins; Vol. 3, The Gulf of Mexico and the Caribbean: New York, Plenum Press, p. 501–552.

——, 1976, Caribbean gravity field and plate tectonics: Geological Society of America Special Paper 169, 79 p.

Bowin, C. O., and Nagle, F., 1982, Igneous and metamorphic rocks of northern Dominican Republic; An uplifted subduction zone complex, *in* Transactions, 9th Caribbean Geological Conference, Santo Domingo, Dominican Republic, 1980: p. 39–50.

Bracey, D. R., and Vogt, P. R., 1970, Plate tectonics in the Hispaniola area: Geological Society of America Bulletin, v. 81, p. 2855–2860.

Breuner, T., 1985, The geology of the eastern Sierra de Neiba [M.S. thesis]: Washington, D.C., George Washington University, 130 p.

Brezsnyánszky, K., Franco, G. L., and Radocz, G., 1983, Perfiles comparativos de las áreas de Cabo Cruz y Maisi, *in* Contribución a la geología de Cuba oriental: Instituto de Geología y Paleontología, Academia de Ciencias de Cuba, p. 169–172.

Briggs, R. P., 1969, Changes in stratigraphic nomenclature in the Cretaceous system, east-central Puerto Rico: U.S. Geological Survey Bulletin 1274–O, p. 1–31.

——, 1971, Geologic map of the Orocovis Quadrangle, Puerto Rico: U.S. Geological Survey Miscellaneous Geologic Investigations Map I–615, scale 1:20,000.

Briggs, R. P., and Aguilar-Cortés, E., 1980, Geologic map of the Fajardo and Cayo Icacos Quadrangles, Puerto Rico: U.S. Geological Survey Miscellane-

ous Geologic Investigations Map I–1153, scale 1:20,000.

Briggs, R. P., and Akers, J. P., 1965, Hydrogeologic map of Puerto Rico and adjacent islands: U.S. Geological Survey Hydrologic Investigations Atlas HA–197, scale 1:240,000.

Briggs, R. P., and Gelabert, P. A., 1962, Preliminary report on the geology of the Barranquitas Quadrangle, Puerto Rico: U.S. Geological Survey Miscellaneous Geologic Investigations Map I–336, scale 1:20,000.

Bronnimann, P., and Pardo, G., 1956, Jurassic–Cretaceous stratigraphy of the carbonate rocks of northern Las Villas province, Cuba: 20th International Geology Congress, Mexico, Abstracts, p. 328.

Bronnimann, P., and Rigassi, D., 1963, Contribution to the geology and paleontology of the area of the city of La Habana, Cuba, and its surroundings: Eclogae Geologicai Helvetiae, v. 56, p. 193–480.

Brouwer, S. B., and Brouwer, P. A., 1982, Geología de la región ambarífera oriental de la República Dominicana, *in* Transactions, 9th Caribbean Geological Conference, Santo Domingo, Dominican Republic, 1980: p. 305–321.

Bucher, W. H., 1947, Problems of Earth deformation illustrated by the Caribbean Sea basin, *in* New York Academy of Sciences Transactions, Series 2, v. 9, p. 98–116.

Burke, K., Coates, A. G., and Robinson, E., 1968, Geology of the Benbow inlier and surrounding area, Jamaica, *in* Transactions, 4th Caribbean Geological Conference, Port of Spain, Trinidad, 1965: p. 249–307.

Burke, K., Fox, P. J., and Sengor, A.M.C., 1978, Buoyant ocean floor and the evolution of the Caribbean: Journal of Geophysical Research, v. 83, p. 3969–3954.

Burke, K., Grippi, J., and Sengor, A.M.C., 1980, Neogene structures in Jamaica and the tectonic style of the northern Caribbean plate boundary zone: Journal of Geology, v. 88, p. 375–386.

Burke, K., Cooper, K., Dewey, J. F., Mann, P., and Pindell, J. L., 1984, Caribbean tectonics and relative plate motions, *in* Bonini, W. E., Hargraves, R. B., and Shagam, R., eds., The Caribbean–South American plate boundary and regional tectonics: Geological Society of America Memoir 162, p. 31–63.

Butterlin, J., 1950, Contribution a l'étude de la gélogie de la Bordure Sud du Cul-de-Sac (Haïti, Grandes Antilles): Societé Haïtienne d'Histoire, de Géographie et de Géologie, Revue no. 76, v. 21, p. 1–79.

——, 1954, La géologie de la République d'Haïti et ses rapports avec celle des régions voisines: Memoires de l'Institut Française d'Haïti, no. 1, 446 p.

——, 1956, La constitution géologique et la structure de Antilles: Paris, Centre National de la Recherche Scientifique, 453 p.

——, 1957, Les formations éocènes sedimentaires et ignées des montagnes Noires (République d'Haïti) et leur importance pour l'histoire géologique des Antilles: Societé Géologique de France, Bulletin, ser. 6, v. 6, p. 163–167.

——, 1960, Géologie générale et regionale de la République d'Haïti: Travaux et Memoires de l'Institut des Hautes Etudes de l'Amérique Latine, v. 7, Université de Paris, 194 p.

——, 1977, Géologie structurale de la région des Caraïbes (Mexique–Amérique Centrale–Antilles–Cordillère Caraïbe): Paris, Masson, 259 p.

Butterlin, J. R., Ramírez, R., and Hoffstetter, R., 1965, Ile d'Haïti, Hispaniola et îles adjacentes, République d'Haïti–Républica Dominicana, *in* Hoffstetter, R., ed., International Geological Congress Stratigraphic Committee; Lexique stratigraphique international, v. 5, Amerique Latine: Paris, Centre National Recherche Science, p. 351–414.

Cabrera, R., Tchunev, D., Ianev, S., and Tzankov, Tz., 1981, Geología y volcanismo de la zona Zaza en las Provincias de Camgüey–Tunas: Resúmenes primer symposio de la Sociedada Cubana de Geología, La Habana, p. 15–16.

Calmus, T., 1983, Contribution à l'étude géologique du Massif du Macaya (Sud-Ouest d'Haiti, Grandes Antilles); Sa place dans l'evolution de l'Orogène Nord-Caraibe [Doctoral Thesis, 3rd cycle]: Paris, France, Université Pierre et Marie Curie, 163 p.

Carey, S. W., 1963, The asymmetry of the Earth: Australian Journal of Earth Science, v. 25, p. 369–383; p. 479–488.

Case, J. E., 1980, Crustal setting of mafic and ultramafic rocks and associated ore deposits of the Caribbean region: U.S. Geological Survey Open-File Report 80–304, 95 p.

Case, J. E., Holcombe, T. L., and Martin, R. A., 1984, Map of geologic provinces in the Caribbean region, *in* Bonini, W. E., Hargraves, R. B., and Shagam, R., eds., The Caribbean–South American plate boundary and regional tectonics: Geological Society of America Memoir 162, p. 1–30.

Cheilletz, A., 1976, Etude géologique et métallogénique des indices à cuivre et molybdène de type porphyre cuprifère de la zone de Vert de Gris-Jean Rabel, Presqu'île du Nord-Ouest, Haïti [Doctoral thesis, 3rd cycle]: Nancy, France, University of Nancy, 177 p.

Cheilletz, A., and Lewis, J. F., 1976, Contribution à l'étude de la bordure meridionale du Massif de Nord NE Haïti, *in* Transactions, 7th Caribbean Geological Conference, Guadeloupe, 1974: p. 244–247.

Cheilletz, A., Kachrillo, J. J., Sonet, J., and Zimmermann, J. L., 1978, Pétrographie et géochronologie de deux complexes intrusifs à porphyres cuprifères d'Haïti, Contribution à la connaissance de la province cuprifère laramienne de l'arc insulaire des Grandes Antilles: Societé Géologique de France Bulletin, ser. 7, v. 20, p. 107–114.

Chen, J. C., 1967, Petrological and chemical studies of Utuado pluton, Puerto Rico [Ph.D. thesis]: Houston, Texas, Rice University, 134 p.

——, 1969, Petrological and chemical studies of Utuado pluton, Puerto Rico: Acta Geologica Taiwana Science Reports, National Taiwan University, no. 13, p. 21–42.

Chubb, L. J., 1960, The Antillean Cretaceous geosyncline; *in* Transactions, 2nd Caribbean Geological Conference, Mayagüez, Puerto Rico: p. 17–26.

Chubb, L. J., and Burke, K., 1963, Age of the Jamaican granodiorites: Geological Magazine, v. 100, p. 524–532.

Cobiella, J. L., 1978, Una melange en Cuba Oriental: Minería en Cuba, v. 4, p. 46–51.

——, 1984, Curso de geología de Cuba: La Habana, Cuba, Editorial Pueblo y Educación, 114 p.

Cobiella, J., Campos, M., Boiteau, A., and Quintas, F., 1977, Geología del flanco sur de la Sierra del Purial: Minería en Cuba, v. 3, (1) p. 55–62; (2) p. 44–53.

Cobiella, J., Quintas, F., Campos, M., and Hernández, M., 1984, Geología de la region central y suroriental de la provincia de Guantánamo: Santiago de Cuba, Editorial Oriente, 125 p.

Cooper, J. C., 1982, Geology of the Fondo Negro region, Dominican Republic [M.S. thesis]: State University of New York at Albany, 145 p.

Cox, D. P., Martin, R. F., M'Gonigle, J. W., McIntyre, D. M., and Rogers, C. L., 1977, Potassium-argon geochronology of some metamorphic, igneous, and hydrothermal events in Puerto Rico and the Virgin Islands: U.S. Geological Survey Journal of Research, v. 5, p. 689–703.

Cuba, 1985a, Mapa Geológico de la República de Cuba: Ministerio de la Industria Básica, Centro de Investigaciones Geológicas, 5 sheets, scale 1:500,000.

——, 1985b, Mapa Tectónico de Cuba: Ministerio de la Industria Básica, Centro de Investigaciones Geológicas, 4 sheets, scale 1:500,000.

De la Beche, H. T., 1827, Remarks on the geology of Jamaica: Geological Society of London Transactions, series 2, v. 2, p. 143–194.

De la Fuente, L., and Ellis, G. M., 1982, Informe sobre la investigación geológica de la Cordillera Oriental, *in* Transactions, 9th Caribbean Conference, Santo Domingo: p. 669–674.

Day, M. J., 1976, The morphology and hydrology of some Jamaican Karst depressions: Earth Surface Processes, v. 1, p. 111–129.

——, 1978, The morphology of tropical humid karst with particular reference to the Caribbean and Central America [Ph.D. thesis]: Oxford, England, Oxford University, 271 p.

Díaz de Villavilla, L., 1985, Proposición para una división de la llamada formación Tobas (Provincias Cienfuegos, Villa Clara y Sancti Spiritus): Serie Geológica, Centro Investigaciones Geológicas, Ministerio de Industria Básica, La Habana, v. 1, p. 133–154.

Dickinson, W. R., and Suczek, C. A., 1979, Plate tectonics and sandstone compositions: American Association of Petroleum Geologists Bulletin, v. 63, p. 2164–2182.

Dilla, M., and García, L., 1985, Nuevos datos sobre la estratagrafia de las provin-

cias de Cienfuegos, Villa Clara y Sancti Spiritus: Serie Geológica, Centro Investigaciones Geológicas, Ministerio de Industria Básica, v. 1, p. 53–77.

Dohm, C. F., 1942, The geology of the Sierra de Neiba and Valles San Juan and Enriquillo in Mosaics Area 16, 17, 21, 23, 24, 25, 32 and 33 Dominican Republic: Unpublished report of the Standard Oil Company, New Jersey, 7 maps, 23 p.

Dolan, J. F., 1986, Changes in sea level recorded in cyclic sedimentation patterns from the Eocene Peralta belt, southern Dominican Republic: Geological Society of America Abstracts with Programs, v. 18, p. 586.

Dolan, J. F., 1988, Paleogene sedimentary basin development in the eastern Greater Antilles: Three studies in active-margin sedimentology [Ph.D. thesis]: Santa Cruz, University of California, 236 p.

Domínguez, H. S., 1987, Geology, hydrothermal alteration, and mineralisation of the El Recodo porphyry copper prospect, southeastern Dominican Republic [M.S. thesis]: Washington, D.C., George Washington University, 203 p.

Donnelly, T. W., 1964, Evolution of eastern Greater Antillean island arc: American Association of Petroleum Geologists Bulletin, v. 48, no. 5, p. 680–696.

——, 1966, Geology of St. Thomas and St. John, U.S. Virgin Islands, *in* Hess, H. H., and others, eds., Caribbean geological investigations: Geological Society of America Memoir 98, p. 85–176.

Donnelly, T. W., and Rogers, J.J.W., 1978, The distribution of igneous rock suites throughout the Caribbean: Geologie en Mijnbouw, v. 57, p. 151–162.

——, 1980, Igneous series in island arcs; The northeastern Caribbean compared with worldwide island-arc assemblages: Bulletin Volcanologique, v. 3, p. 347–382.

Donnelly, T. W., Rogers, J.J.W., Pushkar, P., and Armstrong, R. L., 1971, Chemical evolution of the igneous rocks of the eastern West Indies; An investigation of thorium, uranium and potassium distributions, and lead and strontium isotopic ratios, *in* Donnelly, T. W., ed., Caribbean geophysical, tectonic, and petrologic studies: Geological Society of America Memoir 130, p. 181–224.

Douglas, R. C., 1961, Orbitolinas from Caribbean islands: Journal of Paleontology, v. 35, p. 475–479.

Draper, G., 1978, Coaxial pure shear in Jamaican blueschists and deformation associated with subduction: Nature, v. 275, p. 735–736.

——, 1979, Tectonics of the regionally metamorphosed rocks of eastern Jamaica [Ph.D. thesis]: Jamaica, University of the West Indies, 277 p.

——, 1986, Blueschists and associated rocks in eastern Jamaica and their significance for Cretaceous plate-margin development in the northern Caribbean: Geological Society of America Bulletin, v. 97, p. 48–60.

——, 1987, A revised tectonic model for the evolution of Jamaica, *in* Ahmad, R., ed., Proceedings, Workshop on the status of Jamaican Geology, Kingston, Jamaica, March 1984: Journal of the Geological Society of Jamaica Special Issue, p. 120–150.

Draper, G., and Bone, R., 1981, Denudation rates, thermal evolution, and preservation of blueschist terrains: Journal of Geology, v. 89, p. 601–613.

Draper, G., and Lewis, J., 1982, Petrology, deformation, and tectonic significances of the Amina Schist, northern Dominican Republic, *in* Transactions, 9th Caribbean Geological Conference, Santo Domingo, Dominican Republic, p. 53–64.

Draper, G., and Lewis, J. F., 1989, Petrology and structural development of the Duarte complex, central Dominican Republic; A preliminary account and some tectonic implications, *in* Transactions, 11th Caribbean Geological Conference, Cartagena, Colombia, 1983: p. 103–112.

Draper, G., and Nagle, F., 1985, Circulation of high pressure blocks in subduction complexes; Some insights from northern Hispaniola: Geological Society of America Abstracts with Programs, v. 17, p. 566.

——, 1989, Geological setting and characteristics of blueschist and eclogite-bearing mélanges in northern Hispaniola, *in* 11th Caribbean Geological Conference Transactions, Barbados: p. 33:1–33:9.

Draper, G., Harding, R. R., Horsfield, W. T., Kemp, A. W., and Tresham, A. E., 1976, Low-grade metamorphic belt in Jamaica and its tectonic implications: Geological Society of America Bulletin, v. 87, p. 1283–1290.

Dubreuihl, P., 1982, Contribution à l'étude du bassin Neogene du Plateau Central d'Haiti [Doctoral thesis]: Bordeaux, France, Université de Bordeaux, 156 p.

Ducloz, C., and Vaugnat, M., 1962, A propos de l'age des serpentinites de Cuba: Archives de Sciences Societé de physique et d'Histoire Naturelle de Geneve, v. 15, p. 309–332.

Duplan, L., 1974, Etude photogéologique de la Région Centre de la République d'Haïti: Report Nations Unies, Projet de Développement Minières, 116 p.

Eardley, A. J., 1954, Tectonic relations of Northern and South America: American Association of Petroleum Geologists Bulletin, v. 38, p. 707–773.

—— , 1962, Structural geology of North America, 2nd ed.: New York, Harper and Row, 743 p.

Eberle, W., Hirdes, W., Muff, R., and Pelaez, M., 1982, The geology of the Cordillera Septentrional (Dominican Republic), *in* Transactions, 9th Caribbean Geological Conference, Santo Domingo, Dominican Republic, 1980: p. 619–632.

Edgar, N. T., Ewing, J. J., and Hennion, J., 1971, Seismic refraction and reflection in the Caribbean Sea: American Association of Petroleum Geologists Bulletin, v. 55, p. 833–870.

Edgar, N. T., Saunders, J. B., and others, 1973, Initial reports of the deep sea drilling project, leg 15: Washington, D.C., U.S. Government Printing Office, v. 15, 1137 p.

Eva, A. N., 1976, Biostratigraphy and paleoecology of larger foraminifera of the Yellow Limestone Group in western Jamaica [Ph.D. thesis]: Jamaica, University of the West Indies, 165 p.

—— , 1980, Eocene larger foraminifera from the Sierra El Numero olistostrome, south-central Dominican Republic: 9th Caribbean Geological Conference, Santo Domingo, Dominican Republic, Abstracts: p. 22.

Eva, A. N., and McFarlane, N. A., 1985, Tertiary to early Quaternary carbonate facies relationships in Jamaica, *in* Transactions, 4th Latin American Geological Conference, Port of Spain, Trinidad and Tobago, 1979: p. 210–219.

Evans, C. C., 1986, Facies evolution in a Neogene transpressional basin; Cibao Valley, Dominican Republic [Ph.D. thesis]: Miami, Florida, University of Miami, 103 p.

Ewing, J. I., Antoine, J. W., and Ewing, W. M., 1960, Geophysical measurements in the western Caribbean and Gulf of Mexico: Journal of Geophysical Research, v. 65, p. 4087–4126.

Feigenson, M., 1978a, Petrology and strontium isotope geochemistry of the Loma de Cabrera batholith, Dominican Republic [M.S. thesis]: Washington, D.C., George Washington University, 99 p.

—— , 1978b, The strontium isotope geochemistry of a tonalite batholith from the Dominican Republic: Carnegie Institute of Washington, Annual Report Director Department of Terrestrial Magnetism, p. 870–878.

Fonseca, E., Capote, C, Heredia, M., Santa Cruz, M., and Zelepuguín, V., 1984a, Desarrollo geotectónico, petrología y mineralización de la asociación ofiolítica de Cuba: 27th International Geological Congress, Moscow, Abstracts, v. 111, p. 194.

Fonseca, E., Zelepuquin, V. M., and Heredia, M., 1984b, Particularidades de la estructura de la asociación ofiolítica de Cuba: Ciencias de la Tierra y del Espacio, v. 4, p. 31–45.

Franco, G. L., 1983, Observaciones sobre el Neogeno-Cuaternario de la faja costera del extremo oriental de Cuba, *in* Contribución a la geología de Cuba oriental: Instituto de Geología y Paleontología, Academia de Ciencias de Cuba, p. 144–162.

Frost, S. H., Harbour, L. L., Beach, D. K., Realini, M. J., and Harris, P. M., 1983, Oligocene reef tract development in southwestern Puerto Rico: Sedimentology, v. 9, p. 144.

Furrazola-Bermúdez, G., and 6 others, 1964, Geología de Cuba: La Habana, Ministerio de Industrias, Instituto Cubano Recursos Minerales, 239 p. with maps.

Gealey, W. K., 1980, Ophiolite obduction mechanism, *in* Panayiotou, A., ed., Ophiolites: Proceedings, International Ophiolite Symposium, Cyprus, 1979: Nicosia, Geological Survey Department of Cyprus, p. 228–243.

Geister, J., 1982, Pleistocene reef terraces and coral environments at Santo Domingo and near Boca Chica, southern coast of the Dominican Republic, *in* Transactions, 9th Caribbean Geological Conference, Santo Domingo, 1980:

p. 689–704.

Gerhard, L. C., Frost, S. H., and Curth, P. J., 1978, Stratigraphy and depositional setting, Kingshill Limestone, Miocene, St. Croix, U.S. Virgin Islands: American Association of Petroleum Geologists Bulletin, v. 62, p. 403–418.

Glover, L., III, 1961, Preliminary report on the geology of the Coamo Quadrangle, Puerto Rico: U.S. Geological Survey Miscellaneous Geologic Investigations Map I–335, scale 1:20,000.

—— , 1971, Geology of the Coamo area, Puerto Rico, and its relation to the volcanic arc-trench association: U.S. Geological Survey Professional Paper 636, 102 p.

Glover, L., III, and Mattson, P. H., 1973, Geologic map of the Río Descalabrado Quadrangle, Puerto Rico: U.S. Geological Survey Miscellaneous Geologic Investigations Map I–735, scale 1:20,000.

Green, G. W., 1977, Structure and stratigraphy of the Wagwater Belt, Kingston, Jamaica: Overseas Geological Mineral Research Bulletin, no. 48, 21 p.

Grippi, J., 1978, Geology of the Lucea Inlier, western Jamaica [M.S. thesis]: State University of New York at Albany, 169 p.

—— , 1980, Geology of the Lucea Inlier, western Jamaica: Journal of the Geological Society of Jamaica, v. 19, p. 1–24.

Grippi, J., and Burke, K., 1980, Submarine canyon complex among Cretaceous island-arc sediments, western Jamaica: Geological Society of America Bulletin, v. 91, p. 179–184.

Griscom, A., and Geddes, W. H., 1966, Island-arc structure interpreted from aeromagnetic data near Puerto Rico and the Virgin Islands: Geological Society of America Bulletin, v. 77, p. 153–162.

Groetsch, G. J., 1982, Resedimented conglomerates and turbidites of the upper Tavera Group, Dominican Republic; *in* Transactions 9th Caribbean Geological Conference, Santo Domingo 1980, v. 1, p. 191–198.

Haczewski, G., 1976, Sedimentological reconnaissance of the San Cayetano Formation; An accumulative continental margin in the Jurassic of western Cuba: Acta Geologica Polonica, v. 26, p. 331–353.

Haldemann, E. G., Buchan, R., Blowes, J. H., and Chandler, T., 1979, Geology of laterite nickel deposits, Dominican Republic, *in* Evans, D.J.I., Shoemaker, R. S., and Veltman, E., eds., International Laterite Symposium: American Institute of Mining, Metallurgical, and Petroleum Engineers Society of Mining Engineers, p. 57–84.

Harland, W. B., Smith, A. G., and Wilcock, B., eds., 1964, The Phanerozoic time-scale, a symposium: Geological Society of London Special Publication, 458 p.

Hatten, C. W., 1957, Geologic report on Sierra de los Organos: La Habana, Ministerio de Industrias archives, unpublished report, 140 p., summarized in Furrazola and others, 1964 (see especially Fig. 111 of Furrazola and others, 1964).

—— , 1967, Principal features of Cuban geology; Discussion: American Association of Petroleum Geologists Bulletin, v. 51, p. 780–789.

Hatten, C. W., Schooler, O. E., Giedt, N., and Meyerhoff, A. A., 1958, Geology of central Cuba, eastern Las Villas and western Camagüey provinces, Cuba: La Habana, Ministerio de Industrias archives, unpublished report, 250 p., summarized in Furrazola and others, 1964.

Hatten, C. W., and 5 others, 1989, Tectonostratigraphic units of central Cuba, *in* Transactions, 11th Caribbean Geological Conference, Barbados, 1986: p. 35:1–35:13.

Helsley, C. E., 1971, Summary of the geology of the British Virgin Islands, *in* Transactions, 5th Caribbean Geological Conference, St. Thomas, Virgin Islands, 1968: New York, Queens College Press Geological Bulletin 5, p. 69–73.

Hess, H., and Maxwell, J. C., 1953, Caribbean research project: Geological Society of America Bulletin, v. 64, p. 1–6.

Heubeck, C., 1988, Geology of the southeastern termination of the Cordillera Central, Dominican Republic [M.A. thesis]: Austin, University of Texas, 333 p.

Horsfield, W. T., 1975, Quaternary vertical movements in the Greater Antilles: Geological Society of America Bulletin, v. 86, p. 933–938.

Horsfield, W. T., and Roobol, M. J., 1974, A tectonic model for the evolution of

Jamaica: Journal of the Geological Society of Jamaica, v. 14, p. 31–38.

Ilich, M., and Meyerhoff, A. A., 1980, Status of geosynclinal and geotectonic cycle theories: 26th International Geological Congress, Montreal, Abstracts, v. 1, p. 351.

Ipatenko, S., and Sashina, I. N., 1971, Sobre el levantamiento gravimétrico en Cuba: La Habana, Cuba, Ministerio de Minas, 14 p.

Iturralde-Vinent, M. A., 1969, Principal characteristics of the Cuban Neogene stratigraphy: American Association of Petroleum Geologists Bulletin, v. 53, p. 1938–1955.

—— , 1975, Problems in the application of modern tectonic hypotheses to Cuba and the Caribbean region: American Association of Petroleum Geologists Bulletin, v. 59, p. 838–855.

—— , 1977, Los movimientos tectónicos de la etapa de desarrollo platafórmico en Cuba: Academia de Ciencias de Cuba, Informe Científico-Técnico no. 20, 24 p.

—— , 1978, Los movimientos tectónicos de la etapa de desarrollo platafórmico en Cuba: Geologie en Mijnbouw, v. 57, p. 205–212.

—— , 1981, Nuevo modelo interpretative de la evolución geológica de Cuba: Ciencias de la Tierra y del Espacio, Academia de Ciencias de Cuba, v. 3, p. 51–89.

—— , 1983, An expanding Earth model explanation of the origin and evolution of Cuba, *in* Carey, S. W., ed., Expanding Earth Symposium, Sydney, 1981: University of Tasmania, p. 215–218.

—— , 1988, Naturaleza geológica de Cuba: La Habana, Cuba, Editorial Científico-Técnica, 146 p.

Iturralde-Vinent, M., and 7 others, 1984, Las ofiolitas de Camagüey, Cuba; Naturalezca, posicion tectonica y sedimentos derivados: 27th International Geological Conference, Moscow, Abstracts, v. 111, p. 233–234.

Jackson, T. A., 1977, The petrochemistry and origin of Tertiary volcanics in the Wagwater belt, Jamaica [Ph.D. thesis]: Jamaica, University of the West Indies, 276 p.

Jackson, T. A., and Smith, T. E., 1979, Tectonic significance of basalts and dacites in the Wagwater belt, Jamaica: Geological Magazine, v. 116, p. 365–374.

Jackson, T. A., McFarlane, N. A., Porter, A.R.D., Robinson, E., and Wright, R. M., 1975, Field guide to selected Jamaican geological localities: Kingston, Jamaica, Ministry of Mines and Natural Resources, Mines and Geology Division Special Publication, 57 p.

Jakes, P. 1983, Formaciones vulcanógeno-sedimentarias y sedimentarias de Cuba oriental, *in* Contribución a la geología de Cuba oriental: Instituto de Geología y Paleontología, Academia de Ciencias de Cuba, p. 17–85.

Jiang, M-J., and Robinson, E., 1987, Calcareous nannofossils and large foraminifera in Jamaican rocks of Cretaceous to early Eocene age, *in* Ahmad, R., ed., Proceedings of a workshop on the status of Jamaican geology: Journal of the Geological Society of Jamaica Special Issue, p. 24–53.

Jiménez, J., and Lewis, J. F., 1989, Petrología del area de Restauración, *in* Transactions, 10th Caribbean Geological Conference, Cartagena, Colombia, 1986: p. 445–453.

Jiménez, J., Lewis, J. F., and Amarante, A. J., 1986, Geology, hydrothermal alteration, mineralization, and geochemistry in the area south of Restauración, western Dominican Republic: 11th Caribbean Geological Conference, Barbados, Abstracts: p. 47.

Jolly, W. T., 1971, Potassium-rich igneous rocks from Puerto Rico: Geological Society of America Bulletin, v. 82, p. 399–408.

Jones, R. G., 1918, A geological reconnaissance in Haiti; A contribution to Antillean geology: Journal of Geology, v. 26, p. 728–752.

Joyce, J., 1982, The lithology and structure of the eclogite and glaucophanite-bearing rocks on the Samaná Peninsula, Dominican Republic, *in* Transactions, 9th Caribbean Geological Conference, Santo Domingo, Dominican Republic, 1980: v. 2, p. 417–421.

—— , 1983, The metamorphic mineralogy and P/T conditions of metamorphism of the Samaná Peninsula, Dominican Republic: 10th Caribbean Geological Conference, Cartagena, Colombia, Abstracts, 1983: p. 44.

Joyce, J., and Aronson, J., 1989, K-Ar ages for blueschist metamorphism on the

Samaná Peninsula, *in* Transactions, 10th Caribbean Geological Conference, Cartagena, Colombia, 1983: p. 454–458.

Judoley, C. M., and Furrazola-Bermúdez, G., 1971, Geología del área del Caribe y de la costa del Golfo de México: Cuba, La Habana, 286 p.

Karig, D. E., 1980, Material transport within accretionary prisms and the "knocker" problem: Journal of Geology, v. 98, p. 27–39.

Kashfi, M., 1983, Geology and hydrocarbon potential of Jamaica: American Association of Petroleum Geologists Bulletin, v. 67, p. 2117–2124.

Kaye, C. A., 1956, Notes on the structural geology of Puerto Rico: Geological Society of America Bulletin, v. 68, p. 103–117.

Kemp, A. W., 1971, The geology of the southwestern flank of the Blue Mountains, Jamaica [Ph.D. thesis]: Kingston, Jamaica, University of the West Indies, 307 p.

Kesler, S. E., 1971, Petrology of the Terre-Neuve Igneous Province, northern Haiti, *in* Donnelly, T. W., ed., Caribbean geophysical, tectonic, and petrologic studies: Geological Society of America Memoir 130, p. 119–137.

Kesler, S. E., and Sutter, J. F., 1977, Progress report on radiometric age determination in the Caribbean region: 8th Caribbean Geological Conference, Curaçao: p. 85–86.

Kesler, S. E., and 6 others, 1981, Geology and geochemistry of sulfide mineralization underlying the Pueblo Viejo gold-silver oxide deposit, Dominican Republic: Economic Geology, v. 76, p. 1096–1117.

Khudoley, K. M., 1967a, Principal features of Cuban geology: American Association of Petroleum Geologists Bulletin, v. 51, p. 668–677.

—— , 1967b, Principal features of Cuban geology; Reply: American Association of Petroleum Geologists Bulletin, v. 51, p. 789–791.

Khudoley, K. M., and Meyerhoff, A. A., 1971, Paleogeography and geological history of Greater Antilles: Geological Society of America Memoir 129, 199 p.

Kinghorn, M., 1977, Bibliography of Jamaican Geology: Norwich, England, Geological Abstracts, 150 p.

Knipper, A. L., and Cabrera, R., 1974, Tectónica y geología histórica de la zona de articulación entre en mio- y el eugeosynclinal, y del cinturón hiperbásico de Cuba, *in* Contribución a la geología de Cuba: Academia Ciencias de Cuba, Instituto Geología y Paleontología Publicación Especial 2, p. 15–77.

Kozary, M. T., 1968, Ultramafic rocks in thrust zones of northwestern Oriente province, Cuba: American Association of Petroleum Geologists Bulletin, v. 52, p. 2298–2317.

Krijnen, J. P., and Lee Chin, A. C., 1978, Geology of the northern, central, and southeastern Blue Mountains with a provisional compilation of the entire inlier: Geologie en Mijnbouw, v. 57, p. 243–250.

Krushensky, R. D., 1978, Unconformity between Cretaceous and Eocene rocks in central western Puerto Rico; A concept rejected: Geologie en Mijnbouw, v. 57, p. 227–232.

Krushensky, R. D., and Monroe, W. H., 1975, Geologic map of the Ponce Quadrangle, Puerto Rico: U.S. Geological Survey Miscellaneous Geologic Investigations Map I–863, scale 1:20,000.

Kusnetzov, V. I., Bassov, V. A., Furrazola-Bermúdez, G., García-Sánchez, R, and Sánchez-Orango, J. R., 1977, Résumen estratigráfico de los sedimentos mesozoicos y cenozoicos de Cuba: La Minería en Cuba, v. 3, p. 14–61.

Ladd, J. W., 1976, Relative motion of South America with respect to North America and Caribbean tectonics: Geological Society of America Bulletin, v. 87, p. 969–976.

Ladd, J. W., and Watkins, J. S., 1978, Active margin structures within the north slope of the Muertos trench: Geologie en Mijnbouw, v. 57, no. 2, p. 255–260.

—— , 1979, Tectonic development of trench-arc complexes on the northern and southern margins of the Venezuela Basin, *in* Watkins, J. S., ed., Geological and geophysical investigations of continental margins: American Association of Petroleum Geologists Memoir 29, p. 363–371.

Learned, R. E., Grove, G. R., and Biossen, R., 1973, Geochemical reconnaissance of the island of Vieques, Puerto Rico: U.S. Geological Survey Open-File Report 73–0155, 78 p.

Lebron, M-C., Rodriguez, J., and Lewis, J. F., 1986, Petrology of some unusual high-potash volcanic rocks of Upper Cretaceous age, eastern Dominican Republic: 11th Caribbean Geological Conference, Barbados, Abstracts: p. 57.

Lee, V.J.B., and Mattson, P. H., 1976, Metamorphosed oceanic crust or early volcanic products in Puerto Rico basement rock association, *in* Transactions, 7th Caribbean Geological Conference, Guadeloupe: p. 263–270.

Levchenko, V. A., 1979, Tectonic evaluation of the Mexico–Caribbean region as a result of the expansion of the Earth, *in* The tectonics and geodynamics of the Caribbean region: Moscow, Nauka, p. 117–129.

Lewis, G. E., and Straczek, J. A., 1955, Geology of the south-central Oriente, Cuba: U.S. Geological Survey Bulletin 975–D, p. 171–336.

Lewis, J. F., 1980, Resume of the geology of Hispaniola, *in* Field Guide, 9th Caribbean Geological Conference, Santo Domingo, Dominican Republic, 1980: p. 5–31.

——, 1982a, Cenozoic tectonic evolution and sedimentation in Hispaniola, *in* Transactions, 9th Caribbean Geological Conference, Santo Domingo, Dominican Republic, 1980: v. 1, p. 65–73.

——, 1982b, Granitoid rocks in Hispaniola, *in* Transactions, 9th Caribbean Geological Conference, Santo Domingo, Dominican Republic, 1980: v. 2, p. 391–401.

——, 1982c, Ultrabasic and associated rocks in Hispaniola, *in* Transasctions, 9th Caribbean Geological Conference, Santo Domingo, Dominican Republic, 1980: v. 2, p. 403–408.

Lewis, J. F., and Jiménez, J., 1986, Geological features of the sea floor in central Hispaniola during the early stages of arc evolution: 11th Caribbean Geological Conference, Barbados, Abstracts: p. 58.

Lewis, J. F., Harper, C. T., Kemp, A. W., and Stipp, J. J., 1973, Potassium-argon retention ages of some Cretaceous rocks from Jamaica: Geological Society of America Bulletin, v. 84, p. 335–340.

Lewis, J. F., Draper, G., and Domínguez, H., 1982, Preliminary report on the geology of the Restauración area, Dominican Republic: Dominican Republic, Dirección General de Minería, 18 p.

Lewis, J. F., Draper, G., and Burgi, D., 1983, Geochemistry and petrology of high-magnesium metabasalts of the Duarte complex, Dominican Republic: 10th Caribbean Geological Conference, Cartagena, Colombia, Abstracts: p. 47.

Lewis, J. F., Vespucci, P., Robinson, E., Jiang, M., and Bryant, A., 1989, Paleogene stratigraphy of the Padre Las Casas and adjacent areas in the southeast Cordillera Central, Dominican Republic, *in* Transactions, 10th Caribbean Geological Conference, Cartagena, Colombia, 1983: p. 229–237.

Lidz, B. H., 1982, Biostratigraphy and paleoenvironment of the Miocene–Pliocene hemipelagic limestone; Kingshill Seaway, St. Croix, U.S. Virgin Islands: Journal of Foraminiferal Research, v. 12, p. 205–233.

Llinás, R., 1972, Geología del area Polo Duverge, Cuenca de Enriquillo: Colegio Dominicano de Ingenieros, Arquitéctos y Agrimensores, part 1, no. 31, p. 55–65; part 2, no. 32, p. 40–53.

MacDonald, W. D., and Melson, W. G., 1969, A late Cenozoic Volcanic Province in Hispaniola: Caribbean Journal of Science, v. 9, p. 81–90.

MacGillavry, H. J., 1970, Geological history of the Caribbean: Amsterdam, Koninklijke Nederlandse Akademie van Wetenschoppen, AFdeeling Natuurkunde, Proceedings, v. 73, no. 1, p. 64–96.

Malfait, B. T., and Dinkelman, M. G., 1972, Circum-Caribbean tectonic and igneous activity and the evolution of the Caribbean Plate: Geological Society of America Bulletin, v. 83, p. 251–272.

Mann, P., 1983, Cenozoic tectonics of the northern Caribbean; Structural and stratigraphic studies in Jamaica and Hispaniola [Ph.D. thesis]: State University of New York, Albany, 688 p.

Mann, P., and Burke, K., 1984a, Cenozoic rift formation in the northern Caribbean: Geology, v. 12, p. 732–736.

——, 1984b, Neotectonics of the Caribbean: Reviews of Geophysics and Space Physics, v. 22, p. 309–362.

Mann, P., Burke, K., and Matumotu, T., 1984a, Neotectonics of Hispaniola; Plate motion, sedimentation, and seismicity at a restraining bend: Earth and Planetary Science Letters, v. 70, p. 311–324.

Mann, P., Taylor, F. W., Burke, K., and Kulstad, R., 1984b, Subaerially exposed Holocene coral reef, Enriquillo Valley, Dominican Republic: Geological Society of America Bulletin, v. 95, p. 1084–1092.

Mann, P., Draper, G., and Burke, K., 1985, Neotectonics and sedimentation at a strike-slip restraining bend system, Jamaica, *in* Biddle, K., ed., Strike-slip deformation, basin formation, and sedimentation: Society of Economic Paleontologists and Mineralogists Special Publication 37, p. 211–226.

Martin-Kaye, P.H.A., 1959, Report on the geology of the Leeward and British Virgin Islands: St. Lucia, Voice Publishing Co., 117 p.

Mascle, A., and 6 others, 1980, Field Trip D3, Tertiary sequences south of the Cordillera Central: 9th Caribbean Geological Conference Field Guide, Dominican Republic: p. 107–123.

Matthews, J., and Holcombe, T., 1976, Possible Caribbean underthrusting of the Greater Antilles along the Muertos trough, *in* Proceedings, 7th Caribbean Geological Conference, Guadeloupe: p. 235–242.

Mattson, P. H., 1960, Geology of the Mayagüez area, Puerto Rico: Geological Society of America Bulletin, v. 71, p. 319–362.

——, 1966, Unconformity between Cretaceous and Eocene rocks in central Puerto Rico, *in* Transactions, 3rd Caribbean Geological Conference, Kingston, Jamaica, 1962: p. 49–53.

——, 1968a, Geologic map of the Adjuntas Quadrangle, Puerto Rico: U.S. Geological Survey Miscellaneous Geologic Investigations Map I–519, scale 1:20,000.

——, 1968b, Geological map of the Jayuya Quadrangle, Puerto Rico: U.S. Geological Survey Miscellaneous Geologic Investigations Map I–520, scale 1:20,000.

——, 1973, Middle Cretaceous nappe structures in Puerto Rican ophiolites and their relation to the tectonic history of the Greater Antilles: Geological Society of America Bulletin, v. 84, p. 21–38.

——, 1974a, Cuba, in Spencer, A. M., ed., Mesozoic–Cenozoic orogenic belts: Geological Society of London Special Publication 4, p. 625–638.

——, 1974b, Puerto Rico—Virgin Islands, *in* Spencer, A. M., ed., Mesozoic-Cenozoic orogenic belts: Geological Society of London Special Publication 4, p. 639–661.

——, 1979, Subduction, buoyant braking, flipping, and strike-slip faulting in the northern Caribbean: Journal of Geology, v. 87, p. 293–304.

——, 1984, Caribbean structural breaks and plate movements, *in* Bonini, W. E., Hargraves, R. B., and Shagam, R., eds., The Caribbean-South American plate boundary and regional tectonics: Geological Society of America Memoir 162, p. 131–152.

Mattson, P., and Pessagno, E. A., 1979, Jurassic and Early Cretaceous radiolaria in the Puerto Rican ophiolite; Tectonic implications: Geology, v. 7, p. 440–444.

Maurrasse, F.J.-M., 1973, Sedimentary structures of Caribbean leg 15 sediments, *in* Edgar, N. T., and others, Initial reports of the Deep Sea Drilling Project: Washington, D.C., U.S. Government Printing Office, v. 15, p. 833–845.

——, 1981a, New data on the stratigraphy of the Southern Peninsula of Haiti, *in* Transactions du 1er Colloque sur la Géologie D'Haïti, 1980: Port-au-Prince, Haïti, Le Nateal, S.A., p. 184–199.

——, 1981b, Relations between the geologic setting of Hispaniola and the evolution of the Caribbean, *in* Transactions du 1er colloque sur la Géologie D'Haïti, 1980: Port-au-Prince, Haïti, Le Natal, S.A., p. 2456–264.

Maurrasse, F.J.-M., Husler, J., Georges, G., Schmitt, R., and Damond, P., 1979, Upraised Caribbean sea floor below acoustic reflector B″ at the Southern Peninsula of Haiti: Geologie en Mijnbouw, v. 58, no. 1, p. 71–83.

Maurrasse, F.J.-M., Pierre, Louis, F., and Rigaud, J.-C., 1982, Cenozoic facies distribution in the Southern Peninsula of Haiti and the Barahona Peninsula, *in* Transactions, 9th Caribbean Geological Conference, Santo Domingo, Dominican Republic, 1980: v. 1, p. 161–174.

McFarlane, N. A., compiler, 1977, Geological map of Jamaica: Jamaica, Ministry of Mines and Natural Resources, Mines and Mineral Division, scale 1:250,000.

Mercier de Lepinay, B., Labesse, B., Sigal, J., and Vila, J.-M., 1979, Sédimentation chaotique et tectonique tangentielle Maestrichtiennes dans la presqu'île du Sud d'Haïti (île d'Hispaniola, Grandes Antilles): Paris, Comptes Rendus Academic des Sciences, ser. D, v. 289, p. 887–890.

Mercier de Lepinay, B., Rebillard, P., Chorowicz, J., LeTouzey, P., and Vila, J.-M., 1985, Interpretation structurale de l'île de la Gonave (République d'Haïti) a partir d'images spatiales Landsat-MSS et SEASAT-SAR, *in* Mascle, A., ed., Caribbean geodynamics, Symposium, Paris, February 5-8, 1985: Paris, Éditions Technip, p. 363–369.

Mesnier, H. P., 1980, Exploración minera del área las Cañitas (Provincias de Azua y La Vega, República Dominicana); Informe Final: Bureau de Recherches Géologiques et Minières, Direction des Recherches et du developpement Minières; Secretaría de Industria y Comercio, Dirección General de Minería, 55 p.

Meyerhoff, A. A., and Hatten, C. W., 1968, Diapiric structures in central Cuba: American Association of Petroleum Geologists Memoir 8, p. 315–357.

Meyerhoff, A. A., and Kreig, E. A., 1977a, Jamaican petroleum potential; 1, Future Jamaican exploration is justified, Part 1: Oil and Gas Journal, v. 75, no. 36, p. 79–85.

——, 1977b, Jamaican petroleum potential; 2, Five major cycles make up Jamaican tectonic and structural history, Part 2: Oil and Gas Journal, v. 75, p. 141–146.

Meyerhoff, A. A., Khudoley, K. M., and Hatten, C. W., 1969, Geologic significance of radiometric dates from Cuba: American Association of Petroleum Geologists Bulletin, v. 53, p. 2494–2500.

Meyerhoff, A. A., Kreig, E. A., Cloos, J. D., and Taner, I., 1983, Petroleum potential of Puerto Rico: Oil and Gas Journal, v. 81, p. 113–120.

Meyerhoff, H. A., 1927, The physiography of the Virgin Islands, Culebra, and Vieques: New York Academy of Science Scientific Survey of Puerto Rico and the Virgin Islands, v. 4, pt. 2, p. 145–219.

M'Gonigle, J. W., 1978, Geologic map of the Humacao Quadrangle, Puerto Rico: U.S. Geological Survey Miscellaneous Geologic Investigations Map I–1070, scale 1:20,000.

Michael, R. C., 1978, Geology of the south-central flank of the Cordillera Central and the adjacent portions of the San Juan Valley between Rio San Juan and Rio Yacahueque, Dominican Republic [M.S. Thesis]: Washington, D.C., George Washington University, 162 p.

Michael, R. C., and Lewis, J. F., 1980, Structure and tectonics of the south-central flank of the Massif du Nord–Cordillera Central, and adjacent portions of the Plateau Central–San Juan Valley, Hispaniola: 9th Caribbean Geological Conference, Santo Domingo, Abstracts: p. 50–51.

Millán, G., 1981, Geología del macizo metamórfico de la Isla de la Juventud: Ciencias de la Tierra y el Espacio, v. 3, p. 3–22.

Millán, G., and Myczynski, R., 1978, Fauna jurásica y consideraciones sobre la edad de las secuencias metamórficas del Escambray: Academia de Ciencias de Cuba, Informe Científico-Técnico No. 80, Instituto de Geología y Paleontología, p. 1–14.

Millán, G., and Somin, M. L., 1981, Litología, estratigrafía, tectónica y metamórfismo del macizo Escambray: La Habana, Editorial Academica, 104 p.

——, 1982, Los complejos metamórficas de Cuba: Academia de Ciencias de Cuba, XI Jornado Cientifica del Instituto de Geología y Paleontología, p. 28–33.

——, 1984, El macizo de Escambray; Composición de una gigantesca ventana tectónica en Cuba sur-central: 27th International Geological Congress, Moscow, Abstracts: v. 111, p. 326.

——, 1985a, Nuevos aspectos sobre la estratigrafía del macizo metamorfico de Escambray: Academia de Ciencias de Cuba, Reporte de Investigación del Instituto de Geología y Paleontología, no. 2, p. 1–42.

——, 1985b, Características del metamorfismo del complejo anfibolitico Mabujina, sur de Cuba Central: Academia de Ciencias de Cuba, Reporte de Investigación del Instituto de Geología y Paleontología, no. 2, p. 43–51.

Millán, G., Somin, M. L., and Díaz, C., 1985, Nuevos datos sobre la geología del macizo montañoso de la Sierra del Purial, Cuba Oriental: Academia de Ciencias de Cuba, Reporte del Instituto de Geología y Paleontología, no. 2, p. 52–74.

Monroe, W. H., 1973, Geologic map of the Bayamón Quadrangle, Puerto Rico: U.S. Geological Survey Miscellaneous Geologic Investigations Map I–751, scale 1:20,000.

——, 1976, The karst landforms of Puerto Rico: U.S. Geological Survey Professional Paper 899, 69 p.

——, 1980, Geology of the middle Tertiary formations of Puerto Rico: U.S. Geological Survey Professional Paper 953, 93 p.

Moore, T. C., van Andel, H., Sancetta, C., and Pisias, N., 1978, Cenozoic hiatus in pelagic sediments: Micropaleontology, v. 24, p. 113–138.

Mossakovskiy, A. A., and Albear, J. F., 1978, Nappe structure of western and northern Cuba and history of its emplacement in the light of a study of olistostromes and molasse: Geotectonics, v. 12, p. 225–236.

Moussa, M. T., Seiglie, G. A., Meyerhoff, A. A., and Taner, I., 1987, The Quebradillas Limestone (Miocene–Pliocene), northern Puerto Rico, and tectonics of the northeastern Caribbean margin: Geological Society of America Bulletin, v. 99, p. 427–434.

Nagle, F., 1966, Geology of the Puerto Plata, area Dominican Republic [Ph.D. thesis]: Princeton, New Jersey, Princeton University, 171 p.

——, 1971a, Geology of the Puerto Plata area, Dominican Republic, relative to the Puerto Rico trench, *in* Transactions, 5th Caribbean Geological Conference, St. Thomas, 1968: Queens College Press, Geology Bulletin, p. 79–84.

——, 1971b, Caribbean geology 1970: Bulletin of Marine Science, v. 21, p. 375–439

——, 1972, Chaotic sedimentation in north-central Dominican Republic, *in* Shagam, R., and others, eds., Studies in Earth and space sciences: Geological Society of America Memoir 132, p. 415–428.

——, 1974, Blueschist, eclogite, paired metamorphic belts, and the early tectonic history of Hispaniola: Geological Society of America Bulletin, v. 85, p. 1461–1466.

——, 1979, Geology of the Puerto Plata area, Dominican Republic, *in* Lidz, B., and Nagle, F., eds., Hispaniola; Tectonic focal point of the northern Caribbean; Three geologic studies in the Dominican Republic: Miami Geological Society, p. 1–28.

Nelson, A. E., 1966, Significant changes in volcanism during the Cretaceous in north-central Puerto Rico: U.S. Geological Survey Professional Paper 550–D, p. 172–177.

——, 1967a, Geologic map of the Corozal Quadrangle, Puerto Rico: U.S. Geological Survey Miscellaneous Geologic Investigations Map I–473, scale 1:20,000.

——, 1967b, Geologic map of the Utuado Quadrangle, Puerto Rico: U.S. Geological Survey Miscellaneous Geologic Investigations Map I–480, scale 1:20,000.

Nelson, A. E., and Monroe, W. H., 1966, Geology of the Florida Quadrangle, Puerto Rico: U.S. Geological Survey Bulletin 1221–C, p. 1–22.

Nemec, M. C., 1982, A two-phase model for the tectonic evolution of the Caribbean, *in* Transactions, 9th Caribbean Geological Conference, Santo Domingo, 1980: p. 23–24.

Nicolini, Ph., 1977, Les porphyres cuprifères et les complexes ultra-basiques, du nord-est d'Haïti; Essai gîtologie previsionnelle [Doctoral thesis]: Paris, France, Université Pierre et Marie Curie, 203 p.

Nicolini, P., 1981, Gîtologie Haitienne, *in* Maurasse, F.J-M., ed., Transactions, ler Colloque sur la géologie d'Haïti, 1980: Port-au-Prince, Le Natal, S.A., p. 105–111.

Organization of American States, 1966, Reconocimiento y evaluación de los recursos naturales de la República Dominicana: Washington, D.C., Organization of American States, Pan American Union, v. II, 11 maps, v. III, 169 p.

——, 1972, Géologie République d'Haïti: Organization of American States Map, scale 1:250,000.

OLADE, 1980, Estudio de reconocimiento de las zonas geotérmicas de la República Dominicana y de la República de Haiti: Report Bureau de Recherches Géologiques Minières, Dirección General de Minería, 86 p.

Pagan, P. D., 1976, Bibliografía geológica y paleontológica de la Isla de Santo Domingo (República Dominicana-República de Haiti): Universidad Autónoma de Santo Domingo Publicaciones, v. 212, 219 p.

Palmer, H. C., 1963, Geology of the Monción–Jarabacoa area, Dominican Republic [Ph.D. thesis]: Princeton, New Jersey, Princeton University, 256 p.

——, 1979, Geology of the Moncion–Jarabacoa area, Dominican Republic, *in* Lidz, B., and Nagle, F., eds., Hispaniola; Tectonic focal point of the northern Caribbean; Three geological studies in the Dominican Republic: Miami Geological Society, p. 29–68.

Pardo, G., 1952, Report on stratigraphic studies in Cuba: Part of report to Gulf Oil Company deposited at Institute of Geophysics, University of Texas at Austin, Texas.

——, 1975, Geology of Cuba, *in* Nairn, A.I.M., and Stehli, F. G., eds., The ocean basins and margins; The Gulf of Mexico and the Caribbean: New York, Plenum Press, p. 553–615.

Pease, M. H., Jr., 1968, Cretaceous and lower Tertiary stratigraphy of the Nurumjito and Aguas Buenas Quadrangles and adjacent areas, Puerto Rico: U.S. Geological Survey Bulletin 1253, 57 p.

Pease, M. H., Jr., and Briggs, R. P., 1960, Geology of the Comerio Quadrangle, Puerto Rico: U.S. Geological Survey Miscellaneous Geologic Investigations Map I–320, scale 1:20,000.

Pease, M. H., and Monroe, W. H., 1977, Geologic map of the San Juan Quadrangle, Puerto Rico: U.S. Geological Survey Miscellaneous Geologic Investigations Map I–1010, scale 1:20,000.

Pérez, M., and Equipko, O., 1981, Algunos criterios mineralogo-geoquímicos para subdivider los complejos granitoides de Cuba: Resumenes, Primer Symposio de la Sociedad Cubana de Geología, p. 85.

Perfit, M. R., and Heezen, B. C., 1978, The geology and evolution of the Cayman trench: Geological Society of America Bulletin, v. 89, p. 1155–1174.

Perfit, M. R., and McCulloch, M. T., 1982, Nd- and Sr-isotope geochemistry of eclogites and blueschists from the Hispaniola–Puerto Rico subduction zone: First International Eclogite Conference, France, [abs.]: Terra Cognita, v. 2, no. 3, p. 321.

Perfit, M. R., Heezen, B. C., and Donnelly, T. W., 1980, Chemistry, origin, and tectonic significance of metamorphic rocks from the Puerto Rico trench: Marine Geology, v. 34, p. 125–126.

Perfit, M., Nagle, F., and Bowin, C. O., 1982, Petrology and geochemistry of eclogites and blueschists from Hispaniola; First International Eclogite Conference, France, [abs.]: Terra Cognita, v. 2, no. 3, p. 321.

Pessagno, E. A., 1976, Middle Cretaceous biostratigraphy of the Antillean– Caribbean and eastern Mexico region: Musée Histoire Naturelle de Nice, v. 4, p. 176–182.

Pindell, J. L., 1985, Plate tectonic evolution of the Gulf of Mexico and Caribbean region [Ph.D. thesis]: Durham, England, University of Durham, 287 p.

Pindell, J. L., and Dewey, J. F., 1982, Permo-Triassic reconstruction of western Pangea and the evolution of the Gulf of Mexico/Caribbean region: Tectonics, v. 1, p. 179–211.

Piotrowska, K., 1975, The nappe development in the Sierra de los Organos (western Cuba): Academie Polonaise des Sciences Bulletin, Serie des Sciences la Terre, v. 23, p. 43–52.

——, 1976, First manifestations of volcanism in the Cuban geosyncline: Academie Polonaise des Sciences Bulletin, Serie des Sciences de la Terre, v. 24, no. 3-4, p. 227–234.

——, 1978, Nappe structures in the Sierra de los Organos, western Cuba: Acta Geologica Polonica, v. 28, no. 1, p. 100–170.

Porter, A.R.D., 1970, Geology of the Ginger Ridge granodiorite stock, and associated rocks, St. Catherine, Jamaica [M.Sc. thesis]: Kingston, Jamaica, University of the West Indies, 94 p.

Pszczolkowski, A., 1976a, Nappe structures in the Sierra del Rosario, Cuba: Academie Polonaise des Sciences Bulletin, Serie des Sciences de la Terre, v. 24, no. 3-4, p. 205–215.

——, 1976b, Stratigraphic facies sequences in the Sierra del Rosario, Cuba: Academie Polonaise des Sciences Bulletin, Serie des Sciences de la Terre, v. 24, no. 3-4, p. 193–203.

——, 1978, Geosynclinal sequences of the Cordillera de Guaniguanico in western Cuba; Their lithostratigraphy, facies development, and paleogeography: Acta Geologica Polonica, v. 28, no. 1, p. 1–96.

——, 1982, Cretaceous sediments and paleogeography in the western part of the Cuban miogeosyncline: Acta Geologica Polonica, v. 32, no. 1-2, p. 135–161.

Pushcharovskiy, Ye., M., 1967, Geology and mineral resources of Cuba: Moscow, Akademiya Nauk SSSR, Geologicheskiy Institut, and Academia de Ciencias de Cuba, Trudy, "Nauka," 190 p. (in Russian).

Reblin, M. T., 1973, Regonal gravity survey of the Dominican Republic [M.S. thesis]: Salt Lake City, University of Utah, 129 p.

Redmond, B., 1982a, Sedimentary processes and products; An amber bearing turbidite complex from the northern Dominican Republic [Ph.D. thesis]: Troy, New York, Rensselear Polytechnic Institute, 495 p.

——, 1982b, The Tertiary of the central Cordillera Septentrional, *in* Transactions, 9th Caribbean Geological Conference, Santo Domingo, Dominican Republic: p. 199–210.

Reed, A. J., 1966, Geology of the Bog Walk Quadrangle, Jamaica: Geological Society of Jamaica Bulletin 6, 54 p.

Reeside, J. B., 1947, Upper Cretaceous ammonites from Haiti: U.S. Geological Survey Professional Paper 214–A, p. 1–11.

Reimer, W., 1978, Results of the geological investigations in the northwestern part of the Dominican Republic: Neues Jahrbuch für Geologie und Palaontologie, Heft 3, p. 162–174.

Renz, O., and Verspyck, G. W., 1962, The occurrence of gneissic amphibolite in southwest Puerto Rico: Geologie en Mijnbouw, v. 41, p. 315–320.

Richardson, E. S., 1977, The old Bahama Channel; Past or present plate boundary?: 8th Caribbean Geological Conference, Curaçao, Abstracts: p. 157–158.

Rigassi, D., 1963, Sur la géologie de la Sierra de los Organos, Cuba: Archives de Sciences de physiques et d'Histoire Naturelle de Geneve, v. 16, p. 339–350.

Robinson, E., and Lewis, J. F., 1970, Field guide to aspects of the geology of Jamaica, *in* Donnelly, T. W., ed., International Field Institute Guidebook to the Caribbean island arc system: Washington, D.C., American Geological Institute, 48 p.

Rogers, C. L., 1979, Geologic map of the Caguas Quadrangle, Puerto Rico: U.S. Geological Survey Miscellaneous Geologic Investigations Map I–1152, scale 1:20,000.

Rogers, C. L., Cram, C. M., Pease, M. H., and Tischler, M. S., 1979, Geologic map of the Yabucoa and Punta Tuna Quadrangles, Puerto Rico: U.S. Geological Survey Miscellaneous Investigations Map I–1086, scale 1:20,000.

Roobol, M. J., 1972, Volcanic geology of Jamaica, *in* Transactions, 6th Caribbean Geological Conference, Margarita, Venezuela 1971: p. 100–107.

——, 1976, Post-eruptive sorting of pyroclastic material; An example from Jamaica: Geological Magazine, v. 133, p. 424–444.

Russell, N., and Kesler, S. E., 1980, Field trip B; Gold deposits of Rosario Dominicana, S.A., *in* Field Guide, 9th Caribbean Geological Conference, Santo Domingo, Dominican Republic: p. 51–67.

Russell, N., and 6 others, 1982, Geology and geochemistry of the Pueblo Viejo gold-silver deposit and its host Los Ranchos Formation, Dominican Republic, *in* Transactions, 9th Caribbean Geological Conference, Santo Domingo, Dominican Republic, 1980: p. 263–272.

Rutten, M. G., 1936, Geology of the northern part of the Province of Santa Clara (Las Villas), Cuba: Geographisch Instituut, Utrecht, Geographische en Geologische mededelingen physiographisch-geologische Reeks, ser. 2, no. 11, 59 p.

Sanderson, M. W., and Farr, T. H., 1960, Amber with insect and plant inclusions from the Dominican Republic: Science, v. 131, p. 1313.

Saunders, J. B., Jung, P., Geister, J., and Biju-Duval, B., 1982, The Neogene of the south flank of the Cibao Valley, Dominican Republic; A stratigraphic study, *in* Transactions, 9th Caribbean Geological Conference, Santo Domingo, Dominican Republic 1980: v. 1, p. 151–160.

Sawkins, J. G., 1869, Reports on the geology of Jamaica: Memoir Geological Survey, United Kingdom, Longmans Green and Company, 399 p.

Sayeed, V., Maurrasse, F., Keil, K., Husler, J., and Schmitt, R., 1978, Geochemistry and petrology of some mafic rocks from Dumisseau, southern Haiti: EOS Transactions of the American Geophysical Union, v. 59, p. 403.

Schellekens, J. H., Smith, A. L., and Joyce, J., 1989, Geological studies in western Puerto Rico; A new look at an old problem, *in* Transactions, 10th Caribbean

Geological Conference, Cartagena, Colombia, 1983: p. 222–228.

Scherbakova, B. E., Bovenka, B. G., and Hernández, H., 1977, Structure of the crust beneath western Cuba: Sovetskaya Geologya, no. 8, p. 138–143. (in Russian)

—— , 1978, 1980, Relief on the Mohorovicic discontinuity surface under western Cuba: Doklady Akademia Nauk SSSR, v. 238, no. 3, p. 561–564, translation in Doklady Earth Sciences Section s, v. 238, no. 1, p. 7–9.

Schubert, C., and Cowart, J. B., 1982, Terrazas marinas del Pleistoceno a lo largo de la costa suroriental de la República Dominicana: cronología preliminar, *in* Transactions, 9th Caribbean Geological Conference, Santo Domingo 1980: p. 681–688.

Seiders, V. M., 1971, Cretaceous and lower Tertiary stratigraphy of the Gurabo and El Yunque Quadrangles, Puerto Rico: U.S. Geological Survey Bulletin 1294, p. 1–58.

Seiglie, G. A., and Moussa, M. T., 1984, Late Oligocene–Pliocene transgressive-regressive cycles of sedimentation in northwestern Puerto Rico, *in* Schlee, J. S., ed., Interregional unconformities and hydrocarbon accumulation: American Association of Petroleum Geologists Memoir 36, p. 89–96.

Shein, V. S., and 5 others, 1978, Tektonika Kuby i ieyo shel'fa (Tectonics of Cuba and the surrounding shelf): Sovetskaya Geologya, no. 2, p. 104–119.

Shein, V. S., and 6 others, 1984, Mapa Tectónico de Cuba en escala 1:500,000: 27th International Geological Conference, Moscow, Abstracts, v. 111, p. 401–402.

Shurbet, G. L., and Ewing, W. M., 1956, Gravity reconnaissance survey of Puerto Rico: Geological Society of America Bulletin, v. 67, p. 511–534.

Škvor, V., 1969, The Caribbean area; A case of destruction and regeneration of a continent: Geological Society of America Bulletin, v. 80, p. 961–968.

Smith, T. E., and Jackson, T. A., 1974, Tertiary spilites and quartz keratophyres of the Wagwater belt, Jamaica, West Indies: Bulletin Volcanologique, v. 38, p. 870–890.

Soloviev, O., Skidan, S. A., Skidan, I. K., Pankratov, A. P., and Judoley, C. M., 1964, Comentarios sobre el mapa gravemétrico de la Isla de Cuba: La Habana, Ministerio de Industrias, Revista Tecnológica, v. 2, p. 8–19.

Somin, M. L., 1984, Some aspects of the tectonic environment of the glaucophane metamorphism: Geotectonics, v. 18, p. 460–468.

Somin, M. L., and Millán, G., 1976, Some features of the structure of the metamorphic sequences of Cuba: Geotektonica, v. 5, p. 270–275.

—— , 1977, Sobre la edad de las rocas metamorficas Cubanas: Academia de Ciencias de Cuba, Informe Científico-Técnico, no. 2, p. 1–11.

—— , 1981, Geology of the metamorphic complexes of Cuba (in Russian): Moscow, Nauka, 219 p.

Speed, R. C., 1974, Depositional realm and deformation of Cretaceous rocks, East End, St. Croix, *in* Multer, H. G., and Gerhard, H. C., eds., Guidebook to the geology and ecology of some marine and terrestial environments, St. Croix, U.S. Virgin Islands: West Indies Laboratory Special Publication 5, p. 189–200.

Speed, R. C., Gerhard, L. C., and McKee, E. H., 1979, Ages of deposition, and intrusion of Cretaceous rocks, eastern St. Croix, Virgin Islands: Geological Society of America Bulletin, Part 1, v. 90, p. 629–632.

Sweeting, M. M., 1958, The karstlands of Jamaica: Geographical Journal, v. 125, p. 184–199.

Sykes, L. R., McCann, W. R., and Kafka, A. L., 1982, Motion of Caribbean plate during the last 7 million years and implications for earlier Cenozoic movements: Journal of Geophysical Research, v. 87, p. 10, 656–676.

Taber, S., 1934, Sierra Maestra of Cuba, part of the northern rim of the Bartlett trough: Geological Society of America Bulletin, v. 45, no. 4, p. 567–620.

Talwani, M., Sutton, G. H., and Worzel, J. L., 1959, A crustal section across the Puerto Rico trench: Journal of Geophysical Research, v. 64, p. 1545–1555.

Taylor, F. W., Mann, P., Valastro, T., and Burke, K., 1985, Stratigraphy and radio-isotopic chronology of a subaerially exposed Holocene coral reef, Dominican Republic: Journal of Geology, v. 93, p. 311–332.

Thayer, T. P., and Guild, P. W., 1947, Thrust faults and related structures in eastern Cuba: Transactions of the American Geophysical Union, v. 28, p. 919–930.

Thiadens, A. A., 1937, Geology of the southern part of the Province of Santa Clara (Las Villas): Geographische en Geologische mededelingen physiographisch-geologische Reeks, Geographisch Instituut (Utrecht), v. 12, 69 p.

Tobisch, O. T., 1968, Gneissic amphibolite at Las Palmas, Puerto Rico and its significance in the early history of the Great Antilles island arc: Geological Society of America Bulletin, v. 79, p. 557–574.

United Nations, 1979, Carte géologique d'Haïti: Port-au-Prince, Haïti, Bureau de Mines et de Resources Energetiques, scale 1:200,000.

Vail, P. R., Mitchum, R. M., and Thompson, R. M., 1977, Seismic stratigraphy and global changes in sea level; Part 4, Global cycles of relative changes in sea level, *in* Payton, C. E., Seismic stratigraphy; Applications to hydrocarbon exploration: American Association of Petroleum Geologists Memoir 26, p. 83–97.

van den Berghe, B., 1983, Evolution sedimentaire et structurale depuis le Paleocene de secteur "Massif de la Selle" "Baoruco-nord de la Ride de Beata" dans l'orogene nord Caraiibe (Hispaniola-Grandes Antilles) [Doctoral thesis, 3rd cycle]: Paris, France, Universite Pierre et Marie Curie, 205 p.

van den Bold, W. A., 1974, Neogene of Central Haiti: American Association of Petroleum Geologists Bulletin, v. 58, no. 3, p. 533–539.

—— , 1975, Neogene biostratigraphy (Ostracoda) of southern Hispaniola: Bulletin of American Paleontology, v. 66, p. 549–625.

—— , 1981, Distribution of Ostracoda in the Neogene of Central Haiti: Bulletin of American Paleontology, v. 79, no. 312, 136 p.

Vaughan, T. W., and 5 others, 1921, A geological reconnaissance of the Dominican Republic: Washington, D.C., Gibson Brothers Inc., 268 p.

Versey, H. R., 1957, The White Limestone of Jamaica and the paleogeography governing its deposition [M.S. thesis]: Leeds, England, University of Leeds, 56 p.

Vespucci, P., 1982, Preliminary account of the petrology of the late Cenozoic volcanic province of Hispaniola, *in* Transactions, 9th Caribbean Geological Conference, Santo Domingo, Dominican Republic, 1980: p. 379–390.

—— , 1987, Petrology and geochemistry of the late Cenozoic volcanic rocks of the Dominican Republic [Ph.D. thesis]: Washington, D.C., George Washington University, 286 p.

Vila, J. M., and Feinberg, H., 1982, Les discordances successives à la terminaison sud-est de la Cordillère central dominicaine; Un enregistrement du calendrier tectonique d'Hispaniola (Grandes Antilles): Societé géologique de France Bulletin, v. 25, no. 1, p. 153–156.

Vila, J. M., Butterlin, J., LaBesse, B., and Mercier de Lepinay, B., 1982, Données nouvelles sur les roches metamorphiques de l'île de la Tortue (Hispaniola, Grandes Antilles): Comptes Rendus des Séances de l'Academie des Sciences, Paris, v. 294, ser. II, p. 1103–1106.

Vila, J. M., Butterlin, J., Calmus, T., Mercier de Lepinay, B., and Van den Berghe, B., 1983, *in* Girault, C., ed., Atlas d'Haïti: Bordeaux, CEGET/CNRS, Planche V, Carte géologique, scale 1:1,000,000.

Volckmann, R. P., 1984, Geological map of the Puerto Rico Quadrangle, southwest Puerto Rico: U.S. Geological Survey Miscellaneous Geologic Investigations Map 1-1559, scale 1:20,000.

Wadge, G., and Burke, K., 1983, Neogene Caribbean plate rotation and associated Central American tectonic evolution: Tectonics, v. 2, p. 633–643.

Wadge, G., and Dixon, T., 1984, A geologic interpretation of SEAST–SAR imagery of Jamaica: Journal of Geology, v. 92, p. 561–81.

Wadge, G., and Draper, G., 1977, Tectonic control of speleogenesis in Jamaica: Sheffield, England, British Cave Research Association, Proceedings, 7th International Speleological Congress, p. 416–419.

—— , 1978, Structural geology of southeast Blue Mountains: Geologie en Mijnbouw, v. 57, p. 347–352.

Wadge, G., and Eva, A. N., 1978, The geology and tectonic significance of the Sunning Hill inlier: Journal of the Geological Society of Jamaica, v. 17, p. 1–15.

Wadge, G., Jackson, J. A., Isaacs, M. C., and Smith, T. E., 1982a, Ophiolitic Bath–Dunrobin Formation, Jamaica; Significance for the Cretaceous plate margin evolution in the north-western Caribbean: Journal of the Geological Society of London, v. 139, p. 321–333.

Wadge, G., Draper, G., and Robinson, E., 1982b, Gravity anomalies in the Blue Mountains, eastern Jamaica, *in* Transactions, 9th Caribbean Geological Conference, Santo Domingo, Dominican Republic, 1980: p. 467–474.

Wadge, G., Draper, G., and Lewis, J. F., 1984, Ophiolites of the northern Caribbean; A reappraisal of their roles in the evolution of the Caribbean plate boundary, *in* Gass, I. G., Lippard, S. I., and Shelton, A. W., eds., Ophiolites and oceanic lithosphere: Geological Society of London Special Publication 13, p. 367–380.

Walper, J. L., 1982, Geologic evolution of the Greater Antilles, *in* Transactions, 9th Caribbean Geological Conference, Santo Domingo, Dominican Republic, 1980: p. 13–21.

Wassall, H., 1956, The relationship of oil and serpentine in Cuba: 20th International Geological Congress, Mexico, seccion 3, p. 67–77.

Weaver, J. D., 1958, Utuado pluton, Puerto Rico: Geological Society of America Bulletin, v. 69, p. 1125–1141.

—— , ed., 1977, Geology, geophysics, and resources of the Caribbean; Report of the IDOE Workshop on the Geology and Marine Geophysics of the Caribbean Region and its Resources, Kingston, Jamaica, 1975: Mayagüez, Intergovernmental Oceanographic Commission, UNESCO, University of Puerto Rico Press, 150 p.

Westcott, W., and Etheridge, F. G., 1983, Eocene fan delta-submarine fan deposition in the Wagwater trough, east-central Jamaica: Sedimentology, v. 30, p. 235–247.

Weyl, R., 1941, Bau und Geschichte der Cordillera von Santo Domingo, *in* Meyer-Abich, A., ed., Verroffentlichurgen des Deutsch–Dominikanischen Tropenforschungs instituts v. 2: Jena, Gustav Fischer, 70 p.

—— , 1966, Geologie der Antillen, Band 4, Beitrage zur Regionalen Geologie der Erde, H. J. Martini, ed.: Berlin, Gebrüder Borntraeger, 410 p.

Whetten, J. T., 1966, Geology of St. Croix, Virgin Islands, *in* Hess, H. H., ed., Caribbean geological investigations: Geological Society of America Memoir 98, p. 173–298.

Woodring, W. P., Brown, J. S., and Burbank, W. S., 1924, Geology of the Republic of Haiti: Port-au-Prince, Department of Public Works, Geological Survey of Haiti, Lord Baltimore Press, 631 p.

Wright, R. M., 1976, Aspects of the geology of Tertiary limestones in west-central Jamaica [Ph.D. thesis]: Stanford, California, Stanford University, 283 p.

Zans, V. A., and 5 others, 1962, Synopsis of the geology of Jamaica: Geological Survey of Jamaica Bulletin 4, 72 p.

MANUSCRIPT ACCEPTED BY THE SOCIETY AUGUST 3, 1989

ACKNOWLEDGMENTS

We could not have written this chapter without the cooperation and generous exchange of information provided by our colleagues, and by the support of various institutions.

Lewis acknowledges the valuable assistance given by Georges Pardo, Charles Hatten, Arthur Meyerhoff, and Peter Mattson in the preparation of the Cuban section. Two visits to Cuba arranged in connection with the IGCP for stratigraphic correlation in the Caribbean and correspondence and discussions with many Cuban geologists, particularly Manuel Iturralde-Vinent, Guillermo Millán, Jorge Cobiella, Jorgé Sanchez-Orango, Rustin Cabrera, Eugenia Fonseca, José Oro, and Raúl Flores, were invaluable. Any errors of interpretation of Cuban geology are the responsibility of the author. Financial support for the visits to Cuba came from the Geological Society of America, UNESCO (Cuba), and The George Washington University.

Our work in Hispaniola, principally in the Dominican Republic, has been done in cooperation with the Dirección General de Minería, Universidad Católica Madre y Maestra, and with Rosario Dominicana. We have worked with many people in the last several years and we especially thank Alberto Amarante, Tom Breuner, Carl Bowin, Salvador Brouwer, Warner Cribb, Hugo Dominguez, Walter Eberle, Julio Espaillat, Mark Feigenson, Nelson Gil, George Groetsch, Jorgé Jiménez, James Joyce, Maria-Cristina Lebron, Romeo Llinás, Paul Mann, Bernard Mercier de Lepinay, Richard Michael, Cornelius Monster, Fred Nagle, James Pindell, Brian Redmond, Javier Rodríguez, Norman Russell, Michael Ruth, Ivan Tavares, and Jean-Marie Vila. Lewis was supported financially by National Science Foundation grants INT-8116073 and INT-8511452. Draper was supported by the Latin American Caribbean Center of Florida International University and for work in northern Hispaniola by NSF grants EAR 8306148 and EAR 8509452. All of this financial support is gratefully acknowledged.

The Puerto Rico section was improved by information generously shared by James Joyce, Hans Schellekens, and Alan Smith of the University of Puerto Rico. We also thank them for their expert guidance on a number of field trips on the island.

The members of the Jamaican geological community, both past and present, contributed much to the Jamaica section. Draper thanks in particular his colleagues Rafi Ahmad, Kevin Burke, Anthony Eva, Malcolm Hendry, Trevor Jackson, Geoffrey Wedge, Raymond Wright, and especially Edward Robinson for many stimulating discussions and clarifications of ideas concerning the island's geology.

Finally, we thank Willem van den Bold, T. W. Donnelly, Florentin Maurrasse, and Edward Robinson for sharing their extensive knowledge of northern Caribbean stratigraphy and geology, and for many stimulating discussions.

The Geology of North America
Vol. H, The Caribbean Region
The Geological Society of America, 1990

Chapter 5

Geology of the Lesser Antilles

R. C. Maury
Lab. de Pétrologie et Groupement d'Intérêt Scientifique. "Océanologie et Géodynamique," Université de Bretagne Occidentale, 6, avenue Le Gorgeu, 29283 Brest, France
G. K. Westbrook
School of Earth Sciences, University of Birmingham, P.O. Box 363, Birmingham B15 2TT, United Kingdom
P. E. Baker
Department of Geology, University Park, Nottingham NG7 2RD, United Kingdom
Ph. Bouysse
Dépt. Géologie Marine, Bureau de Recherches Géologiques et Minières, B.P. 6009, 45060 Orléans, France
D. Westercamp*
Institut Mixte de Recherches Géothermiques, Bureau de Recherches Géologiques et Minières, B.P. 6009, 45060 Orléans, France

INTRODUCTION

Ph. Bouysse

The Lesser Antilles and the South Sandwich archipelagoes (Scotia arc) are the only two active island arcs of the Atlantic Ocean. The Lesser Antilles arc (Fig. 1) is on the eastern margin of the Caribbean plate, at the site where the Caribbean plate is underthrust by the subducted Atlantic oceanic crust. The rate of convergence is low compared to other subduction zones; it is generally assumed to be about 2 cm/yr (Jordan, 1975; Minster and Jordan, 1978; Tovish and Schubert, 1978). The convergence vector is thought to be westward oriented, although Sykes and others (1982) and McCann and Sykes (1984) suggest a west-southwest direction. The tip of the Wadati-Benioff zone reaches about 200 km depth: the average dip is 50° to 60° (Girardin and Gaulon, 1983), but it is vertical south of Grenada (Fig. 1c); beneath the present volcanic line, the depth of the subducted slab is 120 to 180 km (Tomblin, 1975; Dorel, 1978, 1981; Stein and others, 1982; Wadge and Shepherd, 1984). As shown in Figure 1c, there is a kink in the subduction zone between Martinique and St. Lucia; this kink may represent the deformation of a single subducting plate or two separate North and South American plates subducting beneath the Caribbean plate (Wadge and Shepherd, 1984).

The Lesser Antilles arc is composed of a score of major islands; it is about 850 km long, and has a radius of curvature of about 450 km. It stretches from the South American continental margin (eastern Venezuela) to the Anegada Passage, which marks the present boundary with the Greater Antilles (Puerto Rico–Virgin Islands platform).

The Lesser Antilles have been described as a double arc (Martin-Kaye, 1969; Fink, 1972). In the southern part of the Lesser Antilles (Fig. 1a), the two arcs coalesce to form a single row of islands and islets. From south to north these are: Grenada, Grenadines archipelago, St. Vincent, St. Lucia, and Martinique. These contain volcanic and sedimentary rocks that range in age from middle Eocene to Holocene (Plate 5A). The two arcs diverge north of Martinique (Bouysse, 1979). The northeastern branch consists of low-lying islands: Marie-Galante, Grande-Terre of Guadeloupe, La Désirade, Antigua, Barbuda, St. Bartholomew, St. Martin, Dog, and Sombrero. Because of the absence of Neogene volcanic centers and the extensive development of middle Eocene to Pleistocene calcareous cover (concealing completely the substratum at Marie-Galante, Grande-Terre, Barbuda, and Sombrero), these islands have been labelled the Limestone Caribbees (Fig. 1a). They also coincide with the so-called outer arc (middle Eocene to Oligocene volcanics and questionable Miocene intrusions), with the exceptions of La Désirade, which has a Mesozoic basement, and possibly of Barbuda (Bouysse, 1984). The northwestern branch, or inner arc, is made of young volcanic islands and was probably initiated during late Miocene; these islands are Dominica, les Saintes, Basse-Terre of Guadeloupe, Montserrat, Redonda, Nevis, St. Kitts, St. Eustatius, and Saba. The axis of the recent or active volcanoes includes the southern and northwestern segments and is called the Volcanic Caribbees, which are characterized by strong relief (the maximum elevation, 1,467 m, is at la Soufrière of Guadeloupe).

To the west, from Guadeloupe southward, the Lesser Antilles Ridge slopes steeply along the eastern border of the Grenada Basin, where the maximum depth is 3,000 m. Farther to the west, the basin is bounded by the Aves Swell, which emerges only at

---

*Deceased.

Maury, R. C., Westbrook, G. K., Baker, P. E., Bouysse, Ph., and Westercamp, D., 1990, Geology of the Lesser Antilles, *in* Dengo, G., and Case, J. E., eds., The Caribbean region: Boulder, Colorado, Geological Society of America, The Geology of North America, v. H.

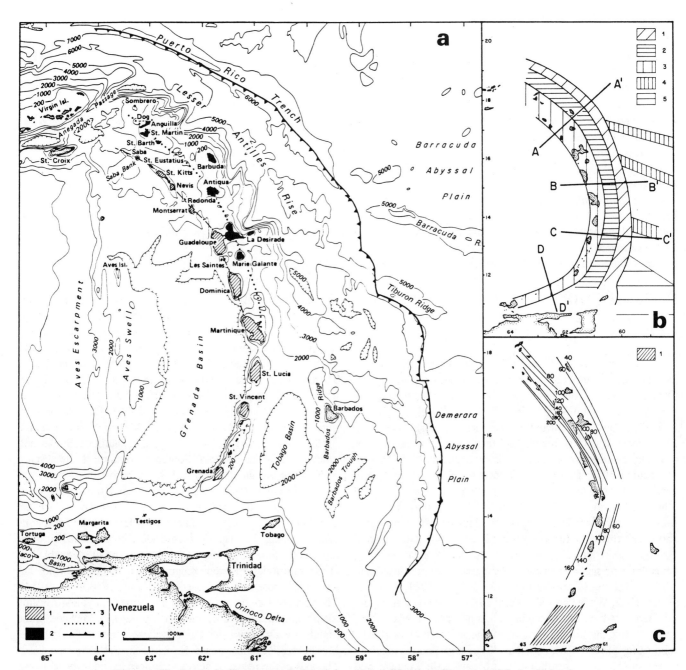

Figure 1. The Lesser Antilles area: a: Bathymetric map (modified from Bouysse, 1984). 1 = Volcanic Caribbees; 2 = Limestone Caribbes; 3 = axis of the inner arc; 4 = axis of the outer arc; 5 = deformation front (after Case and Holcombe, 1980). Isobaths in m. b: Schematic crustal structure of the Lesser Antilles arc. 1 = outer forearc crust; 2 = inner forearc crust; 3 = arc massif; 4 = oceanic basement ridges; 5 = Late Jurassic–Early Cretaceous Atlantic crust. AA′, BB′, CC′, DD′ = lines of sections shown in Figure 3. c: Isobaths (in km) of the Benioff zone beneath the arc (after Wadge and Shepherd, 1984); 1 = vertical part of the southern zone beneath the Venezuelan continental shelf.

the tiny Aves islet, on the northern part of the swell. Aves Swell is interpreted as an extinct island arc that was active from Late Cretaceous to Paleocene (Nagle, 1972; Fox and Heezen, 1975; Pinet and others, 1985). The western side of the swell is connected to the Venezuelan Basin by the Aves escarpment, a 600-km-long rectilinear feature joining the Venezuelan margin to the Greater Antilles. On the eastern side of the Lesser Antilles are two main features: (1) the southeastern termination of the Puerto Rico Trench (more than 6,000 m deep in this area), which is connected to the arc ridge by the Lesser Antilles Rise. The trench rises progressively southward into (2) the Barbados accretionary prism (Westbrook, 1975; Mascle and others, 1977; Westbrook and others, 1984), which culminates on Barbados island.

The submarine morphology of the Lesser Antilles area (Bouysse, 1979; Bouysse and Guennoc, 1983) (Plate 1) shows a sharp contrast between the northern and southern Lesser Antilles. The Southern half, from Grenada to Martinique, is made of one narrow ridge bearing a succession of terraces, the most elongate (170 km long) of which is the Grenada-Grenadines bank. The northern half is much more complicated. The eastern zone, the most developed, is crossed longitudinally by the outer arc and has a series of submarine banks and insular shelves of various sizes. Two of them are quite extensive: the Antigua-Barbuda (4,000 km²) and the St. Barthélémy–Anguilla (4,500 km²) platforms. The eastern slopes of these units are steep, and Neogene deposits are poorly represented, enabling older rocks to crop out. These flanks are made up of a succession of spurs and V-shaped, flat-bottomed sea troughs. One of these slopes, the Desirade escarpment, has a slope of up to 53° for 4,700 m (Bouysse and others, 1983a). The western province is mainly restricted to the inner arc volcanic ridge, which extends northward beyond Saba Island. This northernmost segment is 120 km long and completely submerged; it extends to the Anegada Passage and is now extinct (Bouysse and others, 1985b). West of the inner arc, and to the north, is the Saba bank (2,100 km²), similar in area to the northeastern insular shelves. The western flanks of this province, in contrast with the Atlantic flanks of the northeastern province, are gently sloping and are draped by a thick overburden of Pliocene to Quaternary deposits. These two provinces are separated by the narrow (50 km on average) and elongate (ca. 250 km) Kallinago depression, which stretches from Guadeloupe to the St. Croix basin, one of the small depressions of the Anegada Passage.

Sea-going surveys (Bouysse, 1980; Bouysse and Sigurdsson, 1982) have led to the conclusion that only one active submarine volcano exists in the Lesser Antilles arc (out of the three quoted in the literature; Robson and Tomblin, 1966): Kick'em Jenny, close to the north coast of Grenada (Sigurdsson and Shepherd, 1974). The other two, Hodder's (west of Castries, St. Lucia) and Colombie (in the Guadeloupe archipelago), were thought to be active on the basis of erroneous interpretations of older observations. Historically recorded magmatic, phreatic, or fumarolic activity of subaerial volcanoes (Robson and Tomblin, 1966) has occurred at Soufriere of St. Vincent, Qualibou caldera in St. Lucia, Montagne Pelée in Martinique, Valley of Desolation in Dominica, la Sou-

frière of Guadeloupe, Soufriere Hills of Montserrat, and Mount Misery in St. Kitts (Carr and Stoiber, this volume). There is also hot spring activity on the islands of Nevis and Saba.

CRUSTAL STRUCTURE

G. K. Westbrook

The Lesser Antilles island-arc system stands out on a map of free-air gravity anomalies as an arcuate pair of positive and negative anomalies, extending from the Virgin Islands in the north to Margarita in the south (Plate 7). The positive anomaly lies over the arc massif, and the negative anomaly lies over the edge of the Caribbean plate (Westbrook, 1975; Bowin, 1976). The positive anomaly, although in part produced by the dynamic uplift of the leading edge of the Caribbean plate at the subduction zone, is locally caused by the contrast in density between the denser igneous rocks forming the arc and the water and sediments surrounding it. On a Bouguer gravity anomaly map in which a correction has been made for low density of the water, the locally positive attraction of the arc is still evident (Bowin, 1976; Westbrook and Jackson, 1987). The distribution of the positive gravity anomalies provides a primary guide to the location high in the crust of igneous rocks that form the island-arc massif.

Seismic refraction experiments have shown that the crust of the arc can be broadly divided into three layers (Officer and others, 1959; Dorel and others, 1974; Boynton and others, 1979) (Plates 2 and 3). The uppermost layer is very heterogeneous: it has a wide range of seismic velocities up to 5 km/s^{-1}—the average is about 3.3 km/s^{-1}—and is mainly composed of volcanics (lavas and pyroclastic deposits) and sediment. The middle layer has an average seismic velocity of 6.2 km/s^{-1}, but varies greatly in thickness (2–20 km) and velocity (5.3–7.0 km/s^{-1}), suggesting much lateral variation in composition (Fig. 2). The typical velocity of just over 6 km/s^{-1} suggests that the layer is dominated by plutonic rocks of intermediate composition. The lowest layer has a seismic velocity of 6.9 km/s^{-1}, which suggests a basic composition. The nature of its boundary with the overlying layer varies; in some places it is sharp and produces reflections. The 6.9 km/s^{-1} layer may be the old ocean crust upon which the island arc has been built, subsequently thickened by the addition of mafic plutonic rocks, some of which are cumulates produced in magma chambers in the lower crust. Studies of plutonic nodules have indicated depths of crystallization between 10 and 30 km (Powell, 1978; Arculus and Wills, 1980; D'Arco, 1982). The thickness of this layer has not been established seismically because the rapid thinning of the crust of the arc into the basins on either side and the curvature of the arc severely restrict the observations of first arrivals from seismic waves refracted along the base of the crust beneath the arc. It is only at Martinique that the thickness of the crust (30 km) has been determined from seismic refraction.

Seismic refraction data have been used to constrain the position of major crustal boundaries, and seismic reflection profiles

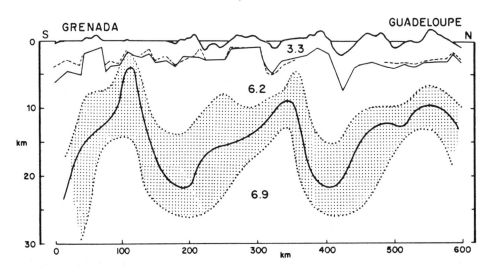

Figure 2. Section along the Lesser Antilles from Grenada to Guadeloupe showing the major seismically defined layers of the arc crust (after Boynton and others, 1979). The top line shows topography and bathymetry (water is stippled). Beneath is the line showing the top of the 6.2 km·s^{-1} layer. The lowest, bold line is the top of the 6.9 km·s^{-1} layer, and the stippled band indicates the uncertainty in the position of this boundary.

have been used to provide information on the thickness of overlying sediments; cross sections of the crustal structure of the arc have been produced by deriving models with a gravitational attraction that matches the gravity anomalies (Westbrook, 1975; Bowin, 1976; Boynton and others, 1979; Bradley, 1979; Ainscough, 1983). These show the total thickness of the arc in the segment between St. Vincent and Guadeloupe to be between 30 and 37 km (Fig. 3). The top of the 6.9 km/s^{-1} layer is generally at about 15 km depth. North of Martinique the separation of the active inner arc from the outer arc is apparent in the crustal section (Fig. 3). North of Guadeloupe the arc platform is much wider, but the crust is also thinner (25 km), so that its cross-sectional area is about the same as it is farther south. The active volcanic islands (Montserrat to Saba) lie over the western flank of arc. The present phase of volcanism has contributed relatively little to the arc massif, which is centered beneath the outer arc. The construction of the active arc on the flank of the Limestone Caribbees has resulted in the creation of a trough between the two arcs. The effect on the crustal models of including the gravitational attraction of the subducted lithosphere is to deepen the Moho beneath the arc by about 3 km.

South of Grenada there are no active volcanic islands, but the continuation of the island-arc massif as far as the island of Margarita is clearly shown by the gravity and magnetic anomalies (Case and others, 1972; Westbrook and Jackson, 1987), seismic reflection profiles (Westbrook and others, 1987), and seismic refraction data (Edgar and others, 1971) (Figs. 3 and 1b), even though it is obscured as a bathymetric feature by sediments that have built up a shelf from South America. The youngest igneous rocks known on this segment of the arc are Eocene (or possibly older) metagranitic rocks of calc-alkaline affinities on Los Testigos (Santamaria and Schubert, 1974). If the 44 to 47 Ma K-Ar

ages are confirmed, the Paleogene volcanic cycle of the Lesser Antilles (outer arc) extended much farther to the southwest.

Seismic reflection lines east of the arc between Grenada and Guadeloupe show that the basement of the island arc, after an initial drop down from the present ridge of the arc, dips relatively gently eastward for about half the width between the arc ridge and the edge at the Caribbean plate, before dipping more steeply downward beneath the accretionary complex (Westbrook and others, 1984). The seismic refraction and gravity models also show the change in dip, which coincides with a transition of crustal structure from thickened island-arc crust to essentially oceanic crust. From Guadeloupe northward, the more gently dipping part of the forearc is represented by bathymetric platforms; the islands of La Désirade and Barbuda are situated on two of these platforms. The steep bathymetric slope on the outer flank of these platforms is contiguous with the more steeply dipping outer part of the forearc crust farther south. The similarity between the parts of the forearc north and south of Guadeloupe is evident on a Bouguer gravity anomaly map, in which the correction density (2.1 gm/cm^{-3}) is similar to that of the sedimentary cover and emphasizes anomalies related to the sediment/basement interface. This map clearly shows the gradient over the steep outer part of the forearc and the more shelflike inner forearc. There is a common style to the anomalies over the inner forearc, and highs similar to those east of Antigua and Guadeloupe also occur off Martinique and St. Lucia. The major difference is that the overall value of the anomalies decreases southward by about 50 mGal at each of two major steps; one occurs south of Guadeloupe and the other south of St. Lucia. These changes reflect the southward deepening of the inner forearc basement from about 1 km off the northern islands to about 7 km off the Grenadines. The southward deepening of the forearc basement is mirrored by a

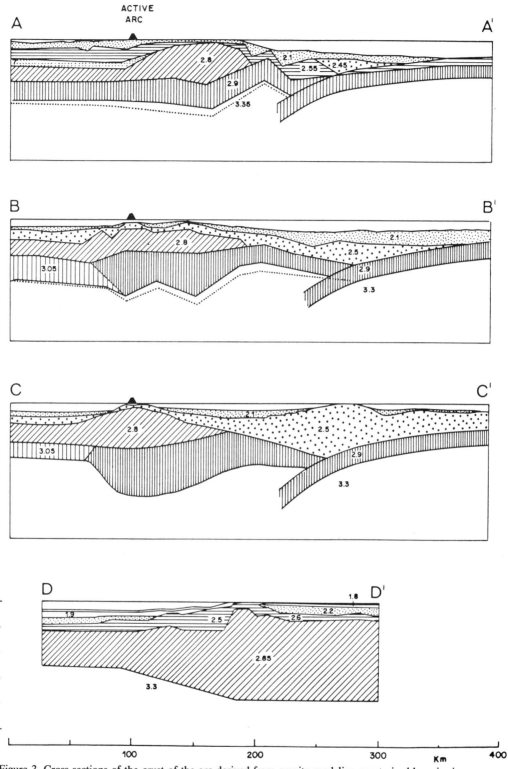

Figure 3. Cross sections of the crust of the arc derived from gravity modeling constrained by seismic refraction and reflection data. The lines of section are shown in Figure 1b. The position of the active volcanic arc is shown by triangle. In section AA′ it lies at the edge of the crustal thickening associated with the main body of the arc. The inactive volcanic arc in section D′ is contiguous with the active arc and joins it south of Grenada. Numbers give the densities of the layers used in the gravity models: 1.8-2.55; sediment: 2.3-3.05, igneous crustal rocks: 3.3, mantle. Position of Moho shown by dotted lines in sections AA′, BB′, from models including gravitational attraction of subducted lithosphere.

southward deepening of the basement of the Grenada Trough behind the island arc. This relative deepening is caused by differential loading of the crust by sediment influx from the south, greater loading of the leading edge of the Caribbean plate by a thicker accretionary complex in the south, and the spreading of the island-arc massif by the divergence of the volcanic trends in the north (in comparison to the south, where the superimposition of volcanism has built the arc higher above the surrounding basement).

The Atlantic lithosphere subducted beneath the Caribbean is cut by many old transform faults and includes ridges and troughs in the oceanic basement (Westbrook and others, 1984). In some places, such as the Barracuda Ridge, these ridges and troughs appear to have influenced the development of the Lesser Antilles (Vogt and others, 1976; Westbrook and McCann, 1986). The trend of these features can be traced beneath the accretionary complex from gravity magnetic and seismic reflection data; the Barracuda Ridge and the Tiburon Rise extend beneath the islands of Barbuda and La Désirade, respectively (Fig. 1b). The high positive anomalies over these islands show them to be farther out of isostatic equilibrium than most of the island arc, presumably as a result of the dynamic uplift produced by the ridges. Farther south, another ridge extends beneath St. Lucia. The intersection of the two southern ridges with the arc also coincides with two major southward-deepening steps in the forearc. In addition to these ridges, there is a major crustal boundary between Late Jurassic and Early Cretaceous oceanic crust produced since the opening of the South Atlantic. This boundary trends northwest, and extends beneath the arc at St. Vincent (Westbrook, 1984).

THE PRE-EOCENE BASEMENT

Ph. Bouysse

Contrary to what was assumed by some authors (e.g., Martin-Kaye, 1969), the oldest rocks found in the Lesser Antilles arc are not of middle (or lower) Eocene age. Since the first contention of the Mesozoic age of La Désirade (Fink, 1968), data derived from submarine dredging and drilling have led to the disclosure of pre-Eocene terranes (Plate 5A). These sites are discussed below.

La Désirade area

La Désirade (ca. 30 km^2) is the easternmost islet of the Guadeloupe group. It is an elongate table (maximum elevation 275 m) of lower Pliocene limestones (Andreieff, in Westercamp, 1980) underlain by an igneous basement complex. The basement complex was thought to be Eocene to lower Miocene in age (Barrabé, 1953; Reynal, 1966), but two features of the geology have aroused considerable debate and have influenced ideas about the geodynamic evolution of the Lesser Antilles: (1) In 1968, Fink claimed a K-Ar age of 142 ±10 Ma (Upper Jurassic) for a trondhjemite outcrop in the center of the northern coast of

the island. (2) The occurrence of a so-called "spilitic-keratophyre assemblage" associated with pillowed basalts and interbedded cherts led some authors to infer an ophiolitic complex of oceanic origin for La Désirade basement (Mattinson and others, 1973, 1980; Fox and Heezen, 1975; Dinkelman and Brown, 1977; Briden and others, 1979).

Due to the scatter of radiometric dates (from 160 to 18 Ma; see Bouysse and others, 1983b) for the basement as a whole, the Jurassic age was disputed by some authors (Dinkelman and Brown, 1977; Briden and others, 1979). Detailed field work (Westercamp, 1980; Bouysse and others, 1983b) had led to the recognition of three successive main units in the igneous basement of La Désirade (Fig. 4).

Unit 1 is the "central acid massif." It is composed of a trondhjemite associated with rhyolitic lava flows. The most reliable dating of this unit is given by Mattinson and others (1973, 1980) who reported a crystallization age of 145–150 Ma (Oxfordian) for a trondhjemite sample, using the $^{206}Pb*/^{238}U$ and $^{207}Pb*/^{206}Pb*$ methods on zircon separates.

Unit 2, the "NE complex," includes pillowed metabasalts and intercalated chert beds intruded by metadacite and metarhyolitic dikes and flows. This unit is characterized by northeast-southwest structural trends. The age of the cherts (Bouysse and others, 1983b) is ascribed to the Lower Cretaceous (Hauterivian-Barremian; i.e., 112–119 Ma). These cherts represent the oldest biostratigraphic assemblage reported up to now in the Lesser Antilles and vindicate the antiquity of unit 1, questioned by some. It implies that unit 1 should be older than unit 2 by some 20 to 30 m.y.

Unit 3, the "upper meta-andesitic group," is poorly represented and occurs mainly as east-west–trending dikes, particularly in the central north coast.

The scatter and the rejuvenation of the ages of the igneous basement can be related to the general epimetamorphism which affected the area in the Cenozoic era. Structural, chronological, mineralogical, and geochemical data led some authors (Donnelly and Rogers, 1978, 1980; Le Guen de Kerneizon and others, 1979; Bouysse and others, 1983b) to discount an ophiolitic origin for La Désirade basement (by obduction of Atlantic or Caribbean crust), suggesting instead that the association was produced by island-arc magmatic processes, but this problem is still debated (Donnelly, this volume).

The Mesozoic basement of La Désirade extends along the Desirade Escarpment which forms the southern flank of La Désirade sea trough. The escarpment is made of "greenstones," along more than 50 km of the scarp (Johnston and others, 1971; Fox and Heezen, 1975; Andreieff and others, 1979). It has been suggested (Bouysse and others, 1983a) that by the Miocene an uplift of some 2,000 to 4,000 m raised the Desirade block with regard to the surrounding features. This dramatic event might have been triggered by the interaction of the Tiburon oceanic ridge (a former Atlantic transform feature) with the subduction system of the Lesser Antilles (Bouysse and Garrabé, 1984).

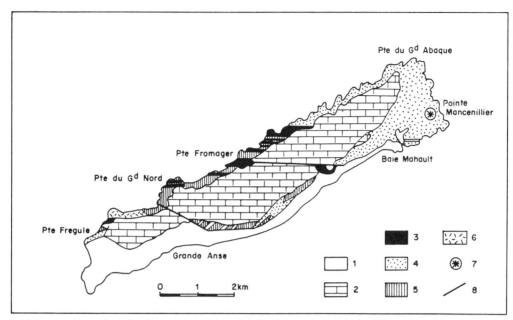

Figure 4. Geological sketch map of La Désirade (after Bouysse and others, 1983b). 1 = Pliocene–Quaternary unconsolidated or reefal deposits; 2 = lower Pliocene calcareous plateau; 3 = upper meta-andesitic series (unit 3); 4 = northeast volcanic complex (unit 2); 5 = central acid massif (unit 1); 6 = undifferentiated igneous basement; 7 = location of dated radiolarian cherts; 8 = fault.

Northeast and northern flanks of the Lesser Antilles Ridge

Pre-Eocene rocks that crop out on the slopes of steep escarpments located east of Antigua, Barbuda, and Anguilla, and north of Sombrero, have been reported by Fox and Heezen (1975). The dredges recovered finely laminated volcanic tuffs composed of altered glass, plagioclase, pyroxene, and to a lesser extent, biogenous material containing Upper Cretaceous radiolaria. These data hint at the existence of coeval active volcanic centers along this part of the Lesser Antilles, supplying material for the deposition of the tuffs via turbidity currents and ash falls.

Dredging along the northern slope of the Anguilla platform (Bouysse and others, 1985a) between –4,100 and –2,500 m recovered volcanic tuffs and marls containing radiolarians, and also planktonic foraminifera and nannofossils providing more or less restricted age ranges: Upper Cretaceous, Upper Senonian (83 to 65 Ma), and Santonian (86 to 83 Ma). Some reworking of neritic biogenous components appears to have occurred, indicating the existence of a shallow platform at those times.

Between the La Desirade and Antigua sea troughs, on the Falmouth spur, an altered quartz diorite was dredged at 1,400 m depth (Andreieff and others, 1979; Bouysse and others, 1980). Several attempts to date this sample radiogenically have failed because of excess degassing during the analytical process. This rock shows some similarities to the La Désirade trondhjemite.

Saba Bank

The wide and shallow Saba bank, located to the west of the northern termination of the Lesser Antilles inner arc, was the site of extensive oil exploration activity. An exploratory well (SB1) drilled in 1977 supplied important data concerning the area (Andreieff and others, 1979; Bouysse and others, 1980; Nemec, 1980; Bouysse and Guennoc, 1983). Beneath some 2,850 m of Cenozoic sedimentary cover, the well penetrated 119 m of a porphyritic andesite underlying lower Eocene reefal limestones. A K-Ar age of 64.5 ±3.7 Ma was claimed for the lower part of the andesitic core. The base of the igneous body was not reached, but multichannel seismic reflection profiles strongly suggest the presence of an extensive underlying Upper Cretaceous sedimentary sequence. This volcanic episode has been related to contemporaneous events known on the nearby island of St. Croix. The data from a second (and still confidential) well (SB2) drilled in 1982 appear to have partially modified these conclusions. Nevertheless, the occurrence of a thick underlying Upper Cretaceous series beneath Saba bank is not in doubt.

St. Croix

St. Croix Island (36 km long) emerges from a SWS–ENE trending submarine ridge (St. Croix Ridge). It is located in the Anegada Passage, near the present tectonic boundary between the Lesser and Greater Antilles. It is equidistant between Saba bank and the Puerto Rico-Virgin Islands platform, and lies to the south (i.e., on the Lesser Antilles side) of the Virgin Islands basin (more than 4,000 m deep). However, the geology of St. Croix (Whetten, 1966) resembles that of the latter: the island is mainly made of Upper Cretaceous sedimentary, plutonic, and volcanic rocks.

Aves Swell

The Aves Swell has been the subject of debate concerning its relations with the Lesser Antilles arc, but there is now broad agreement in considering this ridge as a former island arc (Bunce and others, 1970; Nagle, 1972; Case, 1975; Donnelly, 1975; Fox and Heezen, 1975; Westbrook, 1975; Keary, 1976; Clark and others, 1978; Pinet and others, 1985; Bouysse and others, 1985a). Its structure will be discussed elsewhere (Holcombe and others, this volume).

To the south of the ridge, close to the Venezuelan continental margin, somewhat weathered granodiorites and diabases have been sampled (Fox and others, 1971; Fox and Heezen, 1975). These granodioritic rocks provided K-Ar ages of 89 to 78 Ma (Coniacian to middle Campanian), 67 to 65 Ma (Cretaceous/Cenozoic boundary), and 58 to 57 Ma (upper Paleocene). The ages obtained for the diabases are 57 and 60 Ma. The granitoids were eventually ascribed to a normal island-arc magmatic series. A few other igneous rocks (effusive volcanics) have been dredged elsewhere on the Aves Swell (Nagle, 1972); although these have not been dated, they seem to be capped by post-Paleocene sediments (Nagle, 1972; Fox and Heezen, 1975). The two DSDP holes drilled in the area (holes 30 and 148) did not reach the igneous basement but recovered reworked Paleocene and Upper Cretaceous microfauna (Shipboard Scientific Party, 1973). Later dredging (*Arcante 3* cruise; Bouysse and others, 1985a) carried out on the Aves Escarpment, west of Aves islet, recovered altered island-arc basalts and andesites giving questionable K-Ar ages (along with Eocene to Pliocene deposits, upper Campanian reworked pelagic microfauna, and upper Turonian to lower Senonian neritic tuffaceous limestones), pointing to the presence of a ridge in the Late Cretaceous.

Concerning the striking morphological differences between the northern and southern halves of the Lesser Antilles Ridge and neighboring areas, and the chronological data previously mentioned, it has been suggested (Bouysse, 1979, 1984; Bouysse and others, 1980) that the substratum of the northern Lesser Antilles and of the Aves Swell belongs to an ancient arc related to the Greater Antilles system, whereas the southern half of the Lesser Antilles is younger; the division is somewhere south of the Guadeloupe archipelago. This north-south duality had been previously conjectured by Meyerhoff and Meyerhoff (1972) and Lewis and Robinson (1976).

THE LIMESTONE CARIBBEES

Ph. Bouysse and D. Westercamp

Anguilla, Dog, and Sombrero

Anguilla (91 km^2) is the northernmost island of the Lesser Antilles. Nearly all the island is covered by a subhorizontal neritic facies limestone of basal middle Miocene age (Langhian, N8 zone; P. Andreieff, 1984, personal commun.). A suite of older rocks which dip 40° to the southeast is exposed on the northern coast. A section at Crocus bay shows about 15 m of dark marly limestones and black shales of upper Paleocene age (upper Thanetian, P4 zone; Andreieff and others, 1984) overlain by 60 m of middle Eocene volcaniclastics that contain coarse conglomerates and true hyaloclastites. The top of the sequence contains oysters, indicating a shallowing of the environment. Elsewhere in the same bay and at Road Bay, a highly weathered volcanic basement consisting of basic scoriaceous breccias crops out; it is overlain by volcanic conglomerates and green clays of Eocene age.

A few miles to the northeast is Dog islet, which seems very similar to Anguilla (Martin-Kaye, 1969); with Miocene limestones overlying an altered volcanic basement. Farther to the north, at the margin of the northernmost slopes of the Lesser Antilles Ridge, the tiny islet of Sombrero is exclusively built up by a limestone plateau, rising abruptly some 10 m out of the sea. These neritic limestones, previously assigned to lower Miocene (Schubert, 1935; and see Martin-Kaye, 1969), yield lower Pliocene nannofossils (Bouysse and others, 1985a).

St. Martin

In St. Martin (98 km^2), three types of formations have been recognized (Christman, 1953; Andreieff and others, 1981). From bottom to top, these are as follows.

1. The Pointe-Blanche Formation generally dips 40° to the southeast and is made of a thick sequence of siliceous tuffs (with occasional andesitic flows; Red Pond Bay) corresponding principally to turbidite deposits, although calcareous intercalations are progressively more developed to the top. There are indications of shallowing depositional conditions upward. The lower part of the section, which is not dated because of slight metamorphism and absence of typical microfauna, may be of lower Eocene age; the middle part is middle Eocene, as are the St. Bartholomew limestones. The top of the Pointe-Blanche Formation is upper Eocene (P15 to P17 zones; Andreieff, 1982).

2. Volcanic effusives and intrusives. K-Ar dates (Nagle and others, 1976; Briden and others, 1979) and field work (Christman, 1953; Solomiac, 1974) have established that the Pointe-Blanche Formation is intruded by porphyritic andesites and dacites (dikes and sills) and by diorites and quartz-diorites with associated Pb-Zn-Cu mineralization. According to Briden and others (1979), both andesitic and dioritic activity occurred within a time interval of only 2 or 3 m.y. (perhaps 5 m.y.) corresponding to an age of 33 or 31 to 28 Ma; i.e., lower Oligocene (they discard the 37 Ma and 26 Ma ages of Nagle and others, 1976).

3. The Lowlands Formation consists of nearly horizontal shallow platform limestones and marls of upper Miocene age (N16–N17 zones; Andreieff, 1982) and not of lower Miocene age as previously stated (Drooger, 1951). Tintamarre islet, close to the northeast corner of St. Martin, is made of late lower Miocene limestones (upper Burdigalian, N7 zone; Andreieff, 1982), i.e., slightly older than the Anguilla limestone.

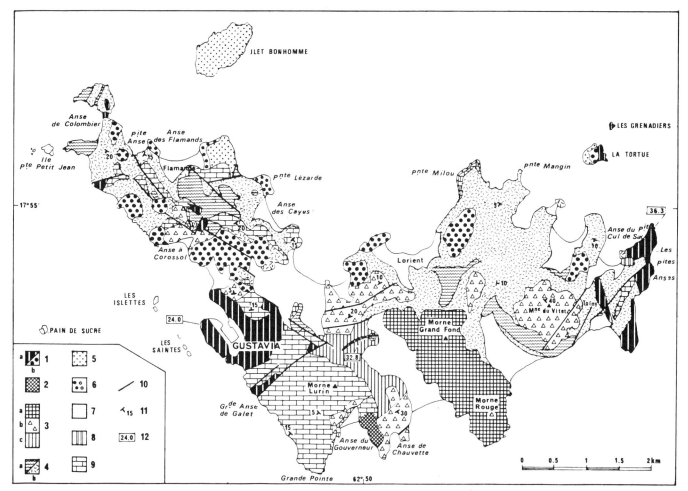

Figure 5. Geological sketch map of St Barthélémy (after Westercamp and Andreieff, 1983b): 1 = upper volcanism (a is massive intrusion; b is intrusive breccia); 2 to 6 = middle Eocene volcanism; 2 = dacitic pipe; 3a = upper dacitic lava flow; 3b = dacitic maar-type breccia; 3c = lower dacitic lava flow; 4a = andesitic lava flow; 4b = upper hyaloclastite deposit; 5 = lower hyaloclastite deposit; 6 = basal unit. 7 = beach and mangrove; 8 = Neogene limestone; 9 = middle Eocene limestone; 10 = fault; 11 = dip; 12 = K-Ar data.

St. Barthélémy

The bulk of St. Barthélémy (25 km^2; Fig. 5) is formed of a submarine volcanic unit (hyaloclastites, maar breccias, massive lava flows, dikes). About ten calcareous horizons composed of reef biomicrites containing variable amounts of volcaniclastics are interbedded within the volcanics; the calcareous horizons correspond to periods of eruptive quiescence. The whole of this volcanic sequence is ascribed to middle Eocene (P12 zone, and possibly part of P11 zone; 39.5–43 Ma). During this short (<3.5 m.y.) time interval, the nature of the volcanism changed from a basic series (perhaps island-arc tholeiites) to calc-alkaline series with andesites and porphyritic dacites containing quartz and ghost-amphiboles. A K/Ar date on an andesite from this unit (Nagle and others, 1976) gave an age of 28.9 ±9 Ma, which is apparently too young with respect to biostratigraphic data (Westercamp and Andreieff, 1983a, 1983b).

After a period of magmatic quiescence, during which the insular platform was uplifted and tilted some 20° to 30° toward the south-southwest, volcanic activity resumed. It was characterized by pipetype features associated with calc-alkaline magmatism (porphyritic andesites and basalts, quartz-microdiorites, quartz-dacites). Four K-Ar dates on this sequence (Nagle and others, 1976; Briden and others, 1979) provided ages ranging from 36.3 to 24 Ma; i.e., a 12 m.y. interval extending from basal late Eocene to the Oligocene/Miocene boundary. This second volcanic cycle was considered by Westercamp and Andreieff (1983a, 1983b) to be of short duration—no longer than 1 m.y.— on the basis of the petrographic uniformity and eruptive style; subsequent metamorphism may have disturbed the K-Ar ages. Consequently, this event should have occurred in late Eocene or in early Oligocene, as on nearby St. Martin. Hydrothermal activity related to this igneous phase induced epimetamorphism and Pb-Zn-Cu mineralization in the volcanic conduits and their country rocks. Basal middle Miocene neritic limestones (N7 zone, Langhian) crop out in the surrounding islets of Roche-Table and Roche-le-Boeuf.

Barbuda

Barbuda (174 km^2) is a low-lying island located some 40 km north of Antigua, on the same submarine bank but substantially offset to the east of the outer arc axis. It is composed of Quaternary limestones (Martin-Kaye, 1959, 1969) that have been uplifted rather recently, producing a plateau some 50 m high. The remainder of the island rises only a few meters above sea level. Brasier and Mather (1975) claimed a middle Miocene age for the oldest deposits (Highlands Formation) because of the occurrence of *Amphistegina rotundata,* but this foraminifer has a broader biostratigraphic range.

Antigua

Antigua (280 km^2) is the southernmost island of the Limestone Caribbees with an exposed Cenozoic volcanic basement (Christman, 1972; Martin-Kaye, 1959). Three major units (Mascle and Westercamp, 1983) form a relatively gentle monocline dipping to the northeast. The lowermost unit is a volcanic complex dominated by submarine primary deposits of hyaloclastite tuffs, which shows a possible evolution from early tholeiitic to later calc-alkaline series. The overlying unit, about 500 m thick (Central Plain) is made of conglomerates, sandstones, and shales resulting from the erosion of the basal unit, with a few intercalated limestone lenses. These two units are ascribed broadly to the Oligocene (Mascle and Westercamp, 1983), but more precise biostratigraphic data are not available. The K-Ar data of Nagle and others (1976) and Briden and others (1979) range from 24.4 to 19.8 Ma (early Miocene) with an isolated age of 39.7 Ma (middle Eocene), and are thus in conflict with micropaleontological data; however, most of Antigua lavas are highly calcitized.

The uppermost unit (Antigua Formation) is a 500-m-thick limestone and marly limestone sequence with scarce volcanic sandstones. These deposits are generally bioclastic and are notable for their fossil corals (Frost and Weiss, 1979) and their larger foraminiferal assemblages. Near the top of the formation, they grade into more pelagic facies. A few horizons rich in nannoplankton and foraminifera allow the Antigua Formation to be ascribed to the upper Oligocene (NP24-NP25 nannozones; i.e., 27 to 23.7 Ma) (Mascle and Westercamp, 1983).

Grande-Terre of Guadeloupe

This island (650 km^2) is completed capped by Pliocene-Quaternary limestones (Andreieff and Cottez, 1976) and is structurally made up of three horsts separated by a central graben. The volcanic substratum was never encountered by the many shallow drillings carried out for water-supply purposes. The longest well (121 m deep) reached pelagic lower Pliocene deposits

(Bouysse and Garrabé, 1984). The Pliocene–Quaternary evolution of Grande-Terre has been studied by Garrabé (1983) and Garrabé and Andreieff (1985). From the middle Pliocene to lower Pleistocene, a shallow-water platform existed, and there were very frequent algal balls. In this platform sequence, volcano-sedimentary horizons are interspersed, and record eruptive activity from the twin island of Basse-Terre. By the upper Pliocene–lower Pleistocene, the algal balls were suddenly replaced by corals. Emergence occurred in two steps, sometime in the Pleistocene: (1) fracturing and emergence of the southwest horst (Grands-Fonds), explaining its more advanced stage of karstification; and (2) fracturing and emergence of the two other horsts. Several uplifted Quaternary marine terraces provide evidence for persistent vertical movements.

Marie-Galante

This island (150 km^2) is entirely covered by a reefal limestone table of Pliocene–Quaternary age, tilted to the southwest. The work of Andreieff and others (1983) has led to a drastic revision of previously published data (Reynal, 1966). The igneous basement does not crop out, and the oldest sedimentary strata (corresponding to a minute outcrop on the eastern shore), characterized by hemipelagic environment, is upper Miocene in age (N17 zone, Messinian). During the early Pliocene, the Marie-Galante seamount was uplifted to a shallow depth, where a neritic platform prevailed and persisted until the Pleistocene. During the Pleistocene, the emergence of the island occurred and was followed by tilting toward the southwest and by faulting, leading to the foundering of the northern part of Marie-Galante. On the whole, the Pliocene–Quaternary history of this island is very similar to that of Grande-Terre (Garrabé and Andreieff, 1985).

Discussion

In conclusion, the following points should be stressed. There is an obvious north-to-south decrease of the maximal ages of the formations that crop out on the islands which protrude from the wide Pliocene–Quaternary submarine platforms (from Thanetian in Anguilla to Messinian in Marie-Galante), the two southernmost islands being practically entirely blanketed by Pliocene-Quaternary reefal limestones. The upper Paleocene rocks of Anguilla are pelagic deposits, contrasting with middle and upper Eocene shallow-water deposits typical of the islands of the Anguilla-St. Bartholomew shelf. This latter environment could possibly be linked to the first regional volcanic phase visible in Dog, Anguilla, St. Martin, and St. Bartholomew. After some minor tectonic readjustments, the second volcanic phase occurred most probably during early Oligocene (possibly latest Eocene to basal upper Oligocene), as evidenced from outcrops on St. Martin to Antigua.

Each island may independently record a complete magmatic evolution, involving eruptive style and petrography, from dominant fissural basaltic series to andesites and dacites restricted to isolated edifices. This evolutionary pattern is exemplified by the volcanism of St. Bartholomew (middle Eocene) and of Antigua (lower Oligocene). It is limited in space (no more than 10 km) and in time (a few m.y.). Cessation of volcanic activity in this part of the Lesser Antilles seems to have occurred by the end of the early Oligocene; i.e., some 10 m.y. earlier than suggested by some authors (Nagle and others, 1976; Briden and others, 1979). This cessation is supported by the evidence of the calcareous character of deposits (without pyroclastic intercalations) during the late Oligocene (Antigua Formation), and the early (or basal middle) Miocene (Anguilla, Tintamarre, and St. Barthélémy islets).

THE SOUTHERN VOLCANIC CARIBBEES

R. C. Maury and D. Westercamp

These islands are characterized—with the noticeable exception of St. Vincent—by the superimposition of Pliocene and Quaternary volcanic units over Miocene volcanics and even, in several cases (Grenada, some of the Grenadines, Martinique), over Eocene–Oligocene sediments, volcanogenic sediments, and associated tuffs and lavas (older arc); see Plate 5A. Andesitic to rhyolitic ash layers of middle Eocene to Oligocene age are also interbedded within the marine deposits (Oceanic Formation) of the emerged accretionary prism or neighboring Barbados Island (Ferragne and others, 1985). With the exception of St. Vincent, the magmatic features of the Southern Volcanic Caribbees show some common characteristics, principally an enrichment in K and other incompatible elements relative to the northern islands (Brown and others, 1977; Rea, 1982; Maury and Westercamp, 1985). The islands are reviewed from south to north.

Grenada

Grenada (ca. 310 km^2) is the southernmost island of the Lesser Antilles. Its geologic history was summarized by Martin-Kaye (1969). Arculus (1973, 1976, 1978) and coworkers (e.g., Shimizu and Arculus, 1975; Hawkesworth and others, 1979), and Graham (1980) and Thirlwall and Graham (1984) performed detailed studies of its unusual lavas, i.e., silica-undersaturated basanitoids and basalts associated with relatively K-rich andesites and dacites (Donnelly, this volume). Briden and others (1979) published 15 K-Ar dates of volcanic rocks from Grenada. The geology of the island is complex, and the determination of the field relations is often difficult because of the particularly large area occupied by reworked volcanic detritus.

The outcropping basement of Grenada consists of a late Eocene to possibly early Oligocene volcanic-sedimentary unit, the Tufton Hall Formation (Martin-Kaye, 1969; Saunders and others, 1985). It includes fine-grained rudites, arenites, and lutites that contain reworked volcanic fragments of andesitic or basaltic composition and isolated minerals of volcanic origin. The magmatic affinities of these volcanic clasts are unknown. Planktonic

foraminifera and radiolaria from mudstones and marlstones give an uppermost Eocene age (Saunders and others, 1985), and a water depth between 2,000 and 3,000 m has been proposed by these authors. The tuffaceous horizons become prominent in the uppermost strata of the Tufton Hall Formation, which is sharply folded and faulted. The axes of the folds strike predominantly east-west, and boudinage features are developed in some localities. Arculus (1973) described a folded dike belonging to the Tufton Hall Formation. The thickness of this unit is at least 250 m and probably much more. Some poorly exposed limestones occur in Grenada. The Tempe-Parnassus limestone (near St. George's) is interbedded with a marl bed which yielded a foraminiferal fauna of middle Oligocene age, and the Hope Vale limestone is of middle Oligocene to middle Miocene age (Saunders and others, 1985). Reef limestone patches found among the volcanics in various parts of the island are thought to be of Pliocene–Pleistocene age.

Several volcanic centers on Grenada have erupted basanitoïds and nepheline-normative basalts together with subalkalic basalts, andesites, and dacites from early Miocene to Holocene times. A distinctive feature of this island is the apparent persistence of magmatic types throughout time (Arculus, 1973, 1976), though important compositional variations occur between volcanic centers as well as within an individual center. The earliest Neogene activity began in the north of Grenada, where several episodes of extrusion of silica-undersaturated basalt and andesite flows and intrusion of andesite domes occurred in the Northern Domes center (Mt. Craven; ca. 21 Ma). After a long period of volcanic quiescence, basanitoid and subalkalic basalt flows, together with andesite domes, were erupted from the South East Mountain (southeast Grenada center, ca. 14–10 Ma), and terminate the Miocene volcanic cycle. Pliocene and Quaternary centers are numerous in Grenada; the main ones are Mt. Maitland center (mainly basaltic; ca. 4–1.5 Ma), Mt. Granby-Fedon's Camp center (basanitoïd to andesite; ca. 3–1 Ma, with progressive shifting of the eruptive centers southward), and Mt. St. Catherine center (basanitoïd to dacite lava and pyroclastic flows surrounding a breached crater containing an andesite dome; ca. 2 Ma, and probably less). After a period of relative quiescence (reef limestone formation), morphologically well-preserved maars and tuff rings of basanitoid to andesitic composition were emplaced throughout the island (St. George, Grand Etang, Lake Antoine, the Punchbowl) and also on Green Island and Caille islets, 2 and 7 km north of Grenada. Close to Caille islet is the only known active submarine volcano in the Lesser Antilles, Kick'em Jenny (8 km north of Grenada). Its crater is presently 160 m below sea level: erupted products include slightly undersaturated amphibole-bearing olivine basalts (Sigurdsson and Shepherd, 1974).

The Grenadines

They are a group (ca. 40) of small islands and islets lying between Grenada and St. Vincent (Fig. 6), which represent the emerged parts of an elongated (~4,500 km^2) bank (The Grena-

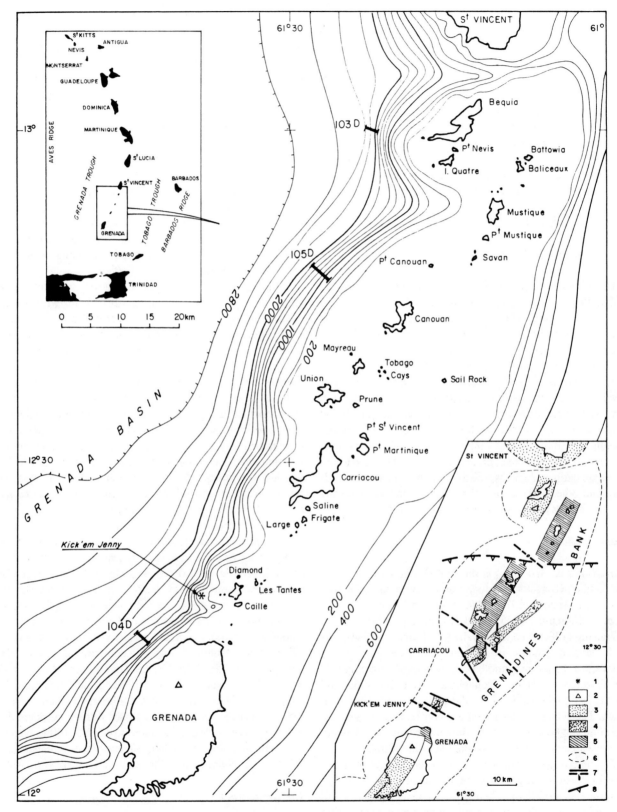

Figure 6. Sketch map of the Grenadines archipelago (after Westercamp and others, 1985): 1 = active submarine volcano; 2 = calc-alkaline Pleistocene volcanism; 3 = early Pliocene calc-alkaline lavas; 4 = middle Miocene andesites; 5 = Oligocene volcanic rocks; 6 = pre-Oligocene ridge; 7 = transverse faults with associated olivine or plagioclase-clinopyroxene-phyric basalts; 8 = deformation front.

dine bank). These islands are known for their long (Eocene to Holocene) and complex geologic histories (Martin-Kaye, 1969), and also for the common occurrence of Mg-rich subalkalic or mildly silica-undersaturated basalts, similar to some of the Grenada basalts (Jackson, 1980; Le Guen de Kerneizon and others, 1985).

The Eocene period is represented in the Grenadines by altered pillow lavas associated with hyaloclastites, which are sometimes intruded by later dikes (Mayreau). These are overlain by limestones containing a rich planktonic microfauna of lowermost middle Eocene age (P10 and P11 zones; Westercamp and others, 1985). The limestones are capped by a volcanic-sedimentary unit of middle Eocene age (P12 zone) that contains large blocks of quartz-bearing rhyolites, and crops out on Jamesby and Baradal islets (Tobago Cays, Fig. 6). Massive limestones of late Eocene age (P17 zone; Robinson and Jung, 1972; Westercamp and others, 1985) have been found in Carriacou.

The Oligocene period is represented in two groups of islands striking NNE–SSW (Fig. 6): a northern group, from Battowia to Savan, including Mustique where there are outcrops of upper Oligocene reworked hyaloclastites (Westercamp and others, 1985); and a southern group, trending from Canouan to Carriacou, where the Windward Formation (Robinson and Jung, 1972) has also been assigned to the upper Oligocene. Most of the hydrothermally altered formations attributed to the Oligocene period are coarse reworked and primary hyaloclastic tuffs intruded by dikes. After a time gap of ca. 10 m.y. near the Oligocene/Miocene boundary (Westercamp and others, 1985), volcanic activity resumed in Carriacou (Belmont Formation) at ca. 18 Ma (Briden and others, 1979). Calc-alkaline lavas were emplaced during the middle Miocene in Petit Martinique and the neighboring islets (Petite Dominique, Petit St. Vincent, and Sail Rock) and Carriacou (Grand Bay Formation) after another period of quiescence that allowed the development of a small sedimentary basin of early middle Miocene age in Carriacou (Carriacou Formation) and Canouan (Canouan Formation) (Martin-Kaye, 1969; Westercamp and others, 1985).

From late Miocene to the present, volcanic activity alternated between calc-alkaline cycles a few m.y. long and short basaltic effusive events of alkaline or subalkaline tendency, controlled by faults striking more or less perpendicular to the island arc (Westercamp and others, 1985; Le Guen de Kerneizon and others, 1985). Two calc-alkaline cycles have been recognized at ca. 8 Ma in Union, and between 6 and 3 Ma in Bequia, Petit Nevis, Quatre, Union, and Carriacou. At least five transverse basaltic events (olivine microphyric basalts or plagioclase and clinopyroxene-phyric basalts) have been recognized at ca. 10.5 Ma in Carriacou, Petite Martinique, Petit St. Vincent, and Union (dikes trend north-south and east-west); at ca. 6.5 Ma in several islands between Ronde and Canouan; at ca. 3.5 Ma south of Carriacou (Saline and Fregate islets group; Ronde); at ca. 2.5 Ma in Diamond and Les Tantes; and at Caille Island and the active (submarine) Kick'em Jenny volcano (Holocene).

In the Grenadines, a number of geologic units from Eocene to middle Miocene age underwent tectonic deformation. Westercamp and others (1985) considered that a complex deformation front migrated progressively northward from Grenada to Canouan during this time range (Fig. 6).

St. Vincent

This island (ca. 390 km^2) is especially well known for its very active northern volcano, Soufriere (1,565 people killed on May 1902; later eruptions in 1971–1972 and 1979). The pyroclastic deposits, lavas, and associated plutonic cumulate nodules from Soufriere have been extensively studied (Aspinall and others, 1973; Lewis, 1973a, 1973b; Roobol and Smith, 1975; Rowley, 1978; Powell, 1978; Graham and Thirlwall, 1979; Shepherd and others, 1979; Arculus and Wills, 1980; Sigurdsson, 1981; Carron and others, 1982; Dostal and others, 1983), but the older central and southern parts of the island are comparatively poorly known. Geologically, St. Vincent differs from the other islands of the southern part of the Lesser Antilles arc and more closely resembles those of the northern part. Sedimentary formations are not known (Martin-Kaye, 1969), and all the volcanic units are younger than 3.5 Ma (Briden and others, 1979; H. Bellon, personal communication, 1984). Acid andesites are exceedingly rare, and more acidic rocks are lacking. Olivine-phyric basalts predominate in the volcanic centers older than Soufriere, which is composed mainly of basaltic andesites and basalts. These olivine-phyric basalts are silica-oversaturated; some of them, especially the oldest ones, are relatively rich in Mg, Cr, and Ni, and thus resemble the magnesian basalts of Grenada and the Grenadines. The volcanic rocks of both Soufrière and older centers are characteristically K-poor (K$_2$O <0.7 wt%) and, from a chemical point of view, resemble those from the K-poor series of the Northern Volcanic Caribbees (e.g., St. Kitts).

Four broad volcanic centers may be identified in St. Vincent (H. Bellon, personal communication, 1984), and their K-Ar ages decrease northward; however, detailed field data on the centers older than La Soufrière are still lacking. The older rocks crop out southwest of Kingstown, on the southern coast (Dike 1 islet; 3.5 Ma), and in the Mesopotamia Valley (ca. 3.4 Ma). These are mainly basaltic flows intruded by some northwest-southeast-trending basaltic dikes. These were followed by two major volcanic centers, the Grand Bonhomme and the Richmond Peak-Mt. Brisbane complex (Westercamp and Tomblin, 1979), which form the axial south-north ridge of St. Vincent. Most of the K-Ar dates of the Grand Bonhomme activity are in the 3–2 Ma range (Briden and others, 1979; H. Bellon, personal communication, 1984). North of Grand Bonhomme, the Richmond Peak–Mt. Brisbane center was active mostly during the 1.9–1.2 Ma period (uppermost Pliocene–early Pleistocene). Volcanism then migrated northward; the oldest ages of Soufrière volcano are ca. 0.7 Ma (Briden and others, 1979).

Four stages in the evolution of Soufriere volcano have been recognized (Robson, 1968; Westercamp and Tomblin, 1979). During the first stage, a large stratovolcano was built up of alternating lava flows and pyroclastic layers. Then, a series of exceedingly violent Plinian explosions destroyed the summit and considerably enlarged the crater. The third stage was a return to lava-flow eruptions alternating with pyroclastic emissions; the fourth stage, now very well documented (Rowley, 1978; Sigurdsson, 1981), showed an increase in explosivity. The actual depth of the magma chamber beneath the volcano is estimated from the study of igneous cumulates to be ca. 15–20 km (Powell, 1978; Arculus and Wills, 1980; Dostal and others, 1983). Found together with the plutonic xenoliths are some calcic hornfels of metasedimentary composition but unknown origin (e.g., Devine and Sigurdsson, 1980).

St. Lucia

St. Lucia (ca. 650 km^2) has several geologic similarities to its neighboring island Martinique. Much attention has been paid to the geology and volcanology of the Holocene Soufriere (Qualibou) volcanic center (Tomblin, 1965; Roobol and others, 1983; Wright and others, 1984), which has spectacular extrusive domes (e.g., Gros Piton, Petit Piton) and pyroclastic deposits. The overall geology of the island has been described by Westercamp and Tomblin (1979) and Le Guen de Kerneizon and others (1983). Thirty-seven radiometric K-Ar dates are available, 10 from Briden and others (1979) and 27 from Le Guen de Kerneizon and others (1983).

Miocene volcanic and volcaniclastic rocks are common. The oldest ages known are from the basalt-andesite agglomerates from the northern end of the island (Cap Estate area), where sedimentary lenses contain a rich planktonic fauna of uppermost middle Miocene age N14 zone (Andreieff in Le Guen de Kerneizon and others, 1983). Spatially associated basalts have given somewhat questionable K-Ar ages of 18.4 Ma (Briden and others, 1979) and 15 Ma (Le Guen de Kerneizon and others, 1983; see the latter authors for discussion). Late Miocene volcanic activity (11 to 7 Ma) was widespread. In the north, numerous basaltic to andesitic flows occur, some typically calc-alkaline and others showing some island-arc tholeiitic tendencies (Le Guen de Kerneizon and others, 1983), especially those in the range 11 to 9 Ma. The Bisé area (west of Castries) rhyolites are ca. 8 Ma, and their origin is ascribed to the differentiation of island-arc tholeiites (Le Guen de Kerneizon and others, 1982). Other Miocene volcanic rocks, mostly calc-alkaline in character, crop out along the Central Ridge of the island (Barre Coulon, Dennery, De Mailly; ca. 10–9 Ma) and at its southern end (Vieux Fort area: ca. 9–7 Ma). A later volcanic event, either calc-alkaline or with some tholeiitic affinities, took place during the uppermost late Miocene (7 to 5.5 Ma), and built up numerous domes in the northern part of the island (Mt. Pimard area) together with the emplacement of basaltic flows in the Soufrière area and acidic pyroclastic deposits near Dennery. After what was apparently a quiescent period, the Pliocene volcanic activity (3–1.5 Ma) began, mainly in the central part of St. Lucia (Mt. Gimie, Migny, Anse La Raye). The magmas erupted during this period are mostly andesitic, and sometimes show relatively high contents of K_2O.

Quaternary volcanism in St. Lucia is represented by the important Soufrière (Qualibou) volcanic center, the activity of which is younger than 1 Ma (Le Guen de Kerneizon and others, 1983); the most recent eruptions are ^{14}C dated (34,000 to 21,000 B.P.; Wright and others, 1984). K-rich and highly silica-oversaturated magmas erupted during this period; they range in composition from andesites to dacites (dacites are predominant), and have [87]Sr/[86]Sr ratios among the highest found in the Lesser Antilles (up to 0.7093). Numerous domes were emplaced within a cirque-shaped depression opening westward, which Tomblin (1965) has considered to be a caldera (the Qualibou caldera). Numerous associated pumice-flow and ash-flow deposits covered the southwest part of St. Lucia. Tomblin (1965) and Westercamp and Tomblin (1979) considered that the deposits originated from the caldera. Recent investigations by Vatin-Pérignon and others (1984) and Wohletz and others (1986) support this opinion. However, Roobol and others (1983) and Wright and others (1984) considered that the deposits were probably erupted from central vents in the highland rainforest area; these authors interpreted the Soufriere depression as a gravity-slide structure.

Martinique

Martinique (1.080 km^2) is the largest island of the Lesser Antilles and displays the most complete geologic pattern (Westercamp and others, 1990; Fig. 7). It is the locus where outer and inner arcs began to diverge, between the late early Miocene and the Miocene/Pliocene boundary. The middle and upper Miocene volcanic units of Martinique and neighboring islands have sometimes been considered as belonging to an "intermediate arc" (Westercamp, 1979).

The oldest terranes are pre-Miocene and crop out in the peninsulas of St. Anne (southeast corner) and Caravelle (protruding from the middle of the east coast) (Fig. 7). They are locally covered by lower Miocene (Aquitanian) reefal limestones. A calcareous intercalation in the volcanics of Morne Castagne (Caravelle peninsula) yielded *Miogypsinoides complanatus* characteristic of the upper Oligocene (P21-P22 zones, ca. 29–24 Ma) (Westercamp and others, 1990). This Oligocene (or even older) volcanic basal complex is suspected to extend beneath a significant part of the insular shelf, particularly well developed off the northeast and east coasts. The visible part of this substratum appears to be composed mainly of subaerial lavas emplaced during a late stage, shortly before cessation of the volcanic activity. The tectonics shows a conjugate north-south and east-west pattern marked by dike orientations.

The middle and upper Miocene units crop out in the southern part of Martinique (Fig. 7). They are characterized by a continuous drifting of the eruptive centers from east to west with temporal variation in composition from submarine-arc tholeiites in the west (Vauclin-Pitault chain, 16 to 12 Ma; i.e., middle Miocene) to calc-alkaline subaerial volcanism cropping out mainly in the eastern half of Trois-Ilets peninsula (8 to 6.5 Ma; i.e., final Miocene). These volcanic products are frequently inter-

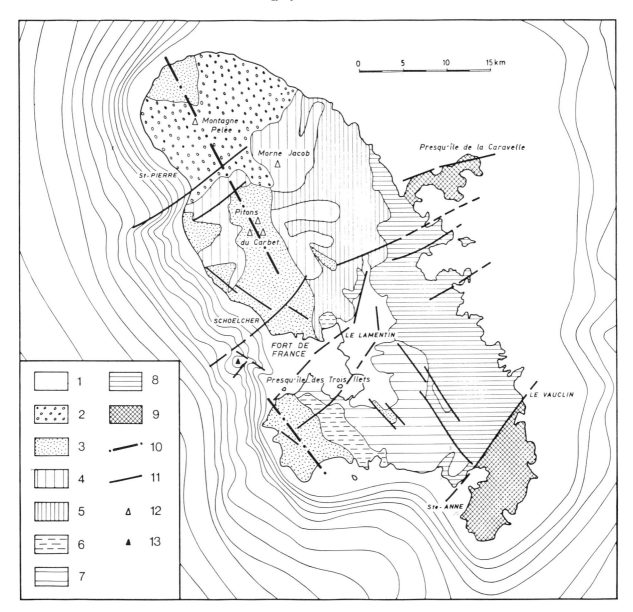

Figure 7. Geological sketch map of Martinique (after Bouysse and others, 1985c): 1 = Lamentin alluvial plain; 2 = Mt. Pelée active volcano; 3 = late Pliocene–Pleistocene volcanism; 4 = Morne Jacob Pliocene volcanism, 1st phase (basic, mainly submarine); 6 = Morne Pavillon effusive volcanism (8–6.5 Ma); 7 = Ducos-Ste Lucie volcanism (12–9 Ma); 8 = Vauclin-Pitault submarine volcanism (16–12 Ma); 9 = volcanic basal complex (>24 Ma); 10 = Pleistocene volcanic front; 11 = fault; 12 = main onshore elevations; 13 = inactive submarine volcano.

bedded with fossiliferous limestones and calcareous tuffs; this allows the K-Ar data (some of which are questionable due to alteration) to be checked. This episode is characterized by northeast-southwest and northwest-southeast conjugate faults.

With the onset of the Pliocene, the volcanic centers shifted back to the northeast. The first phase of this new magmatic cycle appears at Morne Jacob and is composed mainly of submarine lava flows and hyaloclastites of basalt and basic andesite composition. With time, the volcanism migrated westward, forming the Pitons du Carbet (2–0.8 Ma) and becoming much more acidic

(K-rich dacites) and explosive. At the same time, volcanic activity occurred in the western half of Trois-Ilets peninsula, and produced many small volcanoes, some of which are basic and effusive (i.e., the Ilet à Ramiers Mg-rich basalt) and others that are acid and explosive. The latest stage is represented in northern Martinique by Mt. Conil (ca. 0.5 Ma; with effusive volcanism) which was succeeded by Mt. Pelée's activity at about 0.2 Ma (Westercamp and Traineau, 1983). During historic times, four eruptions occurred at Mt. Pelée; 1792, 1851, 1902–1904, and 1929–1932. The dramatic 1902 event caused the death of all the

28,000 inhabitants of St. Pierre (save one) and is one of the most catastrophic eruptions in the history of mankind. Mts. Conil and Pelée are two large calc-alkaline stratovolcanoes characterized by medium-K andesitic series (Westercamp and Tazieff, 1980; Traineau, 1982).

The Pliocene–Quaternary units again display east-west features similar to those of the older arc, but faults and fissures inherited from the Miocene period were reactivated. The complex graben of Lamentin with northeast-southwest transverse faulting is an active tectonic zone that cuts Martinique in two parts, and it is associated with hydrothermal activity.

THE NORTHERN VOLCANIC CARIBBEES

P. E. Baker, D. Westercamp, and Ph. Bouysse

Several common features allow this group of islands to be distinguished from the southern one. First, their volcanic activity is mainly restricted to the Pliocene–Quaternary periods: ages older than 5 Ma are generally lacking, and pre-Pliocene basements are not exposed (with the exception of the northeastern part of Dominica). Secondly, the volcanic series are either of medium-K or low-K types (Carr and Stoiber, this volume). Low-K series predominate in many islands from the northern group (e.g., St. Eustatius, St. Kitts, Montserrat; Brown and others, 1977), and some of them have a number of tholeiitic affinities (e.g., St. Kitts; Baker, 1968, 1984; Hawkesworth and Powell, 1980), although it is questionable whether any should be strictly ascribed to the island-arc tholeiitic series (Smith and others, 1980; Rea and Baker, 1980; Rea, 1982). The volume of volcanic ejecta markedly decreases north of Basse-Terre de Guadeloupe, and the 110-km-long submerged segment north of Saba may be considered extinct (Bouysse and others, 1985c). The islands are reviewed from south to north.

Dominica

Dominica (750 km^2) is made up almost exclusively of volcanic rocks; according to Wills (1974), at least ten volcanic centers have been active during the Pleistocene. Detailed descriptions of the petrology of the lavas and of the volcanology of the partially welded Roseau pyroclastic deposit are given by Wills (1974) and Sigurdsson (1972). Two K-Ar ages (1.8 and 1.1 Ma) from southern Dominica have been published by Briden and others (1979), but a number of unpublished measurements have been made by H. Bellon and J. C. Baubron (1984, personal commun.).

The oldest formations are exposed along the east coast of Dominica (Martin-Kaye, 1969): they are massive lava flows and breccia deposits intruded by numerous NW–SE and NNW–SSE trending dikes resembling some Miocene units from Martinique and St. Lucia. Unpublished K-Ar data (H. Bellon and G. Wadge, 1984, personal commun.) indicate late Miocene ages for the flows and Pliocene ages for the dikes.

During middle Pliocene time, basaltic-andesitic shield volcanoes were built on the southern half of the island and on the western flank of the earlier formation; some of their lower units are pillowed. The basal part of Morne Diablotin overlies early Pliocene limestone (P. Andreieff, 1984, personal commun.), whereas the Foundland and Cochrane areas (basal part of Morne Trois Pitons) appear to be older than was previously stated (Briden and others, 1979); several unpublished K/Ar datings (H. Bellon, J. C. Baubron, 1984, personal commun.) indicate a 3.5 to 1.7 Ma range.

Numerous morphologically well-preserved Pleistocene composite andesitic volcanoes are superimposed over the Pliocene volcanoes. From north to south, they include Morne aux Diables (a small pelean-type edifice), Morne Diablotins (a large strato-volcano), and smaller volcanoes such as Watt Mountain, Morne Anglais, and Morne Plat Pays (ca. 0.5–0.4 m.y. old). An unusually voluminous (for the Lesser Antilles) ignimbritic eruption—the Roseau ignimbrite—occurred at about 30 ka (Sigurdsson, 1972 and unpublished ^{14}C data). Up to 60 km^3 of tephra (equivalent dense-rock value) were erupted (Carey and Sigurdsson, 1980). On land, partly welded and columned ash and pumice flows filled several valleys around Morne Trois Pitons. After this eruption, volcanic activity became much more effusive in character and domes and large dome complexes were erupted, e.g., Micotrin and Morne Trois Pitons; the latter is ca. 25 ka (Roobol and others, 1983). According to field relations, preservation of its morphological shapes, and petrology of its lavas, Grande Soufrière Hills is thought to be contemporaneous with this event. A similar conclusion is drawn for Morne Patates, which was emplaced into a caldera-like depression at the southern end of the island, which may be a gravity-slide structure (Roobol and others, 1983). Very small volcanoes developed near Roseau: Du Mas Estate (a phreato-magmatic crater opened at ca. 1.3 ka) and the phreatic craters of the Valley of Desolation and Boiling lake (the last eruption of which occurred in A.D. 1880). The dominant rock type in Dominica throughout Pleistocene and Quaternary times is medium-K calc-alkaline andesite (Wills, 1974).

Les Saintes

This group of islets south of Guadeloupe (Fig. 8) is formed of medium-K calc-alkaline andesites and subordinate basaltic andesites and dacites. Their K-Ar ages range from 4.7 to ca. 1 Ma (Jacques and others, 1984). During the early periods of activity (4.7 to 3.3 Ma), andesitic flows were emplaced, together with an important dacitic dome (Le Chameau). Phreato-magmatic activity, followed by lava flows and intrusions, occurred from 2.7 to 2.4 Ma and was associated with strong hydrothermal alteration of the older units (airport area, Terre de Haut). The last eruptive episode (1.9 to possibly 0.6 Ma) was mainly restricted to the Terre de Bas volcano (andesitic flows followed by nuées ardentes).

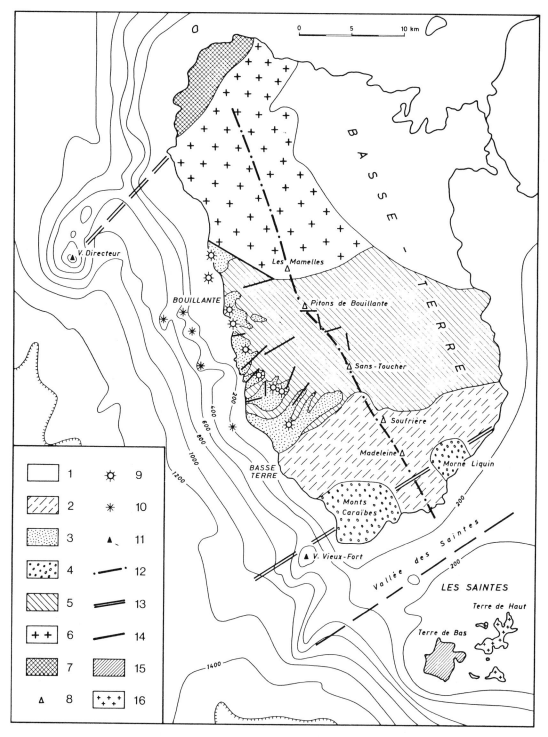

Figure 8. Geological sketch map of Basse-Terre of Guadeloupe and Les Saintes (after Bouysse and others, 1985c): 1 = northeast alluvial plain; 2 = Madeleine-Soufrière volcanism (<0.2 Ma); 3 = Chaîne de Bouillante volcanism (0.5 ?–0.25 Ma); Monts Caraïbes-Morne Liquin volcanism (ca. 0.5 Ma); 5 = Pitons de Bouillante-Sans Toucher (1.25–0.6 Ma); 6 = northern volcanism (3.5 ?–1.15 Ma); 7 = volcanic basal complex (6 ?–4 ? Ma); 8 = main onshore elevations; 9 = onshore eruptive center of Chaîne de Bouillante; 10 = offshore eruptive center of Chaîne de Bouillante; 11 = inactive submarine volcanoes; 12 = main volcanic axis; 13 = conjectural transverse fracture; 14 = fault; 15 = Terre-de-Bas volcanism (ca. 2–1 Ma); 16 = Terre-de-Haut volcanism (ca. 5–2 Ma).

Basse-Terre de Guadeloupe

This island (Fig. 8), the western part of the twin insular system of Guadeloupe, is the second largest island of the Lesser Antilles (950 km^2). Apart from the northeast alluvial plain, the island is entirely igneous. The main structural lineament is oriented NNW–SSE and subparallel to the axis of the island; it controls the distribution of the volcano-structural units. The general pattern is of a north to south shift in the eruptive activity of Basse-Terre (Westercamp and Tazieff, 1980; Gadalia and Westercamp, 1984). Six successive volcanic units have been identified (Fig. 8):

(1) the basal complex, the northernmost unit, is made of massive, highly weathered lava flows; it is thought to be older than 4 Ma.

(2) The northern chain, makes up more than one third of Basse-Terre; it was active between 3.5 and 1.2 Ma and consists of a calc-alkaline series with K$_2$O content higher than in the other units of the island (Dagain, 1981). The following temporal succession is observed: acidic lava flows, dark andesitic flows draping over much of this unit, a quartz-dacite episode with lava flows and nuées ardentes, and, in the south of the area, viscous andesites, dacitic domes, and flows (Les Mamelles).

(3) The Pitons de Bouillante–Sans Toucher axial chain. This unit extends over the center of Basse-Terre and is essentially made of effusive products (1.25–0.6 Ma). This fissural volcanism appears first as extensive submarine eruptions producing hyaloclastites, which were later overlain by andesitic lava flows.

(4) The Monts Caraïbes–Morne Liquin unit was emplaced at about 0.5 Ma (Blanc, 1983). It is characterized by submarine activity of Surtseyan type and seems to have been fed by a transverse ENE–WSW to E–W fracture pattern. Its petrologic nature is more basic than the other units of Basse-Terre (Gunn and others, 1980).

(5) The Bouillante chain is the only unit to be clearly offset from the island's median structural axis, but it displays the same structural directions along the western coastline. Active between 0.5 and 0.25 Ma, it is typified by the small size of its eruptive centers and by the partly subaerial, partly submarine nature of the eruptions. It has been suggested (Bouysse and others, 1983a) that this unit extends off the coastline. Notable hydrothermal activity occurs in the vicinity of Bouillante.

(6) The Madeleine-Soufrière massif is the locus of the present volcanic activity, which started about 0.15 Ma. The petrography of the massif is quite homogenous and is represented by medium-K calc-alkaline basaltic andesites and andesites (Lefèvre and Cocusse, 1985). La Soufrière erupted in 1680, 1695–1696, 1797–1798, 1809, 1837, 1903, 1956, and 1976–1977. All these eruptions had a phreatic origin. The fractured lava dome at the summit of La Soufrière was emplaced in approximately A.D. 1580 (Semet and Vatin-Pérignon, 1979).

Montserrat

On Montserrat (85 km^2), the extinct centers of Silver Hill (ca. 1.6 Ma; Briden and others, 1979) and the Centre Hills (ca. 2 Ma; Le Gall and others, 1983), together with the Harris–Bugby Ridge (ca. 4.4 Ma; Briden and others, 1979) make up the northern half of the island. Massive andesites, agglomerates, and mudflow deposits are the main components of these centers. South Soufrière Hill (ca. 1.6 Ma; Briden and others, 1979) includes a number of more basic lava flows as well as the White River pyroclast fall series of andesitic and basaltic composition. Some units within the White River series contain basic/ultrabasic cumulate blocks, and others show evidence of incomplete mixing of basic and andesitic magma. The original crater of South Soufrière Hill has been obscured by the growth of the Raspberry Hill dome, and the parasitic Roche's Centre includes fragments of tuffaceous limestone thought to be similar to that of St. Kitts and St. Eustatius (Westermann and Kiel, 1961). The Soufriere Hills, which constitute the youngest center on the island, possess a complex nucleus of andesite-dacite domes and the remnants of a large breached crater. An age of 1.1 ±0.25 Ma has been obtained on a sample from Chances Peak dome (Le Gall and others, 1983). Mud-flow and alluvial deposits exposed along the east coast of the island may have been discharged during a catastrophic collapse of the summit prior to the formation of Castle Peak dome within the old crater. Widespread unconsolidated pyroclast flow deposits, mainly of andesitic composition, are exposed in ghauts northeast and southwest of the volcano. Radiocarbon dating shows that the last major series of pyroclast flows was emitted between 17 and 23 ka (Rea, 1974; Baker, 1983). Although there have been no historic eruptions, fumarolic activity persists on the Soufrière Hills, and there have also been periods of enhanced shallow seismicity (Robson and Tomblin, 1966).

Redonda

The small island of Redonda lies between Montserrat and Nevis. It is composed of thin flows of basalt with intervening scoria horizons. These apparently originated from a cone which has its center to the west of the present island (Martin-Kaye, 1969). K/Ar dates reported by Baubron and others (1979) indicate an age of 1.5 ±0.5 Ma, but a more recent determination (D. C. Rex, 1984, personal commun.) suggests an age of less than 1 Ma. The Redonda lavas are olivine-plagioclase-phyric basalts with ca. 49% SiO$_2$, low content of incompatible elements, and some light rare earth element (LREE) enrichment (Baker, 1984).

Nevis

On Nevis (100 km^2), the older Pliocene centers such as Windy Hill, Hurricane Hill, and Cades Bay (3.4–2.7 Ma; Hutton,

1978) occur in the northwest part of the island. Together with slightly younger centers, such as Saddle Hill 1 (1.8 Ma), they are surmounted by the composite cone of Nevis Peak. The summit rises from the rim of an outer crater cutting an older; an inner crater is almost completely filled by a small younger dome (Robson and Tomblin, 1966). Tongues of mudflow and pyroclastic-flow deposits radiate from Nevis Peak to make up much of the lower ground. Hutton (1978) also referred to the extensive development of chaotic ash-and-block flow debris derived from an ancestral Nevis Peak source. According to Hutton (1978), one such deposit contains blocks of poorly fossiliferous limestone "of probable Eocene age." The Nevis lavas are mainly rather siliceous andesites grading into dacites, and resemble the calc-alkaline lavas of southeast St. Kitts; however, they are somewhat more potassic than suites from Montserrat or the northern part of St. Kitts. There have been no historic eruptions on Nevis, but fumarolic activity persists to the present day, and there were seismic swarms below Nevis Peak in 1950–51 and in 1960–61 (Robson and Tomblin, 1966).

St. Kitts

St. Kitts (1975 km^2) is constructed from a series of overlapping volcanic centers aligned along a northwest-southeast axis. Activity has shifted progressively northwestward, and the oldest rocks (ca. 2.3 Ma; Baker, 1969) are exposed in the deeply dissected Salt Pond Peninsula. The South East Range and Middle Range volcanoes largely retain their original form and are likely to be 1–2 m.y. old. The date of 7.5 ±2 Ma cited by Baker (1969) on a lava from the South East Range has now been discarded, following a new determination on a closely associated sample which gave an age of ca. 1 Ma (D. C. Rex, in Baker, 1984). The youngest volcano, Mt. Misery, occupies the northwestern part of the island, and its age is considered to be less than 1 Ma. It is a stratovolcano with an open crater and several parasitic domes, of which Brimstone Hill is the most conspicuous. Pleistocene limestone has been uplifted on the western flank of this dome and also occurs at an elevation of 350 m above sea level in Godwin Gut on the side of the Middle Range. A radiocarbon determination on a coral from the Brimstone Hill limestone indicated an age of 44 ±1.2 ka (Westermann and Kiel, 1961). Basic and andesitic pyroclastic fall deposits of the Mansion Series are widely distributed around Mt. Misery, and much of the succession is less than 40,000 yr old (Roobol and others, 1981). Extensive pyroclastic flow deposits (ca. 2 ka, Roobol and others, 1981; Baker, 1983) are abundant to the north and west of the volcano. The youngest deposits, the Steel Dust Series, are confined to the western slopes, where they form a thin series of pyroclast falls and base-surge deposits dated at ca. 1,650 yr B.P. (Baker, 1983). Despite a predominance of andesite, the Mt. Misery volcanics constitute a distinctive low-K suite of island-arc tholeiite affinity.

St. Eustatius

On St. Eustatius (20 km^2), Westermann and Kiel (1961) recognized three main geological units. The oldest forms the northwestern volcanic hills, composed of agglomerates, tuffs, andesitic lavas, and intrusives that are regarded as the remnants of a stratovolcano originally centered on the present hill of Bergje. The age of this center is <1 Ma (Roobol and others, 1981). The Quill volcano and its deposits make up most of the remainder of the island. This small strato-volcano has no recorded volcanic activity but has almost certainly been active in recent times (Martin-Kaye, 1969). According to Roobol and others (1981), the last eruption occurred approximately 1,500 yr ago. Fragmental successions, including pyroclastic flow deposits, are exposed in coastal sections, and the Quill tuffs are also distributed across the northwestern hills. Round Hill on the northwestern flanks of the volcano is interpreted as a relatively young volcanic dome which just failed to reach the surface. Although andesite is the dominant rock type, there is a wide compositional range from basaltic andesite to rhyolite (D'Arco, 1982). The lavas constitute a low K-calc-alkaline series with a strong resemblance to the St. Kitts suite. The third and smallest unit is the White Wall Formation of Pleistocene limestone located on the southern side of the Quill; it has a steep dip to the south and is thought to have been tilted to its present position by a cryptodome. The White Wall consists of beds of limestone, fossiliferous tuffs, and stratified gypsum. The fossils point to a Pleistocene age, and a radiocarbon date gave an age of 32,640 ±300 yr B.P. (Westermann and Kiel, 1961).

Saba

The small island of Saba (12 km^2, 887 m above sea level), the most northerly of the volcanic chain, is a complex stratovolcano with a summit dome (the Mountain) and several parasitic domes. According to Westermann and Kiel (1961), the basal unit consists of agglomerates, tuffs, and redistributed deposits and occasional andesite lava flows. This gives way to more massive andesites and to the lava flows of Flat Point and those flows behind the Ridge. These lavas extend from the vicinity of Upper Hells Gate down to the airstrip and may be contemporaneous with the uppermost unit. The upper part of Saba is composed of a partially eroded volcanic dome surmounted by remnants of lava spines. A number of plugs and volcanic domes such as Booby Hill cut the older formations on the eastern and southern flanks of the volcano. Younger pyroclastics which include nuées ardentes deposits occur along the south coast and are thought to have originated from the summit dome.

Although andesite is the dominant rock type, basaltic lavas occur in the vicinity of English Quarter and Lower Hells Gate. Amphibole appears in all of the lavas, including the basalts. The volcanic rocks of Saba are broadly comparable with those of other suites in the northern part of the Lesser Antilles, especially Montserrat, but potassium and associated incompatible elements have somewhat higher concentrations than in rocks of neighboring islands such as St. Eustatius. Xenoliths and xenocrysts are common in the lavas, and the high incidence of disequilibrium features may be due in part to magma mixing (Baker and others, 1980).

The submerged northern termination of the Lesser Antilles arc

Bouysse and others (1981) first regarded the Luymes Bank as the northern termination of the active volcanic arc of the Lesser Antilles. It is 25 km northwest of the island of Saba, has a tabular form, and is composed of volcanic rocks capped by sediment. Andesite dredged from the southwest side of the ridge has been dated at 3.6 ±0.6 Ma and is similar to the calc-alkaline andesites exposed on several of the northern islands. Bouysse and others (1985b) described similar calc-alkaline andesites, 4.0 ±0.5 m.y. old, from the Noroit seamount (70 km northward of Luymes Bank), near the Anegada passage, which marks the geodynamic boundary between the Greater and Lesser Antilles. The submerged northern segment of the Lesser Antilles arc is therefore 110 km long (from Saba to the Noroit seamount), and is probably extinct.

GEODYNAMIC EVOLUTION OF THE LESSER ANTILLES

R. C. Maury, Ph. Bouysse, and G. K. Westbrook

Time and space distribution of magmatism

With the exception of La Désirade Upper Jurassic and Lower Cretaceous units, the oldest igneous rocks exposed in the Lesser Antilles area are Late Cretaceous volcanic and plutonic island-arc rocks (Aves Swell, Saba Bank, northern flanks of the Lesser Antilles ridge; Ph. Bouysse, this chapter). They are similar in age and composition to the magmatic rocks that crop out in St. Croix and the Greater Antilles, and may thus be part of the same volcanic arc. Mesozoïc igneous rocks may therefore make up a significant part of the Lesser Antilles arc crust (as discussed below).

The major spatial, chronological, and petrological characteristics of Cenozoic and Quaternary magmatism in the Lesser Antilles are presented in Figure 9. The classical double-arc feature of the Lesser Antilles (Martin-Kaye, 1969; Fink, 1972; Ph. Bouysse, this chapter) is strongly supported by recent data. The older (or outer) arc, of Eocene–Oligocene age, extends from the Limestone Caribbees to Grenada and the Grenadines through Martinique. The inner arc (Volcanic Caribbees) can be subdivided into two segments. The Southern Volcanic Caribbees (from Grenada to Martinique and possibly to Dominica) have been the locus of Miocene volcanism (with the exception of the series on St. Vin-

cent) as well as Pliocene–Quaternary volcanism, but the exposed volcanic rocks are younger than about 5 Ma in the Northern Volcanic Caribbees. The ca. 40 Ma, ca. 15 Ma, and ca. 5 Ma ages seem to correspond to major events in the geodynamic history of the Lesser Antilles, because they correspond respectively to the major activity of the outer arc and to the onset of Miocene and Pliocene–Quaternary volcanic activity along the inner arc. A period of magmatic quiescence about 10 m.y. long occurred near the Oligocene–Miocene boundary, clearly separating the activity of the outer and inner arcs throughout the Lesser Antilles.

The magmatic affinities of the Paleogene island-arc volcanic rocks are generally poorly known, because these have suffered extensive hydrothermal alteration (Gunn and Roobol, 1976). The Neogene and Quaternary lavas can be broadly subdivided into four types (Maury and Westercamp, 1985; Fig. 9; see also Donnelly, this volume):

(1) Mg-, Cr-, and Ni-rich basalts (MgO >8%; Cr >200 ppm; Ni >100 ppm), either alkalic (nepheline-normative) or subalkalic. They occur mainly in Grenada, the Grenadines, and southern St. Vincent, but are also known in Martinique (Ilet à Ramiers) and Redonda.

(2) K-poor volcanic series (K_2O <0.5% for SiO_2 = 50%), with low incompatible element contents and $^{87}Sr/^{86}Sr$ ratios and more or less flat REE patterns, showing sometimes (but not always) the characteristics of island-arc tholeiites. They occur mainly in the northern part of the arc (St. Kitts, St. Eustatius) but also in St. Vincent and in the Miocene series of Martinique and St Lucia.

(3) Medium-K volcanic series (0.5% < K_2O < 0.9% for SiO_2 = 50%) common in the central part of the arc (Montserrat, Grande-Terre, Dominica, Mt. Pelée, Martinique); they show an increase in incompatible element contents and $^{87}Sr/^{86}Sr$ ratios relative to the K-poor series.

(4) Relatively high-K volcanic series (K_2O > 0.9% for SiO_2 = 50%), which are only known to occur in the southern half of the arc (Cochrane, Dominica; Pitons du Carbet, Martinique; Soufrière, St. Lucia; Grenadines and Grenada), and show the highest incompatible element concentrations and Sr isotopic ratios known in the Lesser Antilles, though these enrichments remain moderate with respect to worldwide orogenic series (Brown and others, 1977; Rea, 1982).

The Lesser Antilles Neogene and Quaternary series thus show an overall tendency of increasing incompatible elements and radiogenic strontium toward the south (Brown and others, 1977; Rea, 1982; Dupré and others, 1985). Moreover, in a given area these characteristics usually increase with time during a period of more or less permanent volcanic activity, the earliest series usually being K-poor (Maury and Westercamp, 1985).

Possible geodynamic controls on magmatic features

They have been discussed by a number of authors (e.g., Brown and others, 1977; Hawkesworth and others, 1979; Hawkesworth and Powell, 1980; Smith and others, 1980; Rea

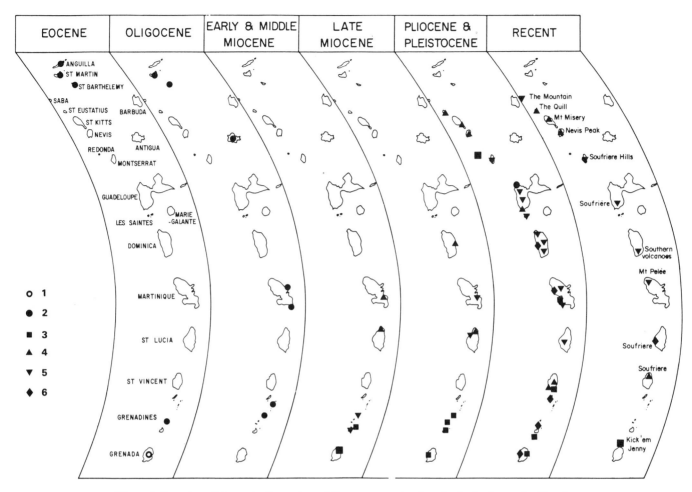

Figure 9. Location of the main Cenozoic and Quaternary volcanic series in the Lesser Antilles: 1 = volcanism of unknown affinity; 2 = orogenic-type volcanism (precise affinities unknown); 3 = Mg-rich alkalic or subalkalic basalts and associated rocks; 4 = Low-K volcanic series; 5 = medium-K volcanic series; 6 = high-K volcanic series.

and Baker, 1980; Rea, 1982; Maury and Westercamp, 1985), though no general agreement arises from this debate (Donnelly and others, Chapter 13, this volume). Recent (1980–1985) data have shown that the thickness (and presumably the composition) of the arc crust remains approximately constant along the arc (Westbrook, this chapter); there are no important variations in dip of the deeper Benioff zone (section I), but its depths are somewhat lower beneath the Southern Volcanic Caribbees (Fig. 1c). The segmentation of the arc crust into fault-bounded blocks (Westbrook, this chapter) also needs to be considered (Rea, 1982), as well as possible variations of the subduction vector obliquity (Donnelly and others, 1971; Brown and others, 1977; Rea and Baker, 1980) or of the subduction rates (Smith and others, 1980). The kink of the Benioff zone between Martinique and St. Lucia (Fig. 1c), which perhaps represents the triple junction of the Caribbean and separates North and South American plates (Wadge and Shepherd, 1984), is not marked by any significant change in the chronology or petrology of volcanism in these two islands, which appear to be very similar to each other

(Maury and Westercamp, this chapter). The occurrence of Atlantic fracture ridges extending beneath Guadeloupe and St. Lucia (Westbrook, this chapter) does not seem to be correlated with special magmatic features. The change in age of the subducted ocean crust south of St. Vincent (Westbrook, this chapter) may be spatially correlated with the major occurrences of silica-undersaturated Mg-rich basalts in Grenada and the Grenadines, but the longevity of alkalic volcanism in Grenada for ca. 20 m.y. remains a puzzle. The apparent spatial, chronological, and/or petrological disconnection of the Mg-rich basalts from the other volcanic series (Thirlwall and Graham, 1984; Westercamp and others, 1985) has been discussed by Maury and Westercamp (1985) who considered that the occurrence of these basalts is linked to transverse faults, which are possibly more common near the southern end of the arc.

Several Sr-Nd-Pb isotopic studies (Hawkesworth and others, 1979; Davidson, 1983; Dupré and others, 1985; J. P. Davidson, B. Dupré, P. Vidal, and W. M. White, 1985, personal commun.) strongly support the participation of subducted sediments in the genesis of the Lesser Antilles magmas as initially proposed by Donnelly and others (1971), though intracrustal contamination may also occur (Thirlwall and Graham, 1984). The observed underthrusting of Atlantic sediments beneath the Barbados accretionary prism (Westbrook and others, 1984) is in accord with this interpretation. The increase in thickness of the Atlantic sediments from the north to the south of the Lesser Antilles area and their corresponding increase in radiogenic isotopes due to the continental components supplied by the Amazon and Orinoco rivers (Dupré and others, 1985) might, in this model, be related to the increase in incompatible elements and radiogenic Sr contents observed in the Lesser Antilles magmas from the north to the south of the inner arc.

Evolution of the arc system

The presence of Cretaceous and Late Jurassic igneous rocks in the crust of the northern Lesser Antilles implies that this part of the arc, at least, formed part of an arc system along the margin of the Caribbean that included the Greater Antilles and Aves Swell and that was active in the Mesozoic; until recently, Bouysse (1979, 1984) has suggested that the arc south of Guadeloupe did not exist before the Eocene, because of the absence of pre-Eocene outcrops.

Also, the narrowness of the bathymetric ridge on which the arc is situated south of Guadeloupe compared with that north of Guadeloupe suggests that it had a much smaller volume and consequently a shorter history of magmatism. Bouysse postulated that before the Eocene a transform fault south of Guadeloupe displaced the subduction zone westward so that there was simultaneous volcanism in Aves Ridge and the Northern Lesser Antilles, which were both in their present relative positions. At the beginning of the Eocene the subduction zone south of Guadeloupe jumped eastward to the same line as that north of Guadeloupe, shifting the line of the arc and creating the Grenada Trough, which would be floored by the old forearc. This hypothesis does not easily explain the continuation of the arc crust southward from Grenada to Margarita, which appears, from the ages of plutonic rocks from Margarita and Los Testigos (Santamaria and Schubert, 1974), to have been active before the Eocene. Also, crustal models of the Lesser Antilles arc, derived from geophysical data (Westbrook, this chapter) show that the volume of arc crust remains virtually constant along the arc. The difference between north and south is that the northern part of the arc is uplifted relative to the south.

An alternative hypothesis to that of Bouysse is that in pre-Eocene times the Aves Ridge and Lesser Antilles were part of a single arc that was split to form the Grenada Trough by back-arc spreading. The Aves Ridge became inactive as it was moved away from locus of island-arc magmatism which remained beneath the Lesser Antilles. The pattern of magnetic anomalies over the Grenada Trough suggests that spreading was not about a simple ridge parallel to the arc (the origin of the Grenada Trough is discussed elsewhere in this volume). An important aspect of this alternative model is that all of the Lesser Antilles is underlain by a basement of Mesozoic arc rocks.

The westward shift of magmatism to the Northern Volcanic Caribbees in the Pliocene appears to have been induced by the subduction of ridges that flank old transform faults in the Atlantic oceanic crust (Bouysse, 1984; Westbrook and McCann, 1986). This may have produced a flattening of the angle of subduction of the lithosphere because of the buoyant effect of the ridges, or narrowing of the forearc by displacement/erosion of part of the forearc by the ridges (Westbrook and McCann, 1986). The forearc off the northern Lesser Antilles is much narrower than that farther south (Fig. 3).

The geological evolution of the Lesser Antilles arc remains perplexing in its complexity. There are many associations and correlations between magmatism, structure, and sedimentation, but their explanations and causes remain undetermined.

REFERENCES CITED

Ainscough, D.P.J., 1983, A study of the crustal structure between the southern part of the Lesser Antilles island arc and the northeastern corner of the South American continent [M.Sc. thesis]: Durham, England, University of Durham, 56 p.

Andreieff, P., 1982, Stratigraphie et micropaléontologie des formations sédimentaires des îles du plateau insulaire d'Anguilla–Saint-Barthélémy (Petites Antilles): Résumé, principaux résultats scientifiques et techniques, Service Géologique National ed. 1981 [abs.]: Bureau de Recherches Géologiques et Minieres, Rapport Annuel Scientifique, p. 56–57.

Andreieff, P., and Cottez, S., 1976, Sur l'âge, la structure et la formation des îles de Grande–Terre et de Marie–Galante (Guadeloupe, F.W.I.): Transactions, 7th Caribbean Geological Conference (Guadeloupe, 1974), p. 329–333.

Andreieff, P., Bouysse, P., and Westercamp, D., 1979, Reconnaissance géologique de l'arc insulaire des Petites Antilles; Résultats d'une campagne à la mer de prélèvements de roches entre Sainte-Lucie et Anguilla (ARCANTE 1): Bulletin du Bureau de Recherches Géologiques et Minières, ser. IV, no. 3–4, p. 227–270.

Andreieff, P., Bizon, G., and Bouysse, P., 1981, Révision de l'âge des formations sédimentaires de l'île de Saint-Martin; Implications sur la chronologie du volcanisme de l'arc insulaire des Petites Antilles: Paris, Académie des Sciences Comptes Rendus, sér. II, v. 292, p. 79–82.

Andreieff, P., Bouysse, P., and Westercamp, D., 1983, Révision géologique de l'île de Marie-Galante (Petites Antilles): Bulletin de la Société Géologique de France, sér. 7, t. 25, no. 6, p. 805–810.

Andreieff, P., Bonneton, J. R., Vila, J. M., and Westercamp, D., 1984, Découverte de Paléocène supérieur à Anguilla, à l'extrémité nord de l'arc des Petites Antilles [abs.]: 10è Réunion Annuelle Sciences de la Terre, Bordeaux, France, Paris, Société Géologique de France (ed.), p. 15.

Arculus, R. J., 1973, The alkali basalt, andesite association of Grenada, Lesser Antilles [Ph.D. thesis]: Durham, England, University of Durham, 349 p.

———, 1976, Geology and geochemistry of the alkali basalt-andesite association of Grenada, Lesser Antilles island arc: Geological Society of America Bulletin, v. 87, p. 612–624.

———, 1978, Mineralogy and petrology of Grenada, Lesser Antilles island arc: Contributions to Mineralogy and Petrology, v. 65, p. 413–424.

Arculus, R. J., and Wills, K.J.A., 1980, Petrology of plutonic blocs and inclusions from the Lesser Antilles island arc: Journal of Petrology, v. 21, p. 743–799.

Aspinall, W. P., Sigurdsson, H., and Shepherd, J. B., 1973, Eruption of Soufrière volcano on St-Vincent island, 1971–1972: Science, v. 181, p. 117–124.

Baker, P. E., 1968, Petrology of Mt. Misery, St. Kitts, West Indies: Lithos, v. 1, p. 124–150.

———, 1969, The geological history of Mt. Misery Volcano, St. Kitts, West Indies: Overseas Geology and Mineral Resources, v. 10, p. 207–230.

———, 1983, Evaluation of volcanic hazards on St. Kitts and Montserrat, West Indies [abs.]: Hamburg, International Union of Geodesy and Geophysics, 18th General assembly, p. 368.

———, 1984, Geochemical evolution of St. Kitts and Montserrat, Lesser Antilles: Geological Society of London Journal, v. 141, p. 401–411.

Baker, P. E., Buckley, F., and Padfield, T., 1980, Petrology of the volcanic rocks of Saba, West Indies: Bulletin Volcanologique, v. 43, no. 2, p. 337–346.

Barrabé, L., 1953, Observations sur la constitution géologique de la Désirade (Guadeloupe): Bulletin de la Société Géologique de France, 6è série, v. III, p. 613–626.

Baubron, J. C., Bouysse, P., Maury, R. C., and Westercamp, D., 1979, L'îlot Redonda, un jalon de l'arc volcanique récent des Petites Antilles: Bulletin du Bureau de Recherches Géologiques et Minières, sec. IV, no. 3–4, p. 273–283.

Blanc, F., 1983, Corrélations chronologiques et géochimiques des formations volcaniques du sud de la Basse-Terre de Guadeloupe (Petites Antilles), [Thèse de 3ème cycle]: Grenoble, Université de Grenoble, 165 p.

Bouysse, P., 1979, Caractères morphostructuraux et évolution géodynamique de l'arc insulaire des Petites Antilles (Campagne ARCANTE 1): Bulletin du Bureau de Recherches Géologiques et Minières, sér. IV, no. 3–4–1976, p. 185–210.

———, 1980, Sur l'existence d'un volcan sous-marin dans l'archipel de la Guadeloupe; Commentaires sur le problème du volcanisme sous-marin historique dans l'arc insulaire des Petites Antilles: Bulletin du Bureau de Recherches Géologiques et Minières, sér. IV, no. 1, p. 3–14.

———, 1984, The Lesser Antilles island arc; structure and geodynamic evolution, *in* Biju-Duval, B., and Moore, J. C., Initial reports of the Deep Sea Drilling Project, Volume 78a: Washington, D.C., U.S. Government Printing Office, p. 83–103.

Bouysse, P., and Garrabé, F., 1984, Evolution tectonique néogène des îles calcaires de l'archipel de la Guadeloupe: Paris, Académie des Sciences Comptes Rendus, sér. II, v. 298, p. 763–766.

Bouysse, P., and Guennoc, P., 1983, Données sur la structure de l'arc insulaire des Petites Antilles, entre Sainte-Lucie et Anguilla: Marine Geology, v. 53, p. 131–166.

Bouysse, P., and Sigurdsson, H., 1982, The "Hodder phenomenon" of 1902; No active submarine volcano off St. Lucia (Lesser Antilles): Marine Geology, v. 50, no. 1–2, p. 1129–1136.

Bouysse, P., Andreieff, P., and Westercamp, D., 1980, Evolution of the Lesser Antilles island arc, new data from the submarine geology: Transactions, 9th Caribbean Geological Conference, Santo Domingo, 1980, p. 75–88.

Bouysse, P., Maury, R. C., Westercamp, D., Baubron, J. C., Andreieff, P., and Cotten, J., 1981, Le banc Luymes, terminaison septentrionale de l'arc récent des Petites Antilles: Bulletin de la Société Géologique de France, v. 23, no. 2, p. 185–194.

Bouysse, P., Robert, S., Guennoc, P., and Monti, S., 1983a, Bathymétrie détaillée (seabeam) et anomalies magnétiques dans les Antilles françaises; Interprétation morphostructurale de la vallée et de l'escarpement de la Désirade et des côtes occidentales de Basse-Terre de Guadeloupe et de Martinique: Documents du Bureau de Recherches Géologiques et Minières, no. 63, 78 p., plus inset maps.

Bouysse, P., Schmidt-Effing, R., and Westercamp, D., 1983b, La Désirade islands

(Lesser Antilles) revisited; Lower Cretaceous radiolarian cherts and arguments against an ophiolitic origin for the basal complex: Geology, v. 11, p. 244–247.

Bouysse, P., Andreieff, P., Richard, M., Baubron, J. C., Mascle, A., Maury, R. C., and Westercamp, D., 1985a, Aves Swell and northern Lesser Antilles ridge; rock–dredging results from Arcante 3 cruise, *in* Mascle, A., ed., Géodynamique des Caraïbes: Paris, Technip, v. 1, p. 65–76.

Bouysse, P., Baubron, J. C., Richard, M., Maury, R. C., and Andreieff, P., 1985b, Evolution de la terminaison nord de l'arc interne des Petites Antilles au Plio–Quaternaire: Bulletin de la Société Géologique de France, sér. 8, t. I, no. 2, p. 181–188.

Bouysse, P., Westercamp, D., Andreieff, P., and Baubron, J. C., 1985c, Le volcanisme sous-marin néogène récent au large des côtes caraïbes des Antilles françaises; Relations avec le volcanisma à terre et évolution du front volcanique: Orléans, France, Géologie de la France, Bureau de Recherche Géologiques et Minières, no. 1, p. 101–114.

Bowin, C., 1976, Caribbean gravity field and plate tectonics: Geological Society of America Special Paper 169, 79 p.

Boynton, C. H., Westbrook, G. K., Bott, M.H.P., and Long, R. E., 1979, A seismic refraction investigation of crustal structure beneath the Lesser Antilles island arc: Royal Astronomical Society Geophysical Journal, v. 58, p. 371–393.

Bradley, A. G., 1979, A gravity study of the continental margin north of the Araya-Paria Peninsula, Venezuela [M.Sc. thesis]: Durham, England, University of Durham, 67 p.

Brasier, M. D., and Mather, J. D., 1975, The stratigraphy of Barbuda, West Indies: Geological Magazine, v. 112, no. 3, p. 271–282.

Briden, J. C., Rex, D. C., Faller, A. M., and Tomblin, J. F., 1979, K-Ar geochronology and palaeomagnetism of volcanic rocks in the Lesser Antilles island arc: Royal Society of London Philosophical Transactions, Royal ser. A., v. 291, no. 1383, p. 485–528.

Brown, G. M., Holland, J. G., Sigurdsson, J., Tomblin, J. F., and Arculus, R. J., 1977, Geochemistry of the Lesser Antilles volcanic island arc: Geochimica et Cosmochimica Acta, v. 41, p. 785–801.

Bunce, E. T., Philips, J. D., Chase, R. L., and Bowin, C. O., 1970, The Lesser Antilles arc and the eastern margin of the Caribbean Sea, *in* Maxwell, A. E., ed., The sea: New York, Wiley-Interscience, v. 4, p. 359–385.

Carey, S. N., and Sigurdsson, H., 1980, The Roseau ash; deep-sea tephra deposits from a major eruption on Dominica, Lesser Antilles arc: Journal of Volcanology and Geothermal Research, v. 7, p. 67–86.

Carron, J. P., Le Guen de Kerneizon, M., and Maury, R. C., 1982, Pétrologie comparée des produits des éruptions de 1902–1979 à la Soufrière de Saint-Vincent (Petites Antilles): Paris, Académie des Sciences Comptes Rendus, sér. II, t. 294, p. 59–62.

Case, J. E., 1975, Geophysical studies of the Caribbean Sea, *in* Nairn, A.E.M., and Stehli, F. G., eds., The ocean basins and margins; the Gulf of Mexico and the Caribbean: New York, Plenum Press, v. 3, p. 107–180.

Case, J. E., and Holcombe, T. L., 1980, Geologic-tectonic map of the Caribbean region: U.S. Geological Survey Miscellaneous Investigations Map I-1100, scale 1:2,500,000.

Case, J. E., Silver, E. A., and others, 1972, Regional gravity anomalies, Venezuela continental borderland: U.S. Geological Survey Open-File Report, OF-73-350, 25 p.

Christman, R. A., 1953, Geology of St. Bartholomew, St. Martin, and Anguilla, Lesser Antilles: Geological Society of America Bulletin, v. 64, p. 65–96.

———, 1972, Volcanic geology of southwestern Antigua, B.W.I., *in* Shagham, R., and 6 others, eds., Studies in earth and space sciences: Geological Society of America Memoir 132, p. 439–448.

Clark, T. F., Korgen, B. J., and Best, D. M., 1978, Heat flow in the eastern Caribbean: Journal of Geophysical Research, v. 83, no. B12, p. 5883–5891.

Dagain, J., 1981, Mise en place du massif volcanique Madeleine-Soufrière, Basse-Terre de Guadeloupe, Antilles, [Thèse de 3è cycle]: Orsay, Université de Paris XI, 156 p.

D'Arco, P., 1982, Contribution à l'interprétation géothermométrique et géobarométrique des paragenèses calco-alcalines de l'arc des Petites Antilles; Cristallisation fractionnée de la série du Quill (Ile de Saint-Eustache) [Thèse de 3è cycle]: Brest, Université de Bretagne Occidentale, 186 p.

Davidson, J. P., 1983, Lesser Antilles isotopic evidence of the role of subducted sediment in island-arc magma genesis: Nature, v. 306, p. 253–256.

Devine, J. D., and Sigurdsson, J., 1980, Garnet-fassaite calc-silicate nodules from La Soufrière, St. Vincent: American Mineralogist, v. 65, p. 302–305.

Dinkelman, M. G., and Brown, J. F., 1977, K-Ar geochronology and its significance to the geological setting of La Désirade, Lesser Antilles, *in* 8th Caribbean Geological Conference, Curaçao, 1977, Abstracts: Geologie en Mijnbouw (special publication), p. 38–39.

Donnelly, T. W., 1975, The geological evolution of the Caribbean and Gulf of Mexico; some critical problems and areas, *in* Nairn, A.E.M., and Stehli, F. G., eds. The ocean basins and margins; Gulf of Mexico and Caribbean: New York, Plenum Press, p. 663–689.

Donnelly, T. W., and Rogers, J.J.W., 1978, The distribution of the igneous rock suites throughout the Caribbean: Geologie en Mijnbouw, v. 57, no. 2, p. 151–162.

——, 1980, Igneous series in island arcs; the northeastern Caribbean compared with worldwide island-arc assemblages: Bulletin Volcanologique, v. 43, no. 2, p. 347–382.

Donnelly, T. W., Rogers, J.J.W., Pushkar, P., and Armstrong, R. L., 1971, Chemical evolution of the igneous rocks of the eastern West Indies; an investigation of thorium, uranium, and potassium distribution, and lead and strontium isotopic ratios, *in* Donnelly, T. W., ed., Caribbean geophysical, tectonic, and petrologic studies: Geological Society of America Memoir 130, p. 181–224.

Dorel, J., 1978, Sismicité et structure de l'arc des Petites Antilles et du bassin atlantique [thèse]: Paris, Université de Paris VI, 326 p.

——, 1981, Seismicity and seismic gap in the Lesser Antilles arc and earthquake hazard in Guadeloupe: Royal Astronomical Society Geophysical Journal, v. 67, p. 679–695.

Dorel, J., Eschenbrenner, S., and Feuillard, M., 1974, Profils sismiques dans les Petites Antilles: Annales de Géophysique, v. 30, p. 117–126.

Dostal, J., Dupuy, C., Carron, J. P., Le Guen de Kerneizon, M., and Maury, R. C., 1983, Partition coefficients of trace elements; application to volcanic rocks of St. Vincent, West Indies: Geochimica et Cosmochimica Acta, v. 47, p. 525–533.

Drooger, C. W., 1951, Foraminifera from the Tertiary of Anguilla, St. Martin and Tintamarre (Leeward Islands, West Indies): Koninklijke Nederlandse Akademie van Wetenschappen Proceedings, ser. B, v. 54, no. 1, p. 54–65.

Dupré, B., White, W. M., Vidal, P., and Maury, R. C., 1985, Utilisation des traceurs couplés (Pb-Sr-Nd) pour déterminer le rôle des sédiments dans la genèse des basaltes de l'arc des Antilles, *in* Mascle, A., ed., Géodynamique des Caraïbes: Paris, Technip, v. 1, p. 91–97.

Edgar, N. T., Ewing, J. I., and Hennion, J., 1971, Seismic refraction and reflection in Caribbean Sea: American Association of Petroleum Geologists Bulletin, v. 55, no. 6, p. 833–870.

Ferragne, A., Parra, M., Bardintzeff, J. M., Desprairies, A., Morin, J. C., and Cadet, J. P., 1985, Les cendres de l'île et de la ride de la Barbade, témoins du volcanisme cénozoïque et quaternaire de l'arc des Petites Antilles, *in* Mascle, A., ed., Géodynamique des Caraïbes: Paris, Technip, v. 1, p. 199–219.

Fink, L. K., Jr., 1968, Marine geology of the Guadeloupe region, Lesser Antilles island arc [Ph.D. thesis]: Miami, University of Miami, 121 p.

——, 1972, Bathymetric and geologic studies of the Guadeloupe region, Lesser Antilles island arc: Marine Geology, v. 12, no. 4, p. 228–267.

Fox, P. J., and Heezen, B. C., 1975, Geology of the Caribbean crust, *in* Nairn, A.E.M., and Stehli, F. G., eds., The ocean basins and margins; Gulf of Mexico and Caribbean: New York, Plenum Press, p. 421–466.

Fox, P. J., Schreiber, E., and Heezen, B. C., 1971, The geology of the Caribbean crust; Tertiary sediments, granitic and basic rocks from Aves Ridge: Tectonophysics, v. 12, p. 89–109.

Frost, S. H., and Weiss, M. P., 1979, Patch reef communities and succession in the Oligocene of Antigua, West Indies: Geological Society of America Bulletin, v. 90, p. 612–616.

Gadalia, A., and Westercamp, D., 1984, Prospection géothermique de la région de Bouillante-Vieux habitants, Guadeloupe: Rapport Service Géologique National 063, Géothermie, France, Bureau de Recherches Géologiques et Minières, 97 p.

Garrabé, F., 1983, Evolution sédimentaire et structurale de la Grande-Terre de Gaudeloupe [thèse de 3è cycle]: Paris, Université de Paris-Sud, 171 p.

Garrabé, F., and Andreieff, P., 1985, Sédimentation et tectonique plio-quaternaires comparées de Marie-Galante et de Grande-Terre (Guadeloupe), *in* Mascle, A., ed., Géodynamique des Caraïbes: Paris, Technip, v. 1, p. 155–160.

Girardin, N., and Gaulon, R., 1983, Microseismicity and stresses in the Lesser Antilles dipping seismic zone: Earth and Planetary Science Letters, v. 62, p. 340–348.

Graham, A. M., 1980, Genesis of the igneous rock suites of Grenada, Lesser Antilles [Ph.D. thesis]: Edinburgh, Scotland, University of Edinburgh, 337 p.

Graham, A. M., and Thirlwall, M. F., 1981, Petrology and the 1979 eruption of Soufrière Volcano, St. Vincent, Lesser Antilles: Contributions to Mineralogy and Petrology, v. 76, p. 336–342.

Gunn, B. M., and Roobol, M. J., 1976, Metasomatic alteration of the predominantly island arc igneous suite of the Limestone Caribbees (E. Caribbean): Geologische Rundschau, v. 65, no. 3, p. 1078–1108.

Gunn, B. M., Roobol, M. J., and Smith, A. L., 1980, Geochemistry of the volcanoes of Basse-Terre, Guadeloupe; an example of intra-island variation: Bulletin Volcanologique, v. 43, no. 2, p. 403–412.

Hawkesworth, C. J., O'Nions, R. K., and Arculus, R. J., 1979, Nd and Sr isotope geochemistry of island arc volcanics, Grenada, Lesser Antilles: Earth and Planetary Science Letters, v. 45, p. 237–248.

Hutton, C. O., 1978, The petrology of Nevis, Leeward Islands, West Indies: Overseas Geology and Mineral Resources, no. 52, 31 p.

Jackson, T. A., 1980, The composition and differentiation of the volcanic rocks of Carriacou, Grenadines, West Indies: Bulletin Volcanologique, v. 43, no. 2, p. 311–324.

Jacques, D., Maury, R. C., and Bellon, H., 1984, Géologie et géochronologie des îles des Saintes, Guadeloupe: Paris, Académie des Sciences Comptes Rendus, sér. 2, t. 299, no. 11, p. 721–726.

Johnston, T. H., Schilling, J. G., Osi, Y., and Fink, L. K., 1971, Dredged greenstones from Lesser Antilles island arc [abs.]: EOS (American Geophysical Union Transactions), v. 52, no. 88, p. 246.

Jordan, T. H., 1975, The present-day motions of the Caribbean plate: Journal of Geophysical Research, v. 80, p. 4433–4439.

Keary, P., 1976, Gravity and seismic reflection investigations into the crustal structure of Aves Ridge, eastern Caribbean: Transactions, 7th Caribbean Geological Conference, Guadeloupe, 1974, p. 311–320.

Lefèvre, C., and Cocusse, P., 1985, Etude pétrographique et minéralogique des laves du massif volcanique Madeleine-Soufrière de Guadeloupe (Petites Antilles); Implications magmatologiques: Bulletin de Minéralogie, v. 108, p. 189–208.

Le Gall, B., Bellon, H., Carron, J. P., and Le Guen de Kerneizon, M., 1983, Données nouvelles sur le volcanisme de l'île de Montserrat (Petites Antilles): Bulletin de la Société Géologique de France, sér. 7, t. 25, no. 6, p. 837–843.

Le Guen de Kerneizon, M., Mascle, A., Maury, R. C., and Westercamp, D., 1979, Les laves de la Désirade (Petites Antilles), témoins d'un magmatisme de marge active; Arguments minéralogiques: Bulletin du Bureau de Recherches Géologiques et Minières, sect. 4, no. 3–4, 1979, p. 285–292.

Le Guen de Kerneizon, M., Bellon, H., Carron, J. P., Maury, R. C., Bellon, H., and Dupuy, C., 1982, Les rhyolites à fayalite et ferroaugite de Sainte-Lucie (arc insulaire des Petites Antilles): Bulletin de Minéralogie, v. 105, p. 203–211.

Le Guen de Kerneizon, M., Bellon, H., Carron, J. P., and Maury, R. C., 1983, L'île de Sainte-Lucie (Petites Antilles); Distinction des principales séries magmatiques à partir de données pétrochimiques et géochronologiques: Bulletin de la Société Géologique de France, sér. 7, t. 25, no. 6, p. 845–853.

Le Guen de Kerneizon, M., Westercamp, D., Carron, J. P., and Bellon, H., 1985, The Grenadines, southern Lesser Antilles; Part II, Major petrochemical features of the volcanic rocks, *in* Mascle, A., ed., Géodynamique des Caraïbes: Paris, Technip, v. 1, p. 119–130.

Lewis, J. F., 1973a, Petrology of the ejected plutonic blocks of the Soufriére Volcano, St. Vincent, West Indies: Journal of Petrology, v. 14, p. 81–112.

——, 1973b, Mineralogy of the ejected plutonic blocks of the Soufriére Volcano, St. Vincent; olivine, pyroxene, amphibole, and magnetite paragenesis: Contributions to Mineralogy and Petrology, v. 38, p. 197–220.

Lewis, J., and Robinson, E., 1976, A revised stratigraphy and geological history of the Lesser Antilles: Transactions, 7th Caribbean Geological Conference, Guadeloupe, 1974, p. 339–344.

Martin-Kaye, P.H.A., 1959, Reports on the geology of the Leeward and British Virgin Islands, St. Lucia: Castries, Voice Publishing Co., 117 p.

——, 1969, A summary of the geology of the Lesser Antilles: Overseas Geology and Mineral Resources, v. 10, p. 172–206.

Mascle, A., and Westercamp, D., 1983, Géologie d'Antigua, Petites Antilles: Bulletin de la Société Géologique de France, sér. 7, t. 15, no. 6, p. 855–866.

Mascle, A., Biju-Duval, B., Letouzey, J., Montadert, L., and Ravenne, C., 1977, Sediments and their deformations in active margins of different geological settings, *in* International Symposium on Geodynamics in the SW Pacific: Paris, Technip, p. 327–344.

Mattinson, J. M., Fink, L. K., and Hopson, C. A., 1973, Age and origin of the ophiolitic rocks on La Désirade Island, Lesser Antilles: Carnegie Institution of Washington Year Book, v. 72, p. 616–623.

——, 1980, Geochronologic and isotopic study of the La Désirade Island basement complex; Jurassic oceanic crust in the Lesser Antilles?: Contributions to Mineralogy and Petrology, v. 71, p. 237–245.

Maury, R. C., and Westercamp, D., 1985, Variations chronologiques et spatiales des basaltes néogènes des Petites Antilles; Implications sur l'évolution de l'arc, *in* Mascle, A., ed., Géodynamique des Caraïbes: Paris, Technip, v. 1, p. 77–89.

McCann, W. R., and Sykes, L. R., 1984, Subduction of aseismic ridges beneath the Caribbean plate; implications for the tectonics and seismic potential of the northeastern Caribbean: Journal of Geophysical Research, v. 89, p. 4493–4519.

Meyerhoff, A. A., and Meyerhoff, H. A., 1972, Continental drift IV; the Caribbean plate: Journal of Geology, v. 80, p. 34–60.

Minster, J. F., and Jordan, T. H., 1978, Present-day plate motions: Journal of Geophysical Research, v. 83, p. 5331–5351.

Nagle, F., 1972, Rocks from the seamounts and escarpments of the Aves Ridge: Transactions, 6th Caribbean Geological Conference, Margarita, 1971, p. 409–413.

Nagle, F., Stipp, J. J., and Fisher, D. E., 1976, K-Ar geochronology of the limestone Caribbees and Martinique, Lesser Antilles, West Indies: Earth and Planetary Science Letters, v. 29, p. 401–412.

Nemec, M. C., 1980, A two-phase model for the tectonic evolution of the Caribbean: Transactions, 9th Caribbean Geological Conference, Santo-Domingo, 1980, p. 23–34.

Officer, C. B., Ewing, J. I., Hennion, J. F., Harkrider, D. G., and Miller, D. E., 1959, Geophysical investigations in the eastern Caribbean; summary of 1955 and 1956 cruises, *in* Ahrens, L. H., and others, eds., Physics and chemistry of the earth: London, Pergamon Press, v. 3, p. 17–109.

Pinet, B., Lajat, D., Le Quellec, P., and Bouysse, P., 1985, Structure of Aves Ridge and Grenada Basin from multichannel seismic data, *in* Mascle, A., ed., Géodynamique des Caraïbes: Paris, Technip, v. 1, p. 53–64.

Powell, M., 1978, Crystallization conditions of low-pressure cumulate nodules from the Lesser Antilles island arc: Earth and Planetary Science Letters, v. 39, p. 162–172.

Rea, W. J., 1974, The volcanic geology and petrology of Montserrat, West Indies: Geological Society of London Journal, v. 130, p. 341–366.

——, 1982, The Lesser Antilles, *in* Thorpe, R. S., ed., Andesites; orogenic andesites and related rocks: Chichester, John Wiley & Sons, p. 167–185.

Rea, W. J., and Baker, P. E., 1980, The geochemical characteristics and conditions of petrogenesis of the volcanic rocks of the northern Lesser Antilles; a review: Bulletin Volcanologique, v. 43, no. 2, p. 325–336.

Reynal, A. de, 1966, Carte géologique du Département de la Guadeloupe au 1:50,000; Feuilles de Marie-Galante et de la Désirade: Paris, Service de la Carte Géologique de France.

Robinson, E., and Jung, P., 1972, Stratigraphy and age of marine rocks of Carriacou: American Association of Petroleum Geologists Bulletin, v. 56, no. 1, p. 114–127.

Robson, G. R., 1968, Field guide trip St. Vincent: Transactions, 4th Caribbean Geologic Conference, Port of Spain, Trinidad, 1965, p. 454–457.

Robson, G. R., and Tomblin, J. F., 1966, Catalogue of the active volcanoes of the world; Part 20, West Indies: Rome, International Association of Volcanology, 56 p.

Roobol, M. J., and Smith, A. L., 1975, A comparison of the recent eruptions of Soufriere, St. Vincent and Mt. Pelée, Martinique: Bulletin Volcanologique, v. 39, p. 214–240.

Roobol, M. J., Smith, A. L., and Wright, J. V., 1981, Revisions in the pyroclastic stratigraphy of Mt. Misery Volcano, St. Kitts, Lesser Antilles; ^{14}C ages and recognition of pyroclast flow deposits: Geological Society of London Journal, v. 138, p. 713–718.

Roobol, M. J., Wright, J. V., and Smith, A. L., 1983, Calderas or gravity-slide structures in the Lesser Antilles island arc?: Journal of Volcanology and Geothermal Research, v. 19, p. 121–134.

Rowley, K., 1978, Late Pleistocene pyroclastic deposits of Soufriere Volcano, St. Vincent, West Indies: Geological Society of America Bulletin, v. 89, p. 825–835.

Santamaria, F., and Schubert, C., 1974, Geochemistry and geochronology of the southern Caribbean–northern Venezuela plate boundary: Geological Society of America Bulletin, v. 85, p. 1085–1098.

Saunders, J. B., Bernoulli, D., and Martin-Kaye, P.H.A., 1985, Late Eocene deep water clastics in Grenada, West Indies: Eclogae Geologicae Helvetiae, v. 78, p. 469–485.

Schubert, C., 1935, Historical geology of the Antillean–Caribbean region: New York, John Wiley & Sons, 811 p.

Semet, M., and Vatin-Perignon, N., 1979, The 16th century activity of La Soufrière de Guadeloupe, F.W.I.; a model for explosive andesitic volcanism in the Lesser Antilles [abs.]: EOS (American Geophysical Union Transactions), v. 60, p. 833.

Shepherd, J. B., Aspinall, W. P., Rowley, K. C., Pereira, J., Sigurdsson, M., Fiske, R. S., and Tomblin, J. F., 1979, The eruption of Soufrière Volcano, St. Vincent, April–June 1979: Nature, v. 282, p. 24–28.

Shimizu, N., and Arculus, R. J., 1975, Rare earth element concentrations in a suite of basanitoïdes and alkali olivine basalts from Grenada, Lesser Antilles: Contributions to Mineralogy and Petrology, v. 50, p. 231–240.

Shipboard Scientific Party, 1973, Site 148, *in* Edgar, N. T. and Saunders, J. B., eds., Initial reports of the Deep Sea Drilling Project, Volume 15: Washington, D.C., U.S. Government Printing Office, p. 217–275.

Sigurdsson, H., 1972, Partly welded pyroclastic flow deposits in Dominica, Lesser Antilles: Bulletin Volcanologique, v. 36, p. 148–163.

——, 1981, Geologic observations in the crater of Soufriere Volcano, St. Vincent: Trinidad, University of the West Indies, Seismic Research Unit Special Publication 1981/1, 25 p.

Sigurdsson, H., and Shepherd, J. B., 1974, Amphibole-bearing basalts from the submarine volcano Kick'em Jenny in the Lesser Antilles island arc: Bulletin Volcanologique, v. 38, no. 4, p. 891–910.

Smith, A. L., Roobol, M. J., and Gunn, B. M., 1980, The Lesser Antilles: a discussion of the island arc magmatism: Bulletin Volcanologique, v. 80, no. 2, p. 287–302.

Solomiac, H., 1974, La géologie et la métallogénie de l'île de Saint-Martin (zone francaise), *in* Livret-guide d'excursion, 7th Conférence géologique des Caraïbes, Guadeloupe, 1974: Paris, Bureau de Recherches Géologiques et Minières, p. 95–108.

Stein, S. Engeln, J. F., and Wiens, D. A., 1982, Subduction seismicity and tectonics in the Lesser Antilles: Journal of Geophysical Research, v. 87, no. B10, p. 8642–8664.

Sykes, L. R., McCann, W. R.,a nd Kafka, A. L., 1982, Motion of Caribbean plate during last 7 million years and implications for earlier Cenozoic movements: Journal of Geophysical Research, v. 87, no. B13, p. 10656–10676.

Thirlwall, M. F., and Graham, A. M., 1984, Evolution of high-Ca, high-Sr C-series basalts from Grenada, Lesser Antilles; the effects of intra-crustal contamination: Geological Society of London Journal, v. 141, p. 427–445.

Tomblin, J. F., 1965, The geology of the Soufrière volcanic centre, St. Lucia: Transactions, 4th Caribbean Geological Conference, Trinidad, p. 367–376.

—— , 1975, The Lesser Antilles and Aves Ridge, *in* Nairn, A.E.M., and Stehli, F. G., eds. The ocean basins and margins: New York, Plenum Press, v. 3, p. 467–500.

Tovish, A., and Schubert, G., 1978, Island arc curvature, velocity of convergence, and angle of subduction: Geophysical Research Letters, v. 5, no. 4, p. 329–332.

Traineau, H., 1982, Contribution à l'étude géologique de la Montagne Pelée, Martinique; Evolution de l'activité éruptive au cours de la période récente [thèse de 3è cycle]: Orsay Université de Paris XI, 209 p.

Vatin-Perignon, N., Chevallier, L., and Blanc, F., 1984, Les évènements dacitiques récents de la Soufrière de Sainte-Lucie, Petites Antilles; Téphrochronologie, dynamismes et structures: Paris, Bulletin Programme Interdisciplinaire de Recherches sur la Prévision et la Surveillance des Eruptions Volcaniques no. 90., Centre National de la Recherche Scientifique-Institut National d'Astronomie et de Géophysique, 31 p.

Vogt, P. R., Lowrie, A., Bracey, D. R., and Hey, R. N., 1976, Subduction of aseismic oceanic ridges; effect on shape, seismicity, and other characteristics of consuming plate boundaries: Geological Society of America Special Paper 172, 59 p.

Wadge, G., and Shepherd, J. B., 1984, Segmentation of the Lesser Antilles subduction zone: Earth and Planetary Science Letters, v. 71, p. 297–304.

Westbrook, G. K., 1975, The structure of the crust and upper mantle in the region of Barbados and the Lesser Antilles: Royal Astronomical Society Geophysical Journal, v. 43, p. 201–242.

Westbrook, G. K., 1984, Magnetic lineations and fracture zones, *in* Speed, R. C., and Westbrook, G. K., eds., Lesser Antilles arc and adjacent terranes: Ocean Margin Drilling Program Regional Atlas Series, Atlas 10, Woods Hole, Massachusetts, Marine Science International, Sheet 5.

Westbrook, G. K. and Jackson, R. J., 1984, Free-air gravity anomalies at sea and Bouguer gravity anomalies on land, *in* Speed, R. C. and Westbrook, G. K., eds., Lesser Antilles arc and adjacent terranes, Atlas 10: Woods Hole, Massachusetts, Marine Sciences International, Ocean Margin Drilling Program Regional Atlas Series, sheet 2.

Westbrook, G. K., and McCann, W. R., 1986, Subduction of Atlantic lithosphere beneath the Caribbean, *in* Vogt, P. R., and Tucholke, B., eds., The western North Atlantic region: Boulder, Colorado, Geological Society of America, The geology of North America, v. M, p. 341–350.

Westbrook, G. K., Mascle, A., and Biju-Duval, B., 1984, Geophysics and the structure of the Lesser Antilles forearc, *in* Biju-Duval, B., Moore, J. C., and others, Initial reports of the Deep Sea Drilling Project, Volume 78A: Washington, D.C., U.S. Government Printing Office, p. 23–38.

Westbrook, G. K., and 6 others, 1984, Depth to acoustic basement, *in* Speed, R. C. and Westbrook, G. K., eds., Lesser Antilles arc and adjacent terranes, Atlas 10: Woods Hole, Massachusetts, Marine Sciences International, Ocean Margin Drilling Program Regional Atlas Series, sheet 8.

Westercamp, D., 1979, Diversité, contrôle structural et origines du volcanisme récent dans l'arc insulaire des Petites Antilles: Bulletin du Bureau de Recherches Géologiques et Minières, sect. 4, no. 3/4–1979, p. 211–226.

—— , 1980, Carte géologique de la Désirade à 1:25,000 et notice explicative: France, Service Géologique Nationale Ed., Bureau de Recherches Géologiques et Minières.

Westercamp, D., and Andreieff, A., 1983a, Saint-Barthélémy et ses îlets; Carte géologique à 1:20,000, avec notice explicative: France, Service Géologique National, Bureau de Recherches Géologiques et Minières.

—— , 1983b, Saint-Barthélémy et ses îles, Antilles francaises; Stratigraphie et évolution magmato-structurale: Bulletin de la Société Géologique de France, sér. 7, t. 25, no. 6, p. 873–883.

Westercamp, D., and Tazieff, H., 1980, Martinique-Guadeloupe-Saint-Martin-La Désirade: Guides géologiques régionaux: Paris, Masson, 135 p.

Westercamp, D., and Tomblin, J. F., 1979, Le volcanisme récent et les éruptions historiques dans la partie centrale de l'arc insulaire des Petites Antilles, Guadeloupe, Martinique, Ste-Lucie, St-Vincent: Bulletin du Bureau de Recherches Géologiques et Minières, sér. 2, no. 3/4–1979, p. 293–321.

Westercamp, D., and Traineau, H., 1983, Carte géologique de la Montagne Pelée au 1:20,000: Orléans, France, Bureau de Recherches Géologiques et Minières.

Westercamp, D., Andreieff, P., Bouysse, P., Mascle, A., and Baubron, J. C., 1985, The Grenadines, southern Lesser Antilles; Part I, Stratigraphy and volcano-structural evolution, *in* Mascle, A., ed., Géodynamique des Caraïbes: Paris, Technip, v. 1, p. 109–118.

Westercamp, D., Andreieff, P., and Baubron, J. C., 1990, Carte géologique de la Martinique au 1:50,000 et notice explicative: France, Service Géologique National, Bureau de Recherche Géologique et Minières (in press).

Westermann, J. H., and Kiel, H., 1961, The geology of Saba and St. Eustatius with notes on the geology of St. Kitts, Nevis, and Montserrat (Lesser Antilles): Uitgaven "Natuurwetenschappelijke Studiekring Voor Suriname en de Nederlandse Antillen" Utrecht, no. 24, 175 p.

Whetten, J. T., 1966, Geology of St. Croix, U.S. Virgin Islands, *in* Hess, H. H., Bowin, C. O., Donnelly, T. W., Whetten, J. T., and Oxburgh, E. R., eds., Caribbean geological investigations: Geological Society of America Memoir 98, p. 177–239.

Wills, K.J.A., 1974, The geological history of southern Dominica and plutonic nodules from the Lesser Antilles [Ph.D. thesis]: Durham, England, University of Durham, 414 p.

Wohletz, K., and 5 others, 1986, The Qualibou caldera, St. Lucia, West Indies: Journal of Volcanology and Geothermal Research, v. 27, p. 77–115.

Wright, J. V., and 6 others, 1984, Late Quaternary explosive silicic volcanism on St. Lucia, West Indies: Geological Magazine, v. 121, no. 1, p. 1–15.

MANUSCRIPT ACCEPTED BY THE SOCIETY DECEMBER 23, 1985

NOTE ADDED IN PROOF

It is now largely admitted that the origin of the Grenada basin results from a back-arc spreading process that occurred during the Paleocene (cf. Bouysse, 1988).

ADDITIONAL REFERENCES

Andreieff, P., Baubron, J. C. and Westercamp, D., 1988, Histoire géologique de la Martinique (Petites Antilles): biostratigraphie (foraminifères), radiochronologie (potassium-argon). Evolution volcano-structurale: Géologie de la France, Bureau de Recherches Géologiques et Minières, Orléans, France, n° 2–3, p. 39–70.

Andreieff, P., Westercamp, D., Garrabe, F., Bonneton, J. R. and Dagain, J., 1988, Stratigraphie de l'île de Saint-Martin (Petites Antilles septentrionales): Géologie de la France, Bureau de Recherches Géologiques et Minières, Orléans, France, n° 2–3, p. 71–88.

Bouysse, P., 1988, Opening of the Grenada back-arc basin and evolution of the Caribbean plate during the Mesozoic and early Paleogene: Tectonophysics, v. 149, p. 121–143.

Bouysse, P., Mascle, A., Mauffret, A., and Mercier de Lepinay, B., 1988, Reconnaissance de structures tectoniques et volcaniques sous-marines de l'arc interne des Petites Antilles (Kick'em Jenny, Qualibou, Montagne Pelée, NW de la Guadeloupe: Marine Geology, v. 81, p. 261–287.

Bouysse, P. and Westercamp, D., 1990, Subduction of Atlantic aseismic ridges and Late Cenozoic evolution of the lesser Antilles island arc: Tectonophysics (in press).

Jacques, D. and Maury, R., 1988, L'archipel des Saintes (Guadeloupe, Petites Antilles): géologie et pétrologie: Géologie de la France, Bureau de Recherches Géologiques et Minières, Orléans, France, n° 2–3, p. 89–99.

Wadge, G., 1986, The dykes and structural setting of the volcanic front in the Lesser Antilles island arc: Bulletin of Volcanology, v. 48, p. 349–372.

Westercamp, D., 1989, Magma generation in the Lesser Antilles: geological constraints: Tectonophysics, v. 149, p. 145–163.

Chapter 6

The Caribbean mountain system, northern South America; A summary

Alirio Bellizzia
Consejo Consultivo de Directores de Servicios Geológicos de Latinoamérica, Apartado 3672, Caracas 1010-A, Venezuela
Gabriel Dengo
Centro de Estudios Geológicos de América Central, Apartado 468, Guatemala, Guatemala

INTRODUCTION

The major tectonic features of northern South America (Fig. 1) are depicted in detail in the tectonic map compiled by Martín (1978), a regional synthesis presented by Bellizzia and others (1981), and a classification of tectonic provinces by Case and others (1984). One of the most prominent features is the Precambrian Guyana shield, a large cratonic block around part of which the Phanerozoic basins and mountain systems are developed. The shield consists mainly of metamorphic and igneous rocks but also includes substantial areas of unmetamorphosed sedimentary and volcanic rocks. Isotopic ages for rocks of the Guyana shield indicate that major geologic events took place between 3.4 and about 1.0 Ma.

The region that extends from the exposed shield to the western Andes, including the Llanos and the Amazonas, was part of the South American craton, at least since the beginning of Paleozoic time (Restrepo and Toussaint, 1988). Proterozoic rocks now form the cores of the major mountain ranges of the Andes, the Sierra de Perijá and the Sierra Nevada de Santa Marta. In the Garzón massif, Colombia, these rocks date from 1,800 to 1,180 Ma (Restrepo and Toussaint, 1988).

Paleozoic sedimentary, metamorphic, and igneous rocks are exposed in the Andes, Perijá, and Santa Marta regions, and small parts of the Caribbean mountain ranges and are known at the subsurface in the basins that separate these mountains from the shield. The Paleozoic sedimentary sequence varies, even in places as close as the Venezuelan Andes, the Cordillera Oriental (Colombia), and Sierra de Perijá. The Cambrian is not yet well understood, but it is certainly represented by metamorphic rocks. Ordovician and Silurian rocks exist in the Venezuelan Andes, in the El Baúl massif (Venezuela), and in the Cordillera Central (Colombia), whereas Devonian rocks, which are unknown to these areas, are well developed in the Cordillera Oriental and the Sierra de Perijá. Carboniferous and Permian rocks are more widespread and are present in all the major mountain ranges, including the Sierra Nevada de Santa Marta. Rocks of these systems are partly metamorphosed in parts of the Venezuelan and Colombian Andes.

The Paleozoic and Mesozoic rocks are separated by an extensive regional unconformity. Thick continental and shallow-water red beds with some intercalated volcanic rocks, probably of Late Jurassic age, form the base of the Mesozoic sequence, which is also very extensive. Marine equivalents of these rocks are found in the Goajira Peninsula, and metamorphosed marine rocks of this age are exposed in the Paraguaná Peninsula and in the Caribbean mountain system.

The Cretaceous is represented by a transgressive sequence of geosynclinal dimensions covering an extensive area from Colombia, across Venezuela, to Trinidad that reaches thicknesses as much as 10 km. In general, it is formed by coarse clastic rocks at the base, followed by massive and thin-bedded limestones and shales. Regressive characteristics appeared at the end of Cretaceous time and extend into the Paleocene.

Mesozoic rocks of different character and tectonic environment occur in other places along the edge of the continent, such as the Caribbean mountain system, which is formed by metamorphosed Late Jurassic and Cretaceous sedimentary and volcanic rocks that must have been north of their present allochthonous position. The same situation is probably true for part of the Goajira Peninsula and the Netherlands Antilles. In the latter, however, mafic igneous oceanic rocks are also present.

Tertiary rocks are also widespread in the northern South America region, but the sedimentary basins were restricted and separated from each other as a result of Late Cretaceous–Eocene orogeny. Tertiary basins with thick sedimentary sequences, mainly clastic but with some limestones, particularly in the late Eocene, are found in the structural depressions that separate the different branches of the Andes. The Atrato, Cauca, Magdalena, and César depressions connect with the Sinú Basin in northwestern Colombia. The characteristics of sedimentation are different for each one. Large Tertiary basins overlying Cretaceous deposits

Bellizzia, A., and Dengo, G., 1990, The Caribbean mountain system, northern South America, *in* Dengo, G., and Case, J. E., eds., The Caribbean Region: Boulder, Colorado, Geological Society of America, The Geology of North America, v. H.

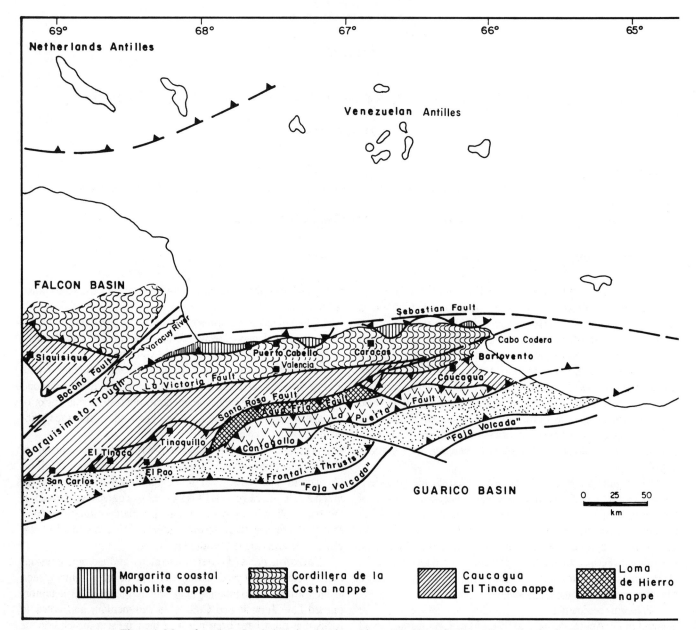

Figure 1. Map of northern South America showing main geographic-geologic features and major faults.

such as the Barinas-Guarico and Oriental Basins, occur between the Guyana shield and the Andes and Caribbean mountain system. In general, uppermost Tertiary and Quaternary rocks are of continental origin.

With the exception of the Guyana shield (Fig. 1), which has remained practically stable since late Precambrian time, the tectonic history of the region has been a complex one, and several metamorphic, igneous, and other deformational episodes have been clearly defined. The initial tectonic events are better known in the Andes. In the Venezuelan Andes, Sierra de Perijá, Cordillera Oriental and Sierra Nevada de Santa Marta, metamorphic events of late Precambrian age are evident. Events that affected the Venezuelan Andes probably occurred during early Paleozoic

(595 to 425 Ma) and late Paleozoic (275 to 175 Ma) times, both accompanied by intrusive activity. Mid-Paleozoic intrusions in this area (400 to 350 Ma) are not related to metamorphism but to milder Devonian-Carboniferous deformation. Ordovician to Silurian intrusives accompanied by metamorphism are found in the Cordillera Oriental of Colombia, in which metamorphic events also occurred duirng Mississippian-Permian time. On the other hand, in the Sierra de Perijá, Devonian intrusions (350 Ma) were not accompanied by metamorphism. Paleozoic volcanism was only local; it is represented by Early Ordovician basalts and by late Paleozoic rhyolites to basalts in the Venezuelan Andes.

Permian to Early Triassic deformation was widespread and, in some cases, e.g., Sierra de Perijá and Cordillera Oriental, was

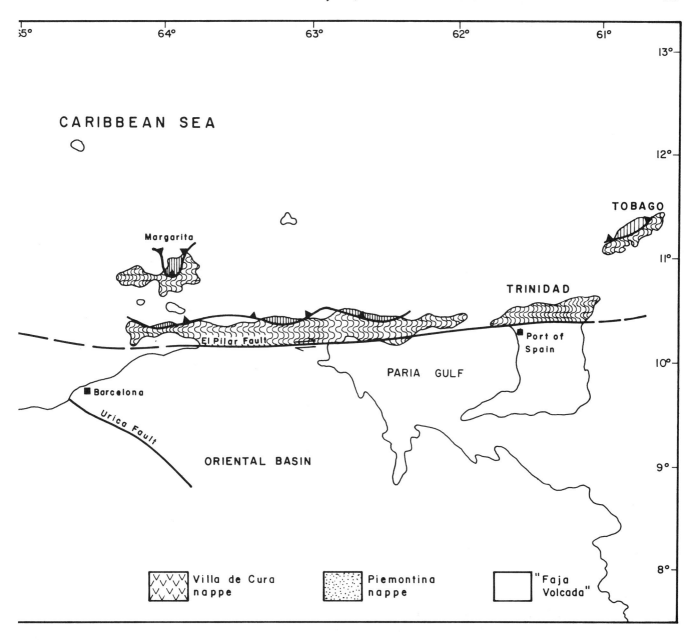

accompanied by intrusive activity (180 Ma). This deformation was followed by a long time span characterized by extensive erosion and deposition of widespread continental deposits in Early Jurassic time, accompanied in some areas by silicic and locally mafic volcanic activity.

The tectonic style developed during the Paleozoic reveals mostly the action of compressional forces, whereas the subsequent Late Cretaceous–Paleocene tectonic deformation produced mainly titled blocks and broad folding. The Mesozoic–early Tertiary deformation in the Andes area was accompanied by granitoid intrusions mostly in the Cordillera Central (Colombia). In this mountain range, deformation was accompanied by widespread volcanism toward the end of the Tertiary and continuing into the Quaternary.

The southwestern part of the Caribbean region, along the coast of South America, differs considerably in crustal characteristics and complexity of tectonism from the Venezuelan and Colombian basins to the north. Due to these differences, the area to the south of the northernmost limits of the Aruba-Curaçao ridge, and roughly following the trace of the continental slope farther to the east, has been named the Venezuelan Borderlands. It extends from the Guajira Peninsula in the west to the Orinoco River Delta in the east.

In the continental section of the margin, from Trinidad in the east toward Guajira Peninsula and the Santa Marta massif in the west, the Caribbean mountain system is formed by a complex section of tectonically superposed units that have been regionally overthrusted repeatedly to the south. This contrasts with the northward fault deformation observed from seismic profiles in the continental margin to the north.

In the Caribbean mountain system, which includes the Goajira Peninsula and Netherlands Antilles, the Mesozoic deformation was entirely different from that of the Andes, and resulted in an Alpine-type mountain range characterized by strong metamorphism, large allochthonous blocks and nappes with a complex structure, and a mixture of rocks of volcanic and sedimentary origin, including slices of oceanic crust. Undoubtedly, it resulted from long-term interactions of oceanic and continental crusts after the primeval Caribbean had formed, probably during Late Triassic–Early Jurassic time.

This chapter deals only with the broad characteristics of the Caribbean mountain system. For geological and geophysical papers on nearby areas, the reader is referred to Bonini and others (1984).

THE CARIBBEAN MOUNTAIN SYSTEM

The Caribbean mountain system, an orographic complex on the northern coastal region of South America, forms an elongated east-west–trending belt of high topography that extends from the Sierra Nevada de Santa Marta and Guajira Peninsula in Colombia, eastward to the island of Tobago and the Northern Range of Trinidad. Its submerged portion forms a series of islands in the southern Caribbean Sea. Its land portion is best exposed in north-central Venezuela, in the ranges known as the Cordillera de la Costa and Serranía del Interior. These ranges are separated on the west from the Venezuelan Andes by the Barquisimeto depression or structural trough. Their continuation to the east is interrupted by Barcelona Bay, which separates them from the ranges of the Araya and Paria Peninsulas, which in turn, are separated from the Northern Range of Trinidad by the Paria Gulf (Fig. 1).

The Caribbean mountain system represents a polyphase series of tectonic units formed by the superposition of several nappes, some of which crop out discontinuously, a fact that has complicated the regional tectonic interpretation. Part of the problem is due to the presence of large and younger transcurrent faults that have caused the lateral displacement of parts of the nappes.

A synthesis of the tectonics of the western part of the mountain system was presented by Menéndez (1967), based mostly on detailed work by Princeton University students under the direction of the late H. H. Hess. Since then, the quantity of geological studies has been overwhelming and the literature is voluminous. Another short synthesis was presented later by Butterlin (1977), and a recent detailed description, tectonic interpretation, and complete list of references has been written by Bellizzia (1989). The summary that follows is based on those publications and therefore does not make specific reference to the detailed studies.

The recognized nappes are, from north to south: (1) Margarita coastal ophiolite nappe, (2) Cordillera de la Costa nappe, (3) Caucagua–El Tinaco nappe, (4) Loma de Hierro–Paracotos nappe, (5) Villa de Cura nappe, and (6) Piemontina nappe. Although their ages vary considerably, they are described here in this same geographic order (Fig. 2).

Margarita coastal ophiolite nappe

This unit, named after Margarita Island, is represented by a narrow belt along the Caribbean coasts of Colombia and Venezuela. It crops out in the Guajira Peninsula to the east, the northern part of the Cordillera de la Costa, the Araya-Paria Peninsulas, and Margarita Island. The predominant rock types are metavolcanics, whose grade of metamorphism varies from one area to another, associated with minor sedimentary rocks. In the Goajira and Paraguaná Peninsulas there are suites of ultramafic rocks that may also belong to the same episode of tectonic emplacement.

In the Cordillera de la Costa, this nappe can be identified in discontinuous but extensive outcrops from the Yaracuy River eastward to Cabo Codera (Fig. 2). The rock types vary from low-grade greenschists to amphibolites, garnet amphibolites, and eclogites. Associated with them are olistoliths of ultramafic rocks.

Farther to the east, rocks of this nappe along the north coast of the Araya-Paria Peninsulas include mainly greenschists with occasional amphibolites and tectonically emplaced serpentinite bodies.

On Margarita Island the sequence includes a variety of rocks, some of which represent a higher-grade metamorphism. These include amphibolitic gneisses, metabasalts, metagabbros, peridotites, serpentinites, and eclogites, associated with minor cherts and metamorphosed limestones.

Cordillera de la Costa nappe

This nappe, together with the Caucagua–El Tinaco nappe, represents materials that originated when the South American paleomargin was sliced. The Cordillera de la Costa nappe constitutes approximately 75 percent of the Caribbean mountain system. Its western and central parts extend from the Caribbean coast south to La Victoria fault. To the east, it forms the Araya-Paria Peninsulas, part of Margarita Island, and the Northern Range of Trinidad. The eastern portion is bounded on the south by El Pilar fault.

The major geologic units in this belt are a pre-Mesozoic basement (Sebastopol complex) unconformably covered by a thick sequence of Jurassic of Lower Cretaceous metasedimentary rocks (Caracas Group) with some intercalations of metamorphosed mafic igneous rocks, and some large granitic intrusions.

The Sebastopol complex, which consists mainly of metagranite, forms the nucleus of the tectonic belt, and its outcrops are confined to a small area west of Caracas. However, gneissic-granitic rocks between Lake Valencia and Puerto Cabello could also belong to this complex.

In the east-central part of the Cordillera de la Costa, the basal sequence of the Caracas Group consists of quartzofeldspathic mica schists that in places grade laterally into augen gneisses. Another sequence of calcareous and graphitic low-grade schists with intercalations of crystalline limestones lies conformably over this.

In the eastern portion, along the Araya-Paria Peninsulas, the stratigraphic sequence is different, although some rocks are similar to the Caracas Group. At the base are mainly quartz-mica schists and graphitic phyllites, with some quartzite and marble intercalations. These are overlain by calcareous-graphitic mica schists and limestones. The sequence is quite variable, and different stratigraphic nomenclatures have been used in various parts of the region. Rocks similar to the lower part of the Caracas Group crop out in the Araya Peninsula and Margarita Island (Juan Griego Group).

In the Northern Range of Trinidad, the rock sequence is essentially the same as in the Paria Peninsula, with the exception of volcanic and volcaniclastic rocks at Sans Souci.

Granite bodies of variable size are found throughout the length of this tectonic belt, and there are considerable discrepancies in age determinations; some of the main granites are intrusive-magmatic; their emplacement ages range from Late Cretaceous to early Tertiary.

The Caucagua–El Tinaco nappe

The Caucagua–El Tinaco nappe, or tectonic belt, is located to the south of the Cordillera de la Costa and is separated from it by La Victoria fault. It extends almost continuously from the Barquisimeto trough eastward to Barlovento. Its southern boundary is defined by the Santa Rosa fault (Fig. 2). It was originally defined in the Caucagua–El Tinaco area, but taking into consideration the geologic characteristics of its westernmost part, Bellizzia and Rodríguez (1976) designated it the Caucagua–El Tinaco–Yumare–Siquisique nappe.

The most complete section of this feature is found in the Tinaco–Tinaquillo–El Pao area. It includes: (1) a Paleozoic or older basement (El Tinaco complex), (2) a mafic-ultramafic complex (Tiñaquillo peridotites), and (3) a discordant volcanic sedimentary sequence on top of Albian-Cenomanian sedimentary formations. Near the village of Siquisique it includes a dismembered ophiolitic unit.

The El Tinaco complex covers 800 km^2 in the north-central part of the state of Cojedes in Venezuela. Two metasedimentary units are recognized: a gneiss intruded by trondhjemite plutons surrounded by a wide belt of injection gneisses (migmatites), and a sequence of pelitic schists. The presence of small bodies of hornblendites is common, hornblendic diorites, and hornblendic basalt dikes intrude the complex. The gneiss represents a sedimentary sequence with minor amounts of volcanic material metamorphosed to the almandine-amphibolite facies. Its supracortical origin is shown clearly by the presence of concordant thin layers of marble and metaconglomerates.

The sequence of greenschist-facies schists and schistose conglomerates that transitionally overlies the gneiss is confined to the northern part of the area. These were derived from arkosic sediments and tuffaceous pelites or mafic tuffs.

Ages of 112 ± 3 Ma and 117 ± 3 Ma (K/Ar) were determined in the biotite and hornblende of the El Tinaco complex, respectively. These Early Cretaceous isotopic ages could represent a thermal event and not the age of the early metamorphism on these rocks.

The oldest rocks that lie unconformably on the El Tinaco complex belong to the Albian; therefore, a pre-Albian age, probably Paleozoic, is usually assigned on the basis of regional correlations.

The volcanic-sedimentary sequence over the El Tinaco complex varies considerably in stratigraphy and degree of deformation from one area to another, and it is difficult to establish proper age and lithologic correlations. In the area north of El Pao, the sequence includes detrital sedimentary rock covered by volcanic breccias, pillow basalts, and diabases, interlayered with cherts and limestones, indicating a submarine origin. In some localities the limestones have been dated as Albian. Toward the east the sequence becomes metamorphosed to greenschist facies.

The previous description allows us to postulate the existence of two megacycles in the volcanic-sedimentary cover: (1) A detrital sequence, deposited in a neritic environment, is formed by arkosic sandstones, coarse quartz, or calcareous conglomerates with abundant fragments of the El Tinaco complex, bioclastic limestones with some benthonic foraminifera, and fine calcareous horizons and chert. The benthonic fauna corresponds to the upper Albian to middle Albian interval. (2) An upper pelagic sequence representing deeper-water environments concordantly overlies the Albian rocks.

An ultramafic complex located north of the town of Tinaquillo appears to be an east-west–oriented sill. It is truncated to the north and to the southwest by a thrust that separates it from low-grade metamorphic schists. To the south, the contact is apparently concordant on the pre-Mesozoic basement of El Tinaco. The ultramafic rocks are less serpentinized than other alpine peridotites of the Caribbean mountain system; their metamorphic fabric is clearly visible, and they represent high-temperature intrusions. This Tinaquillo peridotite is a dunite with thin layers of pyroxenites and amphibolites. Included with the peridotites are tabular masses of hypersthese gabbro.

An area of ophiolitic rocks is near the town of Siquisique. These rocks occur as tectonic slices and include serpentinized dunites, troctolites, gabbros, and pillow basalts. Associated radiolarites have been dated as Jurassic.

Loma de Hierro–Paracotos nappe

This nappe forms a narrow zone about 200 km long, limited by the Santa Rosa fault on the north and the Agua Fría fault on the south (Fig. 2). It is formed mainly of Maastrichtian to Paleocene metasediments that rest conformably on the Loma de Hierro ophiolitic complex. This complex includes a large serpentinite-harzburgite at Loma de Hierro, associated with layered gabbros. Throughout the belt there are smaller serpentinite units, other large mafic intrusions, volcanic breccias, extensive pillow basalts, and associated radiolarian cherts.

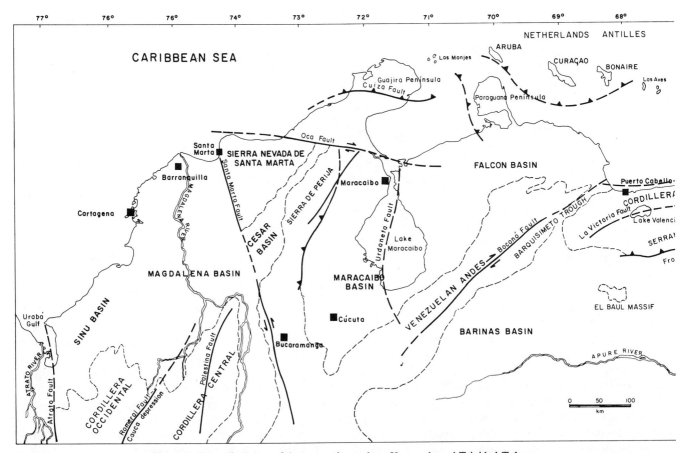

Figure 2. Generalized map of the nappes in northern Venezuela and Trinidad-Tobago.

The Villa de Cura nappe

This tectonic belt is composed of a thick (more than 5,000 m) sequence of metavolcanic rocks and minor intercalations of metasedimentary layers. This is an ophiolitic assemblage that includes mafic lavas (spilitic pillow lavas), metatuff, keratophyres and intercalated meta-cherts, chlorite schists, and phyllites. The Villa de Cura Group covers an elongate area approximately 250 km by 28 km (maximum width). On the north, it is separated from the Caucagua–El Tinaco nappe by the Paracots belt. On the south, this nappe is bound by the Cantagallo thrust fault, along which it is in contact with Upper Cretaceous and lower Tertiary sedimentary rocks of the mountain front (Piemontina belt).

In the southern part of the tectonic belt, between the La Puerta and Cantagallo faults, another thick sequence of metavolcanic rocks (Tiara volcanics) overlies the Villa de Cura Group. It is formed by mafic volcanic rocks associated with serpentinites and gabbros of very low metamorphic grade. Metatuffs from this sequence were dated as Albian (100 ± 10 Ma), which is the upper limit for metamorphism of the Villa de Cura Group.

The Villa de Cura nappe is a fully allochthonous block that probably originated many kilometers north of its present position as part of an island arc and was tectonically emplaced during Late Cretaceous to Paleocene time.

Piemontina nappe

This nappe is bound on the north by the Cantagallo and other faults, and on the south by a series of closely spaced north-dipping thrust faults. In contrast with the other tectonic belts, it consists only of marine sedimentary rocks that range in age from Late Cretaceous to early Eocene. The oldest rocks that crop out in the belt are Cenomanian to Turonian shales and limestones (250 to 500 m thick), followed by a thick (as much as 2,000 m) turbiditic flysch of Coniacian age. This sequence, in turn, is covered by Campanian-Maastrichtian siliceous shales and limestones (as much as 1,500 m thick), followed by another thick flysch (as much as 2,000 m) of Maastrichtian to early Eocene age. The entire sequence is thrust over a narrow zone of overturned Tertiary marine rocks (the "Faja Volcada") at the northern edge of the Guárico sedimentary basin (Fig. 1).

Tectonic history

The major tectonic events that resulted in the complex geology of the Caribbean mountain system, as summarized by Stephan and others (1980), began during Late Jurassic to Early Cretaceous time with the suturing of an oceanic area of Lower Jurassic rocks, located to the north of the South American craton

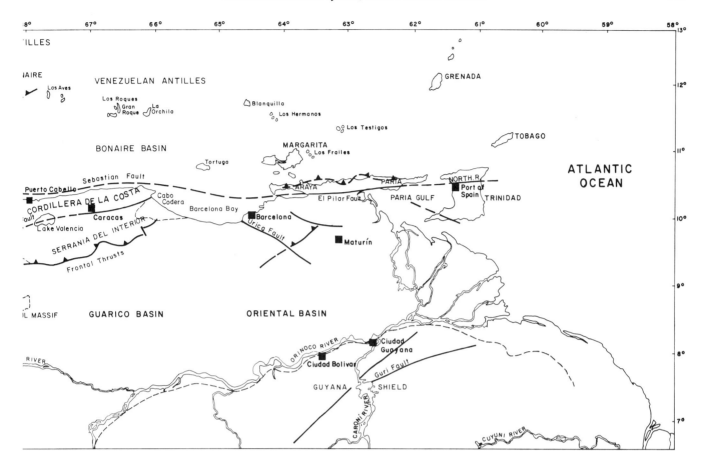

(Guyana shield). This compressive episode produced the first thrust of ophiolitic rocks toward the south (Siquisique ophiolites). Substantial paleogeographic change took place during Aptian-Albian time; it was related to the opening of the South Atlantic Ocean, and was accompanied by major magmatic events. Extensive mafic volcanism occurred from the end of the Albian to the Turonian, at the same time that the basins of the Caribbean originated. The new continental margin was later affected by three important compressive phases during the Senonian, Paleocene, and Eocene, which resulted in large nappes being displaced toward the south and partly superimposed on each other. The Barquisimeto trough corresponds to the border between the overthrust nappes and the Andean mountain ranges.

SOUTH CARIBBEAN ISLAND CHAIN

The South Caribbean island chain includes, from west to east: the Los Monjes archipelago, the Netherlands Antilles, and the rest of the Venezuelan Antilles. These islands lie over several wide platforms developed in a northwest direction and separated from each other by depressions bounded by northwest-striking faults. The Netherlands Antilles and the smaller Venezuelan Antilles are genetically related to each other; the islands are made of volcanic and sedimentary Early Cretaceous to early Tertiary metamorphic rocks, intruded by silicic to intermediate batholiths

and by silicic to mafic dikes and sills. Tertiary to Recent sedimentary rocks cover these batholiths.

The section is best exposed in the Netherlands Antilles, especially on Curaçao (Fig. 3). Here, an Early Cretaceous (Hauterivian) to early Paleocene volcanic-sedimentary sequence underlies Eocene carbonate and clastic deposits (Seroe di Cueba Formation) that are overlain by Miocene to Quaternary limestones. The volcanic-sedimentary sequence includes three units. The lower one contains 1,000 m of Early Cretaceous (118 and 125 Ma, K-Ar) basaltic pillow lavas with a few ultramafic rocks (Curaçao Lava Formation). Trace-element distribution places these basalts in the group of abyssal floor tholeiites. This unit is overlain by a second one, which is essentially sedimentary and contains pelagic silicic rocks grading into very coarse clastics (Knip Group). Minor basaltic flows and andesitic tuffs appear in the lower and upper parts of the unit, respectively. Danian turbiditic volcaniclastic sediments of the third unit (Midden Curaçao Formation) include conglomerates, sandstones, siltstones, and lutites, and cover the Knip Group. Exotic boulders of sialic nature found in the Midden Curaçao Formation suggest the proximity of the South American continent. Late Cretaceous dioritic batholiths intrude the Curaçao Lava Formation, and intermediate sills and dikes intrude the Knip Group and the Midden Curaçao Formation. The whole set is metamorphosed to zeolite facies.

The core of Aruba is made up of a late Senonian tonalitic

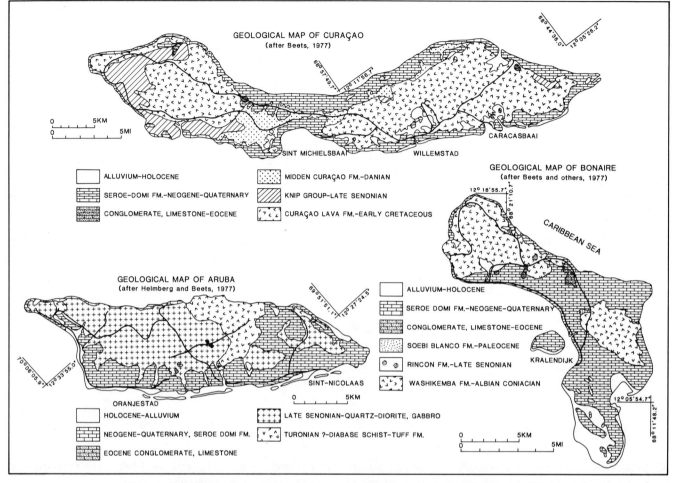

Figure 3. Simplified geologic maps of the Netherlands Antilles (after Helmers and Beets, 1977).

batholith that intrudes the Diabase Schist Formation, which in turn, is composed of pillow basalts and diabase, volcaniclastic conglomerates, sandstones, tuffs and scarce pelagic cherts, and cherty limestones. This sequence is similar to the Curaçao Lava Formation, and the basalts are also low-K abyssal tholeiites.

On Bonaire, the Cretaceous-Paleocene column includes three well-defined lithologic units. The older one is a thick Early Cretaceous to Santonian sequence consisting of andesites, dacites and their related pyroclastics, basalts, diabases, and cherty limestones (Washikemba Formation). In contrast to Aruba and Curaçao, volcanics of this formation are island-arc–type tholeiites. Shallow-water marine sediments of the second unit (Roncón Formation) overlie the volcanic unit with fault contact. Fluviatile conglomerates and lutites of the third unit (Soebi Blanco Formation) cover the Rincón deposits. The presence of pebbles from the Washikemba and Rincón Formations indicate a young age, probably Eocene, for the Soebi Blanco Formation. Similar to the Midden Curaçao Formation, the abundant "foreign" pebbles suggest a sialic source for these sediments, probably derived from the South American continent. The Soebi Blanco Formation is covered unconformably by middle Eocene limestones and marls

that can be correlated with the Seroe di Cueba Formation of Curaçao.

From early Neogene time onward, the Netherlands Antilles gradually emerged, and the resulting depositional record consists of emergent reef talus and several elevated limestone terraces.

In the Venezuelan Antilles (Fig. 1) the exposed area above sea level is small and the section is not complete. The older rocks crop out in La Orchila and consist of chlorite schists, phyllites, amphibole and hornblende gneisses, and epidote gneisses and schists. A few ultramafic bodies of serpentinite and peridotite crop out at the center of the island. Metamorphism is in a transitional facies between greenschist and amphibolite, similar to the metamorphic grade found in the Caribbean Coast Range of Venezuela. Diabases, granites, granodiorites, and pegmatitic and aplitic dikes intrude the metamorphic rocks and are also metamorphosed to chlorite and greenschist facies.

Los Monjes islands consist of orthoamphibolite (116 to 114 Ma, K-Ar) that represent metamorphosed basalt, dolerite or gabbro, with low potassium content. Small bodies of diorite and hornblendic-quartz gabbro crop out in the southern part of the largest island, Monjes del Norte. In the Gran Roque, mafic igneous rocks (meta-diabase and meta-lamprophyre) are intruded by latest Cretaceous (66 to 71 ± 6 Ma, K-Ar) quartz-dioritic irregular bodies, and dikes. Numerous younger pegmatitic and aplitic dikes intrude the quartz diorites.

La Blanquilla Island is almost completely formed by a Late Cretaceous (81 to 64 Ma, K-Ar) batholith, the Garantón Trondhjemite. To the north, it grades to tonalite and is intruded by pegmatitic veins and dikes.

Hornblende gneisses, biotite-epidote schists, amphibolites, and epidosites, intruded by pegmatitic dikes (67 to 71 Ma, K-Ar), crop out on the Los Hermanos islands, which are 15 km southeast of La Blanquilla. These rocks may represent the host rock for the Garantón Trondhjemite.

Tholeiitic basalts and their intrusive equivalents crop out on Los Frailes, whereas Los Testigos consists of a meta-andesitic volcanic complex intruded by a metagranitic pluton (44 to 47 Ma, K-Ar). The volcanic rocks are correlated with the volcanic rocks of Los Frailes (66 Ma, K-Ar).

Finally, at the Las Aves islands, which have a maximum height of 5 m above sea level, a volcanic basement of unknown age is completely covered by Quaternary limestones. Modern beach deposits and coral terraces found several meters above sea level at La Blanquilla, Los Roques, La Orchila, and Los Testigos are evidence for recent uplift of these islands.

REFERENCES CITED

Beets, D. J., 1977, Cretaceous and early Tertiary of Curaçao, *in* Guide to geological excursions on Curaçao, Bonaire, and Aruba: 8th Caribbean Geological Conference, Document series no. 2, p. 7–17.

Beets, D. J., MacGillarry, H. J., and Klaver, G., 1977, Cretaceous and early Tertiary of Bonaire, *in* Guide to geological excursions on Curaçao, Bonaire, and Aruba: 8th Caribbean Geological Conference, Document series no. 2, p. 18–28.

Bellizzia, A., 1989, Sistema Montañoso del Cabribe, una cordillera alóctona en la parte norte de América del Sur: Caracas, VI Congreso Geológico Venezolano, Memorias, (in press).

Bellizzia, A., and Rodríguez, D. G., 1976, Geologia del Estado Yaracuy, *in* IV Congreso Geológico Venezolano, Memorias, v. VI: p. 3317–3415.

Bellizzia, A., Pimentel de Bellizzia, N., and Muñoz, M. I., 1981, Geology and tectonics of northern South America: Venezuela, Ministerio de Energía y Minas Geodynamic Investigations in Venezuela, 140 p.

Bonini, W. E., Hargraves, R. B., and Shagam, R., eds., 1984, The Caribbean–South American plate boundary and regional tectonics: Geological Society of America Memoir 162, 421 p.

Butterlin, J., 1977, Geologic structure de la région des Caraïbes (Mexique–Amerique Central–Antilles–Cordillere Caraiibe): Paris, Masson, 259 p.

Case, J. E., Holcombe, T. L., and Martin, R. G., 1984, Map of tectonic provinces in the Caribbean region, *in* Bonini, W. E., Hargraves, R. B., and Shagam, R., eds., The Caribbean–South American plate boundaries and regional tectonics: Geological Society of America Memoir 162, p. 1–30.

González de Juana, C., Iturralde de Arozena, J. M., and Picard Cadillat, X., 1980, Geología de Venezuela y sus cuencas petrolíferas: Caracas, Ediciones Foninves, 2 tomos, 1031 p.

Helmers, H., and Beets, D. J., 1977, Cretaceous of Aruba, *in* Guide to geological excursions on Curaçao, Bonaire and Aruba: 8th Caribbean Geological Conference, Document series no. 2, p. 29–35.

Martín F., C., 1978, Mapa tectónico, Norte de América del Sur: Venezuela, Ministerio de Energia y Minas, scale 1:2,500,000.

Menéndez, A., 1967, Tectonics of the central part of the western Caribbean mountains, Venezuela, *in* Proceedings, International Conference on Tropical Oceanography: Miami, Florida, University of Miami Studies in Tropical Oceanography, no. 5, p. 103–130.

Restrepo, J. J., and Toussaint, J. F., 1988, Terranes and continental accretion in the Colombia Andes: Episodes, v. 11, no. 3, p. 189–193.

Stephan, J. F., Beck, C., Bellizzia, A., and Blanchet, R., 1980, La Chaine Caraibe du Pacifique à l'Atlantique: 26th Geological International Congress, Résumés C.t., p. 38–59.

MANUSCRIPT ACCEPTED BY THE SOCIETY AUGUST 3, 1989

The Geology of North America
Vol. H, The Caribbean region
The Geological Society of America, 1990

Chapter 7

Geology of the northern Andes; An overview

J. E. Case
U.S. Geological Survey, MS 989, 345 Middlefield Road, Menlo Park, California 94025
Reginald Shagam
Rider College, P.O. Box 6400, Lawrenceville, New Jersey 08648
Robert F. Giegengack
Department of Geology, University of Pennsylvania, Philadelphia, Pennsylvania 19104-6316

INTRODUCTION

The northern Andes in Colombia form three great ranges, the Cordilleras Oriental, Central, and Occidental (Fig. 1). Other ranges include the Sierra Nevada de Santa Marta, Guajira Peninsular ranges, and physiographic extensions of the Cordillera Oriental northeast into Venezuela, including the Sierra de Perijá and the Cordillera de Mérida (Venezuelan Andes). The present physiographic expression is the result of Tertiary (Neogene) uplift. The Cordillera Occidental is underlain by deformed oceanic crust, perhaps allochthonous as judged from the low metamorphic grade of Mesozoic rocks in the north (see chapter by Escalante, this volume; Duque-Caro, 1990); most of the Cordillera Central, Cordillera Oriental, Sierra de Perijá, and Cordillera de Mérida are underlain by continental crust. The Sierra Nevada de Santa Marta and ranges on the Guajira Peninsula are probably underlain by both types of crust, and oceanic segments on the north sides are probably allochthonous. In the following summary of the regional geology, the main mountain ranges will be described from east to west. The Sierra Nevada de Santa Marta, Guajira ranges, and sedimentary basins will be discussed last. Some of the generalized descriptions are modified from Case and others (1984). Geologic maps by Bellizzia and others (1976), Arango C. and others (1976), Martín F. (1978), Case and Holcombe (1980), Etayo-Serna and others (1983, 1986), and Case and others (1984) provide a regional framework for this summary. Bürgl (1961, 1973), Irving (1975), Etayo-Serna and others (1983, 1986) and González and others (1988) provided very useful syntheses of the pre-1960 to 1970 literature for Colombian geology, and González de Juana and others (1980) provided some data for Venezuelan geology. A most helpful synthesis for the region was prepared by Thery (1982). Detailed lithologic-stratigraphic columns for various parts of the region, especially offshore, are shown on Plate 4 (this volume). Shagam and others (1989) have prepared a comprehensive unpublished manuscript

on the geology of the northern Andes, which provides the background for much of this summary.

Shagam (1975) and Shagam and others (1989) recognized Precambrian to Paleozoic "core complexes" for several of the ranges where some of the unmetamorphosed sedimentary cover has been eroded. Abstracts from their descriptions are given here. Although the separate basement terranes in the ranges are somewhat similar, exposing granitic plutons and Barrovian metamorphic suites, significant differences exist for each core area and will be described briefly (Fig. 2). Shagam and others also recognized "orogenic cycles" in some ranges, and there is evidence for structural shortening of some terranes in the core complexes as a result of major thrusting. Although allochthony on a grand scale has not been shown, evidence for large transport is accumulating as detailed mapping is being done by recent (as of 1989) workers.

Intermontane and submontane basins, some of which are prolific producers of hydrocarbons, are described in a brief section of this chapter. Resources are summarized in chapters by Morris and others and Kesler and others (this volume). Pertinent gravity models and inferred crustal structure are shown on Plates 2 and 3 of this volume. Models for the tectonic evolution of the region are included in chapters by Pindell and Barrett, Morris and others, and Mann and others (this volume). Here we provide only a brief discussion of structure and tectonic evolution.

CORDILLERA DE MERIDA

This complex polydeformed and polycomponent structural block (Fig. 3) is characterized by great late Tertiary vertical uplift and a high level of seismicity. The basement includes Precambrian(?) and Paleozoic metamorphic and igneous rocks, which are overlain by Paleozoic sedimentary rocks, by Mesozoic red beds, marine clastic and carbonate strata, and by varying thicknesses of Tertiary marine and continental clastic deposits (Fig. 3). The aggregate thickness of Phanerozoic deposits is greater than

Case, J. E., Shagam, R., and Giegengack, R. F., 1990, Geology of the northern Andes; An overview, *in* Dengo, G., and Case, J. E., eds., The Caribbean region: Boulder, Colorado, Geological Society of America, The Geology of North America, v. H.

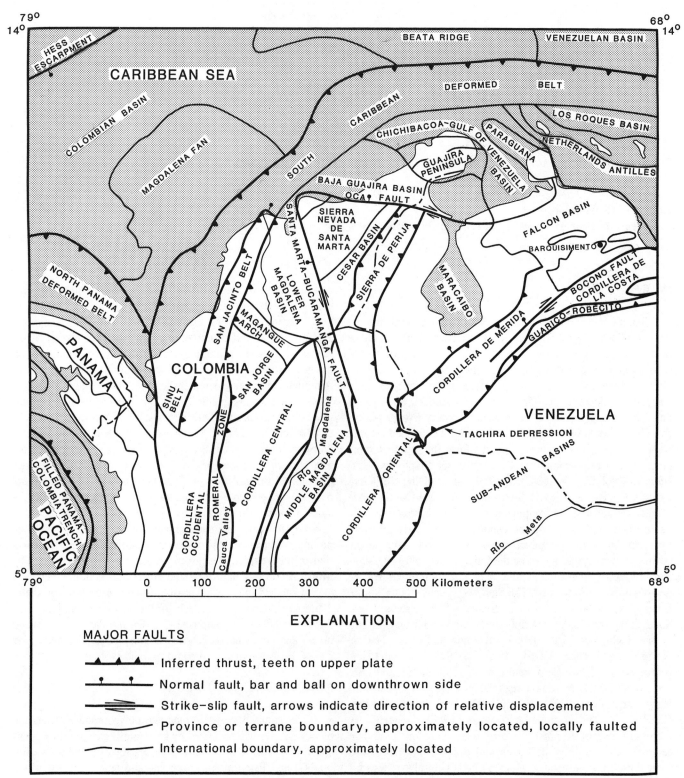

Figure 1. Index map showing major geologic provinces or terranes in the northern Andes and vicinity, simplified from Case and others (1984). In some areas, although province boundaries are shown, names have been deleted for simplicity (westernmost Colombia and Panamá, for example).

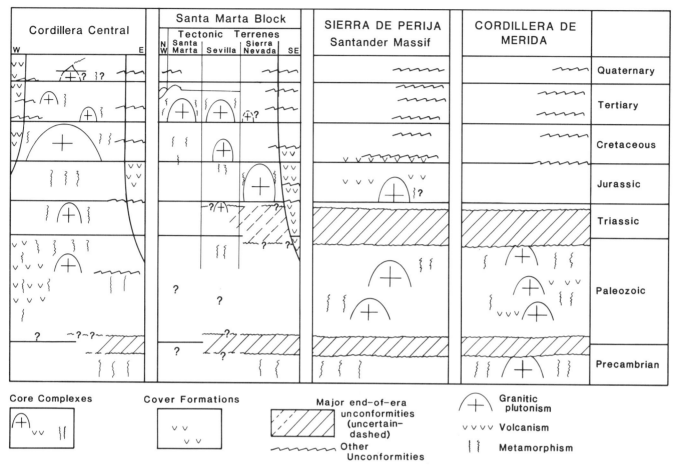

Figure 2. Summary of known or inferred "core" complexes in the northern Andes, from Shagam and others (1989).

10 km. The rocks were complexly deformed during numerous Phanerozoic intervals (summarized by Shagam, 1975; Shagam and others, 1989). Foliations of metamorphic rocks and folds of younger rocks trend generally northeast. The range is bisected by the active Boconó fault zone, which has experienced both right-lateral strike-slip and local vertical components of motion (Schubert, 1982; Giegengack and others, 1976; Giegengack, 1984). The flanking faults are thought to dip beneath the range. A simplified gravity model from the Sierra Nevada de Santa Marta across the Cordillera de Mérida, constructed by Kellogg and Bonini (1982), shows this characteristic of the flanking faults of the range (see Fig. v, Plate 2, this volume).

In the Cordillera de Mérida, the sedimentary rocks of the cover formations rest with marked nonconformity on the igneous-metamorphic complex. The youngest thermal event took place in Permian to Triassic time (Fig. 4). The sharp temporal separation of the igneous-metamorphic complexes from the cover formations becomes less distinct to the north and northwest (Figs. 2 and 4).

A geological controversy surrounds the interpretation of contacts: in older rocks of the Cordillera de Mérida, are they stratigraphic or do they represent metamorphic isograds? Early

workers viewed different metamorphic facies and unmetamorphosed rocks as superimposed time-rock units constituting a "vertical" stratigraphy of Precambrian to Permian age, and contacts of each time-rock unit were considered to be unconformities. Grauch (1971, 1972, 1975) identified gradation, structural conformity, and absence of evidence for hiatus between some metamorphic facies and suggested that the contacts were best viewed as isograds of no stratigraphic significance. Shagam (1972, 1975, 1977) extended this concept into a "horizontal" sequence of metamorphic facies and unmetamorphosed units concentrated in late Paleozoic (principally Pennsylvanian and Permian) time. In a review, Shagam and others (1989) concluded that despite clear evidence for the isograd nature of some contacts, the range of radiometric ages on granitic plutons indicates that on a large scale, some igneous-metamorphic associations must rest nonconformably on older associations of similar type.

A restoration by Shagam and others (1989) of the former extent of the Mucuchachi Formation (Fig. 4; Ms; marine flysch; Carboniferous to Devonian?) over areas currently exposing metamorphic rocks of amphibolite facies brings out a nearly circular array of metamorphic rock units showing the Permian to Triassic granite (G4) in a "bull's-eye," and successively lower-

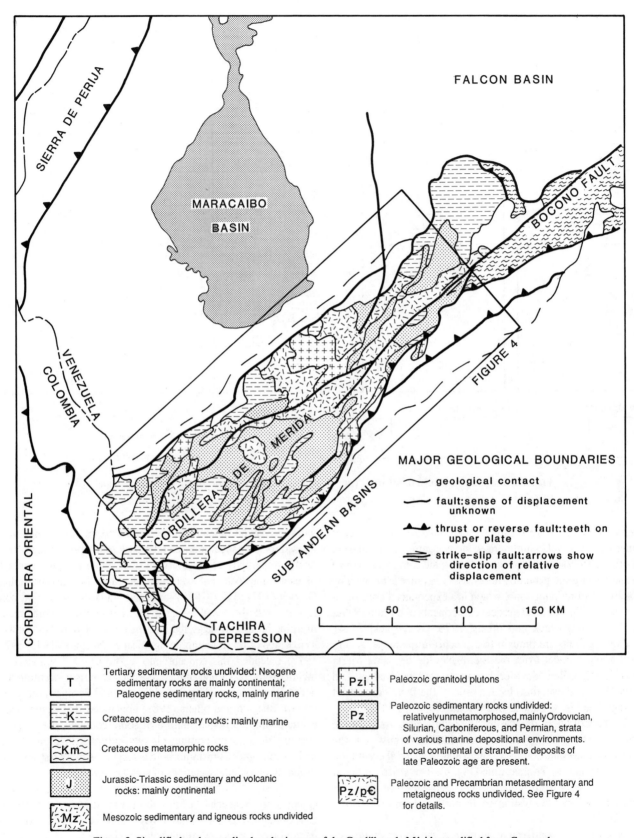

MAJOR GEOLOGICAL BOUNDARIES

〰 geological contact

— fault:sense of displacement unknown

▲▲ thrust or reverse fault:teeth on upper plate

⇒ strike-slip fault:arrows show direction of relative displacement

0   50   100   150 KM

| T | Tertiary sedimentary rocks undivided: Neogene sedimentary rocks are mainly continental; Paleogene sedimentary rocks, mainly marine |

| K | Cretaceous sedimentary rocks: mainly marine |

| Km | Cretaceous metamorphic rocks |

| J | Jurassic-Triassic sedimentary and volcanic rocks: mainly continental |

| Mz | Mesozoic sedimentary and igneous rocks undivided |

| Pzi | Paleozoic granitoid plutons |

| Pz | Paleozoic sedimentary rocks undivided: relatively unmetamorphosed, mainly Ordovician, Silurian, Carboniferous, and Permian, strata of various marine depositional environments. Local continental or strand-line deposits of late Paleozoic age are present. |

| Pz/pЄ | Paleozoic and Precambrian metasedimentary and metaigneous rocks undivided. See Figure 4 for details. |

Figure 3. Simplified and generalized geologic map of the Cordillera de Mérida; modified from Case and Holcombe (1980), Bellizzia and others (1976), and Martín F. (1978). Note that many contacts shown may be faults.

grade rocks outward in concentric belts (Fig. 4). A similar pattern is indicated by the geometry of a staurolite zone that is repeated by faulting into three separate belts (Fig. 4: St_1, St_2, St_3). Restoration of a small portion of a belt of greenschist (Tg), where it is shown trending north on the south side of the Boconó fault, is less certain.

Isotopic ages of granitoid rocks include events of emplacement in late Precambrian, late Cambrian to early Ordovician, Devonian, and Permian to early Triassic times that are summarized by Shagam and others (1989). The principal sources are the compilation by Martín Bellizzia (1968), and studies by Burkley (1976), Kohn and others (1984), and Cordani and others (1985).

The sedimentary cover of the Cordillera de Mérida includes Phanerozoic sedimentary rocks: Ordovician, Silurian, Carboniferous to Permian, Triassic(?), Jurassic, Cretaceous, Tertiary, and Quaternary strata. The Paleozoic strata are mostly marine, but do include Pennsylvanian/Permian red beds. Triassic(?) and Jurassic sedimentary and volcanic rocks are mainly continental. Cretaceous and Paleogene strata are mainly marine, and Neogene and Quaternary deposits are mostly continental. Representative stratigraphic-lithologic sections are shown on Plate 4 (this volume), and additional summary sections are shown in Figure 5. A crustal cross section (Kellogg and Bonini, 1982) is shown as Figure v, Plate 2 (this volume).

The Cordillera de Mérida is characterized by many northeast-trending faults, most of which are high-angle at shallow crustal levels. The Cordillera is separated from the Cordillera Oriental by the Táchira depression (Fig. 3), which is probably a zone of thrusting that decouples the Cordillera de Mérida from the Cordillera Oriental (Macellari, 1984). A Mesozoic-Cenozoic structural high (Salvador, 1986) trends north-northwest across the range. Perhaps the most thoroughly studied structure of the range is the seismically active Boconó fault, which probably has right-lateral displacement as well as local vertical components of displacement and associated small "pull-apart" basins (Schubert, 1982). However, differences of opinion as to the sense of displacement (whether dominantly dip strike or strike slip) remain to be resolved (see discussion by Giegengack and others, 1976; and Giegengack, 1984). Flanking faults are thought to be high-angle reverse faults or thrusts that dip toward the core of the range (e.g., see profile D of Stephan, 1985).

SIERRA DE PERIJA

The Sierra de Perijá is another range uplifted in the Neogene; it has many stratigraphic and structural similarities to the Cordillera de Mérida and Cordillera Oriental (Figs. 3, 5, 6, and 7). Most structural trends are northeast. Precambrian(?) and Paleozoic metamorphic and igneous rocks are only sparsely exposed, mainly on the eastern flank of the range. Paleozoic marine and continental(?) strata are exposed in isolated localities on both the eastern and western flanks of the Sierra. Paleozoic and Mesozoic red beds are exposed along the axis of the range. The Mesozoic red beds were deposited in NNE-trending grabens

(Maze, 1984). Jurassic red beds and Cretaceous marine strata constitute most of the exposures at high elevations. At least five or six episodes of tectonic activity or uplift during Paleozoic to post-Miocene time have been recognized. The range is still seismically active (Plate 10, this volume). Paleomagnetic data on Jurassic rocks suggest different patterns of movement from those of the Cordillera de Mérida (Maze and Hargraves, 1984). Crust is continental, and depth to Moho is about 30 to 35 km (Plate 3, this volume).

Evidence for a core complex in the Sierra de Perijá is less compelling than for the Cordillera de Mérida. Shagam (1975) suggested that there may have been failure to distinguish between metamorphic isograds and stratigraphic contacts as in the Cordillera de Mérida. Sillimanitic schists and interbedded massive quartzites of the Paleozoic sequence could be correlative with calcareous shales and massive quartzites in the basal part of the Devonian section. Hea and Whitman (1960) described greenschist metamorphism in Devonian rocks.

Isotopic ages on crystalline rocks have been reported by Espejo and others (1980) and Dasch (1982) (summarized in tables by Shagam and others [1989]). Ages of about 400, 385, 380, 334, 310, 225, 275, 180, 167, and 168 Ma (Fig. 5) were reported for various rock units by several isotopic methods.

Shagam and others (1989) have summarized contrasting views on the evolution of the Sierra de Perijá and prefer the following explanation. An early orogenic cycle of Cambrian to Ordovician age formed greenschists that grade eastward into schists of the Perijá Formation (amphibolite facies); the last granites of that orogenic cycle are regarded as Silurian in age. The early Paleozoic orogen is overlain by rocks of a late Paleozoic cycle that did not progress to stages of regional metamorphism and plutonism, perhaps because of inadequate thickness of sediment. Structural shortening has brought into close proximity a continuous rock sequence covering most of Devonian to Permian time in Venezuela and a thinner sequence with some pronounced hiatuses in Colombia, and has placed the Paleozoic section over the Jurassic to Cretaceous sequence in the central and northwest areas of the range. Kellogg and Bonini (1982) have constructed balanced cross sections across the Sierra de Perijá in which they have interpreted the range to have been uplifted along a low-angle thrust that extends to midcrustal levels.

Devonian rocks, about 2,200 to 3,800 m thick, include quartzose and ferruginous graywacke, micaceous quartzites, limonitic shales, and sandy siltstones (Miller, 1962; Etayo-Serna and others, 1983). The strata evidently thicken eastward. Carboniferous to Permian rocks, about 800 to 1,500 m thick, include calcareous siltstone, arkosic sandstone, dark sandstones and shales, fossiliferous limestone, and local red beds (Bowen, 1972; Etayo-Serna and others, 1983). Marine fossils occur in Devonian, Carboniferous, and Permian strata.

Triassic(?) and Jurassic red beds and volcanic rocks, ranging from about 1,000 to 3,500 m thick, include conglomerates, sandstones, siltstones, and volcanic rocks of mafic and felsic composition (Fig. 5; Maze, 1984; Etayo-Serna and others, 1983; Kellogg,

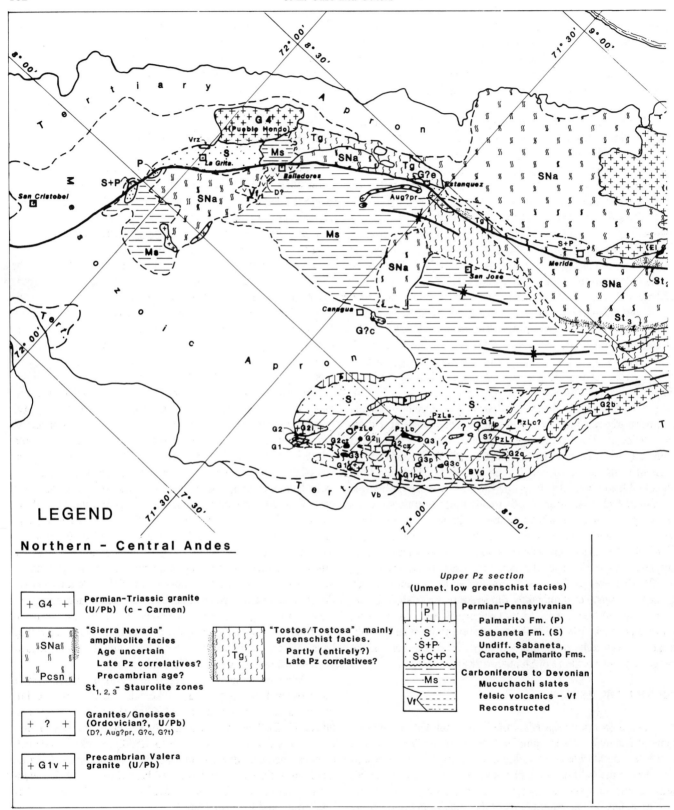

Figure 4. Schematic interpretive map to illustrate problems of stratigraphy and correlation of thermal events in the pre-Triassic igneous and metamorphic rocks of the Cordillera de Mérida. The restoration is mainly north of an imaginary line oriented northwest through the main granitic batholith. North-central Andes makes up most of the range except for a small area in the southern piedmont, which exposes narrow parallel belts of lower Paleozoic (PzL), and Precambrian (BVg) rocks. In the main or central

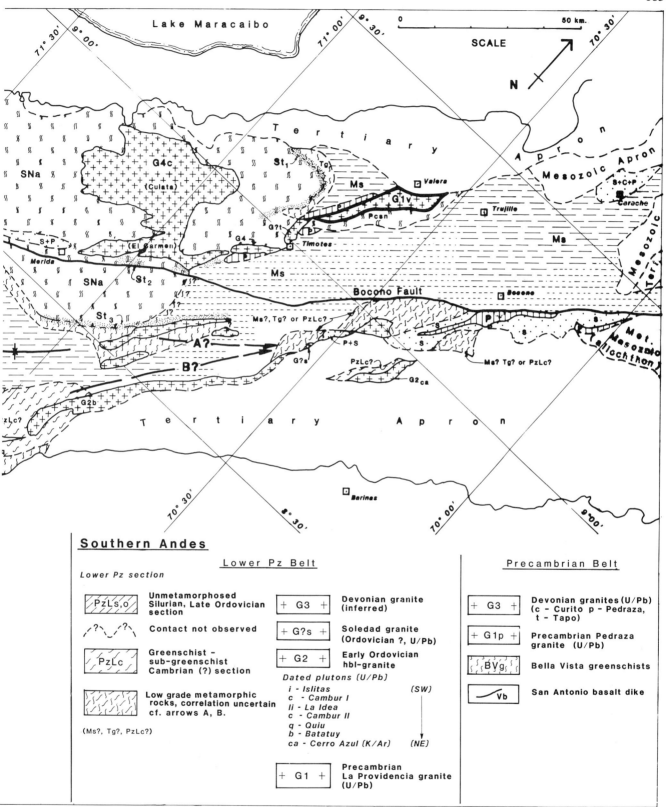

Paleozoic belt, unmetamorphosed fossiliferous Ordovician (PzLo) and Silurian (PzLs) rocks are separated from low-grade metamorphic rocks (PzLc?) to the northeast. Note similar metamorphic rocks of different ages (Tg and BVg) and the problem of correlation on lithological grounds as indicated by arrows A and B.

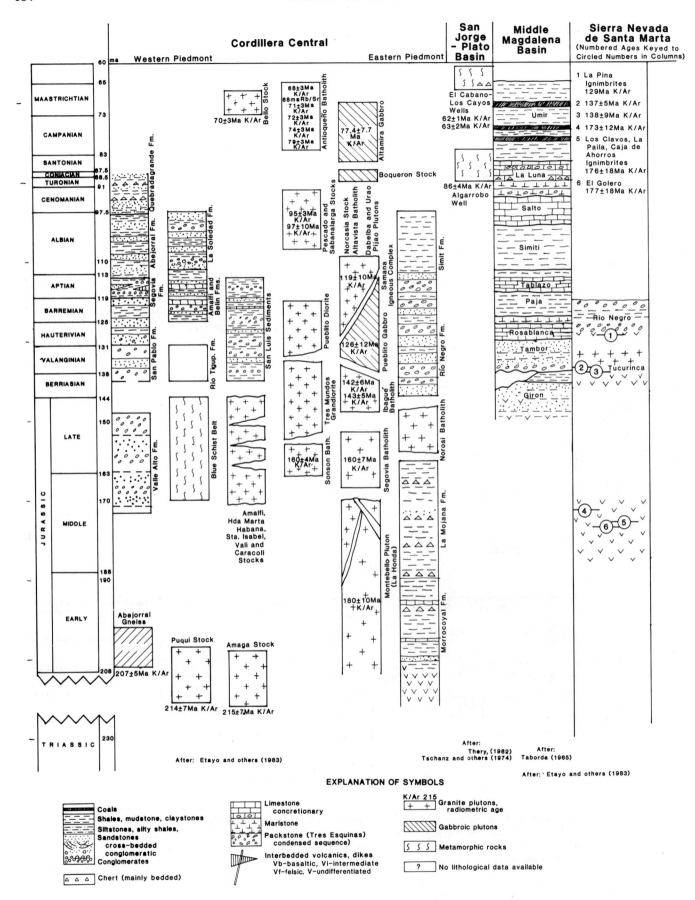

EXPLANATION OF SYMBOLS

Coals

Shales, mudstone, claystones

Siltstones, silty shales,

Sandstones
cross-bedded
conglomeratic

Conglomerates

Chert (mainly bedded)

Limestone
concretionary

Marlstone

Packstone (Tres Esquinas)
condensed sequence)

Interbedded volcanics, dikes
Vb-basaltic, Vi-intermediate
Vf-felsic, V-undifferentiated

K/Ar 215
Granite plutons,
radiometric age

Gabbroic plutons

Metamorphic rocks

? No lithological data available

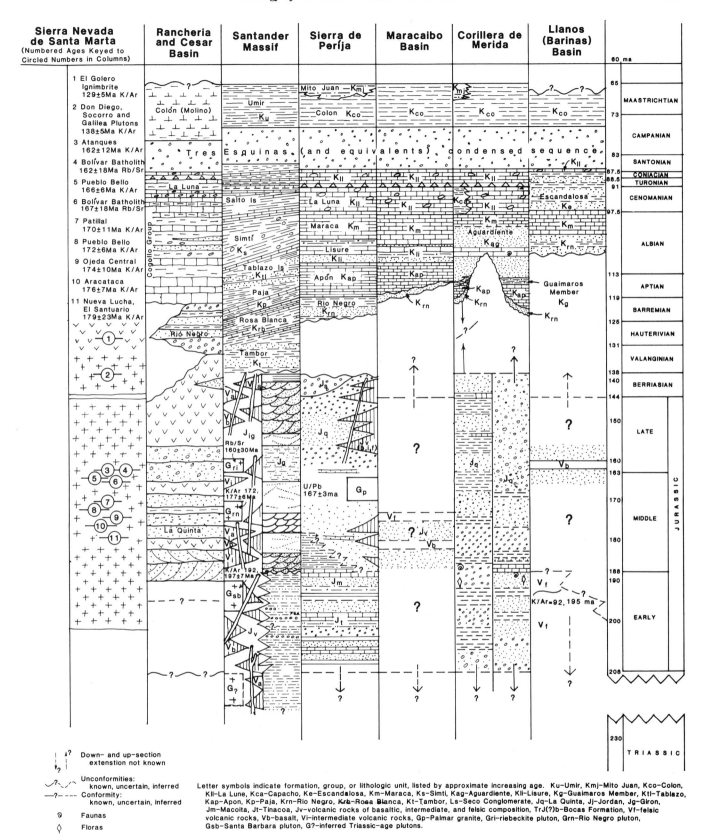

Figure 5. Representative Mesozoic stratigraphic-lithologic columns in the northern Andes (compiled by Shagam and others, 1989; sources of data listed by Shagam and others).

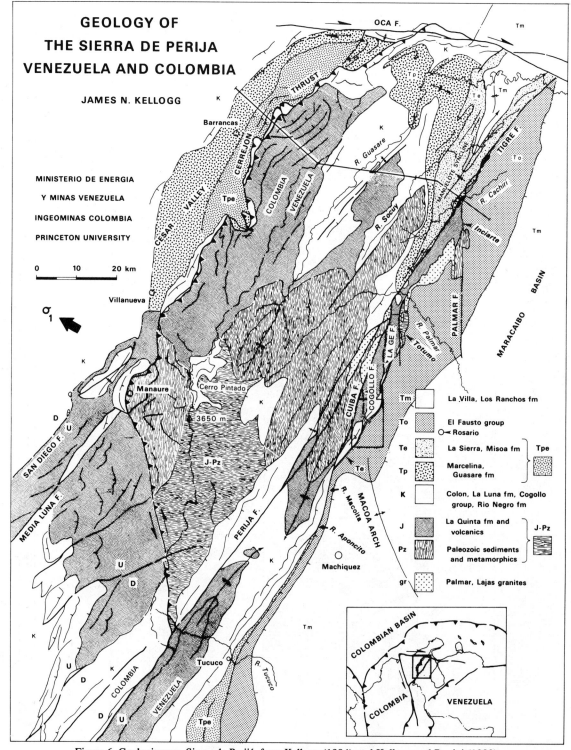

GEOLOGY OF
THE SIERRA DE PERIJA
VENEZUELA AND COLOMBIA

JAMES N. KELLOGG

MINISTERIO DE ENERGIA
Y MINAS VENEZUELA
INGEOMINAS COLOMBIA
PRINCETON UNIVERSITY

Tm	La Villa, Los Ranchos fm
To	El Fausto group O—◀ Rosario
Te	La Sierra, Misoa fm } Tpe
Tp	Marcelina, Guasare fm
K	Colon, La Luna fm, Cogollo group, Rio Negro fm
J	La Quinta fm and volcanics } J-Pz
Pz	Paleozoic sediments and metamorphics
gr	Palmar, Lajas granites

Figure 6. Geologic map, Sierra de Perijá, from Kellogg (1984) and Kellogg and Bonini (1982).

Map Symbols

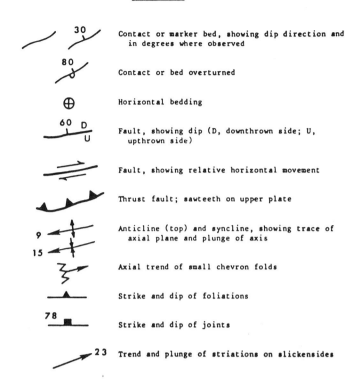

30	Contact or marker bed, showing dip direction and in degrees where observed
80	Contact or bed overturned
⊕	Horizontal bedding
60 D / U	Fault, showing dip (D, downthrown side; U, upthrown side)
	Fault, showing relative horizontal movement
	Thrust fault; sawteeth on upper plate
9 / 15	Anticline (top) and syncline, showing trace of axial plane and plunge of axis
	Axial trend of small chevron folds
	Strike and dip of foliations
78	Strike and dip of joints
23	Trend and plunge of striations on slickensides

1984). Maze postulated that the volcanic–red bed assemblage was deposited in northeast-trending grabens related to tensional and compressional events. Cretaceous strata, about 1,500 to 2,500 m thick, include conglomerates, marine massive reefal and thin-bedded, fetid limestones, various kinds of sandstones, and dark siltstones (Fig. 5).

Faults and broad open folds appear to dominate post-Paleozoic structures of the range; faults on the northwest flank and interior of the range dip mainly southeast; faults on the southeast flank are near vertical or dip northwest (Kellogg and Bonini, 1982). Kellogg and Bonini have postulated that the entire range is allochthonous.

CORDILLERA ORIENTAL

The Cordillera Oriental is a polydeformed uplift with a core of Precambrian and Paleozoic metamorphic and minor igneous rocks overlain by Paleozoic sedimentary rocks; these in turn are overlain by Mesozoic red beds, volcanic rocks, local evaporites; and marine clastic strata; and local thick Cenozoic deposits, mostly continental (Fig. 7). Most folds and faults trend subparallel to the trend of the Cordillera; northeast in the Bogotá leg and roughly north-south in the Santander leg. The thickness of Mesozoic and younger strata exceeds 10 km in places. The Cordillera Oriental was strongly deformed in Paleozoic (and Precambrian?) intervals, during Late Cretaceous to Paleogene time, and the block was greatly uplifted in Miocene and younger time. The range is cut by numerous granitoid plutons of Paleozoic and

Mesozoic age. The Santander massif, within which most of the plutons are exposed, is a distinct subprovince (Fig. 8). Flanking thrusts dip both east (on the west side of the range) and west (on the east side of the range), and there is some evidence that part or all of the Mesozoic sequence is allochthonous. Even though the range may be somewhat allochthonous with respect to its neighbors, paleomagnetic data on Jurassic (193 ± 6 Ma) plutonic rocks yield a stable South American pole (MacDonald and Opdyke, 1972, 1974). The crust is continental (M = 35 to 40 km; Plate 3, this volume).

A large crystalline core complex is exposed in the Santander massif (Figs. 7 and 8). In the massif, Precambrian rocks of highest amphibolite grade (Bucaramanga Gneiss) are nonconformably overlain by metamorphic rocks of greenschist to lower amphibolite facies (Silgará Formation), which are inferred to be of Cambrian to Ordovician age (Ward and others, 1973; Irving, 1975). A sequence of Devonian to Permian strata rests unconformably on these rocks and the orthogneiss; a significant discontinuity probably represents most of Mississippian and Early Pennsylvanian time. Major events of granitic plutonism are partly represented by the orthogneiss that may have been originally intruded in separate late Precambrian to Late Ordovician phases. Ward and others (1973) described local intrusions of Late Permian to Early Triassic age as a minor prelude to the main phase of batholithic emplacement in Late Triassic(?) to Late Jurassic(?) time. They also described metawackes in the Silgará Formation that can be traced continuously along strike into the Bucaramanga Gneiss. Elsewhere, a contact between the Silgará Formation and the Devonian rocks coincides exactly with an isograd. Clearly, the ambivalence in defining contact relations is tied to the isograd versus stratigraphic-contact problem, as in the Cordillera de Mérida.

Precambrian gneisses as old as 1.6 Ga are found in the Garzon massif in the southern part of the Cordillera Oriental (Kroonenberg, 1982; Priem and others, 1989). Isotopic ages for the northern Cordillera Oriental (summarized by Goldsmith and others, 1971; Etayo-Serna and others, 1983; and Shagam and others, 1989) include 945 ± 40 Ma (K/Ar) and 680 ± 140 Ma (Rb/Sr) for the Bucaramanga Gneiss, 546 ± 48 Ma for the late Precambrian–Cambrian quartz monzonite, 471 ± 22 Ma for an Ordovician quartz monzonite, and 394 ± 23 Ma for a Silurian to Devonian monzonite. Isotopic ages of 195 ± 7 Ma and 177 ± 6 Ma have been given for Permian to Jurassic granitoids.

Sedimentary rocks of Devonian to Triassic age overlie the crystalline basement complex of the Santander massif. Some units (Devonian, Carboniferous, and Permian) are fossiliferous. The rocks include conglomerate, sandstone and siltstone, and red beds, especially in the upper part of the sequence. Some units are calcareous. The aggregate thickness is 2,000 to 2,500 m (Ward and others, 1973). Cambrian(?), Devonian, and Carboniferous strata have been reported from the Floresta massif (about 6°N, 73°W). Jurassic and Cretaceous rocks are mainly clastic with local carbonate and cherty phases (Fig. 5). Farther south along the range, near Bogotá (4°45′N), Cretaceous strata become

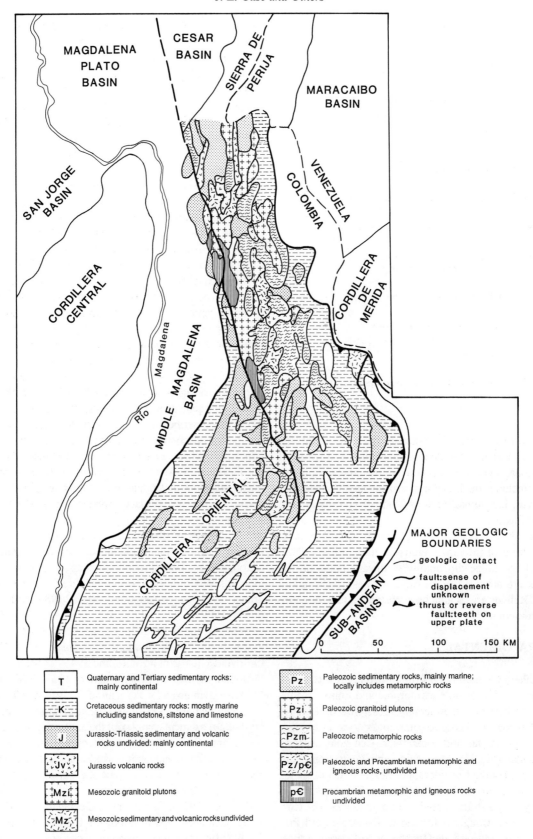

MAJOR GEOLOGIC
BOUNDARIES

— geologic contact

‿ fault:sense of
   displacement
   unknown

▲‿ thrust or reverse
   fault:teeth on
   upper plate

0   50   100   150 KM

| T | Quaternary and Tertiary sedimentary rocks: mainly continental |

| K | Cretaceous sedimentary rocks: mostly marine including sandstone, siltstone and limestone |

| J | Jurassic-Triassic sedimentary and volcanic rocks undivided: mainly continental |

| Jv | Jurassic volcanic rocks |

| Mzi | Mesozoic granitoid plutons |

| Mz | Mesozoic sedimentary and volcanic rocks undivided |

| Pz | Paleozoic sedimentary rocks, mainly marine; locally includes metamorphic rocks |

| Pzi | Paleozoic granitoid plutons |

| Pzm | Paleozoic metamorphic rocks |

| Pz/p€ | Paleozoic and Precambrian metamorphic and igneous rocks, undivided |

| p€ | Precambrian metamorphic and igneous rocks undivided |

Figure 7. Simplified and generalized geologic map of the Cordillera Oriental; modified from Etayo-
Serna and others (1986), Arango. and others (1976), and Case and Holcombe (1980). Note that many
contacts shown may be faults.

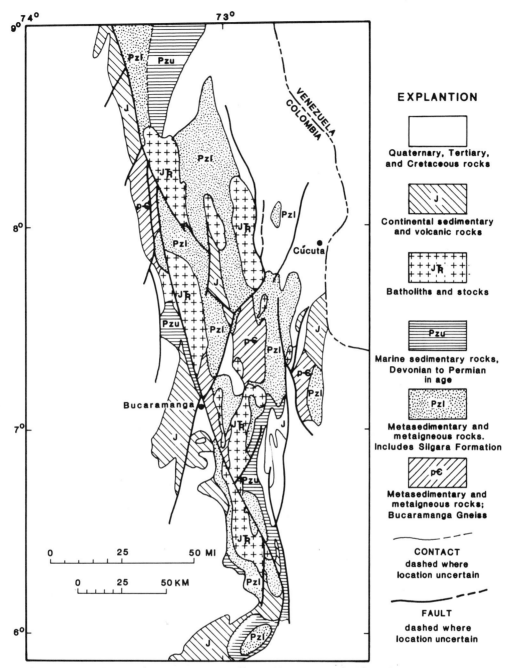

EXPLANTION

Quaternary, Tertiary, and Cretaceous rocks

J
Continental sedimentary and volcanic rocks

JᴿR
Batholiths and stocks

Pzu
Marine sedimentary rocks, Devonian to Permian in age

Pzl
Metasedimentary and metaigneous rocks. Includes Silgara Formation

pЄ
Metasedimentary and metaigneous rocks; Bucaramanga Gneiss

CONTACT
dashed where location uncertain

FAULT
dashed where location uncertain

Figure 8. Geologic map of the Santander massif. Modified and redrafted from Goldsmith and others (1971).

more arenaceous and thicken greatly; a Cretaceous submarine deltaic facies is indicated. Evaporites, perhaps of Cretaceous age, occur near Bogotá and have flowed to produce domes and anticlines (Fig. 9; Bürgl, 1967). The northward extent of the evaporites is unknown.

The northern part of the range is dominated by faults, mostly high-angle (see, e.g., Julivert, 1970; Ward and others, 1973; and Vargas H. and others, 1981). A principal fault is the Santa Marta–Bucaramanga (left-lateral; and a complex scissors displacement along-strike), which is very active seismically, including the well-known "Bucaramanga nest" of earthquakes hav-

ing focal depths of about 150 km (Pennington and others, 1979). Flanking faults tend to be reverse or thrust faults that dip inward toward the range. Folds are broad and open in the north, but folds related to movement of evaporites in the south are more complex (Fig. 9; Campbell and Bürgl, 1965; Julivert, 1970).

CORDILLERA CENTRAL

This range contains a core of Precambrian and Paleozoic metamorphic rocks, overlain on the east by Triassic limestone and Jurassic red beds and calc-alkaline volcanic rocks, and by Cretaceous marine clastic and local carbonate rocks (Fig. 10). A

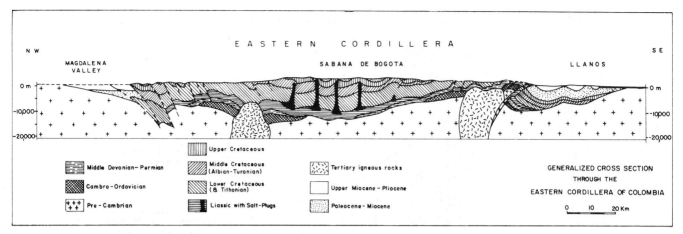

Figure 9. Simplified geologic cross section of the Cordillera Oriental at the latitude of Bogotá, approximately 4°45'N. From Bürgl (1967).

comprehensive synthesis of the regional geology and petrochemistry of Mesozoic and Cenozoic plutons of the Cordillera Central and Cordillera Occidental has been presented by Alvarez A. (1983). The west flank of the Cordillera Central includes oceanic and mantle rocks, probably obducted, in thrust and strike-slip fault zones. Paleozoic and Mesozoic red beds have been reported in the core of the range. Mesozoic units along the east flank are as thick as 4,000 m and are moderately folded and cut by many faults, some of which have large strike-slip components (see, e.g., Feininger, 1970). Most structural trends are north to northeast. Active volcanoes cap the southern part of the area shown in Figure 10, including the Nevado del Ruiz, which erupted in 1985, killing almost 23,000 people. Neogene volcanic deposits are abundant on the east flank of the range, especially south of 5°. The range is seismically active. Paleomagnetic data just south of the map area suggest very large translations and rotations of Triassic rocks (Scott, 1978). The crust is mainly continental, except for obducted slices (M = 35 to 40 km; Plate 3, this volume).

The ostensible core complex of the northernmost part of the range includes both igneous and metamorphic rocks, most of Precambrian or Paleozoic age. East of the Otú and Palestina faults (Fig. 10), the dominant elements of the stratigraphic framework are granulite-facies gneisses overlain by fossiliferous Ordovician rocks metamorphosed to low greenschist facies [Payandé terrane (San Lucas subterrane); see descriptions by Alvarez A., 1983; Etayo-Serna and others, 1983]. South of the area shown on Figure 10, a K/Ar age of 1,360 ± 240 Ma has been reported from a gneiss.

West of the Otú and Palestina faults, the Cordillera Central is dominated by the Antioquian batholith of mainly Cretaceous age. The country rock of the terrane, termed the Cajamarca terrane by Etayo-Serna and others (1983), includes polymetamorphic paragneisses and schists (Toussaint and Restrepo, 1982) generally thought to be Paleozoic, but the age is very uncertain. Paleozoic granitoid plutons, most metamorphosed to a greater or lesser degree, intrude the gneisses and schists of the terrane. Iso-

topic ages of about 343, 312, 270, 227, 207, 205, and 200 Ma have been reported (see summaries and original sources by Restrepo, 1982; Alvarez A., 1983; Etayo-Serna and others, McCourt and others, 1984; Shagam and others, 1989).

Magmatic activity in the Cordillera and adjacent areas has continued intermittently to the present (Millward and others, 1984; Marriner and Millward, 1984). The dominant post-Paleozoic feature is the large Antioquian batholith. On a regional scale, the higher grade facies of the basement schists occur as a broad corona around the Antioquian batholith; greenschist facies rocks become dominant as distance from the batholith increases. This suggests a possible bull's-eye pattern, as in the Cordillera de Mérida, having a radius of roughly 150 km.

To the north, and especially to the west, numerous ultramafic and mafic bodies have been mapped. These are thought to be fragments of upper mantle or lower crust. The method(s) of emplacement of these bodies and their age(s) has been the subject of debate; see, for example, articles by Restrepo and Toussaint (1988) and McCourt and Aspden (1987). One body, Cerro Matoso north of the main Cordillera, is the site of a major nickel laterite deposit.

In the eastern part of the range, one exposure of weakly metamorphosed graptolitic siltstones, associated with quartzites, is of Ordovician age. Otherwise, pre-Triassic(?), Triassic, and Jurassic are the oldest ages for unmetamorphosed stratified rocks over the crystalline basement. These are mainly intermediate to felsic volcanic rocks, interlayered with dark siltstones and red beds having fossil plants. Marine Triassic limestones, just south of the area of Figure 10, have been faunally dated as Late Triassic. Cretaceous sedimentary rocks in the central and eastern part of the Cordillera include conglomerates, various types of sandstones, dark shales, and siliceous shales. In the western part of the range, flyschoid sedimentary strata are interlayered with mafic to intermediate volcanic rocks. Small basins contain Tertiary clastic deposits, mainly continental; north of the range, however, continental, strand line, and shallow marine deposits have been mapped (Duque-Caro, 1979).

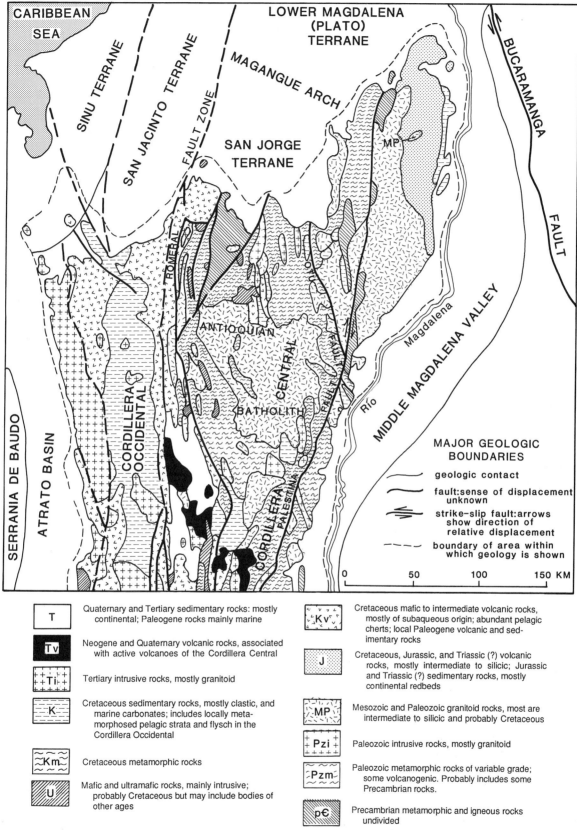

Figure 10. Geologic map of northern Central and Occidental Cordilleras. Greatly simplified from Etayo-Serna and others (1986) and Case and Holcombe (1980). All contacts approximately located. Note that many contacts are faults.

The dominant mapped structures of the main range appear to be high-angle faults that trend northerly, northwest, and northeast (see, e.g., maps by Kassem and others, 1979; and González I. and others, 1980). The eastern flank of the range is highly folded and thrust, especially south of the area of Figure 10 (see cross sections by Butler and Schamel, 1988). Butler and Schamel inferred a west dip on thrusts and axial planes of folds. In contrast, McCourt and Aspden (1987) regarded faults within the range, south of the area of Figure 10, as east dipping with both high-angle reverse and normal displacements. They postulated that rocks of the Cordillera were related to convergence between Paleozoic oceanic crust and an associated island arc (protolith of the Cajamarca sequence), early Mesozoic convergence along the Romeral fault zone, and Paleogene and younger convergence west of the Serranía de Baudó. Restrepo and Toussaint (1988) have emphasized obduction of mafic and ultramafic rocks eastward onto the Cordillera Central, probably in mid- to Late Cretaceous time.

ROMERAL FAULT ZONE

A major tectonic feature of northern South America is the Romeral fault zone, a great suture zone of probable Late Cretaceous and Paleogene age. Superimposed on the suture zone is a graben-like basin, along the Cauca Valley, of much disputed sense of displacement (dip-slip versus strike-slip), which is probably related to strike-slip transform motion. This zone represents the boundary between continental crust on the east and accreted oceanic crust on the west. Direction of dip is controversial: some authors regard it as east dipping, others as west dipping. It appears that high-angle faulting of the Tertiary (Neogene?) is superimposed on older zones of thrusting, as is common with other strike-slip fault systems (Motagua-Polochic zone of Guatemala, for example). The zone has been recently active, as indicated by offset streams and the great Popoyán earthquake of 1983. Direction of strike-slip faulting has been controversial: for example, Campbell (1968) identified a Dolores megashear (which includes the zone later termed the Romeral fault) and postulated right-lateral displacement; Page (1987) presented evidence that the Romeral fault zone is oblique-slip and has roughly equal amounts of high-angle reverse and left-lateral components; Restrepo and Toussaint (1988) have emphasized the importance of older low-angle thrusts along the zone.

The eastern side of the Cauca Valley, along the Romeral and other fault zones, can be regarded as a megamélange, including Mesozoic flyschoid rocks, fragments of ophiolites, Paleozoic(?) metamorphic rocks, and local blueschists, intruded by compositionally variable Mesozoic and Tertiary granitoid plutons. The western side of the valley is a complex zone of high-angle faults, upthrown to the west, and has an aggregate vertical component of displacement of perhaps 2,000 m or more.

The Tertiary basin (Cauca-Patía) contains as much as 3,000 m of mainly continental fluviatile and volcanogenic deposits, although local marine deposits have been reported. These rocks include conglomerates, especially in the upper part, sandstones, shales, and local limestones and cherts. In a representative columnar section, Alvarez A. (1983, Fig. 8) suggested that more than 2,500 m of Maastrichtian and younger strata occur in the basin. These rocks are locally tightly folded, including overturned folds. The inferred crustal setting is shown on Plates 2 and 3 (this volume).

CORDILLERA OCCIDENTAL

No "core complexes," as in ranges to the east, have been identified in the Cordillera Occidental. This complex polycomponent terrane includes local ultramafic and gabbroic bodies and great thicknesses of Cretaceous (and perhaps older) tholeiitic marine basalts and basaltic andesites, pelagic strata, and turbidites, intruded by Tertiary granitoid plutons (Barrero, 1979; Alvarez A., 1983). Local metamorphic belts have been mapped, especially in the southern part of the range. Major fault systems border the east and west flanks of the terrane, but sense of displacement is uncertain. Principal convergent deformation, along north-trending fold and fault systems, took place in pre–middle Miocene time, but major vertical uplift has continued into Holocene time, as indicated by many uplifted terraces. The crust is modified oceanic (M = ±25 km; Plate 3, this volume). Additional details are provided by Alvarez A. (1983); Escalante (this volume); and Duque-Caro (1990).

Alvarez A. (1983) has compiled a generalized columnar section for the northern part of the Cordillera: Lower Cretaceous rocks include a lower flyschoid unit, interlayered with mafic volcanic rocks; a thick sequence of mafic flows and sills, with chert interlayers that extend into the Upper Cretaceous part of the sequence; and an upper flyschoid sequence, with cherts and cherty limestones. The Cretaceous rocks have been dated using marine microfossils (see summary by Alvarez A., 1983). Alvarez has estimated that the sequence is 21 km thick; however, the rocks are highly deformed—folded and probably involved in imbricate thrusting. His estimate may be based on the results of seismic refraction (see Case and MacDonald, this volume). Most mapped (or postulated) faults trend northerly in this heavily forested region, but some trend northwest and others northeast. The layered rocks are tightly folded or overturned.

SIERRA NEVADA DE SANTA MARTA

The Sierra Nevada de Santa Marta is an enormous triangular block that is a complex uplifted polycomponent terrane cored with Precambrian and Paleozoic igneous and metamorphic rocks, and large Mesozoic plutons (Fig. 11; Gansser, 1955; Tschanz and others, 1969, 1974). Foliations trend northeast (Fig. 11). The massif is bordered on the north by the Oca fault (right-lateral) and on the west by the Santa Marta–Bucaramanga fault (left-lateral), both of which show large vertical components of displacement (Campbell, 1968). However, the sense of displacement on these faults is strongly disputed. They are viewed as major strike-slip faults by some and as oblique-slip faults by others. Pertinent discussions are those by Campbell (1968, 1974), Polson and Henao (1968), Julivert (1970), Ward and others (1973), and Kellogg (1984). Faceted spurs occur along parts of the Santa Marta–Bucaramanga fault zone at the base of the range, indicating the youth of the latest faulting.

Patches of Paleozoic sedimentary rocks and thick sequences of Mesozoic volcanic and volcanogenic sedimentary rocks have been mapped. Mesozoic metamorphic rocks crop out to the north in a subterrane (Ruma metamorphic belt; MacDonald and others, 1971; Alvarez, 1971) that may be correlative with similar rocks in the northern Guajira Peninsula, Aruba, the Paraguaná Peninsula, and the Cordillera de la Costa of Venezuela. The Sierra Nevada de Santa Marta complex is intruded by Paleozoic, Mesozoic, and Tertiary granitoid plutons. The crust is continental in the south, but may be oceanic in the north (M = 15 to 25 km; see Kellogg and Bonini, 1982; Plate 3, this volume). The massif is not in isostatic equilibrium; Bouguer anomalies are strongly positive, even at high elevations. Tschanz and others (1974) divided the massif into three geotectonic provinces: the Santa Marta province in the northwest; the Sevilla province just to the southeast; and the Sierra Nevada province covering most of the massif farther to the southeast (Fig. 11). A striking feature of the map is the pattern of scattered patches of granulitic gneiss in large areas of granitoid plutons in the two southeastern provinces, suggesting crustal extension accompanied by massive batholithic invasion.

The Santa Marta province includes mainly greenschists, intruded by a Tertiary granitoid pluton (~46 Ma). In lithology and structural style, rocks of the province, as noted above, are similar to those of the northern parts of ranges on the Guajira Peninsula and the Caribbean coastal ranges (Bellizzia and Dengo, this volume).

The Sevilla belt consists of mafic gneisses possibly overlain by younger schists; these rocks underwent polymetamorphism during latest Permian (~250 Ma) to latest Jurassic time (~147 Ma; MacDonald and Hurley, 1969; Tschanz and others, 1974; Shagam and others, 1989). Anorthosite is locally exposed in the western margin of the province; elsewhere there are some anorthosite and serpentinite bodies. Foliations in the metamorphic rocks trend generally northeast, but there is much local variation.

The principal elements of stratigraphy for the Sierra Nevada province appear in the explanation for Figure 11. The oldest rocks are the Los Mangos granulites, which consist of banded mafic and felsic granulites. They resemble granulitic rocks in the Cordillera Central but are distinctly different and higher grade metamorphic rocks compared to the amphibolitic and greenschist facies rocks that dominate crystalline core areas of the other ranges. The oldest sedimentary rock units are of late Paleozoic age (Devonian? to Pennsylvanian). These crop out at a few isolated localities along the southeastern flanks of the range (Fig. 11), and comprise a few hundred meters of basal sandstone and shale overlain by limestone. Although far thinner, there is clear resemblance to the upper Paleozoic sequence of the Sierra de Perijá. In late Permian(?) to Triassic time, these rocks were dis-

conformably overlain by an interbedded sequence of spilites, basaltic and diabasic volcanic rocks, and dark graywacke siltstones and sandstones. The principal phase of granitic-dioritic plutonism and volcanism followed, mainly through the Jurassic and possibly into earliest Cretaceous time.

Toward the western margin of the Sierra Nevada province the Río Piedras complex of mainly plutonic aspect occupies an extensive area (Fig. 11). This area is characterized by a variety of metamorphic rocks, including metavolcanic rocks, of a wide range of facies (greenschist to amphibolite gneiss) and age (Paleozoic to Early Jurassic).

Isotopic ages for the region have been provided by Tschanz and others (1974) and summarized by Shagam and others (1989). Rb-Sr whole-rock ages on basement granulites are about 1,270 to 1,370 Ma (*in* Kroonenberg, 1982, after MacDonald and Hurley, 1969; Tschanz and others, 1974). A K-Ar age of about 940 Ma was obtained on Los Mangos Gneiss on the western side of the Sierra (Fig. 11). The next youngest age is Jurassic, and Tschanz and others (1974) listed about 18 ages in the Sierra Nevada province in the range ~202 to 129 Ma (Early Jurassic to Early Cretaceous) except for one K-Ar age of 57 Ma (Paleocene) from a Jurassic pluton, which is interpreted to be the thermal effect of intrusion of a small adjacent laccolith.

Stratified cover rocks, exposed mainly on the southeast and north flank of the massif (Fig. 11) include Triassic red beds and red spilitic volcanic rocks, Jurassic ignimbritic and porphyritic rocks, Jurassic to Cretaceous rhyolitic ignimbritic rocks, Cretaceous limestone and shale, Cretaceous to Tertiary shale and limestone, and Tertiary coal-bearing clastic rocks.

The principal structural grain for both foliated rocks and faults of the interior massif is east-northeast. Only a few mapped faults trend northwest; faults of the west side of the massif trend northerly, parallel to the main Santa Marta–Bucaramanga fault system (left-lateral; oblique-slip).

In contrast to the core complex of the Cordillera de Merida, where it appears that Late Permian to Early Triassic plutons were emplaced in upper Paleozoic rocks of the same tectonic cycle, the granites (~200 Ma) in the Sierra Nevada province were intruded into a far older (~1,300 Ma) granulite terrane emplaced by overthrusting. The granites are alien to the granulites, and no bull's eye pattern of thermal products, such as in the Cordillera de Merida, has been observed.

PENINSULA DE LA GUAJIRA

This uplift is a complex polycomponent terrane having a core of Precambrian and Paleozoic metamorphic rocks, overlain by a thick sequence of Mesozoic clastic and carbonate deposits and local volcanic rocks that have been highly folded and faulted, and intruded by felsic plutons (Fig. 12). Most internal structural elements trend northeast to east. To the north, a subterrane of Mesozoic metamorphic and ultramafic rocks (Ruma metamorphic belt) is in fault contact with the southern subterrane. Tertiary basins are superimposed on the older terranes. The crust here is

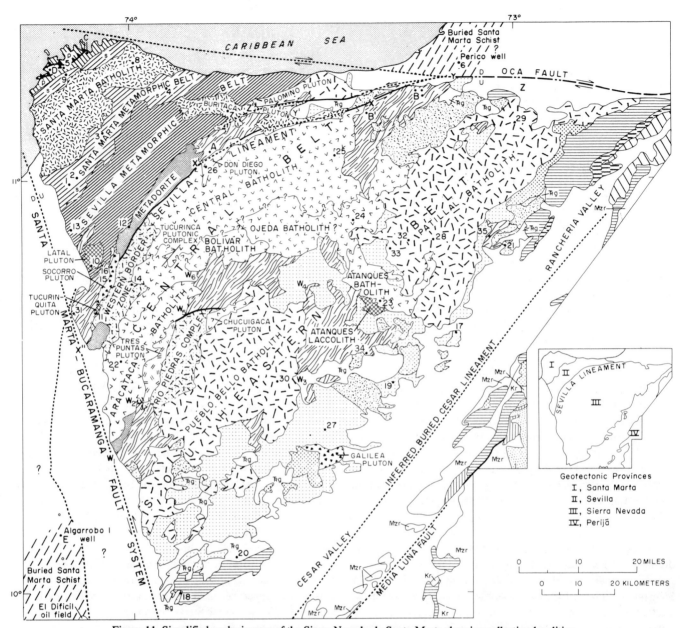

Figure 11. Simplified geologic map of the Sierra Nevada de Santa Marta showing collection localities for radiometrically dated samples. From Tschanz and others (1969, 1974). Left, geologic map; right, explanation.

oceanic, transitional, or continental (not in isostatic equilibrium). Depth to Moho is about 25 km (see Plate 3, this volume). Paleomagnetic data suggest substantial rotations of Cretaceous rocks in the south. Some pertinent references are: Renz (1960), Lockwood (1965), Rollins (1965), Alvarez (1967), MacDonald (1972, 1964), MacDonald and Opdyke (1972), Irving (1972), and Thomas and MacDonald (1976). The oldest dated unit is the Jojoncito gneissic leucogranite, which has a U/Pb age of about 1,250 Ma (P. Banks, cited by W. MacDonald *in* Irving, 1975); Paleozoic(?) to Triassic gneisses and schists in the Guajira arch have minimum K/Ar ages of about 195 and 172 Ma (Etayo-Serna and others, 1983). The Ipapure granodiorite is not well

dated; estimates of Paleozoic(?) to Triassic age have been made, as well as Cretaceous (Etayo-Serna and others, 1983). The Maruayan diorite has a K/Ar age of 120 ± 4 Ma (MacDonald and Opdyke, 1972). The Siapana pluton is a biotite granodiorite of early Mesozoic age (K/Ar date of 195 Ma; MacDonald and Opdyke, 1972).

The Ruma metamorphic zone has rocks of greenschist to amphibolite facies, including small serpentinite bodies; fossil assemblages indicate a Late Cretaceous age. The Ruma zone was probably metamorphosed in Paleocene time, and the Parashi Diorite is probably Eocene (K/Ar age of about 48 Ma; Lockwood, 1965).

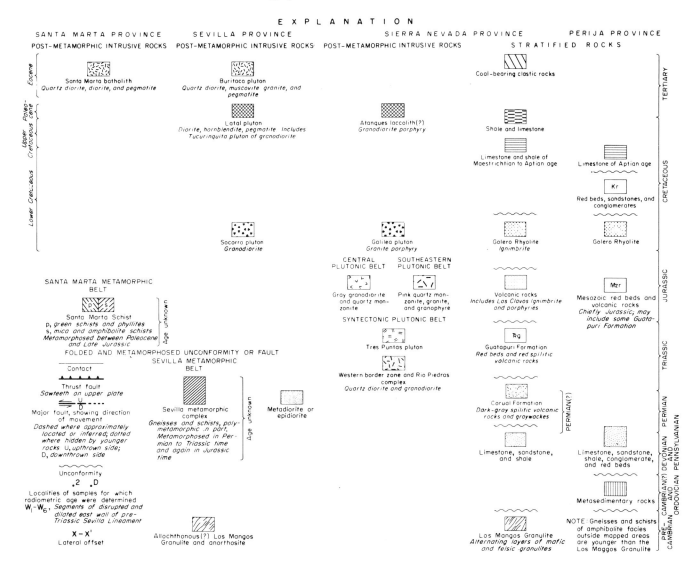

EXPLANATION

| SANTA MARTA PROVINCE | SEVILLA PROVINCE | SIERRA NEVADA PROVINCE | PERIJA PROVINCE |

Mesozoic rocks of the peninsula, southeast of the Ruma zone, are weakly metamorphosed in places. In the north part of the peninsula, low-grade metamorphic rocks of probable Cretaceous age, metamorphosed in Cretaceous-Paleocene time, are dominant. Triassic(?) to Jurassic layered rocks, at least 3,000 m thick, include red beds, siliceous volcanic rocks, sandstones, limestones, siltstones, and shales (Rollins, 1965). The lower parts of the Jurassic and Cretaceous sequences are regarded as continental, and the upper parts of the Jurassic and Cretaceous sequences are marine (MacDonald, 1964). Cretaceous rocks include massive and medium-bedded limestones, dark shales, cherts, and phyllites. Cretaceous strata may exceed 3,000 m in thickness (Rollins, 1965), and are abundantly fossiliferous in the marine shelf sections in the south part of the peninsula.

Tertiary strata on the peninsula are mainly marine clastic and carbonate deposits, but paralic and local continental strata have been drilled. As much as 4,000 m of Tertiary strata have been drilled just off the northwest tip of the peninsula.

The structure is dominated by the northeast-trending Guajira arch, which has a core of Precambrian to Permian or Triassic schist and gneiss. The Ruma metamorphic belt is a remanent of a latest Cretaceous to Paleocene subduction-zone complex that stretched across northern South America from at least the Santa Marta region to the Paraguana Peninsula. South of the Cuiza fault, thought to be right-lateral, the Guajira trough trends northeast to east and contains strongly folded Upper Jurassic and Cretaceous sedimentary rocks. Younger faults bordering the present small ranges trend northwest to west. Case and MacDonald (1973) regarded the structural pattern as related to northwest maximum compressive stress during the Tertiary, probably related in turn to underflow of the Colombian Basin and Beata Ridge beneath the Cretaceous and older rocks of the Sierra Nevada de Santa Marta and the Guajira Peninsula.

MAJOR BASINS

The Tertiary stratigraphy of the basins is extremely complicated in detail because of multiple tectonic events that produced numerous marine incursions and excursions leading to much interfingering of marine and continental facies in the various basins.

The general stratigraphy, structure, regional geologic setting, and oil and gas occurrences and possibilities in basins of Venezuela have been summarized by González de Juana and others (1980). Vásquez and Dickey (1972) and Zambrano and others (1971) provided many details on basins of northwestern Venezuela and northeastern Colombia, including sub-Andean basins south and southeast of the Andes, Maracaibo basin, Chichibacoa–Golfo de Venezuela basin, Baja Guajira basin, and Cesar basin (Fig. 1). Characteristics of the basins are briefly summarized below. Stratigraphic-lithologic columns for some of the basins are shown on Plate 4 (this volume). Geology of basins in Colombia has been summarized by various geologists, and some references are cited for each basin.

Sub-Andean basins

Andean foreland basins south and southeast of the Venezuelan and Colombian Andes are moderately folded and complexly faulted at depth. The Andes are generally thrust south or southeastward over the basins. Tertiary strata of the basins onlap the Precambrian basement of the Guayana Shield, but older rocks have been penetrated by drill holes. Local Paleozoic (Feo-Codecido and others, 1984), some Triassic to Jurassic red beds, and thick Cretaceous and Cenozoic sequences (as much as 4,000 m or more) fill these basins (González de Juana and others, 1980).

Most of the Cretaceous deposits are marine clastic, and the Tertiary deposits include older marine clastic and carbonate rocks and younger continental deposits. Sedimentary rocks rest on a basement composed of various elements of the Precambrian Guayana Shield. Hydrocarbon production has been prolific in the Barinas-Apure basin of Venezuela and the Llanos basin of Colombia along the Colombian-Venezuelan frontier.

Maracaibo basin

One of the world's major petroleum basins contains Triassic to Jurassic red beds, Cretaceous marine carbonate and clastic deposits (1,000 m or more), and 5,000 to 7,000 m of Tertiary deltaic, marine, fluviatile and lacustrine deposits (Zambrano and others, 1971; Vásquez and Dickey, 1972; González de Juana and others, 1980). Deep drill holes in the basin have penetrated "basement" of gray and red granites, greenschists, and carbonaceous phyllites resembling those from the Cordillera de Mérida and Sierra de Perijá (Shagam and others, 1989).

Cesar basin

This asymmetrical Neogene basin, which may be genetically related to both strike-slip and thrust fault systems, appears to be overthrust by the Sierra de Perijá (Kellogg and Bonini, 1982; Kellogg, 1984). It contains Mesozoic strata, continental and ma-

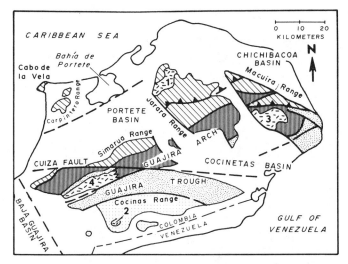

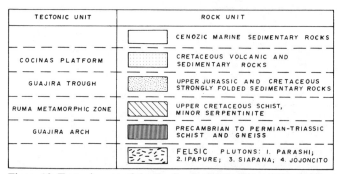

Figure 12. Tectonic map of the Guajira Peninsula (in part after Rollins, 1965; MacDonald, 1964, 1968; MacDonald and Opdyke, 1972; Lockwood, 1965; Alvarez, 1967, 1971; and Thomas, 1972). Pre-Tertiary structural patterns generally trend east-northeast, whereas the northwest Tertiary faults mainly control the trends of the ranges and basins.

rine, that may be as thick as 1,000 m. Older rocks include red beds and intercalated volcanic rocks. Cenozoic marine and continental deposits are as much as 1,000 m thick (Duque-Caro, 1976). Rocks of the basin are broadly folded and cut by northeast-striking, high-angle faults. Major deposits of lignite and coal are present in the northeastern part of the basin. The crust is continental (M = ±30 km; see Plate 3, this volume).

Baja Guajira Basin

North of the right-lateral Oca fault system, this basin contains as much as 4,000 m of Eocene(?) to Pliocene marine and continental deposits. It is (internally) only moderately deformed but may be a pull-apart basin between the Oca and Cuiza faults. The nature of the crust is undefined but probably includes continental crust in the south. One well penetrated schist, marble, and amphibolite similar to rocks of the Santa Marta massif. Pre-Cretaceous calc-alkaline volcanic rocks have been encountered in some drill holes.

Relatively few investigations have been made; they include

reports by Rollins (1965), Zambrano and others (1971), Case and MacDonald (1973), Irving (1975), Duque-Caro (1976), Renz (1977), and Etayo-Serna and others (1983).

Chichibacoa–Golfo de Venezuela basins

These Cenozoic basins, which may have a "pull-apart" origin, contain 4,000 to 7,000 m of Tertiary marine and paralic deposits. Mesozoic strata in the Golfo de Venezuela basin include red beds, carbonates, and minor clastic deposits. The basin has been deformed by many faults of diverse style. The crust is continental or transitional (M = ± 25 km). Some pertinent studies include those by Coronel (1967), Zambrano and others (1971), Thomas (1972), Franco (1975), Thomas and MacDonald (1976), Bonini and others (1977), and Renz (1977).

Middle Magdalena basin

The middle segment of the Magdalena basin is a great intermontane topographic and structural feature between the Cordilleras Oriental and Central north of about 4°30′N. (Figs. 7 and 10). Stratigraphy, structure, and hydrocarbon occurrences have been described by Schamel (1990). It was probably a "foredeep" during Late Cretaceous and Cenozoic time (Van Houten, 1976). Prolific hydrocarbon production occurs in this basin. The Upper Magdalena basin is to the south of the area of Figure 10; the two basins are crossed by a transverse arch, which is characterized by a relative positive gravity anomaly on regional maps. The two basins also differ in that effects of Paleogene compression are dominant in the Middle Magdalena basin but not in the Upper, and the Upper basin is deformed by Miocene and younger events, whereas the Middle Magdalena basin has no intense deformation against its flank with the Cordillera Central. Schamel (1990) has emphasized the importance of ramp structures, with paired anticlines and synclines, along the eastern flank of the Middle Magdalena basin. The Cordillera Oriental is thrust over the basin along east-dipping faults; thick Middle to Upper Cretaceous argillaceous deposits are a primary detachment horizon. In contrast, both west-dipping and east-dipping ramp structures dominate the Upper Magdalena basin to the south. The Upper basin also differs from the Middle basin by the presence of thick volcaniclastic deposits, derived from Miocene and younger stratovolcanoes, along the western flank of the Upper basin (Van Houten, 1976).

Mesozoic strata include older red beds (and volcanic rocks?), clastic, and local carbonate rocks. Cenozoic strata are mainly continental and locally paralic or marine. Marine deposition in the Middle Magdalena basin ceased about the close of the Cretaceous as the Cordillera Central was uplifted and became a source of terrestrial sediments that were deposited along its eastern flanks to a total of possibly more than 8,000 m (Morales and others, 1958; Etayo-Serna and others, 1983). Deposits were coarser grained in the later part of the Tertiary than in the earlier, apparently reflecting increased rate and amount of uplift of the Cordillera Central. Ward and others (1973) and Schamel (1990)

and others have summarized the stratigraphy. For descriptions of Tertiary deposits and their history see reports by Van Houten (1976) and Schamel (1990). Local volcaniclastic deposits, also derived mainly from the Neogene stratovolcanoes, cover parts of the western side of the Middle Magdalena Valley and eastern slopes of the Cordillera Central (Van Houten, 1976; Etayo-Serna and others, 1986). The province is moderately folded and thrust, especially along the flanks. Structural trends are north to northeast. The crust is continental (M = ±30 to 35 km). Some additional investigations were made by Campbell and Bürgl (1965), Thompson (1966), Ward and others (1973), and Irving (1975).

San Jorge–Lower Magdalena (Plato) basin

This moderately deformed basin contains 3,000 to 8,000 m of mainly Tertiary marine and continental strata (Duque-Caro, 1979). Folds and faults trend northeast. The basement includes pre–Late Cretaceous elements of Precambrian and Paleozoic crystalline rocks similar to those of the Cordillera Central. Prolific hydrocarbon production has continued for decades in the basin.

San Jacinto belt

Aggregate thickness of Upper Cretaceous to Neogene strata in this belt, including marine pelagic, turbidite, clastic, fluviatile, and lacustrine deposits, is as much as 10 km. The belt is highly deformed by folds and thrusts that trend north-northeast as a result of Paleogene and Neogene compressional events. Diapirism and intense deformation occurred in Paleogene time. Structures of Paleogene rocks include narrow, elongate, and steep anticlines; and broad and gentle synclines (Duque-Caro, 1984). Local tonalitic plutons intrude Cretaceous strata. The crust is undefined, but probably is deformed oceanic (M = ±25 km; Plate 3, this volume). In many respects, the belt is a northerly extension of the northern Cordillera Occidental. Additional references are Irving (1975) and Duque-Caro (1979).

Sinú belt

This belt includes more than 4,000 m of deformed Oligocene to Pliocene flyschoid strata, mainly in a shaly facies. Duque-Caro (1984) has identified intense deformation and diapirism during Miocene to Pliocene time. He has mapped narrow, elongate, and steep anticlines, broad and gentle synclines, and radial structures. Mud volcanism is a prominent feature of the belt.

CONCLUSION

The evolution of the present-day northern Andes and associated intermontane and foreland basins took place over a relatively short period of geologic time. It began in the Late Cretaceous with the accretion of the Cordillera Occidental to the northwest margin of South America along the Romeral suture zone. A notable feature of the stratigraphy throughout the region is a major hiatus or structural unconformity in about middle Eocene time. Most of the later deformation and uplift occurred from late Miocene to present.

The pre-Andean tectonic history and paleogeography is complex and had a strong influence on the present-day tectonic framework. Although the Precambrian to Paleozoic geology is not fully understood, several orogenic events have been postulated from studying the geologic relations exposed in the various crystalline "core complexes." The Jurassic through Lower Cretaceous sedimentary and volcanic sequences record a period of crustal rifting that is most likely related to the breakup between North and South America. A passive margin phase followed, during which time rich hydrocarbon-generating source rocks were deposited. The Mesozoic grabens were structurally inverted during the Neogene, having localized the present positions of at least the Sierra de Perijá, the Cordillera de Mérida, and the Cordillera Oriental. Differences in deformational styles, rates of uplift, and basin fill and subsidence are the result of the complex interplay of the South American, Nazca, Caribbean, Panamá, and Bonaire Plates and blocks. Assuming a fixed northern South American craton, the uplift of the Andes is probably related to relative eastward convergence of the northern Nazca Plate on the west and relative southward convergence of the Caribbean Plate on the north side of the northern Andean block.

REFERENCES CITED

Alvarez A., J. A., 1983, Geología de la Cordillera Central y el Occidente Colombiano y petroquímica de los intrusivos granitoides Mesocenozoicos: Colombia, Instituto Nacional de Investigaciones Geológico-Mineras, Boletín de Geología, v. 26, no. 2, 175 p.

Alvarez, W., 1967, Geology of the Simarua and Carpintero areas, Guajira Peninsula, Colombia [Ph.D. thesis]: Princeton, New Jersey, Princeton University, 168 p.

——, 1971, Fragmented Andean belt of northern Colombia, in Donnelly, T. W., ed., Caribbean geophysical, tectonic, and petrologic studies: Geological Society of America Memoir 130, p. 77–96.

Arango, C., J. L., Kassem B., T., and Duque-Caro, H., 1976, Mapa geológico de Colombia: Colombia, Instituto Nacional de Investigaciones Geológico-Mineras, scale 1:1,500,000.

Barrero L., D., 1979, Geology of the central Western Cordillera, west of Buga and Roldanillo, Colombia: Colombia Instituto Nacional de Investigaciones Geológico-Mineras, Publicaciones Geológicas Especiales de INGEOMINAS, no. 4, 75 p.

Bellizzia G., A., Pimentel M. N., and Bajo O., 1976, Mapa geológico estructural de Venezuela: Venezuela, Ministerio de Minas e Hidrocarburos, Dirección de Geológia, 27 sheets, scale 1:500,000.

Bonini, W. E., Pimstein de Gaete, C., and Graterol, V., compilers, 1977, Mapa de anomalías de Bouguer de la parte norte de Venezuela y áreas vecinas: Venezuela, Ministerio de Minas e Hidrocarburos, Dirección de Geología, scale 1:1,000,000.

Bowen, J. M., 1972, Estratigrafía del Precretaceo en la parte norte de la Sierra de Perijá, in Memoria, Cuarto Congreso Geológico Venezolano: Venezuela Ministerio de Minas e Hidrocarburos, Dirección de Geología, Boletín de Geología, Publicación Especial no. 5, v. II, p. 729–761.

Bürgl, H., 1961, Historia geológica de Colombia: Revista de la Academía Colombiana de Ciencias, Físicas y Naturales, v. 11, no. 43, p. 137–193.

——, 1967, The orogenesis in the Andean system of Colombia: Tectonophysics, v. 4, p. 429–443.

——, 1973, Precambrian to Middle Cretaceous stratigraphy of Colombia: Translated by Allen, C. G., and Rowlinson, N. R., privately published by N. R. Rowlinson, Bogotá, Colombia, 214 p.

Burkley, L. A., 1976, Geochronology of the central Venezuelan Andes: [Ph.D. thesis]: Cleveland, Ohio, Case Western Reserve University, 150 p.

Butler, K., and Schamel, S., 1988, Structure along the eastern margin of the Central Cordillera, Upper Magdalena Valley, Colombia: Journal of South American Earth Science, p. 109–120.

Campbell, C. J., 1968, The Santa Marta wrench fault of Colombia and its regional setting: Transactions, Caribbean Geological Conference 4, Port-of-Spain, Trinidad, 1965, p. 247–261.

——, 1974, Colombian Andes, in Spencer, A. M., ed., Mesozoic–Cenozoic orogenic belts: Geological Society of London Special Publication 4, p. 705–724.

Campbell, C. J., and Bürgl, H., 1965, Section through the eastern Cordillera of Colombia, South America: Geological Society of America, Bulletin, v. 76, p. 567–590.

Case, J. E., and Holcombe, T. L., 1980, Geologic-tectonic map of the Caribbean region: U.S. Geological Survey Miscellaneous Investigations Map I-1100, scale 1:2,500,000.

Case, J. E., and MacDonald, W. D., 1973, Regional gravity anomalies and crustal structure in northern Colombia: Geological Society of America Bulletin, v. 84, p. 2905–2916.

Case, J. E., Holcombe, T. L., and Martin, R. G., 1984, Map of geologic provinces in the Caribbean region, in Bonini, W. E., Hargraves, R. B., and Shagam, R., eds., The Caribbean–South American plate boundary and regional tectonics: Geological Society of America Memoir 162, p. 1–29, map scale 1:5,000,000.

Cordani, U., García J., R., Pimentel de B., N., and Etchart, H., 1985, Comentario sobre dataciones geocronológicas en la región de los Andes centrales, in Memoria, 6th Congreso Geológico de Venezuela, Caracas, 1985: Venezuela Sociedad Venezolana de Geólogos, v. 3, p. 1571–1585.

Coronel, G. R., 1967, A geological outline of the Gulf of Venezuela, in Proceedings, 7th World Petroleum Congress, Mexico City, March, 1967, v. 2: Amsterdam, Elsevier, p. 799–812.

Dasch, L. E., 1982, U-Pb geochronology of the Sierra de Perijá, Venezuela [M.S. thesis]: Cleveland, Ohio, Case Western Reserve University, 164 p.

Duque-Caro, H., 1976, Características estratigráficas y sedimentarias del Terciario marino de Colombia, in Memoria, 2nd Congreso Latinoamericano de Geología, Caracas, 1973: Venezuela Ministerio de Minas e Hidrocarburos Boletín de Geología Publicación Especial 7, v. 2, p. 945–964.

——, 1979, Major structural elements and evolution of northwestern Colombia, in Watkins, J. S., and others, eds., Geological and geophysical investigations of continental margins: American Association of Petroleum Geologists Memoir 29, p. 329–351.

——, 1984, Structural style, diapirism, and accretionary episods of the Sinú-San Jacinto terrane, southwestern Caribbean borderland, in Bonini, W. E., Hargraves, R. B., and Shagam, R., eds., The Caribbean–South American plate boundary and regional tectonics: Geological Society of America Memoir 162, p. 303–316.

——, 1990, The Chocó block in the northwestern corner of South America; Structural, tectonostratigraphic, and paleogeographic implications: Journal of South American Earth Sciences, v. 3, no. 1, p. 1–14 (in press).

Espejo C., A., Etchart H., L., Cordani, U. G., and Kawashita, K., 1980, Geocronología de intrusivas ácidas en la Sierra de Perijá, Venezuela: Venezuela Ministerio de Energia y Minas, Boletín de Geología, v. 14, p. 245–254.

Etayo-Serna, F., and others, 1983, Mapa de terrenos geológicos de Colombia: Publicaciones Geológicas Especiales del INGEOMINAS, v. 14-1, 235 p.

Etayo-Serna, F., and others, 1986, Mapa geológico de Colombia: Instituto Nacional de Investigaciones Geológico-Mineras Open-File map, scale 1:1,000,000.

Feininger, T., 1970, The Palestina fault, Colombia: Geological Society of America

Bulletin, v. 81, p. 1201–1216.

Feo-Codecido, G., Smith, F. D., Jr., Aboud, N., and de Giaccomo, E., 1984, Basement and Paleozoic rocks of the Venezuelan Llanos basins, *in* Bonini, W. E., Hargraves, R. B., and Shagam, R., eds., The Caribbean–South American plate boundary and regional tectonics: Geological Society of America Memoir 162, p. 175–187.

Franco, A., 1975, Colombia's gas reserves climb: Oil and Gas Journal, v. 73, no. 45, p. 247.

Gansser, A., 1955, Ein Beitrag zür Geologie und Petrographie der Sierra Nevada de Santa Marta (Kolumbien, Sudamerika): Schweizerische Mineralogische und Petrographische Mitteilungen, v. 35, no. 2, p. 209–279.

Giegengack, R. F., 1984, Late Cenozoic tectonic environments of the central Venezuelan Andes, *in* Bonini, W. E., Hargraves, R. B., and Shagam, S., eds., The Caribbean–South American plate boundary and regional tectonics: Geological Society of America Memoir 162, p. 343–364.

Giegengack, R. F., Grauch, R. I., and Shagam, R., 1976, Geometry of late Cenozoic displacement along the Boconó fault, Venezuelan Andes, *in* Memoria, 2nd Congreso Latinoamericano, Caracas, 1973: Venezuela Ministerio de Minas e Hidrocarburos Boletín de Geología Publicación Especial, no. 7, v. 2, p. 1201–1215.

Goldsmith, R., Marvin, R. F., and Mehnert, H. H., 1971, Radiometric ages in the Santander massif, eastern Cordillera, Colombian Andes: U.S. Geological Survey Professional Paper 750-D, p. D44–D49.

González de Juana, C., Iturralde, J., and Picard, X, 1980, Geología de Venezuela y de sus cuencas petrolíferas: Caracas, Ediciones Foninves, 2 volumes, 1031 p.

González I., H., Agudelo C., S., Calle Z., B., and others, 1980, Mapa Geológico, Plancha 187, Departamento de Antioquia: Colombia, Instituto Nacional de Investigaciones Geológico-Mineras, scale 1:1,000,000.

Gonzáles I., H., Nuñez, A., and París, G., 1988, Mapa geológico de Colombia; Memoria explicativa: Bogotá, Instituto Nacional de Investigaciones Geológico-Mineras Memoria, 71 p.

Grauch, R. I., 1971, Geology of the Sierra Nevada south of Mucuchíes, Venezuelan Andes; An aluminum-silicate-bearing metamorphic terrain [terrane] [Ph.D. thesis]: Philadelphia, University of Pennsylvania, 180 p.

—— , 1972, Preliminary report of a late(?) Paleozoic metamorphic event in the Venezuelan Andes, *in* Shagam, R., and others, eds., Studies in Earth and space sciences: Geological Society of America Memoir 132, p. 465–473.

—— , 1975, Geología de la Sierra Nevada al sur de Mucuchíes, Andes Venezolanos; Una region metamórfica de alumino-silicatos: Venezuela, Ministerio de Minas e Hidrocarburos Boletín de Geología, v. 12, no. 23, p. 339–441.

Hea, J. P., and Whitman, A. B., 1960, Estratigrafía y petrología de los sedimentos pre-Cretácicos de la parte norte central de la Sierra de Perijá, Estado Zulia, Venezuela, *in* Memoria, 3rd Congreso Geológico Venezolano, Caracas, 1959: Venezuela, Ministerio de Minas e Hidrocarburos, Boletín de Geología, Publicación Especial, v. 1, no. 3, p. 351–376.

Irving, E. F., compiler, 1972, Mapa geológico de la Peninsula de la Guajira: Instituto Nacional de Investigaciones Geológico-Mineras, Colombia, scale 1:100,000.

—— , 1975, Structural evolution of the northernmost Andes: U.S. Geological Survey Professional Paper 846, 47 p.

Julivert, M., 1970, Cover and basement tectonics in the Cordillera Oriental of Colombia, South America, and a comparison with other folded chains: Geological Society of America Bulletin, v. 81, p. 3623–3646.

Kassem B. T., Alvarez A., J., Arango C., J., and others, 1979, Mapa geológico del Departamento de Antioquia: Colombia, Instituto Nacional de Investigaciones Geológico-Mineras, scale 1:500,000.

Kellogg, J. N., 1984, Cenozoic tectonic history of the Sierra de Perijá and adjacent basins, *in* Bonini, W. E., Hargraves, R. B., and Shagam, R., eds., The Caribbean–South American plate boundary and regional tectonics: Geological Society of America Memoir 162, p. 239–261.

Kellogg, J. N., and Bonini, W. E., 1982, Subduction of the Caribbean plate and basement uplifts in the overriding South American plate: Tectonics, v. 1, no. 3, p. 251–276.

Kohn, B. P., Shagam, R., Banks, P. O., and Burkley, L. A., 1984, Mesozoic–Pleistocene fission-track ages of the Venezuelan Andes and their tectonic implications, *in* Bonini, W. E., Hargraves, R. B., and Shagam, R., eds., The Caribbean–South American plate boundary and regional tectonics: Geological Society of America Memoir 162, p. 365–384.

Kroonenberg, S. B., 1982, A Grenvillian granulite belt in the Colombian Andes and its relation to the Guiana Shield: Geologie en Mijnbouw, v. 61, p. 325–333.

Lockwood, J. P., 1965, Geology of the Serranía de Jarará area, Guajira Peninsula, Colombia [Ph.D. thesis]: Princeton, New Jersey, Princeton University, 237 p.

MacDonald, W. D., 1964, Geology of the Serranía de Macuira area, Guajira Peninsula, Colombia [Ph.D. thesis]: Princeton, New Jersey, Princeton University, 167 p.

—— , 1968, Geology of the Serranía de Macuira area, Guajira Peninsula, northeast Colombia: Transactions 4th Caribbean Geological Conference, Port-of-Spain, Trinidad and Tobago, p. 269–273.

—— , 1972, Características estructurales principales de la Península de la Guajira (Colombia-Venezuela) y el Caribe Sur-Central, *in* Memoria, Cuarto Congreso Geológico Venezolano: Venezuela Ministerio de Minas e Hidrocarburos, Dirección de Geología, Publicación Especial no. 5, v. 4, p. 2463–2476.

MacDonald, W. D., and Hurley, P. M., 1969, Precambrian gneisses from northern Colombia, South America: Geological Society of America Bulletin, v. 80, p. 1867–1872.

MacDonald, W. D., and Opdyke, N. D., 1972, Tectonic rotations suggested by paleomagnetic results from northern Colombia, South America: Journal of Geophysical Research, v. 77, no. 29, p. 5720–5730.

—— , 1974, Triassic paleomagnetism of northern South America: American Association of Petroleum Geologists Bulletin, v. 58, p. 208–215.

MacDonald, W. D., Doolan, B. L., and Cordani, U. G., 1971, Cretaceous–early Tertiary metamorphic K-Ar age values from the south Caribbean: Geological Society of America Bulletin, v. 82, p. 1381–1388.

Macellari, C. E., 1984, Late Tertiary tectonic history of the Táchira depression, southwestern Venezuelan Andes, *in* Bonini, W. E., Hargraves, R. B., and Shagam, R., eds., The Caribbean–South American plate boundary and regional tectonics: Geological Society of America Memoir 162, p. 333–341.

Martín Bellizzia, C., 1968, Edades isotópicas de rocas Venezolanas: Venezuela, Ministerio de Minas e Hidrocarburos (Caracas) Boletín de Geología, v. 10, no. 19, p. 368–380.

Martín F., C., 1978, Mapa tectónico, Norte de América del Sur: Venezuela, Ministerio de Energía y Minas, scale 1:2,500,000.

Maze, W. B., 1984, Jurassic La Quinta Formation in the Sierra de Perijá, northwestern Venezuela; Geology and tectonic environment of redbeds and volcanic rocks, *in* Bonini, W. E., Hargraves, R. B., and Shagam, R., eds., The Caribbean–South American plate boundary and regional tectonics: Geological Society of America Memoir 162, p. 263–282.

Maze, W. B., and Hargraves, R. B., 1984, Paleomagnetic results from the Jurassic La Quinta Formation in the Perijá Range and their tectonic significance, *in* Bonini, W. E., Hargraves, R. B., and Shagam, R., eds., The Caribbean–South American plate boundary and regional tectonics: Geological Society of America Memoir 162, p. 287–293.

Marriner, G. F., and Millward, D., 1984, The petrology and geochemistry of Cretaceous to Recent volcanism in Colombia; The magmatic history of an accretionary plate margin: Geological Society of London Journal, v. 141, p. 473–486.

McCourt, W. J., and Aspden, J. A., 1987, A plate tectonic model for the Phanerozoic evolution of central and southern Colombia, *in* Duque-Caro, H., ed., Transactions, 10th Caribbean Geological Conference, Cartagena, Colombia, p. 38–47.

McCourt, W. J., Aspden, J. A., and Brook, M., 1984, New geological and geochronological data from the Colombian Andes; Continental growth by multiple accretion: Geological Society of London Journal, v. 141, p. 831–845.

Miller, J. B., 1962, Tectonic trends in the Sierra de Perijá and adjacent parts of Venezuela and Colombia: American Association of Petroleum Geologists Bulletin, v. 46, no. 9, p. 1565–1595.

Millward, D., Marriner, G. F., and Saunders, A. D., 1984, Cretaceous tholeiitic volcanic rocks from the western Cordillera of Colombia: Geological Society of London Journal, v. 141, p. 847–860.

Morales, L. G., and the Colombian Petroleum Industry, 1958, General geology and oil occurrences of Middle Magdalena Valley, Colombia, *in* Weeks, L. G., ed., Habitat of Oil: Tulsa, Oklahoma, American Association of Petroleum Geologists, p. 641–695.

Page, W. D., 1987, Quaternary faulting in northwestern Colombia [abs.]: Transactions, 10th Caribbean Geological Conference, Cartagena, Colombia, p. 154.

Pennington, W. D., Mooney, W. D., van Hissenhoven, R., Meyer, R. P., and Ramírez, J., 1979, Results of a reconnaissance microearthquake survey of Bucaramanga, Colombia: Geophysical Research Letters, v. 6, no. 2, p. 65–68.

Polson, I. L., and Henao, D., 1968, The Santa Marta wrench fault; A rebuttal: Transactions, 4th Caribbean Geological Conference, Port-of-Spain, Trinidad and Tobago, p. 263–266.

Priem, H.N.A., Kroonenberg, S. B., Boelrijk, N.A.I.M., and Hebeda, E. H., 1989, Rb-Sr and K-Ar evidence for the presence of a 1.6 Ga basement underlying the 1.2 Ga Garzon-Santa Maria granulite belt in the Colombian Andes: Precambrian Research, v. 42, p. 315–324.

Renz, O., 1960, Geología de la parte sureste de la Península de la Guajira (República de Colombia), *in* Memoria, 3rd Congreso Geológico Venezolano: Venezuela, Ministerio de Minas e Hidrocarburos, Boletín de Geología, Publicación Especial 3, v. 1, p. 317–350.

—— , 1977, The lithologic units of the Cretaceous in western Venezuela, *in* Espejo C., A., and others, eds., Memoria, 5th Congreso Geológico Venezolano: Venezuela, Ministerio de Energía y Mínas, Sociedad Venozolana de Geológos, v. 1, p. 45–58.

Restrepo J., J., 1982, Compilación de edades radiométricas de Colombia: Departamentos Andinos hasta 1982: Boletín Ciencias de la Tierra, v. 7–8, p. 201–247.

Restrepo J., J., and Toussaint, J. F., 1988, Terranes and continental accretion in the Colombian Andes: Episodes, v. 11, no. 3, p. 189–193.

Rollins, J. F., 1965, Stratigraphy and structure of the Goajira Peninsula, northwestern Venezuela and northeastern Colombia: Lincoln, University of Nebraska Studies, n. s., no. 30, 102 p.

Salvador, A., 1986, Comments *on* 'Neogene block tectonics of eastern Turkey and northern South America; Continental applications of the finite difference method' by J. F. Dewey and J. L. Pindell: Tectonics, v. 5, no. 4, p. 697–701.

Schamel, S., 1990, Middle and Upper Magdalena Basin, Colombia, *in* Biddle, K. T., ed., Active margin basins: American Association of Petroleum Geologists Memoir (in press).

Schubert, C., 1982, Neotectonics of Boconó fault, western Venezuela: Tectonophysics, v. 85, p. 205–220.

Scott, G. R., 1978, Translation of accretionary slivers; Triassic results from the Central Cordillera of Colombia [abs.]: EOS Transactions of the American Geophysical Union, v. 59, no. 12, p. 1058–1059.

Shagam, R., 1972, Andean research project, Venezuela; Principal data and tectonic implications, *in* Shagam, R., and others, eds., Studies in Earth and space sciences: Geological Society of America Memoir 132, p. 449–463.

—— , 1975, The northern termination of the Andes, *in* Nairn, A.E.M., and Stehli, F. G., eds., The ocean basins and margins; V. 3, The Gulf of Mexico and the Caribbean: New York, Plenum Press, p. 325–420.

—— , 1977, Stratigraphic models for the northern Andes, *in* Espejo, C., A., and others, eds., Memoria, 5th Congreso Geológico Venezolano: Venezuela, Ministerio de Energía y Minas, Sociedad Venezolana de Geológos, v. 2, p. 855–877.

Shagam, R., Giegengack, R. F., Duque-Caro, H., and Towle, M., 1989, The Santa Marta prong and adjacent areas of eastern Colombia and western Venezuela: unpublished manuscript on file with senior author, ~250 p.

Stephan, J.-F., 1985, Plate II, Section D-D'; Des bassins Caraïbes au craton Guyanais: Coupées Seriées dans l'édifice Andin et la chaîne Caraïbe dans le secteur de la transversal de Barquisimeto, *in* Mascle, A., ed., Caribbean geodynamics, Symposium, Paris, February 5–8, 1985: Editions Technip.

Taborda, B., 1965, Guidebook to the geology of the De Mares Concession: Colombia Society of Petroleum Geologists and Geophysicsts, 25 p.

Thery, J.-M., 1982, Constitution du nord-ouest du continent sud Americaín avant les tectoniques andines, 3 volumes [Doctoral thesis]: Bordeaux, University of Bordeaux, 433 p.

Thery, J. M., Esqevin, J., and Menendez, R., 1977, Significacion geotectonique de datations radiometriques dans des sondages de Basse Magdalena (Colombie): Centre du Recherche et Exploracion Elf-Aquitaine, Bulletin 1, no. 2, p. 475–494.

Thomas, D. J., 1972, Tertiary geology and paleontology (phyllum Mollusca) of the Guajira Peninsula, Colombia [Ph.D. thesis]: Binghamton, State University of New York, 150 p.

Thomas, D. J., and MacDonald, W. D., 1976, Summary of the Tertiary stratigraphy and structure of the Guajira Peninsula, *in* Etayo-Serna, F., and Caceres-Girón, C., eds., Memoria Congreso Colombiano de Geología I, 1969: Universidad Nacional de Colombia, Bogotá, p. 207–216.

Thompson, A. V., 1966, Guidebook of a geological section from Bogotá to the Central Cordillera: Colombian Society of Petroleum Geologists and Geophysicists, 20 p.

Toussaint, J. F., and Restrepo J., J., 1982, Magmatic evolution of the northwestern Andes of Colombia: Earth Reviews, v. 18, p. 205–213.

Tschanz, C. M., Jimeno V., A., Cruz B., J., and others, 1969, Mapa geológico de reconocimiento de la Sierra Nevada de Santa Marta, Colombia: Instituto Nacional de Investigaciones Geológico-Mineras, scale 1:200,000.

Tschanz, C. M., Marvin, R. F., Cruz, B., J., Mehnert, H. H., and Cebula, G. T., 1974, Geologic evolution of the Sierra Nevada de Santa Marta, northeastern Colombia: Geological Society of America Bulletin, v. 85, p. 273–284.

Van Houten, F. B., 1976, Late Cenozoic volcaniclastic deposits, Andean foredeep, Colombia: Geological Society of America Bulletin, v. 87, p. 481–495.

Vargas H., R., Arias T., A., Jaramillo C., L., and Tellez I., N., 1981, Geología del Cuadrángulo I-13, Málaga: Colombia, Instituto Nacional de Investigaciones Geológico-Mineras, Boletín Geológico, 76 p.

Vásquez, E. E., and Dickey, P. A., 1972, Major faulting in northwestern Venezuela and its relation to global tectonics, *in* Transactions 6th Caribbean Geological Conference, Margarita, Venezuela, 1971, p. 191–202.

Ward, D. E., Goldsmith, R., Cruz B., J., and Restrepo A., H., 1973, Geología de los Cuadrángulos H-12 Bucaramanga y H-13 Pamplona, Departamento de Santander: Instituto Nacional de Investigaciones Geológico-Mineras, Boletín Geológico, v. 21, nos. 1–3, 132 p.

Zambrano, E., Vásquez, E., Duval, B., Latreille, M., and Coffinieres, B., 1971, Sintesis paleogeográfica y petrolera del occidente de Venezuela, *in* Memoria, 4th Congreso Geológico Venezolano: Venezuela, Ministerio de Minas e Hidrocarburos, Boletín de Geología, Publicación Especial no. 5, v. 1, p. 483–552.

MANUSCRIPT ACCEPTED BY THE SOCIETY APRIL 12, 1990

ACKNOWLEDGMENTS

Thoughtful and helpful reviews were provided by Carlos Dengo, Gabriel Dengo, Bill MacDonald, and Pete Palmer. Hermann Duque-Caro and Michael Towle contributed much to concepts of this chapter. Steve Schamel kindly provided a preprint of an article on the Middle and Upper Magdalena basins.

Chapter 8

The geology of southern Central America and western Colombia

Gregorio Escalante
Apartado 74 Pavas, San José, Costa Rica

INTRODUCTION

The southern part of Central America, together with the adjacent area to the south, including the Pacific side of Colombia (Fig. 1), contains characteristic stratigraphic and structural features that are quite different from those described from northern Central America. This contrast was first noticed by the early investigators of Central America (Vaughn, 1918; Woodring, 1928; Schuchert, 1935; Sapper, 1937) who divided this area into two distinctive geological provinces: a northern one comprising Guatemala, Honduras, and northern Nicaragua, and a southern province comprising southern Nicaragua, Costa Rica, and Panamá. Schuchert (1935) referred to this southern province as the Isthmian Link, which was later termed the South Central America Orogen (Dengo, 1962a; Lloyd, 1963). Another definition of the northern boundary of the Isthmian Link or South Central America Orogen places most of southern Nicaragua in the northern Central America Province (Nuclear Central America in Schuchert's terminology, later subdivided into the Maya and Chortis blocks by Dengo, 1969).

The area covered in this chapter is one of the most complex of the entire Caribbean region and is characterized by complicated structural patterns, and by stratigraphy developed within narrow and elongate restricted basins (Plate 5B). The region has been the subject of many divergent interpretations as to its tectonic history because it has sustained the interaction of four crustal plates. A clear understanding of the geology of the area is essential in reconstructing a meaningful geological history of the Caribbean and its relationship to the South American and Pacific regions.

The notion of a closer genetic relationship between southern Central America and western Colombia than to the Chortis block has emerged gradually from the work of recent investigators. Dengo (1962a) and Lloyd (1963) emphasized the geological similarities between southern Central America and northwestern South America; Dengo (1985) summarized the concept of a single geological unit incorporating southern Central America and a segment of the South America Plate, including western Colombia, which developed on oceanic crust, whereas the Chortis block developed on continental crust. A question remains, however, as to the nature of the segment of the "South American Plate"

involved in Dengo's concept, which may have constituted one or more independently moving blocks with respect to a cratonic South America. Dengo's hypothesis is followed in this chapter, with reservation and is applied in the explanation of the geological units making up the area covered in this chapter.

Geographically, the area comprises all of Costa Rica, Panamá and a 200-km-wide belt covering northwestern Colombia. It includes land area of approximately 190,00 km^2 and a marine area of about the same size under the Pacific Ocean and the Caribbean Sea. The Pacific side contains tectonic and stratigraphic features that are also common to the Caribbean or that form a part of the boundary of the Caribbean Plate.

The segment of the South American Plate (as defined by Dengo, 1985) is located in a structurally complex area of the South American continent where there is interaction of four tectonic plates (Fig. 2). This large region is bordered by the Caribbean Plate and Chortis block (to the northeast and north), the Cocos and Nazca Plates (to the southwest and west), and a segment of the South American Plate (to the east). The southern part of this segment was placed by Dengo (1985) at the Istmina Arch at about 5° latitude, which coincides with an apparent major interruption of the Cordillera Occidental of Colombia. This southern boundary, however, remains to be properly described. Dengo (1985) subdivided the segment of the South American Plate forming southern Central America and western Colombia into the Chorotega and Chocó blocks; the boundary between these two blocks was placed in central Panamá, at the narrowest part of the isthmus, where a tectonic break is inferred from contrasting gravity values (Case, 1974).

The basement complex of southern Central America and western Colombia is largely composed of mafic igneous flows of oceanic origin that occupies a tectonic belt along the Pacific side of Costa Rica, Panamá, and western Colombia, an elongate area along the Caribbean side of eastern Panamá, and the Cordilleran Occidental of Colombia (Fig. 3). These rocks have been described as the Nicoya Complex in Costa Rica and Panamá, the Complejo Basal in Panamá, and the Chocó volcanic rocks in Colombia. The entire sequence of basement rocks in the region

Escalante, G., 1990, The geology of southern Central America and western Colombia, *in* Dengo, G., and Case, J. E., eds., The Caribbean region: Boulder, Colorado, Geological Society of America, The Geology of North America, v. H.

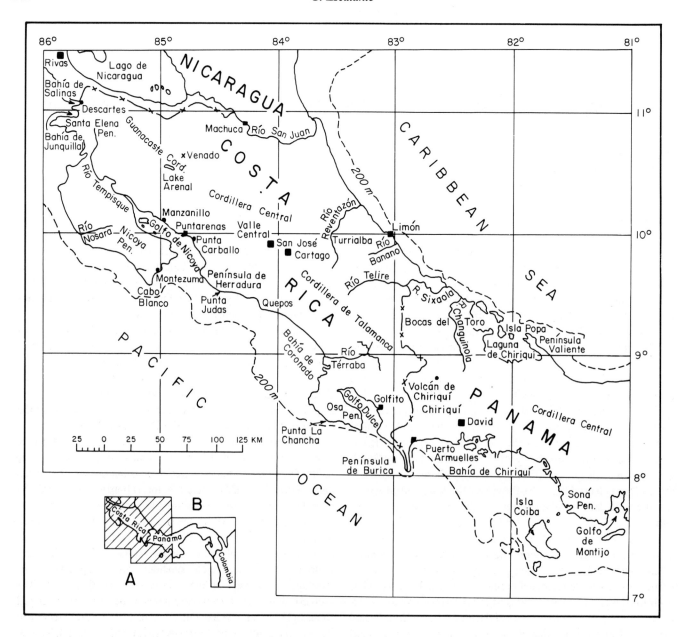

Figure 1a, b. Index map: location of major geographic features in southern Central America and northwestern Colombia.

may be part of a single regional stratigraphic unit extending southward at least as far as Ecuador (Goossens and Rose, 1973; Goossens and others, 1977).

Early Jurassic radiolarites from a sample of chert inbedded in ophiolites in the Nicoya Peninsula of Costa Rica (Fig. 1) have provided the oldest authenticated age determination yet obtained in the entire region (F. Rivier, personal communication, 1982). Late Jurassic (Tithonian) and Early Cretaceous (Hauterivian or presumably Barrenian) radiolarites have also been identified in Costa Rica (Schmidt-Effing and others, 1980). The Early to Late

Cretaceous fauna determined for the basement rocks of Costa Rica, Panamá, and Colombia are compatible with a radiometric date obtained from basalt in the Nicoya Complex of Costa Rica (Barr and Escalante, 1969). Somewhat younger faunal and radiometric age determinations, ranging from Late Cretaceous to early Tertiary, have been determined from basement rocks of northwestern Colombia and eastern Panamá.

The basement complex of Costa Rica, which is thought to be an ophiolite sequence, has been studied in considerable detail since Dengo (1962b) first described and named it from a type

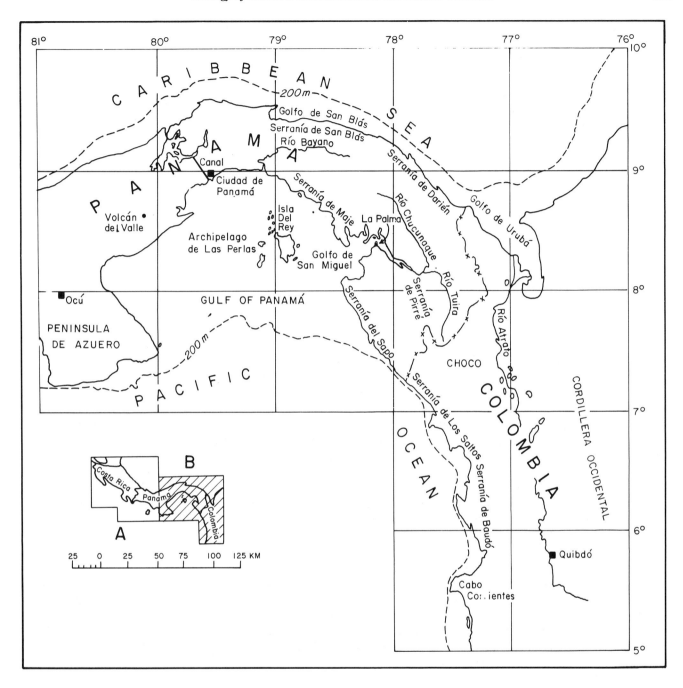

locality in the Nicoya Peninsula of northwestern Costa Rica. On the other hand, the basement rocks in Panamá and Colombia remain to be described in detail.

Cretaceous deposits of marine origin, comprising both carbonate and clastic sequences, have been mapped on the Pacific side of Costa Rica and western Panamá and some local areas of eastern Panamá and western Colombia. On the Caribbean side of southern Central America, however, the Cretaceous marine deposits are represented by a single occurrence of a carbonate section in western Panamá, near the boundary with Costa Rica (Changuinola Formation). None of the wells drilled for petroleum on the Caribbean side of Costa Rica and Panamá have reportedly encountered rocks older than Paleocene.

Marine, volcaniclastic, volcanic, and some continental deposits of Cenozoic age crop out throughout southern Central America and northwestern Colombia. Marine deposits, principally clastic material and sequences of volcaniclastic rocks of various types, are especially thick in various basins extending along the entire region. Most of these basins also contain thick intervals of volcanic rocks, which occur predominantly within the

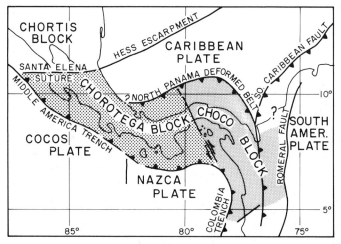

Figure 2. Structural elements of southern Central America and western Colombia.

lower part of the Tertiary section. The stratigraphic units of Cenozoic age, whether of marine or volcanic origin, will be described separately for each defined individual basin. Sedimentary rocks occurring in areas outside of recognized basins will be described for particular areas in Costa Rica and Panamá where they make up important stratigraphic units (Nicoya Peninsula, central Costa Rica, and the Azuero Peninsula of Panamá). Volcanic rocks of mostly late Cenozoic age, widespread in Costa Rica and western Panamá, will be included under the heading of continental volcanics. This section will include also Quaternary rocks of essentially volcanic origin covering over 15 percent of the region. The Quaternary volcanic sequence including various formations blanketing central and northern Costa Rica and a small area of western Panamá are the product of the latest major tectonic event in the region, which includes the currently active volcanism in northern and central Costa Rica.

Igneous intrusive rocks associated with the basement rocks are discussed in the descriptions of various units that make up the older section. Intrusives of Cenozoic age, which appear to be confined to the uppermost Tertiary, are described in conjunction with those of Quaternary age.

Most of the area covered in this chapter can be described in terms of three broad structural units with respect to the Middle America Trench; these are termed the forearc region, magmatic arc, and backarc region. In the Chorotega block, where these structural units are better defined (Fig. 4), a forearc ridge comprises the Pacific side of Costa Rica and westernmost Panamá, including the Santa Elena, Nicoya, Herradura, Osa, Burica, Soná, and Azuero Peninsulas; a magmatic arc comprises the volcanic ranges and Central Talamanca Cordillera of Costa Rica and westernmost Panamá; and the Limón Basin is a backarc feature with respect to the Middle America Trench located along the

Caribbean side of Costa Rica and Panamá. The structural units recognized in the Chorotega block trend in a general northwest to southeast direction and cannot be followed southeastward beyond the Azuero Peninsula. These on-land structural elements likewise tend to disappear northward and are not recognizable features in the southern part of the Chortis block, but the forearc ridge and forearc basin continue as offshore elements.

Other notable differences between the Chorotega and Chocó blocks will be given in the description of the stratigraphy and structure of the region and are summarized as follows:

(1) The oceanic crust common for both blocks may vary significantly in thickness for each block (Matumoto and others, 1977).

(2) The basement rocks common for both blocks, composing ostensible ophiolite complexes, may be in general somewhat older in the Chorotega block.

(3) Ignimbritic volcanic rocks and associated igneous intrusive rocks of Cenozoic age, prevalent rock types within the Chorotega block, are relatively restricted in the Chocó block.

(4) Recent or Quaternary volcanism in the Chocó block has been scant in comparison with the Chorotega block.

THE CHOROTEGA BLOCK

The Chorotega block is separated from the Cocos and Nazca plates on the west by the Middle America Trench, the single largest tectonic feature in the area and is separated from the Caribbean Plate on the east by a southwest-dipping thrust fault system, which forms part of an oceanic feature referred to as the North Panamá Deformed Belt (Case and Holcombe, 1980), which runs parallel to the Caribbean side of Panamá.

The North Panamá Deformed Belt, which is a well-defined oceanographic feature (Lu and McMillen, 1982; Case and Holcombe, 1980), extends eastward to join the South Caribbean Deformed Belt (Case and Holcombe, 1980) at a place just north of the Gulf of Urubá. The South Caribbean Deformed Belt is a major oceanographic feature located outside of the region referred to in this chapter.

The extension of the North Panamá Deformed Belt into the Caribbean side of Costa Rica cannot be established with certainty and is problematic. The fault could possibly be projected inland into the southernmost part of Costa Rica to coincide with an unnamed east-to-west-trending thrust fault system that follows along the valley of the Río Telire (Case and Holcombe, 1980; Saénz, 1982). Dengo (1985), however, assumed that the thrust fault separating the Chorotega block from the Caribbean Plate is located entirely within the Caribbean Sea and that this extends as far north as the Hess Escarpment.

The northern boundary of the Chorotega block with the Chortis is a fault system situated south of the Nicaragua–Costa Rica boundary. This major east-to-west-trending fault, as yet unnamed, is mostly covered by alluvium and late Cenozoic volcanic deposits on the mainland, but is represented to the west, by the

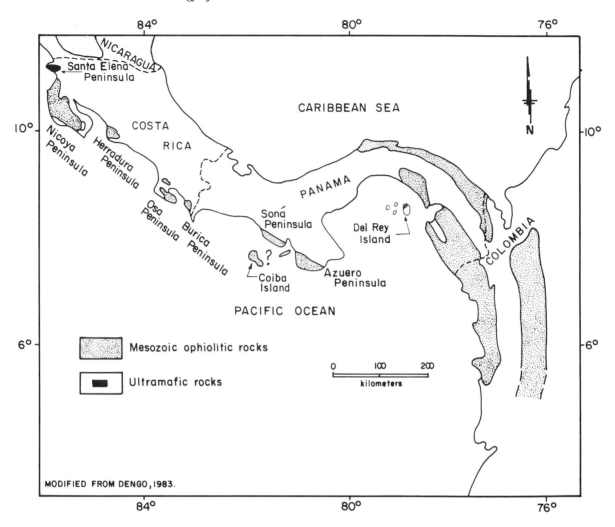

Figure 3. Distribution of basement rocks in southern Central America and western Colombia.

Santa Elena Peninsula fault system of Costa Rica, which brings to the surface a body of serpentinized peridotite. On the east, I believe this fault forms part of the southernmost extension of the Hess Escarpment (Case and Holcombe, 1980). The nature of this fault is not yet well understood but is likely to form part of one of several transcurrent faults recognized on the Santa Elena Peninsula (Dengo, 1962b), and it may also be interpreted as a crustal suture (De Boer, 1979; Dengo, 1985).

The Chorotega block is separated from the Chocó block by an inverted fault or faults that are largely reflected by a major change in the gravity values in both blocks (Case, 1974). This unnamed fault may be a northwest-trending shear zone with left lateral displacement in the central part of Panama (Case and Holcombe, 1980); it is not a recognizable surface feature although faults with a similar trend have been mapped in central Panamá, particularly on the Azuero Peninsula (Case and Holcombe, 1980).

THE CHOCÓ BLOCK

The Chocó block is confined by well-defined structural boundaries except in the area of the Gulf of Urubá. To the west, as is the case with the Chorotega block, the Chocó is bordered by the partly filled trench, which forms a sharp arcuate figure along the Pacific coast of eastern Panamá and western Colombia (Fig. 2). In this area the trench is buried under a great thickness of late Cenozoic deposits (Dengo, 1985) and is not as conspicuous an oceanographic feature as it appears elsewhere along the Pacific of Central America. In contrast to the Chorotega block, the Chocó block is overriding the Nazca Plate rather than the Cocos Plate (Fig. 2).

The Chocó block is separated from the Caribbean Plate by thrust faults of the North Panamá Deformed Belt, which serves as a boundary for the Chorotega block.

The eastern side of the Chocó block, comprising western

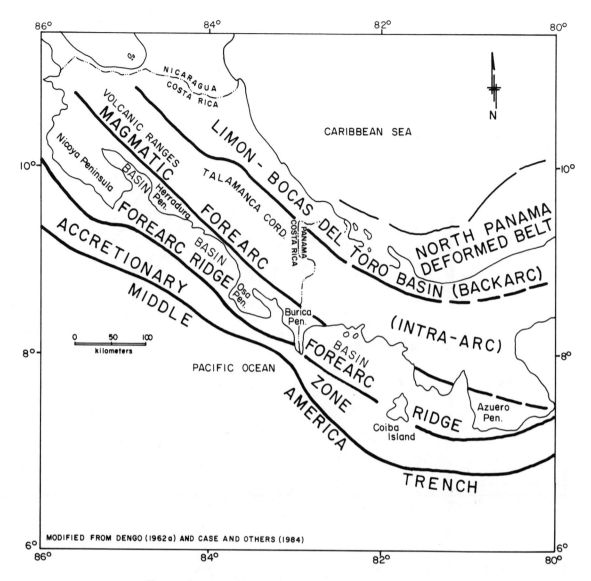

Figure 4. Structural subdivision of Costa Rica and western Panamá.

Colombia, is bordered by the prominent north-to-south-trending Romeral fault zone, which separates this segment of the South American Plate from the main South American craton. The Romeral Fault, which forms part of a megashear system known as the Dolores-Guayaquil megashear (Case and others, 1971), separates a province of "oceanic crust domain" making up the eastern part of the Chocó block from an eastern province of "continental crust domain" (Duque-Caro, 1984). These two provinces correspond respectively to the Cordillera Occidental and Cordillera Central of Colombia. Dengo (1985) did not include the Cordillera Occidental within the Chocó block and placed the eastern boundary of the Chocó at the Atrato Fault, an east-dipping reverse fault zone that extends south from the Urubá Gulf of the Caribbean. The Cordillera Occidental, however, presents geolog-

ical and geophysical characteristics of typical oceanic basement, and I consider the northern part of the Cordillera Occidental to be part of the Chocó block. The Sinú–San Jacinto geologic province of Colombia (Duque-Caro, 1984) is described elsewhere in this volume.

PRE-CRETACEOUS AND CRETACEOUS STRATIGRAPHY

No rocks of pre-Mesozoic age are known in the segment of the South America Plate comprising southern Central America and western Colombia, in contrast to the Chortis block and cratonic South America where rocks of pre-Mesozoic age are important stratigraphic units.

In southern Central America and western Colombia, the pre-Cretaceous and Cretaceous stratigraphic sequence may be divided into two groups: a major one comprising mafic, basically ophiolitic complexes and a younger, more restricted unit, which includes a number of well-defined marine formations of "middle" and Late Cretaceous age.

The extensive mafic basement rocks in the region will be described separately under the heading of ophiolite complexes. Deposits of Cretaceous age, which consist of carbonate and clastic rocks, will also be treated separately under a single heading because most of these units appear as erosional windows in poorly defined basins.

The ophiolite complexes

The oldest rocks in southern Central America and western Colombia comprise rock types generally associated with ophiolitic sequences such as basalt, pillow lava, agglomerate and gabbro, and diabase intrusives, which are associated with chert and siliceous limestone. The term "ophiolite" has been commonly used in the literature to refer to these rocks making up the basement, and the name is used with the reservation that some of the rock types referred to as ophiolitic in this chapter may include mafic or ultramafic rocks of a different type originating as primitive magmatic arcs, oceanic plateaus, or flood basalts rather than at spreading ridges. The ophiolitic complex forming the basement for the Chorotega and Chocó blocks is of mostly Cretaceous and pre-Cretaceous age. Consistently older isotopic age determinations obtained from the Chorotega block, however, seems to point to an older age for this block than for the Chocó where basement rocks as young as 41 ± 3 m.y. have been recognized (Bourgois and others, 1982).

In the Chorotega block, these rocks have been designated the Nicoya Complex (Dengo, 1962b). In the Chocó block, ophiolitic rocks are not as well known as in the Chorotega block, because they cover large areas within the more inaccessible mountainous parts of eastern Panamá and western Colombia. The ophiolitic rocks have been described under various names (e.g., Complejo Basal in Panamá, Basic Igneous Complex of Colombia) and comprise the Serranías de San Blás, Pirré, and Sapo in Panamá; the Serranía de Baudó, shared by Panamá and Colombia; and the Serranía de los Saltos and the Cordillera Occidental in Colombia.

On the basis of chemical composition and other geological considerations, Goossens and Rose (1973) and Goossens and others (1977) were able to establish a correlation between the various mafic igneous groups cropping out in Panamá and western Colombia with the Nicoya Complex; they extended this correlation southward to include the Piñón Formation and the Diabase Porphyry Formation of Ecuador.

The Nicoya Complex. The Nicoya Complex is by far the best described ophiolitic complex in southern Central America. This group of rocks consisting of a folded sequence of basalt, sedimentary units, and intrusive bodies was originally described by Dengo (1962b) and recently, in greater detail, by a large number of investigators who have concentrated their study almost entirely in the Nicoya Peninsula of Costa Rica. Little is known about this stratigraphic unit from other areas of Costa Rica (Herradura, Osa, and Burica Peninsulas) and Panamá (Burica, Soná, and Azuero Peninsulas).

At the type locality, the Nicoya Complex has been divided into two mayor units (De Boer, 1979; Kuijpers, 1980; Schmidt-Effing and others, 1980). The lower portion, of undetermined thickness, consists of massive basalt with characteristic pillow flows. This unit contains little or no intercalated sedimentary material and may be as old as Early Jurassic (F. Rivier, personal communication, 1982). Definite Late Jurassic (Galli-Olivier, 1979) and earliest Cretaceous to Aptian (Kuijpers, 1980) radiolarian age determinations for this unit have also been obtained in the Nicoya Peninsula. The lower unit of the Nicoya Complex has been considered to represent the upper level of uplifted oceanic crust by most of the workers. The serpentinized peridotite of The Santa Elena Peninsula is considered by some (Galli-Olivier, 1979; De Boer, 1979) to be associated ultramafic rocks representing somewhat deeper oceanic crust or upper mantle.

The upper unit of the Nicoya Complex comprises a variety of rock types. The origin, as well as the age, of these heterogeneous sequences has been disputed. De Boer (1979) considered the upper unit to be a volcanic arc complex consisting of an upper unit of pillow lava and volcanic agglomerate intercalated with chert, siliceous limestone, and tuffaceous deposits. Schmidt-Effing (1979) divided the upper unit of the Nicoya Complex into six subcomplexes, which were defined on the basis of the age differences determined from the sedimentary rocks (both as xenoliths and sedimentary cover).

The biostratigraphic correlation of these subcomplexes, according to Schmidt-Effing (1979), indicates that the uppermost Nicoya Complex ranges in age from Maastrichtian to Eocene and is generally 2 to 3 km thick. Kuijpers (1980) described a 300-m-plus upper unit of the Nicoya Complex composed of basalt and ophitic diabase with common occurrences of gabbroic rocks. A Cenomanian to early Santonian age was determined on the basis of a radiolarite intercalation present within the upper part of this unit (Kuijpers, 1980). Kuijpers interpreted the upper unit of the Nicoya Complex to be a nappe of younger oceanic crust that has been thrust over the older oceanic crust of the lower part of the Nicoya Complex. He gave the name Matapalo Unit to the lower part of the Nicoya Complex and Esperanza Unit to the upper.

More recently, Schmidt-Effing and others (1980) presented a simplified subdivision of the Nicoya Complex into a lower and upper part intercalated with a thick sequence of thick, sheet-like, submarine flows. This subdivision does not take into account the peridotites of the Santa Elena Peninsula or other stratigraphic units above the upper Nicoya flows.

Rocks like the Nicoya Complex have been described in lesser detail along other places of the Pacific coastal area of Costa Rica and Panamá, all within the Chorotega block. At one of these localities, the Herradura Peninsula of Costa Rica (Fig. 3), sequences of ophiolitic rocks have been combined into a single stratigraphic unit named the Quepos Subcomplex (Baumgartner, 1984). The age is likely to be younger than the Nicoya Complex: early Cenozoic (Henningsen and Weyl, 1967) near the Paleocene-Eocene boundary (Schmidt-Effing, 1979). Azéma and others (1979) reported Danian microfossils in a limestone (Golfito Formation) associated with the basalts within rocks assigned to this subcomplex. However, I believe the Golfito Formation to be a separate stratigraphic unit as referred to under the heading of other stratigraphic units of Cretaceous and pre-Cretaceous age.

The Osa Peninsula on the southern part of the Pacific coast of Costa Rica was thought to be composed almost entirely of undivided Nicoya Complex rocks (Dóndoli and others, 1968) until Lew (1983) described a Tertiary sedimentary cover over most of the peninsula. He described large xenoliths of Mesozoic and early Tertiary radiolarian and tuffaceous cherts within "massive" basalt flows as well as "intrusive" basalts that cut Paleocene limestones. The interrelation of the two types of basalt cannot be established without proper petrologic and isotope data, but it appears that neither can be older than early Eocene.

No isotopic dates are available for these basement rocks, but in the interior of the peninsula and to the northwest, it is overlain by Eocene (probably middle Eocene) limestones equivalent to the David Limestone of the Chiriquí province of Panamá or the nearby El Cajón Limestone of Costa Rica.

The Burica Peninsula (Fig. 3) also contains rocks that are almost certain to be of the Nicoya type. These rocks were first described by Terry (1941) as forming part of a "backbone of hornblende andesite," but later were reported to be more extensively exposed on the Costa Rican side of the peninsula (Terry, 1956). Some of these rocks consist of pillow basalts with interbedded siliceous units, which resemble those typical of the Nicoya Complex (personal notes).

The basement rocks cropping out in the Azuero Peninsula and the smaller adjacent Soná Peninsula of Panamá generally resemble those typical of the Nicoya Complex in Costa Rica, although this name has not been generally applied to basement rocks of Panamá. Rocks quite different from those in the Nicoya Complex have also been described from the Azuero and Soná Peninsulas; del Giudice and Recchi (1969) mapped schists. Bourgois and others (1982) observed that these are a metamorphosed volcanic-sedimentary sequence and are probably the oldest exposed rocks occurring in Panamá. The schists and basalts are both overlain by pillow basalts and a sedimentary cover including limestones (Ocú Formation) with a late Campanian-Maastrichtian microfauna (del Giudice and Recchi, 1969). Granitoid rocks also occur on the Azuero Peninsula (Terry, 1956; Anonymous, 1976). Terry (1956) reported serpentine described by Dunn from the west side of peninsula and on the coast near the Gulf of Montijo. Some questions remain as to the nature of the rocks that crop out in the poorly known Coiba Island, located between the Burica and Azuero Peninsulas (Fig. 3), which according to Terry (1956) comprises some pre-Eocene rocks.

Hershey (1901) described altered volcanic rocks ("Azuero

Formation"), which he considered to be the oldest in the Peninsula and referred to this broadly as "green eruptive formation." More recently Bourgois and others (1982) discussed extensive occurrences of pre-Tertiary volcanosedimentary rocks on the Azuero Peninsula and dated basalt flows at Playa Venado at 98 Ma. My observations indicate the overall striking similarity of the ophiolitic rocks in the Nicoya and Azuero Peninsulas.

Other complexes. The eastern portion of Panamá and western Colombia, in the Chocó block, contain large areas of basement rocks. Most of these units resemble rock types characteristic of the Chorotega block. Rocks of the Chocó block, however, have not been studied in detail and remain to be compared with the better-known complexes within the Chorotega block. Some of these, however, may not be correctly referred to as ophiolites.

At least half of the surface of eastern Panamá is occupied by igneous rocks forming part of a basement complex. Mafic intrusive and extrusive rocks are particularly common east of the Canal Zone where they are the dominant rock type on the Pacific and Caribbean coastal ranges of the Darién region (Case, 1974). East of the Canal Zone the rugged uplands, referred to as the Serranía de San Blás and Serranía del Darién are entirely composed of igneous rocks that have been broadly mapped as "pre-Tertiary." As in the Pacific ranges, mafic igneous rock types dominate, although granitoid rocks similar to those cropping out in the Cordillera Occidental of Colombia are also present. Granitoid plutons cut the basement of the Serranía del Darién (Kesler and others, 1977; Anonymous, 1976).

Bandy and Casey (1973) identified Late Cretaceous fossils from the sedimentary sequence within the basement around the Gulf of San Miguel where dense, well-preserved pillow basalt and diabase are associated with deformed chert and thin-bedded, siliceous, radiolarian-rich, abyssal, oceanic, sedimentary rocks. Goossens and others (1977) believed that these rocks are closest to oceanic tholeiites in composition. Bourgois and others (1982) compared this basement complex with that of the Quepos and Osa Peninsulas of Costa Rica and that of the Serranía de Baudó of Colombia. Several drill holes (maximum of 740 m) made by the Atlantic-Pacific Interoceanic Canal Commission (1968) along a proposed new canal route north of La Palma, traversed intervals of tuff, diabase, basalt, and agglomerate.

On the northwestern side of the Isla del Rey, the largest of the islands within the Archipelago of Las Perlas, the basement complex is composed of basalt, interbedded sediments (jasper), basalt agglomerate, and associated diorite intrusives (personal notes), but the age is unknown.

The Pacific coastal ranges of eastern Panamá continue into western Colombia as the Serranía de Baudó. This structural unit extends along the western Pacific coast of Colombia as far as Cabo Corrientes, which forms the western border of the Atrato Basin. Within this extensive area, the basement rocks consist of pillow flows, diabases, andesites, serpentinites, tuffs, and volcanic agglomerates (Case and others, 1971; Case, 1974). Etayo and others (1983) also reported peridotites and gabbros from the area.

Late Cretaceous (Campanian) age determinations based on radiolaria and foraminifera (Bandy and Casey, 1973), ammonites (Haffer, 1967), as well as Late Cretaceous radiometric dates from basalt (Bourgois and others, 1982), have been obtained from this sequence of basement rocks in western Colombia and appear to be compatible with most of the age determinations obtained from the Nicoya Complex. Early Miocene nannofauna from a melange (Bourgois and others, 1982), as well as middle Eocene and Oligocene radiometric dates from these rocks, on the other hand, point out the occurrence of much younger basement rock in the Chocó than in the Chorotega block (Nicoya Complex).

The basement rocks of the Cordillera Occidental of Colombia include pillow basalts, gabbros, volcanic breccia, and agglomerates with interbedded chert and tuff of Late(?) Cretaceous age (Alvarez and González, 1978) that are intruded by Tertiary granitoid plutons (Case and others, 1984). The occurrence of local metamorphic belts within this area is in contrast with basement rocks elsewhere in the Chocó block (and Chorotega block) where metamorphic rocks are barely known.

Other stratigraphic units

There still remains some confusion as to which sedimentary rocks are included within the Nicoya Complex. This hinges on the various definitions of the complex as given by different authors. Schmidt-Effing (1979) included rocks as young as Eocene, whereas Henningsen and Weyl (1967) did not consider the complex to extend beyond the Maastrichtian. Galli-Olivier (1979) believed the youngest age limit of the complex to be middle Santonian–early Campanian. This problem in the definition of the Nicoya Complex and associated units of sedimentary rocks is further compounded by the fact that the sedimentary units covering the Nicoya Complex have undergone intensive folding and in some cases appear to be conformable with upper beds of the Nicoya Complex.

Notwithstanding the above, the stratigraphic units of Cretaceous age, whether or not they belong in the Nicoya Complex, are almost entirely restricted to the Pacific side of southern Central America, especially in the Chorotega block and particularly within the Nicoya Peninsula of Costa Rica. Rivier (1983) described the Barbudal Conglomerate Formation, which overlies Nicoya Complex rocks, as the oldest stratigraphic unit in the lower course of the Río Tempisque. The Barbudal (described only from this locality) is a poorly consolidated reddish conglomerate attaining over 100 m in thickness and is considered to be of possible continental origin. Incidentally, this stratigraphic unit may represent evidence for an early emersion of the Nicoya Complex prior to deposition of the Campanian Rivas Formation. The Campanian to middle Eocene Rivas Formation, better known from its type locality in southwestern Nicaragua (Chortis block), consists of tuffaceous shales and siltstones and calcareous graywacke with rare limestone interbeds considered to have been deposited under varying deep and shallow marine conditions.

The formation has been subdivided into many stratigraphic units of apparent local significance in Costa Rica (Sprechmann, 1984). The Sabana Grande Formation, described from the central part of the Nicoya Peninsula, consists of siliceous limestones, chert, and radiolarian phtanites of Senonian (Dengo, 1962b) to Campanian age (Madrigal, 1976), which Laguna (1977) proposed be included within the Rivas Formation. At the southeastern end of the Nicoya Peninsula, Lundberg (1982) introduced the term "sandstone and mudstone of Cabo Blanco" for thin-bedded turbidites considered to be the seaward facies equivalent of the Rivas and Las Palmas (Paleocene) Formations.

The Golfito Formation (Cretaceous and early Paleocene), having a type locality near Golfo Dulce in the southern Pacific region of Costa Rica, is a well-defined stratigraphic unit composed of pelagic, siliceous, dense limestone; shale; and siltstone (Dengo, 1962a). The Sabana Grande, Golfito, and Rivas Formations unconformably overlie rocks belonging to the Nicoya Complex. In Punta Quepos, the Golfito Formation limestone fills erosion surfaces in basalt flows of the upper Nicoya Complex or occurs as interbeds between pillows. Basaltic sands and conglomerates associated with the Golfito limestones indicate the occurrence of submarine erosion contemporaneous to deposition of limestone.

Various stratigraphic units of questionable Cretaceous age, which do not form part of the basement complex, have been recognized within the Azuero Peninsula of Panamá. One of these, the Ocú Formation, composed of fossiliferous limestone has been mapped by del Giudice and Recchi (1969).

On the Caribbean side, however, Cretaceous deposits are known only from a small single inlier of marine and volcaniclastic rocks referred to as the Changuinola Formation, which crops out on the Panamanian side of the Costa Rica–Panamá boundary.

The Changuinola Formation (Fisher and Pessagno, 1965) at its type locality consists of tan, well-bedded, foraminiferal limestones and interbedded tuffs, agglomerates, and lava flows having a total thickness of 1,280 m. The base of the section at Río Changuinola consists of argillaceous white to light gray limestone containing shaly lime mudstone and wackestone rich in planktonic microfossils (personal notes). Within this lower interval, well-bedded olive-green shale, volcanic breccia, and volcanic sand also occur. The thickest intervals of limestone within the formation are the middle and upper part of the section. These rocks consist mostly of very argillaceous, siliceous, and recrystallized limestones occurring interbedded with volcanic sandstone and tuff. Age determinations from microfauna indicate a late Campanian to early Maastrichtian age.

The Changuinola Formation has never been encountered by the drill in exploratory work carried out by petroleum companies on the Caribbean coastal area of Costa Rica and Panamá. This formation, furthermore, has not been found outside of the Río Changuinola area, although the Ocú Formation, which crops out in the Azuero Peninsula, contains limestones of similar age as those in the Changuinola Formation. The relationship between these two units, however, is not known because very little information is available on the Ocú Formation.

Cretaceous units within the Chocó block are generally considered to form part of the basement complex that contains rocks as young as Eocene. Stratigraphic units of Cretaceous age that do not form part of the basement complex have not yet been recognized as independent units.

The Nercua Group, which overlies the Chocó volcanics (basement complex) in the Atrato Basin of Colombia, believed to be mostly of an early Tertiary age, might include a lower interval of Cretaceous age. Late(?) Cretaceous marine deposits in the Cordillera Occidental comprise an unnamed sequence of pelagic carbonates, siliceous beds, and a turbidite sequence overlying basement rocks (Alvarez and González, 1978).

TERTIARY AND QUATERNARY STRATIGRAPHY

Southern Central America contains a large number of narrow and elongated sedimentary basins (Fig. 5) which are not well defined in terms of size and stratigraphy. A limited amount of work has been undertaken in these basins, and they are of difficult access. The stratigraphy of the better known basins, especially those of Limón–Bocas del Toro and the Térraba-Chiriquí (Fig. 5), is derived from surface geological work and meager subsurface information obtained from the intermittent exploratory work carried out by petroleum companies. Regional studies, moreover, are lacking to correlate the stratigraphy of these basins within a single tectonic framework.

Additional stratigraphic information from southern Central America has been obtained from the study of scattered exposures of sedimentary rocks in areas mostly covered by basement complex rocks or appearing as inliers surrounded by younger sequences of volcanic rocks and alluvial material. Occurrences of sedimentary rocks within these particular areas, such as the Nicoya Peninsula, the Central Valley of Costa Rica, and the Azuero Peninsula probably represent extensions of neighboring sedimentary basins or possibly denote the erosional remnants of as yet unidentified basins.

The stratigraphic sequence of Cenozoic age includes a number of volcanic units, such as tuffs, agglomerates, and flows that are interlayered with sedimentary rocks. These are described in the stratigraphy of particular basins. Other volcanic rocks (of mostly late Tertiary age), extensively distributed outside of recognized basins, are referred to under the heading of continental volcanics. Numerous poorly defined and small marine, continental and volcanic deposits of Quaternary age are known in the area.

The stratigraphy of southern Central America will be described for individual sedimentary basins and localities as follows: (a) sedimentary cover of the Nicoya Peninsula and vicinity; (b) sedimentary rocks in central Costa Rica; (c) Pacific coastal basins of Costa Rica and western Panamá; (d) Térraba-Chiriquí Basin; (e) Limón–Bocas del Toro Basin; (f) sedimentary cover of the Azuero Peninsula; (g) Canal Basin, central Panamá; (h) Gulf of Panamá; (i) Bayano, Tuira-Chucunaque, Sambú and Atrato Basins; and (j) continental volcanic deposits.

The Nicoya and Azuero Peninsulas (a and f), the Pacific coastal basins of Costa Rica and western Panamá (c), and the Gulf of Panamá (h) are located, in reference to the Middle America Trench, within the forearc ridge of the Chorotega block. Central Costa Rica and the Térraba-Chiriquí Basin (b and d) are located within the magmatic forearc, and the Limón–Bocas del Toro Basin (e) is a backarc feature within this same block.

The Bayano, Tuirá.-Chucunaque, Sambú, and Atrato Basins (i) are considered to be grabens within the Chocó region, an uplifted block of oceanic crust. The Canal Basin (g) is likely to have developed from faulting associated with the separation of the Chocó and the Chorotega blocks. Continental volcanics of Cenozoic age are widely distributed along the intra-arc of the Chorotega block in both Costa Rica and Panamá and from a few scattered localities within the Chocó block.

Sedimentary cover of the Nicoya Peninsula and vicinity

Kuijpers (1979) subdivided the sedimentary section overlying the Nicoya Complex in the Nicoya Peninsula into two groups: a lower series ranging in age from Campanian to middle Eocene (Sabana Grande, Rivas, and Las Palmas Formations referred to under Cretaceous stratigraphy) and an upper sequence of Miocene and Pliocene age. Late Eocene to early Miocene strata have not been recognized in the Nicoya Peninsula. The upper series of rocks in Nicoya composes from oldest to youngest: the Brito, Masachapa, Punta Carballo, and Montezuma Formations.

The early to middle Eocene Brito Formation, like the Rivas Formation, was first described and defined from southeast Nicaragua, and later recognized in northwestern Costa Rica (Descartes Peninsula and Bahía de Junquillal) by Dengo (1962b). The formation at these two places consists of alternating sequences of sandstones and siltstones with lenticular limestone bodies in its uppermost part. In the Manzanillo area, located on the eastern side of the Gulf of Nicoya (just outside of the Nicoya Peninsula), the formation is represented by conglomerates and tuffaceous sandstones that display the rapid lateral facies changes that characterize the older Rivas and Las Palmas Formations. In the Río Tempisque area, Rivier (1983) described the formation as represented by an alternating sequence of calcilutites, calcarenites, and fine-grained tuffs with some tuffaceous conglomerates in the upper part. Here the Brito Formation is in conformable contact at its base with the "Cerro de Piedra Conglomeratic Formation," referred to originally by Sprechmann (1984). The formation as described by Rivier (1983) is of Paleocene age and consists of volcanic conglomerates and conglomeratic sandstones for a total thickness of 500 m and seems to be restricted to its type locality on the western side of the lower Río Tempisque. As such, the Cerco de Piedra Formation might represent a facies of the Brito. Dengo (1962b) considered the Brito to be transitional with the underlying Las Palmas Formation in the Nicoya Peninsula.

Dengo also suggested extension of the name through the

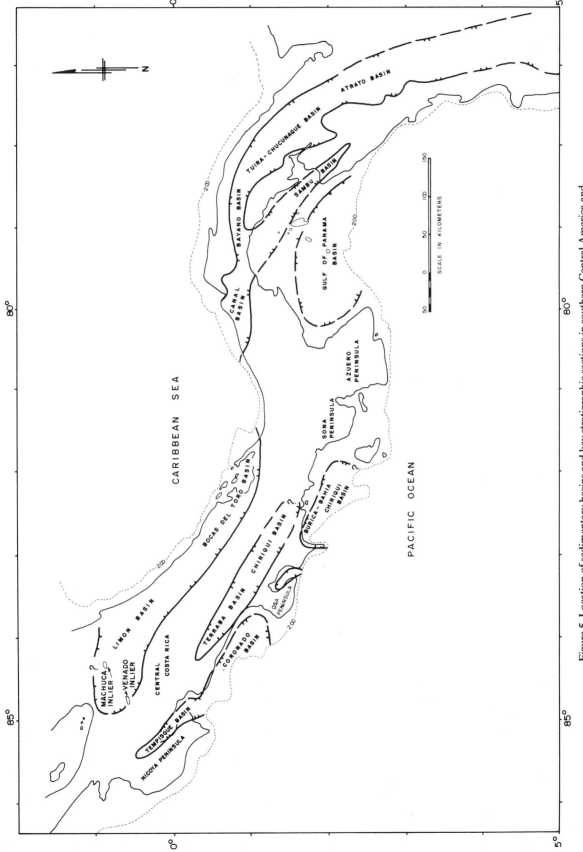

Figure 5. Location of sedimentary basins and key stratigraphic sections in southern Central America and western Colombia.

Pacific region of Costa Rica to the Chiriquí Province of Panamá. Others, such as Baungartner (in Sprechmann, 1984), have preferred to assign separate terminology names to the many local facies variations within the Brito Formation.

The Brito Formation basically displays the same style of deposition shown by the preceeding Rivas and Las Palmas sections and represents the end phase of a cycle of turbidite deposition that began in the Late Cretaceous and ceased toward the end of the Eocene. A final shallowing phase that ended the tectonic cycle led to a widespread limestone facies at the top of the Brito Formation. This can be traced southeastward through the Nicoya Peninsula (Junquillal and Punta Cuevas Limestones), the central Pacific provinces (Damas Limestone), and the Térraba Basin (El Cajón and Fila de Cal Limestones) to the Chiriquí Province of Panamá (David Limestone).

The Masachapa Formation of Oligocene age has been described in detail from a type locality in southwestern Nicaragua (Zoppis Bracci and del Giudice, 1958). Dengo (1962b) recognized the presence of a sedimentary sequence of Oligocene age at two localities within the Nicoya Peninsula, which he tentatively equated with the Masachapa Formation of Nicaragua. At Río Manzanillo, located on the southwestern end of the peninsula, the formation comprises medium-grained thin-bedded sandstones overlain by siltstone, fine-grained sandstone, and calcareous shale. This section resembles lithologically the type section at Masachapa (southwestern Nicaragua).

The other locality is along the lower course of the Río Nosara (situated about 60 km northwest of Manzanillo) where the Masachapa Formation is represented by fine-grain fossiliferous sandstone overlain by light gray, very fossiliferous, arenaceous limestone; calcareous sandstone; and shale. The Massachapa Formation at these localities contains a late Oligocene fauna. The formation in Nicaragua, on the other hand, is considered to be entirely within the lower Oligocene (Zoppis Bracci and del Giudice, 1958).

Detailed surface geological work by students from the University of Costa Rica within small areas on the southern and western side of the Nicoya Peninsula has led to new stratigraphic information and the naming of a large number of lithostratigraphic units of localized significance. One unit, however, the "Sandstone-Shale Sámara Formation," includes the entire Masachapa Formation as well as other overlying and underlying stratigraphic sequences (Sprechmann, 1984). This may be found to have regional significance if equated with the Pacacua and Térraba Formations with type sections in the Central Valley and Térraba River Valley of Costa Rica respectively.

Some confusion exists in regard to the age of the carbonate sequence that crops out in the lower Río Tempisque Valley, which was originally described by Dengo (1962b) as a separate formation (the Barra Honda Formation) of Danian-Montanian age and by Mora (1981) as post-Paleocene age. Rivier (1983) referred to this as a bioherm and biostrome deposit that developed in shallow, clean, and warm waters; it attains a maximum thickness of about 250 m and was tentatively assigned a Miocene age. The formation, described only from the type locality, overlies in sharp angular unconformity rocks as old as Maastrichtian (Rivas Formation).

The Punta Carballo Formation, containing fauna of middle and late Miocene age, is made up mostly of poorly bedded, fine-grained, grayish green, calcareous sandstone. At places the formation is very fossiliferous. Petrographic studies from representative samples of this formation indicate that the rock is highly contaminated by volcanic material and in some cases should be better referred to as a vulcarenite and tuffaceous shale (Baxter, 1976). The Punta Carballo Formation is estimated to be at least 200 m thick at the type locality (just south from the port of Puntarenas) where it unconformably overlies basement rocks.

The Punta Carballo stratigraphic sequence was first mentioned by MacDonald (1920). Dengo (1960) gave the rank of formation to this stratigraphic unit; Madrigal (1970) divided the formation into a lower and upper member, and Baxter (1976) assigned a formational name (Mata de Limón) to the lower member of the Punta Carballo Formation. This last definition has not yet been formalized.

The Montezuma Formation is composed entirely of clastic material, mostly silty to medium-grain fossiliferous sandstone that contains lenticular bodies of coarser sandstone that might be better described, in part, as a lithic graywacke. Friable sandstone samples from this formation have a fairly high porosity and permeability values (personal notes). The formation is characteristically massive and thick bedded, moderately calcareous, and unconformably overlies basalt and chert of the Nicoya Complex at the type locality. The contact is marked in some places by a basal conglomerate. The fauna of the Montezuma Formation indicates deposition in shallow warm marine waters.

The Montezuma Formation was first named and recognized as a stratigraphic entity for Goudkoff and Porter (1942) who assigned a Miocene age based on fossil evidence. Dengo (1962b) judged that the Montezuma Formation was a younger age (possibly late Miocene but more likely Mio-Pliocene) based on the fact that the Punta Carballo Formation, considered middle Miocene, has been subjected to more structural deformation than the Montezuma Formation.

Sedimentary rocks in central Costa Rica

No systematic effort has yet been made to describe the numerous stratigraphic units that crop out as isolated occurrences, small inliers, and erosional remnants in the extensive Quaternary volcanic field that characterizes central Costa Rica. In the Central Valley of Costa Rica and surrounding mountainous country, a number of stratigraphic units have been described and named; most of these sections, however, have not been recognized as formal stratigraphic units, and others may represent facies of well-defined formations from elsewhere in Costa Rica.

The oldest recognized formation in central Costa Rica is a sequence of poorly defined clastic deposits that lithologically resemble the Brito Formation from elsewhere in Costa Rica. The stratigraphic sequence in central Costa Rica contains an interval of dark gray foraminiferal limestone having a very distinctive Eocene fauna known as the Parritilla Limestone (Castillo, 1984). The Parritilla Limestone forms part of a conspicuous carbonate level known under many names elsewhere in the Chorotega block (see Plate 4).

The Pacacua Formation with type section in central Costa Rica (Castillo, 1969) consists of tuffaceous poorly bedded breccia conglomerate and usually well-bedded conglomeratic sandstone, sandstone, siltstone, and shale. Most of the sequence is slightly to moderately calcareous, and the various lithological units range widely in color, with shades of gray and purple prevalent. Castillo (1969) attributed a probable Eocene age to the formation, which according to him, is overlain unconformably at the type locality by deposits of the Oligocene-Miocene Térraba Formation and late Cenozoic and Quaternary volcanic rocks. Rivier (1979), however, assigned the Pacacua a definite Miocene age on paleontological data, and furthermore estimated this to be a facies of the San Miguel, Turrúcares, and Coris Formations, which are distinctive lithological units in the Central Valley of Costa Rica. The question remains, however, as to whether or not the Pacacua may also represent a facies of the Térraba Formation of Oligo-Miocene age, which has not been clearly defined as such within the central part of Costa Rica.

The Turrúcares Formation consisting of fossiliferous conglomerate, limestone, volcaniclastic sediments, and sandstone has yielded a middle and late Miocene fauna (Woodring and Malavassi, 1961; Castillo, 1969; Montero, 1974; Fischer, 1981a, b). The formation crops out within a small area on the western side of the Central Valley of Costa Rica.

The San Miguel Formation of early Miocene age (Carballo and Fischer, 1978) is composed mostly of carbonates and is another distinctive lithological unit in Costa Rica where it crops out intermittently along the southern part of the Central Valley. According to Carballo and Fischer (1978), who described in detail 29 measured sections from different localities, the San Miguel Formation has considerable facies variation and differences in thickness, and they referred to a varied lithology including bioclastic limestone, nodular limestone, crystalline limestone, calcareous sandstone, conglomeratic sandstone, brecciated conglomerate, and shale. Thin sectioning of the limestones reveals this to be mostly packstones with lesser percentages of wackestones and grainstone. Furthermore, Carballo and Fischer (1978), interpreted the paleoenvironment of the San Miguel as offshore sandbar that was emergent at times. Sprechmann (1984) has reinterpreted the paleontological data from the observed biofacies.

Carballo and Fischer's study (1978) defined the stratigraphic contacts of the San Miguel Formation, which is a sharp lithological break between underlying fine-grained calcareous sandstones and an overlying contact with the Coris Formation, which has both transitional contact relationship and sharp lithological breaks.

The Coris Formation, a 360-m-thick tabular body consisting of prevalent quartz arenites, tuff, vulcarenites, and minor shale interbeds is another well-defined stratigraphic unit cropping extensively to the south and southeast of the Central Valley of Costa Rica. The most conspicuous rock type in the formation is a medium- to coarse-grained quartz arenite and true quartzites at some localities. The Coris Formation, which contains a middle to late Miocene fauna, has been summarized in 21 measured columnar sections by Fischer and Franco (1979) indicating sublittoral marine, intermediate, and terrestrial facies corresponding to a regressive cycle.

Much speculation has surrounded the source of the quartz within the Coris Formation because no pre-Miocene source for a large amount of quartz is known anywhere in central Costa Rica and, in fact, nowhere within the northern part of southern Central America. Fischer and Franco (1979) speculated on the erosion of Paleogene volcanic rocks (not clearly defined anywhere in the northern part of southern Central America) as a source. The reported occurrence of metaquartzite fragments and undulose quartz grains in samples of sandstone from the Coris Formation has led others to believe that the source of this detrital quartz is a metamorphic terrane (personal notes). However, no quartzose metamorphic rocks have ever been discovered in southern Central America.

Pacific coastal basins of Costa Rica and western Panama

Limited marine seismic surveys on the Pacific side of Costa Rica and western Panamá indicate a number of relatively small sedimentary basins that have not yet been drilled. None of these have been given a formal name or defined in terms of their size, and all remain to be properly described in the literature. The largest of these basins extends along the central Pacific area of Costa Rica, where the continental shelf is at its widest and covers most of Coronado Bay, the Gulf of Nicoya, and the lower course of the Río Tempisque. This basin informally referred to in this chapter as the Tempisque-Coronado basin (Fig. 5). Several stratigraphic units previously described in the Nicoya Peninsula crop out in the immediate vicinity of the Gulf of Nicoya, and some of these units dip toward the basin; the most relevant being the Montezuma and Punta Carballo Formations.

More significant yet, in this particular basin, is the presence of an unnamed thick section of clastic strata that crops out along the beach at Punta Judas on the central Pacific coastal area of Costa Rica. This unit, recently described in the literature (Seyfried and others, 1985), consists predominately of sandstone and subordinate silty sandstone of greenish blue and greenish gray color, contains minor intervals of conglomerate, and is abundantly fossiliferous (molluscs, echinoids, and trace fossils; Seyfried and others, 1985). They considered the Punta Judas section to have been deposited in an estuarine embayment estimated to exceed 1,200 m in thickness and assumed the sequence to be of middle Miocene age on the basis of foraminifera. Preliminary palynological studies of samples of this section indicate, however, a possible Pliocene age (E. González-Guzmán, personal communication, 1985). The stratigraphic position of the Punta Judas section, however, remains to be properly determined with respect to the Montezuma and Punta Carballo Formations, which are well-defined formations in the central Pacific coastal area of Costa Rica.

The seismic data from the central Pacific shelf area of Costa Rica indicates the presence of two distinctive stratigraphic units, briefly described by Buffler (1982) and Crowe and Buffler (1983). The oldest of these units, referred to under the term "accretionary zone," is characterized by chaotic seismic reflections and refractions and is clearly separated from an overlying unit by a prominent unconformity. In addition, the seismic profiles also indicate the presence of a "slope apron unit," which represents an overlying layered section of inferred sedimentary rocks. According to preliminary interpretations by Buffler (1982), the slope apron unit indicates a number of depositional episodes.

None of these seismic stratigraphic units have yet been correlated with land sections. Crowe and Buffler (1983) stated that the nature and origin of the accretionary complex, as indicated by the seismic records, remains one of the major problems to be resolved in the interpretation of the offshore Pacific area of Costa Rica.

Very little is known about the extensions and interrelations of other sedimentary basins in the offshore of the southern Pacific area of Costa Rica and the contiguous portion of western Panamá. The Burica Peninsula contains a thick sequence of clastic marine deposits of late Tertiary and Quaternary age that overlies a basement complex resembling rocks of the Nicoya Complex. This stratigraphic sequence, exposed along the coastline of the peninsula, has been penetrated by the Corotú-1 well located on the Panamanian side of the peninsula and is also present, at least in part, along the northeastern shore of the Golfo Dulce in Costa Rica. The section exposed on the Panamanian side of the Burica Peninsula comprises mostly conglomerates, sandstones, and claystones, and has been divided into formations that together exceed 2,300 m in thickness. This, however, does not include lower Tertiary strata that occur as restricted inliers overlying basement rocks in the interior of the Burica Peninsula (Terry, 1941; Olsson, 1942), which resemble some of the formations that have been recognized in the Térraba-Chiriquí Basin.

The very fossiliferous post-Eocene section of the Burica Peninsula has been described in great detail. Molluscs have been investigated by Olsson (1942), foraminifera by Coryell and Mossmann (1942), and foraminifera from the Corotú-1 well by Brixley (in Terry, 1956).

The Charco Azul Formation containing late Miocene and Pliocene foraminifera (Coryell and Mossman, 1942) is the oldest of the stratigraphic units cropping out along the Burica Peninsula and is composed mostly of silty shales with rare sandy or limy horizons. A basalt member of this formation, referred to as the Burica Sandstone (Olsson, 1942), contains a basalt conglomerate. The faunal assemblage in the Charco Azul is indicative of gradual deepening of the depositional environment to outer shelf or bathyal depths.

The Armuelles Formation of Pleistocene age, overlies the Charco Azul Formation in sharp angular unconformity. The basal part of this unit is a thick layer of massive conglomerate, interbedded with dark blue sandstones. The section fines upward into well-bedded lignitic shales that tend to be more sandy toward the top of the formation.

Very little is known about the offshore extension of the sedimentary section from the Burica Peninsula because no drilling has been undertaken and no seismic data have yet been released. This offshore sedimentary basin underlies the Bahía de Chiriquí in Panamá and lengthens as a narrow belt into the Golfo Dulce in Costa Rica. A further extension of such a basin might lie under Quaternary alluvium in the coastal plain of southwesternmost Panamá.

The late Tertiary and Quaternary deposits in the Osa Peninsula of Costa Rica are poorly known. The geological map of Costa Rica (Sáenz, 1982) shows the Charco Azul and Armuelles Formation along the coast and inland in the peninsula, although no description of these units is given in the literature. Lew (1983) described in detail a middle Pliocene section of conglomerate, siltstone, and sandstone at Punta La Chancha (Punta La Chancha Formation), which he believed to be a submarine fan deposit, but he failed to correlate this with the neighboring sections at Punta Judas and the Burica Peninsula. Thus the question remains as to whether the section referred to by Lew (1983) forms part of the Burica Basin of Panamá or is an extension of the Coronado Basin of the central Pacific coastal area of Costa Rica.

Térraba-Chiriquí Basin

The Térraba-Chiriquí Basin is mainly an inland feature located on the Pacific side of southern Costa Rica (Térraba Basin) and the adjacent area of western Panamá (Chiriquí Basin or David Basin). The narrow and elongated basin is more than 300 km long and about 50 km wide at its widest (Fig. 5).

Strata totaling more than 7,000 meters in thickness have been described from the Térraba Basin. The oldest strata, consisting predominantly of gray and black shale with thin interbeds of fine- to medium-grain sandstone, forms part of the Paleocene to Eocene Brito Formation (see Nicoya Peninsula).

The Brito Formation, although incomplete, has nearly 1,900 m of section including 140 m of the El Cajón Limestone, a reefoid carbonate sequence that caps the formation and is correlative with similar limestone units elsewhere in the Pacific side of Costa Rica and western Panamá.

The Oligocene and lower Miocene Térraba Formation, at its type section along the Río Térraba, consists entirely of marine clastic deposits and is considered to be a turbidite deposit. The Térraba has been divided into two distinctive members and was described in detail by Mora (1979). The Térraba Formation has been correlated with the Uscari, which crops out on the Caribbean coastal areas of southern Costa Rica and western Panamá (see Limón–Bocas del Toro Basin).

The Curré Formation of middle and late Miocene age,

which rests disconformably on the Térraba Formation, consists largely of medium-grained, brown, tuffaceous sandstone with silty shale and conglomerate interbeds considered by Mora (1979) to represent transitional deltaic and beach deposits. This section has been correlated with the Río Banano and Gatún Formations, which crop out extensively on the Caribbean side of Costa Rica and Panamá.

The Paso Real Formation, of probable Pliocene age, consists entirely of piedmont conglomerates and other coarse clastic deposited during the post-tectonic phase subsequent to the uplift of the neighboring Talamanca Cordillera. The formation has been estimated to be more than 1,500 m thick at its type locality in the Río Térraba.

The stratigraphy of the Panamanian portion of the Térraba-Chiriquí Basin has not been described in the literature. Sedimentary rocks of similar lithology and age to those in the Térraba Valley crop out extensively in the hilly areas of the western Pacific side of Panamá, but have never been identified as lithological entities except for the David Limestone, which correlates with the El Cajón Limestone in the Térraba Basin (Fig. 7). Sedimentary rocks in the Chiriquí Basin are likely to represent lateral extensions of the Brito and Térraba Formations, although a question remains as to the presence in the Chiriquí Basin of younger deposits that could be correlative with the Curré or Gatún Formations in the Río Térraba Valley.

Limón–Bocas del Toro Basin

The Limón Basin of Costa Rica and the Bocas del Toro Basin of Panamá, when taken as a unit, make up the largest sedimentary basin in southern Central America (Fig. 5) and contain an incomplete section of predominantly marine clastic deposits that exceed 7,000 m in thickness. The basin, an elongated feature trending roughly northwest, extends from the Costa Rica–Nicaragua boundary in the north, across the entire length of the Caribbean side of Costa Rica, into the westernmost Caribbean side of Panamá. The widest part of the basin in northern Costa Rica extends for over 150 km from the coast to the foot of the Guanacaste Volcanic Cordillera and gradually narrows southward. At the Panamá–Costa Rica boundary, the inland portion of the basin is less than 50 km wide and becomes an entirely offshore feature about 150 km eastward north of Panamá.

The actual boundary of the basin to the north is difficult to establish because of the thick cover of Quaternary alluvium and volcanic rocks. However, the boundary is believed to coincide with the concealed Hess–Santa Elena Fault System, which separates northern Central America from southern Central America. Two small inliers of sedimentary rocks at Venado and Machuca are the northernmost representative rocks of the Limón Basin. In the Nicaraguan Rise, outside of the Limón Basin (Chortis block), the sedimentary sequence known from extensive drilling differs markedly from that of the Limón Basin.

The stratigraphy of the Limón–Bocas del Toro Basin has been compiled mainly from the extensive field work and explora-

tory drilling carried out by numerous oil companies since the 1920s. However, this exploratory work was concentrated within a relatively small part of the basin, especially in southern Costa Rica and the neighboring areas of Panamá. Very little is known about the geology of the northern part of the basin, which is covered by extensive fields of volcanic rocks and alluvial material. In addition, large parts of the Limón–Bocas del Toro Basin, located at the foot of the Cordillera de Talamanca of Costa Rica and its extension into Panamá, are difficult to reach and remain virtually unexplored.

The synthesized columnar section of the Limón Basin (Fig. 6), albeit incomplete, includes terrigenous and marine deposits as well as volcaniclastic and volcanic rocks that range in age from the Paleocene to Pleistocene. The adjacent Bocas del Toro Basin, containing similar types of deposits, also includes the Late Cretaceous Changuinola Formation, which consists predominantly of carbonates previously described.

The oldest confirmed Tertiary sedimentary unit in the Limón Basin was first described as an informal unit and named by Fisher and Pessagno (1965) from the Río Lari, a tributary of Río Sixaola located near the Panamanian boundary. This section, which contains Paleocene to middle Eocene fauna (Sprechmann, 1984), represents a well-defined and very thick stratigraphic entity that has not been recognized outside of the type locality. The sequence consists of intercalated volcanic rocks and lesser intervals of volcaniclastic and carbonate rocks. The volcanic rocks are basaltic and andesitic lava flows, tuffs, and volcanic breccia, whereas the sedimentary rocks are mostly tuffaceous limestone, calcareous tuff, and rare biomicrites. Rocks similar to those described from the Río Lari are known to crop out extensively near the southwestern boundary of the Limón–Bocas del Toro Basin at the foothills of the Cordillera de Talamanca (personal notes) within an area of very difficult access.

A stratigraphic unit of early and middle Eocene age that crops out extensively in the Limón Basin of Costa Rica is a thick sequence of interbedded sandstones, tuffaceous siltstones and clays, basalt flows, volcanic conglomerates, and breccias (Rivier, 1973). The name "Tuis Formation" has been used informally in private reports to describe the unit. Weyl (1980) briefly referred to the Las Animas Limestone as a facies variation. Castillo (1984) mentioned the type locality at Tuis, near Turrialba, and noted the lack of information on the areal extent of the formation and the nature of the contacts with the overlying and underlying strata. Such information would help in understanding the relationship of the Tuis with the underlying Río Lari unit, which is of similar lithology.

The volcaniclastic character of the stratigraphic units typifying the Paleocene and the early and middle Eocene formations in the Limón Basin (Río Lari and Tuis Formation) has been recognized in various lithologic units cropping out in the Bocas del Toro Basin in Panamá. However, none of these sections has been fully described in the literature; thus, all remain to be correlated with the stratigraphic units of Costa Rica (Fig. 6).

The late Eocene reefoid Las Animas Formation, which con-

216　　　　　　　　　　　　　　　　　　　　　　　　　　　　　*G. Escalante*

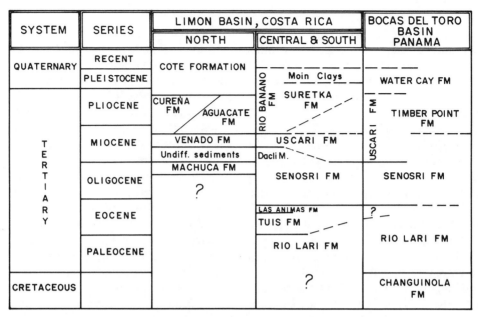

Figure 6. Table of formations, Limón and Bocas del Toro Basins.

sists mostly of massive carbonates and poorly sorted grainstones to packstones, has been described by many investigators (see summary by Rivier, 1973) from its type locality near Turrialba in the valley of the Río Reventazón. The age of the formation, determined on the basis of conspicuous larger foraminifera, is somewhat younger than the limestones in the Brito Formation in the central part of Costa Rica (i.e., Parritilla Limestone). The Las Animas Formation has not been recognized outside of type locality.

The Senosri Formation of early Oligocene age (possibly extending into late Eocene) is represented at the surface by massive, dense, blue-gray, silty, foraminiferal limestone interbedded with argillaceous sandstones, shales, and claystones. A similar rock type is reportedly present in the subsurface of the Limón Basin, varying from an estimated maximum thickness of 750 m to 150 m. Malavassi and Chaves (1970) referred to a surface section which is 1,000 m thick; Rivier (1973) measured 380 m of the formation at Quebrada Grande where he recognized a marly facies, indicating open sea neritic conditions, and a calcareous facies with bentonic foraminifera.

The formation was first described by MacDonald (1919) from a tributary on the Panamanian side of Río Sixaola, which serves as the boundary between Costa Rica and Panamá. The name has gained acceptance and has since been informally used in private reports to describe surface and subsurface sections in the Limón and Bocas del Toro Basins.

A distinctive sequence of silty marls and tuffaceous calcareous siltstones, which appears at places near the upper part of the Senosri Formation, has been termed the Dacli Member (widely used by petroleum companies). This exceeds 1,500 m in some wells drilled in the Limón Basin, but is absent in other places where the Uscari Formation shales rest directly over the Senosri

Formation deposits. The Dacli appears to range in age from late Oligocene to early Miocene.

In contrast to the underlying Senosri Formation, the Uscari Formation is a well-defined lithological entity that has long been described in the literature (Berry, 1921; Olsson, 1922). The Uscari Formation is basically a shale unit whose type locality is situated on the Quebrada Uscari, a northern tributary of the Río Sixaola. The shales are soft and consequently easily eroded to form wide valleys. The dominant shaly sequence of the Uscari Formation contains rare thin interbeds of limestone and calcareous sandstone intervals, particularly toward the upper part of the formation; lignite has also been reported.

The age of the formation appears to be mainly Miocene, but as pointed out by Aguilar (in Sprechmann, 1984), the Uscari seems to be somewhat younger in the area near Puerto Limón than in the type locality in the southwestern part of the Limón Basin (early Miocene).

The Uscari Formation has been recognized as far north as the valley of the Río Reventazón in the Limón Basin and as far south as the valley of the Río Changuinola and other places in the Laguna de Chiriquí, well within the Bocas del Toro Basin. Terry (1956) referred to this formation in Panamá as the "Concho Point Shale." Shaly portions of the formation in Costa Rica have also been given names that have not been adopted by later workers (MacDonald, 1919; Palmer, 1923; Goudkoff and Porter, 1942). The microfauna of the Uscari indicate water deepening eastward into the Caribbean where the formation thickens. Conversely, it thins and grades laterally to shallower facies inland and includes reefal limestones such as those found in the Río Nuevo (a tributary of Río Banano) and Uruchico area in the lower part of Río Telire.

The upper Tertiary stratigraphic sequence of the Limón-Bo-

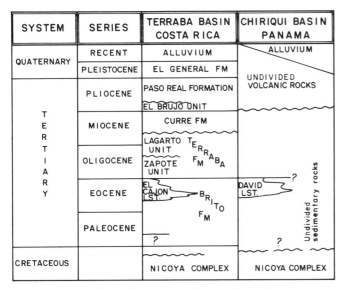

SYSTEM	SERIES	TERRABA BASIN COSTA RICA	CHIRIQUI BASIN PANAMA
QUATERNARY	RECENT	ALLUVIUM	ALLUVIUM
QUATERNARY	PLEISTOCENE	EL GENERAL FM	UNDIVIDED VOLCANIC ROCKS
TERTIARY	PLIOCENE	PASO REAL FORMATION / EL BRUJO UNIT	UNDIVIDED VOLCANIC ROCKS
TERTIARY	MIOCENE	CURRE FM	
TERTIARY	OLIGOCENE	LAGARTO UNIT / ZAPOTE UNIT (TERRABA FM)	
TERTIARY	EOCENE	EL CAJON LST. / BRITO FM	DAVID LST. / Undivided sedimentary rocks
TERTIARY	PALEOCENE	?	?
CRETACEOUS		NICOYA COMPLEX	NICOYA COMPLEX

Figure 7. Table of formations, Térraba-Chiriquí Basin.

cas del Toro Basin has been described under various formational names, which are mostly of local significance. Five distinctive lithofacies described by Taylor (1975) within the Río Banano Formation represent a further stage in the progressive shallowing of the marine paleoenvironment following deposition of the Uscari shales. However, some oscillations occurred between the upper outer sublittoral depths of the Moín Member and the littoral conglomeratic and reefal facies. The Río Banano Formation, as described by Taylor (1975) from its type locality near Puerto Limón, does not include the prevalent sandy facies of the formation that crops out extensively on the Costa Rica side of the Panamá boundary. The formation in Costa Rica characteristically contains beds of lignite that reach a maximum of 2 m thick and in general resembles the Gatún Formation from its type locality in the Canal Basin of Panamá.

Inclusion of the Suretka conglomerates (which forms most of the formation) within the Banano Formation (Taylor, 1975) has not been generally accepted by some geologists who consider the Suretka to be a separate formation as recognized by the early investigators of the Limón Basin.

The Suretka Formation is made up primarily of conglomerates characterized by a wide textural range, and its constituents vary from small clay particles to blocks larger than a meter in diameter. The conglomerate usually appears in well-sorted bedded units including sandstone interbeds and lenticular bodies of clay (Malavassi, 1971). The components in the Suretka conglomerate are basalt, andesite, and quartz diorite (Malavassi, 1971). According to Dengo (1962a), the components in the lower part of the Suretka are derived from the Río Pey volcanics (a continental volcanic sequence of late Tertiary age).

The Río Banano Formation, introduced by Taylor (1975), includes the stratigraphic sequence referred to in the past under various names: Limón and Moín Formations (Gabb, 1881),

Gatún Formation (Olsson, 1922), and the Suretka Conglomerate (Sapper, 1905; Berry, 1921; Sapper, 1937). Taylor (1975) incorporated into the Banano Formation the stratigraphic sequence succeeding the Uscari Formation in the Limón Basin whose fossil evidence indicates an age range from the late Miocene to the Recent, although, according to Taylor (1975), most of the formation is of Plio-Pleistocene age.

Late Tertiary and Quaternary volcanic deposits and alluvium cover a large part of northern Costa Rica, including an area that coincides with the northernmost projection of the Limón Basin where no drilling for petroleum has been undertaken. The stratigraphy of this extensive area is little known, and has been derived almost exclusively from the description of two small inliers that have important sedimentary sections at Machuca and Venado. The better known of these inliers exposed on the Machuca rapids on the Río San Juan (which is the boundary between Costa Rica and Nicaragua) was originally described and named by Hayes (1899), who included information from core drilling in the area. The geologic map of Costa Rica (Saénz-Ruiz, 1982), however, does not indicate any sedimentary rocks near the Machuca rapids and surrounding area.

Hayes (1899) originally described the Machuca section as consisting mainly of tuffaceous and calcareous shale with a subordinate percentage of sandstones, although he did not give any estimate of its thickness. This same investigator assumed a questionable Eocene age for the formation. More recent work in the area, carried out by private interests, is reported to have discovered unquestionable late Oligocene fauna within rocks of this stratigraphic unit.

Hayes (1899) and subsequent investigators of the geology of Central America have referred to the sedimentary section at Machuca as a single stratigraphic unit, and this concept has persisted in the literature ever since. Thus McBirney and Williams (1965) described the lithology of the Machuca Formation in similar terms, although they report finding substantial amounts of silicified limestone. McBirney and Williams (1965), quoting Hoffstetter and others (1960), estimated a thickness of 1,500 m for the Machuca Formation. The question remains, however, as to the nature and age of a section composed of medium to dark gray, slightly indurated, calcareous shale; siltstone; and well-sorted medium-grain sandstone, which crops out intermittently along the Río Infiernito, which flows into the Río San Juan from Costa Rica just west of the Machuca rapids (personal observation).

The Venado inlier, located to the north of lake Arenal, is best known from a section exposed along Río La Muerte, next to the village of Venado where approximately 40 m of marine strata are present (personal notes). About 15 m of the lower part of this section consists of limestone, and the upper part consists of calcareous and fossiliferous sandy siltstone. The Venado limestone is a grainstone containing abundant molluscs, algae, and barnacles.

Small partial sections of clastic deposits have been mapped along the entire inlier. Thickness is unknown because partial sections of clastic deposits have not been correlated. Most of the clastic sequence is dark gray shale and siltstone with subordinate amounts of tuffaceous sandstones. Most of these deposits contain abundant carbonaceous material and occasional lignite beds up to a maximum of 1.25 m thick. The Venado Formation is reported to contain foraminiferal assemblages indicating an inshore, brackish, depositional environment. E. Malavassi (personal communication, 1965) reported finding distinctive late Miocene fauna in samples of the Venado limestone. Thus the Venado limestone is likely to correlate with the late Miocene San Miguel Formation, which crops out in the Central Valley of Costa Rica. The Venado Formation is overlain unconformably by volcanic rocks of continental origin, which may represent two formations (Cote and Aguacate). The base of the unit is not exposed.

The Venado Formation remains one of the least-known stratigraphic units in Costa Rica. A recent geologic map of Costa Rica (Sáenz, 1982) describes the formation, although Sprechmann (1984) did not refer to the Venado Formation in his study of the stratigraphy of Costa Rica.

The late Tertiary stratigraphy of the Bocas del Toro Basin generally resembles that observed in the Limón Basin (Fig. 6), although the sequence has not been separated into defined formations in the literature. A better description of this section is found in private reports. The most important of these was produced by Champlain Oil Company from surface work and exploratory drilling carried out in the 1950s, which describes two late Neogene (post-Uscari) formations. The Timber Point Formation, of probable late Miocene age, consists of an alternating sequence of conglomerates, siltstones, and extrusive volcanic rocks that unconformably overlie the Uscari Formation and older strata within the Bocas del Toro Basin. Although no type section for this formation has been defined, this unit is well exposed at various islands within the Laguna de Chiriquí, especially on the southwest shore of Popa Island.

The Timber Point Formation lacks diagnostic fauna by which to accurately date the formation. However, overlying beds have reportedly been dated as late Miocene, and others cropping out beneath the formation are known to contain early Miocene faunas.

The Water Cay Formation overlies the Timber Point Formation and consists of blue-gray fossiliferous sandstone and siltstone, shale, nodular sandy limestone, lignite, and conglomerates for a total thickness of about 1,500 m. It is overlain by a limestone sequence known as the La Gruta Limestone Member, which is about 450 m thick. The formation contains a late Miocene fauna.

The occurrence of numerous oil seeps in the Limón–Bocas del Toro Basin, on both sides of the Costa Rica–Panamá boundary, has attracted the attention of petroleum explorers since the early part of this century. This large area is the most thoroughly drilled basin in southern Central America, although drilling has been concentrated in a relatively small part of the basin on both sides of the Costa Rica–Panamá boundary. A recent discovery of an oil and gas seep emanating from clastic deposits, the Venado inlier, has greatly enhanced the petroliferous prospects of the northern part of the Limón Basin.

Sedimentary cover of the Azuero Peninsula

The basement rocks making up most of the Azuero Peninsula of Panamá are overlain by deposits of diverse lithology and age, which appear to represent erosional remnants of a poorly defined sedimentary basin or basins. The stratigraphic situation in Azuero generally resembles that of the Nicoya Peninsula in Costa Rica, although the stratigraphic units in the Azuero area are only briefly described in the literature.

One of the sections overlying basement rocks in the Azuero Peninsula, the Ocú Formation of Cretaceous age, has been described previously. Deposits of Cenozoic age represent at least three ill-defined stratigraphic units of essentially marine origin. The oldest of these units, of middle and late Eocene age, known as the "formación lutítico-arenácea" (shale-sandstone formation) comprises an undetermined thickness of shales, sandstones, limestone, and tuffs, covering at least one-fourth of the surface of the Azuero Peninsula, according to del Giudice and Recchi (1969). This stratigraphic unit has also been termed the Bohío Formation, which correlates with the Brito Formation of Nicaragua and Costa Rica. The Tonosí Limestone, an important lithologic unit that occurs at the top of the formation, has received numerous local names such as Búcaro, Azuero, and El Barro Limestones. It contains fauna that is clearly late-middle Eocene in age and is thus correlatable with the David Limestone of the Chiriquí Basin. These limestone facies of late-middle Eocene age have many of the same stratigraphic and structural trends as along the Pacific of Costa Rica and western Panamá. The youngest Tertiary section in the Azuero Peninsula, the Santiago Formation of reported Miocene age, consists of sandstones and conglomeratates of unknown thickness. The formation crops out in rather local parts of the Azuero Peninsula (del Giudice and Recchi, 1969).

Canal Basin, central Panamá

The central part of Panamá has been studied in considerable detail, particularly by many geologists concerned with the engineering of the Panamá Canal. Geological information derived from this work has revealed the presence of a well-defined sedimentary basin. This basin extends across the isthmus from the Pacific to the Caribbean (Fig. 5), forming part of the interconnected narrow and elongated basins which are a characteristic feature of the eastern part of Panamá and western Colombia (the Chocó block). The basin developed in an area where major faulting dissociated the Chorotega and Choco blocks. The stratigraphic record of this basin, therefore, reflects the geological events that led to the separation of these two mayor structural features. The name Madden Basin, which has a local connotation, has been occasionally used in reference to this area (Terry, 1956). However, the term Canal Basin is probably a more appropriate name for the area covered mostly by the former Panamá Canal Zone.

Despite the extensive geological knowledge of central Panamá, there remains considerable confusion as to the proper definition of some formations, especially those within the Canal Basin. This problem is further compounded by the fact that some type localities have been covered by water and others, particularly limestone horizons, have been quarried away, e.g., the Emperador Limestone (Fig. 8) which is no longer present on the surface.

Problems on the stratigraphy of central Panamá, specifically those within the former Panamá Canal Zone (Canal Basin), were described in detail by Woodring (1957, 1970, 1982). A generalized composite section of the stratigraphic units in the basin, indicating their individual thicknesses and comprising at least 2,900 m of deposits (Fig. 8), has been assembled from data contained in a number of publications and is believed to be a fair interpretation of a complex situation.

The oldest stratigraphic unit within the Canal Basin appears to be the middle Eocene and possibly late Eocene Gatuncillo Formation, which consists of fine-grained deposits with algal and foraminiferal limestone intervals. The rich assemblage of macro and microfaunas in the Gatuncillo has been studied by Renz and Bermudez (in Woodring, 1957), Vaughan (1926), Cole (1949, 1952, 1953, 1957), Cooke (1948), and Woodring (1970). Based on lithologic and paleontologic data, Bandy (1970) interpreted the formation to have been deposited in abyssal and bathyal environments.

The Gatuncillo Formation is succeeded by a cobble- and pebble-size conglomeratic facies with interlayers of tuffaceous sandstones and siltstones termed the Bohío Formation (which has also been recognized on the Azuero Peninsula). Bandy (1970) placed the formation in the late Eocene. According to Woodring (1982) the Bohío Formation includes brackish water and some fresh-water species of molluscs. A definite marine facies of the Bohío includes small benthonic foraminifera. Older nomenclature was described by Woodring (1970, 1982).

The Caimito Formation, which contains late Oligocene fauna (Cole, 1952, 1957; Bolli [in Woodring, 1970]; Woodring, 1970), is largely made up of tuffs, tuffaceous siltstones, sandstones, conglomerates, and carbonate members referred to as the Quebrancha and the Chilindrillo Limestones. According to Woodring (1982), the Caimito has a shallow-water and a moderately deep-water facies.

The Caimito Formation is overlain unconformably by the areally restricted Culebra and Cucaracha Formations of early Miocene age. The Culebra is essentially a marine sequence containing carbonaceous shale, lignite, silty mudstone, tuffaceous siltstone, and conglomerate. The Cucaracha Formation consists entirely of massive bentonitic clays. The La Boca Formation of early Miocene age, which crops out in a small area on the Pacific side of Panamá, is of similar lithology to the Culebra Formation.

The middle Miocene Gatún Formation, whose type section is in the Canal Basin, is the principal stratigraphic unit of regional significance. The formation, originally named by Howe (1907), is composed mostly of massive, medium- to very fine-grained, calcareous or marly, somewhat tuffaceous sandstone and siltstone and minor conglomerate. The molluscs from the Gatún have

been studied by Woodring (1957, 1970) and smaller foraminifera by Cushman (1918).

The Gatún is overlain and partially overlapped on the Caribbean side of the Canal Basin by the Mio-Pliocene Chagres Formation, which consists mostly of massive fine-grained sandstone and siltstone. A coquinoid sandstone at the base of the Chagres is commonly referred to as the Toro Limestone member of the Chagres Formation.

Gulf of Panamá

The Gulf of Panamá extends seaward for a distance of 140 km south of Panamá City and is 180 km long at its widest. It is the largest single oceanographic feature with water depths shallower than 200 m in the southern portion of Central America.

The limited stratigraphic information from two drill holes and exposures on the Las Perlas Archipelago, in the middle of the Gulf of Panamá, indicates the presence of a thick section of Pliocene siltstones and claystones with rare sandstone stringers, which is underlain by an Eocene section consisting of siltstone, volcanic conglomerate, and volcanic sandstones in the subsurface of the western side of the Gulf of Panamá. The subsurface data of the eastern side, however, indicate a normal Pliocene to early Miocene stratigraphic sequence containing over 2,000 m of mostly clastic deposits comprising clay, siltstone, minor thin limestones, and some shaly siltstones, which is underlain by an incomplete section of volcanic sandstones and agglomerates. The Archipelago of Las Perlas has at least 7,000 m of marine deposits and volcaniclastic material of unknown age. This thick stratigraphic section overlies volcanic basement rocks at the northwestern side of the Isla del Rey, the largest of the islands in the archipelago. However, the question remains as to whether the surface section of Las Perlas could be more related to the offshore extension of the Sambú Basin rather than the Gulf of Panamá Basin.

No attempt has been made to correlate various isolated sections that are far removed from each other and from the offshore extensions of well-defined sedimentary basins in the inland part of Panamá, such as the Sambú, Bayano, and Canal Basins.

Bayano, Tuira-Chucunaque, Sambú and Atrato Basins

The inland portion of the Chocó Block, which comprises eastern Panamá and western Colombia, is extensively covered by deposits of marine and volcanic origin contained within at least four sedimentary basins, or possibly interconnected subbasins containing a rather similar lithological sequence. The largest and better known of these basins, known as the Tuira-Chucunaque Basin, is contained within the extensive valley of the Tuira and Chucunaque rivers and follows a general N45°W direction along the central portion of eastern Panamá (Fig. 5). This basin includes stratigraphic units that are also present in the neighboring Bayano and Sambú Basins that appear to correlate with formations de-

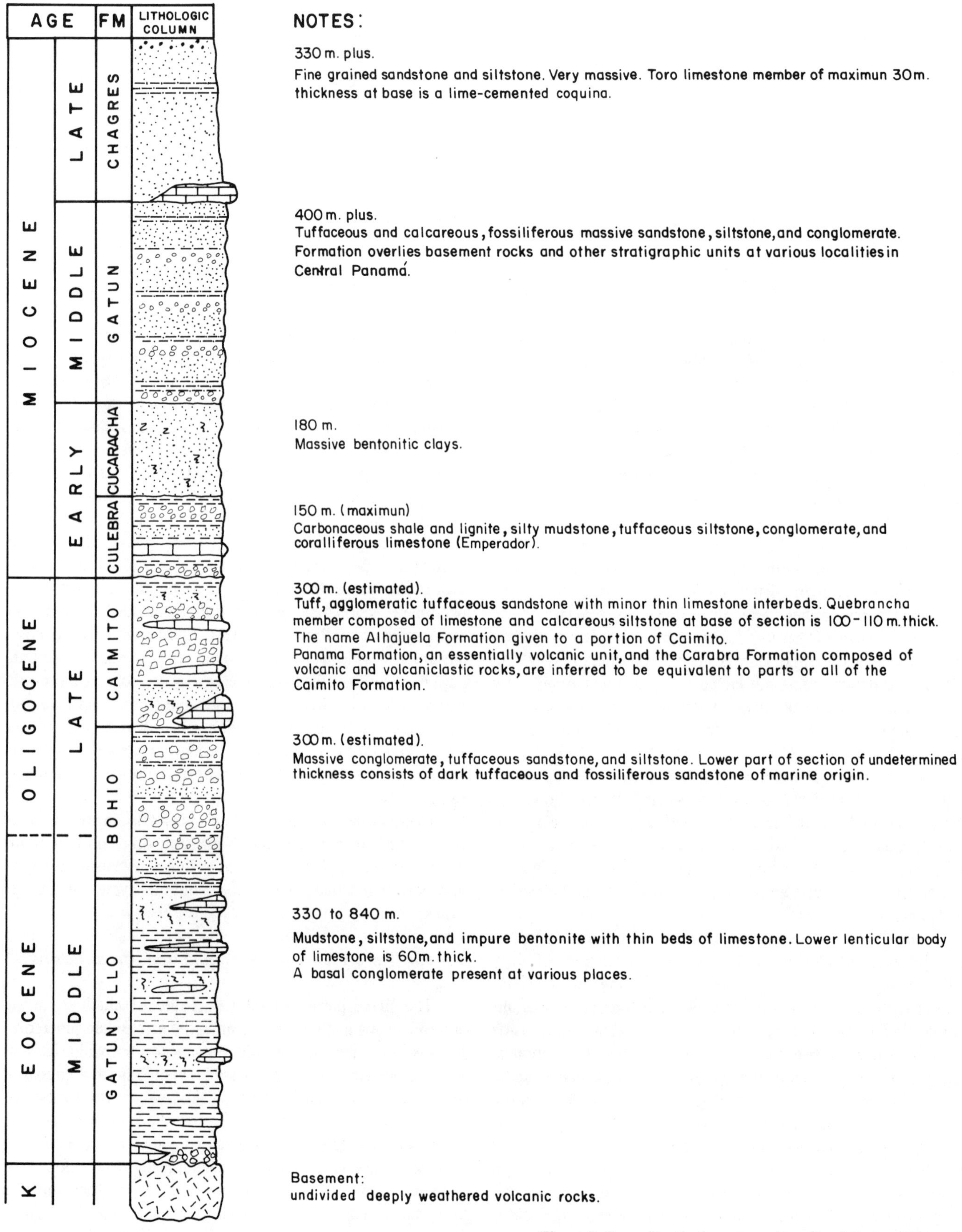

G. Escalante

AGE			FM	LITHOLOGIC COLUMN
M I O C E N E	MIDDLE	LATE	CHAGRES	
			GATUN	
	EARLY		CUCARACHA	
			CULEBRA	
O L I G O C E N E	LATE		CAIMITO	
			BOHIO	
E O C E N E	MIDDLE		GATUNCILLO	
K				

NOTES:

330 m. plus.
Fine grained sandstone and siltstone. Very massive. Toro limestone member of maximun 30m. thickness at base is a lime-cemented coquina.

400 m. plus.
Tuffaceous and calcareous, fossiliferous massive sandstone, siltstone, and conglomerate. Formation overlies basement rocks and other stratigraphic units at various localities in Central Panamá.

180 m.
Massive bentonitic clays.

150 m. (maximun)
Carbonaceous shale and lignite, silty mudstone, tuffaceous siltstone, conglomerate, and coralliferous limestone (Emperador).

300 m. (estimated).
Tuff, agglomeratic tuffaceous sandstone with minor thin limestone interbeds. Quebrancha member composed of limestone and calcareous siltstone at base of section is 100-110 m. thick. The name Alhajuela Formation given to a portion of Caimito. Panama Formation, an essentially volcanic unit, and the Carabra Formation composed of volcanic and volcaniclastic rocks, are inferred to be equivalent to parts or all of the Caimito Formation.

300 m. (estimated).
Massive conglomerate, tuffaceous sandstone, and siltstone. Lower part of section of undetermined thickness consists of dark tuffaceous and fossiliferous sandstone of marine origin.

330 to 840 m.
Mudstone, siltstone, and impure bentonite with thin beds of limestone. Lower lenticular body of limestone is 60m. thick.
A basal conglomerate present at various places.

Basement:
undivided deeply weathered volcanic rocks.

Figure 8. Generalized columnar section, Canal Basin of Panamá.

scribed from the Atrato Basin of western Colombia under different names. (The Tuira-Chucunaque Basin is also occasionally referred to in the literature as the Darién Basin because it is mostly within the Darién Province of Panamá).

Marine strata exceeding 5,500 m in thickness have been measured in the Tuira-Chucunaque Basin. This stratigraphic sequence has been divided into six well-defined formations summarized in the accompanying stratigraphic chart (Fig. 9), which also shows the estimated thickness of each formation. This chart includes an unnamed basal unit consisting of volcanic agglomerates, which is not considered to form part of the basement rocks (Shelton, 1952) and for which no thickness estimate has been given. This mainly volcanic sequence is believed to be of Eocene or older age and reportedly contains some interbedded layers of blue sandstone and thin dark shale beds. Unfortunately, very little has been published on the nature of the deposits and fossil content of the formations recognized in the Tuira-Chucunaque Basin, and thus, little is known about the environment of deposition of formations described by Shelton (1952).

The oldest of these stratigraphic units, the Corcona Formation of late Eocene age, consists of sandstones, shales, and limestones that appear to grade downward into agglomerates and interbeds of dark shale and sandstones. The upper portion of the Corcona Formation, containing more calcareous sandstones and limestones with abundant shell fragments, indicates a relative shallow marine origin.

The Eocene sequence is topped by a distinctive limestone unit of possible late Eocene age, known as the Clarita Formation, that appears to be conformable on the Corcona Formation. This limestone is a hard, dense, crystalline or semi-crystalline rock that becomes thin bedded and shaly toward the top.

The Clarita Limestone is transitionally and conformably overlain by a well-defined section—termed the Arusa Formation of middle Oligocene age (Shelton, 1952)—consisting of uniformly massive, dark brown, calcareous and foraminiferal shale with a subordinate amount of thin sandstone beds. The Arusa Formation is in turn overlain, apparently conformably, by the Aquaqua Formation, which consists of a series of interbedded carbonaceous shales and minor thin-bedded sandstones. Both Olsson (1942) and Terry (1956) considered the stratigraphic unit to be early Miocene. Shelton (1952), on the other hand, suggested that this formation might range into the Oligocene.

The lower Gatún Formation, of middle Miocene age, sometimes separated by a local unconformity from the underlying Aquaqua, is a very heterogenous unit including shales, conglomeratic sandstones, concretionary shales, argillaceous sandstones, and sandy shales. The uppermost part of the formation consistently exhibits massive crossbedded sandstones. The entire stratigraphic unit is very fossiliferous containing fauna comparable to that in the Gatún Formation of central Panamá.

The lower Gatún Formation is overlain by a sequence of late Miocene age consisting of shales, sandstones, and sandy limestones termed the Pucro Formation. The sandstones within the Pucro are characteristically massive and of predominantly dark

blue color. The shales in the formation are essentially black.

The Chucunaque Formation is the youngest Tertiary marine sequence in the Tuira-Chucunaque Basin and consists of a shale-sandstone sequence that occupies the central portion of the basin. The faunas within this formation are comparable to those found in the Gatún Formation of central Panamá, which is considered to be of late Miocene age. Shelton (1952), however, believed that the Chucunaque Formation might extend into Pliocene time.

The Morti Tuffs, Pacific Tuffs, and Sabana Beds described from a small area in the Tuira-Chucunaque Basin are formational names introduced from work carried out by the Atlantic-Pacific Interoceanic Canal Study Commission (1968). The oldest of these units, the Morti Tuffs of early and middle Eocene age, with an estimated thickness of 2,000 m, is correlative with Shelton's Igneous Agglomerate and possibly also with the overlying Corcona Formation (Fig. 9), which is, however, of an entirely different lithology. The Pacific Tuffs, of Oligo-Miocene age (Bandy and Casey, 1973), which have an estimated thickness of 1,500 m, is assumed to be age correlative with the Clarita Limestone (Bandy and Casey, 1973), which was considered by Shelton (1952) to be of early Oligocene and late Eocene age (Fig. 9). On the other hand, the Sabana Bed (Bandy and Casey, 1973), of middle and late Miocene age, which comprises a 2,100-m-thick sequence of fine clastic deposits with minor intervals of limestone and agglomerate, correlates in lithology and age with Shelton's lower Gatún and Pucro Formations and possibly also with the Chucunaque Formation (Fig. 9). Bandy and Casey (1973) established a paleobathymetric history for eastern Panamá indicating a progressively shallower water facies during the middle and later Neogene and culminating in Pliocene-Pleistocene paralic and nonmarine deposits.

The comparatively smaller and narrower Bayano Basin, which is separated from the Tuira-Chucunaque Basin by the Cañazas Platform or Cañazas Dome, appears to contain a similar stratigraphic section to that characterizing the Tuira-Chucunaque Basin. Stewart (1966) estimated the sedimentary sequence at Bayano to be between 2,135 and 3,050 m thick.

The Sambú Basin (Fig. 5) is a narrow small feature that parallels the southeastern end of the Tuira-Chucunaque Basin and contains a section basically similar to the larger basin. The presence of various oil seeps within the small basin has attracted exploratory drilling since the 1920s, which has not penetrated the section below the Aquaqua Formation (Fig. 9).

The Sambú Basin extends northwestward into the Gulf of San Miguel (Fig. 5), where no drilling has yet taken place, and probably joins the seaward extension of the Canal Basin. The question remains, however, as to whether or not the surface section, which crops out at the Archipelago of Las Perlas (referred to in the description of the Gulf of Panamá), represents the stratigraphy of an offshore Sambú Basin.

The Atrato Basin, sometimes referred to as the Chocó Basin of northwestern Colombia, is closely related geologically and geographically to the other basins in eastern Panamá. The Atrato Basin corresponds to the "Quibdo Deep" (Nygren, 1950) in the

AGE	FORMATION	LITHOLOGY	THICKNESS (IN METERS)
RECENT	ALLUVIUM	Sand, gravel, and silt.	Unknown
LATE MIOCENE OR PLIOCENE ?	TUIRA—CHUCUNAQUE	Shale and sandstone	484 - 533
LATE MIOCENE ?	PUCRO	Fossiliferous shale, sandstone and sandy limestone.	106 - 454
MIDDLE MIOCENE	LOWER GATUN	Fossiliferous sandstone, shale, and conglomerate.	354 -1606
LATE OLIGOCENE AND EARLY MIOCENE	AQUAQUA	Shale and sandstone.	242 - 969
MIDDLE OLIGOCENE	ARUSA	Shale	151 - 606
LATE EOCENE AND EARLY OLIGOCENE	CLARITA LIMESTONE	Limestone, sandstone, and shale.	303 - 860
LATE EOCENE	CORCONA	Limestone, sandstone and shale.	90 - 684
EOCENE OR OLDER	IGNEOUS AGGLOMERATE	Mafic igneous agglomerate	Unknown

Modified
From Shelton, 1952

Figure 9. Table of formations, Tuira-Chucunaque Basin.

context of the early concept of the "Bolivar Geosyncline" (referred to by Nygren, 1950) and extends southward from the Panamanian boundary to Cabo Corrientes, coinciding roughly with the assumed southern boundary of the segment of the South America Plate (the Chocó block) that forms southern Central America (Dengo, 1985).

The sedimentary fill of the Atrato Basin is mostly turbiditic and very thick. Nygren (1950) estimated a total thickness of 10,000 m of deposits for this and the contiguous San Juan Basin to the south, which is located outside of the area covered by this chapter. Barlow (1981), on the other hand, estimated a total thickness of deposits in both basins to be about 6,500 m. According to Duque Caro (1979) the section in the Atrato Basin is fully marine and shaly to the north, in contrast to the southern part (the San Juan Basin or sub-basin) where the section becomes more clastic and less marine (Bueno and Govea, 1976; Barlow, 1981), especially within the younger deposits.

Although the stratigraphy of the Atrato Basin has been well documented, some confusion remains as to the naming of some of the stratigraphic units, especially those to which the term "group"

has been applied in the literature. Thus, within the Atrato, the oldest stratigraphic unit referred to as the Nercua Group—comprising conglomerates, limestones, and siltstones—has not been divided into formations or formally established stratigraphic units. This group has been determined to be of Late Cretaceous age, possibly extending into the Paleocene (Bandy, 1970).

The Sautatá Group, as in the case of the Nercua Group, has not been divided into formal stratigraphic units. It comprises several hundred meters of interbedded sandstones, siltstones, and occasional limestones and shales, which have been dated on foraminiferal evidence as middle Paleocene to early Eocene (Bandy, 1970).

The Barrial Group, which overlies conformably the Sautatá Group, likewise has not been subdivided. It comprises siltstones and limestones with interbeds of sandstone and occasional conglomerates to which Bandy (1970) has given a middle Eocene age. The Truandó Group, which unconformably overlies the Barrial Group, comprises the middle Eocene Salaquí Formation and the Oligo-Miocene Uva Formation. The Salaquí consists of limestones, cherty limestones, chert, claystones, sandstones, and a basal tuffaceous and volcanic conglomerate, whereas the Uva Formation, which truncates the Salaquí Formation at its type locality, is basically a carbonate facies (Haffer, 1967).

The Río Salado Group of Bandy (1970) comprises the Napipí and Sierra Formations, as defined by Haffer (1967). The Napipí, considered to be of a middle Miocene age (possibly extending into the late Miocene), is a dominantly claystone sequence that conformably succeeds the Uva Formation. The Napipí Formation varies considerably in thickness throughout the basin. Haffer (1967) described the late Miocene Sierra Formation, another of the stratigraphic units within the Río Salado Group, as a monotonous massive argillaceous siltstone sequence that grades into fine-grained sandstones.

The stratigraphic section in the Atrato Basin is capped by the Quibdó Formation (Haffer, 1967). The formation consists of soft, varicolored, silty claystones interbedded with medium-grained argillaceous sandstones estimated to range in thickness from 700 to 900 m.

No conclusive paleontological data is available for the Quibdó Formation, which is assumed to be no older than late Miocene because it truncates beds of that age.

Continental volcanic deposits

Carr and Stoiber (this volume) have summarized the intense volcanism in Central America. In southern Central America, more than 50 percent of the land area is covered by volcanic and associated igneous intrusive rocks of a definite continental origin. Some of these volcanic units appear interlayered between essentially marine deposits previously described. Such is the case for the Paleocene Río Lari Formation and the Eocene Tuis and Machuca Formations of the Limón Basin, which contain abundant volcanogenic material or actual interlayered sequences of volcanic rocks, including lava flows probably of continental origin. Also important is an unnamed section of reported Eocene or older age comprising volcanic agglomerates that crops out in the Tuira-Chucunaque Basin (Shelton, 1952). It might represent the only exclusively volcanic episode of early Tertiary age within the eastern side of Panamá. Intervals of tuff and volcanic breccia appearing in various formations of Tertiary age throughout southern Central America and westernmost Colombia, especially in the Térraba-Chiriquí and Canal Basins, have been described for each basin. Very little is known, however, on the presence of exclusively continental volcanic rocks in southern Central America, except for an unnamed sequence of tuffs and olivine basalt flows that Weyl (1957) described from the Cordillera de Talamanca, considered by Dengo (1962a) to be early Tertiary in age.

The evidence through the entire Cenozoic indicates a nearly continuous volcanic episode for most of southern Central America, which greatly intensified during the Late Cenozoic, producing widespread deposits of continental volcanic rocks at widely spaced places, especially in central Costa Rica, as well as on the Pacific side and central part of western Panamá. The advent of this major volcanic episode, which has continued to the present, has not been dated accurately, although it must have developed rather suddenly. The volcanism was accompanied by a period of severe tectonic deformation associated with the emplacement of igneous intrusive bodies, especially along the backbone of the Chorotega block. The San Pedrito Formation, composed of tuff and agglomerate, reported to be late-middle Miocene in age, is likely to represent the initiation of this volcanic episode in central Panamá.

The Aguacate Formation, composed of andesitic and basaltic flows, agglomerate, breccia, and tuff may represent the advent of Late Cenozoic volcanism in central Costa Rica. Nomenclature of the Aguacate Formation has been summarized by Sprechmann (1984).

The stratigraphic relations of the Aguacate Formation have not been clearly established. On the western side of the Central Valley of Costa Rica, Castillo (1969) recognized that the formation unconformably overlies deposits of the Térraba, Turrúcares, and Coris Formations and is overlain unconformably by other divided volcanic rocks and lahars. More recently, Bellon and Tournon (1978) were able to obtain Pliocene radiometric dates from Aguacate andesites.

The Río Pey volcanic series, fairly widespread in the Limón Basin (Dengo, 1962a), and the Paso Real volcanic series of the southern Pacific area of Costa Rica (Dengo, 1962a), as well as the poorly defined volcanic sequences of Cureña and Cote (Malavassi and Madrigal, 1970) in the northern part of the country, are likely to be equivalent to the Aguacate Formation. The Aguacate is entirely or partially equivalent to the very thick volcanic sequence of the Nicaragua Sierras (Grupo Coyol), which crops out extensively to the north and outside of the area discussed in this chapter.

The volcanic formations in western and central Panamá are not as well known as those in Costa Rica and have been described only generally. Most of these rocks, like the Aguacate Formation of Costa Rica, probably form part of a single large group. Such might be the case for the San Pedrito and Cañazas Formations, which consist respectively of tuffs and agglomerates and tuffs and lavas, and possibly ignimbrites and tuffs of the La Yeguada Formation. A large number of younger volcanic formations of possible late Pliocene and Pleistocene age have been described from Costa Rica and western Panamá. Most of these are believed to be of local extent, although these have been directly involved in building the volcanic edifices that have become prominent topographic features of the Central Volcanic Cordillera of Costa Rica and the less prominent volcanic mountains of western Panamá (Chiriquí or Barú Volcano).

The Doán Formation of possible Pliocene age, which crops out on the northwestern slope of the Talamanca Cordillera, is composed of massive agglomerates. The original description of this essentially subaerial volcanic sequence (Escalante, 1966; Berrange, 1977) was thought to be of marine deposition by Krushensky (1972).

Other exclusively volcanic units of late Tertiary and Quaternary age have been described from the Central Valley of Costa

Rica. Most of these, of apparent local extent, are part of the volcanic edifices forming the Central Volcanic Cordillera of Costa Rica and surrounding country. Such is the case for the so-called Central Volcanic Group of the Central Valley of Costa Rica, which involves various lithologic units (Sprechmann, 1984); the Irazú Group, which includes four formations (Krushensky, 1972); and other undivided units within this central part of Costa Rica (Sprechmann, 1984). In addition, Williams (1952) described three groups of volcanic rocks of Quaternary age from the Central Valley of Costa Rica ("Meseta Central"), referred to as intracanyon lavas, glowing avalanche deposits, and post-avalanche lavas; Madrigal (1970) described the Orotina Formation, an ignimbrite from the western side of the Central Valley. The Quaternary volcanic rocks from the Guanacaste Cordillera of northwestern Costa Rica are less well known geologically with the exception of two important volcanic units referred to as the Bagaces and Liberia tuffs, which cover extensive areas along the southwestern edge of the cordillera (Dengo, 1962a, 1962b). However, little else is known about the volcanic rocks that form the volcanic cordillera itself (Weyl, 1980) and northeast of the cordillera, an area of difficult access.

The geological map of Costa Rica (Sáenz, 1982) indicates the presence of volcanic rocks in the Talamanca Cordillera in an area where no volcanics of any type had been previously described (Dóndoli and others, 1968). The nature and lithology of these rocks—shown on the map as undivided Tertiary and Quaternary volcanic rocks—remain to be properly evaluated. These rocks appear in areas that display well-preserved geomorphological features, indicating volcanic vents and calderas. This fact suggests a young, possibly Quaternary age for this volcanic series.

Quaternary volcanic rocks have been described as isolated occurrences in the midst of the northeastern Caribbean coastal plain of Costa Rica in the northern part of the Limón Basin. These rocks consisting of olivine basalt (Malavassi and Chaves, 1970) have been derived from at least six small extinct volcanic cones (Dóndoli and others, 1968). The geologic map of Costa Rica (Sáenz, 1982), however, shows the presence of only two volcanic vents and the presence of three different volcanic units within this area. The alkalic composition of these rocks is noteworthy, as pointed out by Carr and Stoiber (this volume).

Very little is known about the nature of the rocks that make up two large areas of Quaternary volcanic rocks in western Panamá and the Chorotega block. One of these is centered around the large stratovolcano of Chiriquí located on the Pacific side near the boundary with Costa Rica; the other contains El Valle, a shield volcano that has a prominent caldera located on the Pacific side between the Azuero Peninsula and Panamá City. No volcanic rocks of proven Quaternary age are known from eastern Panamá and western Colombia (Chocó block), with the exception of a few small isolated outliers of rock referred to as "Tertiary-Quaternary plugs, lavas and basaltic piroclastics" on the geologic map of Panamá (1976). Robert and Jan Stewart have recognized many "young" centers in Panamá from imagery (personal communication to J. E. Case, 1986).

Products of volcanism originating during the Cenozoic in southern Central America and western Colombia have undergone severe tectonic deformation and subsequent alteration, which makes it difficult, if not impossible, to define many centers of volcanism. This is especially true for volcanism developed during the early Cenozoic.

The Quaternary volcanism in southern Central America, on the other hand, has been derived from numerous recognizable centers. In addition, the Quaternary volcanic rocks in the area covered by this chapter have undergone little or no tectonic deformation; thus, it is possible to reconstruct much of the volcanic history of Central America during that period. The very intensive volcanic and associated igneous intrusive activity of the Late Cenozoic produced rocks of important economic value in the entire region covered in this chapter. The finer constituents derived from Quaternary volcanism have given way to the very rich soils that sustain the large centers of population in southern Central America (and northern Central America as well) as exemplified by the Central Valley of Costa Rica, which is inhabited by 80 percent of the population. Late Quaternary and Recent volcanism persisting today is responsible to a large extent for the impressive topographic features that characterize most of the high country in Costa Rica and western Panamá.

Volcanism that was especially important during Late Cenozoic and Recent time in southern Central America (the Chorotega block) was much less significant in eastern Panamá and the adjacent western side of Colombia (the Chocó block), perhaps because of low rates of convergence between the Nazca and Caribbean Plates.

TERTIARY AND QUATERNARY INTRUSIVE ROCKS

The igneous intrusive activity in Costa Rica, as well as that of western Panamá, seems to be mostly restricted to the late Tertiary, coinciding with the advent of the very prominent volcanism that persists to the present. Other intrusive bodies as old as 32.6 Ma (Kesler and others, 1977) have been reported from western Panamá. The regional significance of these periods of igneous intrusive activity and descriptions of the rock types characterizing these episodes are covered in another chapter of this volume. A brief description of the Tertiary intrusive rocks in the area is restricted mainly to the Chorotega block, because only very few scattered and poorly defined intrusive igneous bodies of that age have been described from eastern Panamá: early Tertiary, Cretaceous, and Paleogene plutons in the San Blás area along the Caribbean coast of eastern Panamá (Kesler and others, 1977) and dacitic and granodioritic rocks associated with an eroded Tertiary volcano at Serranía del Majé (del Giudice, 1978). Del Giudice (1978) also describes middle Tertiary quartz monzonites and granodiorites, and late Tertiary diorites from the side of the Cordillera Central of Panama. In western Colombia, granitoid plutons of Tertiary age are reported from the Cordillera Occidental (Etayo, 1983). No igneous intrusive bodies of Tertiary age, however, have been mapped in the basins of eastern Panamá and western Colombia (Case and Holcombe, 1980; Anonymous, 1976). This is in contrast with basins in the Chorotega block, such as the Limón–Bocas del Toro Basin and the Térraba-Chiriquí Basin, where igneous intrusive bodies of various types are a common occurrence. As noted previously, the scarcity of intrusive bodies within the Chocó block serves as an additional criterion to distinguish this block from the Chorotega block.

The rather similar characteristics in age and mode of emplacement of the intrusive bodies in Costa Rica and western Panamá were recognized by the early geologists in Costa Rica (Gabb, 1874) and later brought into a modern perspective by Dengo (1962a) and Berrange (1977). Dengo (1962a) recognized six stocks in the Talamanca Cordillera, including granodiorite, monzonite, and varieties of these. Berrange (1977) named the plutonic rocks the Comagmatic Intrusive Group of Talamanca and described the common occurrence of quartz diorite, granodiorite, and adamellites. He also noted that the more mafic varieties of intrusive rocks in Talamanca are relatively older and more voluminous than the silica facies and that limited radiometric data indicate older ages for mafic rocks and younger ages for the silicic varieties. Rivier (1979) included the rocks of the Escazú Intrusive, located just south of San José, as part of the Talamanca comagmatic group.

The stratigraphic relationship of the Talamanca plutonic rocks to those in eastern Panamá indicates a latest Miocene and Pliocene age, which agrees generally with ages from limited radiometric data.

Intrusive igneous bodies of younger age may also be present as shown by the small bodies that intrude questionable Quaternary volcanic deposits in the central part of the Talamanca Cordillera (Sáenz, 1982). The Cerro Colorado pluton of Panamá has been dated at 3.5 Ma (Kesler and others, 1977). Another at Río Chico on the southern slope of the Cordillera Central of Panamá revealed a date of 7.3 ± 1.6 Ma (del Giudice, 1978). The individual intrusive bodies, which have been described from the Talamanca Cordillera of Costa Rica and its extension into western Panamá, referred to as the Cordillera Central (and sometimes Serranía de Tabasará), have been better described in terms of their size and distribution in the more recent geologic maps of the area (Sáenz, 1982; del Giudice and Recchi, 1969).

TECTONIC HISTORY

Several different views on the origin of southern Central America and western Colombia in terms of modern plate tectonics, and some alternative hypotheses, are described in other chapters of this volume. I believe that much more geological information is required in order to formulate a meaningful theory of the origin of southern Central America and the surrounding region, and to arrive at a clear explanation of the subsequent tectonic history.

The earliest geological episode that can be reconstructed from available data is a prototectonic magmatic phase that developed during the Jurassic and extended into the Early Cretaceous (Fig. 10), and outlined an oceanic plateau of large dimensions. During this episode, oceanic crust formed between North and South America (which separated during Triassic–Early Jurassic). This crust is represented in its earliest stage by remnants of oceanic crust of Jurassic age in the Nicoya Complex in Costa Rica (Schmidt-Effing, 1979). Lloyd (1963) referred to a western archipelago within this large area that supplied material resulting from volcanism and the erosion of the islands. However, the products of this early phase in the tectonic history were mostly the result of submarine extrusive activity, possibly along a very uneven sea floor, as exemplified by the complex depositional patterns developed by sedimentary and volcanic rocks, including submarine landslides. These rocks of the Nicoya Complex of Costa Rica and other related rocks in Panamá and western Colombia (Fig. 3)—and possibly others of similar lithology—crop out as far south as Ecuador and outside of the region covered by this chapter (Goossens and others, 1977). It is not clear how far this volcanic episode extended north of southern Central America, within the Chortis block, where no rocks similar to those of the Nicoya Complex have been found. Case and others (1984) used gravity and seismic evidence for a possible extension of mafic and ultramafic masses similar to the Nicoya and Santa Elena Peninsulas along the Pacific side of the Chortis block.

A mayor deformational stage developed soon after the consolidation of the Nicoya Complex rocks and related stratigraphic units, and prior to the deposition of Late Cretaceous in the entire region. This resulted in the uplift and accretion of a slab of Pacific oceanic crust against the Chortis block in the north (Chorotega block) and the uplift and emergence of oceanic crust against cratonic South America at the south (the Chocó block). The Chorotega block developed from a northeast-oriented stress system associated with formation of the ancestral Middle America Trench. The Chocó block most probably formed as an intra-oceanic feature, either primitive magmatic arc or an uplifted block along faults associated with the ancestral Colombia Trench. The portion of the Chocó block that emerged at this time corresponds to the Panamá Spur (Lloyd, 1963) and probably also contained part of the Cordillera Occidental of Colombia. The accretion of the oceanic crust against the Chortis block took place along the Santa Elena suture; that against the South America Plate occurred along the Romeral fault zone, also a suture (Fig. 10b).

Late Cretaceous marine sedimentation accompanied by moderate volcanic activity (i.e., the volcanic sequences in the Changuinola Formation in the Bocas del Toro Basin) was probably widespread throughout most of the area and preserved only along the Pacific side of Costa Rica and western Panamá and within a restricted part of the Caribbean side of Panamá (Changuinola Formation). The axis of Late Cretaceous deposition, at least within the Chorotega block, must have been located toward the Pacific side.

According to Dengo (1962a), the main orogenic event within the Chorotega block, which began during latest Creta-

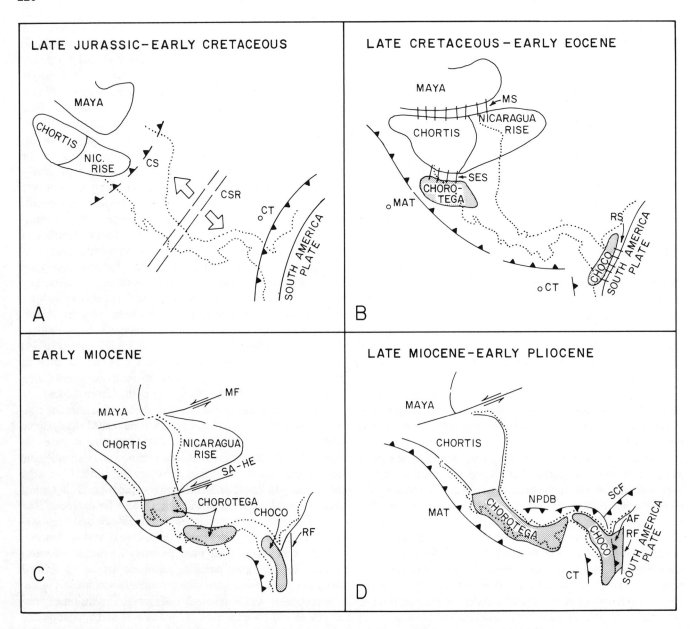

Figure 10. Sketches of relative positions of crustal blocks during their tectonic history: MAT, Middle America Trench; oMAT, ancestral Middle America Trench; CT, Colombia Trench; oCT, ancestral Colombia Trench; MS, Motagua Suture Zone; MF, Motagua Fault; SES, Santa Elena Suture zone; SA-HE, Santa Elena–Hess Escarpment; RS, Romeral Suture Zone; RF, Romeral Fault; NPDB, North Panamá Deformed Belt; SCF, south Caribbean Fault; AF, Atrato Fault; CS, conceptual suture; CSR, conceptual spreading ridge. Modified from Dengo (1985).

ceous time, was uplift along the present axes of both the inner and outer arcs (respectively the intra-arc and backarc) of Costa Rica and western Panamá (Fig. 4). These structural subdivisions have not been defined in the Chocó block. Upwarping of both the Chorotega and Chocó blocks accompanied the downfaulting that defined the basins and troughs that then received thick accumulations of marine and volcaniclastic material. In the Chorotega block, the most outstanding of these basins is a backarc with respect to the Middle America Trend: the Limón-Bocas del Toro Basin. The downfaulting that produced the prominent sedimentary basins throughout the region must have continued at a fairly constant rate during the Cenozoic, because the clastic sedimentation had a generally homogenous character.

The question remains as to when the Chorotega block separated from the Chocó and also the type of faulting tha produced this separation. This certainly must have taken place before the middle Eocene when the earliest deposition took place in the Canal Basin (Gatuncillo Formation), which developed from the separation of these blocks.

The early Tertiary volcanism in eastern Panamá and western Colombia, within the Chocó block, is represented by the Eocene or older sequence of volcanic agglomerate referred to by Shelton (1952), IOCS (1968), and Bandy and Casey (1973) from the Tuira-Chucunaque Basin. Incidentally, well-developed marine deposits of late Eocene age in this same basin, including the Corcona Formation and part of the Clarita Limestone (Fig. 9), have no layers of volcanic rocks and little volcanic influence, in contrast to the Chorotega block where volcanic influence was nearly continuous during the Cenozoic. In the Canal Basin (Fig. 8) between the Chocó and Chorotega blocks, volcanic influence is common throughout the entire Tertiary section.

The early Tertiary volcanism in the area was mainly concentrated in the Chorotega and Chocó blocks. In the Chorotega block, where early Tertiary volcanism was most intense, Dengo (1962a) noted that volcanism was mostly andesitic in the Limón

Basin (and Bocas del Toro Basin) and basaltic in the inner arc (intra-arc). He believed furthermore that volcanism at this time was absent within the outer arc (forearc).

The orogenic phase in southern Central America and western Colombia reached its peak with very intense folding and the emplacement of igneous intrusive rocks during the Miocene, most likely during the later part. This activity again was concentrated within the Chorotega block and gave rise to the Talamanca Cordillera and the contemporaneous intensive volcanism associated with the volcanic Aguacate, Río Pey, and Paso Real Formations in Costa Rica, and other volcanic rocks in western Panamá such as the San Pedrito and Cañazas units. The intense folding and faulting that developed in the Miocene, the result of northeast-trending forces, included thrusting along the Caribbean side of the Chorotega and Chocó blocks (the North Panamá Deformed Belt) and the contiguous area in the southern part of Limón Basin, as well as the comparatively less intense thrusting that developed on the Pacific side of this same block (i.e., the Terraba Basin and the Azuero Peninsula). The S-shaped form of the area described in this chapter also started to develop at this time as a consequence of northeast-trending forces. A final stage in this orogenic phase might have produced the major tensional faulting that broke apart the regional NW-SE–trending fault system across central Panamá, which separates the Chorotega from the Chocó block and another inferred oceanographic feature located along the northeast side of the Azuero Peninsula (Case and Holcombe, 1980).

A final post-orogenic phase within the region covered in this chapter was characterized by general uplift and continued deposition in all the sedimentary basins of the area, and the advent of the extensive volcanism that developed along the NW-SE–trending fault system in Costa Rica and western Panamá associated with convergence of the Middle America Trench, which has continued to the present.

REFERENCES

Alvarez, E., and González, H., 1978, Geología y geoquímica del cuadrángulo I-7, Urrao: Bogotá, Ingeominas, Informe 1761, 347 p., map scale 1:100,000.

Anonymous, 1976, Mapa geológico de Panamá: Panamá City, Instituto Geográfico Nacional "Tommy Guardia," 7 sheets, scale 1:250,000.

Azéma, J., Glacon, G., Tournon, J., and Vila, J. M., 1979, Precisiones acerca del Paleoceno de Puerto Quepos y sus alrededores, Provincia de Puntarenas, Costa Rica: San José, Instituto Geográfico Nacional, Informe Semestral, Julio-Diciembre, p. 77–87.

Atlantic-Pacific Interoceanic Canal Study Commission, 1968, Engineering feasibility studies, geology: Atlantic-Pacific Interoceanic Canal Study Commission, Final Report, Route 25, v. 1, 20 p., 6 appendixes, maps.

Bandy, O. L., 1970, Upper Cretaceous-Cenozoic paleobathymetric cycles, eastern Panama and northern Colombia: Gulf Coast Association of Geological Societies Transactions, v. 20, p. 181–193.

Bandy, O. L., and Casey, R. E., 1973, Reflector horizons and paleobathymetric history, eastern Panama: Geological Society of America Bulletin, v. 84, p. 3081–3086.

Barlow, C. A., 1981, Radar geology and tectonic implications of the Chocó Basin,

Colombia, South America [M.S. thesis]: Fayetteville, University of Arkansas, 113 p.

Barr, K. W., and Escalante, G., 1969, Contribución al esclarecimiento de la edad del complejo de Nicoya, Costa Rica: Guatemala, Publicaciones Geológicas del ICAITI 2, p. 43–47.

Baumgartner, P. O., 1984, El Complejo ofiolítico de Nicoya (Costa Rica); Modelos estructurales analizados en función de los radiolarios (Calloviense a Santoniense), in Sprechmann, P., ed., Manual de geología de Costa Rica, I: Estratigrafía, p. 115–124 (see Sprechmann, p. 1984).

Baxter, S., 1976, Estudio geológico de las formaciones Mata de Limón y Punta Carballo, Costa Rica [Licenciatura thesis]: San José, Escuela Centroamericana de Geología, Universidad de Costa Rica, 66 p.

Bellon, H., and Tournon, J., 1978, Contribution de la geochronométrie K-Ar a l'étude du magmatisme de Costa Rica, Amérique Centrale: Bulletin de la Société Géologique de France 7, XX, no. 6, p. 955–959.

Berrange, J. P., 1977, Reconnaissance geology of the Tapantí Quadrangle, Talamanca Cordillera, Costa Rica: London, Institute of Geological Sciences, Overseas Division report 37, 72 p.

Berry, E. W., 1921, Tertiary fossil plants from Costa Rica: Washington, D.C., Proceedings of the United States National Museum, v. 59, p. 169–185.

Bourgois, J., and 10 others, 1982, Ages et structures des complexes basiques et ultrabasiques de la façade pacifique entre 3°N et 12°N, Colombie, Panama, et Costa Rica: Bulletin de la Société Géologique de France, no. 3, p. 545–554.

Bueno, R., and Govea, C., 1976, Potential for exploration and development of hydrocarbons in Atrato Valley and Pacific coastal and Shelf basins of Colombia, in Halbouty, M. T., and others, eds., Circum-Pacific energy and mineral resources: American Association of Petroleum Geologists Memoir 25, p. 318–327.

Buffler, R. T., 1982, Geologic structure of the forearc region off the west coast of Costa Rica in the vicinity of the Nicoya Peninsula; Results of a multifold seismic reflection survey: University of Texas Institute of Geophysics, 56 p. (unpublished).

Carballo, H.M.A., and Fischer, R., 1978, La Formación San Miguel, Mioceno, Costa Rica: San José, Instituto Geográfico Nacional, Informe Semestral Enero-Junio, p. 45–144.

Case, J. E., 1974, Oceanic crust forms basement of eastern Panama: Geological Society of America Bulletin, v. 85, p. 645–652.

Case, J. E., and Holcombe, T. L., 1980, Geologic-tectonic map of the Caribbean region: U.S. Geological Survey Miscellaneous Investigations Series Map 1-1100, scale 1:2,500,000.

Case, J. E., Durán, S.L.G., López, R. A., and Moore, W. R., 1971, Tectonic investigations in western Colombia and eastern Panama: Geological Society of America Bulletin, v. 82, p. 2685–2712.

Case, J. E., Holcombe, T. L., and Martin, R. G., 1984, Map of geologic provinces in the Caribbean region, in Bonini, W. E., Hargraves, R. B., and Shagam, R., The Caribbean–South American Plate boundary and regional tectonics: Geological Society of America Memoir 162, p. 1–30.

Castillo, M. R., 1969, Geología de los mapas básicos Abra y parte de Río Grande, Costa Rica: San José, Dirección de Geología Minas y Petróleo, Informes Técnicos y Notas Geológicas no. 33, 40 p. (mimeographed report).

——, 1984, Geología de Costa Rica, Una sinopsis: San José, Editorial de la Universidad de Costa Rica, 182 p.

Cole, W. S., 1949, Upper Eocene larger foraminifera from the Panama Canal Zone: Journal of Paleontology, v. 23, no. 3, p. 267–275.

——, 1952, Eocene and Oligocene larger foraminifera from the Panama Canal Zone and vicinity: U.S. Geological Survey Professional Paper 244, 41 p.

——, 1953, Some late Oligocene larger foraminifera from Panama: Journal of Paleontology, v. 27, no. 3, p. 332–337.

——, 1957, Late Oligocene larger foraminifera from Barra Colorado Island, Panama Canal Zone: Bulletin of American Paleontology, v. 37, no. 163, p. 313–338.

Cooke, C. W., 1948, Eocene echinoids from Panama: Journal of Paleontology, v. 22, p. 91–93.

Coryell, H. N., and Mossman, R. W., 1942, Foraminifera from the Charco Azul Formation, Pliocene of Panama: Journal of Paleontology, v. 16, no. 2, p. 233–246.

Crowe, J. C., and Buffler, R. T., 1983, Regional seismic reflection profiles across the Middle America Trench and convergent margin of Costa Rica, in Bally, A. W., ed., Seismic expression of structural styles; a picture and work atlas; vol. 3: American Association of Petroleum Geologists Studies in Geology, no. 15, p. 3.4.2-147 to 3.4.2-162.

Cushman, J. A., 1918, The smaller fossil foraminifera of the Panama Canal Zone: Washington, D.C., United States National Museum Bulletin 103, p. 45–87.

De Boer, J., 1979, The outer arc of the Costa Rican orogen; Oceanic basement complexes of the Nicoya and Santa Elena peninsulas: Tectonophysics, v. 56, p. 595–604.

del Giudice, D., 1978, Características geológicas de la República de Panamá: Universidad Nacional Autónoma de México, Instituto de Geología Boletín 101, p. 4–25.

del Giudice, D., and Recchi, G., 1969, Mapa Geológico del Proyecto Minero de Azuero: Administración de Recursos Minerales, Naciones Unidas, Programa para el Desarrollo, 2 sheets, scale 1:250,000.

Dengo, G., 1960, Notas sobre la geología de la parte central de litoral Pacífico de Costa Rica: San José, Instituto Geográfico de Costa Rica, Informe Semestral, Julio a Diciembre, p. 43–58.

——, 1962a, Tectonic-igneous sequence in Costa Rica, in Engel, A.E.J., James, H. L., and Leonard, B. F., eds., Petrologic studies: Geological Society of America Buddington volume, p. 133–161.

——, 1962b, Estudio Geológico de la Región de Guanacaste: San José, Instituto Geográfico de Costa Rica, 112 p.

——, 1969, Problems of tectonic relations between Central America and the Caribbean: Gulf Coast Association of Geological Societies Transactions, v. 19, p. 311–320.

——, 1985, Mid America; Tectonic setting for the Pacific margin from southern Mexico to northwestern Colombia, in Nairn, A.E.M., and Stehli, F. G., eds., The ocean basins and margins: New York, Plenum Press, v. 7, p. 123–180.

Dondoli, C., Dengo, G., and Malavassi, E., 1968, Mapa Geológico de Costa Rica: San José, Instituto Geográfico Nacional, scale 1:700,000.

Duque-Caro, H., 1979, Major structural elements and evolution of northwestern Colombia, in Watkins, I. S., and others, eds., Geological and geophysical investigations of continental margins: American Association of Petroleum Geologists Memoir 29, p. 329–351.

——, 1984, Structural style, diapirism, and accretionary episodes of the Sinú–San Jacinto terrane; The Caribbean southwestern Colombia borderland, in Bonini, W. E., Hargraves, R. B., and Shagam, R., The Caribbean–South American Plate boundary and regional tectonics: Geological Society of America Memoir 162, p. 307–316.

Escalante, G., 1966, Geología de la Cuenca Superior del Río Reventazón, Costa Rica: Guatemala, Publicaciones Geológicas del ICAITI 1, p. 59–70.

Etayo, F., 1983, Mapa de terrenos geológicos de Colombia: Bogotá, Publicación Especial, Ingeominas 14, 147 p. (preliminary edition).

Fischer, R., 1981a, El desarrollo paleogeográfico del Mioceno de Costa Rica: Porto Alegre, Anales del II Congreso Latino-Americano de Paleontología, p. 565–579.

——, 1981b, Die Herausformung des mittleamerikanischen Isthmus im Moizän Costa Rica: Stuttgart, Ibe. Geologische Palöontologisches, Teil 1, no. 3/4, p. 210–221.

Fischer, R. L., and Franco, J. C., 1979, La Formación Coris; Mioceno, Valle Central, Costa Rica: San José, Instituto Geográfico Nacional, Informe Semestral Enero-Junio, p. 15–17.

Fisher, S. P., and Pessagno, E. A., 1965, Upper Cretaceous strata of northwestern Panama: American Association of Petroleum Geologists Bulletin, v. 49, p. 433–444.

Gabb, W. M., 1874, Notes on the geology of Costa Rica: American Journal of Science, v. 8, p. 388–390.

——, 1881, Descriptions of new species of fossils from the Pliocene clay beds between Limon and Moin, Costa Rica, together with notes on previously known species from there and elsewhere in the Caribbean area: National Academy of Sciences Journal, ser. 2, v. 8, p. 349–380.

Galli-Olivier, C., 1979, Ophiolite and island-arc volcanism in Costa Rica: Geological Society of American Bulletin, v. 90, p. 444–452.

Goossens, P. J., and Rose, W. I., Jr., 1973, Chemical composition and age determination of tholeiitic rocks in the basic igneous complex, Ecuador: Geological Society of America Bulletin, v. 84, p. 1043–1052.

Goossens, P. J., Rose, W. I., Jr., and Flores, D., 1977, Geochemistry of Tholeiites of the basic igneous complex of northwestern South America: Geological Society of America Bulletin, v. 88, p. 1711–1720.

Goudkoff, P. P., and Porter, W. W., 1942, Amoura Shale, Costa Rica: American Association of Petroleum Geologists Bulletin, v. 26, no. 10, p. 1647–1655.

Haffer, J., 1967, On the geology of the Urabá and northern Chocó regions, northwestern Colombia: Bototá, Ecopetrol Open File Report 809, 105 p.

Hayes, C. W., 1899, Physiography and geology of region adjacent to the Nicaragua canal route: Geological Society of America Bulletin, v. 10, p. 285–448.

Henningsen, D., and Weyl, R., 1967, Ozeanische kruste im Nicoya-Komplex von

Costa Rica, Mittelamerika: Geologische Rundschau, v. 57, p. 33–47.

Hershey, O. H., 1901, The geology of the central portion of the Isthmus of Panama: University of California Department of Geology Bulletin, v. 2, no. 8, p. 231–267.

Hoffstetter, R., Zoppis Bracci, L., and Dengo, G., 1960, Lexique stratigraphique international; v. 5, Amerique Latine: Paris, Amerique Centrale, fascicule 2a, 36 p.

Howe, E., 1907, Geology of the Panama Canal: Economic Geology, v. 2, no. 7, p. 639–658.

Kesler, S. E., Sutter, J. F., Issigonis, M. J., Jones, L. M. and Walker, R. L., 1977, Evolution of porphyry copper mineralization in an oceanic island arc; Panama: Economic Geology, v. 72, p. 1142–1153.

Krushensky, R. D., 1972, Geology of the Istarú Quadrangle, Costa Rica: U.S. Geological Survey Bulletin 1358, 46 p.

Kuijpers, E. P., 1979, La geología del complejo ofiolítico de Nicoya, Costa Rica: San José, Instituto Geográfico Nacional, Informe Semestral Julio-Diciembre, p. 15–75.

—— , 1980, The geologic history of the Nicoya ophiolite complex, Costa Rica and its geotectonic significance: Tectonophysics, v. 68, p. 233–255.

Laguna, J., 1977, Geología y sedimentología de tres unidades Paleocenas cerca de Sámara, Península de Nicoya, Provincia de Guanacaste [B.S. thesis]: San José, Universidad de Costa Rica, Escuela Centroamericana de Geología, 79 p.

Lew, L., 1983, The geology of the Osa Peninsula, Costa Rica; Observations and speculations of the outer arc of the southern Central American orogen [M.S. thesis]: University Park, Pennsylvania State University, Department of Geosciences, 91 p.

Lloyd, J. J., 1963, Tectonic history of the south Central American orogen: American Association of Petroleum Geologists Memoir 2, p. 88–100.

Lu, R. S., and McMillen, K. J., 1982, Multichannel seismic survey of the Colombia Basin and adjacent margins, *in* Watkins, J. S., and Drake, C. L., eds., Studies in continental margin geology: American Association of Petroleum Geologists Memoir 34, p. 395–412.

Lundberg, N., 1982, Evolution of the slope landward of the Middle America Trench, Nicoya Peninsula, Costa Rica, *in* Leggett, J. K., ed., Trench-forearc geology; Sedimentation and tectonics on modern and ancient active plate margins: Oxford, Blackwell Scientific Publications, p. 131–147.

MacDonald, D. F., 1919, The sedimentary formations of the Panama Canal Zone with special reference to the stratigraphic relations of the fossiliferous beds: United States National Museum Bulletin 103, p. 525–545.

—— , 1920, Informe final geológico y geográfico de Costa Rica: San José, Revista Costa Rica, part 2, p. 28–32; 50–57; 106–111; 123–125; 139–148.

Madrigal, R., 1970, Geología del mapa básico Barranca, Costa Rica: Dirección de Geología Minas y Petróleo, Informes Técnicos y Notas Geológicas no. 37, p. 55 (mimeographed report).

—— , 1976, Notas del Seminario de Geología de Costa Rica: Escuela Centroamericana de Geología (unpublished report).

Malavassi, V. E., and Chaves, R., 1970, Estudio geológico regional de la zona Atlántica norte de Costa Rica: San José, Dirección de Geología Minas y Petróleo, Informes Técnicos y Notas Geológicas, v. 9, no. 35, 16 p. (mimeographed report).

Malavassi, V. E., and Madrigal, R., 1970, Reconocimiento Geológico de la zona Norte de Costa Rica: Dirección de Geología, Minas y Petróleo, Informes Técnicos y Notas Geológicas 38, 10 p. (mimeographed report).

Matumoto, T., Ohtake, M., Latham, G., and Umaña, J., 1977, Crustal structure in southern Central America: Seismological Society of America Bulletin, v. 67, p. 121–134.

McBirney, A. R., and Williams, H., 1965, Volcanic history of Nicaragua: University of California Press, University of California Publications in Geological Sciences, v. 55, 65 p.

Montero, P. W., 1974, Estratigrafía del Cenozoico del área de Turrúcares, Provincia de Alajuela, Costa Rica [B.S. thesis]: San José, Universidad de Costa Rica, Escuela Centroamericana de Geología, 40 p.

Mora, S., 1979, Proyecto hidroeléctrico Boruca: San José, Estudio Geológico

Regional, Instituto Costarricense de Electricidad, 193 p. (unpublished report).

—— , 1981, Barra Honda: San José, Editorial Universidad Estatal a Distancia, 115 p.

Nygren, W. E., 1950, The Bolivar geosyncline of northwestern South America: American Association of Petroleum Geologists Bulletin, v. 34, p. 1998–2006.

Olsson, A. A., 1922, The Miocene of northern Costa Rica: Bulletin of American Paleontology, v. 9, no. 39, p. 9–20.

—— , 1942, Tertiary and Quaternary fossils from the Burica Peninsula of Panama and Costa Rica: Bulletin of American Paleontology, v. 27, no. 106, 83 p.

Palmer, K.V.W., 1923, Foraminifera and a small molluscan fauna from Costa Rica: Bulletin of American Paleontology, v. 10, no. 40, p. 1–19.

Rivier, F., 1979, Geología del área norte de los Cerros de Escazú, Cordillera de Talamanca, Costa Rica: San José, Instituto Geográfico Nacional, Informe Semestral, Enero-Junio, p. 99–133.

—— , 1983, Sintesis geológica y mapa geológico del área del bajo Tempisque, Guanacaste, Costa Rica: San José, Instituto Geográfico Nacional, Informe Semestral, Enero-Junio, p. 7–30.

Sáenz, R., coordinator, 1982, Mapa Geológico de Costa Rica: San José, Instituto Geográfico Nacional, 9 sheets, scale 1:200,000.

Sapper, K., 1905, Ueber Gebirgsbau und Boden des Südlichen Mittelamerika: Petermanns Geographische Mitt., v. 32, 82 p.

—— , 1937, Mittelamerika; Handbuch der regionalen geologie, 8, 4a: Heidelberg, Steinman and Wilckens, 160 p.

Schmidt-Effing, R., 1979, Alter und Genese des Nicoya-Komplexes, einer ozeanischen Paläokruste, Oberjura bis Eozän, im südlichen Zentralamerika: Geologische Rundschau, v. 68, p. 457–494.

Schmidt-Effing, R., Gursky, H. J., Strebin, M., and Wilberg, H., 1980, The ophiolites of southern Central America with special reference to the Nicoya Peninsula, Costa Rica: Transactions, 9th Caribbean Geological Conference, Santa Domingo, v. 2, p. 423–429.

Schuchert, C., 1935, Historical geology of the Antillean-Caribbean region: New York, John Wiley and Sons, 811 p.

Seyfried, H., Sprechman, P., and Aguilar, T., 1985, Sedimentología y paleoecología de un estuario del litoral Pacífico del Istmo Centroamericano primordial, Mioceno medio, Costa Rica: San José, Revista Geológica de América Central no. 3, Escuela Centroamericana de Geología, p. 1–68.

Shelton, B. J., 1952, Geology and petroleum prospects of Darien, southeastern Panama [M.S. thesis]: Corvallis, Oregon State Unviersity, 62 p.

Sprechmann, P., ed., 1984, Manual de geología de Costa Rica, v. 1: San José, Estratigrafía, Editorial de la Universidad de Costa Rica, 320 p.

Stewart, R. H., 1966, The Río Bayano Basin; A geological report: Office of Interoceanic Canal Studies Open File Memorandum.

Taylor, G. D., 1975, The geology of the Limón area of Costa Rica [Ph.D. thesis]: Baton Rouge, Louisiana State University, 116 p.

Terry, R. A., 1941, Notes on submarine valleys off the Panama coast: Geographic Review, v. 31, no. 5, p. 377–384.

—— , 1956, A geological reconnaissance of Panama: California Academy of Sciences Occassional Papers no. 23, 91 p.

Vaughan, T. W., 1918, Geological history of Central America and the West Indies during Cenozoic time: Geological Society of America Bulletin, v. 29, p. 615–630.

—— , 1926, The stratigraphic horizon of the beds containing *Lepidocyclina Chaperi* on Haut Chagres, Panama: Proceedings of the National Academy of Sciences, v. 12, no. 8, p. 519–522.

Weyl, R., 1957, Contribución a la Geología de la Cordillera de Talamanca de Costa Rica, Centro América: San José, Instituto Geográfico de Costa Rica, 75 p.

—— , 1980, Geology of Central America, 2nd edition: Berlin-Stuttgart, Gebrüder Borntraeger, 371 p.

Williams, H., 1952, Volcanic history of the Meseta Central occidental Costa Rica: Berkeley and Los Angeles, University of California Publications in Geological Sciences, v. 2, no. 4, p. 145–180.

Woodring, W. P., 1928, Tectonic features of the Caribbean region: 3rd Pan-Pacific Scientific Congress, Tokyo, p. 401–431.

——, 1957, Geology and paleontology of Canal Zone and adjoining parts of Panama: U.S. Geological Survey Professional Paper 306-A, 145 p.

——, 1970, Geology and paleontology of Canal Zone and adjoining parts of Panama; Description of Tertiary mollusks: U.S. Geological Survey Professional Paper 306-D, 299 p.

——, 1982, Geology and paleontology of Canal Zone and adjoining parts of Panama; Description of Tertiary mollusks: U.S. Geological Survey Professional Paper 306-F, p. 541–759.

Woodring, W., and Malavassi, V. E., 1961, Miocene foraminifera, mollusks, and a barnacle from the Valle Central, Costa Rica: Journal of Paleontology, v. 35, no. 3, p. 489–497.

Zoppis Bracci, L., and del Giudice, D., 1958, Geología de la costa del Pacífico de Nicaragua: Boletín del Servicio Geológico Nacional de Nicaragua 2, p. 19–68.

MANUSCRIPT ACCEPTED BY THE SOCIETY SEPTEMBER 29, 1987

The Geology of North America
Vol. H, The Caribbean Region
The Geological Society of America, 1990

Chapter 9

Caribbean marine geology;
Ridges and basins of the plate interior

Troy L. Holcombe
Marine Geology and Geophysics Division, National Geophysical Data Center, Boulder, Colorado 80303
John W. Ladd
Lamont-Doherty Geological Observatory of Columbia University, Palisades, New York 10964
Graham Westbrook
School of Earth Sciences, University of Birmingham, Birmingham B15 2TT, England
N. Terence Edgar
Office of Energy and Marine Geology, U.S. Geological Survey, Reston, Virginia 22092
Christopher L. Bowland
Research and Technical Services, ARCO Oil and Gas Company, Plano, Texas 75075

INTRODUCTION

In this chapter we present a summary of the regional geology of the interior of the Caribbean Plate as well as that of the Yucatán Basin. Proceeding from northwest to southeast, the basins and ridges of the Caribbean, exclusive of active plate margins, are the Yucatán Basin and the Cayman Ridge, part of the North American Plate; and the Nicaraguan Rise, Colombian Basin, Beata Ridge, Venezuelan Basin, Aves Ridge, and Grenada Basin, which make up part of the Caribbean Plate.

Geologic history of the subject areas is limited to Mesozoic and Cenozoic time, with the possible exception of the Upper Nicaraguan Rise, which may be partly underlain by a core of pre-Mesozoic rocks. History of crustal formation, probably occurring in the Cretaceous or the Jurassic for most of the Caribbean sea floor, has not been well established because drillholes encountered a basaltic sill/flow sequence, which may postdate initial crustal formation, and because the Caribbean interior is isolated structurally by plate boundaries, relict and active. Identification of magnetic anomaly sequences has been speculative. Time of formation and structural development of the Yucatán and Grenada Basins are as yet also speculative; the basins possibly formed in early Cenozoic time. Evolution of the Caribbean interior is largely that of accumulation of sediments through the Late Cretaceous and Cenozoic, and structural response to stresses applied to existing crust and lithosphere. Some lithosphere was probably consumed along relict subduction zones (upper Nicaraguan Rise, Cayman Ridge, Beata Ridge?, and Aves Ridge) during Late Cretaceous and early Cenozoic time. Apparently, no major plate boundary has extended through the Caribbean interior, except through the Cayman Trough, since the reorganization of

relative plate motions in the Eocene. Miocene-to-Recent time was marked by lithospheric flexure adjacent to active compressional margins, diffuse rifting beneath the western Caribbean, and a great influx of terrigenous sediments, especially from South America. The geomorphology of the Caribbean interior has largely been that of sediment-smoothing of either original spreading-fabric relief, or formation of secondary relief resulting from structural deformation or volcanism.

Discussion of the regional geology for each basin and ridge generally begins with physiography; proceeds through stratigraphy, sediments, and structure; and ends with origin and evolution. Some general features of Quaternary and recent sediments are discussed in the final section. Seismic sections (Plates 8 and 9) are referred to throughout the text. Proper names of features referred to in the text are shown together with generalized bathymetry in Plate 1.

YUCATAN BASIN

The Yucatán Basin, one of the least-known offshore areas of the Caribbean, lies between the arcuate continental/island margin of Yucatán-Cuba, and the ENE–trending Cayman Ridge. It is separated into a deeper (4,000 to 4,600 m) northwestern part containing the Yucatán Plain, and a shallower (2,000 to 3,500 m) southeastern part dominated by a pair of ridges (Camagüey Ridges), which strike northeast across the basin. Linear, sediment-filled basins lie between the Camagüey and Cayman Ridges. The Camagüey Ridges are separated from the Cuban margin by an arcuate eastward extension of the deep basin.

Holcombe, T. L., Ladd, J. W., Westbrook, G., Edgar, N. T., and Bowland, C. L., 1990, Caribbean marine geology; Ridges and basins of the plate interior, *in* Dengo, G., and Case, J. E., eds., The Caribbean Region: Boulder, Colorado, Geological Society of America, The Geology of North America, v. H.

Sedimentary strata

Other than surficial sediments, there is no stratigraphic control for the Yucatán Basin. Surficial pelagic-hemipelagic sediments of the Yucatán Basin consist of foraminifera and pteropod-rich chalk and marl oozes and marl clays (Lamont-Doherty Geological Observatory of Columbia University and Woods Hole Oceanographic Institution, unpublished megascopic core descriptions). Chalk oozes predominate on the elevated southeastern portion of the basin. Marl oozes predominate within the interturbidite lutite sequences of the Yucatán Basin, reflecting influx of sediments from terrigenous sources. Turbidites consist of a heterogeneous series of terrigenous sands and muds (sand/silt/clay or silt/clay) and carbonate sands. Woody plant fragments have been identified in Yucatán Basin turbidites.

Terrigenous sands and muds are fed into the Yucatán Plain from the southwest via the Belize Fan; the primary sediment source area appears to be the mountains of Guatemala and Honduras via the Rivers Polochic, Motagua, Chamelecón, and Ulúa, all of which converge at the head of Belize and Motagua Fans. Yucatán Plain gradients reverse in its eastern extension, leading upslope toward the mouth of the Río Cauto, which drains much of the Sierra Madre Oriental of Cuba. A well-developed drainage network also funnels pelagic carbonate into the Yucatán Plain from the shallower portion of the Yucatán Basin. One such drainage channel breaches the Camagüey Ridges at longitude 82.5°W. Carbonates are likewise brought in from the continental and island slopes of Yucatán and Cuba via canyons. See Plate 1.

The Yucatán Basin contains a sequence of strata generally 0.5 to 1.5 seconds thick, which overlies rough (0.5 to 2 seconds relief) basement (Dillon and others, 1972; Case and Holcombe, 1980). Seismic reflection horizons that occur widely throughout the Caribbean south and east of the upper Nicaraguan Rise are not recognizable in the Yucatán Basin. Higher ridge crests and seamounts of the Camagüey Ridges are locally devoid of sediments, or sediment cover is negligible.

An acoustically well-stratified turbidite sequence up to 1 to 1.25 seconds thick overlies a less reflective sediment sequence in the Yucatán Plain Province, which occupies the structurally deep northern crescent of the basin (Dillon and others, 1972; Plate 1, B). With multichannel seismic reflection data, internal reflectors within the sequence are recognized (Addy and Taylor, 1981; Eric Rosencrantz, personal communication, 1986). Examination of seismic sequences reveals four major intervals, possibly separated by unconformities. The upper two intervals are turbidite sequences thought to be derived from the southwest. The third sequence is similar in appearance to the upper two, but a southwesterly source is not evident. The lowermost sequence is local, discontinuous, and fills in basement lows. In the eastern arm of the Yucatán Plain, seismic sequences appear to be turbidite and fan deposits having an easterly source.

Yucatán Plain sediments are largely undisturbed. An assessment based on study of multichannel seismic reflection lines across the basin is that the basin has been tectonically quiescent during the period of time represented by deposition of the bulk of the sediment section (E. Rosencrantz, personal communication, 1986).

Crustal type and age

Two refraction stations in the Yucatán Basin were occupied by Ewing and others (1960): one station over the shallower southeastern part of the basin adjoining the Cayman Ridge, and one over the deep basin south of the Isle of Pines. Crustal thicknesses and seismic velocities calculated at this latter station are about those "typical" of oceanic crust in the main ocean basins, whereas the southeastern station showed anomalously thick crust. A two-layer crust in the shallower area was indicated in these early refraction sections. Basement relief of the Yucatán Basin (Plate 8, B) has the overall aspect of tilted fault blocks (asymmetry of basement highs; fault-like vertical displacement of the basement), suggesting the possibility that distension, rifting, and foundering of preexisting crust occurred during opening of the basin.

Hall and Yeung (1980) analyzed residual magnetic anomaly patterns and tentatively identified a series of low-amplitude, long-wavelength anomalies, trending northeast in the western Yucatán Basin, and east-northeast in the eastern basin, separated and offset along a fracture zone (Fig. 1). They obtained an uncertain correlation with anomalies that would be generated on one side of a northeast-trending early Cenozoic–Late Cretaceous spreading center formerly lying south of the present basin. This correlation, although speculative, is in general agreement with other indirect age estimates:

1. Heat flow. Mean heat-flow measurements from eleven Yucatán Basin stations (Epp and others, 1970; Erickson and others, 1972) range from 1.5 to 1.79 heat flow units (hfu) and have a mean of 1.45 hfu. Using the Schlater and Tapscott (1979) theoretical description of heat flow versus age, this corresponds to a crustal age range of 40 to 97 Ma, with a mean of 61 Ma. No areal pattern of heat-flow values has been discerned.

2. Basement depth. Basement depth averages about 6,000 m for the deep western Yucatán Basin and about 4,500 m (but highly variable) for the shallower east and southeast. Making a rough allowance for depth adjustment due to isostatic loading by the sediments, basement depths are 5,500 and 4,200 m, respectively. Application of these depths to the Sclater and Tapscott (1979) age-depth relationships yields age estimates of 73 Ma and 24 Ma, respectively. Apparently, heat flow and basement depth are in general agreement for the deep western part of the basin, with depths being slightly greater than heat flow would predict. Basement depths are clearly shallower than heat flow would predict for the southeastern part of the basin.

3. Sediment thickness. Comparing an integrated average thickness (475 m) of the pelagic section from the southeastern elevated part of the basin with sedimentation rate versus time curves from the southeastern Caribbean (Saunders and others, 1973) yields an estimate of 53 Ma. This is probably a low esti-

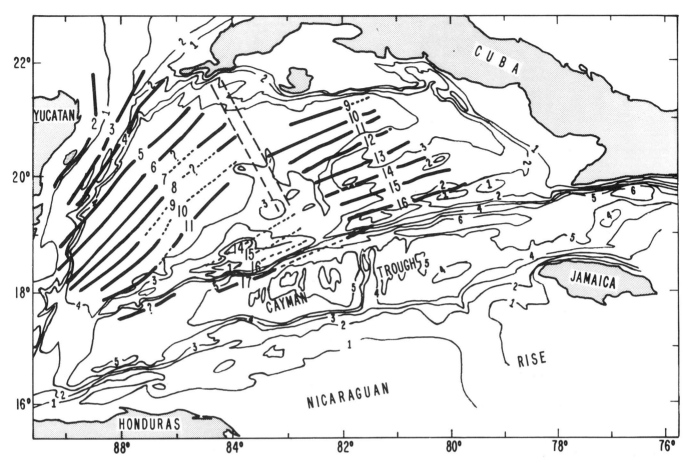

Figure 1. Pattern of residual magnetic anomalies and location of hypothetical fracture zone derived by Hall and Yeung (1980) for the Yucatán Basin. Reprinted by permission. The numbered magnetic anomaly sequence is for labeling purposes and does not imply time sequence or correlation with numbered magnetic lineations recognized worldwide.

mate because of the continuing transport of sediments to the deeper part of the basin. It agrees generally with the heat-flow estimate, but not with the depth estimate, for the southeastern part of the basin.

Models for basin formation

Several models for formation and tectonic evolution of the Yucatán Basin and the northwestern Caribbean have been widely discussed, including: (a) sphenochasmic clockwise rotation of the Honduran (Chortis) block away from Yucatán in a fashion similar to the opening of the Bay of Biscay (Uchupi, 1973; Freeland and Dietz, 1971; Dillon and Vedder, 1973), (b) Emplacement of Pacific crust into the basin behind an advancing Cuban island arc (Malfait and Dinkelman, 1972), and (c) sea-floor spreading behind the Cuban Arc (Hall and Yeung, 1980; Pindell and Dewey, 1982). Sphenochasmic rotation (model a) has been discounted because of evidence for large amounts of left-lateral translation of the Chortis Block with respect to the Yucatán Block in Oligocene-to Recent time. Model b requires a pre–Late Cretaceous crustal age (unless explained by an elegant model for sub-

duction of older crust along basin margins), not in agreement with age estimates derived from residual magnetic anomaly models, heat flow, basement depth, and sediment thickness. Model c, postulating Late Cretaceous–to–Eocene back-arc or inter-arc spreading, appears to be reconcilable with crustal age estimates and what little is known of crustal fabric.

Malfait and Dinkelman (1972) have proposed that, as the collision of the Cuban Arc with the Bahamas propagated eastward, the pole of rotation describing relative movement along the northern Caribbean plate boundary shifted in a series of steps, such that small-circles of rotation, which formerly aligned with the Yucatán Margin, became eventually aligned with the Cayman Trough. This proposition is of interest because it provides a possible explanation for radial patterns of ridges across the southern Yucatán Basin, which could represent relict left-lateral shear zones, ephemerally active during the shift in relative plate motion. These possible shear zones may have continued northeastward through the Cuban Arc, where their position seems to coincide with left-lateral offsets in the core of the arc itself (Case and Holcombe, 1980). This concept of stepwise-propagating shear zones poses a hazard for Late Cretaceous–Early Cenozoic back-arc spreading models because of the overprinting effect that shear zones would have on sediment-distribution patterns, magnetic-anomaly patterns, and age estimates.

The spreading model derived by Hall and Yeung (1980) requires subduction of the spreading center and its southern limb to the south beneath the area now occupied by the Cayman Trough and Nicaraguan Rise. This presumed subduction would logically have proceeded contemporaneously with spreading; such a subduction episode would need to have been complete by the time of the Eocene reorganization of plate boundaries and relative motions. Subduction may have occurred along the north boundary of the basin adjacent to Cuba, as evidenced by what may be a buried trench, with a buried deformational front on its landward side (Plate 8, C).

CAYMAN RIDGE, UPPER NICARAGUAN RISE

Geology of the Cayman Ridge and upper Nicaraguan Rise is known primarily from (1) dredge hauls from the walls of the Cayman Trough, (2) geology of the Cayman Islands, Swan Island, and the Bay Islands, (3) geology of Jamaica and Honduras/Nicaragua, (4) wells drilled on the upper Nicaraguan Rise, and (5) geophysical lines run across the Cayman Ridge and upper Nicaraguan Rise, including seismic reflection and refraction, gravity, and magnetic profiles. The stratigraphy and regional geology of Honduras and Nicaragua (Horne and others, this volume), and the geology of Jamaica (Lewis and others, this volume), are summarized in other chapters.

The Cayman Ridge extends east-northeast across the Caribbean between Belize and Oriente Province, Cuba. Its crestal depth is highly variable (0 to 1,000 m; 3,000 m sill between Grand Cayman and Misteriosa Bank); width varies between 50 and 80 km. Erosional channels dissect the ridge but they are not well delineated by existing data coverage. Its western end is truncated by faulting and/or sediment burial; physiographic expression does not continue across the Belize Fan. Over much of its length a double ridge crest separates small perched basins, valleys, or flats. The Cayman Islands, Misteriosa Bank, and Rosario Reefs cap the highest crests. Refer to Plate 8, B, E.

The upper Nicaraguan Rise extends from Honduras east-northeast across the Caribbean and the island of Jamaica. It includes the broad continental shelf of Honduras/Nicaragua, and the southern island shelf of Jamaica, both carbonate banks, together with a series of other, smaller carbonate banks (including Pedro Bank, Thunder Knoll, Rosalind Bank, Serranilla Bank, and Alice Shoal). These banks are separated by four northwest-trending channels or troughs, which range in maximum depth from less than 400 m to 1,500 m. These channels deepen toward their ends and in most instances merge with canyons leading down the Pedro Escarpment or down into the Cayman Trough. South of Pedro Bank, the channel is floored by a plain at 1,300 to 1,400 m depth. Linear depressions occur along the base of the Pedro Bank Escarpment. The Jamaican Plain occupies one of these depressions. The line of the Pedro Bank Escarpment and this depression is interrupted by the prominent ridge capped by Banco Nuevo. Refer to Plate 8, H.

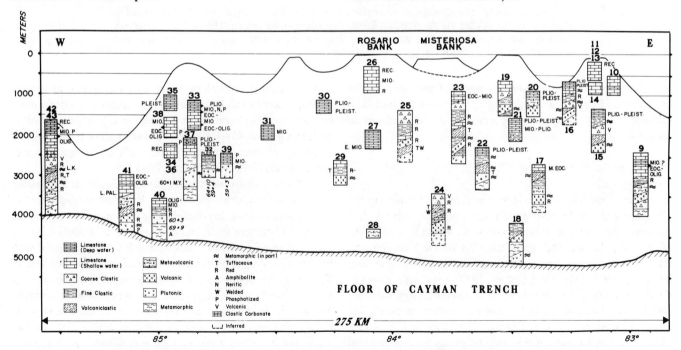

Figure 2. Stratigraphic columns developed from successful dredge hauls for the western sector of the north wall of the Cayman Trough. For precise location of each dredge haul (number above each column) see Perfit and Heezen (1978, Fig. 2). Rock type is shown by symbol. Occurrence of metamorphism, biostratigraphic age dates, radiometric age dates, and occurrence of neritic strata are also shown. From Perfit and Heezen, 1978. Reprinted by permission.

Walls of Cayman Trough

From 50 dredge stations, sampling both walls of the Cayman Trough, Perfit and Heezen (1978) were able to develop a composite stratigraphy. Samples from the north wall of the Cayman Trough are predominantly from the western sector of the trough, opposite Misteriosa and Rosario Banks (Fig. 2). Samples from the south wall of the Cayman Trough are scattered between Jamaica and Swan Island (Fig. 3).

From the deeper (>2,500 m) part of the north wall, exposed rocks are predominantly plutonic, together with metamorphic rocks that may be the metamorphic equivalents of the plutonic rocks. The predominant plutonic rock type is granodiorite. Secondary amounts of volcanic, clastic, and volcaniclastic rocks and metavolcanic rocks, together with some Lower Cretaceous–lower Paleocene shallow-water carbonates, are also present. Potassium-argon dates were obtained from several granodiorite samples (59 ± 3 Ma; 59 ± 4 Ma; 64 ± 10 Ma; 60 ± 3 Ma), and an amphibolite (69 ± 9 Ma). Clastic rocks include volcanic breccias, conglomerates, sandstone, and argillites, some with red-bed equivalents, as well as graywacke and arkose. Volcaniclastic rocks include pyroclastic as well as epiclastic volcanic rocks.

From shallower depths (<3,000 m) interbedded volcanic, clastic, and volcaniclastic rocks predominate over plutonic rocks. Composition of volcanic rocks ranges from basalt to rhyolite but is predominantly andesite and dacite.

Carbonates predominate above 2,500 m in the western portion of the sampled part of the north wall (Fig. 2), and above 1,000 m in the eastern sector of the sampled region. Although some of the limestones, particularly the older rocks, may be inter-

bedded with the deeper volcanic rocks, most are thought to overlie the plutonic/volcanic/volcaniclastic section. Most of the older limestones (lower Cretaceous to Oligocene/Miocene) are characteristic of a neritic carbonate bank or shelf environment. Many of the Miocene-to-Pleistocene limestones are representative of pelagic environments (deeper water outside the neritic zone). Shallow-water limestones of Miocene-to-Recent age also occur, particularly near banks and shallow crests of the Cayman Ridge at depths less than 1,000 m.

A similar stratigraphy characterizes the south wall of the Cayman Trough. Plutonic, extrusive volcanic, and metamorphic rocks were recovered from the deeper walls, but in contrast to the north wall, they do not predominate. Extrusive volcanic rocks are also less abundant. The most abundant rock types are sand-sized clastics and graywackes; also present are breccias, conglomerates, and tuffs. Again, carbonate rocks probably occur interbedded with clastic and volcanic rocks, but they are predominant in the upper, presumed younger, part of the section. The oldest carbonate is Early Cretaceous(?); most ages are Eocene through Recent. Bioclastic limestones of pelagic (deep-water) affinity were recovered, having dates ranging from late Oligocene to Holocene. The shallow-water samples recovered are generally Miocene or older. Based on the samples recovered, deep-water limestones appear to have been deposited earlier on the Nicaraguan Rise wall than on the Cayman Ridge wall.

Cayman Islands

Geology of the Cayman Islands has been summarized by Matley (1926). Hard, shallow-water limestone (The Buff Lime-

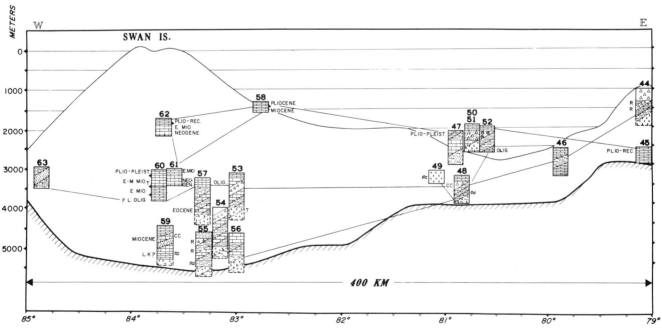

Figure 3. Stratigraphic columns developed from successful dredge hauls for the south wall of the Cayman Trough. For precise location of each dredge haul (number above each column) see Perfit and Heezen (1978, Fig. 2). See Figure 2 for rock types. From Perfit and Heezen, 1978. Reprinted by permission.

stone) forms the core of each island. Paleontologic ages range from mid-Oligocene on Cayman Brac to Miocene on Grand Cayman. The Buff Limestone contains a very low percentage of detritus, all of which could have been transported via wind or ocean currents; therefore, presence of adjacent land areas supplying terrigenous debris is not required. Quaternary coastal deposits, the Ironshore Formation, rest upon the coastal platform; they are described as coralliferous limestone and marl.

Swan Island

On Swan Island, deformed Oligocene or lower Miocene marl oozes, which are structurally aligned east-west parallel to the Cayman Trough, are capped by elevated post–lower Miocene carbonate bank and beach deposits (U.S. Geological Survey, 1967).

Bay Islands

On the Bay Islands of Guanaja and Roatán, a wide variety of meta-igneous, metasedimentary and sedimentary rocks of pre-Tertiary (some sedimentary units may be Tertiary), possibly Paleozoic age, are exposed. Serpentinite and granitic intrusions of unknown age occur. On Roatán, serpentinite is intruded along fault planes. On Utila Island, alkaline basalt has intruded Quaternary coral reef deposits (McBirney and Bass, 1969). Guanaja and Roatán sit atop a mostly submarine ridge that parallels and forms the south wall of the Cayman Trough and is separated from the northern shelf of Honduras by enclosed basins, probably fault-bounded. Thrust faults on Roatán suggest north-south compression; there is no evidence of left-lateral transcurrent displacement.

Recent vertical movement and southward tilting has occurred (McBirney and Bass, 1969). Similarities between the rocks and history of the Bay Islands to that of the Motagua Valley of Guatemala suggest that fault slices of the Motagua Valley terrane have been entrained and carried eastward at least as far as the Bay Islands.

Submerged Nicaraguan Rise

Limited information is available from well control regarding the geology of the submerged portion of the Nicaraguan Rise (Arden, 1975). Of the wells for which stratigraphy is summarized in Figure 4, all but one encounter basement rock at about 2,000 m. Metamorphic rocks (probable), andesite, and granodiorite were encountered in the four wells. The metamorphic basement encountered in the Tuara-1 well (Fig. 4) may be Paleozoic, and the granodiorite intrusives encountered in the Miskito-1 and Pedro Bank-1 wells probably correlate with Upper Cretaceous–lower Cenozoic intrusives found elsewhere on the Nicaraguan Rise. Potassium-argon dates of 53 ± 4.4 Ma were obtained from granodiorite recovered from the Pedro Bank-1 well (G. Draper, personal communication, 1984). The Touche-1 well, which did not reach basement even though it was drilled to 4,500 m, appar-

ently was drilled in a graben. Another well north of the Touche-1, the Main Cape-1, reached Eocene strata at about 3,000 m within this graben. Seismic reflection data reveal that this graben or basin is fault-bounded on the north and east, and that a considerable thickness of sedimentary strata, presumed to be principally Cretaceous in age, lies beneath drilled depths. Total sediment thickness may exceed 10,000 m in this basin (Cáceres Avila and others, 1984). The Touche-1 is the only known well on the submerged Nicaraguan Rise in which Paleocene strata were recognized. In wells outside the fault-bounded basin, middle Eocene marine strata either directly overlie basement or are separated from basement by basal clastic deposits.

Eocene strata encountered in the Nicaraguan Rise wells, and judged by Arden (1975) to occur throughout the area, are predominantly limestones with occasional porous reef rock, containing stringers of calcareous shale; traces of lignite occur. Evaporites are encountered locally near the present coastline of Honduras. Oligocene strata are missing or very thin, documenting an unconformity that extends in time from middle Eocene to Miocene near Honduras.

The Miocene is represented by marine strata, which are marly and gypsiferous, to the north and west, grading to coniniferous in the south and east. Between the Touche-1 and Miskito-1 wells along the Honduras coast, the Miocene facies changes from continental/nearshore fine-grained sandstone (Touche-1) to biogenic carbonates (Miskito-1).

Pliocene and Quaternary strata consist of porous karst-like carbonates, with breccias filling large cavernous zones in reef complexes, and layers of carbonaceous lime mud.

Synopsis of geologic evolution

A Cretaceous and early Cenozoic (pre–middle Eocene) island-arc environment for the Cayman Ridge and the upper Nicaraguan Rise is generally recorded where observed— Jamaica, Honduras/Nicaragua, wells drilled into the submerged portion of the upper Nicaraguan Rise, and walls of the Cayman Trough. Most localities are underlain by a complex assemblage of Cretaceous and lower Cenozoic andesitic and basaltic volcanic rocks, together with volcaniclastic, clastic, and limestone strata, which are locally intruded by granodiorite and metamorphosed in places. Crustal thicknesses of 15 to 20 km, with seismic velocities of the lower crustal layer in the range of 6.2 to 6.7 km/sec (Ewing and others, 1960), are compatible with the conclusion that the Cayman Ridge and upper Nicaraguan Rise are underlain by a core of island-arc rocks. No dated strata or volcanic rocks older than Cretaceous have been reported from Jamaica, the walls of the Cayman Trough, or from wells penetrating water-covered parts of the upper Nicaraguan Rise. Earliest occurrences of volcanic deposits in Honduras suggest that the area became an active island-arc subduction zone beginning in Late Jurassic time (Arden, 1975). As the upper rise is a broad feature, it is possible that there could have been several juxtaposed arcs that may have been active simultaneously or sequentially.

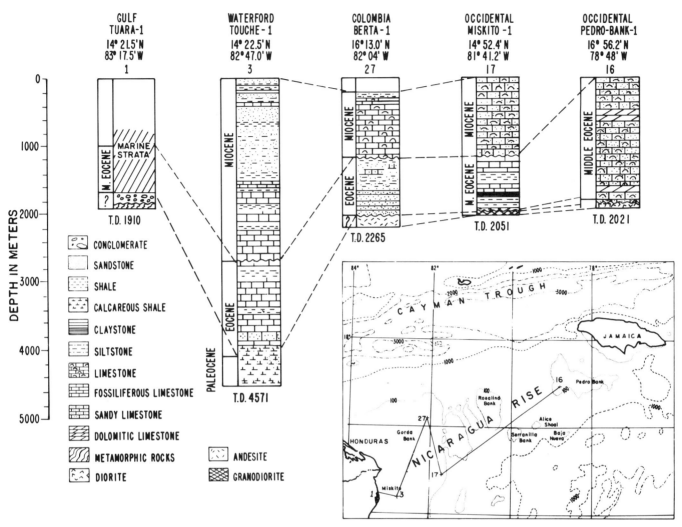

Figure 4. Stratigraphic columns from five wells drilled on the upper Nicaraguan Rise. Location of wells shown in inset map. After Arden, 1975.

Intensity of deformation along the arc peaked during latest Cretaceous and again during early Eocene time, as evidenced by structural deformation in Jamaica (Zans and others, 1963). Uplift and erosion, locally exposing intrusive bodies, was general throughout the upper Nicaraguan Rise during Late Cretaceous–early Eocene. Paleocene and lower Eocene deposits are largely absent except in structural troughs. Although observed only at two localities (Wagwater Trough and Touche-1 offshore well), strata of this age may be present in troughs elsewhere on the upper Nicaraguan Rise. Banks on the rise trend NW–SE, parallel to Wagwater Trough, and are separated from one another by shallow topographic troughs that may correspond to a deeper horst-and-graben structure (see insert map, Fig. 4). Apparently, Paleocene to early Eocene was a time during which extension produced NW–SE–trending grabens. Extensive faulting has been mapped beneath the shallow offshore Nicaraguan/Honduras portion of the rise; many of these faults also trend NW–SE (Case and Holcombe, 1980).

In middle Eocene time, activity ceased along the arc, and submergence was general. Marine Eocene strata are encountered at all locations where exposed or drilled. Submergence was sufficiently complete that local terrigenous sources on Jamaica were submerged and limestones of unusual purity were deposited. Unconformities on Jamaica in late Eocene and at the end of Oligocene time record interludes of minor uplift without appreciable deformation. Emergence in post-Miocene time and initiation of movement along presently active faults is recorded on Jamaica.

The zones of transcurrent faulting and other secondary faulting associated with the plate-boundary zone, which extend through Jamaica (Burke and others, 1980; Lewis and others, this volume) and which are associated with the active plate boundary to the north, probably continue westward along the northern water-covered rim of the Nicaraguan Rise. Several faults that parallel the Cayman Trough and are apparently active at present (judging from the pattern of seismicity and disturbance of sediments as seen in seismic reflection records) extend along the northern rim of the Nicaraguan Rise west of Jamaica (Case and Holcombe, 1980). Similar faulting has been suggested for the Cayman Ridge, where Gough and Heirtzler (1969) proposed that residual magnetic anomalies parallel to the ridge are the result of faulting and transcurrent movement, which has juxtaposed alternately magnetized and relatively nonmagnetized crustal units. Evidence for transcurrent faulting is reported from a northeast-trending fault zone forming the north boundary of the graben or basin, referred to previously, which lies immediately offshore Honduras and Nicaragua (Cáceres Avila and others, 1984).

Within the northern rim of the Nicaraguan Rise province, off Honduras and south and east of the Bay Islands, Pinet (1971) mapped three distinct northeast-trending residual magnetic anomalies arranged in en-echelon pattern. Pinet (1971) interpreted these to be elongated strips of highly magnetized crustal rock, probably ultramafic, which are separated by and are offset along NW–SE–trending transcurrent faults. These faults were interpreted to be secondary to the main ENE–WSW transcurrent fault direction. An alternative, equally plausible explanation is that these magnetized bodies have been offset and rotated along NE–SW transcurrent faults (offshore extensions of NE–SW faults cutting across Honduras).

One of the outstanding unsolved problems of the upper Nicaraguan Rise is how far east the pre-Mesozoic continental crust of the Chortis block extends beneath the rise. Arden (1975) concluded that the offshore portion of the rise is underlain by oceanic island-arc crust, based on crustal thicknesses, seismic velocities, and basement rock types encountered. Others have proposed that at least part of the Nicaraguan Rise is an eastward extension of the pre-Mesozoic continental block based on topographic and structural continuity (Meyerhoff, 1966). Conceivably, the submerged Nicaraguan Rise, particularly the western part, could be underlain, or partly underlain, by pre-Mesozoic crust that has been stretched and fragmented.

LOWER NICARAGUAN RISE

The lower Nicaraguan Rise appears to be a crustal block bounded by escarpments to the northwest (Pedro Bank Escarpment) and southeast (Hess Escarpment), and by rifts on the northeast (Morant Trough) and southwest (San Andrés Trough). The origin of the lower Nicaraguan Rise and its role in the development of the Caribbean area are among the least understood. The Hess Escarpment, a linear northeast-trending escarpment of highly variable relief (100 to 3,000 m), faces the Colombian Basin. Other rift valleys and escarpments, having the same northeast trend as the rift in the San Andrés Trough, occur on the lower Nicaraguan Rise. Scattered volcanic cones rise above the floor of the rise. Overall, the depth of the rise lies at 2,000 to 4,000 m, increasing generally to the southeast. Local relief is highly variable (0 to 3,000 m). Refer to Plate 8, Sections F, G, H, I.

Beneath the Jamaican Plain, acoustically stratified turbidites overlie pelagic sediments, suggesting that they formed late, prob-

ably since the middle Miocene (Plate 8, H). The small plain immediately south of Pedro Bank, as well as the Jamaican Plain, are probably fed from local pelagic and shallow-water carbonate bank sources. These plains appear to be part of an interconnected set of plains and channels that drain to the Colombian Plain. Erosional channels, some fault-controlled and associated with embayments, occur along the Hess Escarpment, especially its northeastern sector near Hispaniola.

Sedimentary strata

Seismic-reflection data suggest that most of the deposits of the lower Nicaraguan Rise are uniformly pelagic and not characteristic of shallow-water deposits. This is substantiated by the Deep Sea Drilling Project (DSDP) site 152 at 15°52.72′N, 74°36.47′W (Plate 8, I; Edgar and others, 1973), the only hole drilled on the lower Nicaraguan Rise, or more specifically, on the Hess Escarpment. The hole was not continuously cored and recovery was poor, but the results clearly demonstrate that pelagic carbonate material mixed with a minor amount of clay was the dominant sediment type from the Campanian to at least the early Eocene and probably throughout the Cenozoic.

The uppermost recovered unit at site 152, lower Eocene to lower Paleocene, consists of siliceous limestone and chalk. The Eocene chert and chalk sequence correlates with seismic reflector A″ (Plate 8, I; the two seismic reflectors encountered at site 152 have been correlated with reflective horizons A″, upper reflector, and B″, lower reflector; see "Venezuelan Basin" section for definition and discussion of these reflectors). Cretaceous strata consist of hard limestones and chalks, some of which are silicified and contain chert. Volcanic constituents are nearly ubiquitous. At the base of the Campanian strata, basalts (horizon B″) contain recrystallized limestone fragments with enclosed Campanian foraminifera. The contact between the Campanian sediments and the basalts was not recovered (Saunders and others, 1973).

Although site 152 was drilled at a water depth of 3,900 m, the preservation of calcareous and siliceous sediments throughout the section to the top of the basalt at 470 m below the sea floor is superior to that found in the Venezuelan Basin at slightly greater depths. This suggests, if we assume that the depth of calcium carbonate compensation was fairly uniform through time in both basins, that the sediments at site 152 were deposited at depths shallower than in the basins. However, neither the cores nor seismic reflection data indicate that the site of deposition was ever as shallow as the upper Nicaraguan Rise is today. The lower rise, therefore, appears to have changed little in its intermediate depth since Late Cretaceous time, although there is evidence of considerable faulting and local vertical movement.

Structure

Despite the apparent regional stability of the lower Nicaraguan Rise over a long period of time, there is considerable evidence of localized deformation. Faults, ridges, troughs, and volcanoes are found throughout the area, and some, if not most, of the activity has been Neogene-to-Recent. Two islands, San Andrés and Providencia, lie on the west end of the rise adjacent to the San Andrés Rift and the Nicaraguan Continental Shelf: Providencia is a volcanic island composed primarily of basaltic and trachytic lavas intruded by diorite dikes (Pagnaccio and Radelli, 1962); San Andrés, on the other hand, is a carbonate island with a deep-seated volcanic base (Milliman and Supko, 1968). San Andrés emerged in post-Miocene time. Kerr (1977) studied the volcanic sequence on La Providencia Island and reported that the oldest outcrop is composed of Miocene-Pliocene pillow basalts (alkaline), and the youngest sequence of volcanic rocks (subalkaline and calc-alkaline) is cut by dikes. He interpreted the chemical assemblage as being representative of both island-arc and oceanic-island volcanism.

San Andrés Trough appears to be an extensional feature separating the acoustically stratified deposits of the Nicaraguan continental margin from the acoustically transparent deposits of the lower Nicaraguan Rise (Plate 8, F). The deposits in the trough are highly stratified and appear to be turbidites that have formed a small abyssal plain. Just beneath the surface of the plain, the strata are folded, suggesting recent tectonic activity. A small rifted basin that appears very similar to the San Andrés Rift lies about 50 km northeast of La Providencia Island on the western side of Roncador Bank (Plate 8, F).

Morant Trough is apparently an active pull-apart basin connecting transcurrent faults of the northern Caribbean plate boundary zone (Mann and others, this volume). The northeasterly structural trend characteristic of the entire rise terminates near its southern flank. Extending southwestward from Morant Trough, another rift-like trough trends north to northeast (Fig. 5). This trough is coincident in trend with other structural lineaments, including the San Andrés Trough and the extension of the Hess Escarpment northeast of DSDP drillsite 152. Trends of these features, although poorly known due to limited data control, were summarized by Case and Holcombe (1980). Together these lineaments form an ill-defined N-to-NE–trending fabric.

Additional evidence for young structural activity and volcanism is seen within the sedimentary sequence covering the Nicaraguan Rise. Seismic horizons beneath and adjacent to the Jamaican Plain appear to be progressively more deformed with depth, suggesting slow deformation continuing to the present (Plate 8, H), and small-displacement faults are observed in various locations on the Nicaraguan Rise (Plate 8, H). Evidence for volcanism is observed in other seismic reflection sections. In one seismic section across the western portion of the rise, a probable young igneous intrusion is observed (Plate 8, G). The deeper seismic reflector has been intruded, and stratification in the overlying deposits has been disrupted. This igneous intrusion has also apparently altered the shape of the sediment surface, so that it is probably a geologically young intrusion. Magmatism that apparently postdates deposition of the sediment section is also observed in an elevated portion of the rise near 78°W adjacent to the Hess Escarpment (Plate 8, H, right center). Adjacent to this presumed

magmatic center, the acoustic character of sediment stratification has been altered, probably as a result of sill emplacement or hydrothermal alteration.

Crustal structure

The crust of the lower Nicaraguan Rise has been defined acoustically by only a few seismic-refraction measurements (Ewing and others, 1960; Edgar and others, 1971). In the central part of the lower Nicaraguan Rise a 4.4-km/sec layer was recorded overlying a 6.3-km/sec layer, whereas on the upper Nicaraguan Rise, about 350 km to the west, a 5.5-km/sec layer lies between 4.8 and 6.7 km/sec layers. At the northeast end of the rise, two reversed refraction profiles yielded consistent results: a 5.1 to 5.4 km/sec layer overlying a 6.5 to 6.7 km/sec layer. These velocities are similar to those recorded in the Colombian Basin, but the 6.7-km/sec crustal layer beneath the rise is about twice as thick as that beneath the basin. The similarities in the acoustic velocities and crustal structure recorded over the eastern part of the rise, the Colombian Basin, and the Beata Ridge to the east suggest that they may have had a common origin. Changes in crustal thickness in various areas may have been one factor responsible for the faulting that separates these various bathymetric features.

Tectonics

The lower Nicaraguan Rise is adjacent to the Chortis block of Central America (continental crust), but it is also adjacent to the region south of the Chortis block where the rocks are believed to be of oceanic origin (Case and others, 1984; Dengo, 1975). The thickness of the crust, its relationship to the upper Nicaraguan Rise (island arc? see discussion in this chapter) and what appears to be a uniform cover of pelagic deposits, lead us to conclude that, like southern Central America, the lower Nicaraguan Rise had an oceanic origin. It was probably created in the Pacific Ocean during the late Mesozoic and became a part of the Caribbean Plate soon after. Unmigrated multichannel seismic reflection data show the Hess Escarpment to have a featureless internal reflection structure and to juxtapose basements with dissimilar elevation and reflection character (Christofferson, 1973; Case and Holcombe, 1980; Bowland, 1984). These attributes suggest a wrench-related, transcurrent origin (Pindell and Dewey, 1982). In the Colombian Basin, the Upper Cretaceous–Recent sediment section fills against and is tectonically undisturbed adjacent to the Hess Escarpment, implying that the escarpment may be as old as Late Cretaceous and represents a very early deformation event in the basin's history. Burke and others (1984) postulated left-lateral movement along the Hess Escarpment as the Caribbean basin crust and the Nicaraguan Rise moved between Mexico and South America from 80 to 53 Ma.

The extensional features referred to previously appear to be late Cenozoic, active rifts, based on the deformation of sediments, seismic activity recorded coincident with the San Andrés Trough

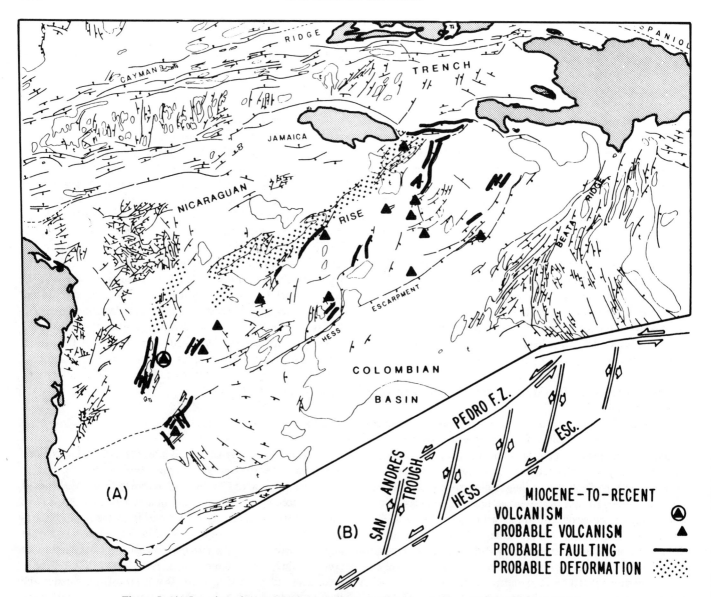

Figure 5. (A) Location of young, probably Miocene-to-Recent volcanism, faulting, and small-scale deformation on the lower Nicaraguan Rise. Tectonic map after Case and Holcombe, 1977. (B) Speculative schematic model for diffuse rifting of the lower Nicaraguan Rise.

(Molnar and Sykes, 1969), and evidence of young volcanic activity from seismic reflection sections. Faulting, volcanism, and small-displacement deformation summarized for the lower Nicaraguan Rise in Figure 5, suggests diffuse, young (Miocene-to-Recent?), probably slow rifting and translation. The trend of rifting may be controlled by an older fabric, as has been suggested by Burke and others (1984) for the San Andrés Trough. A speculative schematic model suggesting the geometry of rifting and translation is also shown in Figure 5.

Late Cenozoic translation along the southern boundary of the lower rise may not have been occurring along the Hess Escarpment itself but north of the escarpment and parallel to it where Bowland (1984) has interpreted wrench faulting (Fig. 6) and where there is other evidence of young tectonic movements,

previously referred to, farther northeast in the vicinity of longitude 78°W (Plate 8, H).

If east-west magnetic anomalies mapped by Christofferson (1976) extend westward across the Hess Escarpment, then possibly the young north-south rifts on the lower Nicaraguan Rise coincide with old fracture-zone trends, suggesting an original north-south and east-west fabric. Later movements along the Hess Escarpment, the Pedro Fracture Zone, and the rifts, probably represent an overprint of younger activity.

Limited data control and the uncertainties inherent in interpreting seismic reflection data do not permit unambiguous structural mapping of the lower Nicaraguan Rise. Therefore, present interpretations, of which the model shown in Figure 5 is but one example, are not well constrained. Wadge and Burke (1983) proposed that late Cenozoic deformation on the lower rise may be related to counterclockwise rotation of the Chortis Block relative to the Colombian Basin. Christofferson (1983) has proposed a pattern of rifts and transforms that represent a plate boundary extending from Costa Rica via the Hess Escarpment trend, and San Andrés Rift, northward across the upper Nicaraguan Rise to the Cayman Trough, across which movement in the left-lateral sense is taking place.

Diffuse rifting of the lithosphere beneath the lower Nicaraguan Rise, accompanied by volcanism, may have locally elevated the rise through increased thermal input and resulting lower densities within the lithosphere. The San Andrés Rift, the rift west of Roncador Bank, the rift south of Morant Trough, and the volcanic center at longitude 78°W near the Hess Escarpment, are all associated with elevated portions of the rise.

COLOMBIAN BASIN, BEATA RIDGE

A large submarine fan (Magdalena Fan) and plain (Colombian Plain) dominates the sea-bottom morphology of the eastern half of the 3,000 to 4,300 m deep Colombian Basin, and a smaller fan (Costa Rica Fan) and plain (Panamá Plain) occupy the southwestern extremity of the basin. Relief ranges from nil to a few tens of meters; higher relief is associated with Mono Rise, uplifted fault blocks, and channels on the fans. See Plate 8, H through U.

The dominant sediment source for the Colombian Plain and Magdalena Fan has obviously been the Río Magdalena that drains a large portion of the Colombian Andes (Muñoz, 1964; Heezen and Muñoz, 1965). Rivers that drain eastern Honduras and Central American mountains supply sediments to a narrow shelf at the head of the Costa Rica Fan. Gradients on the Panamá Plain indicate a mainly western sediment source and have no appreciable north-south component; however, a reversal in gradient reveals that Río Atrato of Colombia is also a contributor of sediments to the plain (see Plate 1). Active folding along the northern margin of Panamá has probably inhibited northward transport of sediments from Panamá to the plain. Channels leading from the shallower Panamá Plain to the deeper Colombian Plain provide a pathway for Central American sediments to reach the center of the basin.

Sediments

Only the upper Miocene-to-Recent part of the stratigraphic section of the Colombian Basin has been sampled by drilling. At DSDP site 154 (11°05.11′N, 80°22.75′W), drilled on a fault-bounded knoll of the Panamá outer ridge, 153 m of Pliocene and younger pelagic deposits (predominantly foram-bearing nannofossil marl) overlie a Pliocene and Miocene terrigenous sequence of deposits (calcareous, ash-bearing clay interspersed with black beds of pyrite and ash) containing turbidites. DSDP site 502, drilled on the Mono Rise (11°29.42′N, 79°22.78′W), was continuously cored. Lithology is similar to that encountered at site

154, but turbidites do not occur in the calcareous clays of the lower unit, the top of which is late Miocene in age. Planktonic foraminifera and calcareous nannofossils are found throughout the section, but radiolaria and diatoms are found only at the top and base of the section. Good preservation and high abundances of microfossils characterize the upper Pliocene and Quaternary but not the lower Pliocene to upper Miocene (Prell and others, 1980).

Sediment accumulation rates at site 502 range from 1.8 to 4.8 cm/1,000 years, with the average being 3.0 cm/1,000 years. Magnetostratigraphy and biostratigraphy indicate continuous deposition over the last 7.5 m.y. (Prell and others, 1982). At this site, sediment accumulation rates decrease with time, being lowest in the Pleistocene. The ratio of noncarbonate to carbonate deposits decreases from late Miocene to 3.6 Ma, then remains constant to the Holocene (Prell and others, 1980). Decreases in the sedimentation accumulation rates and noncarbonate/carbonate ratios are accounted for by decreased influx from terrigenous sources, possibly related to elevation of the site above the level of near-bottom transport. Zimmerman (1982) believed that site 502 was elevated above the level of major near-bottom clay transport at approximately 3.6 Ma (the beginning of a constant noncarbonate/carbonate ratio).

Acoustic stratigraphy and structure

Regional seismic reflection records (Plate 8, K, L, M, N, P, and Q) reveal that one to three seconds (about 1 to 4 km) of strata overlie an irregular oceanic crust in the central and western parts of the Colombian Basin (Lu and McMillen, 1982; Bowland, 1984). To the southeast, sediments thicken to greater than six seconds (>7 km) beneath the Magdalena Fan (Kolla and others, 1984; Lu and McMillen, 1982). In less thickly sedimented parts of the Colombian and Panamá Plains, highly reflective turbidite sequences are observed to overlie more acoustically transparent pelagic and hemipelagic deposits that are generally conformable with oceanic basement. Elevated portions of the basin floor west of Beata Ridge and in the southwestern Colombian Basin are layered by mainly pelagic deposits.

There has been considerable discussion of the occurrence in the Colombian Basin of reflection horizons A″ and B″. (Reflection horizon A″ coincides with the top of Upper Cretaceous–middle Eocene siliceous pelagic carbonates; reflection horizon B″ correlates with the top of Upper Cretaceous basalt sill/flow complex; Ewing and others,1967; Stoffa and others, 1981.) The only stratigraphic control established by drilling is at the northeastern margin of the basin where probable equivalents of horizons A″ and B″ are identified in seismic lines across DSDP site 152 (Edgar and others, 1973). In the northeasternmost Colombian Basin, reflectors that resemble A″ and B″ extend beneath Colombian Plain turbidites where they adjoin the Beata Ridge and Hess Escarpment and are also present locally within the central basin on and around basement structural highs.

Seismic stratigraphic studies of the western Colombian Basin (Lu and McMillan, 1982; Bowland, 1984) have predicted

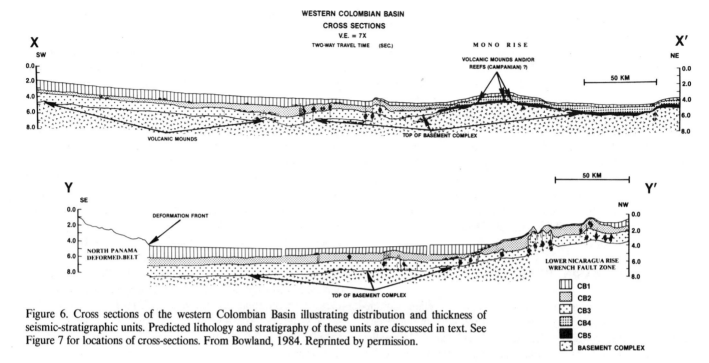

Figure 6. Cross sections of the western Colombian Basin illustrating distribution and thickness of seismic-stratigraphic units. Predicted lithology and stratigraphy of these units are discussed in text. See Figure 7 for locations of cross-sections. From Bowland, 1984. Reprinted by permission.

overall thickness and lithology of sediments and proposed correlations with reflection horizons A″ and B″. Bowland (1984) delineated five seismic stratigraphic units (Fig. 6; and Plate 8, K, L, M, N, P, and Q).

Unit CB5. This unit directly overlies oceanic basement and is correlated with the A″ to B″ interval in the Venezuelan Basin. The interpretation is based on (1) similarities of velocities and internal reflection character, (2) stratigraphic position of unit above basement and below the drilled upper Miocene section, and (3) correlation with Upper Cretaceous pelagic limestones in southern Central America and northwestern Colombia. The unit is believed to be mainly pelagic limestones, chalks, and clays deposited in an open-marine environment. This sequence, about 0.2 seconds thick (about 350 m) over Mono Rise (Plate 8, M, N), regionally thins to basement lows adjacent to the rise. Thinning with depth is explained by transition through the CCD and/or erosion in a strong bottom current regime.

Unit CB4. The top of this unit was sampled at DSDP site 502 where it is an upper Miocene "marine authigenic–volcanic clay facies" containing primarily montmorillonite derived from Central American terranes and deposited by bottom currents (Zimmerman, 1982). Drilling revealed physical conditions in this unit conducive to development of excess pore pressure (Prell and others, 1982). Internal deformation of unconsolidated sediment could explain the unit's contorted seismic facies (Plate 8, K through N).

Unit CB3 and CB2. These are interpreted as turbidites with a complex internal stratigraphy, as if reworked by bottom currents. The units apparently are mid-Eocene to late Miocene in age on the basis of stratigraphic position (time equivalent of unit CB4; Fig. 6). Subtle time-thickness patterns within unit CB2 (Fig. 7)

indicate a northerly sediment source, the western Nicaraguan Rise, where a regional late Eocene through early Miocene unconformity records mid-Tertiary erosion.

Unit CB1. This unit consists of a pelagic sequence where drilled (on uplifted fault block, site 154; Mono Rise, site 502), and gravity-flow deposits elsewhere (Plate 8, K through N). It includes the younger sediment wedge beneath the Panamá Plain and the younger fan sequence underlying the Costa Rica Fan. Sediments of this unit were clearly derived from a southern Central American source (Fig. 7). Formation of rift basins on the lower Nicaraguan Rise probably blocked northern sediment sources.

Stratigraphy of Panamá (Weyl, 1980) and the initiation of a wedge-shaped sediment-filled trough north of Panamá (Unit CB1, Fig. 8) imply that shoaling of the isthmus and development of the North Panamá Deformed Belt (NPDB; Case and Holcombe, 1980) began in the mid-Miocene. Bowland (1984) observed that the structural style and strike of the NPDB deformation front and regional gravity anomalies and seismicity of the fold belt (Bowin, 1976) correlated with crustal structure of the Colombian Basin. He suggested that the Panamá crustal block(s?) is being forced preferentially northwestward between thick oceanic plateau structures, which are difficult to overthrust.

The inception of the NPDB is roughly coeval with the onset of intraplate deformation in the western Colombian Basin. The intraplate deformation is manifested as a 150-km-long, transpressional, northwest-trending fault system (Case and Holcombe, 1980; Bowland, 1984). Multichannel reflection profiles show steep-dipping faults with drag folding of sediments, displacement of basement, and local unconformities within the sedimentary section, indicating episodic uplift. Large, positive free-air gravity

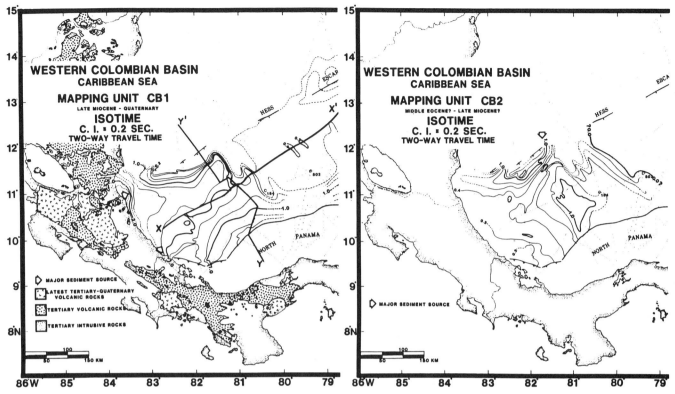

Figure 7. Sediment thickness of seismic-stratigraphic units CB1 and CB2, western Colombian Basin. From Bowland, 1984. Reprinted by permission.

anomalies (Bowin, 1976) are evidence of recent uplift in the fault zone. Drilling at DSDP site 154 on a fault-bounded knoll (Plate 8, J, 0330–0400) showed that a block was uplifted above the level of turbidite deposition in early Pliocene and suggested that surrounding blocks were uplifted at times ranging from Miocene through Pliocene. Concurrent development of this intraplate deformation and the NPDB is probably the response of the western Caribbean Plate to a Neogene NW-SE–oriented stress field (Ladd, 1976; Pindell and Dewey, 1982).

Elevation of site 154 in Miocene-to-Recent time was apparently progressive and was related to the development of an "outer ridge" during structural development of the Panamá convergent margin. The upper transparent section correlates with the upper Pliocene-to-Recent pelagic/hemipelagic deposits, whereas the lower highly reflective sequence correlates in the lower Pliocene and upper Miocene terrigenous deposits. Site 154 was apparently uplifted beyond the range of turbidite deposition in early Pliocene time. The higher knoll at time 0500 to 0530 on Plate 8, J probably was uplifted earlier, some time during the Miocene. Turbidite deposition appears to have continued until the Pleistocene between the two knolls and immediately south of the knoll; during Pleistocene time, these lower elevation areas were also elevated beyond the range of turbidite deposition.

Crustal structure

Crustal layers have velocities within the range of normal oceanic crust, but crustal thickness varies from near normal to more than twice the average for typical oceanic crust. The top of this crust forms a patchwork of regional ridges and basins; crustal thickness mirrors elevation of the crustal surface and is at least 18 km (Ewing and others, 1960) below Mono Rise. Compressional wave velocities within the uppermost basement average 4.6 km/sec.

Much of the basement of the western Colombian Basin, including Mono Rise, is typified by a smooth upper surface and occasionally, well-defined internal reflectors indicating stratification. Reflectors within the basement are absent farther east beneath the distal Magdalena Fan where basement lies deeper and has more typical oceanic crustal thickness (8.5 km; Houtz and Ludwig, 1977) and greater local surface relief (Plate 8, M through Q; Bowland and Rosencrantz, 1988). Reflectors within the now-buried eastern foundation of Mono Rise apparently overlap the rough basement, suggesting that the rise may be younger (Plate 8, P, Q). Heat flow averages 1.57 hfu in the western basin, including Mono Rise, but only 1.6 hfu east of the rise (Epp and others, 1970). In the western basin, heat flow is compatible with crust of latest Cretaceous age, whereas lower heat flow farther east, even after environmental corrections, may indicate a greater crustal age (Bowland, 1984).

Two acoustically distinct crusts in the Venezuelan Basin (Fig. 9), similarities in crustal surface morphologies, velocities, thicknesses, and internal reflection characters among Mono Rise, together with drilled sequences of Late Cretaceous volcanic flows and sills in the Venezuelan and Nauru (western Pacific) basins, and oceanic plateaus of the western Pacific, led Bowland and Rosencrantz (1988) to conclude: (1) the basement of Mono Rise and other positive crustal elements of the western Colombian Basin represent oceanic plateaus constructed of mafic flows and sills, interbedded with marine deposits, emplaced upon older oceanic crust, and (2) the central Colombian Basin is underlain by relatively unaltered crust, possibly of Early Cretaceous or Late Jurassic age. A Late Jurassic or Early Cretaceous formation of primary crust, followed by sedimentation and Late Cretaceous intraplate volcanism, is consistent with the stratigraphy of oceanic rocks, which crop out in the Nicoya Peninsula (Schmidt-Effing and others, 1980) and at other locations in southern Central America and western Colombia.

Beata Ridge

The Beata Ridge consists of a main ridge trending SW from Cape Beata, Hispaniola, and north-south–trending "fingers" or subsidiary ridges that extend diagonally southward and southeastward, away from the main ridge. An escarpment faces the Colombian Basin to the northwest. Topographic expression of the main and subsidiary ridges is terminated southward beneath deposits of the Colombian Plain. Crestal depths (1,000 to 3,000 m) and local relief (a few hundred to 2,000 m) are highly variable. Small plains occupy valleys within the Beata Ridge complex. Local pelagic sediments have filled these plains except at the northern end of the ridge, where gradients suggest that terrigenous sediments from Hispaniola have reached the plains. See Plate 8, U.

Sedimentary cover on the Beata Ridge consists largely of pelagic carbonates at the two sites drilled (Edgar and others, 1973). The Pleistocene-Oligocene sequence of site 151 (15°01.02′N, 73°24.58′W), drilled at the crest of the southern end of the ridge, consists of foraminiferal-nannofossil oozes that unconformably overlie a lower Eocene–Paleocene pelagic sequence of relatively high carbonate content, containing radiolaria. A silicified, brecciated, foraminiferal limestone of Santonian age occurs as a "hard ground" horizon below a major unconformity at the base of the lower Eocene–Paleocene sequence. The bottom 15 m was drilled through a basalt. Drilling rubble from directly above the basalt was dated as Santonian in age. Radiolaria of site 151 are absent or poorly represented in Upper Cretaceous and the lower Eocene strata but are well-enough preserved in the lower Miocene–upper Oligocene sections to permit zonation and comparison with other microfossil groups. Radiolaria are almost entirely missing in sediments younger than early middle Miocene (Saunders and others, 1973).

At site 31 (14°56.60′N, 72°01.63′W) the degree of microfossil preservation has been correlated with proximity to the carbonate compensation depth (CCD). The uppermost strata are Pliocene and contain strongly corroded planktonic foraminifera and great enrichment in discoasters, thus suggesting deposition very near the CCD. Below this unit lies a basal Miocene chalk and a middle Miocene ooze, which show no signs of microfossil

dissolution, indicating deposition well above the planktonic foraminiferal CCD. The basal unit drilled was an upper Oligocene-Miocene indurated chalk containing poorly preserved, corroded planktonic foraminifera, which are assumed to have been deposited near the planktonic foraminiferal CCD. Benson and others (1970) suggested that the ridge had subsided to near the CCD by the late Oligocene, was uplifted somewhat in the Miocene (approximately 1,000 m), and has subsided since the Miocene to its present depth.

Coring and dredging from one locality of the crest of the ridge recovered middle Eocene neritic chalks overlain by Oligocene-to-Recent deep-water carbonate oozes (Fox and others, 1970; Fox and Heezen, 1975; Fig. 8a). Fox and Heezen interpreted seismic reflection records to indicate that reflectors A″ and B″ extend up onto the Beata Ridge with a fairly constant thickness of sediment between A″ and B″ (Fig. 8b; Plate 8, U). The constant thickness of the A″ to B″ interval suggested to them that the topography of the ridge was not formed until well after the time of emplacement of horizon B″. The neritic chalks suggest uplift by mid-Eocene time.

Other evidence indicates that the Beata Ridge was formed as a positive feature after horizon B″ time but well before onset of horizon A″ time. Occurrence of a major Santonian-to-Paleocene unconformity above a "hard-ground" horizon in drillhole 151 suggests current-sweeping of a topographically positive feature, and a depositional scar, probably evidence of a gyre in water circulation in the Venezuelan Basin, remained stable in position for the duration of Santonian-to-Miocene time (Holcombe and Moore, 1977). Initial uplift of the Beata Ridge may have been a consequence of early "Laramide" thrusting events that mechanically thickened oceanic crust (crustal velocities beneath the Beata Ridge are typical of oceanic crust, but the thickness is closer to 15 km, compared to a more typical 5 km thickness for oceanic crust (Edgar and others, 1971). Similar thrusting events may have been responsible for emplacing the basalt sequences in southern Haiti (Maurrasse and others, 1979). Possibly the Beata Ridge evolved episodically, or more or less continually, over an extended period of Late Cretaceous–early Cenozoic time as a "Laramide" structural feature.

Dredging from the western slope of the Beata Ridge included basalts and dolerites (Fox and others, 1970; Fig. 8c). Fox and Heezen (1975) interpreted the Beata Ridge as a series of horsts with normal faults down-dropping the eastern flank. Additional structural detail may be ascertained from Case and Holcombe (1980), who mapped the structure using seismic reflection records. Displacement on the western escarpment decreases to the southwest, where it is buried beneath Colombian Plain turbidites. Many parts of the ridge have a tilted fault-block appearance. One of the large southerly trending subsidiary ridges, lying between latitude 14° and 15° 20′N, is reversed in symmetry to the main NE-SW–trending ridge to the north. It has an east-facing escarpment facing a valley that has the appearance of a rift. One could conclude that rifting has occurred, possibly as a late event in the formation of the ridge.

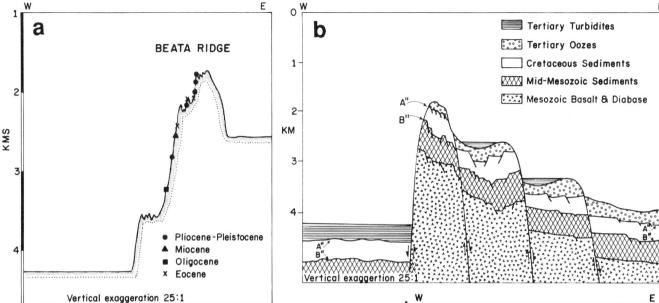

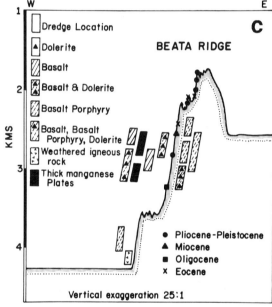

Figure 8. (a) Age dates derived from sediments and sedimentary rocks dredged from the western escarpment of the Beata Ridge, plotted against the probable level from which they were recovered. (b) Schematic crustal section across the Beata Ridge derived from dredged rocks, seismic reflection, and seismic refraction data. Section labeled as "Mid-Mesozoic sediments" is now widely believed to contain flow basalts and basaltic sills. (c) Lithology of rocks dredged from the western escarpment of the Beata Ridge. From Fox and Heezen, 1975. Reprinted by permission.

An imprint of Miocene-to-Recent structural activity has affected the southern end of the Beata Ridge and the Beata Plateau opposite the Aruba Gap. Young faults and folds, as well as distinct horst structures, occur. Displacements on these features offset the entire stratigraphic section and reach a maximum offset of 500 to 1,000 m, 50 to 75 km north of the outer margin of the Curaçao Ridge. These features are quite clearly related to lithospheric flexure accompanying Miocene-to-Recent convergence along the Curaçao Ridge.

Origin of Colombian Basin and Beata Ridge

Neogene development of the Caribbean Plate has been described and discussed in detail (see Pindell and Barrett, and Morris and others, this volume) because of relationships to present plate-boundary configurations and relative movements. Cretaceous and Paleogene development, prior to mid-Cenozoic plate reorganization, is more problematic, and most authors treat this period as cartoons showing the present Colombian Basin and Venezuelan Basin forming as a unit as part of an eastern Pacific plateau. Despite paucity of hard information, it is possible to make certain inferences about origin and evolution, as summarized in preceding sections. We have assembled in broad outline a sequence of events that may be thought of as speculative:

1. Formation of Colombian Basin and Beata Ridge crust no later than Campanian-Maastrichtian time and possibly as early as Jurassic time.

2. Plateau-forming flood-basalt events ending in Late Cretaceous (Campanian-Maastrichtian) time.

3. Structural disturbance, affected a broad zone of the northern Colombian Basin, including the Hess Escarpment. The Beata Ridge was formed and uplifted during this episode. This deformation occurred before horizon A″ time (early Eocene) but no earlier than Campanian-Maastrichtian. Possibly a late rifting event occurred.

4. Thermal(?) uplift and subsidence, probably areally varying depending on crustal inhomogeneities, and associated with high-angle basement faulting. The Beata Ridge subsided after Eocene time, was elevated again during the Miocene, and subsided again in post-Miocene time.

5. Deposition of pelagic sediments over the Colombian Basin since Campanian time and continuing through the Cenozoic. Depositional unconformities on the current-swept Beata Ridge began in the Late Cretaceous and extended through the early Oligocene. Redistribution of sediments by currents may have also occurred in the western Colombian Basin.

6. Possible middle to late Cenozoic wrench-faulting along the northern margin of the westernmost Colombian Basin that may be associated with diffuse rifting on the lower Nicaraguan Rise. Accumulation of turbidites in the westernmost Colombian Basin at about the same time.

7. Accumulation in the Colombian Basin of extensive terrigenous plain and fan deposits in late Cenozoic (Miocene-to-Recent) time, corresponding to uplift in the Andes, Hispaniola, and southern Central America. Formation of the Magdalena and Costa Rica Fans.

8. Middle Miocene-to-Recent intraplate deformation within the Colombian Basin, and development of the deformed belts along the Panamá and Colombian continental margin. Rejuvenation of displacements along old structural trends near the northern and southern ends of the Beata Ridge, on the Beata Plateau, and north of Panamá.

Christofferson (1973) mapped east-trending magnetic anomalies in the Colombian Basin and tentatively suggested a Late Cretaceous (Campanian-Maastrichtian) age for the crust while admitting a great degree of uncertainty. Ghosh and others (1984) tentatively concluded that NE-SW–trending magnetic anomalies in the Venezuelan Basin are Late Jurassic in age. If Christofferson is correct (which we consider unlikely), the crust of the Colombian Basin formed at about the same time as B″ volcanic event of the Venezuelan Basin. If Bowland (1984) is correct and the Colombian Basin crust is pre–Late Cretaceous in age, and overlain by Late Cretaceous constructional volcanic flows and sills, then the crust of both the Colombian and Venezuelan Basins formed prior to the Late Cretaceous.

VENEZUELAN BASIN

The Venezuelan Basin is the largest and deepest (3,000 to 5,000 m) of the interior basins of the Caribbean. Its greatest depths occur at the northern and southern edges of the basin at the approaches to active convergent island and continental margins, respectively. At the northern edge, the Muertos Trough attains a depth of about 5,450 m; it is floored by two small plains. At the southern edge, the Colombian (4,000 to 4,300 m) and Venezuelan Plains (4,800 to 5,000 m) are separated by the Aruba Gap. The eastern margin of the Venezuelan Basin is formed by a fan or apron (Aves Apron) that extends westward from the base of the Aves Plateau. This apron is best developed and reaches its greatest westward extent toward its southern end. Overall basin relief may be characterized as very gentle, ranging from nil to a few tens of meters. A series of regularly spaced isolated knolls, ranging up to 800 m relief, occur adjacent to the Muertos Trough, and one such knoll occurs adjacent to the Aruba Gap; all occur

about 60 to 80 km from the edge of the basin. Refer to Plates 8 and 9, U, V, X, Y, Z, BB.

Gradients show that an easterly source of sediments is important for the Venezuelan Plain, which is a distal extension of the West Aves Apron. Apparently, only small amounts of sediments have reached the Venezuelan Basin from contiguous South American land areas between the Río Magdalena and the longitude of Isla Margarita/Aves Ridge. Terrigenous sediments from directly onshore would be trapped in Lake Maracaibo, the Cariaco Trench, and offshore basins of the Venezuelan Continental Borderland. Sources of sediments for the plains of the Muertos Trough were studied by Forsthoff and Holcombe (1987), who determined that (1) an easterly source is predominant, (2) pelagic sediments from the island slope predominate, (3) terrigenous sediments from Puerto Rico are fed into the eastern plain via Guayanilla Canyon, (4) sediments spill over from the eastern plain to the deeper western plain via the gap, (5) a small amount of terrigenous sediment from Hispaniola apparently enters the western plain from the west, and (6) most sediments from Hispaniola are trapped in offshore basins of the tectonically active island margin.

In the pioneering work on seismic stratigraphy, Ewing and others (1967) surveyed the Venezuelan Basin with the then new seismic reflection profiles and described a general sediment stratigraphy that consisted of the two prominent reflecting horizons. They called these horizons A″ and B″ and thought they were present throughout the Venezuelan and Colombian Basins and over both flanks of the Beata Ridge, the eastern flank of the Nicaraguan Rise, and the western flank of the Aves Ridge (Plates 8 and 9, U to X, Z). These reflecting horizons, discussed repeatedly in this chapter, have been employed, together with drillhole stratigraphy, to develop the Late Cretaceous and Cenozoic history of the Venezuelan Basin (Ladd and Watkins, 1980; Matthews and Holcombe, 1985).

Stratigraphy

Our knowledge of the stratigraphy of the Venezuelan Basin is somewhat better than that of the Colombian Basin due to more extensive seismic surveys and relatively deep penetration of DSDP drilling. DSDP holes 146 and 149 (15°06.99′N, 69°22.67′W; 15°06.99′N, 69°22.74′W; 15°06.25′N, 69°21.85′W) penetrated the sediment section in the western Venezuelan Basin to the level of horizon B″. These holes were nearly continuously cored and provide a 762-m composite section positioned to provide a representative pelagic section for the western Venezuelan Basin (Edgar and others, 1973). No major unconformities were found at this site; therefore, most of the foraminiferal and nannofossil biostratigraphic zones and several of the radiolarian zones were recognized. Recent to lower Miocene deposits are foraminiferal-nannofossil chalk oozes, marl oozes, and clays. Lower Miocene-to-lower Eocene deposits are radiolarian-nannofossil chalks and oozes rich in volcanic material. Below the middle Tertiary lies a lower Eocene(?)–Paleocene(?) section of chert associated with limestone. However, much of the chert was probably associated with a soft stratum that was washed away during recovery. The seismic reflection Horizon A″ correlates with the interface between the unconsolidated or semiconsolidated Miocene–lower Eocene oozes and the consolidated lower Eocene(?)–Paleocene(?) cherts and limestones. The underlying Paleocene section is semilithified clay of volcanic origin, containing no fossils. Upper Maastrichtian deposits are nannofossil marlstones with associated ashes. Lower Maastrichtian–Campanian cherty nannofossil chalk containing radiolaria and very little clay lies beneath the upper Maastrichtian. Santonian–late Turonian radiolarian limestone containing some chert and ash lies below the Campanian and above a dolerite sill. The basal dolerite sill/flow sequence correlates with horizon B″. It encloses a lower Turonian/Coniacian limestone (Edgar and others, 1973).

Site 29 (14°47.11′N, 69°19.36′W), drilled to the south of site 146/149 (Edgar and others, 1973), yielded 250 m of middle Eocene and younger strata. Pleistocene to lower Miocene sediment are soft clay, containing foraminifera, nannofossils, and some silt. A lower Miocene series of clays and chalks, which includes red zeolitic clay (middle Miocene–lower Miocene?), lies unconformably above an unconsolidated radiolarian ooze of middle Eocene age. Horizon A″ corresponds to the contact between the radiolarian ooze and an underlying chert (Benson and others, 1970).

Site 150 (14°30.69′N, 69°21.35′W), located south of site 29, penetrated only 180 m of strata above horizon B″. Pliocene-to-lower Miocene deposits are clays and marls, below which there occurs a major unconformity. A thin unit of lower Eocene–Paleocene zeolitic clay and chert separates the overlying lower Miocene–upper Eocene unconformity from an underlying unconformity that represents the lower Eocene–Santonian. Manganese nodules are associated with the early Miocene–early Eocene unconformity. Santonian/Coniacian/late Turonian marls containing basaltic ash overlie the dolerite of horizon B″ (Edgar and others, 1973).

Site 153 (13°58.33′N, 72°26.08′W), drilled to the southwest of site 150 near the southern end of the Beata Ridge, penetrated 776 m of Late Cretaceous and younger strata. Middle Pliocene nannofossil calcareous clay overlies upper Miocene soft homogeneous clay, which, in turn, overlies middle Miocene clay interbedded with bluish gray, abundantly burrowed calcareous clay. The next two lower intervals are middle Miocene to mid-Oligocene foraminifera-nannofossil chalk. Lower Eocene deposits, hard siliceous limestones and cherts, mark horizon A″. Paleocene limestones, clays, marls, and cherts lie above a Maastrichtiaan silicified breccia similar to the "hard-ground" of site 151. The underlying Cretaceous deposits (poorly recovered Maastrichtian-Coniacian) are limestone with interlayered carbonaceous, phosphatic, and volcanic clay, all containing abundant fish debris. Horizon B″ basalts have a fine-grained vitric ground mass suggestive of a flow (Edgar and others, 1973).

The DSDP drill sites did not penetrate the turbidite-filled abyssal plains on the margins of the Venezuelan Basin. Ladd and Watkins (1980) correlated two seismic units seen on vertical reflection records with the two uppermost lithic units defined in sites 146/149. They traced these units southward to the Venezuelan abyssal plain and found that the lower unit can be traced beneath the turbidites, whereas the upper unit interfingers with the turbidites. This suggests that the early Miocene age for the boundary between these two units is the age of inception of turbidite ponding in the southern Venezuelan Basin.

Most of the western Venezuelan Basin is covered by pelagic deposits of uniform acoustic character with thickness ranging from 600 to 800 m, indicating uniform conditions over a long period of time (Edgar and others, 1971). In general, sediment accumulation rates in the Venezuelan Basin are highest for the Paleocene–Late Cretaceous, early Miocene, and since 3 to 5 Ma. Lower accumulation rates of the Eocene to early Miocene and Santonian to late Paleocene correspond to the unconformities at sites 29 and 150. These unconformities are of similar time span to unconformities found from drilling on the Beata and Aves Ridges. Sites 29 and 150 lie within a concave-northward crescent of thinned deposits mapped by Holcombe and Moore (1977; Plate 8, Section U). They attribute the erosion or nondeposition of sediments within this crescent to more vigorous ocean circulation during Cretaceous to Miocene time when the Tethys was a major globe-encircling seaway. With the development of southern Central America and the Lesser Antilles in mid-Tertiary time, deep-basin circulation in the Caribbean became more restricted, and Miocene-to-Recent deposits have accumulated on previously current-swept crests of the Beata and Aves Ridges and across the entire Venezuelan Basin.

Seismic Horizon B″

Using multichannel seismic reflection systems, Biju-Duval and others (1978) and Diebold and others (1981) showed that the Venezuelan Basin can be effectively divided into a western section, where horizon B″ is a smooth surface forming the boundary between strata with velocities less than 5 km/sec and igneous rocks with velocities greater than 5 km/sec, and a southeastern section where the base of the low-velocity stratum is an irregular surface similar to the top of igneous oceanic crust in the Atlantic Ocean (Fig. 9; Plate 9, Y). The rough-smooth B″ boundary parallels weak magnetic lineations described by Donnelly (1973) and by Watkins and Cavanaugh (1976).

The crust in the region of rough B″ has a velocity structure similar to normal oceanic crust (Diebold and others, 1981; Fig. 10) and is magnetically quiet. Although the top of smooth B″ to the NW is shallower than rough B″ to the SE, velocity results by Diebold and others indicate that smooth B″ is underlain by normal oceanic crust at depths greater or equal to those of rough B″. Seismic lines of Diebold and others (1981) indicate that the rough B″ was covered by sediment at the time of the Cretaceous extrusion event that produced smooth B″.

Wide-angle reflection/refraction profiles interpreted by Diebold and others show that the vertical velocity profile within the Venezuelan Basin is a series of velocity gradients with a marked discontinuity at the base of the sediment column (Fig. 10). This discontinuity was correlated with the B″ reflection. In the area of smooth B″, Diebold and others (1981) found a second discontinuity in the velocity-depth function at 10.1 km with a Moho depth of 15.5 km. This anomalously thick two-part crust was similar to that found by Officer and others (1957). When averaged by Diebold and others (1981), velocity-depth functions within the rough B″ zone produced an average oceanic crustal model similar to that obtained by Edgar and others (1971), except that there are velocity gradients within the crustal layers.

An examination of several multichannel reflection profiles across the Venezuelan Basin indicates that B″ and A″ are coinci-

dent with one reflection peak that is continuous across much of the basin (i.e., A″ and B″ are not composed of a series of en-echelon reflection peaks that change amplitude laterally to form an apparent high-amplitude horizon; Ladd and Watkins, 1980). Vail and others (1977) found that a given amplitude peak or primary seismic reflection is generated by a bedding surface that is more nearly time synchronous than high-amplitude horizons, which are caused by transgressive lithic boundaries. Therefore, in the context of Vail and others (1977), A″ and B″ are approximately time-synchronous events.

A puzzling relationship occurs across the rough-smooth boundary where the reflection peak associated with B″ west of the boundary continues horizontally uninterrupted across the boundary, even though to the west of it the peak reflection is at

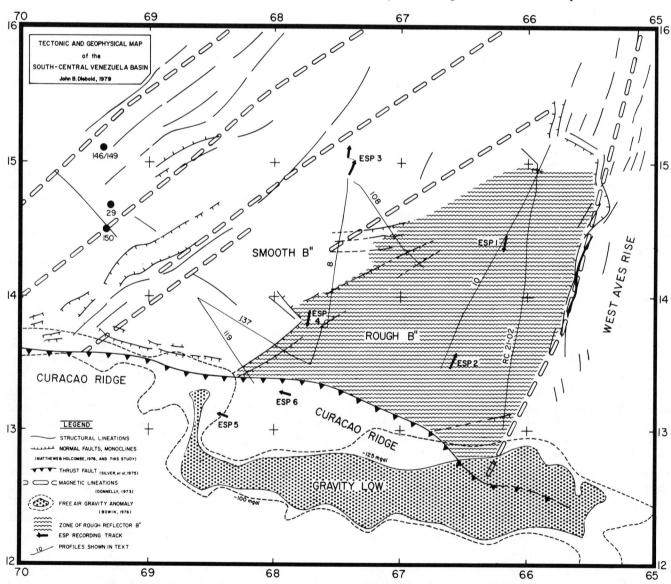

Figure 9. Tectonic and geophysical map of the south-central Venezuelan Basin showing structural trends, magnetic lineations, and the area where horizon B″ has a rough surface. Locations of expanding spread profiles (ESP 1 to 6) from which compressional wave velocity results were obtained and presented in Figure 10 are shown. From Diebold and others, 1981. Reprinted by permission.

the base of the section with velocities less than 5 km/sec, whereas to the east the reflection peak is well up in the low-velocity sediment zone (Plate 9, Y). Some investigators (Diebold and others, 1981), who concentrated on the velocity structure, concluded on the basis of velocities that B″ steps down across the boundary. Seismic stratigraphers (Vail and others, 1977), might conclude that B″ continues uninterrupted across the boundary but that a lateral lithic change occurs below B″. If B″ is defined as the top of 5-km/sec material (not the original definition of Ewing and others, 1967), then B″ does step down across the boundary on Line 108. If B″ is defined as a given amplitude peak on a seismic section (also not the original definition of Ewing and others, 1967), then it does not step down across the boundary. If B″ is a high-amplitude horizon that transgresses several amplitude peaks on a vertical-reflection profile (the original definition), then it does step down across the boundary. These three different working definitions of B″ lead to different conclusions about the nature and meaning of B″. It may be misleading to speak of smooth B″ to the west of the rough-smooth transition and rough B″ to the east. We may be looking at quite different features on either side of the boundary.

The pre–horizon B″ sequence

It has been known since seismic refraction experiments were conducted in the late 1950s that the crust of the Venezuelan Basin is anomalously thick for oceanic crust (Officer and others, 1957, 1959; Ewing and others, 1957). In a review of these seismic

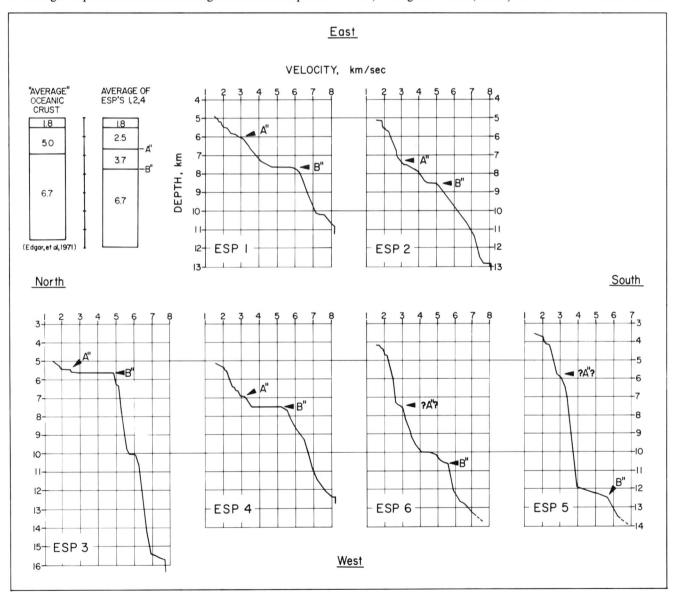

Figure 10. Compressional wave velocities as a function of depth in the south-central Venezuelan Basin, as derived from expanding spread profiles. Locations shown in Figure 9. From Diebold and others, 1981. Reprinted by permission.

refraction experiments, Edgar and others (1971) summarized the crustal structure beneath Horizon B″ as comprising three layers: (i) variable velocity 3.2 to 5.5 km/sec, average thickness 1.3 km; (ii) velocity 6.3 km/sec, thickness 2.5 km; and (iii) velocity 7.3 km/sec, thickness 4.5 km.

Later seismic experiments by Ludwig and others (1975) using sonobuoys showed that the sub-B″ layer (i) has an interval velocity of 3.5 to 5.7 km/sec, although most values were in the range 4.5 to 5.3 km/sec, and thickness varies from 1 to 2.5 km. Multichannel seismic reflection profiles show semiparallel and gently dipping reflections within the sub-B″ layer (Hopkins, 1973; Saunders and others, 1973; Ladd and others, 1977; Biju-Duval and others, 1978; Ladd and Watkins, 1980; Stoffa and others, 1981; Diebold and others, 1981). The presence of these reflections was also noted on single-channel seismic lines by Silver and others (1975). In a careful study of the interval velocities within this layer in the region of the Aruba Gap, Stoffa and others (1981) established that 5 km/sec was the typical value, and low values (3.7 to 3.9 km/sec) quoted earlier by Hopkins (1973) were a consequence of including interlayer multiples in the velocity analysis. This confirmed the work of Ladd and Watkins (1980) who obtained a value of 5.5 km/sec. This high interval velocity strongly suggests an igneous origin for the sub-B″ layer, although the possible presence of limestone should not be ignored.

In the region of smooth B″ in the western Venezuelan Basin, Ladd and Watkins (1980) showed that the section below B″ consists of two units of reflections—an upper unit about one second thick composed of reflections subparallel to B″, and a lower unit composed of gently dipping reflections that extend another second to the top of 7 km/sec material (Plate 9, X). The upper subhorizontal unit is similar to the Cretaceous volcanic complex penetrated during Leg 61 of the Deep Sea Drilling Project within the Nauru Basin of the western Pacific (Larson and others, 1981) where the underlying oceanic crust is thought to be of Jurassic age, based on magnetic anomaly identifications. The Nauru Basin may be part of the much larger region of the Central Pacific, which experienced a major Cretaceous mid-plate volcanic event that included sill intrusions and the development of extrusive volcanic units associated with regional uplift (Houtz and Ludwig, 1979; Schlanger and Premoli Silva, 1981; Menard, 1984; Winterer and Metzler, 1984). This Central Pacific mid-plate volcanism covered an area of approximately 10^6 km^2 and lasted over a period of at least 40 m.y., from Barremian to Campanian-Maastrichtian time. Following the lead of Burke and others (1978), Duncan and Hargraves (1984) suggested that the Caribbean basins formed as part of a Farallon Plate plateau over the Galapagos Hotspot.

The lower unit of dipping reflections within the Venezuelan Basin crust (Plate 9, X) is reminiscent of seaward-dipping crustal reflectors beneath the Voring Plateau offshore Norway, which Mutter and others (1982, 1984) suggested are the result of large subaerial volcanic flows that occurred at the mid-ocean ridge spreading center during the initial stages of continental separa-

tion. Loading of the crust by the thick volcanic pile may have caused rotation of originally horizontal flows toward the accretion center. On the Voring Plateau, single-channel, low-volume air-gun profiles show a smooth acoustic basement over the region where multichannel, large-volume air-gun profiles indicate that the smooth acoustic basement is the top surface of igneous crust containing the seaward-dipping stratification.

Origin and evolution of Venezuelan Basin crust

Magnetic anomalies in the Venezuelan Basin have been studied by Donnelly (1975), Watkins and Cavanaugh (1976), and Ghosh and others (1984). From Project Magnet airborne magnetic profiles, Donnelly (1973) identified NE-SW–trending magnetic anomalies in the northwest part of the Venezuelan Basin and inferred from the similarity in amplitude between airborne measurements and shipborne measurements that the source of the anomalies was probably beneath B″. Watkins and Cavanaugh (1976) also identified the NE-SW–trending anomalies from a shipborne magnetic survey and noted that in the southeast of the basin there appeared to be a magnetically quiet zone. Ghosh and others (1984) produced a synthesis of the magnetic data in the basin (Fig. 11). They confirmed the NE-SW–trending anomalies in the northwest part of the basin, which run parallel to the Beata Ridge, and reported that the source of the magnetic anomalies was beneath B″. They modelled a northeast-southwest spreading ridge between 155 Ma and 127 Ma, at which time the ridge stopped spreading (Fig. 11). These correspond to the M-Series of anomalies, although they were not individually identified.

The magnetically quiet region in the southeast of the basin lies over the region of rough basement, and the anomalies run parallel to the northwest boundary of the region. Ghosh and others (1984) suggested that the crust in this region was formed in Middle Jurassic time during a period of very rapid polarity changes, and that combination of the short wavelengths of the anomalies and the depth of source results in the weak anomalies observed at the surface. In the east of the basin on the flanks of the Aves Ridge, the anomalies are less continuous but commonly have a northeast-southwest trend.

Most investigators believe that the formation of the crust of the Venezuelan Basin predates the formation of Horizon B″, and that formation probably occurred somewhere in the Pacific region. There are various analogies suggested for its anomalous crustal characteristics. Edgar and others (1971) compared it to some of the back-arc regions in the western Pacific. Burke and others (1978) compared it to such regions as the Ontong-Java Plateau and the mid-Pacific mountains. Diebold and others (1981) pointed out similarities with the anomalous crust that occurs at passive continental margins that contain dipping intra-basement reflections (Mutter and others, 1982). This last idea would predict progressively younger crust toward the southeast, opposite to that predicted by Ghosh and others (1984), from the magnetic anomalies.

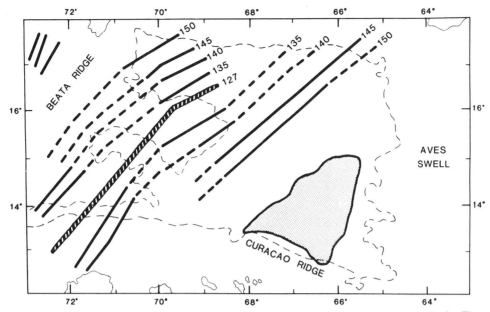

Figure 11. Speculative map of isochrons, in Ma, of crustal formation in the Venezuelan Basin. The isochrons were derived from a synthetic model of the magnetization of the crust computed to give the best fit to the observed magnetic anomalies in the northern and western parts of the basin. The shaded region, which is the area of rough basement topography, is one of low-amplitude magnetic anomalies. From Ghosh and others, 1984. Reprinted by permission.

Mapping of structural features within the deposits of the Venezuelan Basin by Case and Holcombe (1980) and Matthews and Holcombe (1976) suggested a Neogene deformational event that generated a set of northeast-trending and northwest-trending faults and folds. Burke and others (1978) noted the similarity of this pattern to a simple theoretical pattern of deformation involving extrusion flow eastward. This is reminiscent of the analogy drawn by Bucher (1949) between Caribbean geology and glacial flow. He noted an en-echelon pattern of structures in the Greater Antilles and in northern South America, which suggested that the Caribbean sea floor has moved eastward relative to North and South America as a result of north-south compression resulting in east-west crustal extension.

AVES RIDGE, GRENADA BASIN

The Aves Ridge or Aves Plateau extends north-south from the Anegada Passage to the South American continental margin and is about 150 km wide, narrowing toward the southern end. The plateau rises about 1,000 to 2,000 m above the surrounding Venezuelan and Grenada Basins. Its western flank is very straight, running almost due north, but its eastern flank is convex toward the east, with a curvature closely paralleling that of the Lesser Antilles Island Arc. It is capped by a series of pedestals, probably volcanic, which form steep-sided ridge lines. The most prominent ridge line, trending north-south, marks the western extremity of the plateau; other ridges occur within the interior of the plateau and along its arcuate-shaped eastern edge. These pedestals rise 500 to 1,500 m above the plateau; the higher ones crest at 0 to

500 m depth. One breaks the surface to form Aves Island. Refer to Plate 9, CC, DD.

The 150-km-wide arcuate-shaped Grenada Basin separates the Aves Plateau from the Lesser Antilles Island Arc. Its southern sector between 12°N and 15°10'N is the site of the Grenada Plain at a depth of about 2,950 m. Depth decreases to the north within the basin; beyond the plain, relief is moderate (up to a few hundreds of meters). In the south, a small fan dissected by numerous submarine canyons merges with the South American continental slope. A channel network leads from shallower northern portions of the Aves Plateau and Grenada Basin, into the deeper southern sectors. Small-scale, fault-generated relief (escarpments, horsts, tilted blocks) is prevalent over the northern third of the Grenada Basin, accounting for a relief up to a few hundreds of meters but generally in the range of a few tens of meters. Refer to Plate 9, EE, FF.

Sedimentary strata of the Aves Ridge

Apart from the few high peaks and ridges, the Aves Ridge is covered by a drape of strata of moderate thickness over a basement surface of complicated relief (Fig. 12; Plate 9, CC, DD). Local basins in the central region of the ridge are filled with up to 3.5 km of strata. There are major faults on the flanks of the ridge and bounding the local highs (Fig. 12). The sedimentary sequence in the eastern Venezuelan Basin thins slightly over the NNE–trending basement ridge complex at longitude 65° to 66°W, and thickens at the eastern margin of a region of rough basement in a gentle trough beneath the West Aves Apron (Biju-Duval and

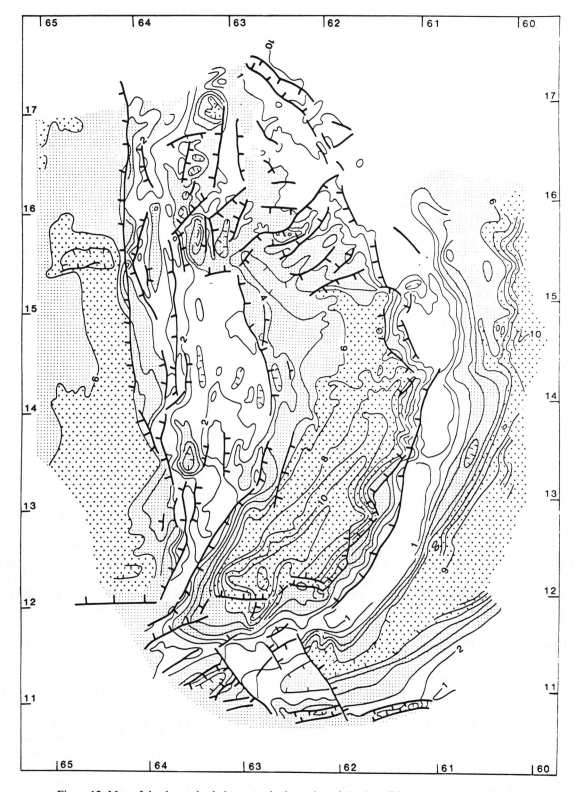

Figure 12. Map of depth to seismic basement in the region of the Aves Ridge and Grenada Trough derived from seismic reflection profiles. Contours at 1-km intervals with patterns indicating the following: 0 to 3 km (blank area), 3 to 6 km (small dots), and >6 km (large dots). Faults marked by ticks on downthrown side. Redrawn from Westbrook and others, 1984. Reprinted by permission.

others, 1978; Plate 9, CC) before continuing up the western flank of the Aves Ridge (Matthews and Holcombe, 1976). Correlation of Horizon A″ from the Venezuelan Basin onto the flanks of the Aves Ridge is made difficult by other strongly reflective horizons in the gentle trough beneath the West Aves Apron and by faulting at the foot of the ridge, but it has been mapped onto the ridge by Mauffret (Westbrook and others, 1984). The lower horizons in the sequence, including A″, however, cannot be followed over the western crest of the ridge because it is interrupted by basement outcrop or subcrop (Westbrook and others, 1984). The sedimentary sequence in the center and on the eastern flank of the ridge can be followed eastward into the Grenada Basin, although a distinct change in facies can be seen in the upper horizons at the margin of the basin (Biju-Duval and others, 1978; Plate 9, EE).

Two DSDP sites, 30 and 148, were drilled on bathymetric highs at the southern end of the ridge. At site 30 (12°52.92′N, 63°23.00′W), at a water depth of 1,211 m, 350 m of Quaternary-to-upper Pliocene calcareous clays and silty clays, and lower Pliocene silts with a high volcanic content, were penetrated before the hole was terminated in Miocene chalk (Bader and others, 1970). At site 148 (13°25.12′N, 63°43.25′W), at a water depth of 1,232 m, 250 m of lower Pliocene to upper Pleistocene clay, calcareous clay, marl, and ash were found to lie unconformably upon volcanic sands and clays containing reworked fossils of Miocene, Paleocene, and Late Cretaceous age (Edgar and others, 1973). The unconformity was marked by a brown, phosphatic iron oxide that implies shallow submarine or subaerial weathering. Both sites showed low carbonate content and an increase in sedimentation rates and ash content throughout the Plio-Pleistocene section, reflecting subsidence of the Aves Ridge and an increase of volcanic activity in the Lesser Antilles.

Dredging in the vicinity of Aves Island has obtained rock of andesitic, basaltic, and dacitic composition (Nagle, 1972). Dredging on the slopes of pedestals of the ridge (Fox and others, 1971; Bouysse and others, 1985), produced (1) volcanic-rich shallow-water sedimentary rock of Turonian to late Senonian age; (2) middle Eocene, late Eocene, Oligocene, and early Miocene shallow-water limestones; (3) Eocene to Pleistocene pelagic limestones; and (4) a variety of igneous rocks including granodiorite, radiometrically dated (K-Ar) at between 89 and 57 Ma, and a diabase, dated at 57 to 60 Ma.

The results of the drilling and dredging indicate significant subsidence (600 to 1,200 m) of the Aves Ridge since the Miocene. The reasons have not been established. The thick cover of deposits over most of the ridge and the absence of young volcanic rocks suggest that the Aves Ridge has been a comparatively inactive feature during most of the Tertiary. Yet there are some perplexing features that seem to contradict this. Heat-flow measurements across the ridge (Clark and others, 1978; Schoonmaker and Ladd, 1984) show that its heat flow is as high as that of the Lesser Antilles. One explanation put forward for this is that the crust of the Aves Ridge may have a high content of radiogenic minerals (Clark and others, 1978).

Also, the pattern of sedimentation, as seen on seismic sections, adjacent to the basement ridges on the western side of the Aves Ridge, has a similar appearance to that of either side of the Lesser Antilles (Plate 9, CC, DD). One cannot say for certain that all the contributions to sedimentation from these ridges have been erosional. The possibility of Tertiary pyroclastic flows remains.

Crust of the Aves Ridge

The results of seismic refraction experiments (Officer and others, 1959; Edgar and others, 1971; Boynton and others, 1979) and modelling of gravity anomalies (Kearey, 1974; Boynton and others, 1979) have shown that the crust beneath the Aves Ridge is thick (approaching 40 km thick at longitude 63°W). Immediately beneath the basement, seen on seismic reflection sections, seismic refraction velocities in the range of 4.1 to 5.5 km/sec suggest a layer of volcanic material beneath which velocities in the range 6.2 to 6.7 km/sec indicate crustal rocks. The presence of a 6.7 km/sec refractor beneath the 6.2 refractor hints at a two-layer crust similar to that of the Lesser Antilles (Boynton and others, 1979). The Aves Ridge is in isostatic equilibrium (Kearey, 1974) except near its southern end (Bowin and Nagle, 1982) where it becomes involved in a zone of convergence between the Caribbean and South American Plates.

The pattern of local gravity anomalies and the shape of the basement surface is compatible with the concept of a heterogeneous upper crustal structure dominated by volcanic centers with plutons beneath them. This crustal character, which is similar to that of the Lesser Antilles, and the types of igneous rock found on the arc, strongly support the hypothesis that the Aves Ridge is primarily an extinct island arc.

Magnetic anomalies over the ridge (see Hall and Westbrook, this volume) show a pattern of local anomalies associated with basement highs and gravity anomaly maxima (Westbrook, this volume) that are superimposed in some areas upon broader trends. In the west of the ridge, a NE-SW–trending pattern of anomalies, similar to those of the northern and western Venezuelan Basin, is broken up by anomalies that are locally associated with the high-standing north-south ridges.

Sedimentary strata of the Grenada Basin

Seismic reflection, refraction, and gravity data (Speed and others, 1984) show that the sedimentary basin underlying the Grenada Basin extends southwest under the slope deposits between the basement of the Aves Ridge and the southwestern extension of the basement of the Lesser Antilles Island Arc that has been covered over by the deposits of the Venezuelan continental shelf and slope (Fig. 12). Depth to apparent acoustic basement in the south of the trough is about 12 km. The basement shallows northward reaching a depth of 6 km west of Guadeloupe. North of the latitude of Guadeloupe (16°), the basement surface becomes very complicated. Southwest-trending basement spurs run down from the Lesser Antilles, and the axis of the basin is shifted to the west where it runs northwestward, close to the Aves Ridge.

A high proportion of the sediment filling the basin is probably of voclaniclastic origin, and sampling of the near-surface sediments with piston cores has shown that the basin contains coarse-grained volcaniclastic gravity flow deposits, many of which are associated with large explosive eruptions in the Lesser Antilles. Reflectivity of acoustic horizons within the turbidites is high (Plate 9, FF) and decreases radially with distance from these known volcanic centers (Holcombe, 1977). These turbidites differ from typical deep fan sequences in the manner in which they develop axial dispersal trends and intercalated sediment from different sources. Silt and clay-sized particles and some air-fall deposits have a much broader area of distribution, including the Aves Ridge (Sigurdsson and others, 1980; Carey and Sigurdsson, 1984). The Río Orinoco is probably the predominant terrigenous source of sediments for the Grenada Plain, as evidenced by the thickly sedimented, continental slope—well-indented by canyons—and the gradient of the plain at the southern end.

At a depth of 1.8 s (2.0 km) beneath the seabed in the center of the basin is a strong seismic reflector with good continuity (Plate 9, EE). It can be traced all over the basin and across the Aves Ridge as far as the western basement ridges where it terminates (Westbrook and others, 1984; Plate 9, DD). By correlation with the sequence on Saba Bank, Saba 1 well, the reflector has been tentatively dated as middle Miocene (Andreiff and others, 1979). This reflector is only slightly deeper in the southern part of the basin than it is in the center, so it appears that most of the subsidence and deposition in the southern part of the basin was pre-Miocene.

Crust of the Grenada Basin

The igneous crust beneath the Grenada Basin has been shown by two seismic experiments at latitude 13°30′N to be 14 km thick (Officer and others, 1959; Boynton and others, 1979). The immediate subsediment basement is a layer of about 1.5 km thickness and 5.3 km/sec seismic velocity. Beneath this are two major crustal layers of 6.2 km/sec, 6.0 km thick, and 7.4 km/sec, 6.5 km thick. This crustal structure is very similar to that of the eastern parts of the Venezuelan Basin, although it is between 1 and 4 km thicker. Gravity modelling constrained by seismic refraction and reflection data show that crustal thickness is fairly uniform throughout the basin except north of 16°N, where it thickens to about 20 km beneath the region of complex basement relief (Speed and others, 1984).

Given the thickness of the crust and the thickness of strata in the trough, the depth of the basement indicates that the crust is older than 40 Ma if one uses the cooling/subsidence curve of oceanic lithosphere as an age predictor (Sclater and Francheteau, 1970). In this narrow basin, however, the effects of subsidence and uplift of the Aves Ridge and Lesser Antilles Arc on its margins should not be overlooked.

Origin of the Aves Ridge and Grenada Basin

As mentioned above, several lines of evidence lead to the conclusion that the Aves Ridge is a former island arc. The convex shape of the eastern flank of the ridge suggests that the arc faced eastward, like the Lesser Antilles Island Arc. The ages of igneous and volcanogenic sedimentary rocks from the ridge indicate that it was active in Late Cretaceous–Paleogene time.

There are two principal hypotheses for the creation of the Grenada Basin. One is that it formed by sea-floor spreading in a back-arc (inter-arc) basin, which split a previous arc into two parts, the Aves Ridge and the Lesser Antilles. The other hypothesis is that the Grenada Basin is former forearc crust that was isolated by an eastward jump of the subduction zone at the beginning of the Eocene. This second hypothesis was put forward by Boynton, Kearey, and Westbrook (reported *in* Kearey, 1974), because of the similarity of the seismic structure of the crust beneath the Grenada Basin to that of the Venezuelan Basin and the similarity of the crust immediately east of the Lesser Antilles to that of the main Atlantic. These similarities suggested to them that the Grenada Basin was part of the original Caribbean Plate, and that the crust east of the Lesser Antilles had been accreted to the edge of the plate. In this hypothesis, the former position of the subduction trace lay beneath the present line of the Lesser Antilles. A modified version of this hypothesis was proposed by Bouysse and Martin (1979), who recognized that the antiquity of rocks in the Lesser Antilles Arc north of Guadeloupe precluded the northern part of the arc from being formed after an early Eocene jump at the subduction zone. Bouysse and Martin noted that the width of the bathymetric arc platform is narrower south of Guadeloupe and inferred that the volume of igneous rocks was less, because of a shorter history of magmatism. Because of this, he proposed that the arc south of Guadeloupe was younger (Eocene-Quaternary), and that only the southern part of the subduction zone had jumped eastward at the beginning of the Eocene. He envisaged that in Late Cretaceous–Paleocene time, a transform fault, running east-west between the present positions of Guadeloupe and Dominica, offset the subduction zone westward in the south, leading to simultaneous volcanism in the northern Lesser Antilles and the Aves Ridge in their present relative positions.

The difficulties encountered by the subduction-jump hypothesis are as follows:

1. There is no sign of any previous accretionary complex in the Grenada Basin, although it may be totally obscured by the Lesser Antilles Arc.

2. The crust of the Grenada Basin does not show the same asymmetry that is shown by the crust of the forearc region of the Lesser Antilles and other island arcs.

3. Geophysical data clearly show that the arc crust of the Lesser Antilles continues southwestward from Grenada to Margarita (Speed and others, 1984). Plutonic rocks on Margarita have been dated as Late Cretaceous, and ages from Los Testigos are Paleocene (Santamaría and Schubert, 1974), showing that

this part of the arc was also active at the same time as the Aves Ridge.

4. Geophysically derived models of the Lesser Antilles Arc (Speed and others, 1984) show that the cross-sectional area of the arc in the south is just as great as the arc north of Guadeloupe. So, the argument that the volume of igneous rocks in the south is less because the arc is younger is unfounded.

5. There is no evidence for the transform fault that should form the northern boundary of the Grenada Basin. The line of the fault proposed by Bouysse and Martin (1979) cuts across basement features and gravity and magnetic anomalies that are continuous.

Consideration of these arguments favors the back-arc spreading origin for the Grenada Basin, which would have been created at the beginning of the Eocene, but this hypothesis is also not without problems. No obvious remnant spreading center has been found in the basin, and the magnetic anomalies run radially to the arc across the basin rather than concentrically to the arc along the basin. So it is clear that whatever form the spreading took, it was not a simple one. An explanation for the origin of the basement features of high relief in the northern part of the basin is not provided by a simple back-arc spreading model.

An important difference between the two models of evolution, which can be tested by drilling, is that the back-arc spreading model predicts a sediment fill for the trough that is no older than Eocene, whereas in the subduction-jump model the deposits could be as old as Jurassic. The similarity of the crust of the Grenada Basin to that of the eastern Venezuelan Basin could be taken to imply that the eastern Venezuelan Basin was also formed by back-arc spreading.

QUATERNARY AND RECENT SEDIMENTS

Biogenic Quaternary and Recent sediments of the Caribbean are predominantly composed of foraminifera and coccoliths. In the Colombian Basin these occur in about equal abundance (Prell, 1978). Pteropods are also found in small and varying amounts (Prell, 1978; Forsthoff and Holcombe, 1987). Overall, the fauna is described as being of warm-water tropical/subtropical aspect (Keigwin, 1982). Studies of benthic foraminifera have led to tentative stratigraphic zonation of interglacial and glacial cycles in the Venezuelan Basin (Sen Gupta, 1984). Siliceous sediments are essentially absent from Quaternary sediments, although a few radiolaria were recovered from the southwest Colombian Basin, as well as older replacement structures of radiolaria and sponge spicules (Riedel and Westberg, 1982).

Quaternary and Recent terrigenous sediments of the Caribbean are primarily composed of the clay minerals illite and montmorillonite and the silt minerals quartz and feldspar. Broad patterns of distribution of the major terrigenous minerals (Griffin and Goldberg, 1969) are illustrated in Figure 13. Quartz, which ranges from 5 to 20 percent of the terrigenous fraction, occurs in greatest abundance adjacent to South America but is also high off

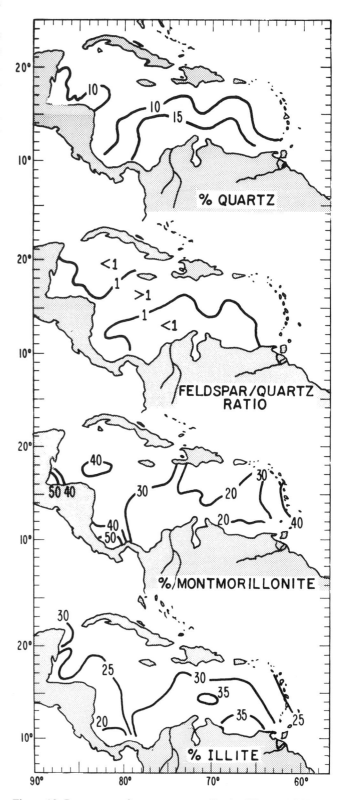

Figure 13. Percentages of quartz, montmorillonite, illite, and feldspar/quartz ratios in deep-sea surficial sediments of the Caribbean Sea. After Griffin and Goldberg, 1969.

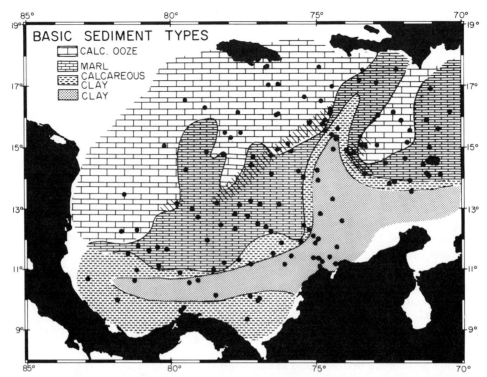

Figure 14. Distribution of surficial sediment types in the Colombian Basin and southern Nicaraguan Rise. Dots indicate location of the 126 samples analyzed. Classification of sediment types is based on percentage of CaCO₃: calcareous ooze = >60 percent CaCO₃; marl = 30 to 60 percent CaCO₃; calcareous clay = 10 to 30 percent CaCO₃; clay = <10% CaCO₃. From Prell, 1978. Reprinted by permission.

northern Central America. Feldspar/quartz ratios are the inverse of quartz content, low off South America and high off the Lesser Antilles, except off northern Central America, where feldspar/quartz ratios and quartz content are both high.

Quartz content is therefore high in areas adjacent to occurrences of high-silicate igneous and metamorphic rocks in the source area (South and Central America). Feldspar content is high adjacent to calc-alkaline volcanic arcs (Lesser Antilles). Quartz and feldspar content are high off northern Central America, probably reflecting the presence of both continental and volcanic-arc terranes in the source area. Montmorillonite content is high adjacent to Central America and the Lesser Antilles, obviously reflecting a volcanic source region. Illite content is high off northern South America and off Yucatán, related to high-silicate continental sources. Kaolinite and chlorite are present in lesser percentages; both apparently increase slightly in abundance off South America. In the southwestern Colombian Basin near southern Central America, Zimmerman (1982) found that the clay-mineral distribution at the surface (high-montmorillonite) is fairly consistent throughout the Quaternary. Montmorillonite content increases back through time at the expense of the other clay minerals, probably due to the influx of volcanogenic components (Zimmerman, 1982). Pyrophyllite is present adjacent to South America reflecting Orinoco and Magdalena sources. Pyrophyllite content in Amazon-transported sediments is significantly smaller. Pyrophyllite content in Venezuelan Basin sediments apparently increased during Quaternary glacial intervals (Bowles and Fleischer, 1985), suggesting that Amazon sediments, which are swept northwestward along the South American shelf and are mixed with Orinoco sediments prior to final deposition in the eastern Caribbean, may not have been brought northwestward in significant quantities during glacial times of lowered sea level and resulting reduction in continental shelf width.

Percentage of carbonates in surficial sediments increases to the north and west across the Caribbean. Using 60 percent carbonate content as a classification limit, foram-nannofossil ooze forms the surficial sediments of the northernmost Venezuelan Basin and the northwestern Caribbean, including the lower Nicaraguan Rise (Lisitzin, 1969; Prell, 1978; Forsthoff and Holcombe, 1987; Fig. 14). Carbonate percentages decrease to that of marl ooze and marl clay approaching the South American continental margin, in the Yucatán Basin near Cuba and Yucatán, and southeastward across the eastern Caribbean (Griffin and Goldberg, 1969; Bowles and Fleischer, 1985). The carbonate compensation depth (CCD) decreases approaching South America where one encounters corrosive bottom waters in a regime of upwelling, high productivity, and high organic content in bottom sediment (Prell, 1978; Gordon, 1967). Elsewhere the CCD is probably at 5 to 5.5 km as it is in the adjoining North Atlantic; therefore, most of the Caribbean sea floor lies above CCD. Excepted are deep fracture zones where deep sea clays occur (Lisitzin, 1969; Hersey and Rutstein, 1958). Another factor in reduced carbonate levels in sediments near South America is increased dilution by terrigenous influx (Prell, 1978; Bowles and Fleischer, 1985).

Percentage of sand-sized grains within surficial sediments is in the range of 10 to 50 percent, higher than that typical of ocean basins (Lisitzin, 1969). Sand percent increases in the northwest Caribbean due to high sand-sized foraminifera content, and adjacent to South America, due to terrigenous influx. Sand content is lowest in the Venezuelan Basin, probably due to the distal character of the terrigenous sediments.

Probably because of the high sand content, Caribbean sediments have been generally unstable on slopes, exhibiting a strong tendency for preferential deposition in valleys. Therefore, relief has been greatly diminished by sediment smoothing throughout the Caribbean. A well-developed drainage network is a manifestation of the efficient movement of sediments from shallower to deeper portions of Caribbean basins.

The extent of Caribbean abyssal plains is shown in Plate 1. Gradients of fans and plains, together with drainage patterns on land, are indicators of probable source areas of sediments moved downslope by gravitational flow. A large number of small plains occur throughout the Caribbean. Terrigenous sediments undoubtedly compose a large component of sediments of the larger plains. However, pelagic carbonate sediments from adjacent slopes also comprise a significant percentage of plain sediments, and probably predominate in high-carbonate areas protected from downslope terrigenous influx. This has been the case for Muertos Trough plains, where turbidite composition is overwhelmingly that of pelagic carbonate (Forsthoff and Holcombe, 1987).

A layer of pelagic sediments constitutes surficial sediment of the abyssal plains throughout much of the extent of the plains. However, there are also a number of occurrences of turbidites at the surface, particularly on the Colombian Plain adjacent to the Magdalena Fan. One concludes here, as elsewhere in the oceans, that turbidity-current deposition has been more extensive during times of lowered sea level than during the Holocene "interglacial."

Most of the plain-forming turbidite sequences of the Caribbean overlie, or are intercalated with, the uppermost part of the pelagic section (Holcombe, 1977). Therefore, the bulk of abyssal plain deposition would appear to be a late Cenozoic phenomenon, probably initiated or accelerated by Miocene-to-Recent uplift, which occurred generally along the Caribbean rim. Significant increases in the rate of sediment deposition outside the plain areas for post-Miocene time are also recorded in the Venezuelan Basin (Edgar and others, 1973) and in the Colombian Basin (Prell and others, 1982). During the last glacial interval, rates of terrigenous clay accumulation were found to increase markedly over interglacial (Holocene) rates, whereas rates of carbonate deposition remained fairly constant (Prell, 1978).

REFERENCES

Addy, S., and Taylor, F. W., 1981, Structure and seismic stratigraphy of Yucatán Basin in the Caribbean [abs.]: American Association of Petroleum Geologists Bulletin, v. 65, p. 888.

Andreiff, P., Bouysse, P., and Westercamp, D., 1979, Reconaissance géologique de l'arc insulaire des Petites Antilles; Resultats d'une campagne a la mer de prelevements de roches entre Sainte-Lucie et Anguille (ARCANTE 1): Bulletin du Bureau de Recherches Géologiques et Minieres (deuxieme série), Section 4, no. 3–4, p. 227–270.

Arden, D., 1975, The geology of Jamaica and the Nicaragua Rise, *in* Nairn, A.E.M., and Stehli, F.G., eds., The Ocean Basins and Margins; v. 3, The Gulf of Mexico and the Caribbean: New York and London, Plenum Press, p. 617–661.

Bader, R. G., Gerard, R. D., and others, 1970, Site 31, *in* Bader, R. G., and others, eds., Initial reports of the Deep Sea Drilling Project: Washington, D.C., U.S. Government Printing Office, v. 4, p. 243–263.

Benson, W. E., Gerard, R. D., and Hay, W. W., 1970, Summary and Conclusions, *in* Bader, R. G. and others, eds., Initial Reports of the Deep Sea Drilling Project: Washington, D.C., U.S. Government Printing Office, v. 4, p. 659–673.

Biju-Duval, B., Mascle, A., Montadert, L., and Wanneson, J., 1978, Seismic investigations in the Colombia, Venezuela, and Grenada Basins and on the Barbados Ridge for future IPOD drilling: Géologie en Mijnbouw, v. 57, no. 2, p. 105–116.

Bouysse, P., and Martin, P., 1979, Caracteres morphostructuraux et évolution géodynamique de l'arc insulaire des Petites Antilles (Campagne ARCANTE 1): Bulletin du Bureau de Recherches Géologiques et Minieres (deuxieme série), Section 4, no. 3–4, p. 185–210.

Bouysse, P., Andrieff, P., Richard, M., Bausbron, J. C., Mascle, A., Maury, R. C., and Westercamp, D., 1985, Aves swell and northern Lesser Antilles Ridge;

Rock-dredging results form ARCANTE 3 cruise, *in* Mascle, A., ed., Caribbean geodynamics: Paris, Editions Technip, p. 65–76.

Bowin, C. O., 1976, Caribbean gravity field and plate tectonics: Geological Society of America Special Paper 169, 79 p.

Bowin, C. O., and Nagle, F., 1982, Igneous and metamorphic rocks of northern Dominican Republic; An uplifted subduction zone complex: Transactions, Ninth Caribbean Geological Conference, Santo Domingo, Dominican Republic, 1980, v. 1, p. 39–50.

Bowland, C. L., 1984, Seismic stratigraphy and structure of the western Colombian Basin, Caribbean Sea [M.S. thesis]: The University of Texas at Austin, 248 p.

Bowland, C. L., and Rosencrantz, E., 1988, Upper crustal structure of the western Colombian Basin, Caribbean Sea: Geological Society of America Bulletin, v. 100, p. 534–546.

Bowles, F. A., and Fleischer, P., 1985, Orinoco and Amazon River sediment input to the eastern Caribbean Basin: Marine Geology, v. 68, p. 53–72.

Boynton, C. H., Westbrook, G. K., Bott, M.H.P., and Long, R. E., 1979, A seismic refraction investigation of crustal structure beneath the Lesser Antilles Island Arc: Royal Astronomical Society Geophysics Journal, v. 58, p. 371–393.

Bucher, W., 1949, Problems of earth deformation illustrated by the Caribbean Sea Basin: New York Academy of Sciences Transactions, ser. 2, v. 9, no. 2, p. 98–116.

Burke, K., Fox, P. J., and Sengor, A.M.C., 1978, Buoyant ocean floor and the evolution of the Caribbean: Journal of Geophysical Research, v. 83, p. 3949–3954.

Burke, K., Grippi, J., and Sengor, A.M.C., 1980, Neogene structures in Jamaica and the tectonic style of the Northern Caribbean plate boundary: Journal of Geology, v. 88, p. 375–386.

Burke, K., Cooper, C., Dewey, J. F., Mann, P., and Pindell, J. L., 1984, Caribbean tectonics and relative plate motions, *in* Bonini, W. E., Hargraves, R. B., and Shagam, R., eds., The Caribbean–South American plate boundary and regional tectonics: Geological Society of America Memoir 162, p. 31–63.

Cáceres Avila, F., Tappmeyer, D. M., Aves, H. S., Gillett, M., and Klenk, C. D., 1984, Recent studies of basins are encouraging for future exploration of Honduras: Oil and Gas Journal, September 1984, p. 139–149.

Carey, S., and Sigurdsson, H., 1984, A model of volcanogenic sedimentation in marginal basins, *in* Kokelar, B. P., and Howells, M. F., eds., Marginal basin geology; Volcanic and associated sedimentary processes in modern and ancient marginal basins: Geological Society of London Special Publication 16, p. 37–58.

Case, J. E., and Holcombe, T. L., 1977, Generalized tectonic map of the Caribbean: Engineering and Mining Journal, v. 178, p. 49–51.

—— , 1980, Geologic–tectonic map of the Caribbean region: U.S. Geological Survey Miscellaneous Field Investigations Map I–1100, scale 1:2,500,000.

Case, J. E., Holcombe, T. L., and Martin, R. G., 1984, Map of the geologic provinces in the Caribbean region, *in* Bonini, W. E., Hargraves, R. B., and Shagam, R., eds., The Caribbean–South American plate boundary and regional tectonics: Geological Society of America Memoir 162, p. 1–30.

Christofferson, E., 1973, Linear magnetic anomalies in the Colombia Basin, central Caribbean Sea: Geological Society of America Bulletin, v. 84, p. 3217–3230.

—— , 1976, Colombian basin magnetism and Caribbean plate tectonics: Geological Society of America Bulletin, v. 87, p. 1255–1258.

—— , 1983, Plate model of the collapsing Caribbean continental margin of Nicaragua and the adjacent San Andrés Island Trough [abs.]: Program and Abstracts of Papers, Tenth Caribbean Geological Conference, p. 32.

Clark, T. F., Korgen, B. J., and Best, D. M., 1978, Heat flow in the eastern Caribbean: Journal of Geophysical Research, v. 83, p. 5883–5891.

Dengo, G., 1975, Paleozoic and Mesozoic tectonic belts in Mexico and Central America, *in* Nairn, A.E.M., and Stehli, F. G., eds., The Ocean Basins and Margins; v. 3, The Gulf of Mexico and the Caribbean: New York and London, Plenum Press, p. 283–323.

Diebold, J. B., Stoffa, P. L., Buhl, P., and Truchan, M., 1981, Venezuela Basin crustal structure: Journal of Geophysical Research, v. 86, p. 7901–7923.

Dillon, W. P., and Vedder, J. G., 1973, Structure and development of the continental margin of British Honduras: Geological Society of America Bulletin, v. 84, p. 2713–2732.

Dillon, W. P., Vedder, J. G., and Graf, R. J., 1972, Structural profile of the northwest Caribbean: Earth and Planetary Science Letters, v. 17, p. 175–180.

Donnelly, T. W., 1973, Magnetic anomaly observations in the eastern Caribbean Sea, *in* Edgar, N. T., Saunders, J. B., and others, eds., Initial Reports of the Deep Sea Drilling Project: Washington, D.C., U.S. Government Printing Office, v. 15, p. 1023–1030.

—— , 1975, The geological evolution of the Caribbean and Gulf of Mexico; Some critical problems and areas, *in* Nairn, A.E.M., and Stehli, F. G., eds., The Ocean Basins and Margins; v. 3, The Gulf of Meixo and the Caribbean: New York and London, Plenum Press, p. 663–685.

Duncan, R. A., and Hargraves, R. B., 1984, Plate tectonic evolution of the Caribbean region, in the mantle reference frame, *in* Bonini, W. E., Hargraves, R. B., and Shagam, R., eds., The Caribbean–South American plate boundary and regional tectonics: Geological Society of America Memoir 162, p. 81–93.

Edgar, N. T., Ewing, J. I., and Hennion, J., 1971, Seismic refraction and reflection in the Caribbean Sea: American Association of Petroleum Geologists Bulletin, v. 55, p. 833–870.

Edgar, N. T., Saunders, J. B., and others, 1973, Initial reports of the Deep Sea Drilling Project: Washington, D.C., U.S. Government Printing Office, v. 15, p. 17–471.

Epp, D., Grim, P. J., and Langseth, M. G., 1970, Heat flow in the Caribbean and Gulf of Mexico: Journal of Geophysical Research, v. 75, p. 5655–5669.

Erickson, A. J., Helsley, C. E., and Simmons, G., 1972, Heat flow and continuous

seismic profiles in the Cayman Trough and Yucatán Basin: Geological Society of America Bulletin, v. 83, p. 1241–1260.

Ewing, J. I., Officer, C. B., Johnson, H. R., and Edwards, R. S., 1957, Geophysical investigations in the eastern Caribbean; Trinidad Shelf, Tobago Trough, Barbados Ridge, Atlantic Ocean: Geological Society of America Bulletin, v. 68, p. 897–912.

Ewing, J. I., Antoine, J., and Ewing, M., 1960, Geophysical measurements in the western Caribbean Sea and in the Gulf of Mexico: Journal of Geophysical Research, v. 65, p. 4087–4126.

Ewing, J. I., Talwani, M., Ewing, M., and Edgar, T., 1967, Sediments of the Caribbean: University of Miami, Studies in tropical oceanography, v. 5, p. 88–102.

Forsthoff, G. M., and Holcombe, T. L., 1987, Quaternary turbidites of the Muertos Trough, northeastern Caribbean Sea; Composition, source, and dispersal patterns: Transactions, Tenth Caribbean Geological Conference (in press).

Fox, P. J., and Heezen, B. C., 1975, Geology of the Caribbean crust, *in* Nairn, A.E.M., and Stehli, F. G., eds., The ocean basins and margins; v. 3, The Gulf of Mexico and the Caribbean: New York and London, Plenum Press, p. 421–466.

Fox, P. J., Ruddiman, W. F., Ryan, W.B.F., and Heezen, B. C., 1970, The geology of the Caribbean crust; I, Beata Ridge: Tectonophysics, v. 10, p. 495–513.

Fox, P. J., Schreiber, E., and Heezen, B. C., 1971, The geology of the Caribbean crust; Tertiary sediments, granitic and basic rocks from the Aves Ridge: Tectonophysics, v. 12, p. 88–109.

Freeland, G. L., and Dietz, R. S., 1971, Plate tectonic evolution of Caribbean–Gulf of Mexico region: Nature, v. 232, p. 20–23.

Gordon, A. L., 1967, Circulation of the Caribbean Sea: Journal of Geophysical Research, v. 72, p. 6207–6223.

Ghosh, N., Hall, S. A., and Casey, J. F., 1984, Seafloor spreading magnetic anomalies in the Venezuelan Basin, *in* Bonini, W. E., Hargraves, R. B., and Shagam, R., eds., The Caribbean–South American plate boundary and regional tectonics: Geological Society of America Memoir 162, p. 65–80.

Gough, D. I., and Heirtzler, J. R., 1969, Magnetic anomalies and tectonics of the Cayman Trough: Royal Astronomical Society Geophysical Journal, v. 18, p. 33–49.

Griffin, J. J., and Goldberg, E. D., 1969, Recent sediments of the Caribbean Sea, *in* McBirney, A. R., ed., Tectonic relations of northern Central America and the western Caribbean: American Association of Petroleum Geologists Memoir 11, p. 258–268.

Hall, S. A., and Yeung, T., 1980, A study of magnetic anomalies in the Yucatán Basin: Transactions, Ninth Caribbean Geological Conference, p. 519–526.

Heezen, B. C., and Muñoz J., N. G., 1965, Magdalena turbidites in deep-sea sediments [abs.]: Transactions, Fourth Caribbean Geological Conference, p. 342.

Hersey, J. B., and Rutstein, M. S., 1958, Reconnaissance survey of Oriente Deep with a precision echo sounder: Geological Society of America Bulletin, v. 69, p. 1297–1304.

Holcombe, T. L., 1977, Caribbean bathymetry and sediments, *in* Weaver, J. D., ed., Geology, geophysics, and resources of the Caribbean; A report of the IDOE Workshop on the geology and marine geophysics of the Caribbean region and its resources: UNESCO Intergovernmental Oceanographic Commission, p. 27–62.

Holcombe, T. L., and Moore, W. S., 1977, Paleocurrents in the eastern Caribbean; Geological evidence and implications: Marine Geology, v. 23, p. 35–56.

Hopkins, H. R., 1973, Geology of the Aruba Gap abyssal plain near Deep Sea Drilling site 153, *in* Edgar, N. T., Saunders, J. B., and others, eds., Initial reports of the Deep Sea Drilling Project: Washington, D.C., U.S. Government Printing Office, v. 15, p. 1039–1050.

Houtz, R. E., and Ludwig, W. J., 1977, Structure of Colombian Basin, Caribbean Sea, from profiler–sonobouy measurements: Journal of Geophysical Research, v. 82, p. 4861–4867.

—— , 1979, Distribution of reverberant sub-bottom layers in the southwest

Pacific Basin: Journal of Geophysical Research, v. 84, p. 3497–3504.

Kearey, P., 1974, Gravity and seismic reflection investigations into the crustal structure of the Aves Ridge, eastern Caribbean: Royal Astronomical Society Geophysical Journal, v. 38, p. 435–448.

Keigwin, L. D., Jr., 1982, Neogene planktonic foraminifera from Deep Sea Drilling Project sites 502–503, *in* Prell, W. L., Gardner, J. V., and others, eds., Initial reports of the Deep Sea Drilling Project: Washington, D.C., U.S. Government Printing Office, v. 68, p. 269–277.

Kerr, J. M., 1977, The volcanic and tectonic history of La Providencia Island, Colombia [M.S. thesis]: New Brunswick, New Jersey, Rutgers University, 62 p.

Kolla, V., Buffler, R. T., and Ladd, J. W., 1984, Seismic stratigraphy and sedimentation of the Magdalena Fan, southern Colombian Basin, Caribbean Sea: American Association of Petroleum Geologists Bulletin, v. 68, p. 316–332.

Ladd, J. W., 1976, Relative motions of South America with respect to North America and Caribbean tectonics: Geological Society of America Bulletin, v. 87, p. 969–976.

Ladd, J. W., and Watkins, J. S., 1980, Seismic stratigraphy of the western Venezuela Basin: Marine Geology, v. 35, p. 21–41.

Ladd, J. W., Worzel, J. L., and Watkins, J. S., 1977, Multifold seismic reflection records from the northern Venezuela Basin and the north slope of the Muertos Trench, *in* Talwani, M., and Pitman, W. C., eds., Island arcs, deep sea trenches, and back-arc basins: American Geophysical Union, Maurice Ewing Series, v. 1, p. 41–56.

Ladd, J. W., Shih, T., and Tsai, C. J., 1981, Cenozoic tectonics of central Hispaniola and adjacent Caribbean Sea: American Association of Petroleum Geologists Bulletin, v. 65, no. 3, p. 466–489.

Larson, R. L., Schlanger, S. O., and others, eds., 1981, Initial reports of the Deep Sea Drilling Project, Leg 61: Washington, D.C., U.S. Government Printing Office, v. 61, 885 p.

Lisitzin, A. P., ed., 1969, Maps of sediment deposits, Atlantic Ocean; (1) sediment types, (2) distribution of calcium carbonate, (3) sediment grain-size sand (>0.1 mm), (4) sediment grain-size silt (0.1-0.01 mm), and (5) sediment grain-size clay (<0.01 mm): Moscow, Joint Geophysics Committee, Academy of Sciences of the Soviet Union, scale 1:20,000,000.

Lu, R. S., and McMillen, K. J., 1982, Multichannel seismic survey of the Colombia Basin and adjacent margins, *in* Watkins, J. S., and Drake, C. L., eds., Studies in continental margin geology: American Association of Petroleum Geologists Memoir 34, p. 395–410.

Ludwig, W. J., Houtz, R., and Ewing, J., 1975, Profiler sonobuoy measurements in Colombia and Venezuela Basins, Caribbean Sea: American Association of Petroleum Geologists Bulletin, v. 59, p. 115–123.

Malfait, B. T., and Dinkelman, M. G., 1972, Circum-Caribbean tectonic and igneous activity and the evolution of the Caribbean plate: Geological Society of America Bulletin, v. 83, p. 251–272.

Matley, C. A., 1926, The geology of the Cayman Islands (British West Indies), and their relation to the Bartlett Trough: Geological Society of London Quarterly Journal, v. 82, p. 352–387.

Matthews, J. E., and Holcombe, T. L., 1976, Regional geological/geophysical study of Caribbean Sea (Navy Ocean area NA-9); 1, Geophysical maps of the eastern Caribbean: U.S. Naval Oceanographic Office, Reference Publication RP3, scale 1:2,000,000.

——— , 1985, Venezuela Basin of the Caribbean Sea; Stratigraphy and sediment distribution: Marine Geology, v. 68, p. 1–23.

Maurrasse, F.J.M.R., Husler, J., Georges, G., Schmitt, R., and Damond, P., 1979, Upraised Caribbean sea-floor below acoustic reflector B″ at the southern peninsula of Haiti: Géologie en Mijnbouw, v. 58, p. 71–83.

McBirney, A. R., and Bass, M. M., 1969, Geology of the Bay Islands, Gulf of Honduras, *in* McBirney, A. R., ed., Tectonic relations of northern Central America and the western Caribbean: American Association of Petroleum Geologists Memoir 11, p. 229–243.

Menard, H. W., 1984, Darwin reprise: Journal of Geophysical Research, v. 89, p. 9960–9968.

Meyerhoff, A. A., 1966, Bartlett Fault System-age and offset, *in* Transactions, Third Caribbean Geological Conference: Jamaica Geological Survey Publication 95, p. 1–7.

Milliman, J. D., and Supko, P. R., 1968, On the geology of San Andrés Island, western Caribbean: Géologie Mijnbouw, v. 47, p. 102–105.

Molnar, P., and Sykes, L. R., 1969, Tectonics of the Caribbean and middle American regions from focal mechanisms and seismicity: Geological Society of America Bulletin, v. 80, p. 1639–1684.

Muñoz J., N. G., 1964, Magdalena turbidites in deep-sea sediments [M.S. thesis]: Palisades, New York, Columbia University, 211 p.

Mutter, J. C., Talwani, M., and Stoffa, P., 1982, Origin of eastward-dipping reflectors in oceanic crust off the Norwegian margin by subaerial seafloor spreading: Geology, v. 10, p. 353–357.

——— , 1984, Evidence for a thick oceanic crust adjacent to the Norwegian margin: Journal of Geophysical Research, v. 89, p. 483–502.

Nagle, F., 1972, Rocks from the sediments of escarpments on the Aves Ridge, *in* Transactions, Sixth Caribbean Geological Conference: Caracas, Venezuela, Impreso por Cromotik, p. 409–413.

Officer, C. B., Ewing, J. I., Edwards, R. S., and Johnson, H. R., 1957, Geophysical investigations in the eastern Caribbean; Venezuelan Basin, Antilles Island Arc, and Puerto Rico Trench: Geological Society of America Bulletin, v. 68, p. 359–378.

Officer, C. B., Ewing, J. I., Hennion, J. F., Harkrider, D. G., and Miller, D. E., 1959, Geophysical investigations in the eastern Caribbean; Summary of 1955 and 1956 cruises, *in* Ahrens, L. H., Press, F., Rankama, K., and Runcorn, S. K., eds., Physics and chemistry of the Earth, v. 3: New York, Pergamon Press, p. 17–109.

Pagnaccio, P. F., and Radelli, F., 1962, Note on the geology of the isles of Providencia and Santa Catalina (Colombia, Caribbean Sea): Géologia Colombiana, v. 3, p. 125–132.

Perfit, M. R., and Heezen, B. C., 1978, The geology and evolution of the Cayman Trench: Geological Society of America Bulletin, v. 89, p. 1155–1174.

Pindell, S., and Dewey, J. F., 1982, Permo–Triassic reconstruction of western Pangea and the evolution of the Gulf of Mexico/Caribbean region: Tectonics, v. 1, p. 179–212.

Pinet, P. R., 1971, Structural configuration of the northwestern Caribbean plate boundary: Geological Society of America Bulletin, v. 82, p. 2027–2032.

Prell, W. L., 1978, Upper Quaternary sediments of the Colombia Basin; Spatial and stratigraphic variation: Geological Society of America Bulletin, v. 89, p. 1241–1255.

Prell, W. L., Gardner, J. V., and others, 1980, Hydraulic piston coring of late Neogene and Quaternary sections in the Caribbean and equatorial Pacific; Preliminary results of Deep Sea Drilling Project, Leg 68: Geological Society of America Bulletin, part I, v. 91, p. 433–444.

Prell, W. L., Gardner, J. V., and others, 1982, site 502; Colombia Basin, western Caribbean Sea, *in* Prell, W. L., Gardner, J. V., and others, eds., Initial reports of the Deep Sea Drilling Project: Washington, D.C., U.S. Government Printing Office, v. 68, p. 15–162.

Riedel, W., and Westberg, M. J., 1982, Neogene radiolarians from the eastern tropical Pacific and Caribbean, Deep Sea Drilling Project, Leg 68, *in* Prell, W. L., Gardner, J. V., and others, eds., Initial reports of the Deep Sea Drilling Project: Washington, D.C., U.S. Government Printing Office, v. 68, p. 289–300.

Santamaría, F., and Schubert, C., 1974, Geochemistry and geochronology of the southern Caribbean–northern Venezuela plate boundary: Geological Society of America Bulletin, v. 85, p. 1085–1098.

Saunders, J. B., Edgar, N. T., Donnelly, T. W., and Hay, W. W., 1973, Cruise synthesis, *in* Edgar, N. T., Saunders, J. B., and others, eds., Initial reports of the Deep Sea Drilling Project: Washington, D.C., U.S. Government Printing Office, v. 15, p. 1077–1111.

Schlanger, S. O., and Premoli Silva, I., 1981, Tectonic, volcanic, and paleogeographic implications of redeposited reef faunas of Late Cretaceous and Tertiary age from the Nauru Basin and the Line Islands, *in* Larson, R. L., Schlanger, S. O., and others, eds., Initial reports of the Deep Sea Drilling

Project: Washington, D.C., U.S. Government Printing Office, v. 61, p. 817–827.

Schmidt-Effing, R., Gursky, H. J., Strebin, M., and Wildberg, H., 1980, The ophiolites of southern Central America with special reference to the Nicoya Peninsula (Costa Rica): Transactions, Ninth Caribbean Geological Conference, Santo Domingo, Dominican Republic, v. 2, p. 423–429.

Schoonmaker, J. E., and Ladd, J. W., 1984, Heat flow in Lesser Antilles Arc and adjacent terranes, *in* Speed, R. C., Westbrook, G. K., and others, eds., Ocean Margin Drilling Program Regional Atlas Series, Atlas 10: Woods Hole, Massachusetts, Marine Science International, 27 sheets.

Sclater, J. G., and Francheteau, J., 1970, The implications of terrestrial heat flow observations for current tectonic and geochemical models of the crust and upper mantle of the Earth: Royal Astronomical Society Geophysical Journal, v. 20, p. 509–542.

Sclater, J. G., and Tapscott, C., 1979, The history of the Atlantic: Scientific American, v. 240, p. 156–174.

Sen Gupta, B. K., 1984, Post glacial benthic foraminifera of the Venezuela Basin [abs.]: EOS (Transactions of the American Geophysical Union), v. 64, p. 1076.

Sigurdsson, H., Sparks, R.S.J., Carey, S., and Huang, T. C., 1980, Volcanic sedimentation in the Lesser Antilles Arc: Journal of Geology, v. 88, no. 5, p. 523–540.

Silver, E. A., Case, J. E., and MacGillavry, H. J., 1975, Geophysical study of the Venezuelan Borderland: Geological Society of America Bulletin, v. 86, p. 213–226.

Speed, R. C., Westbrook, G. K., and others, 1984, Lesser Antilles Arc and adjacent terranes, Ocean Margin Drilling Program Regional Atlas Series, Atlas 10: Woods Hole, Massachusetts, Marine Science International, 27 Sheets.

Stoffa, P. L., Mauffret, A., Truchan, M., and Buhl, P., 1981, Sub-B″ layering in the southern Caribbean; The Aruba Gap and Venezuela Basin: Earth and Planetary Science Letters, v. 53, p. 131–146.

Uchupi, E., 1973, Eastern Yucatán continental margin and western Caribbean tectonics: American Association of Petroleum Geologists Bulletin, v. 57, p. 1075–1085.

U.S. Geological Survey, 1967, Geology of Swan Island: U.S. Geological Survey Professional Paper 575, p. A127.

Vail, P. R., Mitchum, R. M., Jr., Todd, R. G., Widmier, J. M., Thompson, S., III, Sangree, J. B., Bubb, J. N., and Hatlelid, W. G., 1977, Seismic stratigraphy and global changes of sea level, *in* Payton, E. C., ed., Seismic stratigraphy; Applications to hydrocarbon exploration: American Association of Petroleum Geologists Memoir 26, p. 49–212.

Wadge, G., and Burke, K., 1983, Neogene Caribbean plate rotation and associated Central American tectonic evolution: Tectonics, v. 2, p. 633–643.

Watkins, J., and Cavanaugh, T., 1976, Implications of magnetic anomalies in the Venezuelan Basin: Transactions, Seventh Caribbean Geological Conference, Conference Géologique des Caraibes, San Francois, Guadeloupe, p. 127–138.

Westbrook, G. K., Mauffret, A., Munschy, M., Jackson, R., Biju-Duval, B., Mascle, A., and Ladd, J. W., 1984, Depth to acoustic basement, and depth to intermediate horizons, *in* Speed, R. C., Westbrook, G. K., and others, eds., Lesser Antilles Arc and adjacent terranes, Ocean Margin Drilling Program Regional Atlas Series, Atlas 10: Woods Hole, Massachusetts, Marine Science International, 27 Sheets.

Weyl, R., 1980, Geology of Central America (second revised edition): Berlin, Stuttgart, Gebrüder Borntraeger, p. 371.

Winterer, E. L., and Metzler, C. V., 1984, Origin and subsidence of guyots in Mid-Pacific Mountains: Journal of Geophysical Research, v. 89, p. 9969–9979.

Zans, V. A., Chubb, L. J., Versey, H. R., Williams, J. B., Robinson, E., and Cooke, D. L., 1963, Synopsis of the geology of Jamaica: Geological Survey of Jamaica Bulletin 4, 72 p.

Zimmerman, H. B., 1982, Lithologic stratigraphy and clay mineralogy of the western Caribbean and eastern equatorial Pacific, Leg 68, Deep Sea Drilling Project, *in* Prell, W. L., and Gardner, J. V., eds., Initial reports of the Deep Sea Drilling Project: Washington, D.C., U.S. Government Printing Office, v. 68, p. 383–395.

MANUSCRIPT ACCEPTED BY THE SOCIETY AUGUST 17, 1988

ACKNOWLEDGMENTS

D. D. Arden, T. Kinder, and E. Rosencrantz reviewed sections of the text and made valuable suggestions. Unpublished seismic reflection sections were kindly made available by W. J. Ludwig, and E. Rosencrantz. C. Fisher provided able editorial assistance during all phases of manuscript preparation. Support of the authors' employing institutions—U.S. National Geophysical Data Center, U.S. Naval Ocean Research and Development Activity, Lamont-Doherty Geological Observatory of Columbia University, University of Durham, University of Birmingham, U.S. Geological Survey, and ARCO Oil and Gas Company—is gratefully acknowledged.

The Geology of North America
Vol. H, The Caribbean region
The Geological Society of America, 1990

Chapter 10

Caribbean marine geology; Active margins of the plate boundary

John W. Ladd*
Lamont-Doherty Geological Observatory of Columbia University, Palisades, New York 10964
Troy L. Holcombe
Marine Geology and Geophysics Division, National Geophysical Data Center, 325 Broadway, Boulder, Colorado 80303
Graham K. Westbrook
School of Earth Sciences, University of Birmingham, Birmingham B15 2TT, England
N. Terence Edgar
Office of Energy and Marine Geology, U.S. Geological Survey, Reston, Virginia 22092

INTRODUCTION

The margins of the Caribbean plate are characterized by varying amounts of strike-slip faulting and compressional folding, thrusting, warping, and extensional faulting. The Cayman Trough is a predominantly strike-slip transform boundary except for a short segment of a spreading ridge (Macdonald and Holcombe, 1978; Holcombe and Sharman, 1983). The Barbados Ridge–Lesser Antilles Arc system and the Middle America Trench–Central America Arc system are predominantly compressional, convergent boundaries. The other boundaries have experienced Neogene strike-slip faulting, compression, and extension across a broad plate boundary zone. Because we are dealing with several rigid plates in relative motion with respect to each other, we believe that the Neogene pattern has undergone slow second-order changes with time (Dewey, 1975). The Neogene and Quaternary pattern has been quite different from Paleogene and Cretaceous patterns of plate boundary organization and deformation (Ladd, 1976; Pindell and Dewey, 1982; Pindell and Barrett, this volume). In this chapter we will review the northern, southern, and eastern boundaries of the Caribbean; the western boundary with the Cocos plate is reviewed only briefly here and more fully in the eastern Pacific volume (von Huene, 1989). Place names referred to in this chapter can be found in Plate 1.

MIDDLE AMERICA TRENCH

The western boundary of the Caribbean plate is a broad zone that has developed during (and perhaps before) the Neogene by convergence of the Cocos and Caribbean plates to the northwest of the Azuero Peninsula and by more oblique convergence, possibly involving some strike-slip faulting, between the Nazca

and Caribbean plates south of Panama to the east. The Cocos-Caribbean boundary runs northwest from the Nazca-Cocos-Caribbean triple junction at the intersection of the north-south–trending Panama Fracture Zone and Central America (Lonsdale and Klitgord, 1978), and includes the Middle America Trench, the broad fore-arc basin underlying the continental shelf that is interrupted by several peninsulas including the Nicoya Peninsula, and the parallel volcanic belt. To the northwest the Middle America Trench continues apparently uninterrupted across the boundary between the Chortis block on the Caribbean plate and the Maya block on the North American plate, where the intersection of the Motagua-Polochic fault system with the Middle America Trench forms a trench-trench-transform triple junction that is unstable (in the terms of McKenzie and Morgan, 1969). This instability is reflected in the intense deformation on the Chortis block south of the Motagua-Polochic plate boundary zone (Plafker, 1976; Burkart, 1978, 1983; Wadge and Burke, 1983). The onshore geology has recently been summarized by Weyl (1980) and Dengo (1985). Dengo divided the land between the trans-Mexican volcanic belt and northwestern Colombia into five lithostratigraphic terranes, including the Oaxaca and Maya blocks of the North American plate (see Donnelly and others, this volume), the Chortis block of the Caribbean plate, and the Chorotega and Chocó blocks of the South American plate.

Molnar and Sykes (1969), Dean and Drake (1978), and McNally and Minster (1981) have determined that seismicity and earthquake focal mechanisms within the area indicate convergence of the Cocos and Caribbean plates. Minster and Jordan (1978) determined estimates of the convergence rate of roughly 8 cm/yr offshore Guatemala based on worldwide measurements of relative plate-motion vectors. Foci associated with the subduction process define a northeastward-dipping Benioff Zone that extends

---

*Present address: National Science Foundation, Rm 609, 1800 G. St. NW, Washington, D.C. 20550.

Ladd, J. W., Holcombe, T. L., Westbrook, G. K., and Edgar, N. T., 1990, Caribbean marine geology; Active margins of the plate boundary, *in* Dengo, G., and Case, J. E., eds., The Caribbean region: Boulder, Colorado, Geological Society of America, The Geology of North America, v. H.

to depths of greater than 200 km beneath Central America (Carr, 1976). The Central American volcanic chain is a product of the subduction process (Carr and others, 1974).

Recent work offshore Oaxaca (Watkins and others, 1981; Moore and Shipley, 1988; Watkins, 1989), offshore Guatemala (Aubouin and others, 1982, 1984; von Huene, 1989), and on-shore and offshore Costa Rica (Lundberg, 1982; Shipley and others, 1982; Shipley and Moore, 1986) suggests that the style of deformation along the inner slope of the Middle America Trench has great spatial and temporal variability: the Nicoya Peninsula of Costa Rica was uplifted in Late Cretaceous time, whereas the Guatemala shelf was uplifted in late Paleocene or early Eocene time. Offshore Oaxaca, tectonic accretion and underplating (Shipley and others, 1982) occurred during late Tertiary time following a period of tectonic erosion (Karig and others, 1978), whereas crustal accretion (structural stacking of crustal rocks; Ladd and others, 1982) or strike-slip juxtaposition of terranes (see von Huene, 1989) occurred during early Tertiary time offshore Guatemala and was followed by late Tertiary tectonic erosion and/or sediment bypassing (von Huene and others, 1980). During the late Tertiary, sediment accretion and underplating has occurred at the toe of the slope off the Nicoya Peninsula of Costa Rica (Silver and others, 1985).

CAYMAN TROUGH

Geomorphology

The Cayman Trough extends east-northeast across the northwestern Caribbean Sea and forms part of the boundary between the Caribbean and North American plates. The presence of the trough was first revealed by hydrographic surveys in the late nineteenth century (Hill, 1898) and was named the Bartlett Deep. Subsequent bathymetric data, which include swath bathymetry (CAYTROUGH, 1979), have provided the basis for the preparation of fairly detailed bathymetry. These data have been enhanced by the use of sidescan imagery in the central region of the trough (Edgar and others, 1989a, b).

In broad outline the Cayman Trough is a rhomb-shaped trough about 1,200 km long and about 90 to 110 km wide. Narrow, 50-km-wide extensions of the trough continue beyond the northeast and southwest corners of the rhomb, eastward to the Windward Passage and westward into the Gulf of Honduras.

Steep north (Cayman Ridge) and south (Nicaraguan Rise) bounding walls descend to a relatively level floor. The greatest depth, 6,800 m, occurs in longitudinal deeps (Bartlett deep) adjacent to the north wall between Grand Cayman Island and Cuba, which is the deepest place in the Caribbean Sea and second-greatest depth in the Atlantic Ocean after the Puerto Rico Trench. The central region of the trough floor is characterized by northerly oriented ridges that shallow symmetrically toward a central rift valley at about long 81°45′W. This region is referred to as the Mid-Cayman Rise (Fig. 1; Plate 8, D). Local relief in this region is highly variable, and reaches 3,000 m. East and west

of the Mid-Cayman Rise, the trough deepens, and the relief is subdued by sediment cover. West of Swan Island, the trough shallows toward the Gulf of Honduras.

Width of the rift-valley floor varies from about 3 to 18 km, and its depth increases from about 5,000 m at the center of the trough to about 6,000 m at both ends. The rift joins the deep marginal trough at a nodal basin at the base of the Cayman Ridge through a broad curvature that has a radius of about 10 km. A similar curvature and basin connects the southern end of the rift to the marginal trough that lies to the west. Large-scale relief within the rift valley is oblique (337°) to the trend (355°) of the valley walls.

A large topographic high protrudes into the rift valley at about the midpoint between the trough walls. South of this high, high-relief topography trends obliquely (337°) across the valley from the east wall to the west wall. The northern half of the valley is characterized by lower relief, which also trends obliquely across the valley but at a lesser angle.

Fine-scale morphology (10 to 50 m) of the spreading axis is described as a series of volcanic ridges, cones, and depressions in a 2- to 3-km-wide belt that parallels the valley walls (CAYTROUGH, 1979).

The rift-valley walls rise abruptly from the edge of the rift valley and consist of a series of fault escarpments and ledges that form inward-facing steps a few meters to tens of meters in relief. Subsequent erosion and the formation of talus ramps have modified the small-scale morphology to a minor extent.

Sea-floor morphology of the Mid-Cayman Rise east and west of the rift valley is well described by sidescan imagery. North-oriented linear topography throughout the trough floor records a history of sea-floor spreading consistent with that currently active. These lineations are clearly evident on both the swath bathymetry and sidescan images and are predominantly confined within the arc between 335° and 358°, a range of 23° and an average of 350°. A few divergent lineations are evident, such as those at about 82°W, 18°N, which trend 016°. Another set of lineations that has an orientation inconsistent with that of the rest of the trough floor lies along the southern margin east of the rift valley. This 5-km-wide belt extends from the rift valley eastward but does not extend westward where the topography is north-trending. Offsets of the north-trending topography are evident (Figs. 2 and 3), but displacements appear to be less than 10 km. None appears to offset the rift-valley walls. Evidence of off-axis volcanism is rare, but features at 82°40′W, 18°15′N, and 80°45′W, 19°00′N have a morphology similar to a volcano.

The deformation zone associated with motion along the Oriente transform fault is evident on the mosaic, particularly in the eastern part where the surface of abyssal plain sediments has been disturbed. East of this deformation, the fault can be traced along a lineation south of a major easterly trending ridge that parallels the wall of the trough. The trace of the Swan Island transform fault (Fig. 3) is not clearly displayed along the short segment surveyed at its eastern terminus, but the base of the south wall, displayed as a fine white band, approximates its trend.

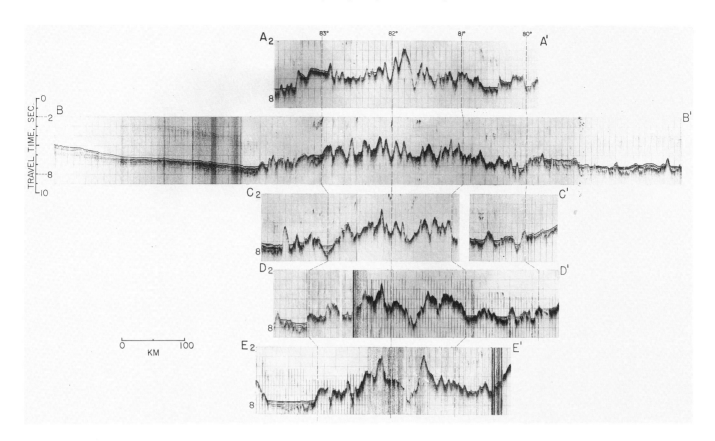

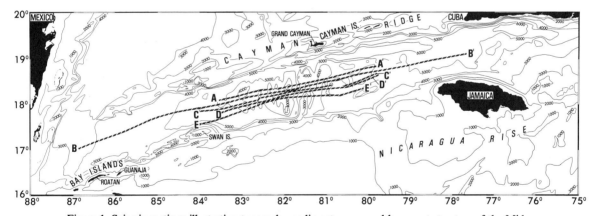

Figure 1. Seismic sections illustrating topgraphy, sediment cover, and basement structure of the Mid-Cayman spreading center. Sections are normalized to lat 82° W. Location of sections is shown in the index map. Section B-B′ extends westward across the Motagua Fan. The rift valley is at long 81° 40′ W. Sections were run by U.S. Naval Oceanographic Office ships USNS *Kane* in 1972 and USNS *Wilkes* in 1973. Both seismic systems recorded single-channel, unprocessed seismic profiles.

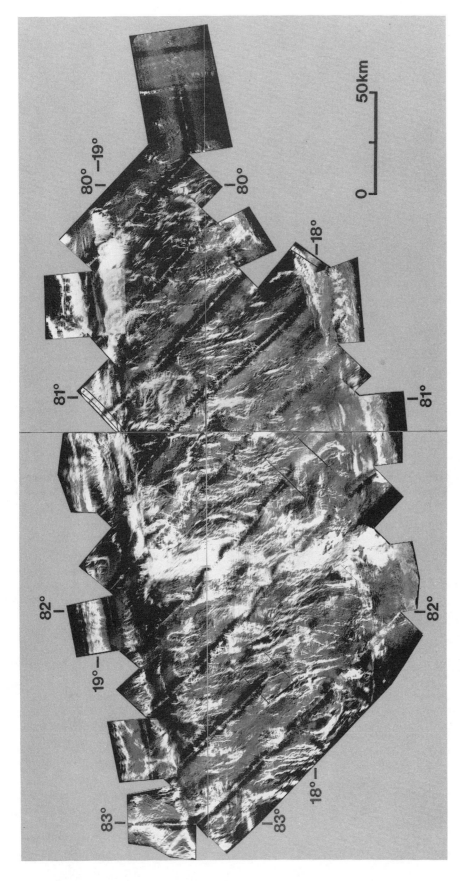

Figure 2. GLORIA sidescan mosaic provides a regional perspective of the morphology of the mid-Cayman Rise and part of the adjacent walls from about long 79°W to 83°W. The bright northerly trending band in the central part of the mosaic is caused by strong reflected returns from the sediment-free surface of the floor and walls of the rift valley. Dark areas represent lower levels of reflected signals caused primarily by sediment cover and low incident angles between the outgoing signal and the sea floor. From Edgar and others (1989a, 1989b).

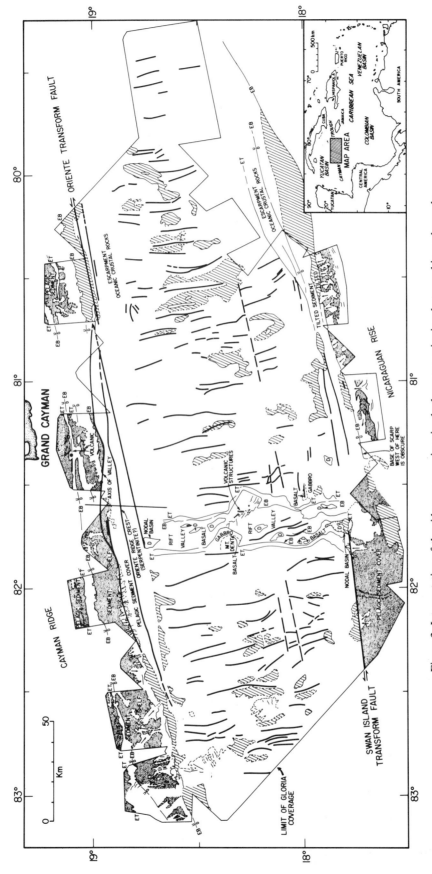

Figure 3. Interpretation of the side-scan mosaic using bathymetry, seismic, photographic, and sample data. ET, top of escarpment; EB, base of escarpment; heavy solid line, ridge: U/D, normal fault; solid line with apposing arrows, transcurrent fault; D, depression; dashed contour, sediment-rock contact; cross-hatching, abyssal plain; stippling, pelagic sediment accumulations; small arrows along Nicaragua Rise and Cayman Ridge, down direction in submarine canyons.

The north wall of the trough is dominated by a major step that separates two escarpments. The step has a maximum width of about 8 km and extends about 110 km along the wall. A particularly large, well-developed canyon that serves as a sediment pathway to a deep-sea fan and abyssal plain lies west of the rift-transform intersection at about 82°45′W.

Sediment accumulation

Sediment accumulation on the Cayman Trough floor is known principally from seismic reflection lines, sidescan sonar, a few piston cores and dredge hauls, and diving observations. To date there has been no sediment sampling with deep-sea drilling.

Because the floor of the trough is underlain by rough oceanic basement, sediment thickness is highly variable on the Mid-Cayman Rise (Fig. 1). Greatest thicknesses (generally >1.5 sec) occur at the western end, where sediments spilling out eastward over the basement have created the Motagua Fan, and in the eastern end (up to 1.5 sec) near Cuba, Jamaica, and Hispaniola. Exposed basement, thin pelagic sediments, or sediment pockets lying in the valleys characterize the Mid-Cayman Rise. East of the Mid-Cayman Rise, between long. 77° and 80° west, sediment thickness generally varies between 0.2 and 0.8 sec, analogous to basement relief, although that relief is largely buried. Because the Mid-Cayman Rise is elevated, and flanked by deep transform-fault valleys, it is to a large degree shielded from influx of terrigenous and pelagic sediments brought in via gravity flow. All but the deepest valleys are above carbonate compensation depth; consequently, the predominant sediment type is pelagic carbonates. These sediments are unstable on the slopes of the oceanic basement, and there has been a tendency for them to accumulate as flat-lying strata in valley bottoms, implying remobilization and downslope transportation via turbidity flow. This pattern of deposition is typical for pelagic carbonate provinces where sea-floor topography is rough. Although seismic records indicate exposed basement, direct observations within the rift and on the rift walls (CAYTROUGH, 1979; Stroup and Fox, 1981) reveal that pelagic sediment covers all but the steep slopes and active spreading axis.

Sediments brought into the trough by gravity flow from the adjacent walls are probably deposited in the southern end of the rift valley, which lies downslope from the trough walls. It is possible that such sediment brought into the active rift would be elevated by the tectonic uplift mechanism that forms the rift walls. Such a mechanism may explain why sediments containing Miocene and Pliocene fossil fragments were dredged from the walls of the rift valley (Perfit and Heezen, 1978); the age of the sediments is not consistent with models of spreading rates based on magnetic anomalies and seismicity.

Generally, sediment cover overlying the Mid-Cayman Rise increases with increasing distance east and west of the axial rift (Fig. 1). This observation applies not only to pocketed valley sediments, but also to the pelagic drape. Sediments within the fracture-zone valleys are probably a mixture of terrigenous sediments and pelagic carbonates; sediments sampled from the plain within Oriente Deep consist of terrigenous lutite (red clay) interbedded with turbidite layers containing terrigenous detritus, including shell fragments, beach pebbles, and wood (Hersey and Rutstein, 1958).

East of long. 79°30′W, gravity-flow sediments have filled the fracture valleys along the south wall and spilled across the oceanic basement topography of the trough floor, which here slopes strongly from south to north (Plate 8, E).

Within the deeper Oriente transform-fault zone, sediment deposition generally increases eastward, away from the active rift and toward Cuba. Some deformation of sediments has been noted (Plate 8, E). It is possible that some of the older sediments, due to continuing deformation, may have been incorporated into what is now recognized as acoustic basement along this fracture zone.

The entire western end of the trough has been inundated with sediments that have formed the eastward-sloping Motagua Fan and its distal plains. Gradients on the fan indicate that the rivers Ulua and Chamelecon of Honduras and the rivers Motagua and Polochic of Guatemala, which debouch into the bight of the Gulf of Honduras, are the principal sediment sources. As Banks and Richards (1969) have pointed out, sediments derived from Honduras farther east would be trapped in offshore basins south of the Cayman Trough. Surface irregularities on the fan probably reflect structural offset as well as the presence of distributary channels (Plate 8, A). The fan surface also slopes southward toward the active Swan Island transform-fault zone, where tectonic disturbance of the sedimentary section has been observed (Plate 8, A). Core samples collected by Erickson and others (1972) from the Motagua Fan yielded Pleistocene sediments, mostly turbidites, partly terrigenous, containing plant debris, calcarenite sands, shale fragments, and graded beds.

Crustal rocks

Crustal rocks of the floor of the Cayman Trough are known from samples dredged from the western sector of the Mid-Cayman Rise (Eggler and others, 1973), from a longitudinal ridge bordering the rise (Perfit and Heezen, 1978), and from intensive sampling—via dredge and submersible—of the walls of the active rift (Perfit and Heezen, 1978; CAYTROUGH, 1979; Stroup and Fox, 1981). The rocks sampled are ocean-floor tholeiites and ultramafics that are first-order compositional equivalents of rocks dredged from rifts, transforms, and spreading ridges of the mid-oceanic ridge. Important variations in major- and trace-element percentages, however, distinguish Mid-Cayman Rise rocks from those typical of the mid-ocean ridge basalts.

An assemblage of pillow basalts with local occurrence of flow basalts dominates the rift floor (CAYTROUGH, 1979). Basalts from the zones of active volcanism are fresh and glassy with little or no manganese coating, whereas those elsewhere on the rift floor are manganese coated and subjected to secondary alteration. Rocks dredged and sampled from the walls of the rift include gabbros (olivine gabbro, orthopyroxene and clinopyroxene gabbro, troctolite), diabase, pillow and crystalline basalt, metamorphosed gabbro and basalt, serpentinized rocks (harzburgite, lherzolite, dunite, and wehrlite), and highly altered, brecciated, and mylonitized rocks (Stroup and Fox, 1981). Gabbroic rocks predominate; basalts are sampled infrequently and have a possible preference for the top of the rift walls. Ultramafic rocks are interspersed within the gabbros in an apparently complex fashion. A clear pattern of spatial distribution of rock types is not recognized, and there is no clear correlation between outcrop type (i.e., massive, fractured, banded) and rock type. In addition, a clear pattern of crystal fractionation or zoning, either at the scale of thin sections or with depth on the rift wall, is not observed. An extremely complex pattern is implied for magma injection, fracturing and/or jointing, hydrothermal alteration, metamorphism, and injection of serpentinized ultramafic rocks.

The relative absence of pillow basalts strongly suggests that the upper extrusive crustal layer of pillow basalts, flows, and sheeted dikes is very thin (a few hundred meters) compared to that of "typical" oceanic crust (1 to 2 km), as deduced from seismic refraction studies, studies of ophiolite complexes, and deep-ocean drilling. To explain the almost complete absence of extrusive basalts from the rift walls, White and Stroup (1979) and Stroup and Fox (1981) have proposed a model in which the presumed thin topmost crustal layer is downfaulted along outward-facing faults that produce grabens underlying the ledges in the rift walls; these grabens are then filled with talus and sediments that cover the basalt. The random occurrence of ultramafic rocks presumably injected into the gabbroic rocks suggested to Stroup and Fox (1981) that the lower crustal layer is also anomalously thin (fault throws that generated the inward-facing fault scarps are generally no more than a few hundred meters), or that injection of subcrustal ultramafic material has penetrated to the top of the lower crustal layer.

Granodiorites and tonalites and their metamorphic equivalents have been dredged from escarpments bordering the Oriente Deep opposite one of the northeast-trending ridges of horst-block aspect northeast of Jamaica and from side walls of this ridge (Perfit and Heezen, 1978). These intrusive rocks are in marked contrast to other dredged rocks of the Cayman Trough floor in that they are generally associated with island arcs rather than with ocean floor. One could speculate that the horst-block features represent pieces of island-arc crust, which were separated by rifting during early phases of crustal distension associated with early opening of the Cayman Trough. Similar island-arc intrusives occur along the adjacent coast of Cuba in the Sierra Maestra, in Jamaica, and beneath the Cayman Ridge (north wall of Cayman Trough). A K-Ar date of 83 ± 2 Ma (Late Cretaceous) was obtained from a tonalite sample (Perfit and Heezen, 1978). This is older than dates obtained for Sierra Maestra intrusives (46 to 58 Ma (Khudoley and Meyerhoff, 1971) and for Cayman Ridge intrusives (59 to 69 Ma; Perfit and Heezen, 1978), but it compares favorably with dates obtained for granodiorite intrusives exposed in Jamaica (75 to 85 Ma; Lewis and others, 1973).

The oceanic nature of the crust underlying the Cayman Trough floor is also demonstrated by refraction studies of the 1950s. Refraction lines from the eastern trough floor at long. 75° to 80°W (Ewing and others, 1960) and from one line west of the spreading center (Dowling, 1967) reveal a thin (<1 km) uppermost 2 km/sec sedimentary layer, a thin (<2 km) 4.0 to 5.5 km/sec upper crustal layer, a 3- to 6-km-thick 6.2 to 6.8 km/sec lower crustal layer, and clearly determined 8.0 to 8.3 km/sec mantle velocities. Layer sequence and interval velocities are typical of oceanic crust as recorded in earlier refraction measurements. Overall, the crust is probably thinner (5 to 7 km) than the average for oceanic crust. The M discontinuity occurs at about 11 to 13 km below sea level.

In three refraction stations near the spreading center (Ewing and others, 1960; Dowling, 1967), mantle arrivals were not recorded. It is significant that in one east-west section, over and parallel to the south wall of the Oriente transform, a 7.5 km/sec velocity was obtained directly below 2.0 km/sec sediments (Dowling, 1967). Unusually high velocities for upper (5.4 to 5.8 km/sec) and lower (7.1 to 7.2 km/sec) crust were obtained at the western end of the trough (Dowling, 1967), and in two stations at the eastern end of the trough between Cuba and the western peninsula of Haiti (Edgar and others, 1971). This extra thickness can be explained either by consolidation of a thick overburden of sediments, or by the presence of an upper crustal layer of granitoid or intermediate composition. The unusually high velocities in the lower crust might be explained by the occurrence of a greater than normal percentage of ultramafic rocks. This heightened presence of ultramafic material included as injections or intrusive bodies within the lower crustal layer is borne out by the results of rift-wall studies (CAYTROUGH, 1979; Stroup and Fox, 1981).

Explaining the Cayman Trough crust in terms of a two-layer model in which upper crustal rocks are predominantly basalt lavas and flows underlain by sheeted dikes, and lower crustal rocks are predominantly gabbroid intrusives, as the refraction data would indicate, is problematic because, where intensively sampled at the rift walls basaltic extrusives are rarely encountered, if at all. The degree of fracturing and the processes and degree of secondary alteration are possibly important determinants of crustal velocity in the upper crustal layers beneath the Cayman Trough.

Mechanism of opening, structural evolution

Views regarding the origin and evolution of the Cayman Trough have evolved with the development of geological thought and with accumulating geological evidence. One of the earliest views regarding the origin of the Cayman Trough was that of Spencer (1895), who proposed that the Cayman (Bartlett) Trough was a gigantic gorge, the product of stream erosion during a time when the whole Antillean region stood above sea level. Hill (1898) and Ballore (1906) thought of the trough as a syncline in an east-west fold belt, which would account for the parallel, elevated, linear, structurally positive features adjoining or extending beyond the limits of the trough in Central America, Cuba, Jamaica, and Hispaniola.

Various models of north-south compression have been proposed that presume folding and high-angle thrust faulting within or adjacent to the trough (Suess, 1909; Woodring, 1928; Meyerhoff, 1933; Lewis and Straczek, 1955; Hersey and Rutstein, 1958). Later compressional models incorporate a component of transcurrent faulting (Bucher, 1947; Meyerhoff, 1954; Meyerhoff, 1966). Any model for structural evolution for the area must take into account ample evidence for north-south compression found in the circum-trough area; for example, in Oriente province, Cuba, in Hispaniola (Lewis and Straczek, 1955; Goreau, 1983), and in the Bay Islands (McBirney and Bass, 1969).

Vaughan (1918), Taber (1922), and Schuchert (1935) envisioned the Cayman Trough as a gigantic block-faulted graben formed in a tensional regime. Cited as evidence for such rifting were the relatively straight, precipitous walls, the relatively flat trough floor, truncation of strata exposed in fault scarps along the Cuban and Jamaican coasts, and the apparent confinement of seismicity to the area of the trough walls. Early to middle Miocene strata are truncated by faulting along the Cuban coast (Meyerhoff, 1966); therefore, a post-Miocene initiation of faulting was proposed, with active faulting continuing to the present.

Large-scale left-lateral strike-slip faulting through the Cayman Trough region was proposed by Hess and Maxwell (1953), on the basis that metamorphic belts in Cuba and Hispaniola, which are now fragmented, once formed a continuous linear zone. Two large-displacement transcurrent faults were proposed, extending along the northern and southern walls of the trough, respectively. This idea found credence in the plate-tectonic era, when Sykes and Ewing (1965) and Molnar and Sykes (1969) presented interpretations requiring large-scale left-lateral transcurrent movements, as evidenced by (1) focal-mechanism solutions from earthquake events occurring within the floor of the Cayman Trough, (2) linearity of the trough, and (3) lack of intermediate- and deep-focus seismicity. Once gravity and refraction studies established that the Cayman Trough was underlain by thin oceanic crust (Ewing and Heezen, 1955; Ewing and others, 1960; Bowin, 1968) and it was recognized that the Cayman Trough was a fundamentally distinct feature from the Puerto Rico Trench, a tensional origin for the trough, with upwelling of oceanic crustal material, was suggested (Ewing and others, 1960). Models that combine components of transcurrent movement with components of tensional movement (transtension) were proposed (Bowin, 1968; Erickson and others, 1972).

Recognition of north-south basement ridges and all the morphologic features of a transversely oriented spreading center (north-south rift; overall symmetry including symmetric depths increase away from rift; rough sediment-free basement) led to the proposal that the Cayman Trough is a short transverse spreading center between two long transforms, the active limbs of which coincide with the north wall east of the north-south rift (Oriente transform fault) and the south wall west of the rift (Swan transform fault) (Holcombe and others, 1973). This model is consist-

ent with morphologic criteria for active rifts and transforms, with geophysical evidence for thin oceanic crust, and it also explains the pattern of seismicity, which largely coincides with the rift and the active limbs of the transforms. It also explains the high heat-flow observations taken from the floor of the trough (Erickson and others, 1972). Heat-flow measurements average 2.01 hfu, higher than the world average and the Caribbean average (1.6 hfu), but compare favorably with the average for mid-oceanic ridges. Recent studies of oceanic crustal rocks from the Cayman Trough (Perfit and Heezen, 1978) and extensive geological investigations of the rift floor and walls, including petrology of crustal rocks, geomorphology, structural patterns, and volcanism (CAYTROUGH, 1979; White and Stroup, 1979; Stroup and Fox, 1981), have generally supported and refined the short transverse rift–long transform interpretation.

Seismicity and evidence of currently active tectonic displacements are not confined to the Cayman Trough proper, but are distributed along a 200-km-wide belt characterized as a "plate boundary zone" (Burke and others, 1980) that includes Jamaica, the northern Nicaraguan Rise, the Oriente Province of Cuba, and the Cayman Ridge. Although primary movement along the plate boundary is probably confined to the rift and transform within the floor of the trough, secondary movements of varying style and orientation occur throughout the plate boundary zone.

Age and rates of opening

North-south orientation of magnetic lineations from the Cayman Trough are of low amplitude and are not well defined. An inversion solution was obtained for one magnetic profile; magnetic anomalies 1 through 4 were identified within 150 km of the spreading center and modeled with a block model (Macdonald and Holcombe, 1978). A total spreading rate of 2 cm/yr was obtained for 0 to 2.4 Ma and a rate of 4 cm/yr was obtained for 2.4 to 6.0 Ma. The 2.4 to 6.0 Ma rate is in good agreement with long-term slip rates inferred by Sykes and others (1982) from patterns of seismicity in the Lesser Antilles subduction zone. The inversion solution of Macdonald and Holcombe (1978) yielded a crustal magnetization of 2 amps/m, a value significantly lower than that typical of oceanic crust found at a spreading center. Higher magnetization has been found to occur in pillow lavas and flows of the volcanic crustal layer than in the sheeted dikes and the gabbroic layer; this would suggest that the contribution to crustal magnetization is primarily from the gabbroic layer. Such a conclusion lends credence to the conclusion reached from rift-wall studies (CAYTROUGH, 1979; Stroup and Fox, 1981) that the volcanic upper crustal layer is anomalously thin beneath the Cayman Trough.

Sykes and others (1982) questioned whether a slowdown in North American–Caribbean relative plate motion occurred at 2 Ma; they proposed that since 2 Ma, half of the total relative motion not recorded across the Cayman Trough spreading center has been accommodated by slip along secondary faults along and south of the south wall of the trough east of the spreading center.

On the other hand, Mocquet and Aggarwal (1983) have presented evidence for seismic slip rates of about 2 cm/yr in Hispaniola, rates in agreement with that obtained for spreading in the Cayman Trough from 0 to 2.4 Ma. Rosencrantz and Sclater (1986) offered an alternative identification of observed magnetic anomalies for all the USNS *Wilkes* traverses; their spreading rates of 1.5 cm/yr (0 to 30 Ma) and 3.0 cm/yr (30 Ma to ?) are more consistent with spreading rates determined from crustal subsidence. These rates were modified slightly by Rosencrantz and others (1988) to 1.5 cm/yr (0 to 26 Ma) and 2.5 to 3.0 cm/yr (26 to 50 Ma) after invoking four ridge jumps.

All but one of the USNS *Wilkes* lines (Fig. 1) cross a large gabbroic block that juts into the rift valley at about its midpoint. The central aomaly overlies this crustal block, which forms the wall of the rift valley; one of the USNS *Wilkes* lines crosses the rift valley south of this block, but no typical central anomaly was recorded (Edgar and others, in preparation).

Edgar and others (1989b) accepted the premise of Sykes and others (1982) that, if the Caribbean plate is anchored to the mesosphere by subduction at the Lesser Antilles and Central America (Jordan, 1975), then the average relative motion between the North American and Caribbean plates should be equivalent to the total North Atlantic spreading rate. They determined this rate to be 2.6 cm/yr, based on Atlantic rates from Klitgord and Schouten (1986).

Extrapolation of the 4 cm/yr rate back in time using the present opening mechanism would place the time of initial opening of the deep rhombic-shaped part of the trough at about 25 Ma. According to this rate, the opening of the deep oceanic part of the Cayman Trough could have occurred in its entirety since late Oligocene time. Rosencrantz and others (1988) extrapolated their rates to 50 Ma or early middle Eocene time for the time of initial opening. A rate of 2.6 cm/yr (Edgar and others, in preparation) yields 42 Ma, or an early late Eocene time for the initial opening.

The northeast-trending horst-block terrane between Jamaica and Cuba probably records an earlier episode of Cayman Trough opening. Presence of a thicker crust with a 5.4 km/sec layer and the recovery of granodiorites from scarps in this area lead one to speculate that this part of the trough represents an initial rifting and extension or stretching of a thicker island-arc crust. This left a horst-and-graben terrane of rifted blocks of thick crust interspersed with volcanic intrusions, prior to formation of a cleanly breaking rift accompanied by generation of oceanic crust. Therefore, initiation of the earlier episode of rifting that produced the horst and graben terrane could have occurred earlier, in Oligocene or Eocene time.

Beyond the floor of the Cayman Trough, along the North American–Caribbean plate boundary zone, the history of relative movements has been complex and diffuse; on the other hand, it is more accessible to observation. One problem has been finding evidence for 750 to 1,500 km of late Cenozoic transcurrent movement through Central America and the Greater Antilles. Perhaps the solution will emerge as investigation continues. Bur-

kart (1983) has uncovered convincing evidence, to us, of transcurrent movements totaling several hundred kilometers in the past 10 to 12 m.y. along the Polochic, Jocotán, and Motagua faults in Guatemala.

NORTHERN CARIBBEAN PLATE BOUNDARY ZONE

Except for the Mid-Cayman spreading center and associated transform faults, the Neogene-Quaternary boundary between North America and the Caribbean plate lies within continental crust (Burkart, 1978, 1983; Dengo, 1985) or Cretaceous-Paleogene island-arc material. Because of this, deformation along the northern Caribbean plate boundary is spread over a 200-km-wide plate boundary zone in which deformation includes dominant strike-slip motion and secondary extension and compression in response to horizontal simple shear (Burke and others, 1980, 1984). Superimposed on this horizontal simple shear is a compressional couple caused by the convergence of North America and South America across the Caribbean region (Ladd, 1976). This convergence has led to the development of zones of overthrusting and associated topographic trenches along the northern and southern margins of the Greater Antilles (Ladd and Watkins, 1978a, b; Molnar, 1977; Frankel and others, 1980; Biju-Duval and others, 1982a).

As observed today, the northern Caribbean plate boundary zone includes the Motagua-Polochic-Jocotán fault zones in Guatemala, the Cayman Trough, southern Cuba, Hispaniola, Puerto Rico, the Virgin Islands, the Puerto Rico Trench, and the Muertos Trough. Throughout the Greater Antilles, including northern Cuba, and along the Central American plate boundary lie the remains of Cretaceous to Paleogene orogenic zones that suggest a much different plate boundary configuration for this earlier time period. Along the north side of the Polochic fault, the Sierra de Santa Cruz ophiolite overlies the Late Cretaceous wackes of the Sepur Formation. The Sierra de Santa Cruz is one of a number of ophiolite bodies that lie along the suture zone between the Maya and Chortis blocks (for more details see Donnelly and others, this volume). A well on Pedro Bank on the Nicaraguan Rise bottomed in an Eocene granodiorite. In Jamaica, a thick section of late Campanian to Maastrichtian volcanic, plutonic, and volcaniclastic rock is exposed in the southwestern Blue Mountains. In the Massif de la Selle of southern Haiti, the Cretaceous Dumisseau Formation, composed of basalts, dolerites, pelagic limestones, volcanogenic turbidites, cherts, and siliceous siltstones, shows deformation increasing westward, which in some areas has led to formation of a tectonic mélange (Maurrasse, 1982). Maurrasse (1981), noting the contrast in structural grain and lithologic composition between southern Haiti and the rest of Hispaniola, suggested the existence of two Late Cretaceous island arcs: a southern arc including southern Haiti, Jamaica, and the Nicaraguan Rise, and a northern arc including the rest of Hispaniola, Puerto Rico, and Cuba. Similarly, Mann and Burke (in preparation) interpret the pattern of outcrops from Guatemala to south-

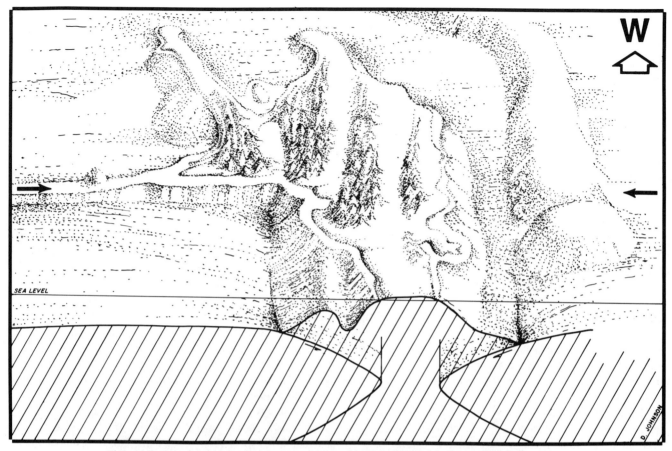

Figure 4. Interpretive drawing, looking west, shows crust of North America plate (right foreground) and ocean crust of Caribbean plate (left foreground) underthrusting eastern Hispaniola. Bold arrows in background indicate convergence of Beata Ridge (left) and Bahama platform (right) across central Hispaniola giving rise to compressive basin-and-range structure in central Hispaniola. All relative motions indicated are minor vector components of major Caribbean plate–North American plate relative motion which is predominantly strike slip (Caribbean plate out of page, North American plate into page). From Ladd and others (1981).

ern Haiti as indicating a southern island arc that flourished in Cretaceous time and collided with the Yucatan platform in latest Cretaceous time. They suggest that Neogene strike-slip motion along the northern Caribbean plate boundary zone has smeared this Cretaceous arc eastward to its present configuration.

Mann and Burke, following the suggestions of many previous authors, including Malfait and Dinkelman (1972), Maurrasse (1981), and Pindell and Dewey (1982), also conclude that a northern island arc existed from Cretaceous to late Eocene time, remnants of which stretch from northern Cuba to the Virgin Islands. This arc ceased functioning as the result of progressive Eocene collision with the Bahama platform; this led to a plate boundary reorganization, and by early Oligocene time the present boundary zone configuration had formed, with dominant east-west strike-slip motion and secondary north-south compression.

Muertos Trough

Where oceanic crust lies adjacent to the Greater Antilles island platform, the north-south convergence is accommodated by the oceanic crust underthrusting the island platform. Where

thicker crust lies adjacent to the island platform, as is the case with the Beata Ridge and the Bahamas, the convergence is accommodated by folding and thrust faulting within the island platform (Ladd and others, 1981; Biju-Duval and others, 1982a) (Fig. 4). South of Haiti, west of the Beata Ridge, and south of the Dominican Republic and Puerto Rico, east of the Beata Ridge, as well as along the Puerto Rico Trench, seismic reflection records show the development of typical convergent-margin morphology and structure; a topographic trench marks the seaward limit of a highly deformed sediment wedge (Garrison, 1972; Matthews and Holcombe, 1974; Ladd and others, 1977; Goreau, 1983; compare seismic sections from the Muertos Trough depicted in these papers with seismic sections across the Nankai Trough published by Aoki and others, 1982) (Plate 9, AA and BB). South of the Greater Antilles, the stratigraphy of the Venezuelan Basin can be traced northward beneath the deformed sediment wedge on seismic reflection profiles. The trench axis contains a Pliocene-Pleistocene turbidite fill that in places shows minor deformation at the toe of the deformed sediment wedge.

Our only clues to the age relations within the sediment

wedge on the southern flank of the Greater Antilles come indirectly from seismic reflection data, which can be correlated with sections onshore in Hispaniola and drilled sections in the Venezuelan Basin (Plate 5b). The Paleogene section drilled in the Venezuelan Basin can be traced beneath the turbidite fill of the Muertos Trough, indicating that the turbidite fill is Neogene in age. Because the existing drill hole calibrating the Venezuelan Basin section is far to the south, and because the seismic reflection record in the vicinity of the Muertos Trough does not clearly delineate reflectors immediately beneath the turbidites, the turbidite fill could possibly be limited in age to the late Neogene and/or Quaternary. Existing data are not definitive.

San Pedro Basin is a large basin that lies on the island platform just south of the Dominican Republic and contains several kilometers of mildly deformed sediments ponded behind a structural high at the southern boundary of the island platform (Ladd and others, 1981) (see Plate 9, AA). The cross-sectional form of the basin and outer ridge are similar to fore-arc basins and structural highs at the shelf edge seen on many convergent margins (Karig, 1974a; Karig and Sharman, 1975; Seely, 1979). The basin is confined at either end by salients of the island platform, but igneous basement beneath the basin may be oceanic crust (see generalized scheme in Fig. 3; Seely, 1979). The stratigraphy within the basin can be tentatively correlated with the stratigraphy of Cristóbal Basin onshore, indicating that the basin fill may represent most of the Tertiary. The northward dip and onlapping relations of basin fill on the north flank of the structural high suggest that the southern boundary ridge has been growing throughout the period of basin filling. A thick stratified section lies beneath a strong angular unconformity within the southern boundary ridge. This unconformity continues beneath the basin, indicating that the structural high formed on the site of an earlier depocenter. North-south compression has foreshortened the basin on the flank of the island platform, and the depocenter has moved northward with time.

Terraces extend discontinuously along the southern flank of the Greater Antilles in water depths of 1 to 5 km. They are most striking just south of Mona Passage, the seaway that separates Puerto Rico and Hispaniola (Ladd and Watkins, 1978a), but can also be seen along the slope south of Hispaniola. The terraces, which are unrelated to sea-level terraces found subaerially and in shallow water, are formed much like the San Pedro Basin and consist of mildly deformed sediment filling small basins above an irregular basement. The older, deeper strata within these terrace basins dip islandward, attesting to lower slope uplift and deformation during the period of sediment basin fill. Seismic sections south of Mona Passage also show suggestions of landward-dipping horizons, which might be interpreted as landward-dipping thrust faults (Seely and others, 1974).

The entire southern margin of the Greater Antilles, except where the Beata Ridge interrupts the slope, may have developed during the Neogene and possibly earlier by accretionary processes related to convergence (Seely and others, 1974). The wedge of sediments beneath the island flank may be continually deforming and uplifting as new material is added at the toe of the slope by folding and thrusting. Sediment accretion south of the Greater Antilles may take place at rates even faster than in some Pacific margins, where the plate-convergence is an order of magnitude faster, but tectonic accretion apparently has not occurred during the Neogene (Aubouin and others, 1982; von Huene and others, 1985; Hilde, 1983). The southern boundary ridge south of the Dominican Republic overlies an irregular horizon that is deformed into an anticline which has been growing during the Neogene; this indicates the compressional nature of this zone and suggests that the material beneath the slope is a sediment wedge (Plate 9, BB). One must be cautious about this conclusion, however, because before drilling, the wedge of material beneath the continental slope offshore Guatemala was thought to be sediment (Seely and others, 1974). Drilling there has determined that the wedge of material between the trench inner slope and the basal décollement off Guatemala is composed primarily of fractured ultramafic rock having seismic velocities >4 km/sec (von Huene and others, 1985).

North of Puerto Rico and the Virgin Islands is the Puerto Rico Trench, which ends north of eastern Hispaniola where the Bahama Platform impinges on the Greater Antilles. The Puerto Rico Trench, which has been the subject of numerous research papers (e.g., Tucholke and Ewing, 1974; Perfit and others, 1980; McCann and Sykes, 1984), is similar in morphology and gravity expression to Pacific deep-sea trenches.

Farther west, north of Haiti, seismic reflection work of Austin (1983) shows compressive folds and thrusts with northward vergence on the flank of the island platform resulting from collision of the Bahamas and the Greater Antilles. Austin also noted normal faults, which he attributed to tension at the crest of compressive folds.

SOUTHERN CARIBBEAN PLATE BOUNDARY ZONE

Like the Greater Antilles, the southern margin of the Caribbean plate is a broad zone of deformation involving strike-slip faulting, compressional folding and faulting, and extensional folding and faulting. In the region of Costa Rica and Panamá east of the Panama Fracture Zone, the boundary zone between the Caribbean plate and the Nazca plate is about 400 km wide, and there is compressional folding and thrusting offshore Panamá to the north (Case, 1974b; Lu and McMillen, 1982; Breen and others, 1988), and folding, thrusting (Lowrie, 1978), and possibly strike-slip faulting offshore Panamá to the south (Lonsdale and Klitgord, 1978). Farther east in Colombia and western Venezuela, the boundary zone between the Caribbean plate and the South American plate is about 600 km wide from the northern flank of the South Caribbean deformed belt (Case, 1974b) to the southeastern flank of the Venezuelan Andes (Biju-Duval and others, 1982c). Eastward in Venezuela the boundary zone narrows to 400 km from the north flank of the Curaçao Ridge to the south flank of the Caribbean Coastal Range and to perhaps only 200 km in width in the region of Trinidad-Tobago. Within this plate boundary zone there are discrete blocks at all scales, from micro-plates and terranes to outcrop-sized fault blocks (Silver and others, 1975; Bowin, 1976; Dengo, 1985; Muessig, 1984; Burke and others, 1984).

Panama and Colombia

As with the Greater Antilles, the geology of the South Caribbean plate boundary zone is the product of Mesozoic and Tertiary evolution during a long period of constantly changing tectonic regimes. However, the offshore part of this zone is primarily the result of Neogene and Quaternary convergence and simple shear. Edgar and others (1971) recognized the similarity of the Caribbean margin of Panamá to other convergent margins of the world in that the Caribbean margin has a sharp boundary between deformed material beneath the continental margin and more seaward undeformed rocks and sediments (Plate 8, J). Lu and McMillen (1982) published a number of deep-penetration seismic profiles across the Panamá margin that show the deformation of the margin increasing in intensity landward; reflections from deep layers in the Colombian Basin extend under the toe of the deformed belt (Plate 8, K and L). Breen and others (1988) and Reed and others (1989) used side-scan sonar techniques to map a series of folds and thrusts and associated mud diapirs within the north Panamá thrust belt (see Fig. 5). Considerations of the angle between the topographic slope and the underlying oceanic crust, together with the observed mixed landward and seaward vergence of individual thrusts and the associated mud diapirs, suggested very low shear stress along the base of the accretionary prism, indicating pore-fluid pressures along the décollement >0.95 of lithostatic pressure. From considerations of gravity data and onshore geology in Panamá, Case (1974a) concluded that the basement framework of eastern Panamá is oceanic and has been thickened and uplifted to its present elevation by convergence and overthrusting between the Farallon plate and the Caribbean plate. The timing of this process is uncertain, but seismic data indicate active thrusting, and paleobathymetric conclusions of Bandy and Casey (1973) indicate progressive shoaling in middle and late Neogene time for eastern Panama and shoaling in Eocene time for the Canal Zone area. Keigwin (1978) suggested the possibility of surface-water communication between the Atlantic and Pacific until 3.1 Ma in the early Pliocene. The geographic position of Panamá and Costa Rica with respect to South America during the early Cenozoic is uncertain. The present landmass of Costa Rica and Panamá may have been assembled throughout the Tertiary from widely separated terranes that have collided with each other as a result of subduction or transform processes (see von Huene, 1989); Gose (1983) found a 14° northward translation of the Pacific coastal zone of Costa Rica in post-Eocene time. It is not clear how large an area of Costa Rica and Panamá experienced this translation. This is similar to the translation reported by MacDonald and Opdyke (1972) for Cretaceous units found in the Guajira Peninsula of Colombia. The tectonic summaries by Burke and others (1984) and Duncan and Hargraves (1984) suggest that the Central American Arc formed on the western side of an oceanic plateau in Late Cretaceous or early Tertiary time and was emplaced in more or less its present position in Oligocene-Miocene time (see chapter by MacDonald, this volume).

Farther east, off the coast of Colombia, the South Caribbean deformed belt lies offshore from a complex region of folding, thrusting, strike-slip faulting, and vertical uplift (see Plate 1 for location). From structural trends in the Sierra de Perijá and from gravity anomalies and earthquake focal-mechanism studies, Kellogg and Bonini (1982) found that in the region of the Caribbean margin of Colombia, Caribbean–South American convergence has produced northwest-southeast compression in the overriding South American plate and nonmagmatic subduction of Caribbean oceanic crust beneath South American continental crust along the South Caribbean marginal fault. They estimated a convergence rate of about 2 cm/yr based on the 390-km length of the southeastward-dipping seismic zone beneath the Maracaibo Basin. This convergence has led to the deformation of the South Caribbean deformed belt and uplift of continental blocks by 7 to 12 km in the past 10 m.y. to form the Venezuelan Andes, Sierra de Perijá, and the Sierra Nevada de Santa Marta. This southeastward convergence of the Caribbean plate with respect to South America in the region of northern Colombia is consistent with the results of Jordan (1975), but is inconsistent with the results of Sykes and others (1982) (see Ladd and others, 1984). The approximate present relative motions between the Caribbean and South American plates have probably persisted since the late Eocene plate reorganization (Ladd, 1976; Sykes and others, 1982). Aggarwal (1983a, b) and Aggarwal and others (1983) obtained strikingly different results for Caribbean–South America convergence based on the occurrence of great earthquakes in northern South America. From focal mechanism solutions for shallow earthquakes within the Venezuelan Andes, they obtained an ENE–WSW oblique convergence. They considered the Boconó fault to be part of the Caribbean–South America plate boundary. Kellogg and Bonini (1982), on the other hand, considered offsets along the Boconó fault to be related to Nazca–South America plate convergence. The South Caribbean deformed belt continues onshore as the Sinú belt of folded Neogene turbidites (Duque-Caro, 1979, 1984). Late Holocene uplift of the coast south of Cartagena within the Sinu Belt is indicated by a raised marine terrace (Page, 1983).

Offshore much of western Colombia, the South Caribbean deformed belt is swamped by the rapid sedimentation of the Magdalena Fan (Shepard, 1973; Breen, 1989) (Plate 1). Seaward of the 1,500-m contour off the mouth of the Magdalena River, deep penetration seismic reflection records show very little deformation of the fan sediments (Kolla and others, 1984). Landward of the 1,500 meter contour, however, profiles show intense deformation that is probably related to mud diapirism that occurs along the coast off Colombia. This mud diapirism is probably activated by horizontal stress applied to an overpressured Miocene shale layer by Caribbean–South American convergence (Duque-Caro, 1984; Davis and Engelder, 1985).

The fan extends about 250 km offshore from the mouth of the Magdalena River; more than 5 km of sediment are beneath the upper fan, which tapers to less than 2 km of sediment on the lower fan abyssal plain region. Seismic reflection data permit the sediment section beneath the fan to be divided into six seismic sequences based on fan-wide unconformities and contrasting reflection character of adjacent units. The bottom three units thin both landward and seaward and may be an early Tertiary continental-rise deposit. The upper three units thicken landward and were probably deposited in the Neogene and Quaternary, contemporaneous with major Andean orogeny (Kolla and others, 1984).

East of the Sierra Nevada de Santa Marta, the fan gives way to the intensely deformed sediment wedge of the South Caribbean deformed belt. Seismic lines that extend northwest from the Guajira Peninsula across this belt show a highly deformed sediment wedge lying on top of a seaward-dipping basement surface beneath the upper continental slope, and a landward, southeastward-dipping surface beneath the lower slope (Ladd and others, 1984; Ladd and Truchan, 1984). The deformed sediment wedge is overlain in most places by a mildly deformed seaward-prograding sediment apron. The deformed sediment wedge abuts the thick undeformed sediments of the Colombian Basin along a sharp deformation front coincident with Kellogg and Bonini's (1982) South Caribbean marginal fault. On some seismic lines, deep Colombian Basin horizons can be followed beneath the seaward toe of the deformed wedge. A mid-slope basin, the Ranchería Basin, lies along part of this margin; the basin contains 2 to 3 km of undeformed deposits overlying an irregular acoustic basement. The basin separates the undeformed prograding sediments of the upper continental slope from the highly deformed sediments of the lower slope, much in the way a fore-arc basin separates the continental massif from the accretionary prism along many Pacific active margins. The irregular basement beneath the Rancheria Basin is continuous with the basement that rises southward toward the Guajira Peninsula. Available well information offshore Guajira (Baquero, 1983) is difficult to tie to this basement surface because of the irregular relief on basement in the vicinity of the wells. The acoustic basement may be over-pressured, highly deformed Miocene shales, or Mesozoic crystalline rock. The lack of ponded sediment within the depressions in the topography on the lower slope attests to the recent nature of the lower slope deformation.

Venezuelan Margin

From the Guajira Peninsula east to Isla Margarita, the main elements of the continental margin of South America are: (1) the Venezuelan Andes and Caribbean Coastal Range, which thrust southward over the Precambrian Guyana Shield (Maresch, 1974); (2) the Falcón Basin and its offshore eastward extension, the Bonaire Basin (Muessig, 1984); (3) the island ridge of the Netherlands and Venezuelan Antilles (Beets and MacGillavry, 1977); and (4) the South Caribbean deformed belt and its eastward extension, the Curaçao Ridge, which were thrust northward over the Venezuelan Basin (Silver and others, 1975; Biju-Duval and others, 1982c; Ladd and others, 1984). In the region of the Cariaco Trough just west of Margarita, the South Caribbean deformed belt narrows considerably where a series of northwest-southeast–trending strike-slip faults offset the east-west–trending strike-slip shear zone of the southern Caribbean plate boundary zone (Case and Holcombe, 1980; Pérez and Aggarwal, 1981). The elements of the Caribbean–South America plate boundary zone have their analogs in other convergent continental margins (Jordan and others, 1983; Suarez and others, 1983) that are bounded on the oceanic side by a subduction zone and tectonized fore-arc zone and separated from a foreland fold and thrust belt on the continental side by a zone of uplift and normal faulting.

The Caribbean Coast Range and Leeward Antilles were emplaced during a Cretaceous through Eocene period of southward overthrusting (Bellizzia, 1972; Maresch, 1974) with renewed thrusting in the late Miocene (Biju-Duval and others, 1982c; see also the chapter on northern South America in this volume).

Muessig (1984) described the development of the Falcón Basin and its offshore continuation, the Bonaire Basin, in terms of Oligocene and Miocene extensional tectonics associated with right-lateral motion along offset, east-west–trending transcurrent faults. The offsets in the transcurrent faults led to the development of northwest- to north-trending normal faults throughout the Falcon and Bonaire basins. The Venezuelan and Netherlands Antilles are separated from each other by grabens that developed with this extension. This phase of deformation was followed by late Miocene–Pliocene north-south compression, which led to the development of east-west–trending folds and reverse faults.

The South Caribbean deformed belt and its eastward extension, the Curaçao Ridge, form the northern edge of the South American–Caribbean plate boundary zone and are an expression of the convergence (perhaps oblique) of these two plates and associated underthrusting of the Venezuelan Basin along the South Caribbean marginal fault. On seismic reflection profiles the Curaçao Ridge appears as a highly deformed wedge of sediments lying above southward-dipping, deep Venezuelan Basin reflections (Ladd and others, 1984; Plate 9, W and Z). Wide-angle seismic reflection measurements of Diebold and others (1981) indicate the sedimentary nature of the ridge. The Curaçao Ridge is separated from the Venezuelan Antilles island platform by the Los Roques Basin. The lack of ponded sediments on the folded surface topography of the ridge indicates Holocene deformation of the ridge. Biju-Duval and others (1982c) suggested that the Curaçao Ridge is no older than Neogene because its small volume compared to volumes of Venezuelan Basin deposits indicates only modest accretion of Venezuelan Basin rocks and sediments. However, the large negative free-air gravity anomalies over the Curaçao Ridge (Bowin, 1976; Case and others, this volume) suggest that a large volume of low-density material lies beneath

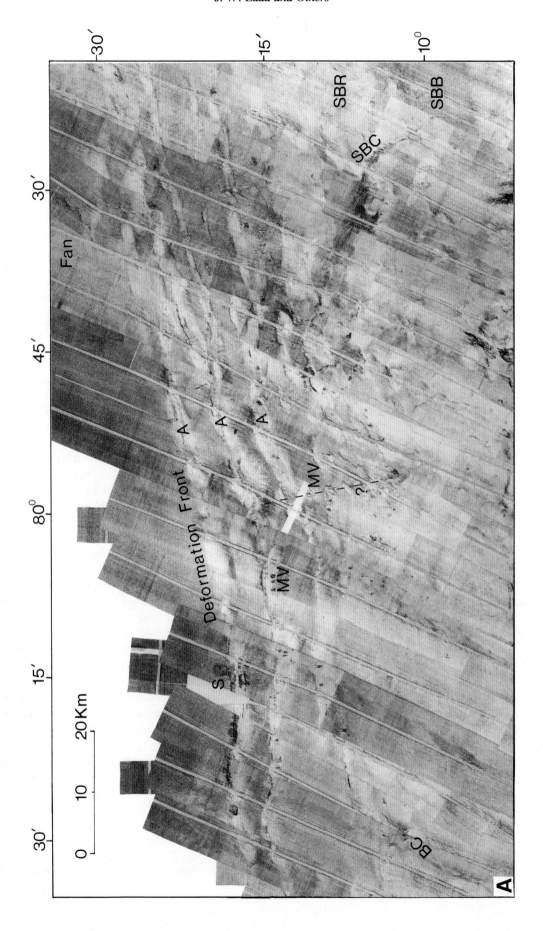

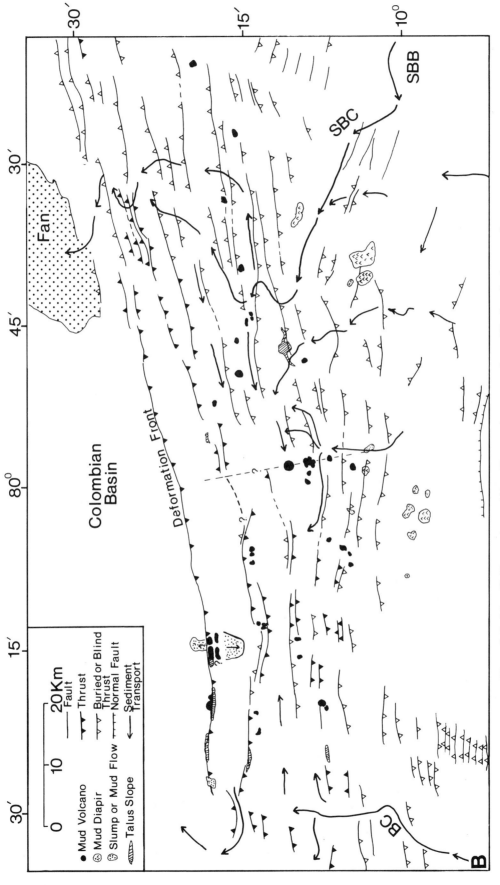

Figure 5. SeaMarc II side-scan image (A) and interpretive structural map (B) of mud volcano region on the northern margin of Panama. Regions of low reflectivity are shown in white, outlining anticlinal ridges (A). Highly reflective regions such as the turbidite deposits of the slope basins and Colombia Basin are darker. Mud volcanoes (MV) characterized by dark circular or elliptical regions are typically found on the anticlinal ridges. SBB = San Blas basin. SBC = San Blas canyon. SBR = San Blas ridge. BC = Boundary canyon. S = slump. From Reed and others (1989).

the ridge. The topographic Curaçao Ridge may be sitting on a large sediment basin. Farther west, where the Los Roques Basin does not separate the South Caribbean deformed belt from the Venezuelan continental margin, an apron of mildly deformed or undeformed sediments prograde out over the deformed accretionary prism. Near the Netherlands Antilles, the undeformed apron may be equivalent to the undeformed Neogene limestones and clastic deposits that overlie highly deformed Cretaceous and Paleogene volcanic-sedimentary sequences. Farther north the age of the base of the apron may become progressively younger, as does the age of the deformed accretionary prism. However, drilling in a similar environment offshore Guatemala has warned us to be careful about such interpretations. Offshore Guatemala an undeformed apron prograde across a deformed wedge. There, drilling found the apron-wedge contact to be Neogene sediment over ultramafic rock having little or no evidence of Neogene accretion. Similarly, the South Caribbean deformed belt could be the result of a Paleocene accretionary phase that did not continue into the Neogene. This is unlikely considering the apparent recent deformation of the Curaçao Ridge; but until more detailed data are available regarding the age of the deformed complex within the South Caribbean deformed belt, our conclusions must remain tentative.

EASTERN CARIBBEAN TRENCH AND FORE-ARC REGION

The fore-arc region of the Caribbean's margin with the Atlantic exhibits a wide range of geologic structures in response to the subduction of Atlantic oceanic lithosphere beneath the Caribbean. It appears that for at least the latter part of the Tertiary period, the rate of subduction has been between 2 and 4 cm/yr, and the direction has been west to west-southwest. Evidence for the rates and directions of subduction during the Tertiary is discussed elsewhere (Pindell and Barrett, this volume; Westbrook and McCann, 1986). The variety of the response of the margin to subduction is expressed in the morphology of the fore arc. North of Puerto Rico, a pronounced trench 8.0 km deep lies 160 km from the inactive island arc. East of Grenada there is no trench, and the foot of the subduction-accretion complex lies at a depth of 4 km, 470 km from the active island arc. The Puerto Rico Trench curves around the arc southeastward, gradually diverging from the arc and shallowing until it disappears at lat. 17°N. This divergence and shallowing of the trench is a consequence of the increase in width of the accretionary complex, which as it accumulates more sediment, grows forward out of the tectonic trench caused by the flexure of the lithosphere into the subduction zone. Farther south a very broad accretionary complex with a complicated morphology is developed. Near its western margin lies the Barbados Ridge, on which is the island of Barbados. Between the Barbados Ridge and the Lesser Antilles is the Tobago Trough (Speed and others, 1989).

The edge of crystalline crust of the Caribbean plate (not including the accretionary complex) is marked by the axis of the negative Bouguer gravity anomaly, an increase in seismicity, the truncation of WNW–trending magnetic anomalies associated with Atlantic oceanic fracture zones, and a deepening of the igneous basement of the Caribbean and Atlantic plates shown by seismic refraction and reflection data. The edge of the plate remains at a constant distance of about 160 km from the active volcanic arc (Speed and others, 1984).

The sediments on the lithosphere entering the northern part of the subduction zone are thin (200 to 500 m north of 17°N) and predominantly pelagic. Deep Sea Drilling Project (DSDP) hole 543, drilled on the northern flank of a basement ridge, the Tiburon Rise, at lat. 15° 45′N, penetrated a complete Tertiary sequence of muds and mudstones, some with nannofossils, radiolarian clays and claystones, pelagic clays, with intercalated ash beds in the Oligocene-Quaternary sequence, that terminates in calcareous ferruginous claystones of Campanian age overlying basalts (Moore and others, 1982). At the latitude of the Barracuda Ridge there is an occasional terrigenous turbidite in the sedimentary sequence, as shown in DSDP hole 27 (Bader and others, 1970). Farther south, the total thickness of sediment increases with increasing proximity to the South American continent and the proportion of terrigenous turbidites increases greatly. At lat. 11°N the total thickness of sediment is 6 km, of which the proportion of post-Miocene terrigenous turbidites is probably 75 percent (Westbrook and others, 1984b). Sidescan sonar shows that a submarine fan of the Río Orinoco extends along the ocean floor at the base of the complex as far north as 13°N; some elements apparently extend even farther north (Belderson and others, 1984).

The fore-arc region can be divided into two main provinces: (1) the accretionary complex, which overlies both Caribbean and Atlantic igneous crust; and (2) the undeformed arc outer shelf and slope and residual fore-arc basins situated on Caribbean crust between the accretionary complex and the volcanic island arc.

The accretionary complex

The complex is most extensively developed east of the Lesser Antilles, where it is called the Barbados Ridge Complex (Westbrook, 1982), but it exists in attenuated form north of Puerto Rico. The presence of deformed rocks on the island of Barbados had been known since the last century (Jukes-Brown and Harrison, 1892), but deformational structures at the toe (eastern edge) of the complex shown by seismic reflection profiles were first reported by Chase and Bunce (1969). Subsequent single and multichannel reflection profiling by many organizations has revealed the great extent and variety of deformation of the accretionary complex (Bunce and others, 1971; Marlow and others, 1974; Westbrook, 1975; Peter and Westbrook, 1976; Biju-Duval and others, 1978, 1982b; Westbrook and others, 1982, 1984a, 1988; Westbrook and Smith, 1983; Mauffret and others, 1984). The reflection data and sea-bed imaging techniques such as GLORIA (long range side scan sonar; Stride and others, 1982) and Seabeam (bathymetric swath mapping; Biju-Duval and others, 1982b) show that laterally (ocean to arc) the complex may be broadly divided into four zones (Fig. 6) (Westbrook and others, 1984b; Beck and others, 1984).

Zone of initial accretion. This zone forms the front (eastern margin) of the complex. In this zone the upper part of the sequence of sediments on the ocean floor is deformed and detached from the remainder of the sequence, which passes farther beneath the complex. The zone is about 50 km wide and has a steeper bathymetric slope than the rest of the complex. The typical structure developed at the leading edge of the complex is an asymmetric, eastward-vergent anticline riding up a westward-dipping thrust fault. The wavelengths of the folds (spacing between thrusts) vary greatly along the complex and depend directly on the thickness of the sequence of sediment that is being deformed and accreted. The ratio of wavelength to thickness is about three to one. In the southern part of the complex, wavelengths of 3 or 4 km are common (Plate 9, NN). In the northern part of the complex, where sediments on the ocean floor are thin, wavelengths become so short that the structures cannot be clearly resolved on a seismic section (Plate 9, KK). These initial fold-thrust blocks have considerable continuity along strike, exceeding 50 km in the southern part of the complex (Biju-Duval and others, 1982b). As they are uplifted by continued thrusting and accretion of new blocks, the blocks are compressed, shortening the spacing between thrusts. Several blocks back from the front of the complex, new overthrusts develop, which cut through and displace the first-formed structures (Westbrook and Smith, 1983; Westbrook and others, 1984a; Mascle and others, 1988). These overthrusts appear as long west-dipping reflectors on seismic sections, and occasionally develop as ramps with intervening flats (Plate 9, LL and MM).

Farther westward, the structures become more complex, and consequently more obscure on seismic sections. This is accompanied by a decrease in the slope of the complex and a gradual increase in the thickness of the apron of sediment deposited directly on the complex.

Zone of stabilization. This zone forms the broad region behind the zone of initial accretion where the overall bathymetric slope to the east is gentle and local westward slopes are common. The zone is covered by an apron of sediment of varying thickness, 50 to 1,000 m, that is little deformed in general. It appears that horizontal strain rates in this region are low. Deformation is localized in narrow zones and usually has a strong component of vertical displacement. In the thicker sequences of cover sediment lying on the accreted rocks below, the lower strata show more deformation and displacement by faults than the upper strata, which, being younger, have had less opportunity to be deformed. The apron sediments therefore provide a stratigraphic record of deformation of the complex after initial accretion (Plate 9, JJ).

Zone of supracomplex basins. In the south of the complex, west of the zone of initial accretion, are sedimentary basins containing up to 4 km of material that overlie the accretionary complex. The largest of these is the Barbados Trough (Plate 9, II). These basins are part of the zone of stabilization, except that there is less horizontal shortening and local relative subsidence. The sequences of tilted horizons and unconformities within these basins also record the deformational history of the complex. North of the latitude of Barbados, bathymetric troughs appear to be the equivalent of the basins farther south, except they are not filled because of the absence of local supply of sediment, such as the Orinoco farther south. They may also be young features. Some well-bedded sediments that appear in the trough are now uplifted on intervening ridges (Peter and Westbrook, 1976).

Barbados Ridge uplift. Extending from Tobago through Barbados, as far north as 15°N, is a ridge that forms the westernmost component of the complex in the south. In the ridge, deformed rocks that appear to be part of the complex that was accreted from ocean-floor sediments in the past have been uplifted so that they crop out in the Scotland District of Barbados (Speed and Larue, 1982) and on the ridge north of Barbados. Additionally, old fore-arc basin or slope-apron sediments (now lithified where exposed on Barbados), the Oceanic and related formations (Speed and Larue, 1982), crop out locally on Barbados and elsewhere on the ridge. Both groups of rock form a "basement" that is seismically incoherent and overlain by varying thicknesses of mainly post-Miocene strata (Biju-Duval and others, 1978; Speed and others, 1984). The western flank of the ridge forms the eastern margin of the fore-arc basin, and strata in the basin are uplifted on the flanks of the ridge (Plate 9, GG and HH).

Western deformation front. The western boundary of the accretionary complex with the fore-arc basin is generally deformational. The strata of the fore-arc basin are deformed and uplifted at this boundary, so much so that the lower strata lose coherence and become part of the seismic "basement" of the Barbados Ridge uplift. This deformational boundary can be traced as an active feature from the northern Lesser Antilles, where it extends close to the base of the steep slope down from the arc massif, to the Tobago Trough, where it extends just to the east of the center of the trough at the foot of the Barbados Ridge uplift. South of 12°30'N, however, the boundary dies away as an active feature and is overstepped by post-Miocene strata (Biju-Duval and others, 1978; Speed and others, 1984; Torrini and Speed, 1989; Plate 9, GG).

All the zones of the complex become narrower toward the north. The Barbados Ridge uplift is absent north of 15°N, and the supracomplex basins are absent north of 15°20'N.

Fore-arc Basins

A large fore-arc basin underlies the Tobago Trough and the region to the north as far as Guadeloupe, which includes the so-called Lesser Antilles Trench (Peter and Westbrook, 1976; Speed and others, 1989). Seismic reflection, seismic refraction, and gravity anomalies show that the igneous basement dips eastward, down from the island arc, and becomes steeper under the eastern part of the basin as it extends under the accretionary complex (Westbrook, 1975; Westbrook and others, 1984a, b).

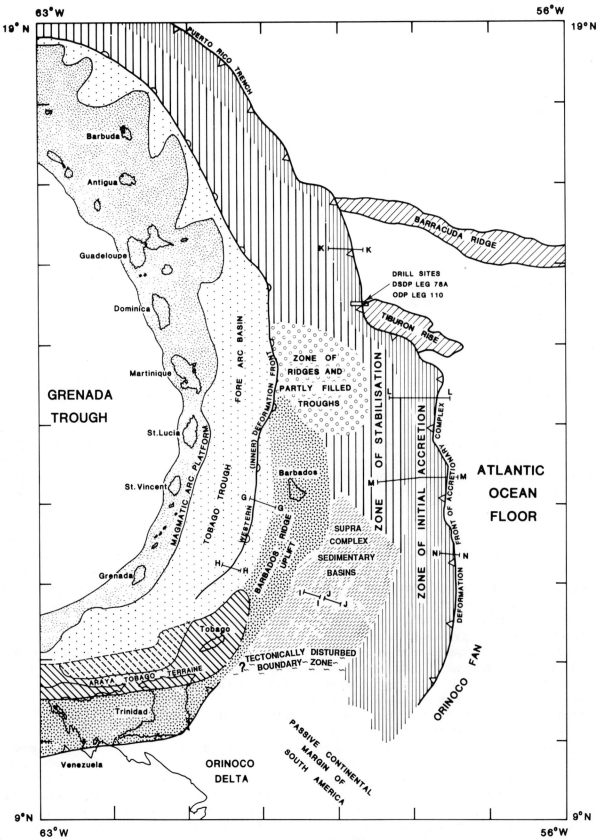

Figure 6. Map of the eastern Caribbean showing the principal tectonic provinces of the forearc region.

The eastern flank of the basin is formed by the accretionary complex, and consequently, growth of the complex has controlled the development of the basin. Seismic reflection profiles show 6 sec (about 10 km) of undeformed sediment in the basin west of Barbados. Within the basin a prominent unconformity has been dated as latest Miocene–early Pliocene by tying into wells on the Trinidad Shelf (Speed and others, 1984; Biju-Duval and others, 1982b). In thicker parts of the basin, there are 2 km of Pliocene-Pleistocene sediment above this unconformity. Piston core sampling has shown that sediment near the arc is sandy and has a high volcanogenic content, but that farther east the sediments are mainly silts derived from the Amazon and Orinoco Rivers (Keller and others, 1972). The basin continues southwestward beneath the South American continental shelf almost as far as the island of Margarita (Feo-Codecido, 1977; Westbrook and others, 1984b), although it becomes shallower and is interrupted by faulting.

North of Guadeloupe, the fore-arc basin is not a continuous feature, but occurs as separate small basins filling reentrants in the arc massif. The eastern margins of these basins are formed by the accretionary complex, which has deformed and uplifted the basin sediments, the deeper horizons being tilted back toward the island arc. The uplifted platforms and spurs along the northern margin of the arc are the equivalent of basement that underlies the fore-arc basin farther south (see Maury and others, this volume). Off Puerto Rico and the Virgin Islands, larger fore-arc basins are developed, but they are segmented to some extent by basement ridges.

Southern margin of the fore-arc

Along its southern boundary the fore-arc assemblage impinges upon the strike-slip northern boundary of the South American continent and its Atlantic passive continental margin. The island of Tobago is situated on a metamorphic basement terrane that plunges northward beneath the Barbados Ridge and forms the southeastern margin of the Tobago Trough south of 11°N. This terrane stretches along the Araya-Paria coast of Venezuela (Speed and others, 1984; Fig. 6) and has been postulated to be allochthonous, either being obducted onto the edge of the Caribbean sometime in Miocene time (Ainscough, 1983) or thrust beneath the leading edge of the Caribbean plate (Speed, 1985). East of the Araya-Tobago terrane lies a poorly defined boundary between the accretionary complex and the Atlantic continental margin of South America. Along strike from the El Pilar fault system there is a zone that is incoherent on seismic reflection sections, with undeformed sediments to the south and deformed sediments to the north. Farther east, however, there is a gradual southward lessening in the deformation of the strata.

The northern fore-arc region—Puerto Rico Trench

Alvin dives on the south wall of the trench indicate that huge sections have been normally faulted and dropped toward the trench floor, exposing intensely tectonized metamorphic rocks (Heezen and others, 1985). Along the south wall, Fox and Heezen (1975) discovered early Tertiary shallow-water limestone at 3,500 m, suggesting extensive subsidence of the edge of the island platform since early Miocene time; during this same time interval, central Puerto Rico has been uplifted by anticlinal warping (Horsfield, 1975). Below the trench-slope break at 3,500 m are marble, schist, and serpentinite (Perfit and others, 1980) similar to rocks that crop out farther west in the northern blueschist belt of Hispaniola. *Gloria* side-scan surveys of the Puerto Rico Trench have shown an extensive system of submarine canyons on the south slope of the trench. Just north of Puerto Rico, the *Gloria* surveys revealed a huge amphitheater created by the slumping of 4,000 km^3 of rock (Scientific staff, 1987; Dillon and others, 1987; see Fig. 7).

The part of the fore-arc region that is clearly of accretionary origin is very narrow (20 km) north of Puerto Rico and the Virgin Islands. Northward narrowing of the complex is generally due to decreasing thickness of sedimentation on the ocean floor and the increasing obliquity of convergence. However, locally in the trench north of Puerto Rico, turbidites of many hundreds of meters thickness fill the base of the trench (Conolly and Ewing, 1967). These turbidites may have been transported down the Mona Canyon. Probable reasons for the narrow accretionary wedge may be one or a combination of the following: the turbidites may only be recent (Pliocene-Pleistocene); significant convergence across the Puerto Rico Trench, in addition to strike-slip motion, is Pliocene-Pleistocene or younger; and/or the previous accretionary wedge was removed by the sweeping action of the northwestward extensions of the Barracuda Ridge and Tiburon Rise as they obliquely entered the subduction zone. McCann and Sykes (1984) placed the last such sweeping event as occurring during the past 3.5 m.y. They considered that the Main Ridge northeast of Puerto Rico is an accreted segment of the Barracuda Ridge. If this is so, then most of the fore-arc north of Puerto Rico must be accreted Atlantic Ocean crust. The great thickness of undisturbed sediments in basins west of Main Ridge and the continuity of reflectors up the slope to the island platform are not easily accounted for by this hypothesis. It seems certain that the impingement of oceanic ridges and possibly continental fragments from the Bahamas has played an important role in the development of the fore-arc assemblage of Puerto Rico and the Virgin Islands, but the exact nature of that role remains to be established.

Barbados

The Barbados Ridge Complex emerges above sea level as the island of Barbados. Most of the island is covered by a cap of Pleistocene coral reef deposits up to 200 m thick, derived from fringing coral reefs that grew outward as the island emerged above sea level. The old reef fronts form concentric cliff lines in the island's topography. The main axis of uplift extends northeast-southwest through the center of the island (Mesolella and others,

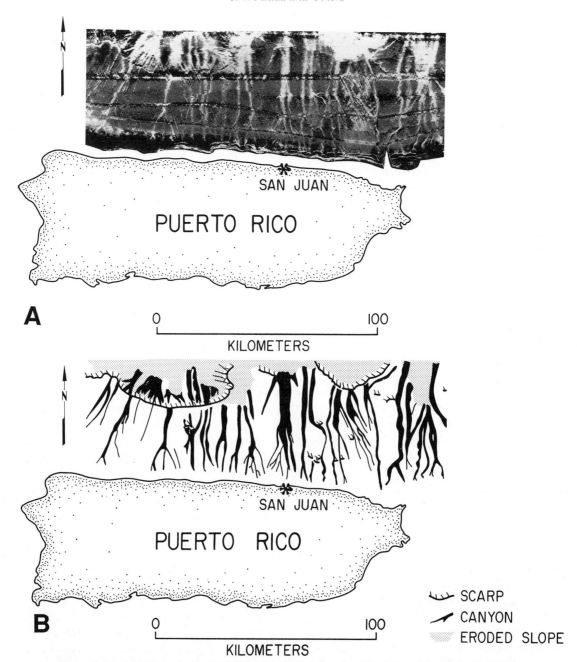

Figure 7. Gloria side-scan image (A) and interpretive line drawing (B) of part of the south slope of the Puero Rico Trench north of Puerto Rico. From Dillon and others (1987). Regions of high reflectivity are shown in white.

1970). The age of the oldest reef deposits at the center of the island is 0.6 to 0.7 Ma, and the maximum rate of uplift of the island has been 0.45 mm/yr (Bender and others, 1979).

Beneath the Pleistocene coral lie two principal groups of rocks: a predominantly pelagic group, which is mostly the Oceanic deposits of Jukes-Brown and Harrison (1892); and a basal complex that is mainly terrigenous rocks of the Scotland Formation of Senn (1940) (Fig. 8). The rocks of the Oceanic formation lie above the terrigenous rocks and were formerly thought to have been unconformably deposited upon them. The ages of the two groups are now known to overlap. The rocks of the Oceanic formation are early Eocene to middle Miocene, whereas the terrigenous rocks are Paleocene to late Eocene (Saunders and others, 1984). A structural discordance, commonly represented by a foliated clay-rich zone and truncating the bedding of the rocks of the Oceanic formation as well as the terrigenous rocks, forms the boundary between the two groups.

The Oceanic formation consists mainly of nannoplanktonic radiolarian marls, commonly including foraminifera that were deposited at abyssal or bathyal depths (Saunders and others,

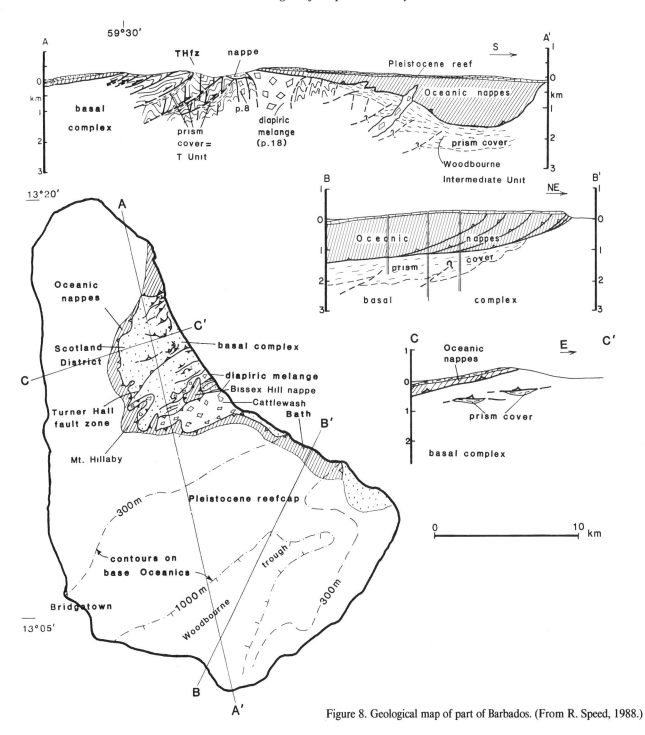

Figure 8. Geological map of part of Barbados. (From R. Speed, 1988.)

1984). Intercalated within the Oceanic deposits are numerous ash bands of Eocene age. It appears that these rocks, which generally have gentle dips, were emplaced as a number of thrust nappes (Torrini and others, 1985). Locally they are tightly folded about east- to northeast-trending axes and are cut by thrust faults. An isolated nappe occurs at Bissex Hill, where a basal unit of very deformed Eocene and Oligocene pelagic rocks is unconformably overlain by the Bissex Hill Formation of early Miocene age (Saunders, 1979). An arenaceous unit within the Bissex Hill Formation is composed of upper bathyal foraminifera (Steineck and others, 1984).

The terrigenous rocks of the Scotland Group form the bulk of the basal complex (Speed and Larue, 1982) and are, for the most part, turbidites that range from coarse quartzose units up to

90 m thick to fine muddy units. Minerals in the coarser units indicate provenance from a high-grade metamorphic terrane, presumably in South America (Senn, 1940). These rocks once formed a submarine-fan sequence (Pudsey and Reading, 1982) and may very well have been deposited in a fore-arc trench (Speed, 1981). Within the basal complex there are two other lithologic suites that constitute only a very small proportion of the whole. One is a hemipelagic suite consisting of radiolarite, mudstone, and distal quartzose turbidite, believed to have been an abyssal ocean-floor cover. The other is a mélange, the Joes River beds of Senn (1940), that consists of blocks of terrigenous and hemipelagic rocks in an organic-rich scaly clay matrix derived from Paleocene-Eocene rocks. The mélange bodies are diapiric in nature, but it is not firmly established whether the mixing of rock materials is a consequence of diapirism or an earlier development as a debris flow. Exploration boreholes have shown that the rocks of the basal complex extend to a depth of at least 4.5 km (Baadsgard, 1960).

The rocks of the basal complex have undergone polyphase deformation, although they are essentially unmetamorphosed. They lie in many fault-bounded packets that are 10 to 1,000 m thick. The bounding faults have an east-northeast strike and are generally vertical, although in the northern part of the outcrop they dip steeply to the north. The earliest phase of deformation was pervasive and predominantly tectonic. It produced shortening normal to the packet boundaries, with a sense of overriding to the north-northwest in present-day geographic coordinates. The axes of early folds that have not been refolded have a shallow plunge and lie in or close to the fault surfaces bounding the packets. Faults within packets postdate, predate, or were synchronous with the folding.

A group of terrigenous and hemipelagic strata of Oligocene-Miocene age was recognized in wells in southern Barbados and called the "T unit" by Baadsgard (1960). The T unit appears to be deposited on the basal complex but tectonically intercalated with it to some degree. It underlies the Oceanic nappes (Speed, 1983).

The interpretation of the geologic history of the rocks of the island produced by R. C. Speed (1983) and his coworkers (Speed and Larue, 1982; Torrini and others, 1985) is that the rocks of the basal complex were accreted at the toe of the accretionary wedge in Eocene time and that the turbidites were deposited upon the hemipelagic rocks prior to accretion. The faults bounding the "packets" originated as thrusts along which the "packets" became decoupled from the ocean-floor sedimentary sequence as they were accreted. The Oceanic deposit was laid down contemporaneously in a fore-arc basin, an antecedent of the Tobago Trough. In the early Miocene, the rocks of the Oceanic formation began to be thrust over the accretionary wedge. During the Miocene, the Oceanic nappes also overrode the strata of the T unit, which had been deposited in an upper slope basin, analogous to the present-day Barbados Trough. The tectonism of this period also intercalated the T unit with the basal complex and reactivated and created faults in the basal complex. Relative to present-

day geographic coordinates, this thrusting of the basal complex was directed southward. During this whole period the region of Barbados had been slowly rising as a consequence of the thickening of the accretionary complex due to its continued growth. A major problem in the interpretation of the tectonics of Barbados is that the trend of all the major structures is east-northeast rather than north. A northern trend would be parallel to the island arc and the grain of the accretionary complex near its eastern margin and approximately perpendicular to the direction of convergence. A markedly different configuration of the island arc in the past allowing south-southeast convergence is not easy to justify, so subsequent tectonic rotation of the island seems the most likely explanation, although evidence for this is scant. During the Neogene the Caribbean plate has been compressed against South America, which may have produced strike-slip motion along the suture between the Caribbean and the Atlantic with consequent rotation of material close to the suture.

Gas hydrates

Bottom-simulating reflectors (BSR) attributed to the formation of gas hydrate occur widely in the active margins of the Caribbean. Their occurrence in the fore arc of the Middle America Trench was reported by Shipley and Didyk (1981), and samples of the hydrate were obtained during DSDP Leg 67 drilling into the fore-arc complex off Guatemala. BSR are seen on reflection sections across the southern Caribbean margin between Panamá and the Curaçao Ridge (Lu and McMillen, 1982; Ladd and others, 1984) and in the Barbados Ridge Complex south of 15°N (Westbrook and Smith, 1984; Westbrook and others, 1984a). A common factor in these areas is the presence of terrigenous turbidites, which probably have a significant content of vegetable debris. The principal source of turbidites in the southern Caribbean is the Magdalena River, and for the Barbados Ridge Complex the source is the Orinoco River. Hydrate stability is pressure and temperature dependent. It is the change in physical properties of the rock arising from solid hydrate to a methane-water mixture that gives rise to the BSR. Because of the temperature dependency of this change, the depth of the BSR beneath the sea bed can be used to estimate the geothermal gradient and, consequently, the heat flow. Using this approach, heat flow has been estimated over the accretionary complexes along the southern and eastern margins of the Caribbean and was found to be generally in the range of 35 to 50 mW/m^2. This is typically about 60 to 80 percent of the value for the subducting ocean floor, and the reduction arises from the thermal blanketing effect of relatively cool sediments being rapidly thickened by accretion.

Radial variations in the structure of the accretionary complex

The width of the accretionary complex changes greatly from south to north, and this change in width is accompanied by a change in the maximum thickness of the complex; beneath Bar-

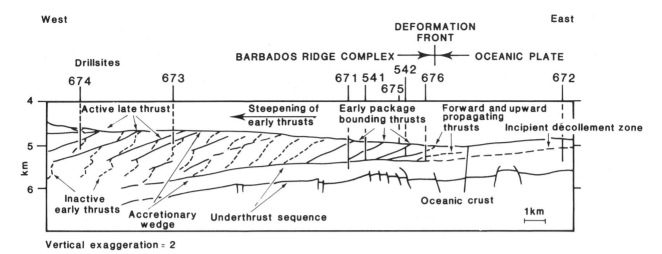

Figure 9. Schematic cross-section through the drill sites of DSDP Leg 78A and ODP Leg 110 at 15° 32′ N based on seismic section and drilling results. From Mascle and others (1988).

bados the thickness is at least 20 km, but off Antigua it is only about 8 km (Westbrook, 1975; Westbrook and McCann, 1986; see also Fig. 3 in the Lesser Antilles chapter of this volume). The reason for this general change in width and thickness is the northward lessening of the volume of accreted sediment, which is a consequence of the thinning of the sediment on the Atlantic floor away from the South American sources of terrigenous sediment (Bunce and others, 1971).

There are, however, more local changes in the accretionary complex that originate from the influence on the complex of ridges in the Atlantic oceanic basement, such as the Barracuda Ridge and Tiburón Rise, that bound old transform faults (Westbrook, 1982, 1984). These ridges have a two-fold effect on the complex. By providing local variations in the thickness of sediment supplied to the complex, they control the forward growth of the complex, so that the deformation front lies farther out over troughs than ridges. Also, because of the damming effect of the ridges on sediment supplied from the south, the sediments are thicker on southern sides of a ridge, so that the front of the complex swings eastward when traced southward across a ridge. In addition, the ridges have a directly dynamic effect, because they trend obliquely (west-northwest) across the direction of subduction. This produces an effect on the complex similar to that of a snowplow, banking up the complex on their southern sides. The complex drops down northward by a kilometer across each of the traces of where the Barracuda Ridge, Tiburón Rise, and a buried ridge opposite Barbados pass beneath it.

Processes in the accretionary complex

It has already been mentioned that the front of the accretionary complex sediment is accreted by the forward propagation of successive thrusts that decouple folded "slices" of sediment from the ocean-floor sediment sequence. These thrust faults root in a décollement that separates the accretionary complex from the remainder of the sedimentary sequence passing beneath it, apparently undeformed, upon the subducting oceanic lithosphere (Plate 9, KK, LL, MM). The extent to which these undeformed sediments can be traced beneath the complex westward toward the island arc exceeds 110 km (Westbrook and others, 1988), and this décollement has been observed to be widespread beneath the whole of the frontal part of the complex (Fig. 9). The low angle of slope of the surface of the complex requires there to be very low shear stresses on the décollement, otherwise the stresses imparted to the complex would compress it further and steepen the slope. Davis and others (1983) likened this to the behavior of earth in front of a bulldozer. High pore-fluid pressures at about 95 percent of the lithostatic load are needed to reduce the shear stress on the décollement (Westbrook and others, 1982; Davis and others, 1983).

The frontal part of the accretionary complex was drilled during DSDP Leg 78A and ODP Leg 110, on the northern flank of the Tiburon Rise (Fig. 6). Drilling proved the thrust faulting and demonstrated that the faults act as conduits for fluids expelled from the wedge, which have reduced salinity and act as an agent of heat transport (Moore and others, 1984; Mascle and others, 1988) (Fig. 9). The décollement was penetrated at site 671, showing it to be a 40-m-thick zone of sheared clays of early Miocene age with a scaly fabric. The rocks accreted into the wedge were predominantly Neogene hemipelagic clays and mudstones with intercalated ash layers, but in the sequence of mainly Paleogene claystones beneath the décollement, silty-sandy horizons were encountered. In the décollement zone, pore fluids contained thermogenic methane that must have originated from farther landward beneath the wedge, where temperatures were higher. This clearly indicates that the décollement has acted as a channel for the lateral flow of fluids, whereas the absence of methane in the wedge above shows that the fluid regimes of the wedge and the sequence beneath the décollement are essentially separate in this region.

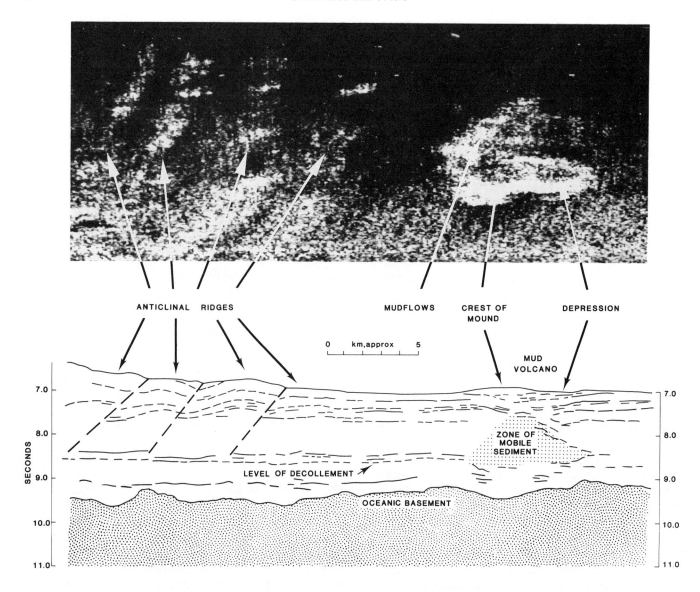

Figure 10. a. GLORIA sonograph of mud volcano on ocean floor in front of accretionary complex at 14° 20′ N. Area east of summit of mound is a depression and bright area to north is composed of mud flows. To the west, the first two folds of the accretionary wedge are imaged (after Langseth and others, 1988; Westbrook and Smith, 1983). b. Cross-section of mud volcano and front of accretionary complex based on interpretation of seismic section shown as LL in Plate 9 and high-resolution water gun seismic profile.

Increased thickening of the accretionary complex cannot continue by rotation and flattening of the accreted thrust slices beyond a certain point unless extremely high strains occur, which does not appear to be the case from structures observed on seismic sections. One mechanism for allowing continued thickening is the development of new thrusts that cut through the accreted thrust slices. These longer westward-dipping thrusts occur farther back in the complex and can be observed on seismic sections between 13°N and 17°N (Plate 9, LL and MM). At drill sites 673 and 674, about 12 and 16 km landward of the toe of the wedge, respectively, thrust faults associated with the accretion processes

are cut and displaced by these younger lower angle faults, which are not easily seen on the seismic sections.

Another mechanism of thickening the complex is the addition of sedimentary material from beneath. This appears to be associated with the development of ramps that allow the décollement beneath the complex to change level. These ramps can be seen in seismic sections east of Barbados, where there are at least three levels of décollement (Plate 9, section LL). The complex has to flex up over the ramps as the ocean crust passes beneath, forming hanging-wall anticlines. The extra stresses required to form these anticlines, associated strain hardening, and/or an increase in shear stress on the upper décollement resulting from a drop in pore-water pressure or the loss of a lubricating clay horizon, can induce the ramp to move forward, thus isolating a block of the underlying sequence as a "horse," which then becomes incorporated in the accretionary complex.

The extent to which undeformed sediments have been traced beneath the complex has been limited by the distribution of seismic profiles with sufficient penetration to image the strata. The sediments presumably extend much farther, but whether they reach as far as the leading edge of the crystalline crust of the Caribbean plate, as they appear to do on a deeply penetrating seismic line east of Guadeloupe (Westbrook and others, 1988), and whether they are subducted into the deeper parts of the subduction zone can only be speculated at present. The Barbados Ridge uplift may be caused by material being added to the base of the complex (subcreted) at the edge of the Caribbean plate. Isotopic ratios and trace elements in the igneous rocks of the Lesser Antilles strongly suggest the involvement of subducted sediment in magma genesis beneath the arc (White and Dupre, 1986; Davidson, 1983).

The presence of high pore-water pressures in the complex is indicated by the numerous mud diapirs and their surface expressions—mud volcanoes—that occur in the accretionary complex south of the Tiburon Rise. Side-scan sonar images show that they are widely distributed (Stride and others, 1982; Brown and Westbrook, 1987, 1988) and increase in number toward the south. They can also be seen on seismic sections (Biju-Duval and others, 1982b; Plate 9, II). Not all reach the surface, and some of these are old mud volcanoes covered by later sedimentation. A few mud volcanoes occur in the ocean-floor sediments a few kilometers east of the front of the complex, where the presence of overpressured pore water may also aid the development of décollements and thrusts (Westbrook and Smith, 1983; Langseth and others, 1988; see Fig. 10). The expulsion of fluids from beneath the wedge into the sequence of sediments in front of the wedge was confirmed by the discovery of pore water enriched with thermogenic methane in clays with dilation veining at the same stratigraphic level as the décollement 7 km oceanward of the toe of the wedge, at drill site 672.

Submarine slides from the slope at the front of the complex on the ocean floor have been observed at two places with side-scan sonar (Stride and others, 1982), and at one of the locations, can also be seen on seismic sections. They have a rough surface, and their internal structure is chaotic. The slide deposits will be accreted into the complex as mélange units. The submarine slides appear to have been caused by an oversteepening of the initial slope that was produced by the "snowplow" action of oceanic basement ridges.

Evolution of the fore-arc regions

A fundamental feature of the accretionary complex is that it has grown in width and thickness with time, but there is plenty of evidence to show that this growth has been episodic rather than continuous. Apron sediments on the complex are truncated by deformation near the front of the complex rather than thinning gently, and their internal strata show many unconformities. The history of rocks on Barbados Island is episodic. A change in subduction rate may be one factor. It would change the dynamic balance of the subduction zone, producing uplift or subsidence. A major change in thickness and type of sediment on the ocean floor would also produce a rapid change. This probably occurred when the eastward-moving Caribbean plate came into contact with the Orinoco submarine fan. The accretion of the allochthonous Araya-Tobago terrane had a profound effect on the southern part of the complex. The subduction of the oceanic basement ridges has had pronounced local effects in the north part of the complex.

SUMMARY

The margins of the Caribbean are complex, active tectonic belts that have been evolving throughout the Cenozoic (see the chapter in this volume by Mann and others on Caribbean neotectonics and the chapter by Pindell and Barrett on plate tectonic interpretations). The eastern and western boundaries are predominantly convergent, with well-developed seismic Benioff zones and volcanic arcs, though even these boundary zones show evidence of strike-slip faulting and normal faulting, particularly along the Middle America convergent zone. The Cayman Trough is dominantly a strike-slip zone that extends into Central America and includes a zone of extension and associated normal faulting south of Grand Cayman. The southern boundary from Panama to Trinidad is a broad zone of convergence and strike-slip faulting, but also includes zones of extensional normal faulting between offset strike-slip faults. Similarly, the northern boundary from Cuba and Jamaica to the Virgin Islands is a broad zone of strike-slip faulting and convergence between the North American plate and the Caribbean plate.

REFERENCES CITED

Aggarwal, Y., 1983a, Present-day boundary and motion of the Caribbean Plate relative to South America [abs.]: 10th Caribbean Geological Conference, Cartagena, Colombia, Program and Abstracts of Papers, p. 16.

—— , 1983b, A new model for the present-day and Pliocene tectonics of the southern Caribbean [abs.]: EOS Transactions of the American Geophysical Union, v. 64, p. 831.

Aggarwal, Y., Soulas, J., and García, D., 1983, Contemporary tectonics of the Venezuelan Andes and northern Colombia [abs.]: 10th Caribbean Geological Conference, Cartagena, Colombia, Program and Abstracts of Papers, p. 17.

Ainscough, D.P.J., 1983, A study of the crustal structure between the southern part of the Lesser Antilles island arc and the northeastern corner of the South American continent [M.S. thesis]: Durham, United Kingdom, University of Durham, 55 p.

Aoki, Y., Tamano, T., and Kato, S., 1982, Detailed structure of the Nankai Trough from migrated seismic sections, *in* Watkins, J. S., and Drake, C. L., eds., Studies in continental margin geology: American Association of Petroleum Geologists Memoir 34, p. 309–322.

Aubouin, J., von Huene, R. E., and others, 1982, Leg 84 of the Deep Sea Drilling Project; Subduction without accretion; Middle America Trench off Guatemala: Nature. v. 297, p. 458–460.

—— , 1984, Initial reports of the Deep Sea Drilling Project, Volume 84: Washington, D.C., U.S. Government Printing Office, 967 p.

Austin, J. A., Jr., 1983, Overthrusting in a deep-water carbonate terrane, *in* Bally, A. W., ed., Seismic expression of structural styles: American Association of Petroleum Geologists Studies in Geology, Series 15, v. 3, p. 3.4.2.167–3.4.2.172.

Baadsgard, P. H., 1960, Barbados W.I. exploration results 1950–1958: Proceedings of the 21st International Geological Congress, v. 18, p. 21–27.

Bader, R. G., and 8 others, 1970, Initial reports of the Deep Sea Drilling Project, Volume 4: Washington, D.C., U.S. Government Printing Office, p. 93–112.

Ballore, F. M., 1906, Tremblements de Terre: Paris, A. Colin, 374 p.

Bandy, O. L., and Casey, R. E., 1973, Reflector horizons and paleobathymetric history, eastern Panama: Geological Society of America Bulletin, v. 84, p. 3081–3086.

Banks, N. G., and Richards, M. L., 1969, Structure and bathymetry of western end of Bartlett Trough, Caribbean Sea, *in* McBirney, A. R., ed., Tectonic relations of northern Central America and the western Caribbean; The Bonacca Expedition: American Association of Petroleum Geologists Memoir 11, p. 258–268.

Baquero, S. E., 1983, Estructura y litologia de una area al NW de la Peninsula Guajira: Una Estratigraphía Sismica [thesis]: Universidad Nacional de Colombia, Departamento de Geociencias, 117 p.

Beck, C., Mascle, A., Saunders, J. B., Speed, R. C., and Westbrook, G. K., 1984, Structural features, *in* Speed, R. C., Westbrook, G. K., and others, eds., Lesser Antilles Arc and adjacent terranes; Atlas 10, Ocean Margin Drilling Program, Regional Atlas Series: Woods Hole, Massachusetts, Marine Science International, sheet 16.

Beets, D. J., and MacGillavry, H. J., 1977, Outline of the Cretaceous and Early Tertiary history of Curaçao, Bonaire, and Aruba (Guide to the Field Excursions on Curaçao, Bonaire, and Aruba, Netherlands, Antilles): 8th Caribbean Geological Conference, p. 1–6.

Belderson, R., Kenyon, N. H., and Stride, A. H., 1984, Morphology and structural trends of the Barbados Ridge Complex in the vicinity of the Deep Sea Drilling Project Sites 541, 542, and 543, as revealed by GLORIA long range side scan-sonar, *in* Biju-Duval, B., Moore, J. C., and others, Initial reports of the Deep Sea Drilling Project, Volume 78A: Washington, D.C., U.S. Government Printing Office, p. 79–81.

Bellizzia, A. G., 1972, Is the entire Caribbean Mountain Belt of Venezuela allochthonous?, *in* Shagam, R., and others, eds., Studies in the earth and space sciences: Geological Society of America Memoir 132, p. 363–368.

Bender, M. L., Fairbanks, R. G., Taylor, F. W., Matthews, R. K., Goddard, J. G.,

and Broecker, W. S., 1979, Uranium-series dating of the Pleistocene reef tracts of Barbados, West Indies, 1: Geological Society of America Bulletin, v. 90, p. 557–594.

Biju-Duval, B., Mascle, A., Montadert, L., and Wanneson, J., 1978, Seismic investigations in the Colombia, Venezuela, and Grenada Basins, and on the Barbados Ridge for future IPOD drilling: Geologie en Mijnbouw, v. 57, no. 2, p. 105–116.

Biju-Duval, B., Bizon, G., Mascle, A., and Muller, C., 1982a, Active margin processes; Field observations in southern Hispaniola, *in* Watkins, J. S., and Drake, C. L., eds., Studies in continental margin geology: American Association of Petroleum Geologists Memoir 34, p. 325–344.

Biju-Duval, B., Le Quellec, P., Mascle, A., Renard, V., and Valery, P., 1982b, Multibeam bathymetric survey and high resolution seismic investigation on the Barbados Ridge Complex (eastern Caribbean); A key to the knowledge and interpretation of an accretionary wedge: Tectonophysics, v. 86, p. 275–304.

Biju-Duval, B., Mascle, A., Rosales, H., and Young, G., 1982c, Episutural Oligo-Miocene basins along the north Venezuelan margin, *in* Watkins, J. S., and Drake, C. L., eds., Studies in continental margin geology: American Association of Petroleum Geologists Memoir 34, p. 347–358.

Bowin, C. O., 1968, Geophysical study of the Cayman Trough: Journal of Geophysical Research, v. 73, p. 5159–5173.

—— , 1976, Caribbean gravity field and plate tectonics: Geological Society of America Special Paper 169, 79 p.

Breen, N. A., 1989, Structural effect of Magdalena Fan deposition of the northern Colombia convergent margin: Geology, v. 17, p. 34–37.

Breen, N. A., Tagudin, J. E., Reed, D. L., and Silver, E. A., 1988, Mud-cored parallel folds and possible melange development in the North Panama thrust belt: Geology, v. 16, p. 207–210.

Brown, K. M., and Westbrook, G. K., 1987, The tectonic fabric of the Barbados Ridge accretionary complex: Marine Petroleum Geology, v. 4, p. 71–81.

—— , 1988, Mud diapirism and subcretion in Barbados Ridge accretionary complex; Role of fluids in accretionary processes: Tectonics, v. 7, p. 613–640.

Bucher, W. H., 1947, Problems of earth deformation illustrated by the Caribbean Sea basin: Transactions of the New York Academy of Sciences, ser. 2, v. 9, p. 98–116.

Bunce, E. T., Phillips, J. D., Chase, R. L., and Bowin, C. O., 1971, The Lesser Antilles Arc and the eastern margin of the Caribbean Sea, *in* Maxwell, A. E., ed., The Sea, Volume 4, Part II: New York, Wiley-Interscience, p. 359–385.

Burkart, B., 1978, Offset across the Polochic fault of Guatemala and Chiapas, Mexico: Geology, v. 6, p. 328–332.

—— , 1983, Neogene North America–Caribbean plate boundary across northern Central America; Offset along the Polochic fault: Tectonophysics, v. 99, p. 251–270.

Burke, K., Grippi, J., and Sengor, A.M.C., 1980, Neogene structures in Jamaica and the tectonic style of the northern Caribbean plate boundary zone: Journal of Geology, v. 88, p. 375–386.

Burke, K., Cooper, C., Dewey, J. F., Mann, P., and Pindell, J. L., 1984, Caribbean tectonics and relative plate motions, *in* Bonini, W. E., Hargraves, R. B., and Shagam, R., eds., The Caribbean–South American plate boundary and regional tectonics: Geological Society of America Memoir 162, p. 31–64.

Carr, M. J., 1976, Underthrusting and Quaternary faulting in northern Central America: Geological Society of America Bulletin, v. 87, p. 825–829.

Carr, M. J., Stoiber, R. E., and Drake, C. L., 1974, The segmented nature of some continental margins, *in* Burke, C. A., and Drake, C. L., eds., The geology of continental margins: New York, Springer-Verlag, p. 105–116.

Case, J. E., 1974a, Oceanic crust forms basement of eastern Panama: Geological Society of America Bulletin, v. 85, p. 645–662.

—— , 1974b, Major basins along the continental margin of northern South America, *in* Burk, C. A., and Drake, C. L., eds., The geology of continental margins: New York, Springer-Verlag, p. 733–741.

Case, J. E., and Holcombe, T. L., 1980, Geologic-tectonic map of the Caribbean region: U.S. Geological Survey Miscellaneous Field Investigations Series Map I-1100, scale 1:2,500,000.

CAYTROUGH, 1979, Geological and geophysical investigations of the Mid-Cayman Rise spreading center; Initial results and observations, *in* Talwani, M., Harrison, C. G., and Hayes, D. E., eds., Deep drilling results in the Atlantic Ocean; Ocean crust: American Geophysical Union Maurice Ewing Series, v. 2, p. 66–93.

Chase, R. L., and Bunce, E. T., 1969, Underthrusting of the eastern margin of the Antilles by the floor of the western North Atlantic Ocean, and origin of the Barbados Ridge: Journal of Geophysical Research, v. 74, no. 6, p. 1413–1420.

Connolly, J. R., and Ewing, M., 1967, Sedimentation in the Puerto Rico Trench: Journal of Sedimentary Petrology, v. 37, p. 44–59.

Davidson, J. P., 1983, Lesser Antilles isotopic evidence of the role of subducted sediment in island arc magma genesis: Nature, v. 306, p. 253–256.

Davis, D. M., and Engelder, T., 1985, The role of salt in fold-and-thrust belts: Tectonophysics, v. 119, p. 67–88.

Davis, D. M., Suppe, J., and Dahlen, F. A., 1983, Mechanics of fold-and-thrust belts and accretionary wedges: Journal of Geophysical Research, v. 88, p. 1153–1172.

Dean, B. W., and Drake, C. L., 1978, Focal mechanism solutions and tectonics of the Middle America Arc: Journal of Geology, v. 86, p. 111–128.

Dengo, G., 1985, Mid America; Tectonic setting for the Pacific margin from southern Mexico to northwestern Colombia, *in* Nairn, A.E.M., and Stehli, F. G., eds., The ocean basins and margins; Volume 7, The Pacific, New York, Plenum Press, p. 123–180.

Dewey, J. F., 1975, Finite plate rotations; Some implications for the evolution of rock masses at plate margins: American Journal of Science, v. 275A, p. 260–284.

Diebold, J. B., Stoffa, P. L., Buhl, P., and Truchan, M., 1981, Venezuelan Basin crustal structure: Journal of Geophysical Research, v. 86, p. 7901–7923.

Dillon, W. P., Edgar, N. T., Scanlon, K. M., and Klitgord, K. E., 1987, Geology of the Caribbean: Oceanus, v. 30, no. 4, p. 42–52.

Dowling, J. J., 1967, Annual report of the Geosciences Division, 1966–1967: Dallas, Texas, Southwest Center for Advanced Studies, p. 12–13.

Duncan, R. A., and Hargraves, R. B., 1984, Plate tectonic evolution of the Caribbean region in the mantle reference frame, *in* Bonini, W. E., Hargraves, R. B., and Shagam, R., eds., Caribbean–South American plate boundary and regional tectonics: Geological Society of America Memoir 162, p. 81–93.

Duque-Caro, H., 1979, Major structural elements and evolution of northwestern Colombia, *in* Watkins, J. S., Montadert, L., and Dickersn, P. W., eds., Geological and geophysical investigations of continental margins: American Association of Petroleum Geologists Memoir 29, p. 329–352.

—— , 1984, Structural style, diapirism, and accretionary episodes of the Sinu-San Jacinto terrane, southwestern Caribbean borderland, *in* Bonini, W. E., Hargraves, R. B., and Shagam, R., eds., The Caribbean–South American plate boundary and regional tectonics: Geological Society of America Memoir 162, p. 303–316.

Edgar, N. T., Ewing, J. I., and Hennion, J., 1971, Seismic refraction and reflection in Caribbean Sea: American Association of Petroleum Geologists Bulletin, v. 55, p. 833–870.

Edgar, N. T., Parson, L. M., Dillon, W. P., Jacobs, C., Scanlon, K. M., and Holcombe, T. L., 1989a, Central Cayman Trough: Gloria mosaic, interpretation, and track map: U.S. Geological Survey Miscellaneous Field Studies Map MF-2083, scale 1:375,000.

—— , 1989b, Geophysical and Gloria sidescan data in the central Cayman Trough (in preparation).

Eggler, D. H., Fahlquist, D. A., Pequegnat, W. E., and Herndon, J. M., 1973, Ultrabasic rocks from the Cayman Trough, Caribbean Sea: Geological Society of America Bulletin, v. 84, p. 2133–2138.

Erickson, A. J., Helsley, C. E., and Simmons, G., 1972, Heat flow and continuous seismic profiles in the Cayman Trough and Yucatan Basin: Geological Society of America Bulletin, v. 83, p. 1241–1260.

Ewing, J. I., Antoine, J., and Ewing, M., 1960, Geophysical measurements in the western Caribbean Sea and in the Gulf of Mexico: Journal of Geophysical Research, v. 65, no. 12, p. 4087–4126.

Ewing, M., and Heezen, B. C., 1955, Puerto Rico Trench topography and geophysical data: Geological Society of America Bulletin, v. 62, p. 255–268.

Feo-Codecido, G., 1977, Un esbozo geologico de la plataforma continental Margarita-Tobago, *in* Memorias, Congreso Latino Americano de Geología, II, Caracas, Venezuela, 1973, Ministerio de Minas e Hidrocarburos: Boletín de Geologia Publicación Especial, v. 3, no. 7, p. 1923–1945.

Fox, P. J., and Heezen, B. C., 1975, Geology of the Caribbean crust, *in* Nairn, A.E.M., and Stehli, F. G., eds., Ocean basins and margins; Volume 3, The Caribbean and Gulf of Mexico: New York, Plenum Press, p. 412–466.

Frankel, A., McCann, W. R., and Murphy, A. J., 1980, Observations from a seismic network in the Virgin Islands region; Tectonic structures and earthquake swarms: Journal of Geophysical Research, v. 85, p. 2669–2678.

Garrison, L. E., 1972, Acoustic reflection profiles, eastern Greater Antilles: U.S. Department of Commerce, National Technical Information Service and U.S. Geological Survey Document GD–72–004, 19 p.

Goreau, P.D.E., 1983, The tectonic evolution of the north central Caribbean plate margin [Ph.D. thesis]: Woods Hole Oceanographic Institute/Massachusetts Institution of Technology, WHOI–83–34, 244 p.

Gose, W. A., 1983, Late Cretaceous–early Tertiary tectonic history of southern Central America: Journal of Geophysical Research, v. 88, p. 10585–10592.

Heezen, B. C., Nesteroff, W. D., Rawson, M., and Freeman-Lynde, R. P., 1985, Visual evidence for subsidence in the western Puerto Rico Trench: Geodynamique des Caribes, Symposium, Paris, 5-8 February 1985, Edition Technip, 27 Rue Ginoux, 75015 Paris, p. 287–304.

Hersey, J. B., and Rutstein, M. S., 1958, Reconnaissance survey of Oriente Deep with a precision echo-sounder: Geological Society of America Bulletin, v. 69, p. 1297–1304.

Hess, H. H., and Maxwell, J. C., 1953, Caribbean research project: Geological Society of America Bulletin, v. 64, p. 1–6.

Hilde, T.W.C., 1983, Sediment subduction versus accretion around the Pacific: Tectonophysics, v. 99, p. 381–397.

Hill, R. T., 1898, The geological history of the isthmus of Panama and portions of Costa Rica: Cambridge, Massachusetts, Harvard University, Bulletin of the Museum of Comparative Zoology, v. 28, p. 151–285.

Holcombe, T. L., and Sharman, G. F., 1983, Post-Miocene Cayman Trough evolution; A speculative model: Geology, v. 11, p. 714–717.

Holcombe, T. L., Vogt, P. R., Matthews, J. E., and Murchison, R. R., 1973, Evidence for sea-floor spreading in the Cayman Trough: Earth and Planetary Science Letters, v. 20, p. 357–371.

Horsfield, W. T., 1975, Quaternary vertical movements in the Greater Antilles: Geological Society of America Bulletin, v. 86, p. 933–938.

Jordan, T. E., 1975, The present-day motions of the Caribbean Plate: Journal of Geophysical Research, v. 80, p. 4433–4439.

Jordan, T. E., Isacks, B. L., Allmendinger, R. W., Brewer, J. A., Ramos, V. A., and Ando, C. J., 1983, Andean tectonics related to geometry of subducted Nazca Plate: Geological Society of America Bulletin, v. 94, p. 341–361.

Jukes-Brown, A. J., and Harrison, J. B., 1892, The geology of Barbados; Part 2, The oceanic deposits: Geological Society of London Quarterly Journal, v. 48, p. 170–226.

Karig, D. E., 1974a, Evolution of arc systems in the western Pacific: Annual Review Earth and Planetary Sciences, v. 2, p. 51–76.

—— , 1974b, Tectonic erosion of trenches: Earth and Planetary Science Letters, v. 21, p. 209–212.

Karig, D. E., and Sharman, G. F., III, 1975, Subduction and accretion in trenches: Geological Society of America Bulletin, v. 86, p. 377–389.

Karig, D. E., Cardwell, R. K., Moore, G. F., and Moore, D. G., 1978, Late Cenozoic subduction and continental margin truncation along the northern Middle America Trench: Geological Society of America Bulletin, v. 89, p. 265–276.

Keigwin, L. D., Jr., 1978, Pliocene closing of the Isthmus of Panama based on biostratigraphic evidence from nearby Pacific Ocean and Caribbean Sea cores: Geology, v. 6, p. 630–634.

Keller, G. H., Lambert, D. N., Bennet, R. H., and Rucker, J. B., 1972, Mass physical properties of Tobago Trough sediments: Transactions 4th Caribbean Geologic Conference, Margarita, Venezuela, p. 405–408.

Kellogg, J. N., and Bonini, W. E., 1982, Subduction of the Caribbean Plate and basement uplifts in the overriding South America Plate: Tectonics, v. 1, p. 251–276.

Khudoley, K. M., and Meyerhoff, A. A., 1971, Paleogeography and geological history of the Greater Antilles: Geological Society of America Memoir 129, 199 p.

Klitgord, K. D., and Schouten, H., 1986, Plate kinematics of the central Atlantic, *in* Vogt, P. R., and others, eds., The western North Atlantic region: Boulder, Colorado, Geological Society of America, The Geology of North America, v. M, p. 351–378.

Kolla, V., Buffler, R. T., and Ladd, J. W., 1984, Seismic stratigraphy and sedimentation of the Magdalena Fan, southern Colombian Basin, Caribbean Sea: American Association of Petroleum Geologists Bulletin, v. 68, p. 316–332.

Ladd, J. W., 1976, Relative motion of South America with respect to North America and Caribbean tectonics: Geological Society of America Bulletin, v. 87, p. 969–976.

Ladd, J. W., and Truchan, M., 1984, Compressional features across the Caribbean margin of Colombia; Lamont-Doherty seismic line C–130, *in* Bally, A. W., ed., Seismic expression of structural styles: American Association of Petroleum Geologists Studies in Geology, v. 3, ser. 15, p. 3.4.2–163.

Ladd, J. W., and Watkins, J. S., 1978a, Active margin structures within the north slope of the Muertos Trench: Geologie en Mijnbouw, v. 57, p. 255–260.

—— , 1978b, Tectonic development of trench-arc complexes on the northern and southern margins of the Venezuela Basin, *in* Watkins, J. S., Montadert, L., and Dickerson, P., eds., Geological and geophysical investigations of continental margins: American Association of Petroleum Geologists Memoir 29, p. 363–372.

Ladd, J. W., Worzel, J. L., and Watkins, J. S., 1977, Multifold seismic reflection records from the northern Venezuela Basin and the north slope of the Muertos Trench, *in* Talwani, M., and Pitman, W. C., III, eds., Island arcs, deep sea trenches, and back-arc basins: American Geophysical Union Maurice Ewing Series I, p. 41–56.

Ladd, J. W., Shih, T. C., and Tsai, C. J., 1981, Cenozoic tectonics of central Hispaniola and adjacent Caribbean Sea: American Association of Petroleum Geologists Bulletin, v. 65, p. 466–489.

Ladd, J. W., Ibrahim, A. K., McMillen, K. J., Latham, G. V., and von Huene, R., 1982, Interpretation of seismic reflection data of the Middle America Trench offshore Guatemala, *in* Aubouin, J., and others, Initial reports of the Deep Sea Drilling Project, Volume 67: Washington, D.C., U.S. Government Printing Office, p. 675–689.

Ladd, J. W., and 7 others, 1984, Seismic reflection profiles across the southern margin of the Caribbean, *in* Bonini, W., Hargraves, R., and Shagam, R., eds., Caribbean–South American plate boundary and regional tectonics: Geological Society of America Memoir 162, p. 153–159.

Langseth, M. G., Westbrook, G. K., and Hobart, M. A., 1988, Geophysical survey of a mud volcano seaward of the Barbados Ridge accretionary complex: Journal of Geophysical Research, v. 93, p. 1049–1062.

Lewis, G. E., and Straczek, J. A., 1955, Geology of south-central Oriente, Cuba: U.S. Geological Survey Bulletin 975D, p. 171–336.

Lewis, J. F., Harper, C. T., Kemp, A. W., and Stipp, J. J., 1973, Potassium-argon retention ages for some Cretaceous rocks from Jamaica: Geological Society of America Bulletin, v. 84, p. 335–340.

Lonsdale, P., and Klitgord, K. D., 1978, Structure and tectonic history of eastern Panama Basin: Geological Society of America Bulletin, v. 89, p. 981–999.

Lowrie, A., 1978, Buried trench south of the Gulf of Panama: Geology, v. 6, p. 434–436.

Lu, R., and McMillen, K. J., 1982, Multichannel seismic survey of the Colombia Basin and adjacent margins, *in* Watkins, J. S., and Drake, C. L., eds., Studies in continental margin geology: American Association of Petroleum Geologists Memoir 34, p. 395–410.

Lundberg, N., 1982, Evolution of the slope landward of the Middle America Trench, Nicoya Peninsula, Costa Rica, *in* Leggett, J. K., ed., Trench-forearc geology; Sedimentation and tectonics on modern and ancient plate margins: Geological Society of London, p. 131–150.

Macdonald, K. C., and Holcombe, T. L., 1978, Inversion of magnetic anomalies and seafloor spreading in the Cayman Trough: Earth and Planetary Science Letters, v. 40, p. 407–414.

MacDonald, W., and Opdyke, N., 1972, Tectonic rotations suggested by paleomagnetic results from northern Colombia, South America: Journal of Geophysical Research, v. 77, p. 5720–5730.

Malfait, B., and Dinkelman, M. G., 1972, Circum-Caribbean tectonic and igneous activity and the evolution of the Caribbean plate: Geological Society of America Bulletin, v. 83, p. 251–272.

Maresch, W. V., 1974, Plate-tectonics origin of the Caribbean Mountain System of northern South America; Discussion and proposal: Geological Society of America Bulletin, v. 85, p. 669–682.

Marlow, M. S., Garrison, L. E., Martin, R. G., Trumbull, J.V.A., and Cooper, A. K., 1974, Tectonic transition in the northeastern Caribbean: U.S. Geological Survey Journal of Research, v. 2, no. 3, p. 289–302.

Mascle, A., Moore, J. C., and others, 1988, Proceedings of the Ocean Drilling Program, initial reports (Part A), 110: College Station, Texas, Ocean Drilling Program, 603 p.

Matthews, J. E., and Holcombe, T. L., 1974, Possible Caribbean underthrusting of the Greater Antilles along the Muertos Trough: Proceedings, 7th Caribbean Geologican Conference, Guadalupe, p. 235–242.

Mauffret, A., Westbrook, G. K., and Truchan, M., and Ladd, J., 1984, The relief of the ocean basement and the structure of the front of the accretionary complex in the region of sites 541, 542, and 543, *in* Biju-Duval, B., Moore, J. C., and others, Initial reports of the Deep Sea Drilling Project, Volume 78A: Washington, D.C., U.S. Government Printing Office, p. 42–62.

Maurrasse, F.J-M.R., 1981, Relations between the geologic setting of Hispaniola and the origin and evolution of the Caribbean, *in* Maurasse, F.J-M.R., ed., Presentations Transactions du ler Colloque sur la Geologie d'Haiti, Port-au-Prince, 27-29 Mars 1980: p. 246–264.

—— , 1982, Survey of the geology of Haiti: Guide to the Field Excursions in Haiti of the Miami Geological Society, 103 p.

McBirney, A. R., and Bass, M. N., 1969, Geology of Bay Islands, Gulf of Honduras, *in* McBirney, A. R., ed., Tectonic relations of northern Central America and western Caribbean; The Bonacca Expedition: American Association of Petroleum Geologists Memoir 11, p. 229–243.

McCann, W. R., and Sykes, L. R., 1984, Subduction of aseismic ridges beneath the Caribbean plate; Implications for the tectonic and seismic potential of the northeastern Caribbean: Journal of Geophysical Research, v. 89, no. B6, p. 4493–4519.

McKenzie, D. P., and Morgan, W. J., 1969, Evolution of triple junctions: Nature, v. 224, p. 125–133.

McNally, K. C., and Minster, J. D., 1981, Nonuniform seismic slip rates along the Middle America Trench: Journal of Geophysical Research, v. 86, p. 4949–4959.

Mesolella, K. J., Sealy, A., and Matthews, R. K., 1970, Facies geometrics within Pleistocene reefs of Barbados, West Indies: American Association of Petroleum Geologists Bulletin, v. 54, no. 10, p. 1899–1917.

Meyerhoff, A. A., 1966, Bartlett Fault system-age and offset: Transactions of the 3rd Caribbean Geological Conference, Jamaica Geological Survey Publication 95, p. 1–7.

Meyerhoff, H. A., 1933, Geology of Puerto Rico: Rio Peidras, Puerto Rico, University of Puerto Rico, p. 77–89, 166–168.

—— , 1954, Antillean tectonics: New York Academy of Sciences Transactions, ser. 2, v. 16, p. 149–155.

Minster, J. B., and Jordan, T. H., 1978, Present-day plate motions: Journal of Geophysical Research, v. 83, p. 5331–5334.

Mocquet, A., and Aggarwal, Y. P., 1983, Seismic slip rates in the Greater and Lesser Antilles; Implications for the present-day motion of the Caribbean Plate relative to North America [abs.]: EOS Transactions of the American Geophysical Union, v. 64, p. 832.

Molnar, P., 1977, Gravity anomalies and the origin of the Puerto Rico Trench: Royal Astronomical Society Geophysical Journal, v. 51, p. 701–708.

Molnar, P., and Sykes, L. R., 1969, Tectonics of the Caribbean and Middle America regions from focal mechanisms and seismicity: Geological Society of America Bulletin, v. 80, p. 1639–1684.

Moore, G. F., and Shipley, T. H., 1988, Mechanisms of sediment accretion in the Middle America Trench off Mexico: Journal of Geophysical Research, v. 93, p. 8911–8927.

Moore, J. C., Biju-Duval, B., and others, 1982, Offscraping and underthrusting of sediment at the deformation front of the Barbados Ridge; Deep Sea Drilling Project Leg 78A: Geological Society of America Bulletin, v. 93, p. 1065–1077.

—— , 1984, Tectonic synthesis, Deep Sea Drilling Project Leg 78A, Structural evolution of offscraped and underthrust sediment northern Barbados Ridge complex, *in* Biju-Duval, B., Moore, J. C., and others, Initial reports of the Deep Sea Drilling Project; Volume 78: Washington, D.C., U.S. Government Printing Office, p. 601–621.

Muessig, K. W., 1984, Structure and Cenozoic tectonics of the Falcon Basin, Venezuela, and adjacent areas, *in* Bonini, W., Hargraves, R., and Shagam, R., eds., Caribbean–South American plate boundary and regional tectonics: Geological Society of America Memoir 162, p. 217–230.

Page, W. D., 1983, Holocene deformation of the Caribbean coast, northwestern Colombia, *in* General geology, gemorphology, and neotectonics of northwestern Colombia: Field Trip C, 10th Caribbean Geological Conference, p. A1–A20.

Pérez, O. J., and Aggarwal, Y. P., 1981, Present-day tectonics of the southeastern Caribbean and northeastern Venezuela: Journal of Geophysical Research, v. 86, p. 10791–10804.

Perfit, M. R., and Heezen, B. C., 1978, The geology and evolution of the Cayman Trench: Geological Society of America Bulletin, v. 89, p. 1155–1174.

Perfit, M. R., Heezen, B. C., Rawson, M., and Donnelly, T. W., 1980, Chemistry, origin, and tectonic significance of metamorphic rocks from the Puerto Rico Trench: Marine Geology, v. 34, p. 125–156.

Peter, G., and Westbrook, G. K., 1976, Tectonics of southwestern North Atlantic and Barbados Ridge complex: American Association of Petroleum Geologists Bulletin, v. 60, no. 7, p. 1078–1106.

Pindell, J., and Dewey, J. F., 1982, Permo-Triassic reconstruction of western Pangaea and the evolution of the Gulf of Mexico/Caribbean region: Tectonics, v. 1, p. 179–212.

Plafker, G., 1976, Tectonic aspects of the Guatemala earthquake of 4 February 1976: Science, v. 93, p. 1201–1208.

Pudsey, C. J., and Reading, H. G., 1982, Sedimentology and structure of the Scotland Group, Barbados, *in* Leggett, J. K., ed., Trench and forearc geology; Sedimentation and tectonics in ancient and modern active plate margins: Geological Society of London Special Publication 10, p. 291–308.

Reed, D. L., Silver, E. A., Tagudin, J. E., Shipley, T. H., and Vrolijk, P., 1989, Relations between mud volcanoes, thrust deformation, slope sedimentation, and gas hydrate, offshore North Panama: Marine and Petroleum Geology (in press).

Rosencrantz, E., and Sclater, J. G., 1986, Depth and age in the Cayman Trough: Earth and Planetary Science Letters, v. 79, no. 1-2, p. 133–144.

Rosencrantz, E., Ross, M. I., and Sclater, J. G., 1988, Age and spreading history of the Cayman Trough as determined from depth, heat flow, and magnetic anomalies: Journal of Geophysical Research, v. 93, no. B3, p. 2141–2157.

Saunders, J. B., 1985, Field guide to Trinidad, Tobago, and Barbados: Fourth Latin American Geological Congress, 1979, Port of Spain, Trinidad and Tobago, Arina, Trinidad, Trinidad and Tobago Printing & Packaging Ltd.

Saunders, J. B., and others, 1984, The stratigraphy of the late Eocene to early Oligocene in the Bath Cliffs Section, Barbados, West Indies: Micropaleontology, v. 30, p. 390–425.

Schuchert, C., 1935, Historical geology of the Antillean–Caribbean region: New York, Wiley, 811 p.

Scientific Staff, 1987, Atlas of the U.S. Exclusive Economic Zone, Gulf of Mexico and eastern Caribbean areas; A. Gulf of Mexico, B. Eastern Caribbean, EEZ-SCAN '85: U.S. Geological Survey Miscellaneous Investigations Series I-1864A, 104 p; B, 57 p.

Seely, D. R., 1979, The evolution of structural highs bordering major forearc basins, *in* Watkins, J. S., Montadert, L., and Dickerson, P. W., eds., Geological and geophysical investigations of the continental margins: American Association of Petroleum Geologists Memoir 29, p. 245–260.

Seely, D. R., Vail, P. R., and Walton, G. G., 1974, Trench slope model, *in* Burk, C. A., and Drake, C. L., eds., The geology of continental margins: New York, Springer-Verlag, p. 249–260.

Senn, A., 1940, Palaeogene of Barbados and its bearing on the history and structure of the Antillean–Caribbean region: Geological Society of America Bulletin, v. 24, p. 1548–1610.

Shepard, F. P., 1973, Sea floor of Magdalena delta and Santa Marta area, Colombia: Geological Society of America Bulletin, v. 84, p. 1955–1972.

Shipley, T. H., and Didyk, B. M., 1981, Occurrence of methane hydrates offshore southern Mexico, *in* Moore, J. C., Watkins, J. S., and others, Initial reports of the Deep Sea Drilling Project, Volume 66: Washington, D.C., U.S. Government Printing Office, p. 547–555.

Shipley, T. H., and Moore, G. F., 1986, Sediment accretion, subduction, and dewatering at the base of the trench slope off Costa Rica; Seismic reflection view of the décollement: Journal of Geophysical Research, v. 91, p. 2019–2028.

Shipley, T. H., Ladd, J. W., Buffler, R. T., and Watkins, J. S., 1982, Sedimentation in different tectonic environments of the Middle America Trench, southern Mexico and Guatemala, *in* Leggett, J. K., ed., Trench-forearc geology; Sedimentation and tectonics on modern and ancient active plate margins: Geological Society of London, p. 95–106.

Silver, E. A., Case, J. E., and MacGillavry, H. J., 1975, Geophysical study of the Venezuelan borderland: Geological Society of America Bulletin, v. 86, p. 213–226.

Silver, E. A., Ellis, J. M., Breen, N. A., Shipley, T. H., 1985, Comments on the growth of accretionary wedges: Geology, v. 13, p. 6–9.

Speed, R. C., 1981, Geology of Barbados; Implication for an accretionary origin, International Geological Congress, Paris, Colloquium G 3.6: Oceanologic Acta, Supplement v. 4, p. 259–265.

—— , 1983, Structure of the accretionary complex of Barbados; 1, Chalky Mount: Geological Society of America Bulletin, v. 94, p. 92–116.

—— , 1985, Cenozoic collision of the Lesser Antilles Arc and continental South America and the origin of the El Pilar Fault: Tectonics, v. 4, no. 1, p. 41–69.

Speed, R. C., 1988, Geologic history of Barbados: A preliminary synthesis Transactions of 11th Caribbean Geological Conference, 1986; Bridgetown, Barbados, Energy Division Ministry of Finance, p. 29–1 to 29–11.

Speed, R. C., and Larue, D. K., 1982, Barbados; Architecture and implications for accretion: Journal of Geophysical Research, v. 87, no. 85, p. 3633–3643.

Speed, R. C., Westbrook, G. K., and others, 1984, Lesser Antilles arc and adjacent terranes: Ocean Margin Drilling Program, Atlas 10, Regional Atlas Series: Woods Hole, Massachusetts, Marine Science International, scale 1:200,000.

Speed, R. C., Torrini, R., Jr., and Smith, P. L., 1989, Tectonic evolution of the Tobago Trough forearc basin: Journal of Geophysical Research, v. 94, p. 2913–2936..

Spencer, J. W., 1895, Reconstruction of the Antilles Continent: Geological Society of America Bulletin, v. 6, p. 103–140.

Steineck, P. L., and others, 1984, Middle Eocene and Oligocene deep-sea Ostracoda from the Oceanic formation, Barbados: Journal of Paleontology, v. 58, no. 6, p. 1463–1496.

Stride, A., Belderson, R., and Kenyon, N., 1982, Structural grain, mud volcanoes, and other features on the Barbados Ridge Complex revealed by GLORIA long-range side-scan sonar: Marine Geology, v. 49, p. 187–196.

Stroup, J. B., and Fox, P. J., 1981, Geologic investigations in the Cayman Trough; Evidence for thin oceanic crust along the Mid-Cayman Rise: Journal of Geology, v. 89, p. 395–420.

Suarez, G., Molnar, P., and Burchfiel, B. C., 1983, Seismicity, fault plane solutions, depth of faulting, and active tectonics of the Andes of Peru, Ecuador, and southern Colombia: Journal of Geophysical Research, v. 88, p. 10403–10428.

Suess, E., 1909, Das Antlitz der Erde, v. 3, no. 2: Vienna, Tempsky, 789 p.

Sykes, L. R., and Ewing, M., 1965, The seismicity of the Caribbean region: Journal of Geophysical Research, v. 70, p. 5065–5074.

Sykes, L. R., McCann, W. R., and Kafka, A. L., 1982, Motion of Caribbean Plate during last 7 million years and implications for earlier Cenozoic movements: Journal of Geophysical Research, v. 87, p. 10656–10676.

Taber, S., 1922, The great fault troughs of the Antilles: Journal of Geology, v. 30, p. 89–113.

Torrini, R., Jr., and Speed, R. C., 1989, Tectonic wedging in the forearc basin-accretionary prism transition, Lesser Antilles forearc: Journal of Geophysical Research v. 94, p. 10, 549–10, 584.

Torrini, R., Jr., Speed, R. C., and Mattioli, G. S., 1985, Tectonic relationships between forearc-basin strata and the accretionary complex at Bath, Barbados: Geological Society of America Bulletin, v. 96, p. 861–874.

Tucholke, B. E., and Ewing, J. I., 1974, Bathymetry and sediment geometry of the Greater Antilles outer ridge and vicinity: Geological Society of America Bulletin, v. 85, p. 1789–1802.

Vaughan, T. W., 1918, Geological history of Central America and the West Indies during Cenozoic time: Geological Society of America Bulletin, v. 29, p. 625–626.

von Huene, R., 1989, The Middle America convergent plate boundary, *in* Winterer, E. L., Hussong, D. M., and Decker, R. W., The eastern Pacific Ocean and Hawaii: Boulder, Colorado, Geological Society of America, The Geology of North America, v. N, p. 535–550.

von Huene, R., Aubouin, J., and others, 1980, Leg 67; The Deep Sea Drilling Project Mid-American Trench Transect off Guatemala: Geological Society of America Bulletin, Part 1, v. 91, p. 421–432.

von Huene, R., Aubouin, J., and others, 1985, Initial reports of the Deep Sea Drilling Project, Volume 84: Washington, D.C., U.S., Government Printing Office, 957 p.

von Huene, R., Miller, J., Taylor, D., and Blackman, D., 1985, A study of geophysical data along the IPOD active margin transect off Guatemala, *in* Aubouin, J., von Huene, R., and others, Initial reports of the Deep Sea Drilling Project, Volume 84: Washington, D.C., U.S. Government Printing Office, p. 895–910.

Wadge, G., and Burke, K., 1983, Neogene Caribbean Plate rotation and associated Central American tectonic evolution: Tectonics, v. 2, p. 633–643.

Watkins, J. S., 1989, The Middle America Trench off southern Mexico, *in* Winterer, E. L., Hussong, D. M., and Decker, R. W., eds., The Eastern Pacific Ocean and Hawaii: Boulder, Colorado, Geological Society of America, The Geology of North America, v. N, p. 523–534.

Watkins, J. S., Moore, J. C., and others, 1981, Initial reports of the Deep Sea Drilling Project, Volume 66: Washington, D.C., U.S. Government Printing Office, 864 p.

Westbrook, G. K., 1975, The structure of the crust and upper mantle in the region of Barbados and the Lesser Antilles: Royal Astronomical Society Geophysical Journal, v. 43, p. 201–242.

—— , 1982, The Barbados Ridge Complex; Tectonics of a mature forearc system: Geological Society of London Special Publication 10, p. 275–290.

—— , 1984, Magnetic lineations and fracture zones, *in* Speed, R. C., Westbrook, G. K., and others, eds., Lesser Antilles Arc and adjacent terranes; Atlas 10, Ocean Margin Drilling Program, Regional Atlas Series: Woods Hole, Massachusetts, Marine Science International, sheet 5.

Westbrook, G. K., and Smith, M. J., 1983, Long decollements and mud volcanoes; Evidence from the Barbados Ridge Complex for the role of high pore-fluid pressure in the development of an accretionary complex: Geology, v. 11, p. 279–283.

—— , 1984, Migrated seismic sections across edge of accretionary complex, *in* Speed, R. C., Westbrook, G. K., and others, Lesser Antilles Arc and adjacent terranes; Atlas 10, Ocean Margin Drilling Program, Regional Atlas Series: Woods Hole, Massachusetts, Marine Science International, sheet 23.

Westbrook, G. K., and McCann, W. R., 1986, Subduction of Atlantic lithosphere beneath the Caribbean, *in* Vogt, P. R., and Tucholke, B. E., eds., The western North Atlantic region: Boulder, Colorado, Geological Society of America, The Geology of North America, v. M, p. 341–350.

Westbrook, G. K., and others, 1982, Extensive underthrusting of undeformed sediment beneath the accretionary complex of the Lesser Antilles subduction zone: Nature, v. 300, p. 625–628.

Westbrook, G. K., Mascle, A., and Biju-Duval, B., 1984a, Geophysics and the structure of the Lesser Antilles forearc, *in* Biju-Duval, B., Moore, J. C., and others, Initial reports of the Deep Sea Drilling Project, Volume 78A: Washington, D.C., U.S. Government Printing Office, p. 23–38.

Westbrook, G. K., and 6 others, 1984b, Seismic reflection ship tracks, depth to acoustic basement, depth to intermediate seismic reflectors, thickness of sediment above acoustic basement, thickness of sedimentary sequences above intermediate reflectors, *in* Speed, R. C., Westbrook, G. K., and others, Lesser Antilles Arc and adjacent terranes; Atlas 10, Ocean Margin Drilling Program, Regional Atlas Series: Woods Hole, Massachusetts, Marine Science International, sheets 7–11.

Westbrook, G. K., Ladd, J. W., Buhl, P., Bangs, N., and Tiley, G. J., 1988, Cross section of an accretionary wedge; Barbados Ridge complex: Geology, v. 16, p. 631–635.

Weyl, R., 1980, Geology of Central America (second edition): Berlin, Gebruder Borntraeger, 371 p.

White, G. W., and Stroup, J. B., 1979, Distribution of rock types in the Mid-Cayman Rise, Caribbean Sea, as evidence for conjugate normal faulting in slowly spreading ridges: Geology, v. 7, p. 32–36.

White, W. M., and Dupre, B., 1986, Sediment subduction and magma genesis in the Lesser Antilles; Isotopic and trace element constraints: Journal of Geophysical Research, v. 91, p. 5927–5941.

Woodring, W. P., 1928, Tectonic features of the Caribbean region: Tokyo, National Research Council of Japan, Proceedings of the 3rd Pan-Pacific Science Congress, v. 1, p. 401–431.

MANUSCRIPT ACCEPTED BY THE SOCIETY AUGUST 22, 1989

ACKNOWLEDGMENTS

The authors wish to thank various agencies, including the United States Navy, the National Science Foundation, the National Oceanic and Atmospheric Administration, and the U.S. Geological Survey for support during the writing of this text. Our thanks also to Jim Case, Pete Palmer, Casey Moore, and Eli Silver, who read early versions of this chapter.

The Geology of North America
Vol. H, The Caribbean region
The Geological Society of America, 1990

Chapter 11

Seismicity, large earthquakes, and the margin of the Caribbean Plate

William R. McCann
Department of Geology, University of Puerto Rico, Mayagüez, Puerto Rico 00708
Wayne D. Pennington
Exploration and Production Technology, Marathon Oil Company, P.O. Box 269, Littleton, Colorado 80160

INTRODUCTION

The distribution of small earthquakes recorded during the last 35 years, of large earthquakes during the last 400 years, as well as focal mechanisms determined for moderate earthquakes, have provided insights into the location of, and style of motion on, the margin of the Caribbean plate. In this chapter we review information gained by seismological means to help define the nature of the Caribbean plate and its boundaries. The location of the Caribbean plate boundary is more clearly defined along its eastern, western, and northwestern margins (the Lesser Antilles and Central America); other portions are more complex and still subject to general debate (Fig. 1). The first Caribbean-wide study of seismicity by Sykes and Ewing (1965) delineated several features, including westerly and southerly dipping seismic zones in the Lesser Antilles and eastern Greater Antilles, respectively; a strong source of intermediate-depth events beneath eastern Hispaniola; and shallow-focus earthquakes extending from Central America through the Greater Antilles, as well as along northern South America. Work by Molnar and Sykes (1969) determined the general shape of the easterly dipping seismic zone in Central America, several focal mechanisms consistent with underthrusting of sea floor along the eastern and western margins of the Caribbean plate, and left- and right-lateral motion along segments of the northern and southern margins, respectively. They also estimated 0.5 and 2.0 cm/year as the minimum rates of seismic slip at the Lesser Antilles and Middle America subduction zones. These and other studies clearly demonstrated that the Atlantic Ocean sea floor of the Americas (North American and/or South American) plate moves westerly with respect to the Caribbean, and is underthrust at the eastern edge of the Caribbean plate at the Lesser Antilles arc, and that near Puerto Rico and the Virgin Islands, sea floor is underthrust obliquely, as the direction of relative motion is nearly parallel to the trench (Frankel, 1980, 1982; Fischer and McCann, 1984). They also showed that the Cocos plate moves northeast, subducting beneath the western edge of the Caribbean plate at the Middle American trench.

With the general outline and direction of motion of the Caribbean plate determined, subsequent studies have further enhanced our knowledge of various details; local seismic networks contributed substantially to this increase in knowledge. These networks now cover extensive portions of the plate margin; no fewer than ten organizations participate in the operation of 200 stations covering 85 percent of its margin (Table 1).

Numerous catalogs of significant earthquakes have documented the hazard that large earthquakes pose to the peoples of the region (Scherer, 1912; Reid and Taber, 1919a, b, 1920; Centeno-Grau, 1940; Fiedler, 1961; Robson, 1964; and Tomblin and Robson, 1977). These listings, as well as the instrumental catalogs of Gutenberg and Richter (1954) and Rothè (1969), allowed Kelleher and others (1973) to estimate rupture zones for the strongest circum-Caribbean earthquakes. More recent regional studies of individual shocks indicate that nearly all of the margin of the Caribbean plate has experienced a large or great earthquake in historic times. Notable exceptions are the southern Lesser Antilles and the region near the Cayman Islands. The documentation of large historical earthquakes has allowed the definition of the plate boundary where more recent seismicity is sparce. When combined, the data often point to wide zones of recent deformation rather than a narrow, simple zone of plate interaction.

In the following sections we will review, in a regional manner, available data pertaining to the occurrence of earthquakes around and within the Caribbean plate, including instrumentally recorded shocks, historic earthquakes, and source mechanisms indicating styles of faulting. A map of the seismicity of the Caribbean is shown on Plate 10. Figures 2-9 present various characteristics of the observed seismicity, including: contours for depth to the Wadati-Benioff zone (Fig. 2); locations of cross sections and seismicity clusters in the eastern Caribbean (Fig. 3); seismicity cross sections (Fig. 4); stereographic view of the intermediate-depth seismicity around the Caribbean (Fig. 5);

McCann, W. R., and Pennington, W. D., 1990, Seismicity, large earthquakes, and the margin of the Caribbean Plate, *in* Dengo, G., and Case, J. E., eds., The Caribbean region: Boulder, Colorado, Geological Society of America, The Geology of North America, v. H.

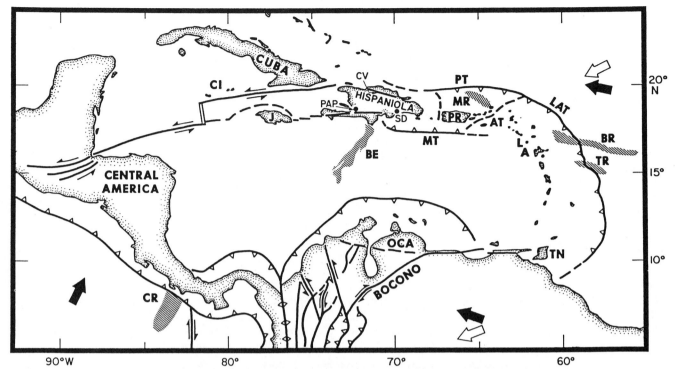

Figure 1. Generalized neotectonic features of the Caribbean region (after Mann and Burke, 1984). Northwestern, western, and eastern margins are comparatively simple; along the other margins, platelets form a buffer zone between the large plates. Features identified by abbreviations on this map are: the Cayman islands (CI), Port-au-Prince (PAP), Santo Domingo (SD), Cibao valley (CV), Puerto Rico trench (PT), Main ridge (MR), Puerto Rico (PR), Muertos trough (MT), Beata ridge (BE), Anegada trough (AT), Lesser Antilles trench (LAT), Lesser Antilles (LA), Barracuda ridge (BR), Tiburon rise (TR), Trinidad (TN), and the Cocos ridge (CR). The black arrows indicate convergence directions of plates relative to the Caribbean according to Minster and Jordan (1978); the white arrows according to the model of Sykes and others (1982).

large earthquakes in the northeastern Caribbean (Fig. 6), Central America (Fig. 7), and northern South America (Fig. 8); and a seismotectonic model for the Cocos–North American–Caribbean triple junction area (Fig. 9). These figures will be referred to frequently in the text. Throughout the paper, magnitudes of earthquakes determined by surface-wave studies are abbreviated Ms, and those determined by body-wave studies are abbreviated mb. In some cases, magnitudes have been determined in other papers by the intensity of shaking over various regions; if no specific magnitude scale was intended, we use M, otherwise, the correlative scale (Ms or mb) intended by the original authors is used in reporting here.

EASTERN SUBDUCTION ZONE

Configuration of seismic zone

Atlantic Ocean sea floor slips beneath the eastern and northeastern margin of the Caribbean plate at the Lesser Antilles–Puerto Rico subduction zone. Intermediate-depth seismicity indicates penetration of the (North or South) American lithosphere to at least 200 km depth in the Lesser Antilles (Figs. 2, 3,

4). The deepest extent of the continuous seismic zone dipping to the south from the trench gradually shoals westward along the trench, to about 70 km near the Dominican Republic. In the Lesser Antilles, the seismic zone dips westerly about 55° except at its northern and southern end where dips are closer to 30° (Dorel, 1981; McCann and Sykes, 1984; Figs. 4, 5). The large variations in the shape of the shallow zone appear to correlate with variations of the local tectonic regime. In the south, a wide accretionary prism about 20 km thick on its landward edge lies above the shallower part of the zone of underthrusting (Ladd and others, this volume). In the north, the shallow-dipping seismic zone, which developed in late Miocene time, is probably a result of the subduction of aseismic ridges (McCann and Sykes, 1984).

Near Puerto Rico, the seismic zone dips southerly at 57° (Fischer and McCann, 1984; Fig. 4D). The west-to-east transition from this seismic zone to the westerly-dipping one in the northern Lesser Antilles is found in a 300-km-long zone relatively devoid of teleseismically recorded shocks. A microearthquake network in the region has provided data suggesting that the downgoing seismic zone is continuous and undergoes a smooth change in dip from westerly to southerly with no major breaks (McCann and Sykes, 1984).

Shallow seismicity: Distribution and focal mechanisms

Small and moderate shocks of shallow focus are not distributed evenly along the eastern margin of the Caribbean plate. This uneven distribution results in part from aftershock sequences of strong earthquakes, as well as from shocks clustered near the subduction of tectonic features such as major fracture zones and aseismic ridges. Eight spatial clusters and five inactive zones are observed in the data of the last 35 years (Fig. 3). Numerous focal mechanisms have been determined for events near this subduction zone. Taken together these two data sets describe the direction of motion between the plates, but also indicate the complexity of the subduction process.

Clusters A and F (Fig. 3) are aftershocks of large earthquakes in 1953 (7.0 Ms) and 1969 (7.2 Ms), respectively (also seen on Fig. 6). The 1953 event (Cluster A) lies at the western edge of the rupture zone of the 1946 (8.1 Ms) earthquake, which took place along the northeast coast of Hispaniola. Although no mechanism is available for the 1946 event, the dimensions of the aftershock zone (75 by 175 km) suggest it ruptured along a shallowly dipping thrust fault that extends to the west from the zone of thrusting that is observed near Puerto Rico. The 1953 event is also located at the westernmost extent of a region of presumed underthrusting. The 1969 event (Cluster F) is a normal faulting sequence in the North American plate and will be discussed below (under "Large Historic Earthquakes").

Clusters C and D lie just east of Hispaniola, along sections of the Puerto Rico trench that have anomalous characteristics. A shallow block of crust near western Puerto Rico occupies the inner wall of the trench at this location. McCann and Sykes (1984) suggested that it is a portion of the Bahama Bank that was sutured to the Caribbean plate in the last few million years. In addition, this block may be the easternmost extension of the subduction complex material that has recently translated to the west and now lies along the north coast of Hispaniola (Joyce, personal communication, 1985). North of the easternmost Virgin Islands (just east of Puerto Rico) lies the Main ridge, a northwest-trending fracture zone on the North American plate (Fig. 1). The Main ridge enters the subduction zone in a region of high seismic activity (Cluster D) (McCann and Sykes, 1984). These two regions appear to produce higher amounts of seismic activity than nearby regions because of the more complex interplay between the plates. In the case of the block northwest of Puerto Rico, the major thrust zone may, because of its youth, contain more small seismic asperities than other regions, or the block may not be firmly attached to Puerto Rico. In the case of the Main ridge, the seismic activity occurs on the plate boundary and within the adjacent plates, and appears to be associated with the warping of the two plates as they adjust to the incoming topographic features arriving at the subduction zone. Kafka and others (1981) and Frankel (1982) demonstrated the unusual nature of the plate motions in this region. Their focal mechanisms of earthquakes near the intersection of the Main ridge with the subduction zone demonstrate that relative motion between the upper and lower

TABLE 1. SEISMIC NETWORKS IN THE CARIBBEAN AREA

Country/ Region	No. of Stations	Date Opened	Organization
Colombia	1		WWSSN (BOG)
National	8		Univ. Javeriana, Inst. Geofisica
Costa Rica			
North	10	May 1974	Inst. Costarricense de Electricidad
Geothermal	17	June 1977	Univ. Nacional
National	14	1984-1985	Observatorio Vul. y Sis. de Costa Rica
Cuba	3		Academy of Science, Havana
Dominican Republic			
North/Central	15	Dec. 1979	Coporacion Dominicana de Electricidad
East	8	1986	Instituto Sismologico Universitario
El Salvador	1		WWSSN (LPS)
National	3		Centro de Invest. Geo.
Guatemala			
National	37	1974-1979	INSIVUMEH
Jamaica	12		Seis Res Unit, Univ. of West Indes
Lesser Antilles	41		same as above
	1		WWSSN (TRN)
Nicaragua	15		Inst. Nicar. de Est. Territorialies
Panamá	1		WWSSN (BHP)
USA	1		WWSSN (SJG)
Puerto Rico and Virgin Is.	20	1974	University of Puerto Rico
Venezuela	1		WWSSN (CAR)
North	10		Inst. Sismologico
Guri	10		Inst. Sismologico
Southwest	4		Univ. de los Andes
French West Indies	29		Institute de Physique de Globe, Univ. of Paris

plate takes place on a southerly dipping fault plane, but that slip is directed south of west, indicating oblique thrusting.

Little seismicity is recorded teleseismically from the southern margin of Puerto Rico, but local seismic networks and the historic record indicate significant earthquake activity (Asencio,

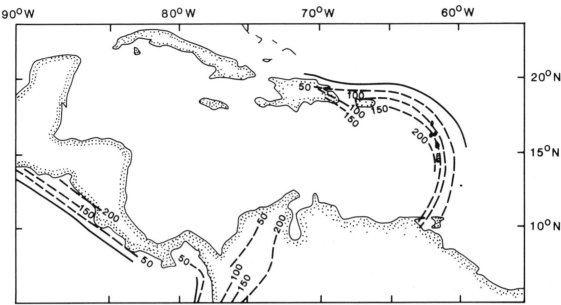

Figure 2. Depth contours for small earthquakes around the Caribbean plate. Contour intervals are drawn every 50 km where possible. Hypocenters are from the International Seismological Centre (1963 to 1982). Note that the deep seismic zone in the Lesser Antilles continues to the north beneath Puerto Rico and terminates in the complex zone of seismicity beneath the Dominican Republic. In northwestern South America, the seismic zone is difficult to define because of the low rate of seismic activity, but may extend to 200 km depth. The seismic zone beneath Middle America is considerably more simple.

1980; McCann, 1985), suggesting that Puerto Rico is not rigidly attached to the Caribbean plate (see also Ladd and others, 1977). The seismically active Anegada trough, which cuts northeast across the Virgin Islands, joins the Muertos trough to the Puerto Rico trench near 63°W (Fig. 1). Seismic-profiler records of the sea floor of the passage demonstrate that the passage represents a pull-apart basin defining the eastern edge of the Puerto Rico platelet (Murphy and McCann, 1979).

Cluster E, in the northern Lesser Antilles, lies at the intersection of the presumed subducted extension of the Barracuda ridge with the seismic zone. The seismically active region is bounded on its northern and southern edges by strong offsets in the bathymetric contours on the inner wall of the trench, suggesting that an integral block, delimited by transverse features, has been activated by the subduction of the Barracuda ridge (McCann and others, 1982). Tomblin (1972) proposed that a WSW–trending transverse fracture passes through this region, one of a series of similarly oriented features cutting the Lesser Antilles arc. Seismic events within the overriding plate have oblique slip or normal faulting mechanisms, and some thrust mechanisms are found in the subduction zone (Molnar and Sykes, 1969; Stein and others, 1982). The vertical P-axis of the upper-plate normal fault suggests strong interplate contact in the region of the subduction of the ridge (McCann and others, 1982).

Cluster G in the center of the Lesser Antilles arc lies updip and south of a cluster of intermediate-depth shocks. Molnar and Sykes (1969) reported a thrusting earthquake in this group; Dorel (1981) reported a dip-slip mechanism.

Cluster H is an updip extension of an intense source of intermediate-depth shocks at the southern edge of the Lesser Antilles arc. No mechanisms are available for these events.

The remaining segments of the eastern subduction zone show comparatively little seismic activity. These sites are generally in between regions subducting aseismic ridges and, therefore, probably have relatively simple plate interactions, and flexural deformation of the plates is probably at a minimum.

Subduction of aseismic ridges

The distribution of seismicity along the eastern subduction zone does not appear to be random; regions of high seismic activity are related to the subduction of anomalous features on the incoming sea floor. As numerous ridges now interact with the subduction zone, the plate boundary has become segmented into tectonic elements some 200 km long. This segmentation has led to a complicated distribution of small and large earthquakes. The overall dip of the seismic zone appears to have been affected by the subduction of the ridges. For example, the central Lesser Antilles has a steeply dipping seismic zone and subducts old (>80 Ma), normal sea floor. However, in the northern Lesser Antilles, where old sea floor also subducts, the recent entrance of a relatively buoyant segment of lithosphere into the subduction zone had led to a shallowly dipping seismic zone and hence a wide zone of contact between the plates. At the northeastern corner of the Caribbean plate, where the northerly trending Lesser Antilles intersects the westerly trending Greater Antilles, the Caribbean plate boundary strikes northwesterly. Fracture-zone trends on the incoming sea floor also strike northwest. McCann and Sykes

(1984) suggested that the trench at the northern Lesser Antilles meets incoming fracture zones and aseismic ridges nearly broadside, and that these features, therefore, affect a large segment of the subduction zone nearly simultaneously. They further suggested that such a broadside collision recently took place, with the entrance of the aseismic Main-Barracuda ridge into the subduction zone. An earlier feature, an extension of the buoyant Bahama Bank, entered the subduction zone in late Miocene time. This event occurred at about the time the locus of volcanism shifted from the present-day Limestone Caribees to the more westerly post-Miocene volcanic chain, suggesting that the collision of the Bahama Bank caused a shoaling in the dip of the downgoing seismic zone.

Large historic earthquakes

Large, damaging earthquakes are numerous in the long historic record of the eastern Caribbean (see Fig. 6). The largest shock was in 1843, when intensities as high as VIII and IX on the Modified Mercalli scale occurred along 150 km of the northern and central Lesser Antilles (Robson, 1964; McCann and Sykes, 1986; Bernard and Lambert, 1988). Kelleher and others (1973) and McCann and Sykes (1984, 1986) interpreted this event as having ruptured along the main thrust zone. McCann and Sykes (1984) suggested that rupture during this event was bounded by the presence of aseismic ridges on the downgoing plate. Stein and others (1986) do not agree with that interpretation and suggested

that thrust events are not likely in the Lesser Antilles as it slowly subducts old sea floor, making it similar to the Marianas. They suggested that this event may have occurred in the region of the trench, not near the islands.

Other significant, shallow earthquakes took place in 1690, 1831, 1839, 1888, 1897, 1946, 1969, and 1974 in the Lesser Antilles, and in 1787, 1867, 1918, and 1943 along the Puerto Rico–Virgin Islands segment (Reid and Taber, 1919a, b, 1920; Robson, 1964; McCann and others, 1982). Of all of these early shocks, only the largest, in 1843, can confidently be associated with the main thrust zone. This is so because of the similarity to isoseismal shapes from known thrust events in other subduction zones (McCann and Sykes, 1986), whereas other events, being significantly smaller in maximum dimension, do not provide convincing evidence that they were interplate in nature. Some of these smaller events probably did occur on the interface between the plates, although others, perhaps being somewhat deeper or shallower, occurred within one of the abutting plates.

Two events, in 1969 and 1974, are well understood in terms of their source characteristics. The earlier event, offshore of Guadeloupe, occurred within the Atlantic sea floor near the seaward edge of the accretionary prism (and was followed by the aftershocks of Cluster F, shown in Fig. 3). Stein and others (1982), who determined a normal-fault mechanism for the main event, suggested that this large shock involved failure of the North American plate as it bends to descend beneath the Caribbean plate. The vent in 1974 (7.2 Ms) has been studied by several

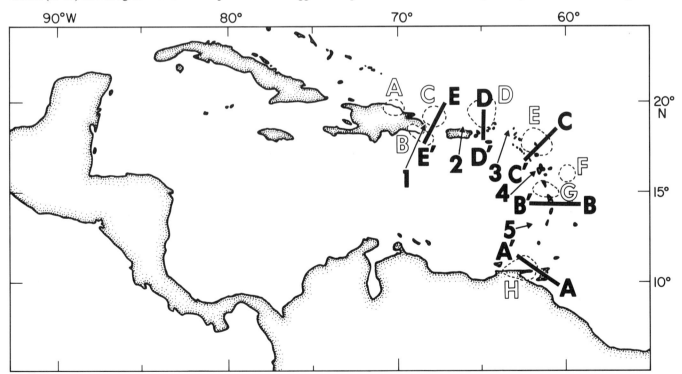

Figure 3. Location map for vertical cross sections and generalized spatial/temporal clusters of seismicity in the eastern Caribbean. Locations of vertical cross sections are indicated by lines marked by solid letters; clusters of earthquakes are indicated by dashed line regions labeled with open letters A to H; notable zones of quiescence are numbered 1 to 5.

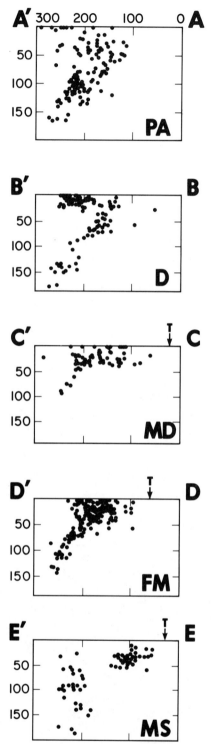

Figure 4. Vertical cross sections whose locations are shown in Fig. 3; scale is in kilometers. These sections demonstrate that oceanic lithosphere has been underthrust beneath the Caribbean plate from the southeast, east and north. Cross sections are from Perez and Aggarwal (PA, 1981) and McCann and Sykes (MS, 1984) who used National Earthquake Information Service catalog data; McCann and others (MD, 1982) who jointly located a teleseismic data set, and Dorel (D, 1981) and Fischer and McCann (FM, 1984) who both used local network data.

researchers (Tomblin and Aspinall, 1975; McCann and others, 1982; Stein and others, 1982). It occurred on a normal fault within the Caribbean plate and had aftershocks located from near the plate interface at 35 km depth to within 10 km of the surface (McCann and others, 1982). The unusual source mechanism of this event is attributed to the increasingly oblique convergence along this segment of the arc (compared with the direct convergence along the central and southern Lesser Antilles) and/or the subduction of the Barracuda ridge.

Near Puerto Rico and the Virgin Islands, large shocks are not evenly distributed; most shocks occur northwest of Puerto Rico near the recent cluster of activity and the shallow block on the inner wall of the trench. The great length of the historic record of Puerto Rico (450 years) allows us to confidently conclude that the unevenness of the observed distribution of shocks is not an artifact of a short catalog. Only one event, that of 1787, is inferred to be great (M = 8 to 8.25). This event is not as well reported as the 1843 shock in the Lesser Antilles. McCann and Sykes (1984) suggested that it took place on the plate boundary.

Throughout the eastern subduction zone, much of the interplate slip must occur aseismically. By comparison with other subduction zones consuming sea floor of similar age, McCann and Sykes (1984) estimated that about two-thirds of the interplate slip occurs aseismically. Stein and others (1982, 1986) saw this subduction zone as analogous to a more extreme case of aseismic subduction, such as in the Marianas, making thrust events very unlikely.

Intermediate-depth events

The intermediate-depth earthquakes define a Wadati-Benioff zone in the Lesser Antilles that dips to the west (Figs. 2, 4, and 5). Strong intermediate-depth earthquakes are few in the eastern subduction zone. Since the beginning of instrumental recording about 80 years ago, 20 shocks with mb > 6.0 have occurred; most of these have been located along the Lesser Antilles seismic zone, the others beneath eastern Hispaniola. The largest shock, mb = 7.4, was located beneath the central Lesser Antilles. Stein and others (1982) determined a strike-slip mechanism for an event located within a cluster of intermediate-depth shocks; this event probably represents motion along a preexisting zone of weakness (i.e., a fracture zone or old plate boundary) within the subducted slab.

A strong intermediate-depth cluster of activity can be found near the southern edge of the arc northwest of Trinidad (downdip of Cluster H). From well-located events, Perez and Aggarwal (1981) determined a northwest-dipping seismic zone, which appears to be the southernmost edge of the eastern subduction zone. They found an event to have a tensional axis plunging northwest in the direction of the dip of the seismic zone; this implies to them that the observed seismic activity represents a subducted slab. But as of yet there is no satisfactory explanation for the very high level of seismic activity found there.

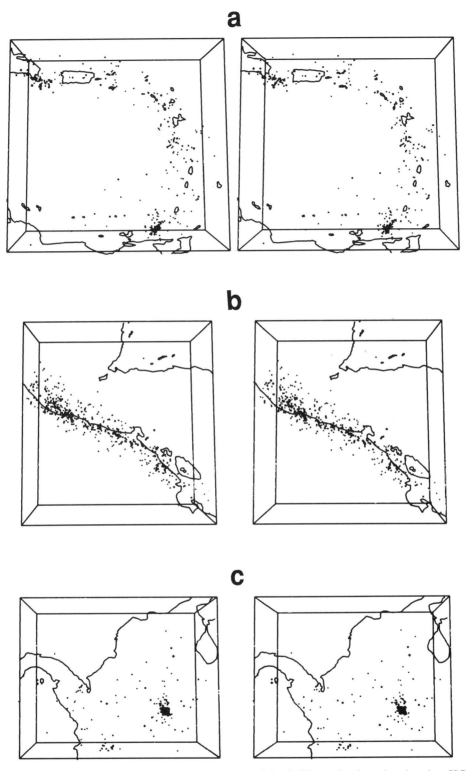

Figure 5. Stereo-pairs of the seismicity of various parts of the Caribbean plate boundary, based on ISC data (1964-1982, mb ≥4.2, depth ≥70 km). Top pair is the Lesser Antilles subduction zone including the Puerto Rico and the eastern tip of Hispaniola. The middle pair is the Central American subduction zone. The bottom pair is the northwestern margin of South America, including the Bucaramanga nest. In all of the pairs, the top of the box is drawn at 10 km depth and the bottom of the box is drawn at 250 km depth.

TECTONIC TRANSITION ZONE: HISPANIOLA

Complex seismic zone

Hispaniola lies at the junction of numerous structural elements in the Caribbean, and the seismic activity reflects this tectonic complexity. Near Puerto Rico, to the east, seismicity defines a relatively simple, southerly dipping seismic zone that extends from the Puerto Rico trench (section D–D′ on Fig. 4; also see Fig. 5). In marked contrast, seismicity near Hispaniola defines complex structures, a southerly dipping seismic zone in the north, a northwesterly striking region with no seismic activity, as well as a northwest-striking zone of intermediate depth shocks dipping nearly vertically, and shallow activity throughout the island and the region offshore to the south (section E-E′ on Fig. 4; also see Fig. 5). Intermediate-depth earthquakes are not found west of central Hispaniola (Fig. 2). Thus, Hispaniola lies on the transition zone from underthrusting in the east to strike-slip tectonics in the west. The complex nature of the seismicity in Hispaniola, when coupled with the marine geophysical data (e.g., see Ladd and others, 1977), suggests underthrusting beneath the south and north coasts, and land geology suggests post-Miocene strike-slip and vertical motions along the north and southwest sectors of the island. Taken together, these data delineate a multi-branched plate boundary that is surely more complex than the boundary to the east. The region near the Lesser Antilles can be characterized as a simple subduction zone; the region near Puerto Rico as an oblique subduction zone, with a buffer platelet containing Puerto Rico and the Virgin Islands lying in the zone of interplate motion.

Near Hispaniola the platelets in the complex boundary are less clearly defined, and faults appear to cut through the island rather than pass around it as they seem to do near Puerto Rico. Mann and Burke (1984) have referred to this region as a plate-boundary zone. Plate motion occurs to the east on the thrust zone that crops out at the Puerto Rico trench. But the trench pinches out to the west, north of Hispaniola (Fig. 1), clogged with the topography of the Bahama Bank. Motion between the plates appears to occur along the thrust zone in the shallow westerly extension of the Puerto Rico trench and on high-angle faults in the northern part of the island, such as Septentrional in the Cibao valley (Fig. 1). Motion along faults in the south of the island extend offshore into a region of low seismic activity, the Muertos trough. The Muertos trough is a site of active plate convergence, as evidenced by a strong shock in 1984. That event represents thrusting of the Caribbean sea floor beneath the island of Hispaniola (Byrne and others, 1985).

Strong historic shocks

Large shocks of Hispaniola, although fewer in number than the smaller events, span a much longer period of time and represent most of the seismic energy released during the last few centuries. They more clearly delineate major faults in the plate-boundary zone found along the northern and southern coasts of the island (Fig. 1). Zones of intense shaking from events in 1946, 1842, and 1887 cover the northern coast. Other significant shocks are listed in the 400 years of written records, but the above events are by far the most significant (Scherer, 1912; Lynch and Bodle, 1948; Kelleher and others, 1973; Aggarwal and Mocquet, 1983). The events in 1842 and 1887 are presumed to have taken place along the high-angle faults in the WNW–trending Cibao valley (Fig. 1) or their offshore extensions to the west, although there are no reports of surface rupture: both events caused damage along the southern coast of Cuba as well.

The 1946 earthquake (8.1 Ms) affected a large part of the Dominican Republic. Most intense shaking took place in the northeast region. Both isoseismals and aftershocks define a northwest-trending region encompassing the near-shore and offshore regions as well. No permanent deformation, either uplift or subsidence, was observed in association with this shock, even though a large sea wave accompanied it. Similarly, ground faulting was not observed with the shocks in the Cibao valley and along the northern coast of Haiti (Scherer, 1912). As noted before, this shock probably occurred on the western extension of the thrust zone of Puerto Rico, and not on the high-angle faults of the Cibao valley, which lie at the southern part of the aftershock zone.

Mann and others (1984) reported a compressional feature, often observed with across-strike offsets of strike-slip faults, in the Cibao valley, tentatively relating it to the shock of 1842. Winslow (personal communication, 1986) also reports a 50-km-long scarp near the central/eastern part of the valley; it, too, may be related to the 1842 earthquakes, although the freshness of the scarp may indicate association with the 1946 event.

The southern margin of Hispaniola also has a history of violent earthquakes. The shock in 1751 destroyed or severely damaged most towns along the southern part of the Dominican Republic (Fig. 6; Scherer, 1912). The occurrence of a sea wave with this event argues, weakly, for an offshore source. The Muertos trough, San Pedro Basin, and the accretionary prism between them exhibit a morphology typical of convergent zones. The event in 1751 may have taken place on a northerly dipping thrust zone emerging at the Muertos trough. A large earthquake shook the region near Port-au-Prince, Haiti, about one month after the Dominican shock. These events, though closely related in time, probably occurred on different faults, but on a tectonically related fault system.

Port-au-Prince (Fig. 1) was once again shaken by a severe shock in 1770; destruction also could be found to the west along the southern peninsula of Haiti. In 1860, a shock occurred even farther west along that peninsula (Fig. 6). The shocks of 1751, 1770, and 1860 define the second of the two belts of activity cutting through Hispaniola. These belts appear to define the southern and northern boundaries of an independent block that moves with respect to both the Caribbean and North American plates. This block, as defined by two belts of large earthquakes,

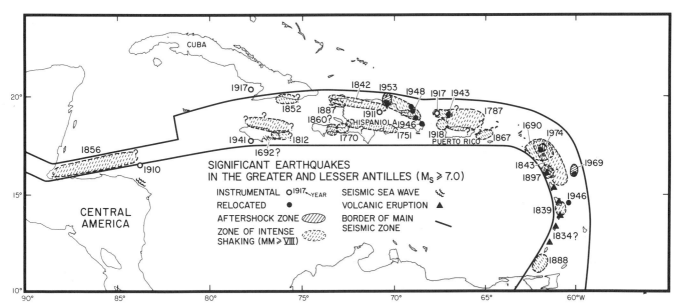

Figure 6. Historic and strong, recent earthquakes of the eastern and northern margins of the Caribbean region. Large earthquakes of the last few centuries cover most of the seismic zone. Major exceptions are the southern Lesser Antilles and the region west of Jamaica. Historic reporting in the latter region is probably incomplete. Two distinct bands of earthquakes are found from Hispaniola through Cuba and Jamaica, suggesting the existence of a buffer plate between the North American and Caribbean plates.

extends west through Jamaica and Cuba, ending near the spreading center south of the Cayman Islands (Fig. 1).

Intermediate-depth events

The region of intermediate-depth seismic activity in and near Hispaniola, noted by Sykes and Ewing (1965) and later discussed by Molnar and Sykes (1969) and Bracey and Vogt (1970), is probably more complicated than had been envisioned by those earlier researchers. Beneath Cluster B (Fig. 3) in eastern Hispaniola lies a northwest-trending, nearly vertically dipping seismic zone (Section E-E′ in Fig. 4, also Fig. 5). Spatially, it is separated from a seismic zone that dips shallowly to the south from the Puerto Rico trench by a northwest-trending, 60-km-wide belt with no seismic activity (schematically indicated in Fig. 2). These two seismic zones may represent two separate slabs underthrust during two different episodes of subduction at the Puerto Rico trench (McCann and Sykes, 1984). One zone may be associated with recent underthrusting of the North American plate at the Puero Rico trench, the other a previous, but recent, episode of convergence from the same trench. Collision of the Bahama Bank (and/or the allochthonous Septentrional terrane north of the Cibao valley) with the trench may have caused the earlier subducted slab to break off from the surface plate, causing the observed 60-km gap in seismic activity.

This deeper, more southerly zone of intermediate depth activity is one of the most prominent seismic regions in the Caribbean. Focal mechanisms of events in this region are few, but show nearly vertical tensional axes consistent with the nearly vertical, but slightly southerly dip of the seismic zone. The events from 100 to 150 km appear to define an east-west–striking zone, whereas the deeper shocks define a northwesterly trend. If all of these shocks are occurring in the same slab, then it must be contorted. Because some of these events lie close to the part of the Caribbean plate underthrust at the Muertos trough, a collisional interaction of the underthrust Caribbean plate with the deeper slab may mean that there are two distinct sections of underthrust lithosphere producing this intense seismic activity. So, in the Hispaniola region there may be three distinct slabs of lithosphere that are each producing intermediate-depth earthquakes. First, the events at the lower edge indicate a slab that is underthrust presently at the Puerto Rico trench; second, the events at the leading edge of the Caribbean plate indicate that the plate is being underthrust at the Muertos trough; third, the deepest events occur in the lithosphere, which was underthrust at the Puerto Rico trench prior to a collisional event in the trench (near western Puerto Rico and northern Hispaniola) in latest Miocene-Pliocene time.

The complicated distribution of intermediate-depth events in this region is primarily related to events associated with the blocking of the subduction zone near the western end of the Puerto Rico trench with the topography of the Bahama Bank. In a more general sense, however, it may be related to the fact that this is the western terminus of subduction along the eastern subduction zone of the Caribbean and to the fact that plate motions here are nearly parallel to the strike of the subduction zone. To the west, tectonic movements, although exhibiting compressional motions, are more related to strike-slip motions than true subduction.

TRANSFORM BOUNDARY: CUBA, JAMAICA, CAYMAN ISLANDS, AND WEST TO CENTRAL AMERICA

Seismicity

Tectonic movements, as reflected in seismic activity, delineate the westward continuation of the northern and southern edges of the block that lies between the North American and Caribbean plates observed in Hispaniola (Figs. 1 and 6). Small earthquakes of the last 35 years are few between Hispaniola and Central America. A group of shocks is found in the vicinity of the Cayman spreading center, just south of the Cayman islands (Fig. 1). To the west of this, the North American and Caribbean plates appear to be in direct contact along the left-lateral Swan fracture zone, although most of that fracture zone has not been seismically active during the last 35 years; near the northern coast of Honduras, a 200-km-long segment of low-level seismic activity is observed within the Swan fracture zone.

There are three focal mechanisms available in the region, one on the northern limb of double zone of seismicity and the other two to the west of the Cayman spreading center. They all show left-lateral strike-slip faulting. The Pliocene-Recent uplift of the Sierra Maestra of Cuba (Horsfield, 1973) and the post-Miocene deformation of Jamaica (Burke and others, 1980) attest to the need for vertical, as well as transcurrent, movements along the edges of the plates.

Historic earthquakes

Earthquakes in the historic record provide firm evidence for at least two branches of seismic activity near Cuba and Jamaica (Fig. 6). Near Cuba, strong earthquakes are generally felt near the southernmost coast near the Sierra Maestra (Taber, 1920, 1922; Cárdenas, 1945; Salterain, 1883). And while some of these shocks were felt strongly in Jamaica, destruction is limited to Cuba itself (Tomblin and Robson, 1977). Similarly, shocks destructive in Jamaica were only felt in Cuba, with little damage caused. The largest events in Cuba occurred in 1551, 1678, 1766, 1852, and 1932 (Cárdenas, 1945). Those in Jamaica were in 1692, 1812, and 1907. Other more recent strong shocks include those of 1900, 1917, and 1943. The 1900 event (7.9 Ms) is poorly located, and, even though it took place in the region near Cuba, there are no reports of damage on that island. That event was probably located farther west along one of the plate boundaries.

One large earthquake off the northern coast of Honduras occurred in 1856. This shock was associated with strong shaking along the coast of Honduras to the south of the Swan fracture zone. In that same region, damage was caused by a destructive seismic sea wave. This event may have ruptured along the Swan fracture zone itself, and despite the fact that it was associated with a tsunami, the rupture may have occurred along a strike-slip fault. The occurrence of the sea wave may be accounted for by sec-

ondary slumping of sediments along the steep slopes in the region, or a small but significant portion of the total motion was vertical rather than horizontal.

TRANSFORM FAULTING IN CENTRAL AMERICA

Distribution of faulting

In 1976 a large earthquake ruptured a 230-km-long segment of the Motagua fault in Guatemala (Plafker, 1976). The Motagua fault is part of a system of southwest-to-west–striking, left-lateral faults that begin in the east where the Swan fracture zone intersects the coast in the Gulf of Honduras and are lost to the west beneath the late Tertiary/Quaternary volcanic cover in the volcanic chain of Middle America. The Motagua fault appears to take up about 20 mm per year of the relative motion between the Caribbean and North American plates. Other relative plate motion may take place as extensional deformation of the wedge-shaped region of the Caribbean plate extending south of the Motagua fault, west of the Honduras depression and east of the Middle America trench. Although older historic events in the vicinity are known, only one, in 1775, may have occurred on the Motagua fault.

Other important, but perhaps not as well-known, faults in the region include the Jocotan, which lies to the south and nearly parallels the Motagua, and the Polochic, which trends nearly east-west to the north of the Motagua (see Schwartz and others, 1979). The Polochic appears to have been important in Miocene deformation and can account for 130 km of the middle Miocene to recent motion totaling 300 km (Burbach and others, 1984). The geologic evidence, however, suggests that this fault is not active today, at least to the degree that the Motagua is active or that the Polochic was in the past. No historic earthquakes are identified with this fault.

The best-studied region is that of the Motagua fault and the rupture zone of the 1976 Guatemala earthquake. Source studies of this event show it to have occurred on a left-lateral strike-slip fault. Several sub-events are apparent, indicating that the fault is splayed or offset at various points along the portion that ruptured in 1976. Aftershocks are well distributed along the 230-km-long fault segment that displays from 0.7 to 3.4 m of left-lateral offset. Several aftershocks are located to the south of the western part of the rupture zone. Normal faulting appears to be the predominant mode of rupture for these events, consistent with the Basin and Range–type deformation hypothesized for this region.

CENTRAL AMERICAN SUBDUCTION ZONE

The western Caribbean plate boundary lies along the Mid-America trench, where oceanic lithosphere of the Cocos plate is underthrust and subducted beneath continental and uplifted oceanic crust of Central America (Fig. 5). The northwesternmost boundary of the Caribbean plate is not readily recognized from seismicity, and may be diffuse, lying in the Guatemala-Chiapas (Mexico) region near the Isthmus of Tehuantepec (see later section). The remainder of the western boundary is well-defined seismically and extends offshore of Guatemala to southern Costa Rica. With the exception of the Cocos ridge offshore Costa Rica, the Cocos plate consists of normal oceanic crust where it is convergent with the Caribbean plate, perhaps accounting for the apparent simplicity of subduction along the Caribbean-Cocos boundary.

Down-going seismic zone

Two recent studies have reviewed the seismicity of the Cocos-Caribbean (and North American) interaction, and their results are summarized here. Le Fevre and McNally (1984) compiled most available earthquake focal mechanisms and hypocentral locations (from the National Earthquake Information Service) for all earthquakes of mb > 4.0 in an effort to evaluate the effect of bathymetric features on the stress distribution and coupling between plates. Burbach and others (1984), on the other hand, used only carefully selected earthquake locations (from the International Seismological Center [ISC]), well-determined focal mechanisms, and comparison of the selected ISC locations with both local-network locations and new locations determined by Joint Hypocenter Determination (JHD). Although Le Fevre and McNally (1984) used thousands of earthquake locations and 187 focal mechanisms, and Burbach and others (1984) selected 220 earthquake locations and 53 focal mechanisms, the results of the two studies are in excellent agreement. (About half the events in each study are along the Cocos–North American boundary). A trend-surface analysis of hypocentral locations (Bevis and Isacks, 1984) also produced a similar geometric interpretation.

The Benioff zone beneath Central America is fairly simple geometrically. The seismicity defines a curved surface dipping at angles up to 70° (Fig. 5). Local-network locations yield steeper dips for the deeper events, but this appears to be a result of systematic mislocation caused by neglecting the effect of the high-velocity subducted lithosphere on seismic-ray paths (McLaren and Frohlich, 1985). Other studies using teleseismic earthquake locations defining the Central American Benioff zone include those by Dewey and Algermissen (1974, using JHD), Carr (1974, using JHD), Molnar and Sykes (1969), Isacks and Molnar (1971), Dean (1976), Dean and Drake (1978), Aubouin and others (1982), and Isacks and Barazangi (1977). Local seismograph networks with the published observations of Benioff-zone seismicity in Central America include those in Nicaragua (R. White, *in* Burbach and others, 1984) and Costa Rica (T. Matumoto, *in* Burbach and others, 1984).

From the Mexico-Guatemala border southeast to northwestern Costa Rica, the Benioff zone dips smoothly at about 60°, follows the strike of the offshore Middle American trench, and extends to just over 200 km depth in some locations. Volcanoes overlie the Benioff zone in this region, where the Benioff zone is 130 to 150 km depth, and some authors have used the volcanic lineations to define segmentations in the subducted lithosphere (e.g., see Stoiber and Carr, 1974). However, most interpretations

consider the Benioff zone here to be laterally continuous, and not segmented in any gross fashion. Northwest of the Mexico-Guatemala border, the Benioff zone flattens out and the line of volcanism is broken, apparently due to a change in relative motion of the overlying plate (either North American or the north-westernmost corner of the Caribbean plate; see Burbach and others, 1984, and Guzman-Speziale and others, 1989, for discussions). In southern Costa Rica, the Benioff zone becomes ill-defined and the line of volcanism terminates well before reaching the Caribbean-Cocos-Nazca triple junction at the Panama fracture zone. A local seismic network in Costa Rica has identified a shallow-dipping Benioff zone that extends to less than 100 km depth (Burbach and others, 1984). The local-network observations support the presence of a tear in the subducted lithosphere (Cocos plate), allowing subduction of the Cocos ridge at a shallow angle.

Historic earthquakes

Numerous very strong earthquakes have taken place along the Pacific coast of Central America in the last few centuries (Fig. 7). Based on the location of the most intense shaking, most of these shocks are probably due to the subduction of the Cocos plate. Some shocks are related to the chain of active volcanoes that lies north and east of the Pacific coast, but the larger shocks are clearly subduction related events. The instrumental record demonstrates that large shallow earthquakes (h < 70 km; Ms ≤ 7.0) commonly occur here (Fig. 7).

Kelleher and others (1973) delineated the rupture zones of the large, twentieth century earthquakes in Middle America. For segments along the Mexican coast to the North, large shocks tended to occur every 30 to 35 years, but the data were less clear for the remainder of Middle America. R. White (written communication, 1989) reported historic shocks near Middle America. The large events are much more frequent than the great or near-great earthquakes in the historic record. In fact, a section of the subduction zone near the southeast edge of the 1773 earthquake may not have ruptured in 200 years (Fig. 7).

Aftershock zones along the Caribbean-Cocos plate boundary in Central America tend to be of small to moderate size, and the magnitudes of the largest shocks of this century are about 8.0. The region of greatest historic activity in the 1700s and 1800s (Guatemala-Honduras) was again very active this century. In general, these shocks have larger rupture zones than those farther southeast along the margin (near Costa Rica). A large region of little seismic activity divides these distinctly different zones; during this century, only two shocks (in 1921 and 1926) have occurred in this quiet area.

CARIBBEAN–SOUTH AMERICAN PLATE BOUNDARY

Although there is considerable seismicity in northern South America and the adjacent Caribbean sea floor, there is not wide-

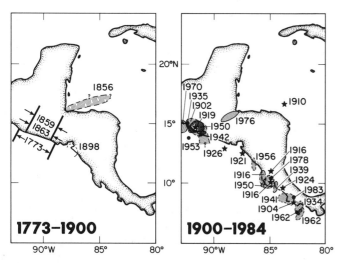

Figure 7. Historic earthquakes of Central America (after R. White, personal communication, 1989). The pre-twentieth century record for the southern part of Central America is incomplete. See text for details. The bars indicate the lateral extent of ruptures from 1773 to 1900, and the hachured patterns (which are varying in orientation only to permit visual differentiation) indicate the probable extent of ruptures for events from 1900 to 1984.

spread agreement on the location of the plate boundary defined by the seismicity (Figs. 1, 5). This now appears to be due to the complex nature of the boundary (partly transform, along multiple branches, and partly convergent, although at a slow rate) and to the short historic record of large earthquakes and their long recurrence intervals.

Multi-branched transform seismic zone

Mann and Burke (1984) have termed the plate boundary along northwestern South America a plate-boundary "zone," where the plate boundary is diffuse and multi-branched. In this section of the chapter, we will discuss the seismicity apparently related to transform motion; seismicity related to possible subduction is deferred to a later section, and seismicity related to the triple junctions (Nazca-Caribbean–South America and Cocos-Nazca-Caribbean) near Panamá will be treated in detail in a separate section. Varying interpretations of the seismicity in northwestern South America have led to a large number of models for the plate boundaries, yet in the framework of a plate-boundary "zone," the various interpretations may reduce to different levels of emphasis placed on specific branches of the boundary zone.

Pennington (1981) identified a feature he called the Andean block, a roughly triangular piece of crust between the Colombian portion of the Peru-Chile trench, the Caribbean Sea, and the "eastern Andean frontal fault zone," a seismically defined boundary that runs from the region of the Gulf of Guayaquil in Ecuador along the eastern Andes and the Bocono fault zone to the Caribbean margin of northwestern Venezuela (see Fig. 1). He suggested

that this block behaves somewhat independently of both the Caribbean and South American plates. Kellogg and Bonini (1982) essentially retain this model, with the inclusion of a smaller Maracaibo block (see also Silver and others, 1975; Bowin, 1976) bounded by the Santa Marta, Oca, and Bocono faults within the limits of Pennington's Andean block. That model finds only weak support from the seismicity, but apparently strong support from geology (e.g., see Kellogg, 1984). Perez and Aggarwal (1981) have emphasized the significance of the faults in Pennington's eastern Andean frontal zone, and consider them to compose a wide plate boundary between the South American and Caribbean plates; they assign the Andean block entirely to the Caribbean. The differences between these models, again, are ones of emphasis, and the seismicity of northwestern South America is sufficiently diffuse to prevent an unambiguous interpretation. The diffuse seismicity, however, supports the concept of a plate-boundary zone, which is further supported by various geologic features (Mann and Burke, 1984), and which is capable of including to varying degrees all of the major features of the seismically derived model described above. The major transform features probably include the seismically active faults of the eastern Andean frontal system (which may also be somewhat compressive) and the less seismically active Santa Marta and Oca faults, as well as other faults in the area.

The major Caribbean–South American plate boundary in northeastern Venezuela is a series of strike-slip faults, all exhibiting some seismicity (Molnar and Sykes, 1969), although some of that seismicity may be complex (Rial, 1978). Additional diffuse seismicity may be related to some underthrusting of the Caribbean plate beneath South America or microplates such as the Andean or Maracaibo blocks, or to details of deformation within the plate-boundary zone.

Subduction of the Caribbean beneath South America

One of the remaining disagreements in southern Caribbean tectonics is the significance of earthquakes at intermediate depths beneath South America. Pennington (1981) showed that these earthquakes lie along an apparent Benioff zone continuous with oceanic crust of the Caribbean Sea north of Colombia, and presumed that they represented active subduction of the Caribbean plate beneath the overriding Andean block. Kellogg and Bonini (1982) studied the seismicity in detail, and showed how subduction of the Caribbean plate was related to regional geologic features in northern Colombia. Pérez and Aggarwal (1981), on the other hand, considered the seismicity to be a remanent feature, and concluded that current subduction, if there is any, is insignificant.

One of the most peculiar seismicity patterns on Earth lies in the apparent Benioff zone beneath Colombia. The Bucaramanga nest of intermediate depth seismicity lies at about 161 km depth near 6.820°N, 73.165°W (Fig. 2 and Plate 10). Tryggvason and Lawson (1970) studied the nest from teleseismic observations, and concluded that it occupied a very small volume. Dewey

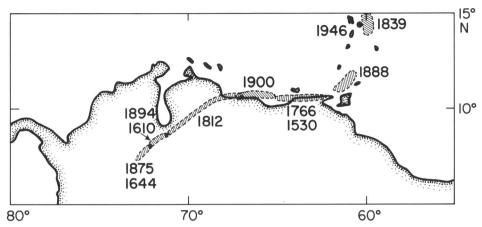

Figure 8. Historic shallow-focus earthquakes of the northern margin of South America (after Aggarwal and Mocquet, 1983). The hachured patterns indicate the extent of ruptures.

(1972) showed that it was teleseismically indistinguishable from a point source. Pennington and others (1979) reported on a short reconnaissance survey of the nest using portable microearthquake recording units, and Schneider and others (1987) reported on a detailed microearthquake survey using several digital micro-earthquake recorders. The nest, although producing an average of over 1.5 events per month with mb ⩾4.2, has produced only one known event with magnitude of 6.0, and none greater than that (Pennington and others, 1979). The bulk of the seismic activity lies within a volume of about 8 km (northwest) by 4 km (north-east) by 4 km (depth), and several focal mechanisms of varying orientations are present (Schneider and others, 1987). The origin of such a peculiar feature is not known, although its small size may limit the maximum-magnitude event possible (Pennington and others, 1979). Schneider and others (1987) speculated that the nest may originate from melting or from phase transformations of subducted crust, following the general models of McGarr (1977) and Pennington (1983, 1984).

Large historic earthquakes in northern South America

Numerous large earthquakes have taken place in northern South America in the last few centuries. Shocks in the historic record (Fig. 8) have occurred along the northern coast of South America in 1530 and 1766 (repeat) and 1900. These earthquakes are probably associated with the El Pilar fault system that trends east-west along the coast just offshore Venezuela.

The northeasterly trend of earthquakes (1610, 1644, 1812, 1875, 1894) broke portions of the Bocono fault system (Aggar-wal, 1983). This fault is now the most seismically active fault between the core of South America and the blocks to the north-west, that may or may not be rigidly attached to the Caribbean plate. The Oca fault, a westerly extension of the El Pilar system that produced the event in 1900 and 1766, apparently ceased motion in the Pliocene. The absence of large, or even small, earthquakes in the offshore region of northwestern Venezuela should not be taken as evidence that those faults are not active

today, but rather may suggest that in the last few hundred years the activity has concentrated on the inland faults, or that the slip is aseismic.

SEISMICITY OF THE TRIPLE JUNCTIONS

Considering the major plates surrounding the Caribbean, there should exist four major triple junctions along the Caribbean plate boundary. The diffuse nature of the seismicity and, in turn, of the plate-boundary "zones," tends to complicate this picture. In this section we discuss the seismicity associated with the expected triple-junction locations.

Caribbean-Cocos–North American triple junction

The surface trace of the Motagua-Polochic fault system in western Guatemala may be inferred to extend to the west through Chiapas, Mexico to the Pacific coast, where it is covered by coastal plain deposits, and offshore to the Middle America Trench (Dengo, 1985; Mapa Geologico de Chiapas, 1989), al-though the overlying deposits make identification of the Carib-bean–North American plate boundary uncertain (Fig. 9). Likewise, the sparse seismicity in westernmost Guatemala and southern Chiapas also makes any seismic identification of that plate boundary and the Caribbean-Cocos–North American triple junction uncertain. Although most models for the Caribbean–North American plate boundary assume that it follows an extension of the seismically active Motagua and Polochic fault systems (e.g., Muehlberger and Ritchie, 1975; Bowin, 1976; Plafker, 1976; Burkhart, 1983), the distribution and fault-plane solutions of aftershocks of the 1976 Guatemala earthquake (Langer and Bollinger, 1979) strongly suggest that the Motagua fault, at least, does not continue to the west of its known surface trace. On the other hand, a lineation of seismicity oriented northwest-southeast has been recognized, located to the north-west of the Polochic fault system, and extension to the isthmus of Tehuantepec (Guzmán-Speziale and others, 1989). This lineation could represent deformation internal to the North American plate, or it could, as Guzmán-Speziale and others (1989) suggest, represent a significant plate (Caribbean–North American) boundary. In their model, the region of Chiapas (and offshore) bounded by this lineation, the Salina Cruz fault in the isthmus of Tehuantepec, the Middle American trench, and roughly the Guatemala-Mexico border is a small wedge of the Caribbean plate trapped between the North American and Caribbean plates. It may also be undergoing significant internal deformation. If this wedge is deforming internally, it could be considered a diffuse triple junction; if it behaves more rigidly, and is a part of the Caribbean plate, the triple junction must lie in the region of the Salina–Cruz–Middle American trench intersection. There is no strong evidence from seismicity or regional geology to favor the latter model, but neither does there seem to be overwhelming evidence supporting the model that this wedge is rigidly attached to the Caribbean plate. In fact, normal-faulting earthquakes south of the western edge of the Motagua fault (Langer and Bollinger, 1979) suggest that the wedge (with a diffuse southwestern boundary "zone") may be moving somewhat independently of all the neighboring plates.

The simple model of a trench-transform-trench triple junction is inherently unstable. The complexity that is exhibited by the seismicity in the region of the expected Caribbean–Cocos–North American triple junction is, no doubt, a result of the contemporary (and transitory) response of a small piece of lithosphere to the large-scale driving forces of the neighboring plates. The seismicity apparently yields a snapshot view of a long and complex pattern of strain accumulation and relief.

Caribbean-Nazca-Cocos and Caribbean–Nazca–South American triple junctions

These two triple junctions, in a simplified plate-tectonic view, should lie near the western and eastern edges of Panamá, respectively (Fig. 1). The northeastern corner of the Cocos plate lies at the juncture of the Middle America trench and the Panamá fracture zone, and the northeastern edge of the Nazca plate must lie along the Colombian portion of the Perú-Chile trench. The problem comes in defining the Caribbean-Nazca and Caribbean–South American plate boundaries in the region of Panamá and Colombia (see Fig. 1, and also earlier discussion in this chapter). A number of physiographic features could be assigned as boundaries, but the seismicity is relatively sparse and diffuse.

One solution is to simply assign the entire Panamá region to a diffuse zone of deformation, from the Panamá basin in the Pacific Ocean to the northern edge of the Panamá deformed belt to the Caribbean Sea, and conclude that motion appropriate to both triple junctions is accommodated there. There is some seismicity and focal-mechanism evidence to support this model (Pennington, 1981). This model lacks detail, however, and the seismicity present should be sufficient to provide a clearer picture. Adamek and others (1988) proposed the existence of one or more microplates in the Panamá region; of most relevance to

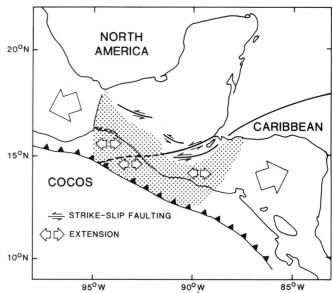

Figure 9. The Cocos-North American-Caribbean triple junction region, based on models presented by Dengo (1985) and Guzmán-Speziale and others (1989). The stippled pattern indicates a zone of crustal extension.

Caribbean seismicity is the apparent convergence of the Caribbean and Panamá crustal material, with a seismically defined thrust plane (perhaps an incipient Benioff zone) dipping south beneath Panamá from the edge of the north Panamá deformed belt. This implies that the southern edge of the Caribbean plate can be defined along the margin of the Panamá deformed belt. Seismicity farther south, in the eastern Panamá basin, suggests that Panamá is not strongly coupled to the Nazca plate, and that it may exist as its own platelet (Adamek and others, 1988). Additional seismicity within the proposed platelet further suggests that the platelet is not behaving rigidly. Thus, the seismicity appears to describe a region of weak deformation, perhaps a "soft platelet" surrounded by the major plates, and accommodating the motion required of the two triple junctions expected to exist in a simple model.

Caribbean–North American–South American triple junction

Plate-tectonic models usually require the existence of separate North American and South American plates (e.g., see Minster and Jordan, 1978; or Ladd and others, 1977), yet evidence for the North American–South American plate boundary is not obvious from seismicity. The triple junction that marks the point of interaction of the North and South American plates with the Caribbean plate is elusive. Wadge and Shepherd (1984) suggest that it may lie in the region of Martinique and St. Lucia (near section B-B′ as drawn on Fig. 3), based on the changes in the dip of the Lesser Antilles seismic zone from northwesterly in the south to southwesterly in the north. Aggarwal (1983) deduced a pole that lies north of Puerto Rico, and estimated the location of the triple junction to lie near the Central Lesser Antilles. He concluded that focal mechanisms of events east of the Lesser Antilles are consistent with a pole north of Puerto Rico. Stein and others (1982) examined focal mechanisms of strong earthquakes that occurred in the region east of the Lesser Antilles subduction zone, and concluded that there is no direct evidence for the North American–South American plate boundary in those data.

REFERENCES CITED

Adamek, S., Frohlich, C., and Pennington, W. D., 1988, Seismicity of the Caribbean-Nazca boundary; Constraints on microplate tectonics of the Panama region: Journal of Geophysical Research, v. 93, p. 2053–2075.

Aggarwal, Y. P., 1983, Seismic gaps and earthquake hazard in Venezuela, *in* Proceedings of a Symposium on Neotectonics, Seismicity, and Geologic Risk in Venezuela and the Caribbean: Caracas, Venezuela, p. 26.

Aggarwal, Y. P., and Mocquet, A., 1983, Seismic-slip rates in the Greater and Lesser Antilles, *in* Proceedings of a Symposium on Neotectonics, Seismicity, and Geologic Risk in Venezuela and the Caribbean: Caracas, Venezuela, p. 30.

Asencio, E., 1980, Western Puerto Rico seismicity: U.S. Geological Survey Open-File Report 80–192, 135 p.

Aubouin, J., and others, 1982, The Middle America trench in the geological framework of Central America, *in* Initial reports of the Deep Sea Drilling Project: Washington, D.C., U.S. Government Printing Office, v. 67, p. 747–755.

Bernard, P., and Lambert, J., 1988, Subduction and seismic hazard in the northern Lesser Antilles; Revision of the historical seismicity: Bulletin of the Seismological Society of America, v. 78, p. 1965–1983.

Bevis, M., and Isacks, B., 1984, Hypocentral trend surface analysis; Probing the geometry of Benioff zones: Journal of Geophysical Research, v. 89, p. 6153–6170.

Bowin, C., 1976, Caribbean gravity field and plate tectonics: Geological Society of America Special Paper 169, 79 p.

Bracey, D. R., and Vogt, P. R., 1970, Plate tectonics in the Hispaniola area: Geological Society of America Bulletin, v. 81, p. 2855–2860.

Burbach, G. V., Frohlich, C., Pennington, W. D., and Matumoto, T., 1984, Seismicity and tectonics of the subducted Cocos plate: Journal of Geophysical Research, v. 89, p. 7719–7735.

Burke, K., Grippi, J., and Sengor, A., 1980, Neogene structures in Jamaica and the tectonic style of the northern Caribbean plate boundary zone: Journal of Geology, v. 88, p. 375–386.

Burkhart, B., 1983, Neogene North American–Caribbean plate boundary across northern Central America; Offset along the Polochic fault: Tectonophysics, v. 99, p. 251–270.

Byrne, D., Suárez, G., and McCann, W. R., 1985, Muertos Trough subduction; Microplate tectonics in the northern Caribbean?: Nature, v. 317, p. 420–421.

Cárdenas, H., 1945, Estudio de las principales fallas de Cuba: Havana, Cuba, Tesis de Grado, 66 p.

Carr, M. J., 1976, Underthrusting and Quaternary faulting in northern Central America: Geological Society of America Bulletin, v. 87, p. 825–829.

Centeno-Grau, M., 1940, Estudios seismológicos: Caracas, Venezuela, Litografía del Comercio, p. 210–300.

Dean, B., 1976, Focal mechanism solutions and tectonics of the Middle America Arc [M.A. thesis]: Hanover, New Hampshire, Dartmouth College, 81 p.

Dean, B., and Drake, C., 1978, Focal mechanism solutions and tectonics of the Middle America Arc: Journal of Geology, v. 86, p. 111–128.

Dengo, G., 1985, Mid America: tectonic setting for the Pacific margin from southern Mexico to northwestern Colombia, *in* Nairn, A.E.M., Stehli, F. G., and Uyeda, S., eds., The Ocean basins and Margins, v. 7A, The Pacific Ocean: New York, Plenum Press, p. 123–180.

Dewey, J. W., 1972, Seismicity and tectonics of western Venezuela: Bulletin of the Seismological Society of America, v. 62, p. 1711–1751.

Dewey, J. W., and Algermissen, S. T., 1974, Seismicity and the Middle America arc-trench system near Managua, Nicaragua: Bulletin of the Seismological Society of America, v. 64, p. 1033–1048.

Dorel, J., 1981, Seismicity and seismic gap in the Lesser Antilles arc and earthquake hazard in Guadeloupe: Geophysical Journal of the Royal Astronomical Society, v. 67, p. 679–695.

Fiedler, G., 1961, Areas afectadas por Terremotos en Venezuela: Boletin Geologia, v. 3, p. 1791.

Fischer, K., and McCann, W. R., 1984, Velocity modeling and earthquake relocation in the northeast Caribbean: Bulletin of the Seismological Society of America, v. 74, p. 1249–1262.

Frankel, A., 1980, Source parameters and scaling relationship of small earthquakes in the northern Caribbean: Bulletin of the Seismological Society of America, v. 71, p. 1173–1190.

—— , 1982, A composite focal mechanism for microearthquakes along the northeastern border of the Caribbean plate: Geophysical Research Letters, v. 8, p. 511–514.

Gutenberg, B., and Richter, C. F., 1954, Seismicity of the Earth: Princeton, New Jersey, Princeton University, 310 p.

Guzmán-Speziale, M., Pennington, W. D., and Matumoto, T., 1989, The triple junction of the North America, Cocos, and Caribbean plates; Seismicity and tectonics: Tectonics, v. 8, p. 981–998.

Horsfield, W. T., 1973, Late Tertiary and Quaternary crustal movements in Jamaica: Journal of the Geological Society of Jamaica, v. 13, p. 6–13.

Isacks, B. L., and Barazangi, M., 1977, Geometry of Benioff zones; Lateral segmentation and downwards bending of the subducted lithosphere, *in* Talwani, M., and Pitman, W., eds., Island arcs, deep sea trenches, and back-arc basins: American Geophysical Union, p. 99–114.

Isacks, B., and Molnar, P., 1971, Distribution of stresses in the descending lithosphere from a global survey of focal-mechanism solutions of mantle earthquakes: Reviews of Geophysics and Space Physics, v. 9, p. 101–174.

Kafka, A., Taitel, J., Quittmeyer, R., and Frankel, A., 1981, Some problems with retrieval of earthquake source parameters from Rayleigh wave spectra; Two earthquakes north of the Virgin Islands [abs.]: EOS Transactions of the America Geophysical Union, v. 62, p. 950.

Kelleher, J., Sykes, L., and Oliver, J., 1973, Possible criteria for predicting earthquake locations and their applications to major plate boundaries of the Pacific and the Caribbean: Journal of Geophysical Research, v. 78, p. 2547–1585.

Kellogg, J. N., 1984, Cenozoic tectonic history of the Sierra de Perija, Venezuela-Colombia, and adjacent basins, *in* Bonini, W. E., Hargraves, R. B., and Shagam, R., eds., The Caribbean–South American plate boundary and regional tectonics: Geological Society of America Memoir 162, p. 239–262.

Kellogg, J. N., and Bonini, W. E., 1982, Subduction of the Caribbean plate and basements in the overriding South American plate: Tectonics, v. 1, p. 251–276.

Ladd, J., Worzel, J., and Watkins, J., 1977, Multifold seismic reflection records from the northern Venezuela Basin and the north slope of the Muertos Trench, *in* Talwani, M., ed., Island arcs, deep sea trenches, and back-arc basins: American Geophysical Union Maurice Ewing Series, v. 1, p. 41–56.

Langer, C. J., and Bollinger, G. A., 1979, Secondary faulting near the terminus of a seismogenic strike-slip fault; Aftershocks of the 1976 Guatemala earthquake: Bulletin of the Seismological Society of America, v. 69, p. 427–444.

Le Fevre, L., and McNally, K., 1984, Stress distribution and subduction of aseismic ridges in the Middle America subduction zone: Journal of Geophysical Research, v. 90, 4495–4510.

Lynch, J., and Bodle, R., 1948, The Dominican earthquakes of August 1946: Bulletin of the Seismological Society of America, v. 38, p. 1–17.

Mann, P., and Burke, K., 1984, Neotectonics of the Caribbean: Reviews of Geophysics and Space Physics, v. 22, p. 309–362.

Mann, P., Burke, K., and Matumoto, T., 1984, Neotectonics of Hispaniola; Plate motion, sedimentation, and seismicity at a restraining bend: Earth and Planetary Science Letters, v. 70, p. 311–324.

Mapa Geologico de Chiapas, 1989: Mexico, Comision Federal de Electricidad, scale 1:500,000.

McCann, W. R., 1985, On the earthquake hazard of Puerto Rico and the Virgin Islands: Bulletin of the Seismological Society of America, v. 75, p. 251–262.

McCann, W. R., and Sykes, L. R., 1984, Subduction of aseismic ridges beneath the Caribbean plate; Implications for the seismicity and seismic potential of the northeastern Caribbean: Journal of Geophysical Research, v. 89, p. 4493–4519.

—— , 1986, Reply *to* comment *by* Stein and others: Journal of Geophysical Research, v. 91, p. 787–791.

McCann, W. R., Dewey, J., Murphy, A. J., and Harding, J., 1982, A large normal-fault earthquake in the overriding wedge of the Lesser Antilles subduction zone; The earthquake of October 8, 1974: Bulletin of the Seismological Society of America, v. 72, p. 2267–2284.

McCarr, A., 1977, Seismic moments of earthquakes beneath island arcs, phase changes, and subduction velocities: Journal of Geophysical Research, v. 82, p. 256–264.

McLaren, J. P., and Frohlich, C., 1985, Model calculations of regional network locations for earthquakes in subduction zones: Bulletin of the Seismological Society of America, v. 75, p. 397–414.

Minster, J., and Jordan, T., 1978, Present-day plate motions: Journal of Geophysical Research, v. 83, p. 5331–5354.

Molnar, P., and Sykes, L., 1969, Tectonics of the Caribbean and Middle America regions from focal mechanisms and seismicity: Geological Society of America Bulletin, v. 80, p. 1639–1684.

Muehlberger, W., and Ritchie, A. W., 1975, Caribbean-Americas plate boundary in Guatemala and southern Mexico as seen on Skylab IV orbital photography: Geology, v. 3, p. 232–235.

Murphy, A. J., and McCann, W. R., 1979, Preliminary results from a new seismic network in the northeastern Caribbean: Bulletin of the Seismological Society of America, v. 69, p. 1497–1513.

Pennington, W. D., 1981, Subduction of the eastern Panamá Basin and seismotectonics of northwestern South America: Journal of Geophysical Research, v. 86, p. 10753–10770.

—— , 1983, The role of shallow phase changes in the subduction of oceanic crust: Science, v. 220, p. 1045–1047.

—— , 1984, The effect of oceanic crustal structure on phase changes and subduction: Tectonophysics, v. 102, p. 377–398.

Pennington, W. D., Mooney, W., van Hissenhoven, R., Meyer, H., Ramirez, J., and Meyer, R., 1979, Results of a microearthquake reconnaissance survey of Bucaramanga, Colombia: Geophysical Research Letters, v. 6, p. 65–68.

Perez, O., and Aggarwal, Y., 1981, Present-day tectonics of the southeastern Caribbean and northeastern Venezuela: Journal of Geophysical Research, v. 86, p. 10791–19804.

Plafker, G., 1976, Tectonic aspects of the Guatemala earthquake of 4 February 1976: Science, v. 193, p. 1201–1208.

Reid, H., and Taber, S., 1919a, The Puerto Rico earthquakes of October–November 1918: Bulletin of the Seismological Society of America, v. 9, p. 95–127.

—— , 1919b, The Puerto Rico earthquake of 1918: Washington, D.C., House of Representatives Document 269, 74 p.

—— , 1920, The Virgin Islands earthquakes of 1867–1868: Bulletin of the Seismological Society of America, v. 10, p. 9–30.

Rial, J., 1978, The Caracas, Venezuela, earthquake of July 1967; A multiple-source event: Journal of Geophysical Research, v. 83, p. 5405–5414.

Robson, G., 1964, An earthquake catalog for the eastern Caribbean 1530–1960: Bulletin of the Seismological Society of America, v. 54, p. 785–832.

Rothé, J., 1969, The seismicity of the Earth 1953–1965: Paris, UNESCO, 336 p.

Salterain, P., 1883, Legera Reseña de los Temblores de Tierra Ocurridos en la Isla de Cuba: Boletín de la Commisión del Mapa de España, Madrid, v. 10, p. 371–385.

Scherer, J., 1912, Great earthquakes in the island of Haiti: Bulletin of the Seismological Society of America, v. 2, p. 161–180.

Schneider, J. F., Pennington, W. D., and Meyer, R. P., 1987, Microseismicity and focal mechanisms of the intermediate-depth Bucaramanga nest, Colombia: Journal of Geophysical Research, v. 92, p. 13913–13926.

Schwartz, D. P., Cluff, L. S., and Donnelly, T. W., 1979, Quaternary faulting along the Caribbean–North America plate boundary in Central America: Tectonophysics, v. 52, p. 431–445.

Silver, E. A., Case, J. E., and MacGillavry, H. J., 1975, Geophysical study of the Venezuelan borderland: Geological Society of America Bulletin, v. 86, p. 213–226.

Stein, S., Engeln, J., Wiens, D., Speed, R., and Fujita, K., 1982, Subduction seismicity and tectonics in the Lesser Antilles arc: Journal of Geophysical Research, v. 87, p. 8642–8664.

Stein, S., Wiens, D., Engeln, J., and Fujita, K., 1986, Comment *on* 'Subduction of aseismic ridges beneath the Caribbean Plate; Implications for the tectonics and seismic potential of the northeastern Caribbean' by McCann, W., and Sykes, L.: Journal of Geophysical Research, v. 91, p. 784–786.

Stoiber, R. E., and Carr, M. J., 1974, Quaternary volcanic and tectonic segmentation of Central America: Bulletin Volcanologique, v. 37, p. 304–325.

Sykes, L., and Ewing, M., 1965, The seismicity of the Caribbean region: Journal of Geophysical Research, v. 70, p. 5065–5074.

Sykes, L. R., McCann, W. R., and Kafka, A. L., 1982, Motion of Caribbean Plate during last 7 million years and implications for earlier Cenozoic movements: Journal of Geophysical Research, v. 87, p. 10656–10676.

Taber, S., 1920, Jamaica earthquakes and the Bartlett Trough: Bulletin of the Seismological Society of America, v. 10, p. 55–89.

—— , 1922, The great fault troughs of the Antilles: Journal Geological, v. 30, p. 89–114.

Tomblin, J., 1972, Seismicity and plate tectonics of the eastern Caribbean, *in* 6th Conference on the Geology of the Caribbean: Margarita, Venezuela, p. 177–282.

Tomblin, J., and Aspinall, W., 1975, Reconnaissance report of the Antigua West Indies earthquake of October 8, 1974: Bulletin of the Seismological Society of America, v. 65, p. 1533.

Tomblin, J., and Robson, G., 1977, A catalogue of felt earthquakes for Jamaica, with reference to other islands in the Greater Antilles, 1564–1791: Kingston, Jamaica, Ministry of Mining and Natural Resources, 243 p.

Tryggvason, E., and Lawson, J. E., 1970, The intermediate earthquake source near Bucaramanga, Colombia: Bulletin of the Seismological Society of America, v. 60, p. 269–276.

Wadge, G., and Shepherd, J., 1984, Segmentation of the Lesser Antilles subduction zone: Earth and Planetary Science Letters, v. 71, p. 297–304.

MANUSCRIPT ACCEPTED BY THE SOCIETY AUGUST 25, 1989

The Geology of North America
Vol. H, The Caribbean Region
The Geological Society of America, 1990

Chapter 12

Review of Caribbean neotectonics

Paul Mann
Institute for Geophysics, University of Texas at Austin, 8701 Mopac Blvd., Austin, Texas 78759-8345
Carlos Schubert
Centro de Ecología, Instituto Venezolano de Investigaciónes Científicas, Apartado 21827, Caracas 1020A, Venezuela
Kevin Burke
Lunar and Planetary Institute, 3303 NASA Road 1, Houston, Texas 77058, and Department of Geosciences, University of Houston/University Park, Houston, Texas 77004

INTRODUCTION

Studies of active plate boundaries have shown that geodetic and earthquake records from historic periods are insufficient for completely understanding fault behavior and regional patterns of crustal movements. Several pioneering studies have demonstrated that geologic studies of the Holocene and late Pleistocene epochs (Sieh, 1981) can provide valuable information on crustal processes, such as seismogenic fault slip and aseismic uplift, which often exhibit long-term temporal and spatial variations. Realization of the importance of the longer, more extensive geologic record of crustal movements has led to many recent advances in *neotectonics,* a multidisciplinary field emphasizing the relationship between Neogene relative plate motions and structural, sedimentary, volcanic, and earthquake processes.

We have previously defined the time span of the "neotectonic" phase of Caribbean development as Neogene (Mann and Burke, 1984a). The selection of the Miocene for the beginning of the period during which neotectonic structures form is consistent with most Caribbean tectonic models that show the approximate configuration of present-day plate boundaries established by the Miocene (see Pindell and Barrett, this volume).

Our purpose is to review the neotectonics of the Caribbean Plate with particular emphasis on recent results from geologic studies of major strike-slip fault systems along the northern and southern edges of the plate and subaerial fault systems within arc systems at the eastern and western edges of the plate. Caribbean tectonic studies have traditionally focused on either earthquakes (e.g., Molnar and Sykes, 1969; Sykes and others, 1982) or mapping Paleogene and Cretaceous rocks (e.g., volume edited by Donnelly, 1971). Until recently (e.g., volume edited by Bonini and others, 1984, and studies such as that of Bizon and others, 1985, in volume from the Symposium on Caribbean Geodynamics, Paris, 1985), there has not been widespread interest in mapping Neogene rocks or structures within a plate-tectonic

framework. The occurrence of several major natural disasters in the Caribbean during this century (e.g., 1902 volcanic eruption of Mount Pelée, Martinique; 1972 Managua earthquake; 1976 Guatemala earthquake; 1985 volcanic eruption of the Nevado del Ruíz, Colombia; 1985 Mexico City earthquake) and the dense populations in many potentially hazardous areas indicate the need for improved neotectonic data bases and models for predicting long-term patterns of crustal movement.

We begin by reviewing the neotectonic setting of the Caribbean Plate and follow this with descriptions of the major neotectonic features of the various plate boundaries. Because of space constraints, we have included only a selection of the more recent neotectonic studies in the region and we have condensed the results of these studies into map or tabular form. A more complete—though less up-to-date—review of Caribbean neotectonics, was given by Mann and Burke (1984a). The more recent data included in this review support the general conclusions of this earlier and more interpretive paper.

NEOTECTONIC SETTING OF THE CARIBBEAN

The distribution of recorded earthquakes, active calc-alkaline volcanoes, and spreading ridges, defines four rigid plates in the Caribbean and Middle American regions: North America, South America, Caribbean, and Cocos (Fig. 1). Geologic and seismic studies indicate that the Caribbean is moving eastward relative to the Americas, and this movement is accommodated by left-lateral faults along its northern boundary within continental, island arc, and oceanic lithosphere bounding the North American Plate, and right-lateral faults along its southern boundary within continental, island arc, and oceanic lithosphere bounding the South American Plate. Oceanic lithosphere of the North and South American Plates is consumed along the eastern edge of the

Mann, P., Schubert, C., and Burke, K., 1990, Review of Caribbean neotectonics, *in* Dengo, G., and Case, J. E., eds., The Caribbean region: Boulder, Colorado, Geological Society of America, The Geology of North America, v. H.

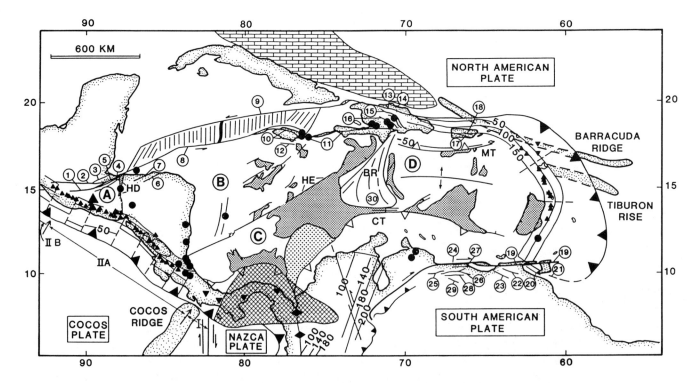

Figure 1. Tectonic map of the Caribbean (modified from Mann and Burke, 1984a). Major strike-slip fault zones are identified by numbers and documented in Tables 1 and 2. Active calc-alkaline volcanoes are shown by upright triangles above subducted slabs. Depth contours are given in kilometers on the upper surface of subducted slabs. I, IIA, and IIB indicate slab segment boundaries proposed by Burbach and others (1984) as an alternative to the more closely spaced boundaries of Carr (1976), which are unlabeled but shown arcward of the trench. Aseismic ridges are stippled, and extinct calc-alkaline volcanoes are indicated by inverted triangles. Late Neogene intraplate and plate boundary zone alkaline volcanoes are shown as black dots; note that plate boundary zone alkaline volcanoes are usually found in pull-apart segments of strike-slip faults. Abyssal plains of the Nicaraguan Rise and Colombian and Venezuelan basins are shown by the fine regular dot pattern and consist of relatively undeformed terrigenous turbidite sequences. The coarse dot pattern indicates coarser submarine-fan material of the Magdalena Fan in the Colombian Basin. Letters A to D indicate blocks within the Caribbean Plate that are separated by major fault zones (HD, Honduras Depression; HE, Hess Escarpment; BR, Beata Ridge; CT, Curaçao or South Caribbean Thrust; and MT, Muertos Thrust). The brick pattern north of Cuba indicates the Bahamas carbonate platform. The grid pattern in the area of Panamá and Colombia is the area in which focal mechanism solutions of earthquakes suggest that the greatest stress is east-west compression with a north-south intermediate stress axis (Pennington, 1981). Data on depth of the Benioff zones are from the following sources: northwestern South America (Pennington, 1981; Kellogg and Bonini, 1982); Middle America (Carr, 1976; Burbach and others, 1984); and the Lesser Antilles (Tomblin, 1975).

Caribbean at the Lesser Antilles subduction zone, and oceanic lithosphere of the Cocos Plate is consumed along the western edge at the Middle America subduction zone (Fig. 1).

The Caribbean Plate itself consists mostly of a rim of accreted Cretaceous-Paleogene arc terranes about a central marine basin with a thickness intermediate between that of oceans and continents (Fig. 1). Seismic refraction measurements in the Caribbean Sea reveal crustal thicknesses of 12 to 15 km that are much greater than the 6-km thickness typically observed beneath the main ocean basins (Fox and Heezen, 1975). The basin is 4 to 5 km deep and, therefore, anomalously shallow for ocean floor

generated in Cretaceous or earliest times. The shallow depth of the Caribbean, averaging 1 to 2 km less than the predicted, has been attributed to the emplacement of extensive basaltic sills about 80 Ma. The thickened area of the Caribbean has been compared to western Pacific oceanic plateaus, like the Manihiki and Ontong Java, which are similar in scale and age (Burke and others, 1978). The thicker-than-normal crust of the Caribbean may explain why the Caribbean is unusual among the plates of the world in that it is not presently subducted at typical island arcs along its perimeter (Sykes and others, 1982; Fig. 1). An area in the southeastern corner of the Colombian Basin has been

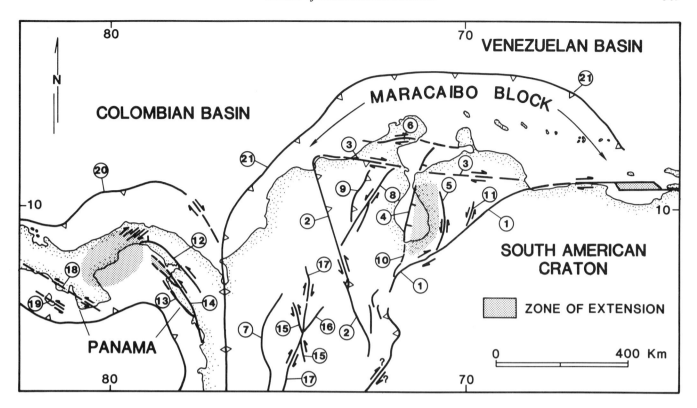

Figure 2. Compilation map showing major faults in northwestern South America and Panamá. Faults are identified by number and documented in Table 3. Note that faults in this region generally strike northeasterly or northwesterly and are not parallel to westerly striking, strike-slip faults of the southern Caribbean PBZ to the east. In northwestern South America, late Neogene tectonics appears to have been dominated by the northward motion of a triangular wedge (the "Maracaibo Block") defined by the Boconó (no. 1) and Santa Marta–Bucaramanga Fault Zones (no. 2) into the Venezuelan and eastern Colombian Basins. Complex extension within the Maracaibo Block accompanied northward movement. In Panamá, late Neogene left-lateral strike-slip faulting and accompanying extension appears to accommodate motion of the present isthmus northwestward over the Colombian Basin.

shown by Stoffa and others (1981) to be underlain by normal oceanic crust.

Plate tectonics within continental and island-arc lithosphere in areas like the Caribbean are well recognized to be more complicated than in the oceans because of the existence of many older faults that act as planes of weakness and because silica and feldspar-rich rocks of continents and island arcs deform more easily at low temperatures than oceanic basalts. The existence of both of these conditions in the Caribbean makes the distinction difficult between structures and earthquakes associated with interplate relative motion and those structures and earthquakes associated with internal plate deformation. Deformation associated with Caribbean plate motion occurs in broad plate boundary zones (PBZ) up to 250 km wide, rather than the much narrower plate boundaries found in oceanic crust. The geologic and seismologic complexities occurring within the broad Caribbean plate boundary zones have generated much controversy among geologists and geophysicists on the location and character of the present plate boundaries.

ORGANIZATION OF THIS CHAPTER

We have divided our discussion of Caribbean neotectonics into five sections corresponding to five distinct plate boundary zones: (1) North America–Caribbean strike-slip PBZ; (2) South America–Caribbean strike-slip PBZ; (3) North America–Caribbean PBZ (Lesser Antilles subduction zone); (4) Cocos-Caribbean PBZ (Middle America subduction zone); and (5) Panamá Arc–South America collisional PBZ (region of Panamá, Colombia, and western Venezuela; Fig. 2). All geographic localities mentioned in the text are shown on Plate 1. General subtopics on the northern and southern strike-slip zones that are particularly emphasized in the text of this chapter and the accompanying tables and plate include: (1) distribution of major strike-slip faults; (2) fault offsets and rates of displacement; (3) areas and rates of Neogene subsidence and uplift; (4) relation of Neogene volcanism to tectonic setting; (5) groundbreaks associated with earthquake faulting; and (6) relationship of faulting to earthquake distribution. Subtopics number 4 (volcanism) and number 6 (earthquakes) are only briefly discussed because these topics are discussed in more detail by Carr and Stoiber (this volume) and McCann and Pennington (this volume). Recent faulting in the Caribbean Sea and along the active subduction margins is only briefly covered here and on Plate 11; it is covered in more detail in chapters by Holcombe and others (this volume) and by von Huene (in Winterer and others, 1989).

The general emphasis of this chapter and its accompanying tables and plate is to present the existing regional geologic and tectonic data on which our present understanding of Caribbean neotectonics is based. The localities of studies discussed in the text are shown on Plate 11 and keyed by number to the references given at the end of this paper. Because systematic neotectonic studies in the Caribbean have only begun fairly recently, there is a paucity of quantitative data on fault movement histories, especially in late Neogene time. For this reason, many neotectonic characteristics of mapped fault and fault-related structures, such as those depicted on the 1:2,500,000 compilation map of Case and Holcombe (1980), remain poorly known. However, it is hoped that this compilation of geologic and geophysical information will help guide workers in formulating the type of detailed neotectonic studies (e.g., detailed mapping, fault trenching, coral reef studies) that are now needed in the region.

INTRODUCTION TO CARIBBEAN-NORTH AMERICA AND CARIBBEAN-SOUTH AMERICA PLATE BOUNDARY ZONES

The compilation of strike-slip faults and their known or apparent offsets are given in Tables 1 and 2 and are identified by number on Figure 1. Although Neogene strike-slip faulting is known to occur in the Panamá–South America collision PBZ, we consider these faults to occupy a distinctly different neotectonic plate boundary zone and discuss them in a later section. However, the fault characteristics of the Panamá–South America PBZ are described in a similar fashion on Table 3 as those of the northern and southern Caribbean. Faults in the Panamá–South America region are identified by number on Figure 2.

Neogene offsets have been proposed for only some of the faults listed in Tables 1, 2, and 3, and virtually none of these are reliably based on offset piercing points intersecting opposite sides of the fault plane. The remaining faults are suggested to be strike-slip mainly because: (1) they parallel known strike-slip faults; (2) they occur within the plate boundary earthquake zone and are commonly associated with elongate zones of active seismicity (see Figs. of McCann and Pennington, this volume); (3) they are closely associated with elongate, historical rupture zones; and (4) they generally form prominent linear fault valleys or coastlines (see Plate 11).

Strike-slip offsets are difficult to establish because strike-slip faults in both the northern and southern Caribbean tend to parallel Late Cretaceous–Paleogene thrust faults associated with arc-continent collision zones and/or outcrop entirely within Mesozoic rocks, making estimation of Cenozoic movement diffi-

cult. However, some offsets have been established using four criteria of varying reliability: (1) displaced streams, terraces, and alluvial fans provide lines that meet the fault at piercing points and are adequate to determine fault slip; these features have yielded Quaternary slip rates such as from the displaced river terraces along the Motagua Fault Zone of Guatemala (Table 1); (2) displaced contacts of rock units are widely used as evidence for strike-slip faulting although they are less reliable indicators than those of criterion 1 because the contacts of rock units on geologic maps are based on the intersection of a geologic plane that predates the fault movement and a topographic surface that postdates the fault movement (e.g., offsets along the Enriquillo–Plantain Garden Fault Zone in Jamaica and Hispaniola); (3) length of pull-apart basins can provide a minimum amount of offset, provided overlapping strike-slip fault traces and basin geometry are well mapped (see Mann and others, 1983, for a discussion of uncertainties in determining the dimensions of pull-aparts); and (4) juxtaposition of dissimilar continental or arc basement terranes is a less reliable indicator of Neogene strike-slip offset because displacement may have occurred during Late Cretaceous–Paleogene thrusting (e.g., Hispaniola Fault Zone).

The criterion or criteria used for determining Caribbean strike-slip fault offsets are listed in Tables 1, 2, and 3. It can readily be seen from the large number of unknown characteristics that improvement of these fault data should be a priority area for future research.

NORTH AMERICA–CARIBBEAN STRIKE-SLIP PLATE BOUNDARY ZONE

Distribution of major strike-slip faults

The North America–Caribbean PBZ consists of a broad zone of Neogene left-lateral strike-slip deformation extending from the northern Lesser Antilles volcanic arc in the east to the Middle America volcanic arc in western Guatemala and southern Mexico in the west (Fig. 1; Plate 11). Recent mapping and data compilation in the northeastern Caribbean (Mann and others, 1984b) has shown that the Neogene strike-slip system there consists of two distinct but parallel left-lateral strike-slip fault zones (Plate 1). A northern strike-slip zone strikes eastward from the Puerto Rico Trench and passes through: (1) northern Hispaniola (Septentrional Fault Zone); (2) along the southern margin of Cuba (Oriente Fault Zone) and into a zone of sea-floor spreading (Mid-Cayman Spreading Center) at the center of the Cayman Trough; (3) north of Honduras (Swan Fault Zone); and (4) through Central America (Motagua and Polochic fault zones) toward the Middle America Trench (Table 1 and Plate 11).

A southern strike-slip zone strikes westward from central Hispaniola (Enriquillo Fault Zone) and passes through: (1) the southern peninsula of Haiti ("Décrochement senestre sud-Haïtien" of Calmus, 1983, and Bizon and others, 1985); (2) the Jamaica Passage between Haiti and Jamaica; and (3) Jamaica as a series of reverse and thrust faults, which constitute a local compressional or "restraining bend" segment on the strike-slip fault (Table 1 and Plate 11). The fault appears to exit the northwest coast of Jamaica as a single east-west strike-slip fault (Duanvale Fault Zone), which strikes westward until it appears to merge with the unnamed southeastern fracture zone of the Cayman Trough. Mann and others (1984b) renamed the part of this fault that extends from central Hispaniola to eastern Jamaica, the "Enriquillo-Plantain Garden Fault Zone" based on its distal segments in Hispaniola and eastern Jamaica.

On a gross scale, the North American–Caribbean strike-slip PBZ is fairly well defined by two major throughgoing strike-slip fault zones from central Hispaniola to the area west of Jamaica (Fig. 1). The southern zone in Hispaniola, the Enriquillo–Plantain Garden Fault Zone, does not strike eastward across eastern Hispaniola and Puerto Rico. Instead, left-lateral displacement on the Enriquillo–Plantain Garden Fault Zone appears to be locally transformed into northeast-striking normal faults with associated Plio-Pleistocene volcanoes, dikes, and shallow intrusions in central Hispaniola (Plate 11). These normal faults may connect the two strike-slip zones of Hispaniola as a complex pull-apart structure or the normal faults may simply represent a fault termination structure on the Enriquillo–Plantain Garden Fault Zone.

The importance of strike-slip faulting as a neotectonic process is poorly known in Puerto Rico and the Virgin Islands. Although strike-slip fault offsets of post-Cretaceous and Neogene age have been reported from Puerto Rico (Table 1), there appears to be no recognizable throughgoing left-lateral strike-slip fault zone that connects with those to the west in Hispaniola. Evidence has been presented for discontinuous normal faults of Neogene age in southern Puerto Rico (Monroe, 1972) and the Virgin Islands (Holmes and Kindinger, 1985). The largest and most active fault zone in this area appears to be the Anegada Passage Fault Zone, which extends for 375 km in a northeast direction and defines the eastern boundary of the Virgin Islands Platform. Hess and Maxwell (1953) regarded the Anegada Passage Fault Zone as a left-lateral strike-slip fault, whereas Houlgatte (1983) has interpreted this feature as an active right-lateral strike-slip fault along which the St. Croix and Sombrero basin have formed as late Neogene pull-apart basins (Plate 11).

Strike-slip fault offsets

A wide range of left-lateral offsets has been mapped on faults within the North America–Caribbean PBZ (Table 1 and Plate 11). By far the largest offset (1,100 km) is that observed on the Swan and Oriente Fault Zones, which bound the Cayman Trough pull-apart basin (Holcombe and Sharman, 1983; Fig. 1). The existence of the Cayman Trough pull-apart provides compelling evidence for large-scale, post-Eocene(?) left-lateral strike-slip movement between the Caribbean and North American plates. Although the trough is approximately 1,400 km long, the amount of left-lateral strike-slip offset required to produce the pull-apart structure is given by the length of oceanic crust generated by the Mid-Cayman Spreading Center in the central part of

the trough and the length of stretched crust, which is now found in the distal ends of the trough and formed prior to the formation of the Mid-Cayman Spreading Center. Pindell and Barrett (this volume) and Rosencrantz and Sclater (1986) took into account basement extension at the ends of the trough and estimated about 1,100 km of total left-lateral offset across the Cayman Trough in post-Eocene(?) time.

Most of the fault offsets in the PBZ are much less than the Cayman Trough offset and range from less than 100 m to 250 km (Table 1). We have included many poorly known faults, which were probably, or known to be, active in pre-Miocene time (e.g., Hispaniola Fault Zone and Great Northern and Southern Fault Zones of Puerto Rico). These faults may have been active in Neogene time because they form prominent topographic lineaments; lie well within the seismogenic PBZ and parallel known Neogene strike-slip faults. We have also included faults in Table 1 for which there is no geologic evidence for strike-slip movement (Chamelecón-Jocotán, San Augustín, Aguán, La Ceiba, South Jamaica, Camú, Los Pozos–San Juan, and Río Jueves). As in the case of pre-Neogene faults included in Table 1, these poorly known faults were included in the compilation because they: (1) parallel known strike-slip faults; (2) occur within the plate boundary earthquake zone and are often associated with elongate zones of active seismicity and/or elongate rupture zones of historic earthquakes; and (3) they generally form prominent linear fault valleys or coastlines (Plate 11).

Rates of strike-slip fault displacement

Reliable rates of Neogene strike-slip displacement have been determined for only a few of the major strike-slip faults in the northern Caribbean (Fig. 1 and Plate 11). The Motagua Fault Zone in Guatemala (Fig. 1) offsets a staircase of Quaternary stream terraces whose ages suggest an average late Pleistocene-Holocene rate of 6 mm/yr left-lateral displacement (Table 1). Rates of strike-slip displacement are also well known along the Polochic Fault Zone of Guatemala and southern Mexico with estimates of offsets from various features ranging from 1.3 to 20 mm/yr over the last 15 m.y. The rate of sea-floor spreading in the Cayman Trough can be derived from crustal cooling curves. Interpretations of these data suggest that early Oligocene to present spreading occurred at rates of 15 ± 5 mm/yr. Estimates of rates of left-lateral displacement from onshore faults in the northeastern Caribbean (Jamaica and Hispaniola) since middle Miocene time range from 6 to .75 mm/yr and may be inaccurate because they are based on apparent offsets of geologic contacts (Table 1).

Minster and Jordan (1978) used data from the Cayman Trough, earthquake slip vectors, and the three-plate closure condition to calculate a rate of 19.4 mm/yr along interplate slip lines, which predict pure strike-slip motion along most of the length of the North America–Caribbean PBZ. Sykes and others (1982) used earthquake slip vectors and the configuration of the subducted slab in the northeastern Caribbean to calculate a much

TABLE 1. DATA ON FAULTS WITHIN THE NORTH AMERICAN-CARIBBEAN PLATE BOUNDARY ZONE

Number (Indicated in Fig. 1)	Name of Fault and location	Amount and Type of Offset/ Displacement	Offset Displaced Features	Timing of Offset	Slip Rate and Time Interval During Which Movement Occurred	Selected References
1	Motagua FZ, Guatemala	58.3 m left-lateral	Stream terraces	Late Pleist.- Holocene	6 mm/yr (10,000 yr)	Schwartz and others (1979)
2	Polochic FZ, Guatemala	130 km left-lateral	Drainages, Cretaceous rocks, Late Cretaceous folds	Post-middle Miocene (~15 Ma)	≥8.6 mm/yr (~15 m.y.)	Burkart (1983)
2	Polochic FZ, Guatemala and Mexico	130 km left-lateral	Distinctive clast types from source	10.3 to 6.6 Ma	1.3 mm/yr (10 m.y.)	Deaton and Burkart (1984)
2	Polochic FZ, central Guatemala and Mexico	60 to 120 m left-lateral	Drainages	Late Quat.	10 - 20 mm/yr (6000 yr)	Kupfer and Godoy (1967)
3	Polochic FZ, eastern Guatemala (also known as North Izabal FZ)	≥1.1 km	Alluvial fans	Pleistocene (1.6 Ma)	≥7 mm/yr (1.6 m.y.)	Schwartz and Swan (1979), Burkart (1983)
4	Chamelecón-Jocotán FZ, Guatemala and Honduras	Unknown	Unknown	——	——	Donnelly and others (1968)
5	San Augustín FZ	Unknown	Unknown	——	——	Plafker (1976)
6	Aguan FZ, Honduras	Unknown	Unknown	——	——	Muehlberger (1976)
7	La Ceiba FZ, Honduras	Unknown	Unknown	——	——	Muehlberger (1976)
8	Swan FZ, Cayman Trough	1100 km left-lateral	Length of oceanic and stretched floor of the Cayman Trough pull-apart	Eocene(?) to Present	15 ± 5 mm/yr (last 30 m.y. only)	Rosencrantz and Sclater (1986)
9	Oriente FZ, Cayman Trough	1100 km left-lateral	Length of oceanic and stretched floor of the Cayman Trough pull-apart	Eocene(?) to Present	15 ± 5 mm/yr (last 30 m.y. only)	Rosencrantz and Sclater (1986)
10	Eight faults in Jamaica	33 km left-lateral (cumulative)	Cret.-Eocene rocks and other faults	Late Miocene to present (10-0 Ma)	~4 mm/yr (10 m.y.)	Burke and others (1980)

(Table 1 continues on next page.)

TABLE 1. (CONTINUED)

Number (Indicated in Fig. 1)	Name of Fault and location	Amount and Type of Offset/ Displacement	Offset Displaced Features	Timing of Offset	Slip Rate and Time Interval During Which Movement Occurred	Selected References
11	Enriquillo-Plantain Garden FZ, Jamaica	10-12.8 km left-lateral	Cretaceous rocks and associated gravity/magnetic highs	Middle to late Miocene to present (17-0 Ma)	~0.75 mm/yr (17 m.y.)	Mann and others (1985)
11	Enriquillo-Plantain Garden FZ, Jamaica	25-30 km left-lateral	Cretaceous and late Miocene rocks	Pliocene to present (5-0 Ma)	5-6 mm/yr (5 m.y.)	van den Berge (1983), Calmus (1983)
12	South Jamaica FZ, Nicaraguan Rise (inferred from earthquake data)	Unknown	Unknown	——	——	Mann and Burke (1984a)
13	Septentrional FZ, Hispaniola	100 km(?) left-lateral	Cretaceous rocks	Unknown	——	Eberle and others (1980), Mann and others (1984b)
14	Camú FZ, Hispaniola	Unknown	Unknown	——	——	Mann and others (1984b)
15	Hispaniola FZ, Hispaniola	250 km(?) left-lateral	Juxtaposes dis-similar Cretaceous basement terranes	Middle to latest Oligocene	——	Mann and others (1984b)
16	Los Pozos-San Juan FZ, Hispaniola	Unknown	Unknown	——	——	Mann and others (1984b)
17	Esmeralda FZ, (Great Southern FZ) Puerto Rico	10 km left-lateral	Cretaceous rocks	Post-Campanian Maastrichtian	——	Glover (1971)
17	Río Jueves FZ (Great Southern FZ) Puerto Rico	Unknown	Unknown	——	——	Glover (1971)
18	Quebrada Vincente FZ (Great Northern FZ), Puerto Rico	28 km left-lateral	Cretaceous-Paleogene rocks	——	——	Briggs and Pease (1968)
18	Cerro Mula FZ (Great Northern FZ), Puerto Rico	33 km left-lateral	Cretaceous-Paleogene	——	——	Briggs and Pease (1968)

TABLE 2. DATA ON FAULTS WITHIN THE SOUTH AMERICAN-CARIBBEAN PLATE BOUNDARY ZONE

Number (Indicated in Fig. 1)	Name of Fault and location	Amount and Type of Offset/ Displacement	Offset Displaced Features	Timing of Offset	Slip Rate and Time Interval During Which Movement Occurred	Selected References
19	El Pilar FZ, Venezuela and Trinidad	20 km right-lateral	Barremian-Aptian rocks	Post-early Cretaceous	----	Vierbuchen (1984), Schubert (1970)
19	El Pilar FZ, Trinidad	35-40 km right-lateral	Caroni Basin (Late Miocene)	Post-late Miocene	5 mm/yr for 40 km of offset in 8 m.y.	Robertson (1986), Robertson and Burke (1986)
20	El Soldado FZ, Trinidad	10.5 km right-lateral	Easterly trending structures (age not given)	Post-middle Pliocene	7-11 mm/yr	Perez and Aggarwal (1981)
21	Los Bajos FZ, Trinidad	10.5 km right-lateral	Offset Neogene sediments	Post-middle Pliocene	7-11 mm/yr	Wilson (1968)
22	San Francisco FZ, Venezuela	Unknown	Does not affect Late Miocene and younger rocks	----	----	Rosales (1972), Robertson (1986)
23	Urica FZ, Venezuela	35 km right-lateral	Basement gravity anomaly	----	----	Munro and Smith (1984)
24	Morón FZ	70 km right-lateral	Cariaco pull-apart basin	Last 2 m.y.	12.5-50 mm/yr (based on 25-100 km of offset to form Cariaco Basin	Schubert (1982b), Schubert and Krause (1984)
25	La Victoria FZ, Venezuela	30 km right-lateral	Offset based on geometry of Lake Valencia	Plio-Pleistocene	1-2.5 mm/yr based on 2-5 km of offset to form Lake Valencia in 2 m.y.	Schubert (1986)
26	Tácata FZ, Venezuela	3.5 km	Offsets Pleisto-cene drainage	Pleistocene	----	Schubert (1986)
27	Avila FZ, Venezuela	17 km	Offset based on Guarenas-Guatire pull-apart basin	Pleistocene	----	Schubert (1984)
28	Santa Rosa FZ, Venezuela	0.1 km	Offsets Pleisto-cene drainage	Pleistocene	----	Schubert (1986)
29	Guárico FZ, Venezuela	Unknown	Unknown	----	----	Schubert (1984)
30	Pecos FZ, Caribbean Sea	Unknown	Unknown	----	----	Stoffa and others (1981)

faster rate of interplate motion (37 ± 5 mm/yr over the last 7 m.y.). The calculated direction of relative plate motion predicts a larger component of plate convergence in the Hispaniola and Puerto Rico Trench area and pure strike-slip motion to the west in the Cayman Trough and in Central America.

In summary, the most reliable rates of North America–Caribbean interplate displacement on major strike-slip faults in late Neogene times range from 1.3 to 20 mm/yr in Central America; 15 ± 5 mm/yr in the Cayman Trough; and between 6 and 7.5 mm/yr from onshore areas of the northeastern Caribbean (Table 1). The total rate of interplate motion may be somewhat higher, as suggested by Sykes and others (1982; i.e., 37 ± 5 mm/yr), because of undetected cumulative displacements on minor faults, rotation of blocks between major faults, vertical uplift and subsidence at fault bends, and ductile flow in warm lithosphere.

Strike-slip–related subsidence and uplift

The Neogene horizontal strike-slip displacements described above have been accompanied by extensive vertical tectonic movements in both the northern and southern strike-slip PBZs of the Caribbean. The magnitude of these vertical movements is readily seen in the high topography (2 to 3 km) of peninsulas and islands relative to their small land areas as well as in deep (>1 km), fault-bounded submarine troughs in coastal areas. We have attempted to plot as much data on Neogene subsidence and uplift on Plate 11 in order to establish the typically strike-slip mechanism of these vertical movements.

Previous studies of Caribbean subsidence and uplift can be grouped into several categories: (1) geologic studies of Neogene strike-slip related sedimentary basins and push-up blocks; (2) studies of elevated and submerged Pleistocene coral reefs; (3) studies of late Neogene, elevated erosional terraces; and (4) geodetic releveling surveys. Many of these studies were carried out on a very local scale and without considering the seismic and neotectonic setting of the area. The purpose of this section is to provide a better conceptual basis for the tectonic interpretation of these data.

The most dramatic examples of Neogene tectonic uplift and subsidence in both the northern and southern Caribbean strike-slip PBZs can be related to bends or irregularities in the traces of the major strike-slip fault zones that are shown in Figures 1 and 2 and Plate 11. In general, Neogene sedimentary basins within both PBZs mark long-lived zones of strike-slip–related tectonic subsidence and are found offshore or in topographically low on-land depressions or valleys. Oligocene strike-slip basins like the Falcón (Muessig, 1984) or Tavera (Mann and Burke, 1984a) have often been deformed by Neogene strike-slip displacements and are found on land.

Using nomenclature developed by geologists in California and New Zealand, we have broadly classified Caribbean strike-slip related basins into five basin types or categories based on their bounding fault structure: (1) *pull-apart basins* produced by

extension at a discontinuity or "step" along a strike-slip fault; (2) *fault-wedge basins* occurring at intersections of bifurcating faults; (3) *fault-angle depressions* parallel to a single strike-slip fault traces; (4) *fault-flank depressions* between transverse secondary folds or normal faults; and (5) *ramp basins* between reverse or thrust faults related to strike-slip movement (all basin types are diagramatically shown in Fig. 3 and discussed in more detail by Mann and Burke [1984a]).

Areas of most rapid tectonic uplift in both the northern and southern Caribbean region are often localized on restraining bend strike-slip fault segments or "push-ups" produced by compression at a discontinuity or "step" along a throughgoing strike-slip fault. Because these bends are usually the sites of rapid, long-term (>5 m.y.) uplift, they typically form deeply eroded mountainous areas that are typically structural domes exposing Cretaceous and older basement rocks. The late Neogene emergence of several of the islands and peninsulas of the Caribbean region can be attributed to the restraining bend mechanism (Soná Peninsula, Panamá; Jamaica; southwestern peninsula of Haiti; Araya-Paria Peninsula of Venezuela; Gonâve Island, Haiti; and possibly Tobago—Plate 11).

Studies of late Neogene elevated erosional terraces and Pleistocene elevated and submerged constructional coral reef terraces have been carried out in the North American–Caribbean strike-slip PBZ for a number of years. Uplift and subsidence data based on coral reef and terrace data, were taken from many papers and plotted on Plate 11. In general, the results of these studies along with general geology and topography indicate localized tectonic uplift in late Neogene time at restraining bend structures shown on Plate 11.

Use of terrace and reef studies for tectonic problems requires: (1) obtaining precise radiometric ages from unrecrystallized coral from the reef, or, in the case of erosional terraces, obtaining accurate ages from *in situ* organic matter, coral, or shell material from the terrace veneer; and (2) being able to account for the rapid and large variations in eustatic sea level that have occurred through Neogene time. Because of the large uncertainties in Quaternary sea-level history, even during the Holocene (e.g., Taylor and others, 1985), the tectonic history of many reefs may be difficult to resolve.

Horsfield (1975) previously summarized much of the data shown on Plate 11 and noted that raised coral reefs are highest and most numerous in northwestern Haiti where as many as 28 Pleistocene constructional coral reef terraces rise to an elevation of 430 m. Because of tropical weathering effects, radiometric dating was possible only for the lower three terraces. After accounting for eustatic sea-level fluctuations, these ages suggest an average uplift rate of 0.3 mm/yr over the last 130,000 yr (Dodge and others, 1983). The rapid tectonic uplift of this area is consistent with its geologic position on an active, thrust-bound anticline in a major restraining bend structure centered on west-central Hispaniola (Mann and others, 1984b). The Gonâve Island to the south is a similar type of fault-bounded anticline (Mercier de Lepinay and others, 1985). To the east, late Holocene corals in certain areas of

TABLE 3. DATA ON FAULTS WITHIN THE NORTHWESTERN SOUTH AMERICA-PANAMA PLATE BOUNDARY ZONE

Number (Indicated in Fig. 1)	Name of Fault and location	Amount and Type of Offset/ Displacement	Offset Displaced Features	Timing of Offset	Slip Rate and Time Interval During Which Movement Occurred	Selected References
1	Boconó FZ, Venezuela	60-100 m right-lateral	Late Pleistocene glacial moraines	Late Pleistocene	3-14 mm/yr (18,000 yr)	Schubert (1982a)
1	Boconó FZ, Venezuela	~100 km right-lateral	Eocene thrust fault	Late Tertiary	----	Schubert (1982b)
2	Santa Marta-Bucaramanga FZ, Colombia and Venezuela	100-115 km left-lateral	Offset Tertiary basin	Pliocene to Recent	----	Tschanz and others (1974)
2	Santa Marta FZ, Colombia	0-6 km dip-slip displacement (west side down)	Offset Precambrian rocks	Cenozoic	----	Tschanz and others (1974), Case and MacDonald (1973)
3	Oca-Chirinos FZ, Colombia and Venezuela	65-98 km right-lateral	Offset Mesozoic basement rocks	Cenozoic	----	Tschanz and others (1974), Vasquez and Dickey (1972)
3	Oca FZ, Colombia	0-6 km dis-slip displacement (north side down	Offset Precambrian rocks	Cenozoic	----	Tschanz and others (1974), MacDonald (1973), Feo-Codecido (1972), Doolan and MacDonald (1976)
4	Urdanera FZ, Venezuela	Normal (east side down)	Post-Oligocene sediments	Post-Oligocene	----	Borger and Lenert (1959)
5	Valera FZ, Venezuela	1.4-2 km left-lateral	Based on deformed Quaternary deposits and a pull-apart basin	Quaternary	<1 mm/yr Quaternary	Soulas (1985)
6	Cuiza, FZ Colombia	15-25 km right-lateral	Not given	----	----	Alvarez (1971), MacDonald (1968)
7	Romeral FZ, Colombia	Interpreted as reverse, left-lateral or lateral	Unknown	----	----	Feininger and Bristow (1980), Cline and others (1981)
8	Tigre FZ, Colombia	Interpreted as thrust or left-lateral fault	En echelon folds along trace	----	----	Rod (1956), Kellogg and Bonini (1982)
9	Cerrejón FZ, Colombia	16 ± 8km thrust (west side up	Cenozoic sediments	Late Cenozoic	----	Kellogg and Bonini (1982)
10	Avispa FZ, Venezuela	Interpreted as thrust or normal	Not given			
11	Humocaro FZ	Presumed left-lateral	Not given	----	----	Rod (1956)

(Table 3 continues on next page.)

TABLE 3. (CONTINUED)

Number (Indicated in Fig. 1)	Name of Fault and location	Amount and Type of Offset/ Displacement	Offset Displaced Features	Timing of Offset	Slip Rate and Time Interval During Which Movement Occurred	Selected References
12	Sansón Hills FZ, Panama	Left-lateral	En echelon folds along trace	----	----	Rod (1956)
13	Jaqué River FZ, Panama	Presumed left-lateral	----	----	----	Wing and MacDonald (1973)
14	Sambú FZ, Panama	Presumed left-lateral	----	----	----	Lowrie and others (1982)
15	Otú FZ, Colombia	70 km left-lateral	Offsets Pre-cambrian and Paleozoic rocks	----	----	Feininger (1970)
16	Cimitarra FZ, Colombia	Presumed strike-slip	----	----	----	Feininger (1970)
17	Palestina FZ, Colombia	27 km right-lateral	Offsets pre-Cenozoic rocks	----	----	Feininger (1970), Collins and others (1981)
18	Azuero-Soná FZ	Left-lateral strike-slip	Skewed river courses, restraining bend structure	----	----	Mann and others (1986)
19	Coiba FZ	Left-lateral strike-slip	Small pull-apart basin	----	----	Mann and others (1986)
20	North Panama FZ	Thrust	Displaces late Neogene deposits	----	----	Lu and McMillen (1983), Bowland (1984)
21	South Caribbean FZ	Thrust	Displaces late Neogene deposits	----	----	Ladd and others (1984)

the tectonically active Enriquillo Valley are about 2 m higher in elevation than corals of similar age described at other localities in the Caribbean and western Atlantic (Taylor and others, 1985). Based on this preliminary study, apparent uplift is attributed to either deformation along thrust and strike-slip faults bounding the valley or to underestimation of paleosea levels during the Holocene by previous workers conducting reef studies in the region. Mapping and radiometric dating in northeastern and southeastern Dominican Republic has indicated a 3- to 6-m-high coral terrace level that actually consists of two reefs of different ages, with one thinly veneering the other and separated by a horizontal unconformity (Geister, 1980; Schubert and Cowart, 1980; Taylor, unpublished data, 1986). This is a common relationship found globally on stable coastlines and developed when two reefs had grown and become superimposed during the previous two interglacials about 130 and 220 ka, times when sea level was near its presently high level. This widespread relationship indicates that eastern Hispaniola has not been tectonically uplifted—at least for

the past 200,000 yr. This lack of tectonic uplift is consistent with the fact that eastern Hispaniola is topographically subdued relative to the more tectonically active central and western areas of the island.

Along the very steep and topographically rugged southern coast of Cuba adjacent to the Cayman Trough, Liliyenberg and others (1981) found very rapid uplift and subsidence rates based on geodetic releveling surveys in the periods from 1952 to 1965 and from 1970 to 1976. Proposed rates of uplift/subsidence range from 2 to 8 mm/yr. In this same area, Oro and others (1982) and Kartashov and Mayo (1972) identified several areas of folding and faulting of Neogene sediments. In central and western Cuba, studies by Shanzer and others (1975) and Ducloz (1963) identified a series of higher-level erosional surfaces and coastal marine terraces. The higher erosional terraces of probable Mio-Pliocene age are slightly deformed tectonically.

In Jamaica, the site of another active restraining bend system (Mann and Burke, 1980; Mann and others, 1985), uplifted

STRIKE-SLIP BASIN TYPES

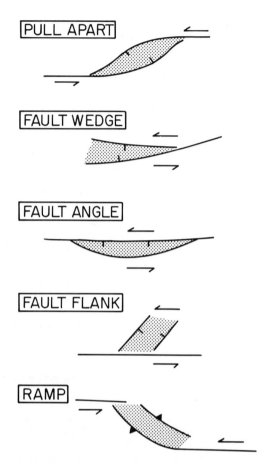

Figure 3. Common types of sedimentary basins that are formed along strike-slip fault zones. These basin models, which were largely developed by workers in California and New Zealand, can explain most of the local areas of tectonic subsidence and Neogene sedimentation in the northern and southern Caribbean. These basins typically are adjacent to strike-slip compressional zones (or "push-ups") such as Jamaica or the Araya-Paria Peninsula of Venezuela (Fig. 1). These uplifted areas are quickly eroded and contribute large amounts of clastic sediments to basinal areas.

Pleistocene coral terraces are most common along the northern coast, where at one locality, seven coral reef levels are present up to 180 m in elevation. Radiometric ages of these terraces indicate uplift rates there of 0.14 mm/yr (Cant, 1973). Horsfield (1972) measured the elevation of a well-developed, late Pleistocene sea-level notch along a 30 km segment of northern Jamaica. The present variable elevation of the notch, at heights ranging from 2 to 12 m above sea level, suggests a pattern of late Pleistocene tectonic uplift controlled by block movements along northeast-striking normal(?) faults perhaps produced by secondary extension along the left-lateral Duanvale Fault (see fault-flank basin

mechanism of Fig. 3). The similarities of notch profile and dimensions and the existence of only one notch at any given locality suggest that the notches were all formed during the same period. Land and Epstein (1970) previously pointed out that the notch probably formed during a regression about 105,000 yr ago, which followed the 130-ka interglacial high stand. Coral terraces in westernmost Jamaica at Negril are tilted to the south, and the general lack of terraces along the south coast of Jamaica suggests relative subsidence in this direction (Horsfield, 1975).

A study of late Tertiary high-level planation surfaces and uplifted marine fossil assemblages by Robinson (1971) suggests that Jamaica began to emerge from the sea in middle Miocene time and that the main fault movements in Jamaica occurred during the middle to late Pliocene. The concordant elevations of higher level erosional surfaces suggested to Robinson (1971) that the origin of higher level planation surfaces was due to changes in eustatic sea level. Steineck (1974) computed values of Neogene uplift in northern Jamaica using paleodepth estimates from fossil assemblages and sedimentary thicknesses. He estimated 450 m of late Miocene and early Pliocene uplift and a post-middle Pliocene uplift of 1,000 m. From the middle Miocene, long-term, down-to-the-south tilting consistent with tilts of Pleistocene coral reefs is indicated by southward thickening of Neogene carbonate units (Arden, 1975).

Neogene tilting and vertical movements have been suggested for the Nicaraguan Rise by Bock (1972) and Horsfield (1975). Navassa Island, the Cayman Islands, the Swan Islands, and the Bay Islands all occupy similar structural positions as emergent crests of elongate submarine ridges either within or adjacent to major strike-slip fault zones (Plate 11). Horsfield (1975) suggested that Neogene carbonate rocks of the Cayman Islands are tilted to the west with a general decrease in elevation of the islands in this direction. In a more recent work, Emery (1981) found no evidence for tectonic uplift or warping of the 2-m-high last interglacial (~125 ka) erosional terrace on Grand Cayman Island. Brunt and others (1973) suggested early Pleistocene subsidence based on facies analysis of onshore limestone outcrops. Tilting of Neogene carbonate units has also been suggested for Navassa Island (Burne and others, 1974), the Swan Islands (Ivey and others, 1980), and the Bay Islands (Horsfield, 1973, 1974).

In Puerto Rico, the concordance of various erosional terrace levels and Pleistocene reefs indicates a minimum amount of differential tectonic movement in late Pleistocene time (Monroe, 1968; Weaver, 1968, 1971). However, Alonso-Harris and others (1983) suggested that mid-Oligocene to early Pleistocene deposits of the southern slope of the Puerto Rico Trench have differentially subsided toward the trench on the lower slope and have been uplifted on the upper slope toward the island by hundreds of meters over the past 4 m.y. Fox and Heezen (1975) documented the existence of early Tertiary shallow-water limestone at a depth of 3,500 m in the Puerto Rico Trench. This observation led them to conclude that there had been extensive subsidence of the southern slope of the trench since early Miocene time. Monroe (1972) pointed out that the middle Tertiary strata of northern

Puerto Rico form a north-dipping monocline interrupted by only a few small folds and minor faults, whereas rocks of equivalent age in southern Puerto Rico are more intensely deformed by a complex system of early Miocene to Pleistocene faults. Tilting and late Pleistocene faulting on the Virgin Island Platform has been described by Holmes and Kindinger (1985).

Relation of Neogene volcanism to strike-slip faults

Wadge and Wooden (1982) reviewed data on nine occurrences of Miocene to Holocene volcanic centers within the North America–Caribbean PBZ (Plate 11). Most of these centers consist of alkalic basalts, which were either erupted as volcanoes or intruded as shallow plugs generally along northeast-striking, normal faults produced as a secondary response to east–west-trending left-lateral simple shear (Fig. 3). At least two of these Neogene basalt occurrences (Low Layton, northeast coast of Jamaica, and a submarine outcrop in the Jamaica Passage; Plate 11) appear to have been erupted into small pull-apart basins along east-west strike-slip faults.

Groundbreaks associated with faults

The February 4, 1976 (M = 7.5) Guatemala earthquake is the only historical surface-faulting earthquake in the northern Caribbean for which there are detailed data on both coseismic and afterslip displacement. This event resulted in about a meter of left-lateral offset along a 230-km-long, well-defined rupture (Plafker, 1976) that coincided with a previously mapped late Quaternary fault known to mark part of the southern side of the Motagua Valley (Schwartz and others, 1979; Plate 11). Afterslip measurements along the Motagua Fault Zone in the months following the 1976 coseismic rupture revealed as much as a 42 percent increase in displacement over the coseismic displacement (Bucknam and others, 1978). Coseismic surface faulting showing normal slip also occurred along the Mixco fault of Guatemala during the February 4 Motagua rupture and during a separate Mixco earthquake two days after the main February 4 event (Plafker, 1976; Langer and Bollinger, 1979).

Relation of earthquake to plate boundary zone faults

In this section we would like to briefly point out the seismic expression of previously described northern Caribbean PBZ faults by referring to seismicity map by McCann and Pennington (this volume). This map indicates a 200- to 250-km-wide seismic zone that approximately defines the two major strike-slip fault zones in the northern Caribbean (Fig. 1 and Plate 11). The northern strike-slip fault zone is relatively well defined by an alignment of scattered shallow epicenters in the Puerto Rico Trench; northern Hispaniola (Septentrional Fault Zone); southern Cuba (Oriente Fault Zone); Cayman Trough (Mid-Cayman Spreading Center); and north of Honduras (Swan Fault Zone; Fig. 1). The southern mapped strike-slip fault zone—the Enriquillo-Plantain Garden

Fault Zone—is poorly defined by recorded events in southern Hispaniola and Jamaica, but better defined by the inferred rupture zones of historical earthquakes (review by Mann and others, 1984b, their Fig. 2D).

The relationship of historical seismicity to the following northern Caribbean faults is given in these references: Motagua (Schwartz and others, 1979); Polochic (White, 1985); Swan (Osieki, 1981); Jamaican faults (review by Mann and others, 1985); Hispaniola (Sykes and others, 1982); and Puerto Rico and the Virgin Islands (McCann, 1985).

Plate motion models

The predicted direction and total rate of present-day North America–Caribbean interplate motion remains controversial. West of central Hispaniola, surface faulting (Mann and others, 1984b) and shallow seismicity (Sykes and others, 1982) suggest pure east-west strike-slip movement in accord with that predicted from global plate calculations (Minster and Jordan, 1978). However, in eastern Hispaniola, Puerto Rico, and the Virgin Islands, seismicity indicates west-southwesterly oblique underthrusting of the North American Plate at the Puerto Rico Trench (Frankel, 1982; Sykes and others, 1982; Fischer and McCann, 1984). The global plate model for this area (Minster and Jordan, 1978) predicts a small component of interplate extension in the vicinity of Puerto Rico and the Virgin Islands. Byrne and others (1985) have presented a microplate model for this region based on regional seismicity. This model proposes three small platelets bounded by the Puerto Rico Trench, the Muertos Trough, and other less well-known faults. These smaller microplates may be moving independently of the larger Caribbean and North American plates, as shown by the recent occurrence of a large earthquake along the proposed microplate boundary along the Muertos Trough.

SOUTH AMERICA–CARIBBEAN STRIKE-SLIP PLATE BOUNDARY ZONES

Distribution of major strike-slip faults

The South American–Caribbean strike-slip PBZ is classified here for convenience as the approximately 200-km-wide zone of right-lateral strike-slip faults that lies east of the Boconó Fault Zone (at approximately 68°W) and extends along the Venezuelan coastal margin to the Lesser Antilles subduction zone near Trinidad and Tobago (Fig. 1). Because much of the faulting occurs offshore, the character and lateral extent of strike-slip faults is becoming better known from study of marine seismic records (e.g., Schubert and Krause, 1984; Leonard, 1983; Robertson and Burke, 1989). The onshore faults have been fairly well studied along the Venezuelan coastal margin, within the Caribbean Mountains to the south, and westward into eastern Venezuela and Trinidad (Soulas, 1985) (Plate 11). The principal onshore strike-slip fault zone in northern South America is the Morón–El

Pilar Fault System, which passes eastward from a continuous but strongly curved juncture with the northeast striking Boconó Fault Zone (Schubert, 1984) and then passes along the Venezuelan coastal margin (Morón Fault Zone). Schubert (1984) has also included the eastern submarine extension of Oca-Chirinos Fault Zone (Plate 11) to the north as part of the Morón Fault Zone. This collective Morón Fault Zone steps southward across and terminates at the Cariaco pull-apart basin (Plate 11). The southern margin of this active pull-apart is the El Pilar Fault Zone, which extends eastward through northern Trinidad. A small push-up structure occurs in the Cerros de las Minas on the Araya-Paria Peninsula (Plate 11) in eastern Venezuela and shifts the trace of the El Pilar Fault Zone 5 km to the north (Perez and Aggarwal, 1981; Vierbuchen, 1984). Analysis of marine seismic reflection data to the north and east of Trinidad, and deformation of mud diapirs (Robertson and Burke, 1989), suggest that the El Pilar Fault Zone extends 100 km east of Trinidad in an east-northeasterly direction toward the Lesser Antilles subduction zone. Robertson and Burke (1989) identified two other east-northeasterly striking submarine faults to the north of the El Pilar Fault Zone, which we show on Plate 11.

In the Caribbean Mountains south of the Morón Fault Zone, there are several east-west to west-southwesterly striking right-lateral faults of which the La Victoria Fault Zone appears to be the most important (Table 2 and Plate 11). Other faults in this zone include the Tácata and Avila Fault Zones (Table 2). A curious set of west-northwesterly striking right-lateral faults are found near the southern limit of the PBZ (Guárico, Urica, San Francisco, El Soldado, and Los Bajos) and most appear to change strike and terminate on northeasterly striking thrust faults. However, the Urica Fault Zone appears not to terminate on a thrust but has been suggested to extend 185 km eastward to south of Trinidad (Munroe and Smith, 1984).

Strike-slip fault offsets

A wide range of right-lateral offsets have been mapped on faults within the South America–Caribbean PBZ (Table 2 and Plate 11). Unlike the northern Caribbean where the Cayman Trough provides direct evidence for large-scale Tertiary left-lateral strike-slip displacement, up to now there have been no large (>100 km) right-lateral offsets observed in the southern Caribbean (Table 2). However, no one strike-slip fault such as the El Pilar need account for more than a fraction of the total inter-plate motion since at least the Oligocene, and all strike-slip faults shown in Figure 2 need not have been active simultaneously.

Muessig (1984) has pointed out that east-west striking strike-slip faults and associated pull-apart basins were active in northern Venezuela as early as the Oligocene. Early offsets along these older faults are now difficult to detect because these faults parallel Eocene and older thrusts of the Caribbean nappe province and because of subsequent Neogene deformation, particularly that related to the northward motion of the Maracaibo Block relative to the rest of South America (Mann and Burke, 1984a).

We have included many poorly known faults in Table 2 for which there is no geologic evidence for strike-slip movement (e.g., San Francisco and Guárico). These poorly known faults were included in the compilation because they often: (1) parallel known strike-slip faults; (2) occur within the plate boundary earthquake zone and are often associated with elongate zones of active seismicity and/or elongate rupture zones of historic earthquakes; and (3) they generally form prominent linear fault valleys or coastlines (Plate 11).

Rates of strike-slip fault displacement

As in the northern Caribbean, there is limited direct geologic or geodetic data for the rates of offset in the South America–Caribbean strike-slip PBZ. A major problem in determining rates of Neogene displacement is that most of the major strike-slip faults crop out within and offset Mesozoic rocks. However, some offsets of Neogene rocks have been established. Installation of geodetic networks is planned across the El Pilar Fault Zone on the Araya-Paria Peninsula (Schubert, 1979).

According to Wilson (1968) and Perez and Aggarwal (1981), the El Soldado and Los Bajos Fault Zones of Trinidad both offset post-middle Pliocene deposits and structures by about 10.5 km (Table 2). Perez and Aggarwal (1981) treated these adjacent faults as a composite structure with a total of 22 km of right-lateral offset of late Neogene deposits and calculated an average slip rate of about 7 to 11 mm/yr. Using the geometry of late Neogene pull-apart basins along the El Pilar–Morón Fault System (Cariaco Basin) and the La Victoria Fault Zone (Lake Valencia; Plate 11), Schubert (1984) calculated rates of 12.5 to 50 mm/yr (based on 25 to 100 km of offset in 2 m.y.) and 1 to 2.5 mm/yr (based on 2 to 5 km of offset in 2 m.y.) on the two faults, respectively. It should be noted that rates of displacement based on pull-apart basin geometry should be treated with caution because of problems in defining their exact dimensions as well as the precise age of their sedimentary fill. Robertson and Burke (1986) postulated 35 to 40 km of apparent right-lateral offset along the submarine extension of the El Pilar Fault Zone to the east of Trinidad. The fault apparently offsets the late Miocene Caroni Basin, which outcrops in northern Trinidad. This offset of 35 to 40 km, if produced at a constant rate over the last 6 to 8 m.y., suggests an average rate of offset of 5 mm/yr. Robertson and Burke (1989) proposed an additional 85 km of right-lateral offset south of the El Pilar Fault Zone, based on the geometry of sheared elliptical mud diapirs.

Strike-slip related subsidence and uplift

The pattern of vertical uplift and subsidence in the Caribbean–South America PBZ conforms well to a model of a wide plate boundary zone of right-lateral strike-slip on a few major east-west striking, right-lateral fault strands (Plate 11). Areas of most rapid uplift and subsidence seem to be localized at bends or stepovers in the major strike-slip faults. For example, the Cariaco

Basin (Schubert, 1982b) is a 1,400-m-deep submarine depression formed within a 200-m-deep coastal shelf at a 35-km-wide step-over between the Morón and El Pilar Fault Zones (Plate 11). The basin contains a minimum sediment thickness of 1 km. A minimum age of 2 Ma for this sedimentary fill can be calculated using the sedimentation rate of 0.5 mm/yr determined during analysis of a core from the upper sedimentary horizons. Other late Neogene pull-aparts at bends in right-lateral strike-slip zones include the Guarenas-Guatire Basin along the Avila Fault Zone and the Lake Valencia Basin along the La Victoria Fault Zone (Plate 11). Both basins are bounded by active faults and filled with several hundred meters of Plio-Pleistocene alluvial and lacustrine sediments. Other recent strike-slip–related basins include Santa Lucía–Ocumare del Tuy—a fault-wedge basin at the junction of the Tácata and La Victoria Fault Zones—and several late Neogene basins in the Trinidad area (e.g., Caroni), which are elongate and synclinal fault-angle depressions parallel to major strike-slip faults (Robertson and Burke, 1989).

The South America–Caribbean PBZ differs from the North America–Caribbean boundary by having significantly less major restraining bend or compressional segments along strike-slip faults (Plate 11). One exception is the Cerros de la Minas push-up on the El Pilar Fault Zone on the Araya-Paria Peninsula. This push-up may be responsible for the topographic uplift of the central part of the peninsula. Uplift between and along the El Pilar Fault Zone and adjacent offshore faults appears to closely control the elongate alignment of basement metamorphic rocks on the Araya-Paria Peninsula of Venezuela, the northern coast range of Trinidad, and the islands of Tobago (Robertson and Burke, 1989), Margarita, Coche, and Tortuga (Schubert and Krause, 1984; Plate 11).

An interesting feature of the South America–Caribbean deformation zone in Trinidad and eastern Venezuela is the close association of active mud diapirs with secondary thrust faults and anticlines produced by right-lateral strike-slip displacement (Higgins and Saunders, 1974). The parent material of the diapirs is Miocene delta front muds deposited during northward progradation of the proto-Orinoco River (Michelson, 1976). Elliptical mud diapirs within the strike-slip PBZ near Trinidad appear to have undergone right-lateral ductile shear and have been used to delineate the active zone of strike-slip displacement (Robertson, 1986).

Studies of uplifted planation surfaces and coral reef terraces have been carried out in the South America–Caribbean strike-slip PBZ for a number of years. Uplift and subsidence data based on coral reef and terrace data were taken from the following papers and plotted on Plate 11: Aruba, Bonaire, Curaçao, and La Blanquilla Islands (Herweijer and Focke, 1978; Schubert and Szabo, 1978); La Orchila Island (Schubert and Valastro, 1976); Cordillera de la Costa of Venezuela (Schubert and others, 1977); western tip of Araya Peninsula (Vignali, 1972); and Margarita (Graf, 1972).

Radiometric dating of the lower unrecrystallized limestone terraces of Curaçao (10 m above sea level), La Blanquilla Island (7 to 10 m above sea level), and La Orchila Island (1 to 3 m above sea level) show that these constructional terraces formed about 130,000 yr ago during the last major interglacial when sea level was slightly higher than today. No equivalents of the Barbados I and II terraces were found, which indicates that these islands have been less uplifted then the tectonically active island of Barbados. Nevertheless, Schubert and Valastro (1976) suggested that the submarine ridge on which all of the islands are located has been subjected to gradual uplift since late Tertiary time.

A single fission track age of an apatite from the Venezuela Caribbean Mountains yielded a latest Miocene age of uplift (6.1 ± 1.3 Ma; Kohn and others, 1984). The authors point out that this uplift age conforms with abundant evidence for synchronous uplift in the mountain ranges of the Maracaibo Block to the west.

Relation of Neogene volcanism to strike-slip faults

There are no reported occurrences of Neogene volcanism along strike-slip faults, although aligned hot springs, fumaroles, and sulfur deposits are present along the active trace of the El Pilar Fault Zone on the Araya-Paria Peninsula (Schubert, 1979; Plate 11). This apparent lack of fault-related volcanism, which contrasts with the northern strike-slip boundary, may simply reflect the fact that many of the major South American faults are submarine and may have small areas of associated submarine volcanism that have been buried by sediment and are therefore difficult to detect.

Groundbreaks associated with faults

Paige (1930) reported extension and shear cracks from the epicenter area of the 1929 Gulf of Cariaco earthquake (M = 6.9) near Cumaná in the vicinity of the El Pilar Fault Zone. The orientation of the cracks suggested right-lateral strike-slip motion on an east-west fault.

Relation of earthquakes to plate boundary zone faults

In this section we would like to briefly point out the seismic expression of previously described southern Caribbean PBZ faults by referring to the seismicity map by Pennington and others (this volume). This map indicates a diffuse east-west band of shallow earthquakes parallel to the El Pilar Fault Zone in eastern Venezuela, but this band virtually disappears to the west along the Morón Fault Zone of central Venezuela and the adjacent offshore borderlands area (Kafka and Weidner, 1981). Microearthquake surveys along the El Pilar Fault Zone from the Gulf of Cariaco to the Gulf of Paria reveal concentrations of microearthquakes along the El Pilar Fault Zone from the Gulf of Cariaco to as far as the town of El Pilar on the Araya-Paria Peninsula (Perez and Aggarwal, 1981; Plate 11). The southern limit of major seismic activity in eastern Venezuela is approximately aligned along the strike of the Urica Fault Zone (Perez and Aggarwal, 1981) (Fig. 1).

Plate motion models

As in the northern Caribbean, the direction and rate of Caribbean–South America interplate motion remains controversial. Several groups of workers have suggested on the basis of theoretical plate calculations, geologic evidence, and seismicity that the South American Plate has been converging in a westnorthwesterly direction on the southern boundary of the Caribbean Plate since the late Tertiary (Minster and Jordan, 1978; Perez and Aggarwal, 1981). This convergence has produced a PBZ of west-northwesterly, right-lateral strike-slip faults such as the Urica, San Francisco, Los Bajos, El Soldado, and Guárico Faults and related northeast-trending thrust faults. The westnorthwesterly strike of these faults is thought to mark the direction of plate convergence. Speed (1985) has recently elaborated this idea of oblique convergence and has suggested this convergence began in late Eocene or Oligocene time in western Venezuela and progressed eastward to a point today on the Araya-Paria Peninsula. In his model the El Pilar Fault is a north-dipping thrust along a "sutured" collisional front to the west of the Araya-Paria Peninsula. On the other hand, Mann and Burke (1984a) have suggested that long-term Neogene interplate strike-slip motion extending to the Lesser Antilles arc is recorded by major strikeslip faults like the Morón–El Pilar Fault System, which extend as far east as Tobago (Robertson and Burke, 1989). The geometry of associated pull-apart and push-up segments along these faults suggests an east-west direction of relative plate motion parallel to the strike of the major faults, as in the northern Caribbean. The interpretation is consistent with truncation of west-northwesterly striking family of faults on throughgoing east-west striking faults like the El Pilar (Plate 11).

The relation of the east-west striking right-lateral faults of the South America–Caribbean PBZs (e.g., Morón–El Pilar) to both east-west (Oca-Chirinos) and northwest striking (Boconó) strike-slip faults of the Maracaibo Block is not clear (Plate 11). Schubert and Krause (1984) have shown through interpretation of satellite radar imagery and marine data that the Boconó Fault Zone changes strike abruptly at the Yaracuy pull-apart basin and is directly continuous with the Morón Fault Zone to the east. Furthermore, they extended the Oca-Chirinos Fault Zone eastward without interruption to north of the Gulf of Cariaco (Plate 11). Dewey and Pindell (1985) suggested that the Cretaceous-Paleogene Aruba-Orchila island arc has been internally deformed as the Maracaibo Block overrode the relatively eastward moving Caribbean Plate at this juncture. This internal deformation has resulted in the formation of small Neogene basins between the islands. In the offshore area to the east of the Paraguana Peninsula, Barbot and others (1980) have identified a complex zone of north-to-northwesterly striking, mostly normal faults that deform Quaternary sediments. On Curaçao, Schubert and Scheidegger (1986) measured joints in outcrops of Quaternary reef limestone and determined that the direction of maximum compression has an azimuth of 170° This direction is slightly different from a direction of maximum compression with azimuth of 130°, deter-

mined using joints in outcrops of Mesozoic rocks and Quaternary sediments in the Coastal Range of Venezuela (Table 1). In the next section we discuss the neotectonics of the Maracaibo Block and its surroundings in greater detail.

PANAMA ARC–SOUTH AMERICA COLLISIONAL PLATE BOUNDARY ZONE

Introduction

The Caribbean PBZ in northwestern South America (area west of the Boconó Fault Zone in Venezuela and north of approximately 5°N) and Panamá (Fig. 2) contrasts with the eastern and western island arc boundaries and the northern and southern strike-slip boundaries in: (1) not exhibiting widespread active calc-alkaline volcanoes; (2) having major active strike-slip faults that strike northeasterly and northwesterly (Fig. 2); (3) having a wider, more complex pattern of earthquakes (Kafka and Weidner, 1981; Pennington and others, this volume); (4) having seismic zones (downgoing slabs) that reach farther into the mantle (Pennington, 1981); and (5) having many complex Neogene sedimentary basins that frequently occur between two inwardly dipping reverse faults ("ramp basins"; cf. Fig. 3).

The plate-tectonic framework of the area has remained obscure because no throughgoing strike-slip faults or other plate boundary features can be mapped between the Morón Fault Zone in Venezuela and the active arc systems of Costa Rica and Colombia (Fig. 2). This observation suggests that the region represents a complex PBZ in which Caribbean plate motion is transformed from the relatively simple and predictable southern Caribbean strike-slip zone into other, more complex tectonic styles. In order to better understand deformation and plate motion in this region, we shall discuss the following topics: (1) distribution of major faults; (2) fault offsets; (3) rates of fault displacement; (4) collision-related subsidence and uplift; (5) relation of faults to earthquakes; and (6) plate-motion models. A compilation of offsets, timing of offsets, and slip rate is shown in Table 3. Major structural features and sources of information are plotted on Plate 11.

Distribution of major faults

Detailed and systematic mapping of Neogene structures along fault zones on a regional scale has only begun in recent years (e.g., Schubert, 1982a). Faulting in Panamá has been poorly studied but has become better known because of advances in side-looking radar imagery, which provides synoptic views of regions such as eastern Panamá that are often cloud covered (Wing and MacDonald, 1973).

Most of the major faults in northwestern South America are right-lateral strike-slip or thrust faults and strike north to northeast, roughly following the arcuate northwestern edge of the South American craton (Fig. 2; Table 3; Plate 11). Three notable exceptions occur: the right-lateral, east-west-striking Oca-

Chirinos and Cuiza fault zones of Colombia and Venezuela and the north-northeast–striking left-lateral Santa Marta–Bucaramanga Fault Zone of Colombia (Fig. 2; Table 3). The Boconó Santa Marta–Bucaramanga, and South Caribbean Deformed Belt define a wedge-shaped area referred to as the "Maracaibo Block" (Bowin, 1976; Mann and Burke, 1984a). Faulting within the Maracaibo Block is extremely complex, and the nature of the major faults (e.g., El Tigre, Avispa, Valera, Carache, Humocaro; Table 3) is not well understood.

Two orthogonal sets of poorly studied strike-slip faults have been identified in Panamá: northeasterly striking right-lateral faults and northwesterly striking left-lateral faults (Fig. 2; Table 3). The northwesterly striking faults appear to be the dominant set; they form prominent fault valleys on the Azuero and Soná peninsulas of western Panamá and may continue to the northwest into Costa Rica (Plate 11).

Major fault offsets

A wide variety of types and amounts of fault offsets have been mapped within the region of Panamá and northwestern South America. A summary of known and unknown fault characteristics is given in Table 3 and plotted on Plate 11. Probably the best-studied fault of those listed in Table 3 is the Boconó Fault Zone of Venezuela because of its proximity to large population areas and because of its much higher rate of shallow seismic activity than other faults like the Morón or Santa Marta–Bucaramanga Fault Zones (McCann and Pennington, this volume). Despite the attention it has received, the total amount and timing of right-lateral offset on the Boconó is controversial; geologic estimates range from 9 to 290 km (see Table 1 of Schubert, 1982a). Based on semiquantitative plate vector diagrams, Dewey and Pindell (1985) predicted a total right-lateral offset of 290 km over the last 9 m.y. in a zone parallel to the Boconó Fault within the northeasterly striking Mérida Andes. Schubert (1982a) has identified three active pull-apart basins along the trace of the Boconó Fault Zone and thereby established its dominantly right-lateral strike-slip character. The youngest feature with a reported offset (other than that of the Quaternary glacial features) are thrust sheets of the Caribbean nappe province, which developed mostly during the Eocene collision of a south-facing island arc with the South American continent (Stephan, 1985). The Boconó Fault Zone apparently offsets the leading edge of the thrust sheets by 80 km in a right-lateral sense. An even larger offset along the Boconó fault is suggested by correlation of arc and ophiolitic rocks of the Venezuelan Mountains with those in the Falcón region and the Guajira and Paraguaná peninsulas (Mann and Burke, 1984a). Oligocene and Neogene deposits of the Falcón Basin obscure much of the intervening area and make precise correlations of arc and ophiolite rocks in the two areas difficult. Salvador (1986) has pointed out that existence of a broad but continuous pre-Cretaceous basement arch across the Boconó Fault Zone that precludes the possibility of large (>10 km) strike-slip offset. Resolution of the discrepancy in the amount of pro-posed strike-slip offset along the Boconó Fault Zone remains a priority area for future mapping.

The Santa Marta–Bucaramanga Fault Zone has been mapped as a continuous feature for 550 km from the Caribbean coast to the eastern Cordillera of Colombia where, like the Boconó Fault Zone, it appears to terminate on a series of thrusts (Campbell, 1968; Fig. 2). The Santa Marta and Bucaramanga fault segments are linked at a major compressional push-up structure, which is marked by exposures of Precambrian basement rocks (Tschanz and others, 1974). The presence of a prominent topographic scarp, a right-stepping push-up, faceted spurs, and sinistrally skewed stream channels (Campbell, 1968) suggests active, left-lateral displacement along the fault. Vertical relief in the triangular-shaped Santa Marta Massif, bounded by the Santa Marta–Bucaramanga and Oca Fault Zones (Plate 11), is very large, with Precambrian rocks exposed at elevation of 6 km above sea level. Structural relief on the base of the Tertiary section is at least 15 km between the crest of the Santa Marta Massif and the adjacent deep Colombian and Venezuelan basins (Case and Holcombe, 1980). Major left-lateral offsets, approximately equivalent to the 100 km suggested by Stephan (1985) offset on the Boconó, have been suggested on the basis of structural and stratigraphic similarities between the César and Middle Magdalena basins (offset of 110 km; Campbell, 1968) and correlation between outcrops and subcrops of metamorphic rocks on either side of the fault (Tschanz and others, 1974).

The Oca-Chirinos Fault Zone has been mapped for 190 km from the northeastern coast of Colombia to the northern end of Lake Maracaibo. Sixty-five km of apparent right-lateral offset is inferred from offset metamorphic rocks along the Sierra de Santa Marta (Tschanz and others, 1974). Although the modern and historic seismicity is very low, the Oca-Chirinos Fault displaces a series of Quaternary beach strandlines and a shell horizon with an age of 2,500 yr (Kellogg and Bonini, 1982). Vasquez and Dickey (1972) have suggested that the Oca-Chirinos Fault extends eastward through the basement of the Oligocene Falcón Basin on the basis of right-stepping en echelon folds. A right-lateral offset of 98 km was calculated using the geometry of the en echelon folds. Sedimentary facies maps suggest that the age of displacement was post-medial Miocene.

The Cuiza Fault Zone of the Guajira Peninsula apparently offsets Cretaceous and Paleozoic rocks by 15 to 25 km (Alvarez, 1971). Offsets on other faults within the Maracaibo Block are listed on Table 3. Many of these faults seem to have a predominantly vertical component of movement and have acted as important controls on post-Eocene sedimentation in the Lake Maracaibo area (see Mann and Burke, 1984, for a review).

Faults with major known offsets to the southwest of the Maracaibo Block in Colombia and Ecuador include the Palestina Fault Zone with 27.7 km of apparent right-lateral offset on a variety of lithologic units (Feininger, 1970) and the Otú Fault with a left-lateral offset of 70 km (Fig. 2). Offsets on the Romeral, Nus, and Cimitarra faults are not known. The Romeral Fault forms a major tectonic boundary in northern South America by separating continental crust on the southeast from oceanic crust to the northwest.

In Panamá, no well-mapped offsets on faults have been demonstrated, although en echelon folds and pull-apart segments indicate active, left-lateral displacement on major, northeast-striking onshore faults such as the Sansón Hills, Jaqué River, and Sambú Fault Zones (Mann and others, 1986; Table 3). Vitali and others (1985) have suggested the presence of an offshore northwest-striking left-lateral fault parallel to the North Panama Ridge in the Colombian Basin.

Rates of strike-slip movement

The best-known rates of movement are for the Boconó Fault Zone, which offsets late Pleistocene (18 ka) glacial moraines from which a local slip rate of 3 to 14 mm/yr can be calculated (Schubert, 1982a). The configuration and size of Quaternary pull-apart basins suggest a Quaternary right-lateral offset rate of 1.4 to 1.8 mm/yr. Recent geodetic measurements across the Boconó Fault have shown a right-lateral offset of 27 mm between 1975 and 1981, corresponding to an offset of 4.5 mm/yr (Henneberg, 1983).

Tectonic subsidence and uplift

A large number of fault-bounded sedimentary basins are present in the Panamá–South America collisional zone. The most prominent of these are the Maracaibo, Barinas, and Magdalena in northwestern South America (Plate 11). The fact that these basins did not assume their present-day morphology until Oligocene or Miocene time suggests that rapid Neogene uplift has occurred along the fault-bounded mountain fronts that define their edges (see Mann and Burke, 1984a, for review). For example, the uplift of the Mérida Andes by reverse and thrust faulting at its edges was responsible for the symmetrical presence of the Maracaibo and Barinas Basins on its flanks.

Schubert (1985) has reviewed Quaternary uplift data from the Mérida Andes. According to Schubert (1985), uplifted oxisoils, suggested as major evidence for recent uplift by Weingarten (1977), were never dated and may be younger (middle Quaternary age) and probably formed at higher elevations than previously thought by Weingarten. Quaternary uplift of the soils may have been on the order of 2 km in the late Quaternary, assuming they formed at lower (800 m) elevations. Alluvial terraces high above present river levels in the Venezuelan Andes apparently have formed very recently (since the beginning of Wisconsinan time) and probably close to their present elevation.

Local geodetic networks for measuring vertical and horizontal crustal movements have been established in the Venezuelan Andes and Lake Maracaibo area since 1956 (Henneberg, 1983). Geodetic installations to measure movements along the Boconó Fault began in 1973 at three locations. The main result of this network was to show that the magnitudes of observed vectors are principally directed toward the fault (indicating horizontal com-

pression perpendicular to the strike of the Venezuelan Andes), although most vectors also show an additional right-lateral slip component. The net horizontal creep rate varies between the networks, from 1 mm in 5 months to 100 mm in 2 years. The net vertical movements suggest the southeast side of the fault has been uplifted 46 mm above the north side since measurements began in 1973.

In the Lake Maracaibo geodetic network, measurements indicate that subsidence related to oil extraction has been as rapid as 5 m in 57 years (1925–1982) on the eastern edge of the lake.

Shagam and others (1984) have determined 56 fission-track ages from apatite, sphene, and zircon concentrates from rocks collected in the mountain ranges in western Venezuela and eastern Colombia that constitute the triangular Maracaibo Block. These ages indicate that late Cenozoic uplift occurred sporadically with uplift in progress in the Sierra de Perijá (western Venezuela) by latest Oligocene, in the Santander Massif (eastern Colombia) by the early mid-Miocene, and in the Venezuelan Andes by the late Miocene. A major uplift of all of the mountain ranges within the Maracaibo Block occurred in unison during Pliocene-Pleistocene time at accelerating rates.

Local vertical movements have accompanied the development of mud volcanoes along the northwestern coast of Colombia (Plate 11). Mud diapirism began in the middle Miocene and continues to the present as a result of east-west shortening and gravity loading of pelagic mudstones with denser turbiditic sandstones (Duque-Caro, 1984; Vernette and others, 1985). Recent emergence of this foldbelt, which strikes offshore into the Southern Caribbean Deformed Belt (Ladd and others, 1984), has been suggested by Burel and Vernette (1981) and by Duque-Caro (1984) on the basis of late Pliocene–Pleistocene marine deposits now 200 m above sea level.

The Neogene uplift history of the Panama landbridge can be inferred from sedimentary and geochemical differences between the Caribbean/Atlantic and Pacific Oceans following uplift of the land bridge. These differences suggest shoaling of Panama about 4 Ma (Keigwin, 1982). Interchange of terrestrial faunas between North and South America across the Panama land bridge occurred during the Pliocene (~3 Ma; see Mann and Burke, 1984a, for review).

Relation of faults to earthquakes

Maps of earthquake epicenters (McCann and Pennington, this volume) suggest present activity on only one of the major faults listed in Table 3: the Boconó Fault and a possible extension of the Boconó Fault southward along the eastern front of the Andes in Colombia and Ecuador ("Eastern Andean Frontal Fault Zone" of Pennington, 1981). Most of the earthquakes along the Boconó Fault Zone are shallow (<35 km) and have right-lateral focal mechanisms solutions. Historical records indicate that the most destructive event along the Boconó fault was the 1812 earthquake, which appeared to rupture the entire central and northern segments of the fault in addition to the western end of the Morón Fault Zone. Low seismic activity since 1930 and a lack of great earthquakes along the Oca-Chirinos Fault suggest that it has been less active than the Boconó, at least during the historic period (see review by Mann and Burke, 1984).

Plate motion models

Previous plate models of the complex neotectonics of northwestern South America and Panamá can be broadly classified into two groups of hypotheses. The first group attempted to identify a regional stress field by using either the pattern of major faults (e.g., Kellogg and Bonini, 1982) or earthquake focal mechanisms (e.g., Kafka and Weidner, 1981). Kellogg and Bonini (1982) emphasized the role of shallow subduction of the Caribbean Plate beneath northern South America as a mechanism for producing regionally consistent compressive stresses (that is, roughly northwest to southeast crustal shortening across thrust faults). Both Kellogg and Bonini (1982) and Kafka and Weidner (1981) suggested specific directions of maximum compressive stress, ranging from westerly to northwesterly, that is released on variously oriented zones of weakness over the region of northwestern South America.

A second group of hypotheses attempts to account for the complex neotectonics in a more direct fashion by identifying the various rigid plates or blocks involved in the deformation and by defining their rate and direction of relative motion (Silver and others, 1975; Bowin, 1976; Pennington, 1981; Wadge and Burke, 1983; Mann and Burke, 1984a; Dewey and Pindell, 1985). This second group of hypotheses all emphasize the role of the Maracaibo Block, a triangular wedge of crust that is actively moving northward over the Caribbean Plate along the Boconó and Santa Marta–Bucaramanga Fault Zones (Fig. 2). This second group of hypotheses seems to offer a simpler solution to neotectonics in an area where the regional stress field must be exceedingly complicated by the presence of small fault-bounded blocks or microplates composed of anisotropic continental, arc, and oceanic lithosphere and containing preexisting faults oblique to the present-day, interblock movement directions.

Many workers have postulated that the event that initiated northward movement of variously defined blocks of northwestern South America into the Caribbean and uplift of the northern Andean Mountains was the collision of the Panama island arc with the northwestern margin of South America in the latest Miocene to early Pliocene (Wadge and Burke, 1983). Some workers have assumed that the Maracaibo Block is a rigid lithospheric block and have calculated its direction and rate of motion relative to the surrounding larger plates using vector triangle diagrams (Bowin, 1976; Dewey and Pindell, 1985; Kellogg and others, 1985). If one assumes that these blocks behave rigidly, it is possible to construct block vector diagrams that sum relative motions on block mosaics and allow semiquantitative analysis of the directions and slip rates of interblock relative motions as well as slip rates and trends at postulated but often poorly defined block boundaries (Bowin, 1976; Dewey and Pindell, 1985; Kellogg and others, 1985). It is difficult to compare the results of

these analyses, because each group of workers defined different block boundaries and assumed different rates of relative motion. However, all the models suggest northwesterly convergence of the northwest corner of South America (Maracaibo Block, *sensu lata*) over the Colombian Basin. Predicted rates of convergence vary from 1.7 cm/yr (Kellogg and others, 1985) to 0.5 cm/yr (Bowin, 1976). Dewey and Pindell (1985) predicted 300 km of post-late Miocene (<9 Ma) of underthrusting of the Colombian Basin beneath the northwest corner of South America. This northwesterly direction of convergence is consistent with more deformed sediments in the western South Caribbean Deformed Belt than in the eastern belt. A prediction of 290 km of right-lateral offset along the Boconó Fault Zone by Dewey and Pindell (1985) using the same method has been challenged by Salvador (1986) on the basis of stratigraphic data.

A qualitative approach based on compilation of regional geologic data by Mann and Burke (1984) suggested a more northerly convergence direction of the Maracaibo Block on the southern Caribbean. This interpretation was based on regional geologic relations such as: (1) the Neogene uplift of the Beata Ridge to the north of the Maracaibo Block; (2) movement of the Maracaibo Block appears mechanically more likely in a northerly direction, roughly parallel to the bisector of the angle defined by the bounding Boconó and Santa Marta–Bucaramanga Fault Zones; and (3) the presence of Neogene normal faults within the Maracaibo Block suggests that east-west extension of the block occurs during its northward displacement in a manner similar to that of tectonically similar blocks in other areas such as in western Turkey (see Mann and Burke, 1984a, their Fig. 13).

In the Panamá region, a similar rigid plate vector analysis by Minster and Jordan (1978) using a global data set predicted roughly east-west left-lateral strike-slip motion (N71°E ± 5°) at a rate of 54 ± 5 mm/yr between the Nazca and Caribbean plates. Using a compilation of regional geologic data, Mann and Burke (1984a) suggested that Panamá constitutes a northwesterly striking diffuse left-lateral shear zone between the Caribbean and Nazca plates (Fig. 2) rather than a rigid block. These faults segment Panamá, accentuate its oroclinal bend, and displace it northwesterly over the Colombian Basin (Lu and McMillen, 1983; Bowland, 1984). The northward displacement of the Maracaibo Block and the northwesterly displacement of Panamá relative to cratonic South America were interpreted by Mann and Burke (1984a) as movement or "escape" of arc (Panama) and continental (Maracaibo Block) material away from a collisional area presently seismically active in eastern Panamá and western Colombia (McCann and Pennington, this volume).

COCOS–CARIBBEAN–NORTH AMERICA PLATE BOUNDARY ZONE: MIDDLE AMERICA ARC SYSTEM

Introduction

The Middle America region is an area of intense volcanic, seismic, and tectonic activity primarily related to the subduction of Miocene oceanic crust of the Cocos Plate beneath the North American and Caribbean plates (Plate 11). The calculated convergence rate increases southward from about 7 cm/yr off Mexico to more than 10 cm/yr off Costa Rica (Minster and Jordan, 1978). The purpose of this section is to summarize our present knowledge of crustal faulting and vertical movements in the overriding Caribbean Plate. The reader interested in more detailed information on volcanism or seismicity of the Middle America region is referred to the chapters of this volume by Carr and Stoiber (volcanism) and McCann and Pennington (seismicity). Marine data bearing on the tectonics and Neogene development of the submarine trench, slope, and forearc sequence of the Middle America Trench are summarized by von Huene in Winterer and others (1989).

The pattern of onshore Neogene faulting in the overriding plate of the Middle America arc is more complex than the predictable strike-slip fault patterns along the northern and southern Caribbean and is difficult to clearly relate to a single tectonic mechanism. However, recent progress has been made toward identifying certain tectonic mechanisms that can explain regional patterns of faulting, subsidence, and uplift. We organize this discussion around four of the most widely accepted mechanisms believed to affect the Middle America Subduction Zone: (1) arc-parallel extension and strike-slip faulting along the volcanic axis; (2) segmentation of the subducted Cocos Plate; (3) subduction of the Cocos Ridge; and (4) interaction of North America and the Caribbean plates in northern Middle America. Although this approach to the discussion necessarily mixes interpretation with data, the approach does have the advantage of placing a large amount of seemingly unrelated data into a clearer neotectonic framework.

Arc-parallel extension and strike-slip faulting

A prominent Quaternary structural depression coinciding roughly with the belt of active arc volcanoes extends approximately 600 km from the northern Gulf of Fonseca in El Salvador to the Caribbean Sea in Costa Rica (Case and Holcombe, 1980; Table 1). This feature is most prominent in Nicaragua where it is occupied by two major lakes (Managua and Nicaragua) and is known as the Nicaraguan Depression (McBirney and Williams, 1965). Active volcanic centers occur close to the southern margin of the Nicaraguan Depression (approximate width: 75 km) and in the Gulf of Fonseca (approximate width: 40 km). Near the Nicaragua–Costa Rica border, the floor of the depression becomes filled with Quaternary lahar deposits, and the active volcanic centers are located very near the southwestern boundary fault. North of the Gulf of Fonseca in El Salvador, the depression abruptly changes from a northwesterly to more west-north-westerly strike. The depression in El Salvador is intersected by a large number of transverse faults (Carr, 1976) and does not form a continuous topographic feature. However, in El Salvador it can be traced as discontinuous topographic depressions, locally called the "Salvador Graben" or "Median Trough," to the Guatemala

border (Weyl, 1980; Carr, 1976). In Guatemala the Median Trough disappears under the deposits of large volcanoes, although the very striking linear configuration of the volcanic chain and the sharp topographic drop of more than 2,000 m down to the Pacific Coastal Plain might be regarded as evidence of a continuation of the feature (Weyl, 1980).

Structural information on the Nicaraguan Depression–Median Trough is best summarized by McBirney and Williams (1965), Williams and Meyer-Abich (1955), and Carr (1976). The boundary faults of the Nicaraguan Depression are well defined in central and southern Nicaragua (Plate 11). South and west of Lake Managua, the Mateare Fault forms the southwestern margin of the depression and extends as a slightly eroded scarp for 70 km in weakly consolidated volcaniclastic material (Plate 11). The fault appears to be a high-angle normal fault of large displacement along which the Nicaraguan Depression has subsided as an asymmetric half-graben (see McBirney and Williams, 1965, their Fig. 10). Normal faulting along the other, northeastern edge of the graben is traceable continuously from the Gulf of Fonseca to the southeastern tip of Nicaragua. Faulting along this edge occurs on a smaller scale but does act to tilt young sediments to the southwest. Sediments on the southwestern side of the graben appear to be tilted seaward away from the Mateare Fault (Plate 11).

No visible northwestward projection of the Mateare Fault is observed until the fault enters El Salvador where an irregular belt of faulting divides the irregular central depression of that country from seaward-tilted beds along the southwestern margin of the graben. Carr (1976) presented a map of the Median Trough of western El Salvador and southeastern Guatemala (his Fig. 4), which shows the long axis of the trough bounded by right-lateral strike-slip faults that offset other faults by 6 to 9 km (Plate 11). Williams and Meyer-Abich (1955) have suggested that the Median Trough formed in the Pliocene or early Pleistocene as a graben with bedded sediments on the graben shoulders dipping away from the basin floor. As in Nicaragua, most of the Quaternary volcanoes in western El Salvador developed over fissures close to the southern margin of the trough, although in eastern El Salvador, most of the volcanoes rose in the center of the depression and therefore tend to obscure its presence. Information on the many discontinuous faults of the Median Trough is summarized by Williams and Meyer-Abich (1955).

Faults intersecting the depression at high angles in Nicaragua and El Salvador have been emphasized by several authors as seismogenic hazards (Carr, 1976; Plafker, 1976), particularly after the disastrous Managua earthquake of 1972 (M = 5.6). This earthquake occurred at shallow depths (8 to 10 km) along four subparallel, left-lateral strike-slip faults that strike perpendicular to the long axis of the Nicaraguan Depression (Brown and others, 1973). The fault breaks were mappable on land for a distance of 1.6 to 5.9 km. Aftershock data indicated that the faulting extends at least 6 km northeast of the city beneath Lake Managua. Horizontal displacements varied, with the maximum aggregate left-lateral slip ranging from 2 to 38 cm (Brown and others,

1973). Carr (1976) described three Quaternary left-lateral fault zones in El Salvador that strike N30°E to N40°E and offset the boundary faults of the Median Trough by 5 km.

An interesting feature of the Quaternary volcanoes of the Middle America arc is that many display a secondary north-south alignment of vents and tension fractures that intersect the major northwest axis at angles of about 45° (Plate 11). In the northern arc chain in El Salvador, aligned vents have a slightly north-northwesterly strike. North-south striking aligned vents of Neogene alkali volcanoes are also present in the back-arc region of Costa Rica (Wadge and Wooden, 1982) and north-south striking normal faulting has been described offshore in the Colombian Basin by Bowland (1984). These aligned volcanic centers and parallel normal faults suggest that the azimuth of maximum horizontal compression within the volcanic arc and a wide back-arc area of the western Caribbean Plate is not oriented parallel to the northeasterly direction of Cocos–Caribbean Plate convergence (as found in other arcs like the Aleutians; Nakamura and others, 1977) but is oriented in a north-south direction oblique to interplate convergence (Plate 11).

Much of the evidence for the character of active faulting along the Nicaraguan-Median Trough has come from focal mechanism and aftershock studies of large shallow earthquakes. To the south of the Nicaraguan Depression proper in the Valle Central of Costa Rica (Plate 11), Montero and Dewey (1982) suggested on the basis of their study of shallow-focus (<30 km) seismicity that faulting occurs on left-lateral fault planes perpendicular to the arc, and right-lateral fault planes striking parallel to the arc. The shallow seismic belt coincides with the east-southeasterly striking topographic Valle Central and forms (offsets?) the southern margin of the active volcanic arc. Relocation of hypocenters of shallow-focus earthquakes near Managua (Dewey and Algermissen, 1974) showed that earthquakes are closely associated with the western boundary of the Nicaraguan Depression and with Quaternary volcanoes. No shallow earthquakes were located near the eastern boundary of the depression. These authors pointed out the correspondence of the 1972 Managua earthquake faulting to an apparent right-lateral offset in the line of volcanic centers (Case and Holcombe, 1980) and suggested that the offset is formed by an "oceanic-type" transform that accommodates spreading between the two volcanic centers (i.e., left-lateral slip, apparent right-lateral offset). Another larger apparent right-lateral offset of the active volcanic axis is present near the southern end of Lake Nicaragua.

Carr (1976) interpreted the focal mechanism of the 1965 El Salvador earthquake as right-lateral strike-slip parallel to the Median Trough. Burbach and others (1984) were skeptical of using shallow strike-slip events (such as the 1965 El Salvador event and those interpreted by Dean and Drake, 1978) as evidence for transverse breaks perpendicular to the arc or movements parallel to the arc depression because of possible errors in location of the shallow events.

Harlow and White (1985) reviewed evidence for shallow earthquakes and presented a model for right-lateral slip along the volcanic chain similar to the model proposed by Carr (1976) using geologic data. Harlow and White (1985) attributed right slip in the arc to oblique convergence of the Cocos Plate by 5° to 20° to the downward dip of the Benioff zone. However, the direction of plate motion as determined from earthquake focal mechanisms (Burbach and others, 1984) and global tectonic data (Minster and Jordan, 1978) appears to be perpendicular to the arc.

In summary, geologic and seismic data indicate that much of the neotectonic activity associated with subduction along the Middle America Trench is concentrated in a topographic, fault-bounded depression subparallel to the line of active volcanoes. Possible mechanisms for the formation of this feature are: (1) extension of the active volcanic axis and/or back-arc extension associated with the subduction process; (2) subsidence between right-lateral strike-slip faults forming the edges of the trough; or (3) some combination of processes 1 and 2. Little geologic evidence has been presented for continuous right-lateral strike-slip movement paralle to the active arc. Existing data suggest that the Nicaraguan Depression near Managua is a half-graben with vertical displacement much greater along the southwestern boundary (Mateare Fault Zone). Transverse faults perpendicular to the depression may result as "oceanic-type" transform faults connecting offset and widening volcanic centers, or as described in the next section, the transverse faults may reflect crustal breaks above tears or segment boundaries in the subducted Cocos Plate.

Segmentation of the subducted Cocos Plate

Carr (1976) suggested that zones of Quaternary left-lateral strike-slip faults in Guatemala and El Salvador could be directly related to transverse tears or segment boundaries found in the underthrust Cocos Plate (Fig. 1). These tears bound breaks between slabs of different dip. Burbach and others (1984) tested this hypothesis by reexamining teleseismic earthquake locations in the Middle America region and found that the subducting plate appears to have only three major segment boundaries rather than the dozen smaller segments proposed by Carr (1976; both sets of segments shown on Fig. 1). The southernmost segment boundary of Burbach and others (1984) is located southeast of the Nicoya Peninsula and divides a shallowly dipping slab containing the subducted Cocos Ridge to the south from a steeper dipping slab to the north. This segment boudnary may represent an actual fault in the subducted Cocos Plate between an area to the south of slowed or stopped subduction associated with underthrusting of the shallow-dipping Cocos Ridge and an area to the north, which is experiencing "normal" subduction at a steeper angle. A middle segment boundary of Burbach and others (1984) is located below northern Guatemala and is defined by a smooth, unbroken contortion of the slab, which to the north of the segment boundary dips at a shallower angle to the northwest. This curved segment boundary was probably produced by the eastward motion of the North American Plate relative to the Caribbean along the left-lateral Motagua and Polochic strike-slip faults. This lateral motion of North America relative to the Caribbean during the Neogene has pushed the modern trench axis westward in southern Mexico without significantly affecting the geometry of subduction below. Movement of the North American Plate westward relative to the trench axis explains the broad and discontinuous pattern of arc-related volcanism on the North American Plate in southern Mexico (Trans-Mexican Volcanic Belt). In contrast, the narrow alignment of volcanoes on the Caribbean Plate in Middle America suggests that the Caribbean Plate has remained stationary relative to the volcano-producing area of the subducted Cocos Plate (Plate 11).

In summary, Burbach and others (1984) suggested that the resolution of the teleseismic data is not great enough to show conclusively the existence of smaller scale segmentation, especially in the upper 50 km of the subducted plate. The origin of transverse strike-slip faulting as described by Carr (1976) in the northern Middle America magmatic arc remains enigmatic, although strike-slip interactions of the North America and Caribbean plates may provide a possible alternative explanation.

North America–Caribbean Plate interactions

Several authors have attributed Neogene faulting transverse to the northern Middle America arc in Guatemala, El Salvador, and Honduras to internal deformation of the Caribbean Plate as it moves eastward relative to the North American Plate along convex southward, arcuate left-lateral faults of the Motagua–Polochic system (e.g., Pfafker, 1976; Langer and Bollinger, 1979; Wadge and Burke, 1983; Mann and Burke, 1984a; Burkart and Self, 1985). Burkart and Self (1985) provide the most comprehensive discussion of this mechanism and its effects on recent faulting and volcanism.

Burkart and Self (1985) defined four morphotectonic zones of the arc chain in Guatemala and El Salvador. These zones reflect varying amounts of roughly east-west oriented crustal extension and related volcanism as the area (Area "A" in Fig. 1 and Plate 11) rotated eastward relative to both North America and the subduction-controlled ribbon of subcrustal melt. Bifurcation of the volcanic axis in Guatemala and El Salvador with a somewhat older chain lying landward of the active chain was interpreted as eastward movement of crustal blocks away from the subduction-controlled ribbon of melt. In summary, this type of model interprets the recent transverse faulting of the northern Middle America arc in terms of differential movement of upper-crustal blocks over a zone of magma production and contrasts with the model of Carr (1976), which attributes surficial faulting to transverse breaks in the subducted Cocos slab.

This model of localized extension in Area A does not explain widespread east-west extension of other areas to the west in Honduras (Honduras Depression), Nicaragua (Estelí Valley), the submarine grabens of the southwestern Nicaraguan Rise, or the scattered occurrences of late Neogene alkaline basalts in Honduras, Nicaragua, Costa Rica, or the Nicaraguan Rise (Plate 11).

Mann and Burke (1984a) suggested a previous phase of east-west extension of northern Central America and the Nicaraguan Rise (Zone B) associated with post-Cretaceous eastward displacement of the Caribbean relative to the northern Central America promontory. These earlier extensional features appear to have been reactivated by present-day east-west extensional forces, whose origin is poorly understood.

Cocos Ridge collision

The Cocos Ridge is a thickened mass of oceanic crust formed by volcanic activity between 22 and 17 Ma near an oceanic spreading center in the eastern Pacific. The crest of the ridge lies at 1 to 2 km below sea level with an average relief of 3 km above the surrounding sea floor. Studies of marine magnetic anomalies in the eastern Pacific suggest that the Cocos Ridge, which is a linear feature trending northeasterly and extending approximately 200 km in width, entered the Costa Rican segment of the Middle America Trench about 1 Ma and has penetrated less than 40 km below Costa Rica (Lonsdale and Klitgord, 1978). The subduction of the Cocos Ridge has been emphasized by many workers as a mechanism for the shallow-dipping Benioff Zone and the neotectonic fault and uplift patterns of the southern Middle America arc (e.g., Burbach and others, 1984; Heywood, 1984). In this section we will briefly review some of the neotectonic data on this zone and discuss its possible relation to the Cocos Ridge subduction.

Burbach and others (1984) reviewed the seismicity of the southern Middle America subduction zone and pointed out that the Benioff Zone in the approximate area of the Cocos Ridge between the Panamá Fracture Zone and the Nicoya Peninsula is poorly defined and is characterized by a noticeable absence of hypocenters deeper than 100 km (Plate 11). To the north, the Benioff Zone is well defined and steeply dipping. This suggested the presence of a tear in the downgoing slab, perhaps related to a difference in dip angle between the shallowly inclined Cocos Ridge segment and the "normally" inclined segment to the north.

Topographically, Costa Rica is higher than any other part of southern or central Middle America with peaks more than 3,500 m. This area of high topography coincides approximately with the 200 km width of the subducting Cocos Ridge. Moreover, this region is characterized by rugged peninsulas along the Pacific coast (Burica, Azuero, Osa, and Nicoya), which are commonly within 50 km of the Middle America Trench and also (with the exception of Nicoya) are in approximate alignment with the subducting Cocos Ridge. A major spatial gap occurs in the active volcanic arc opposite the Cocos Ridge and is very similar to other volcanic gaps in other areas produced by subduction of aseismic ridges (McGeary and others, 1985).

Studies of tectonic uplift have been carried out in both the mainland and peninsulas of Costa Rica. Marine Miocene deposits of the Valle Central are now situated between 600 and 1,890 m above sea level. Kruckow (1974) gave the rate of uplift as between 0.040 and 0.095 mm/yr. River terraces studied by the same author indicate periods of rapid uplift followed by periods of relative quiesence. Miyamura (1975) calculated a present rate of uplift for the central mountain range of Costa Rica at 1 to 2 mm/yr based on a geodetic releveling survey. Hare and Gardner (1985) studied four large-scale high-level erosion surfaces of unknown age on the Nicoya Peninsula and suggested that the peninsula has undergone differential and intermittent tectonic uplift since Oligocene-Miocene emergence. Madrigal (1977) has mapped a series of up to six erosional marine terraces of Pleistocene(?) age on the east coast of the Osa Peninsula, Costa Rica, which are tilted toward the north and northeast. Fischer (1980) identified recent to sub-recent differential movements along northeasterly striking faults exposed on the coast from the Nicoya to Burica peninsulas by observing deformation of the coastal bioerosional morphology. The fault blocks were elevated to different heights 1 to 2 m above their original position. Alt and others (1980) have proposed an extremely high uplift rate of 25 mm/yr for the Coastal Range based on a single radiocarbon date of raised fluvial terraces at the mouth of the Rio Terraba.

The pattern of faulting in Neogene sediments in Costa Rica appears to reflect predominately horizontal shortening perpendicular to the trench and is consistent with the width of the subducting Cocos Ridge (Heywood, 1984). Vertical uplift may also be related to the buoyancy of the subducted Cocos Ridge. Major Neogene faults are typically reverse faults that strike parallel to the arc and dip steeply to the northeast. The faults mapped by Fischer (1980) may represent synchronous normal faults perpendicular to this trend. Along strike in Nicaragua, the structural pattern changes rapidly to an extensional half-graben that is much lower in elevation.

In summary, attempted subduction of the Cocos Ridge appears to provide a good working hypothesis for interpreting the existing neotectonic data from the southern Middle America Trench.

NORTH AMERICA–SOUTH AMERICA–CARIBBEAN PLATE BOUNDARY ZONE: LESSER ANTILLES SUBDUCTION ZONE

Introduction

The Lesser Antilles subduction zone extends from the vicinity of Trinidad to as far north as western Puerto Rico and marks the site of subduction of very old (~100 Ma) oceanic lithosphere of the Atlantic Ocean at a slow convergence rate (~2 to 4 cm/yr; Plate 11). The purpose of this section is to summarize our present knowledge of crustal faulting and vertical movements in the Lesser Antilles subduction zone with particular emphasis on land areas in the volcanic arc, forearc (Barbados), and back-arc region (Aves Island). The reader interested in other aspects of the Neogene geology of this region is referred to the chapters in this volume by Maury and others (Lesser Antilles), Carr and Stoiber (volcanism), McCann and Pennington (seismicity), and Holcombe and others (active tectonic margins). Excellent reviews of

the geologic and tectonic evolution of the Lesser Antilles are given by Bouysse (1984) and Speed and others (1984).

As in the Middle America subduction zone, Neogene faulting and crustal movements in the overriding Caribbean Plate in the Lesser Antilles are often difficult to clearly relate to a single tectonic mechanism. Moreover, determination of neotectonic deformation patterns in the Lesser Antilles using earthquakes is difficult because subduction at shallow depths is largely aseismic and many of the larger events appear to reflect complex internal plate deformation rather than interplate deformation (Stein and others, 1982). We organize this discussion around four of the currently most popular mechanisms for crustal faulting in the overriding Caribbean Plate: (1) subduction of aseismic ridges; (2) segmentation of the subducted plate; (3) back-thrusting of forearc over the Grenada Basin; and (4) sedimentary diapirism. Readers interested in the submarine effects of frontal accretion along the sedimentary deformation front of the arc are referred to chapters on marine geology in this volume by Holcombe and others.

Subduction of aseismic ridges

Several aseismic ridges, most noticably the Barracuda Ridge and the Tiburon Rise (Fig. 1), appear to have been obliquely subducted beneath the Lesser Antilles island arc and have been interpreted as possible mechanisms for the uplift and deformation of the overriding plate. Stein and others (1982) pointed out that the Barracuda Ridge is a nonbuoyant feature that may represent a fossil flanking ridge of a transform fault. McCann and Sykes (1984) interpreted the Barracuda Ridge as a continuation of the 15°20'N central Atlantic fracture zone. These authors suggested that the Barracuda Ridge is a continuous feature *beneath* the overriding northeastern corner of the Caribbean Plate and emerges as the Main Ridge in the Puerto Rico Trench. Other nonbuoyant aseismic ridges to the south—such as the Tiburon, an unnamed ridge at 14°30'N, and the Santa Lucia Ridge north of Barbados (Plate 11)—have been suggested by McCann and Sykes (1984) and Westbrook (1982) as having major effects on the geologic uplift, volcanism, and seismicity of the overriding Caribbean Plate.

Possible effects related to the subduction of these aseismic ridges include: (1) shoaling in the dip of the descending slab from 55° to 35° in late Miocene time and shifting of the locus of volcanism some 50 km to the west as an ancient and unnamed ridge was subducted; extensive K-Ar age dating of arc volcanic rocks by Briden and others (1979) has shown a distinction between a range of 37 to 10 Ma in the now-extinct outer arc to the east (Limestone Caribbees) and less than 7.7 Ma in the active inner arc to the west (Volcanic Caribbees; Plate 11); (2) disruption of deposits of the inner wall of the Puerto Rico Trench as the Main Ridge was subducted; (3) uplift of the outer edge of the Caribbean Plate above the subducted Barracuda Ridge based on the alignment of banks and the islands of Barbuda, Anguilla, St. Martins, and St. Bartholomew, although there is presently no direct geologic evidence for tectonic uplift of any of these islands; (5) generation of anomalously large earthquakes such as the 1843 event (see Stein and others, 1986, for an alternative interpretation); (6) uplift of the island of Barbados by underthrusting of the Santa Lucia Ridge (Westbrook, 1982); and (7) flexure and normal faulting of the Caribbean Plate above subducting aseismic ridges such as the Barracuda; this is a possible cause of the 1974 Antigua earthquake (Stein and others, 1982).

With the exception of Barbados, there is insufficient quantitative data on Neogene tectonic movements in the Lesser Antilles islands to test this idea of differential uplift of island areas above subducted ridges. We have plotted the available data on Plate 11 and discuss it briefly below.

Horsfield (1975) noted that except for Anegada, most of the Virgin Islands have no Quaternary raised marine deposits, and therefore lack indications of Quaternary emergence. Tomblin (1975) noted that the pattern of deformation in Antigua is recorded in the deformation of well-stratified Oligocene limestones that suggest the whole island underwent northeastward tilting, which is almost imperceptible (2°) in the northeast but increases progressively to the southwest and reaches a maximum of around 20°. Lewis and Robinson (1976) have noted that the general lack of fossiliferous deposits of post-middle Miocene age in the northern part of the Lesser Antilles suggests uplift in late Miocene time perhaps associated with the late Miocene migration of volcanism to the inner arc. Brasier and Mather (1975) have studied in detail the Neogene stratigraphy of Barbuda and found that this island has remained stable during the Neogene and has not experienced periods of rapid tectonic uplift. On the other hand, Martin-Kaye (1963) has identified tectonic warping of the prominent 20 fathom submarine banks around Barbuda and Anegada. This author has also pointed out that 300-m (1,000 ft) summits, which are ubiquitous on the Lesser Antilles islands, may be remnants of a distinct erosion level of unknown age that has not suffered appreciable differential tectonic movements since its formation. Froidefond and others (1985) have identified submerged reef terraces around Martinique and interpreted their distribution and water depths in terms of vertical tectonics. Garrabé and Andreiff (1985) have studied Plio-Quaternary limestones on Guadeloupe and suggested Quaternary uplift and tilting episodes.

Slab segmentation

As in Middle America, segmentation of the downgoing Atlantic sea floor has been proposed by several authors as an important tectonic control on volcanism and faulting in the Lesser Antilles arc. Tomblin (1975) proposed segmentation of the Benioff Zone into three major slabs based on variations in the dip of the seismic zone (slab boundaries indicated in Fig. 1). Westercamp (1979) suggested segmentation of the Lesser Antilles islands into 17 tectonic blocks bounded by high-angle, mostly submarine, northeast-striking faults, which were located using morphology, distribution of shallow earthquakes, and island geology. These faults are interpreted as resulting from underlying

discontinuities in the downgoing plate and serve as conduits for alkaline and subalkaline magmas. Wadge and Shepherd (1984) identified a "kink," or abrupt change in strike, in the subducting slab at the latitude of Martinique and suggested this kink may represent deformation of a single subducting plate or two separate North and South American plates subducting beneath the Caribbean Plate with a triple junction in the region of Martinique. This kink aligns with a major strike change and gap in the 10-km-wide band of active volcanoes between Martinique and St. Lucia. Moreover, the kink separates mid-Miocene dike populations of different orientations on the islands to the north and south. Although theoretical models of plate motion (e.g., Minster and Jordan, 1978) predict the existence of relative motion between two distinct North and South American plates in the vicinity of the Lesser Antilles arc, there has been no clear bathymetric or seismic evidence for the boundary in the Atlantic other than the change in orientation of the subducting slab described by Wadge and Shepherd (1984).

McCann and Sykes (1984) summarized evidence for a continuous downgoing seismic zone that dips westerly beneath the Lesser Antilles arc and smoothly changes its dip to southerly beneath the Virgin Islands. The presence of the Anegada Passage Fault Zone above this continuous slab in the Virgin Islands area suggests that slab segmentation is not a likely mechanism for the origin of this major, right-lateral(?) fault (Houlgatte, 1983).

Because the level of seismicity is low in the southern half of the Lesser Antilles arc, models relating slab segmentation to faulting in the overriding Caribbean Plate are controversial. Perez and Aggarwal (1981) used seismic data to suggest that the subduction of the Atlantic sea floor beneath the Caribbean terminates in the vicinity of the Los Bajos–El Soldado right-lateral faults near Trinidad (Table 2) and that these faults represent the surface expression of hinge faulting formed as a result of vertical motion between the southwestern edge of the subducted Atlantic slab and the South American continent. Interpreting local network data, Wadge and Shepherd (1984) disagreed with the results of Perez and Aggarwal (1981). Wadge and Shepherd (1984) determined that the dip of the subducted slab in the Trinidad area was vertical, and the resulting lack of an overlying mantle wedge explains the absence of subduction magmatism on the overlying Venezuelan continental shelf.

Geologic evidence for prominent transverse faults in the Lesser Antilles that could correspond to slab segment boundaries is poor. The results of detailed studies of marine seismic data such as those by Bouysse (1984) in the northern Lesser Antilles and Torrini and Speed (in preparation) for the Barbados area and the compilation maps made by Speed and others (1984) for the entire Lesser Antilles do not reveal the presence of prominent transverse faults in the overriding Caribbean Plate. Recent scarps on the sea floor tend to be isolated, discontinuous features that often are parallel to the length of the arc (Plate 11). Exceptions include the transverse Desirade scarp, which extends over 70 km in an east-northeast direction to the north of and parallel to La Desirade Island, and the transverse Anegada Fault Zone (Plate 11).

Regional studies of joints in Eocene to Miocene rocks along the length of the Lesser Antilles suggest a relatively uniform stress field in which one of the principal stress directions strikes to the northwest (Bonneton and Scheidegger, 1981). The authors assumed that the northwest-southeast direction is the direction of maximum compression, which is roughly tangential to the west-northwesterly striking small circles of relative motion between the Caribbean and Atlantic plates predicted by Minster and Jordan (1978), but not to the southeast-striking small circles predicted by Sykes and others (1982). Bonneton and Scheidegger (1981) pointed out that the direction of maximum compression obtained from joints agrees well with the northwest-striking orientation of recent extensional volcanic fissures at the Soufrière in Guadeloupe (i.e., long axes of fissures are proposed to have opened parallel to the direction of maximum compressive stress). Westercamp (1979) noted northwesterly striking fissures of early Miocene age in Martinque, of Quaternary age in St. Kitts, and Quaternary age in Martinique. In Martinque, northerly striking fissures are also present.

However, Westercamp (1979) also observed northeasterly striking aligned Quaternary volcanic craters in Guadeloupe and northeasterly striking alignment of Plio-Pleistocene craters in Grenada. He explained the two sets of northeast- and northwest-striking faults as a conjugate pair of strike-slip faults produced by north-south shortening of the entire eastern Caribbean Plate (Burke and others, 1978).

Bouysse (1984) noted that the highly mafic character of the basal Pliocene monogenetic volcano of Redonda to the north of Guadeloupe is a rather uncommon feature in the Lesser Antilles and may be related to a major transverse fault. Wadge and Shepherd (1984) suggested that mid-Miocene dike swarms in Martinique strike northwesterly and those in St. Lucia strike northeasterly. They interpret these dikes as recording a mid-Miocene stress regime with the least principal stress direction perpendicular to the arc. This is not the stress system that is usually inferred from island arc dike azimuths in other arcs such as the Aleutians where dikes and maximum principal stress directions are perpendicular to the arc (Nakamura and others, 1977).

In summary, there is no good evidence for geologic effects of slab segmentation in the Lesser Antilles, and there is no consensus on the regional Neogene stress field. However, the stress field may be fairly uniform over wide areas, as inferred from joint and dike studies.

Back-thrusting of forearc deposits over the Grenada Basin

Interpretation of marine seismic data has shown that the structural high of the accretionary prism of the Lesser Antilles (the Barbados Ridge) has overthrusted the Tobago Trough forearc basin along an eastward-dipping fold-fault system (Speed and others, 1984; Plate 11). The mechanism for this arcward thrusting is probably the result of long-term horizontal compressional forces that formed the prism (Westbrook, 1982). These forces arise principally from shear stresses applied to the base of the sediment pile by the subducting ocean crust. These shear stresses are opposed by the reaction of the island arc and consequently achieve a maximum value at the Barbados Ridge. The surficial axis of the Barbados Ridge is centered approximately 20 km above the line along which the ocean crust of the Atlantic is subducted beneath the crystalline crust of the Caribbean (see Fig. 3 of Westbrook, 1982).

Torrini and Speed (1989) have also argued for eastward (trenchward) thrusting of early Eocene to early middle Miocene pelagic strata over contemporary and older terrigenous deposits exposed on Barbados, Biju-Duval and others (1985) were skeptical of large-scale thrusting because the incompetent marls and chalks of the upper pelagic unit do not show any evidence of strong internal folding or cleavage development.

The late Neogene uplift history of the island of Barbados at the crest of the Barbados Ridge has been well studied using uranium series dating methods on Pleistocene reef terraces (Bender and others, 1979). The reef terraces of Barbados consist of both constructional and erosional features, which form a fairly continuous record of sea-level change and tectonic uplift back to 700 ka. The reef substrate consists of marine sedimentary rocks believed to have been deposited and deformed in the proto–Lesser Antilles trench. Anticlinal warping of the coral cap of the island along a northeast trend has locally exposed the sedimentary basement of the island. Rates of uplift as fast as 0.2 to 0.45 mm/yr have been documented on reefs located along this anticlinal structure, and it seems likely that uplift has proceeded at similar rates throughout the Quaternary. A localized mechanism for the rapid uplift of Barbados may be the presence of active or recently active mud diapirism beneath the island and/or the presence of a subducted aseismic ridge such as the Santa Lucia below the island (Westbrook, 1982; Plate 11).

Sedimentary diapirism

Side-scan sonar surveys of the forearc region of the southern Lesser Antilles have revealed extensive areas of mud diapirs on the sea floor (Speed and others, 1984) (Plate 11). The general distribution of these features shows that they increase in abundance southward toward the known mud diapir field near Trinidad and the Neogene delta of the Orinoco River (Michelson, 1976). Many diapirs are randomly scattered, but others (such as to the southwest of Barbados) show alignment suggesting either fault or fold control.

Arc basins and the Aves Ridge

Two major arc basins parallel to the strike of the arc are found in the Lesser Antilles: (1) the Kallinago Basin stretches from the north of Guadeloupe to the Anegada Passage and probably formed in the late Miocene by the westward migration of the volcanic line from the Limestone Caribbees to its present site; and (2) the Grenada Basin, which may have formed as a trapped basin in Eocene(?) time as the locus of volcanism migrated eastward from the Aves Ridge to its present site (Bouysse, 1984). The Kallinago Basin reaches depths of 2,000 m and contains at least 1 km of fault-bounded post-middle Miocene sediments. The Kallinago Basin is not a typical extensional rift basin related to back-arc spreading because the volcanic line jumped westward away from the trench and not toward the trench as commonly found in most back-arc basins (Bouysse, 1984). The Grenada Basin is locally fault bounded, reaches a maximum depth of 2,800 m, and contains 7 km of strata of unknown age. The western side of the Grenada Basin is bounded by the Aves Ridge. The Aves Ridge is exposed only at the tiny island of Aves, which is covered with Quaternary shallow marine sands. On the basis of dredged rocks, the rate of subsidence of Aves Ridge can be estimated as 0.038 to 0.06 mm/yr, although this rate is insufficient to explain historical changes in size and sedimentary distribution of Aves Island and its platform (Schubert and Laredo, 1984).

INTERNAL DEFORMATION OF THE CARIBBEAN PLATE

Introduction

Although the interior of the Caribbean Plate is relatively aseismic in comparison to its boundaries, there are indications of active deformation well within the plate interior that include: (1) occasional intraplate earthquakes with magnitudes as large as M = 5.1 (Kafka and Weidner, 1979); (2) a vague belt of intraplate seismicity along the Caribbean coast of Nicaragua (McCann and Pennington, this volume); (3) intraplate faulting affecting Neogene sediments seen on reflection profiles (Holcombe and others, this volume); and (4) late Neogene intraplate volcanism (Wadge and Wooden, 1982; Plate 11).

Prominent structures within the plate permit subdivision into four zones (A to D in Fig. 1): (1) a Central American zone (Zone A in Fig. 1) bounded by the Middle America arc, the Honduras Depression, and left-lateral strike-slip faults of the North America–Caribbean PBZ; (2) the Nicaraguan Rise (Zone B) north of the Hess Escarpment; (3) the Venezuelan Basin (Zone D) between the Beata Ridge and the Aves Ridge; and (4) the Colombian Basin (Zone C) between the Hess Escarpment and the Beata Ridge. The small amount of seismic activity within the Caribbean Plate relative to the surrounding PBZs suggests very slow or episodic intraplate block movements.

The purpose of this section is to briefly describe the main characteristics of each of the zones and comment on their neotectonic significance.

Central American zone

This area is characterized by east-west extension across roughly north-south–striking grabens such as those reviewed by Plafker (1976) in Honduras, Guatemala, and El Salvador. This rifting has been explained as localized extension produced as the Caribbean Plate attempts to move eastward about a continental

promontory of the North American Plate in northern Central America (Mann and Burke, 1984a).

Nicaraguan Rise and Hess Escarpment

Unlike Zone A in Central America, the dominant fault trend on the Nicaraguan Rise is southwesterly and parallel to the Hess Escarpment. With the exception of the Hess Escarpment, the character and history of these faults is poorly studied. The Hess Escarpment extends for 1,000 km in a southwesterly direction and forms a prominent bathymetric break between the Colombian Basin to the south (Zone C) and the Nicaraguan Rise to the north (Zone B). Despite its linearity, studies of marine seismic records indicate fault movements on the Hess Escarpment are probably pre-Cenozoic. Bowland (1984) has shown that sedimentary units, which are thought to range in age from Late Cretaceous to Recent, form an undeformed onlap sequence (at least locally) over the escarpment. However, the Hess Escarpment does appear to form a major crustal boundary separating blocks with differing Neogene fault styles and basement characteristics. Immediately to the north of the southwestern end of the Hess Escarpment, Neogene and possibly Quaternary north-south–striking normal faults extend the crust to form a series of horsts and grabens (Bowland, 1984; Plate 11). The zone of normal faulting extends northward along the Nicaragua margin and correlates with: (1) a zone of weak seismicity (McCann and Pennington, this volume); (2) late Miocene volcanism exposed on Providencia Island (Wadge and Wooden, 1982); and (3) tilting and fracturing of reef terraces on Providencia and San Andrés Island (Geister, 1972, 1975; Plate 11).

Colombian Basin

To the south of the Hess Escarpment in the Colombian Basin (Zone C), recent faults strike northwest and bound a pronounced basement and topographic high—the Mono Rise (Bowland, 1984). A major unconformity suggests that uplift along presently active northwest-striking fault zones bounding the Mono Rise began in middle Miocene time. Bowland (1984) attributed this deformation to reactivation of basement features triggered by northwestward overthrusting of the Panamá deformed belt over the Colombian Basin (Lu and McMillen, 1983). The southeastern edge of the Colombian Basin is bounded by the South Caribbean Marginal Fault (Ladd and others, 1984).

Beata Ridge

The Beata Ridge is marked by a triangular-shaped uplifted area at a place where the Caribbean is narrowest, between the Guajira Peninsula of Colombia and Hispaniola. The Beata Ridge forms a heavily faulted boundary between the Colombian Basin (Zone C) and the Venezuelan Basin (Zone D; Fig. 1). Fox and Heezen (1975) suggested that the structure of the Beata Ridge consists of a steep fault-scarp bounding its western edge and a series of fault blocks that step down to the floor of the Venezuelan Basin. From seismic profiles, Ladd and others (1981) were unable to confirm whether the east flank of the Beata Ridge is a series of fault blocks or whether it consists of parallel volcanic ridges. The Beata Ridge extends onshore into southern Hispaniola as a zone of late Neogene normal and strike-slip faults (Taylor and others, 1984).

Venezuelan Basin

The Venezuelan Basin (Zone D) is bounded on the north by the Muertos Trench, on the east by the Lesser Antilles arc, on the south by the South Caribbean Marginal Fault, and on the west by the Beata Ridge. Faults within the Venezuelan Basin trend northeasterly and northwesterly (Matthews and Holcombe, 1985). Burke and others (1978) suggested that the structural pattern of the apparently conjugate faults resembled a modified Prandtl cell developed in response to north-south shortening. The direction of faulting indicated by a focal mechanism determined by Kafka and Weidner (1979) is opposite to that predicted in the Prandtl cell model.

More prominent than faults in the Venezuelan Basin is an east-west–trending arch parallel to the long axis of the basin (Fig. 1). This arch may reflect an outer swell produced by intraplate flexing related to Neogene oblique underthrusting at the Muertos and South Caribbean marginal fault zones (Biju-Duval and others, 1983).

Model for internal deformation

Two active mechanisms for the internal deformation of the Caribbean are proposed: (1) northerly motion of the Maracaibo Block relative to cratonic South America with convergence on the southern margin of the Caribbean (Mann and Burke, 1984a; Dewey and Pindell, 1985), and (2) easterly motion of the Caribbean Plate relative to North America about a continental promontory in northern Central America with east-west intraplate extension of the northern Caribbean Plate (Wadge and Burke, 1983; Mann and Burke, 1984a; Burkart and Self, 1985). Motion of the Maracaibo Block results in deformation mostly of Zones C and D (Colombian and Venezuelan basins) and was probably initiated in the late Miocene or Pliocene (Biju-Duval and others, 1983). Motion of the Caribbean about the Central American promontory results in active deformation of Zone A (area of Central America west of the Honduras Depression) and previously resulted in a similar style of rift formation in Zone B (Jamaica and the Nicaraguan Rise) during earlier eastward motion of the Caribbean in the Paleogene. Therefore, from about the late Miocene, both mechanisms have been active and have deformed opposite edges of the plate. Present-day extension of the Nicaraguan Rise (Zone B) appears to have reactivated Cenozoic rifts associated with earlier (Paleocene-Miocene) internal plate deformation. The tectonic mechanism of this present-day east-west extension across the Nicaraguan Rise (Zone B) is poorly understood.

CONCLUSIONS

The main conclusions of this data compilation and comparison to current models for the neotectonics of the Caribbean are as follows.

1. The precise rate and direction of Neogene Caribbean Plate motion relative to surrounding plates remains imprecisely known because of geological and seismological complexities produced in wide (200–250 km) PBZs of deformation developed in thickened oceanic, island arc, and continental crust (Plate 11). Based on fault data, the Caribbean Plate appears to be moving in an easterly direction relative to the North and South American plates at a rate of 1 to 2 centimeters a year (Tables 1, 2, and 3). Relatively rigid microplates within these broad PBZs may move independently of their larger neighbors and produce geologic and seismic complexities.

2. The total amount of Cenozoic offset across the Caribbean strike-slip boundaries is controversial, although the existence of the Cayman Trough pull-apart basin provides compelling evidence for significant (~1,100 km) post-Eocene(?), left-lateral offset between North America and the Caribbean. Within the broad northern and southern strike-slip PBZs, no one strike-slip fault zone need account for more than a fraction of the total motion, and all mapped strike-slip faults need not be active simultaneously.

3. The pattern of Neogene faulting in the northern and southern strike-slip boundaries of the Caribbean conforms well to deformation patterns produced along vertical, roughly east-west striking, strike-slip fault planes. The most dramatic examples of Neogene tectonic uplift and subsidence in the northern and southern Caribbean can be related to bends or irregularities in the traces of major strike-slip fault zones (Plate 11). These bends either form localized areas of extension or compression, depending on the fault geometry (Fig. 3).

4. The Neogene pattern of deformation in northwestern South America and Panamá can be interpreted within the framework of the late Miocene to present collision of the Panamá island arc with the northwestern margin of South America. Compression produced by this event appears to have induced northward strike-slip displacement of a triangular, fault-bounded area of northwestern South America—the Maracaibo Block—into the southern Caribbean at a rate of up to 14 mm/yr (Table 3). The total amount of offset on the strike-slip faults bounding the Maracaibo Block (Santa Marta–Bucaramanga and Boconó) remains controversial and is a priority area for future research. The structural relationships between the northward moving Maracaibo Block and the eastward moving Caribbean Plate relative to South America are poorly understood but may involve significant internal deformation. Convergence between the Maracaibo Block and the Caribbean is suggested as a mechanism for late Neogene internal deformation of the Caribbean Plate. A general lack of seismic activity from within the Caribbean Plate suggests very slow or episodic intraplate block movements.

5. Onshore Neogene faulting in the Middle America and

Lesser Antilles areas is often difficult to relate to a single tectonic mechanism. Possible deformation mechanisms include: (1) arc-parallel extension and faulting along the volcanic axis; (2) internal deformation produced by adjacent interplate motion; and (3) subduction of aseismic ridges.

6. Because systematic neotectonic studies in the Caribbean have only begun fairly recently, there is a paucity of quantitative data on fault-movement histories, especially in late Neogene time. Detailed geologic studies, such as trenching of active faults and studies of uplifted and deformed coral reefs, should prove valuable in building an improved Caribbean neotectonic data base for better understanding of tectonic processes. This knowledge may prove valuable in better understanding and eventually forecasting the type of major earthquake and volcanic disasters which have occurred in the Caribbean during this century.

REFERENCES CITED

(Numbers refer to Plate 11)

1. Alsonso-Harris, R., Krieg, E. A., and Meyerhoff, A., 1983, Post-early Pliocene age of the Puerto Rico Trench: Transactions Caribbean Geological Conference, 10th, Cartagena, Colombia, Abstracts, p. 17–18.
2. Alt, J. N., Harpster, R. E., and Schwartz, D. P., 1980, Late Quaternary deformation and differential uplift along the Pacific coast of Costa Rica: Geological Society of America Abstracts with Programs, v. 12, p. 378–379.
3. Alvarez, W., 1971, Fragmented Andean belt of northern Colombia, *in* Donnelly, T. W., ed., Caribbean Geophysical, Tectonic and Petrologic Studies: Geological Society of America Memoir 130, p. 77–96.
4. Arden, D. D., Jr., 1975, Geology of Jamaica and the Nicaragua Rise, *in* Nairn, A.E.M., and Stehli, F. G., eds., The Ocean Basins and Margins, Volume 3: The Gulf of Mexico and the Caribbean: New York, Plenum, p. 617–661.
5. Barbot, J. P., Butenko, J., Espinoza, E., Daza, J., and Malave, G., 1980, El Cuaternario del Golfo de la Vela y su importancia geotécnica para la exploración y explotación petrolera: Transactions Caribbean Geological Conference, 9th, Santo Domingo, Dominican Republic, p. 541–553.
6. Bender, M. L., Fairbanks, R. G., Taylor, F. W., Matthews, R. K., Goddard, J. G., and Broecker, W. S., 1979, Uranium-series dating of the Pleistocene reef tracts of Barbados, West Indies: Geological Society of America Bulletin, v. 90, p. 577–594.
7. Biju-Duval, B., and 6 others, 1985, The terrigenous and pelagic series of Barbados Island; Paleocene to middle Miocene slope deposits accreted to the Lesser Antilles margin, *in* Proceedings, Géodynamique des Caraïbes Symposium, Paris, France, February, 1985: Paris, Éditions Technip, p. 187–197.
8. Biju-Duval, B., Mascle, A., Rosales, H., and Young, G., 1983, Episutural Oligo–Miocene basins along the north Venezuelan margin, *in* Watkins, J. S. and Drake, C. L., eds., Studies in continental margin geology: American Association of Petroleum Geologists Memoir 34, p. 347–358.
9. Bizon, G., Bizon, J. J., Calmus, T., Muller, C., van den Berghe, B., 1985, Stratigraphie du Tertiaire du sud d'Hispaniola (Grandes Antilles); Influence de la tectonique décrochante sur la paléogéographie et l'histoire sédimentaire, *in* Proceedings, Géodynamique des Caraïbes Symposium, Paris, France, February, 1985: Paris, Éditions Technip, p. 371–380.
10. Bock, W. K., 1972, The use of foraminifera as indicators of subsidence in the Caribbean: Transactions, Caribbean Geological Conference, 6th, Caracas, Venezuela, p. 439–440.
11. Bonini, W. E., Hargraves, R. B., and Shagam, R., eds., 1984, The Caribbean-South American Plate boundary and Regional Tectonics: Geological Society of America Memoir 162, 421 p.
12. Bonneton, J.-R., and Scheidegger, A. E., 1981, Relations between fracture patterns, seismicity, and plate motions in the Lesser Antilles: Journal of Structural Geology, v. 3, p. 359–369.
13. Borger, H. D., and Lenert, E. F., 1959, The geology and development of the Bolivar Coastal Field at Maracaibo, Venezuela: Proceedings, World Petroleum Congress, 5th, Mexico City, p. 481–498.
14. Bouysse, P., 1984, The Lesser Antilles island arc; Structure and geodynamic evolution, *in* Biju-Duval, B., and Moore, J. C., eds., Initial reports of the Deep Sea Drilling Project: Washington, D.C., U.S. Government Printing Office, v. 78A, p. 83–103.
15. Bowin, C., 1976, The Caribbean; Gravity field and plate tectonics: Geological Society of America Special Paper 169, 169 p.
16. Bowland, C. L., 1984, Seismic stratigraphy and structure of the western Colombian Basin, Caribbean Sea [M.S. thesis]: Austin, University of Texas, 248 p.
17. Brasier, M., and Mather, J., 1975, The stratigraphy of Barbuda, West Indies: Geological Magazine, v. 112, p. 271–282.
18. Briggs, R. P., and Pease, M. H., Jr., 1968, Large- and small-scale wrench faulting in an island arc segment [abs.]: Geological Society of America Special Paper 115, p. 24.
19. Briden, J. C., Rex, D. C., Faller, A. M., and Tomblin, J. F., 1979, K-Ar geochronology and paleomagnetism of volcanic rocks in the Lesser Antilles arc: Philosophical Transactions of the Royal Society of London, v. 291, no. 1383, p. 485–528.
20. Brown, R. D., Jr., Ward, P. L., and Plafker, G., 1973, Geologic and seismologic aspects of the Managua earthquakes of December 23, 1972: U.S. Geological Survey Professional Paper 838, 34 p.
21. Brunt, M. A., Giglioli, M.E.C., Mather, J. D., Piper, D.J.W., and Richards, H. G., 1973, The Pleistocene rocks of the Cayman Islands: Geological Magazine, v. 110, p. 209–221.
22. Bucknam, R. C., Plafker, G., and Sharp, R. V., 1978, Fault movement (afterslip) following the Guatemala earthquake of February 4, 1976: Geology, v. 6, p. 170–173.
23. Burbach, G. V., Frohlich, C., Pennington, W. D., and Matumoto, T., 1984, Seismicity and tectonics of the subducted Cocos Plate: Journal of Geophysical Research, v. 89, p. 7719–7735.
24. Burel, T. and Vernette, G., 1981, Evidencias de cambios de nivel del mar en el Cuaternario de la region de Cartagena (Bolivar): Revista Centro Interamericano de Fotointerpretación (CIAF) (Colombia), v. 6, p. 77–92.
25. Burkart, B., 1983, Neogene North American-Caribbean plate boundary across northern Central America; Offset along the Polochic fault: Tectonophysics, v. 99, p. 251–270.
26. Burkart, B., and Self, S., 1985, Extension and rotation of crustal blocks in northern Central America and effect on the volcanic arc: Geology, v. 13, p. 22–26.
27. Burke, K., Fox, P. J., and Sengör, A.M.C., 1978, Buoyant ocean floor and the evolution of the Caribbean: Journal of Geophysical Research, v. 83, p. 3949–3945.
28. Burke, K., Grippi, J., and Sengör, A.M.C., 1980, Neogene structures in Jamaica and the tectonic style of the Northern Caribbean Plate Boundary Zone: Journal of Geology, v. 88, p. 375–386.
29. Burne, R. V., Horsfield, W. T., and Robinson, E., 1974, The geology of Navassa Island: Caribbean Journal of Science, v. 14, p. 109–114.
30. Byrne, D. B., Suarez, G., and McCann, W. R., 1985, Muertos Trough subduction; Microplate tectonics in the northern Caribbean?: Nature, v. 317, p. 420–421.
31. Calmus, T., 1983, Décrochement senestre sud-haïtien; Analyses et conséquences paléogéographiques dans la region de Camp–Perrin (Massif de Macaya, presqu'île du Sud d'Haïti): Extrait des Annales de la Société Géologique du Nord (Lille, France), séance du 10 Juin 1983, p. 309–316.
32. Campbell, C. J., 1968, The Santa Marta wrench fault of Colombia and its regional setting: Transactions, Caribbean Geological Conference, 4th, Trinidad, p. 247–261.
33. Cant, R. V., 1973, Jamaica's Pleistocene reef terraces: Geologie en Mijnbouw, v. 52, p. 157–160.

34. Carr, M. J., 1976, Underthrusting and Quaternary faulting in Central America: Geological Society of America Bulletin, v. 87, p. 825–829.

35. Case, J. E., and Holcombe, T. L., compilers, 1980, Geologic-tectonic map of the Caribbean region: U.S. Geological Survey Miscellaneous Investigations Series Map I-1100, scale 1:2,500,000.

35A. Case, J. E., and MacDonald, W. D., 1973, Regional gravity anomalies and crustal structure in northern Colombia: Geological Society of America Bulletin, v. 84, p. 2905–2916.

36. Cline, K. M., and 6 others, 1981, Quaternary activity on the Romeral and Cauca faults, northwest Colombia: Revista Centro Interamericano de Fotointerpretación (CIAF) (Colombia), v. 6, p. 115–116.

37. Collins, D. E., Benalcazar, G., and Page, W. K., 1981, Quaternary activity on the Palestina fault zone, northwestern Colombia: Revista Centro Interamericano de Fotointerpretación (CIAF) (Colombia), v. 6, p. 117–118.

38. Dean, B. W., and Drake, C. L., 1978, Focal mechanism solutions and tectonics of the Middle America arc: Journal of Geology, v. 86, p. 111–128.

39. Deaton, B. C., and Burkart, B., 1984, Time of sinistral slip along the Polochic Fault Zone of Guatemala: Tectonophysics, v. 102, p. 297–313.

40. Dewey, J. F., and Pindell, J. L., 1985, Neogene block tectonics of eastern Turkey and northern South America; Continental applications of the finite difference method: Tectonics, v. 4, p. 71–83.

41. Dewey, J. W., and Algermissen, S. T., 1974, Seismicity of the Middle America arc-trench system near Managua, Nicaragua: Seismological Society of America Bulletin, v. 64, p. 1033–1048.

42. Dodge, R. E., Fairbanks, R. G., Benninger, L. K., and Maurrasse, F., 1983, Pleistocene sea levels from raised coral reefs of Haiti: Science, v. 219, p. 1423–1225.

43. Donnelly, T. W., ed., 1971, Caribbean geophysical, tectonic, and petrologic studies: Geological Society of America Memoir 130, 224 p.

44. Donnelly, T. W., Crane, D., and Burkart, B., 1968, Geologic history of the landward extension of the Bartlett Trough; Some preliminary notes: Transactions, Caribbean Geological Conference, 4th, Port-of-Spain, Trinidad, p. 225–228.

45. Doolan, B. L., and MacDonald, W. D., 1976, Structure and metamorphism of schists of the Santa Marta area, Colombia: Memorias Primer Congreso Colombiano de Geología, Bogota, p. 187–205.

46. Ducloz, C., 1963, Étude géomorphologique de la région de Matanzas, Cuba: Archives des Sciences de Genève, v. 16, fasc. 2, p. 351–402.

47. Duque-Caro, H., 1984, Structural style, diapirism, and accretionary episodes of the Sinú-San Jacinto terrane, southwestern Caribbean borderland, *in* Bonini, W. E., Hargraves, R. B., and Shagam, R., eds., The Caribbean–South American Plate Boundary and Regional Tectonics: Geological Society of America Memoir 162, p. 303–316.

48. Eberle, W., Hirdes, W., Muff, R., and Palaez, M., 1980, The geology of the Cordillera Septentrional: Transactions, Caribbean Geological Conference, 9th, Santo Domingo, Dominican Republic, p. 619–632.

49. Emery, K. O., 1981, Low marine terraces of Grand Cayman Island: Estuarine, Coastal, and Shelf Science, v. 12, p. 569–578.

50. Feininger, T. and Bristow, C. R., 1980, Cretaceous and Paleogene geologic history of coastal Ecuador: Geologisches Rundschau, v. 69, p. 849–874.

51. Feininger, T., 1970, The Palestina fault, Colombia: Geological Society of America Bulletin, v. 81, p. 1201–1216.

52. Feo-Codecido, G., 1972, Breves ideas sobre la estructura de la falla de Oca, Venezuela: Transactions, Caribbean Geological Conference, 6th, Caracas, Venezuela, p. 184–190.

53. Fischer, K. M., and McCann, W. R., 1984, Velocity modeling and earthquake relocation in the northeast Caribbean: Bulletin of the Seismological Society of America, v. 74, p. 1249–1262.

54. Fischer, R., 1980, Recent tectonic movements of the Costa Rican Pacific coast: Tectonophysics, v. 70, p. T25–T33.

55. Fox, P. J., and Heezen, B. C., 1975, Geology of the Caribbean crust, *in* Nairn, A.E.M., and Stehli, F. G., eds., The Ocean Basins and Margins: Volume 3, The Gulf of Mexico and the Caribbean: New York, Plenum, p. 421–466.

56. Frankel, A., 1982, A composite focal mechanism for microearthquakes along the northeastern border of the Caribbean Plate: Geophysical Research Letters, v. 9, p. 511–514.

57. Froidefond, J. M., Berthois, L., Griboulard, R., Julius, C., and Pons, J. D., 1985, Terrasses submergées du'origine récifale, variations du niveau marin et activité néotectonique sur le plateau sud et est de la Martinique, *in* Proceedings, Géodynamique des Caraïbes Symposium, Paris, France, February, 1985: Paris, Éditions Technip, p. 143–154.

58. Garrabé, F. and Andreiff, P., 1985, Sédimentation et tectonique plio-quaternaires comparées de Marie-Galante et de Grande-Terre (Guadeloupe), *in* Proceedings, Géodynamique des Caraïbes Symposium, Paris, France, February, 1985: Paris, Éditions Technip, p. 155–160.

59. Geister, J., 1972, Nota sobre la edad de las calizas coralinas del Pleistoceno marino en las islas de San Andrés y Providencia (Mar Caribe occidental, Colombia): Mitteilungen des Instituto Colombiano-Alemán de Investigaciones Científicas (Colombia), v. 6, p. 135–140.

60. ——, 1975, Riffbau und geologische Entwicklungsgeschichte der Insel San Andrés (westliches Karibisches Meer, Kolumbien): Stuttgarter Beiträge zur Naturkunde, Series B (Geologie und Paläontologie), no. 15, 203 p.

61. ——, 1980, Pleistocene reef terraces and coral environments at Santo Domingo and near Boca Chica, southern coast of the Dominican Republic: Transactions, Caribbean Geological Conference, 9th, Santo Domingo, Dominican Republic, p. 689–703.

62. Glover, L., III, 1971, Geology of the Coamo area, Puerto Rico, and its relation to the volcanic arc-trench association: U.S. Geological Survey Professional Paper 636, 102 p.

63. Graf, C. H., 1972, Sedimentos del Terciario Superior y Cuaternario de la peninsula de Macanao, Margarita, Venezuela: Transactions, Caribbean Geological Conference, 6th, Caracas, Venezuela, p. 414–417.

64. Hare, P. W., and Gardner, T. W., 1985, Geomorphic indicators of vertical tectonism along converging plate margins, Nicoya Peninsula, Costa Rica, *in* Hack, J., and Morisawa, M., eds., Tectonic Geomorphology: Proceedings, 15th Geomorphology Symposia series, Binghamton, New York, p. 76–104.

65. Harlow, D. H., and White, R. A., 1985, Shallow earthquakes along the volcanic chain in Central America; Evidence for oblique subduction? [abs.]: Earthquake Notes (Eastern Section of the Seismological Society of America), v. 56, p. 28.

66. Henneberg, H. G., 1983, Geodetic control of neotectonics in Venezuela: Tectonophysics, v. 97, p. 1–15.

67. Herweijer, J. P., and Focke, J. W., 1978, Late Pleistocene depositional and denudational history of Aruba, Bonaire, and Curacao (Netherlands Antilles): Geologie en Mijnbouw, v. 57, p. 177–187.

68. Hess, H. H., and Maxwell, J. C., 1953, Caribbean research project: Geological Society of America Bulletin, v. 64, p. 1–6.

69. Heywood, C. E., 1984, Forearc deformation in southern Costa Rica: A consequence of the collision of the aseismic Cocos Ridge [M.S. thesis]: Santa Cruz, University of California, 104 p.

70. Higgins, G. E., and Saunders, J. B., 1974, Mud volcanoes; their nature and origin, *in* Jung, P., ed., Contributions to the geology and paleobiology of the Caribbean and adjacent areas: Basel, Verhandlungen der Naturforschenden Gesellschaft, v. 84, p. 101–152.

71. Holcombe, T. L., Personal communications, 1985.

72. Holcombe, T. L., and Sharman, G. F., 1983, Post-Miocene Cayman trough evolution; A speculative model: Geology, v. 11, p. 714–717.

73. Holmes, C. W., and Kindinger, J. L., 1985, Late Pleistocene–Holocene geology of the central Virgin Island Platform: Marine Geology, v. 64, p. 41–64.

74. Horsfield, W. T., 1972, A late Pleistocene sealevel notch and its relation to block faulting on the north coast of Jamaica: Journal of the Geological Society of Jamaica, v. 12, p. 18–22.

75. ——, 1973, Late Tertiary and Quaternary crustal movements in Jamaica: Journal of the Geological Society of Jamaica, v. 13, p. 6–13.

76. ——, 1974, Major faults in Jamaica: Journal of the Geological Society of Jamaica, v. 14, p. 1–14.

77. ——, 1975, Quaternary vertical movements in the Greater Antilles: Geological Society of America Bulletin, v. 86, p. 933–938.

78. Houlgatte, E., 1983, Étude d'une partie de la frontiére nord-est de la plaque Caraïbe [Diplome d'Etudes Approfondies]: Brest, France, Université de Bretagne Occidentale, 69 p.

79. Ivey, M. L., Jr., Breyer, J. A., and Britton, J. C., 1980, Sedimentary facies and depositional history of the Swan Islands, Honduras: Sedimentary Geology, v. 27, p. 195–212.

80. Kafka, A. L., and Weidner, D. J., 1979, The focal mechanisms and depths of small earthquakes as determined from Rayleigh-wave radiation patterns: Bulletin Seismological Society of America, v. 69, p. 1379–1390.

81. ——, 1981, Earthquake focal mechanisms and tectonic processes along the southern boundary of the Caribbean Plate: Journal of Geophysical Research, v. 86, p. 2877–2888.

82. Kartashov, I. P., and Mayo, N. A., 1972, Principales rasgos del desarrollo geologico de Cuba oriental en el Cenozoico Tardio: Transactions, Caribbean Geological Conference, 6th, Caracas, Venezuela, p. 108–112.

83. Keigwin, L., 1982, Isotopic paleoceanography of the Caribbean and east Pacific; Role of Panama uplift in late Neogene time: Science, v. 217, p. 350–353.

84. Kellogg, J. N., Oguijiofor, I. J., and Kansakar, D. R., 1985, Cenozoic tectonics of the Panama and North Andes blocks, *in* Memoirs, Latin American Congress, 6th, Bogota, Colombia: Consejo Consultivo de Directores de Servicios de Latinoamerica, p. 40–59.

85. Kellogg, J. N., and Bonini, W. E., 1982, Subduction of the Caribbean Plate and basement uplifts in the overriding South American Plate: Tectonics, v. 1, p. 251–276.

86. Kohn, B. P., Shagam, R., and Subieta, T., 1984, Results and preliminary implications of sixteen fission-track ages from rocks of the western Caribbean Mountains, Venezuela, *in* Bonini, W. E., Hargraves, R. B., and Shagam, R., eds., The Caribbean–South American Plate Boundary and Regional Tectonics: Geological Society of America Memoir 162, p. 415–421.

87. Kruckow, T., 1974, Landhebung im Vallee Central und Wachstum der Kustenebenen in Costa Rica (Mittelamerika): Jahrbuch Wittheit zu Bremen, v. 18, p. 247–263.

88. Kupfer, D. H., and Godoy, J., 1967, Strike-slip faulting in Guatemala [abs.]: EOS American Geophysical Union Transactions, v. 48, p. 215.

89. Ladd, J. W., and 7 others, 1984, Seismic reflection profiles across the southern margin of the Caribbean, *in* Bonini, W. E., Hargraves, R. B., and Shagam, R., eds., The Caribbean–South American Plate Boundary and Regional Tectonics: Geological Society of America Memoir 162, p. 153–159.

90. Ladd, J. W., Shih, T. C., and Tsai, C. J., 1981, Cenozoic tectonics of central Hispaniola and adjacent Caribbean Sea: American Association of Petroleum Geologists Bulletin, v. 75, p. 466–489.

91. Land, L. S., and Epstein, S., 1970, Late Pleistocene diagenesis and dolomitization, north Jamaica: Sedimentology, v. 14, p. 187–200.

92. Langer, C. J., and Bollinger, C. A., 1979, Secondary faulting near the terminus of a seismogenic strike-slip fault; Aftershocks of the 1976 Guatemala earthquake: Bulletin of the Seismological Society of America, v. 69, p. 427–444.

93. Leonard, R., 1983, Geology and hydrocarbon accumulations, Colombus Basin, offshore Trinidad: American Association of Petroleum Geologists Bulletin, v. 67, p. 1081–1093.

94. Lewis, J., and Robinson, E., 1976, A revised stratigraphy and geological history of the Lesser Antilles: Transactions, Caribbean Geological Conference, 7th, Guadeloupe, p. 339–344.

95. Liliyenberg, D. A., Blanco-Secundo, P., Venereo-Morales, A., Díaz-Díaz, J., and Hernández-Santana, J., 1981, New data on the relationship between Holocene vertical movements, seismicity, and structural differential in eastern Cuba: Doklady Earth Science Section, v. 257, p. 188–191.

96. Lonsdale, P., and Klitgord, K. D., 1978, Structure and tectonic history of the eastern Panama Basin: Geological Society of America Bulletin, v. 98, p. 981–999.

97. Lowrie, A., Stewart, J., Stewart, R. H., Van Andel, T. J., and McRaney, L., 1982, Location of the eastern boundary of the Cocos Plate during the Miocene: Marine Geology, v. 45, p. 261–279.

98. Lu, R. S., and McMillen, K. J., 1983, Multichannel seismic survey of the Colombia Basin and adjacent margins, *in* Watkins, J. S., and Drake, C. L., eds., Studies in Continental Margin Geology: American Association of Petroleum Geologists Memoir 34, p. 395–410.

99. MacDonald, W. D., 1968, Geology of the Serranía de Macuira area, Guajira Peninsula, northeast Colombia: Transactions, Caribbean Geological Conference, 4th, Port-of-Spain, Trinidad, p. 267–273.

100. Madrigal, R., 1977, Terrazas marinas y tectonismo en peninsula de Osa, Costa Rica: Revista Geográfica (Costa Rica), v. 86–87, p. 161–166.

101. Mann, P., and Burke, K., 1980, Neogene wrench faulting in the Wagwater belt, Jamaica: Transactions, Caribbean Geological Conference, 9th, Santo Domingo, Dominican Republic, p. 95–97.

102. ——, 1984, 1984a, Neotectonics of the Caribbean: Reviews of Geophysics and Space Physics, v. 22, p. 309–362.

103. Mann, P., Burke, K., and Matsumoto, T., 1984b, Neotectonics of Hispaniola; Plate motion, sedimentation, and seismicity at a restraining bend: Earth and Planetary Science Letters, v. 70, p. 311–324.

104. Mann, P., Draper, G., and Burke, K., 1985, Neotectonics of a strike-slip restraining bend system, Jamaica, *in* Biddle, K. T., and Christie-Blick, N., eds., Strike-slip deformation, basin formation, and sedimentation: Society of Economic Paleontologists and Mineralogists Special Publication 37, p. 211–226.

105. Mann, P., Hempton, M. R., Bradley, D. C., and Burke, K., 1983, Development of pull-apart basins: Journal of Geology, v. 91, p. 529–554.

106. Mann, P., Taylor, F. W., Burke, K., Kulstad, R., 1984a, Subaerially exposed Holocene coral reef, Enriquillo Valley, Dominican Republic: Geological Society of America Bulletin, v. 95, p. 1084–1092.

107. Mann, P., Corrigan, J., and Miranda, R., 1986, Geologic constraints on the Late Neogene Caribbean-Nazca Plate Boundary Zone in Panama [abs.]: EOS American Geophysical Union Transactions, v. 67, p. 1199.

108. Martin-Kaye, P.H.A., 1963, Accordant summit levels in the Lesser Antilles: Caribbean Journal of Science, v. 3, p. 181–184.

109. Matthews, J. E., and Holcombe, T. L., 1985, Venezuela Basin of the Caribbean Sea; Stratigraphy and sediment distribution: Marine Geology, v. 68, p. 1–23.

110. Mattson, P. H., 1984, Caribbean structural breaks and plate movements, *in* Bonini, W. E., Hargraves, R. B., and Shagam, R., eds., The Caribbean–South American Plate Boundary and Regional Tectonics: Geological Society of America Memoir 162, p. 131–152.

111. McBirney, A. R., and Williams, H., 1965, Volcanism in the southern part of El Salvador: University of California Publications in Geological Sciences, v. 32, p. 1–64.

112. McCann, W. R., 1985, On the earthquake hazards of Puerto Rico and the Virgin Islands: Bulletin of the Seismological Society of America, v. 75, p. 251–262.

113. McCann, W. R., and Sykes, L. R., 1984, Subduction of aseismic ridges beneath the Caribbean Plate; Implications for the tectonics and seismic potential of the northeastern Caribbean: Journal of Geophysical Research, v. 89, p. 4493–4519.

114. McGeary, S., Nur, A., and Ben-Avraham, Z., 1985, Spatial gaps in arc volcanism; The effect of collision or subduction of oceanic plateaus: Tectonophysics v. 119, p. 195–221.

115. Mercier de Lepinay, B., Rebillard, Ph., Chorowicz, J., Letouzey, P., and Vila, J. M., 1985, Interprétation structurale de l'île de la Gonâve (République d'Haïti) à partir d'images spatiales LANDSAT-MSS et SEASAT-SAR, *in* Proceedings, Géodynamique des Caraïbes Symposium, Paris, France, February, 1985: Paris, Éditions Technip, p. 363–369.

116. Michelson, J. E., 1976, Miocene deltaic oil habitat, Trinidad: American Association of Petroleum Geologists Bulletin, v. 60, p. 1502–1519.

117. Minster, J. B., and Jordan, T. H., 1978, Present-day plate motions: Journal

of Geophysical Research, v. 83, p. 5331–5354.

118. Miyamura, S., 1975, Recent crustal movements in Costa Rica disclosed by relevelling surveys: Tectonophysics, v. 29, p. 191–198.

119. Molnar, P., and Sykes, L., 1969, Tectonics of the Caribbean and Middle America regions from focal mechanisms and seismicity: Geological Society of America Bulletin, v. 80, p. 1639–1684.

120. Monroe, W. H., 1968, High-level Quaternary beach deposits in northwestern Puerto Rico: U.S. Geological Survey Professional Paper 600-C, p. C140–C143.

121. ——, 1972, Tectonic contrast between northern and southern Puerto Rico: Transactions, Caribbean Geological Conference, 6th, Caracas, Venezuela, p. 274–276.

122. Montero, W., and Dewey, J. W., 1982, Shallow-focus seismicity, composite focal mechanism, and tectonics of the Valle Central of Costa Rica: Bulletin of the Seismological Society of America, v. 72, p. 1611–1626.

123. Muehlberger, W. R., 1976, The Honduras Depression, *in* Transactions, Geological Conference of Central America, 4th, Guatemala: Guatemala, Instituto Centroamericano de Investigación y Technología Industrial, p. 43–51.

124. Muessig, K. W., 1984, Structure and Cenozoic tectonics of the Falcón Basin, Venezuela, and adjacent areas, *in* Bonini, W. E., Hargraves, R. B., and Shagam, R., eds., The Caribbean-South American Plate Boundary and Regional Tectonics: Geological Society of America Memoir 162, p. 217–230.

125. Munro, S. E., and Smith, F. D., Jr., 1984, The Urica fault zone, northeastern Venezuela, *in* Bonini, W. E., Hargraves, R. B., and Shagam, R., eds., The Caribbean–South American Plate Boundary and Regional Tectonics: Geological Society of America Memoir 162, p. 213–215.

125A. Nakamura, K., Jacob, K., and Davies, J., 1977, Volcanoes as possible indicators of tectonic stress orientation; Aleutians and Alaska: Pure and Applied Geophysics, v. 115, p. 87–112.

126. Oro, J., Hernandez, J., Marquez, M., Barrientos, A., and Perez, E., 1982, Naturaleza de los movimientos neotectónicos de la cuenca de Guatanamo: Instituto de Geología y Paleontología, Academia de Ciencias de Cuba, Jornada Científica, v. 9, p. 43–47.

127. Osieki, P. S., 1981, Estimated intensities and probable tectonic sources of historic (pre-1898) Honduran earthquakes: Seismological Society of America Bulletin, v. 71, p. 865–881.

128. Paige, S., 1930, The earthquake at Cumaná, Venezuela, January 17, 1929: Seismological Society of America Bulletin, v. 20, p. 1–10.

129. Pennington, W. D., 1981, Subduction of the eastern Panama Basin and seismotectonics of northwestern South America: Journal of Geophysical Research, v. 86, p. 10753–10770.

130. Perez, O. J., and Aggarwal, Y. P., 1981, Present-day tectonics of the southeastern Caribbean and northeastern Venezuela: Journal of Geophysical Research, v. 86, p. 10791–10804.

131. Plafker, G., 1976, Tectonic aspects of the Guatemala earthquake of 4 February 1976: Science, v. 193, p. 1201–1208.

132. Robertson, P., and Burke, K., 1986, Evolution of a plate boundary hinge zone during the last 20 million years in the southeastern Caribbean [abs.]: EOS American Geophysical Union Transactions, v. 67, p. 1210.

132A. Robertson, P., and Burke, K., 1989, Evolution of southern Caribbean plate boundary, vicinity of Trinidad and Tobago: American Association of Petroleum Geologists, v. 73, p. 490–509.

133. Robinson, E., 1971, Late Tertiary erosion surfaces and Pleistocene sea levels in Jamaica: Transactions, Caribbean Geological Conference, 5th, St. Thomas, Virgin Islands, p. 213–221.

134. Rod, E., 1956, Strike-slip faults of northern Venezuela: American Association of Petroleum Geologists Bulletin, v. 40, p. 457–476.

135. Rosales, H., 1972, La falla de San Francisco en el oriente de Venezuela: Boletín Geología (Venezuela), Publicación Especial no. 5, v. 4, p. 2322–2339.

136. Rosencrantz, E., and Sclater, J. G., 1986, Depth and age in the Cayman Trough: Earth and Planetary Science Letters, v. 79, p. 133–144.

137. Rosencrantz, E., Personal communication, 1986.

138. Salvador, A., 1986, Comment *on* "Neogene block tectonics of eastern Turkey and northern South America: continental applications of the finite difference method": Tectonics, v. 5, p. 697–701.

139. Schubert, C. and Valastro, S., 1976, Quaternary geology of La Orchila Island, central Venezuelan offshore, Caribbean Sea: Geological Society of America Bulletin, v. 87, p. 1131–1142.

140. Schubert, C., Valastro, S., and Coward, J. B., 1977, Evidencias de levantamiento reciente de la costa norte-central (Cordillera de la Costa), Venezuela: Acta Científica Venezolana, v. 28, p. 363–372.

141. Schubert, C., and Szabo, B. J., 1978, Uranium-series ages of Pleistocene marine deposits on the islands of Curacao and La Blanquilla, Caribbean Sea: Geologie en Mijnbouw, v. 57, p. 325–332.

142. Schubert, C., 1979, El Pilar Fault Zone, northeastern Venezuela: brief review: Tectonophysics, v. 52, p. 447–455.

143. Schubert, C., and Cowart, J. B., 1980, Terrazas marinas del Pleistoceno a lo largo de la costa suroriental de la Republica Dominicana; Cronología preliminar: Transactions, Caribbean Geological Conference, 9th, Santo Domingo, Dominican Republic, p. 681–688.

144. Schubert, C., 1982a, Neotectonics of Boconó fault, western Venezuela: Tectonophysics, v. 85, p. 205–220.

145. ——, 1982b, Origin of Cariaco Basin, southern Caribbean Sea: Marine Geology, v. 47, p. 345–360.

146. ——, 1984, Basin formation along the Boconó–Morón–El Pilar fault system, Venezuela: Journal of Geophysical Research, v. 89, p. 5711–5718.

147. Schubert, C., and Krause, F. F., 1984, Morón fault zone, north-central Venezuelan borderland; Identification, definition, and neotectonic character: Marine Geophysical Researches, v. 6, p. 257–273.

148. Schubert, C., 1985, Comments *on* "Subduction of the Caribbean plate and basement uplifts in the overriding South America Plate": Tectonics, v. 4, p. 781–783.

149. Schubert, C. and Laredo, M., 1984, Geology of Aves Island (Venezuela) and subsidence of Aves Ridge, Caribbean Sea: Marine Geology, v. 59, p. 305–318.

150. Schubert, C., and Scheidegger, A. E., 1986, Recent joints and their tectonic significance in the Coastal Range of Venezuela and Curacao: Journal of Coastal Research, v. 2, p. 167–172.

151. Schubert, C., 1986, Aspectos neotectónicos de la zona de falla de la Victoria y orígen de la cuenca de Santa Lucía-Ocumare del Tuy, Venezuela: Acta Científica Venezolana, v. 37, p. 278–286.

152. Schwartz, D. P., and Swan, F. H., III, 1979, Quaternary faulting and deformation along the eastern Chixoy–Polochic Fault Zone, Guatemala: Geological Society of America Abstracts with Programs, v. 11, p. 512.

153. Schwartz, D. P., Cluff, L. S., and Donnelly, T. W., 1979, Quaternary faulting along the Caribbean–North American plate boundary in Central America: Tectonophysics, v. 52, p. 431–445.

154. Shagam, R., and 6 others, 1984, Tectonic implications of Cretaceous-Pliocene fission-track ages from rocks of the circum-Maracaibo Basin region of western Venezuela and eastern Colombia, *in* Bonini, W. E., Hargraves, R. B., and Shagam, R., eds., The Caribbean–South American Plate Boundary and Regional Tectonics: Geological Society of America Memoir 162, p. 385–412.

155. Shanzer, E. V., Petrov, O. M., and Franco, G., 1975, Sobre las formaciones costeras del Holoceno, las terrazas pleistocenicas de la region Habana-Matanzas y los sedimentos vinculados a ellas: Academia de Ciencias de Cuba, Serie Geológica, no. 21, p. 1–26.

156. Sieh, K. E., 1981, A review of geological evidence for recurrence of large earthquakes *in* Earthquake prediction; An international review, Washington, D.C.: American Geophysical Union, p. 181–207.

157. Silver, E. A., Case, J. E., and MacGillavry, H. J., 1975, Geophysical study of the Venezuelan Borderland: Geological Society of America Bulletin, v. 86, p. 213–226.

158. Soulas, J. P., 1985, Neotectónica del flanco occidental de los Andes de Venezuela, entre 70°30′ y 71°00′ W (fallas de Boconó, Valera, Tuname,

Pinango, y del piedemonte): Memoir, Venezuelan Geologic Congress, 6th, Caracas, Venezuela, v. 4, p. 2687–2711.

158A. —— , 1985, Neotectónica Geologico Venezolano: Memoir, Venezuelan Geologic Congress, 6th, Caracas, Venezuela, v. 10, p. 6639–6656.

159. Speed, R. C., 1985, Cenozoic collision of the Lesser Antilles arc and continental South America and the origin of the El Pilar fault: Tectonics, v. 4, p. 41–69.

160. Speed, R. C., and 8 others, 1984, Lesser Antilles arc and adjacent terranes, Atlas 10, Ocean Margin Drilling Program, Regional Atlas Series: Woods Hole, Massachusetts, Marine Science International, 27 sheets, scale 1:2,000,000.

161. Stein, S., Engeln, J. F., Wiens, D. A., Speed, R. C., and Fujita, K., 1982, Subduction seismicity and tectonics in the Lesser Antilles arc: Journal of Geophysical Research, v. 87, p. 8642–8664.

162. Stein, S., Wiens, D. A., Engeln, J. F., and Fujita, K., 1986, Comment *on* "Subduction of aseismic ridges beneath the Caribbean Plate; Implications for the tectonics and seismic potential of the northeastern Caribbean": Journal of Geophysical Research, v. 91, p. 784–786.

163. Steineck, P. L., 1974, Foraminiferal paleoecology of the Montpelier and Lower Coastal Groups (Eocene–Miocene), Jamaica, West Indies: Palaeogeography, Palaeoclimatology, Palaeoecology, v. 16, p. 217–242.

164. Stephan, J. F., 1985, Andes et chaîne Caraïbe sur la transversale de Barquisimeto (Venezuela); Évolution géodynamique, *in* Proceedings, Géodynamique des Caraïbes Symposium, Paris, France, February, 1985: Paris, Éditions Technip, p. 505–529.

165. Stoffa, P. L., Mauffret, A., Truchan, M., and Buhl, P., 1981, Sub-B" layering in the southern Caribbean; The Aruba Gap and Venezuela Basin: Earth and Planetary Science Letters, v. 53, p. 131–146.

166. Sykes, L. R., McCann, W. R., and Kafka, A. L., 1982, Motion of Caribbean Plate during last 7 million years and implications for earlier Cenozoic movements: Journal of Geophysical Research, v. 87, p. 10656–10676.

167. Taylor, F. W., Mann, P., Valastro, S., Jr., and Burke, K., 1985, Stratigraphy and radiocarbon chronology of a subaerially exposed Holocene coral reef, Dominican Republic: Journal of Geology, v. 93, p. 311–332.

168. Taylor, F. W., Mann, P., and Deveaux, E., 1984, Neotectonics of the Beata Ridge; Integration of observations from the Caribbean Sea and southern Hispaniola [abs.]: EOS American Geophysical Union Transactions, v. 65, p. 1109–1110.

169. Tomblin, J. F., 1975, The Lesser Antilles and Aves Ridge, *in* Nairn, A.E.M., and Stehli, F. G., eds., The Ocean Basins and Margins, Vol. 3, The Gulf of Mexico and the Caribbean: New York, Plenum, p. 467–500.

170. Torrini, R., Jr., and Speed, R. C., 1989, Structure and tectonics of the forearc basin/accretionary prism transition, Lesser Antilles forearc: Journal of Geophysical Research, v. 94, p. 10,549–10,584

171. Tschanz, C. M., Martin, R. F., Cruz, B. J., Mehnert, H., and Cebula, G. T., 1974, Geologic evolution of the Sierra Nevada de Santa Marta, northeastern Colombia: Geological Society of America Bulletin, v. 85, p. 273–284.

172. Van den Berghe, B., 1983, Evolution sédimentaire et structurale depuis le Paleocene du secteur "Massif de la Selle" (Haïti)–"Baoruco" (Republique Dominicaine); "Nord de la Ride de Beata" dans l'orogene nord Caraïbe (Hispaniola–Grandes Antilles) [Ph.D. thesis]: Paris, Université Pierre et Marie Curie, 205 p.

173. Vasquez, E. E. and Dickey, P. A., 1972, Major faulting in northwestern Venezuela and its relation to global tectonics: Transactions, Caribbean Geological Conference, 6th, Caracas, Venezuela, p. 191–202.

174. Vernette, G., Klingebiel, A., Chassaigne, B., and Zarki, H., 1985, Tectonisme et organisation des provinces morpho-sédimentaires sur le littoral Caraïbe de Colombia, *in* Proceedings, Géodynamique des Caraïbes Symposium, Paris, France, February, 1985: Paris, Éditions Technip, p. 463–474.

175. Vierbuchen, R. C., 1984, The geology of the El Pilar Fault zone and adjacent areas in northeastern Venezuela, *in* Bonini, W. E., Hargraves, R. B., and Shagam R., eds., The Caribbean-South American Plate Boundary and Regional Tectonics: Geological Society of America Memoir 162,

p. 189–212.

176. Vignali, M., 1972, Excursion geologica al extremo occidental de Araya: Transactions, Caribbean Geological Conference, 6th, Caracas, Venezuela, p. 44–47.

177. Vitali, C., Mauffret, A., Kenyon, N., and Renard, V., 1985, Panamanian and Colombian deformed belts; An integrated study using Gloria and SEABEAM transits and seismic profiles, *in* Proceedings, Géodynamique des Caraïbes Symposium, Paris, France, February, 1985: Paris, Éditions Technip, p. 451–461.

178. Wadge, G., and Wooden, J. L., 1982, Late Cenozoic alkaline volcanism in the northwestern Caribbean; Tectonic setting and Sr isotopic characteristics: Earth and Planetary Science Letters, v. 57, p. 35–46.

179. Wadge, G. and Burke, K., 1983, Neogene Caribbean Plate rotation and associated Central American tectonic evolution: Tectonics, v. 2, p. 633–643.

180. Wadge, G., and Shepherd, J. B., 1984, Segmentation of the Lesser Antilles subduction zone: Earth and Planetary Science Letters, v. 71, p. 297–304.

181. Weaver, J. D., 1968, Terraces in western Puerto Rico: Transactions, Caribbean Geological Confernece, 4th, Port-of-Spain, Trinidad, p. 243–245.

182. —— , 1971, Review of geomorphological and Pleistocene research in the Caribbean: Transactions, Caribbean Geological Conference, 5th, St. Thomas, Virgin Islands, p. 201–206.

183. Weingarten, B., 1977, Tectonic and paleoclimatic significance of a paleosol in the central Andes of Venezuela [M.S. thesis]: Philadelphia, University of Pennsylvania, 67 p.

184. Westbrook, G. K., 1982, The Barbados Ridge Complex; Tectonics of a mature forearc system, *in* Leggett, J. K., ed., Trench-forearc geology; Sedimentation and tectonics on modern and ancient active plate margins: Geological Society of London Special Publication no. 10, p. 275–290.

185. Westercamp, D., 1979, Diversité, controle structural et origines du volcanisme recent dans l'arc insulaire des Petites Antilles: Bulletin de Recherches Geologiques et Minieres (2nd series), section IV, no. 3/4, p. 211–226.

186. Weyl, R., 1980, Geology of Central America (second edition): Berlin, Gebrueder Borntraeger, 371 p.

187. White, R. A., 1985, The Guatemala earthquake of 1816 on the Chixoy–Polochic fault: Seismological Society of America Bulletin, v. 75, p. 455–473.

188. Williams, H., and Meyer-Abich, H., 1955, Volcanism in the southern part of El Salvador: University of California Publications in Geological Sciences, v. 32, p. 1–64.

189. Wilson, C. C., 1968, The Los Bajos fault: Transactions, Caribbean Geological Conference, 4th, Port-of-Spain, Trinidad, p. 87–89.

190. Wing, R., and MacDonald, H., 1973, Radar geology; Petroleum exploration technique, eastern Panamá and northwestern Colombia: American Association of Petroleum Geologists Bulletin, v. 57, p. 825–840.

Winterer, E. L., Hussong, D. M., and Decker, R. W., 1989, The Eastern Pacific Region: Boulder, Colorado, Geological Society of America, The Geology of North America, v. N, 577 p.

MANUSCRIPT ACCEPTED BY THE SOCIETY AUGUST 6, 1987

ACKNOWLEDGMENTS

Field studies by Mann and Burke related to this review were funded by the NASA Geodynamics Program (contracts NAG 5155 and NA55-28139 to Burke) and the University of Texas Institute for Geophysics. Field studies by Schubert in Venezuela were partially supported by CONICIT (Grants S1-0374 and S1-727) and Universidad de los Andes (Grant Fo-100-79). This paper is University of Texas Institute for Geophysics Contribution no. 660 and Lunar and Planetary Institute Contribution no. 596. The LPI is operated by the Universities Space Research Association under Contract NASW-4066 with the National Aeronautic and Space Administration. Special thanks to J. Case, J. Matti, J. Schwartz, and F. Taylor for helpful reviews and to E. Clark, R. Mason, and K. Moser for typing and retyping the manuscript. We thank A. Mauffret, J. Stephan, and R. Torrini for providing preprints.

Printed in U.S.A.

The Geology of North America
Vol. H, The Caribbean Region
The Geological Society of America, 1990

Chapter 13

History and tectonic setting of Caribbean magmatism

Thomas W. Donnelly
Department of Geological Sciences, State University of New York at Binghamton, Binghamton, New York 13901
Dirk Beets
Rijks Geologische Dienst, Postbus 157, Haarlem 24931, Netherlands
Michael J. Carr
Department of Geological Sciences, Rutgers University, New Brunswick, New Jersey 08903
Trevor Jackson
Department of Geology, University of the West Indies, Mona, Kingston 7, Jamaica
Gerard Klaver
Institute of Earth Sciences, Free University, 1507 MC Amsterdam, Netherlands
John Lewis
Department of Geology, George Washington University, Washington, D.C. 20052
Rene Maury
Laboratoire de Pétrologie, Université de Bretagne Occidentale, 29283 Brest Cedex, France
Hans Schellenkens and Alan L. Smith
Department of Geology, University of Puerto Rico, Mayagüez, Puerto Rico 00708
Geoffrey Wadge
Department of Geography, University of Reading, Reading RG6 2BA, England
Denis Westercamp
B.R.G.M., 6-8 Rue Chasseloup-Labat, 75737 Paris Cedex, France

INTRODUCTION

The Caribbean area has a rich and varied igneous history, especially in the Late Cretaceous and Cenozoic. The emphasis of this chapter will be on that portion of the igneous history that began with Mesozoic separation of South and North America and has continued to the Holocene. Pre-Jurassic magmatism is recorded in northern Central America, Venezuela, and Colombia, and will be discussed briefly in other chapters of this volume.

The aim of this chapter will be to describe igneous rock associations according to magmatic styles that characterize certain time intervals of the Caribbean and to suggest how these styles relate to contemporary tectonics. A recurring theme will be the close relationship among widespread igneous rock occurrences which might have prompted special interpretations in the past.

Because the volcanic units that form the backbone of this account are mainly named stratigraphic units, much of this account will refer to these units. Further discussion may be found in other chapters of this volume.

MAGMATO-TECTONIC ASSOCIATIONS OF THE CARIBBEAN

The classification of magmatic suites used here is a very general one that follows the lines of Donnelly and Rogers (1978, 1980). The major igneous associations of Caribbean igneous suites are (1) a Jurassic to mid-Upper Cretaceous widespread Cretaceous oceanic basalt and accompanying minor mafic and siliceous small plutons, and (2) several series of mid-Upper Cretaceous to Holocene, dominantly calc-alkaline volcanic and plutonic suites, and (3) middle Tertiary to Holocene alkalic basaltic suites. The basaltic suite has the attributes of an ophiolite where it occurs on land; in addition, it has been recovered from five Deep Sea Drilling Project (DSDP) sites in the Venezuelan and Colombian basins. Basaltic rocks have the affinities of mid-ocean ridge basalt (MORB) as well as ocean-island basalt (OIB). The calc-alkaline suites include a Cretaceous primitive island arc (PIA) suite, a Cretaceous shoshonite suite, and many widespread Late Cretaceous to Holocene normal calc-alkaline (CA) suites. In addition, there are several suites which cannot be assigned readily to

Donnelly, T. W., Beets, D., Carr, M. J., Jackson, T., Klaver, G., Lewis, J., Maury, R., Schellenkens, H., Smith, A. L., Wadge, G., and Westercamp, D., 1990, History and tectonic setting of Caribbean magmatism, *in* Dengo, G., and Case, J. E., eds., The Caribbean region: Boulder, Colorado, Geological Society of America, The Geology of North America, v. H.

any of these categories; some of these are tholeiitic to calc-alkalic basaltic to bimodal suites associated with rifting events, and others include high-alkali variants of the calc-alkaline association. Representative chemical analyses of the rocks of these suites are given in Table 1.

The Caribbean igneous suites are among the most extensive and thoroughly studied orogenic igneous rock associations of the world. The elucidation of their relationship to plate motions is essential for a reconstruction of the tectonic evolution of the Caribbean area.

THE CIRCUM-CARIBBEAN CRETACEOUS BASALT ASSOCIATION

The most voluminous post-Paleozoic igneous rock series in the Caribbean realm is a dominantly Early to middle Cretaceous mafic and ultramafic complex, which occurs within the Venezuelan and Colombian basins, throughout the Greater Antilles, along the northern coast of South America from Trinidad to the Guajira Peninsula of Colombia, and along the Pacific margin from central Guatemala south to Ecuador (Fig. 1).

The grouping of the widespread basalt occurrences as a single province is a recent concept and stems largely from the recognition of similar and coeval basalt in the basement of the Venezuelan and Colombian basins, found during deep-sea drilling on Leg 15 (Donnelly, 1973a; Donnelly and others, 1973b).

The mafic associations bear a close resemblance to the contemporary concept of an ophiolite (Coleman, 1977), and many have been so labeled (e.g., Wadge and others, 1984).

Lithology and composition of the basaltic association

Some occurrences of this association are dominantly serpentinite, whereas others are dominantly basalt, and many consist of highly deformed and scattered mafic lithologies mixed in a serpentinite matrix. The dominant mafic lithology is basalt, which is generally pillowed and less commonly in hyaloclastic (rarely pyroclastic) beds. Less widespread lithologies consist of dolerite (very rarely as sheeted dikes), cumulate gabbro, peridotite, and plagiogranite. Amphibolite of basaltic composition is abundant at many localities, but eclogite is relatively rare.

Because of structural complexity, in no place has the thickness of this association been accurately determined, but at several localities it is evidently several hundred meters and in some areas probably several kilometers (estimated from regional gravity anomalies) thick.

Associated sedimentary rocks include pelagic facies, such as radiolarian cherts or pelagic limestones; in other places the sedimentary rocks are thick and coarse, and are either terrigenous or consist of epiclastic mafic igneous debris. Radiolaria are the most widespread associated fossils, and ammonites have been found in many localities. Foraminifera have been found in a few localities. Intercalated shallow-water molluscs are rare.

The composition of the basalt and associated mafic litholo-

gies is mainly oceanic (low-K), and many occurrences have been compared closely with MORB. Other compositions, however, include both low-Ti, high-Mg picrites, and low- to high-Mg basalts with high titanium and potassium. These latter occurrences resemble OIB. Other lithologies (plagiogranite, peridotites, gabbros) bear a close compositional resemblance to their counterparts in ophiolite complexes elsewhere.

Age of basalt occurrences

The basalt occurrences have been dated by both fossil (Fig. 2) and radiometric (Fig. 3) methods. Most of the fossil dates are in the range Aptian to Cenomanian, but some are earlier and a few later. As Figure 2 shows, the age of the termination of basaltic eruptive activity is essentially coeval over a very broad area. At several localities, sedimentary rocks immediately overlying the basalt are Campanian. The age for the end of the basalt event is further constrained by tectonic emplacement of mafic allochthons, and by intrusion of these allochthons by plutons of other magmatic affinities. In Hispaniola, in DSDP site 152 on the Beata Ridge, and possibly in Jamaica, there is evidence for magmatic activity continuing into the Campanian. Some basalt occurrences along the Pacific coast include small volumes of early Tertiary basalts, but in no case do they appear to be voluminous.

Numerous attempts have been made to date these rocks by K/Ar techniques. Because of the low K contents of these rocks, this method has, not surprisingly, proven unreliable. Figure 3 shows histograms for basalts, gabbros, and amphibolites belonging to this association. The ages are taken as given in publications; virtually all would be found to be slightly older if modern decay constants were used. Although the ages are approximately correct, many are clearly too young. In some localities, radiometric ages are younger than fossil ages of overlying sedimentary rocks (cf. Bourgois and others, 1982a, and Bandy and Casey, 1973) or younger than the age of tectonic emplacement of the basalt (cf. Bertrand and others, 1980, and Rosenfeld, 1981). Amphibolite dates are especially problematic; the partitioning of argon and potassium among phases during metamorphism is not known, and the age refers neither clearly to the original magmatism nor to the metamorphism. Published ages are valuable in many cases to establish that certain mafic igneous bodies belong to this association, but the probable error of these ages limit their value.

Northern border of South America

The major exposures of the basalt association in northern South America are on the offshore islands of Aruba and Curaçao, and as allochthonous bodies of the Villa de Cura complex and the Paraguaná Peninsula of northern Venezuela. The Sans Souci Formation of Trinidad, Tinaquillo peridotite, Paraguaná Peninsula gabbros, and Siquisique ophiolitic debris of Venezuela are notable smaller occurrences (Plates 5A, 5C). A few minor exposures are found in northeastern Colombia.

1. Venezuela. The Venezuelan basalt exposures are found

TABLE 1. CHEMICAL ANALYSES* OF REPRESENTATIVE, INDIVIDUAL CARIBBEAN VOLCANIC ROCKS

Cretaceous Basalt Association

No.**	DSDP		Aruba	Curaçao		Duarte		Gorgona I.		Nicoya		Hispaniola	
	1	2	3	4	5	6	7	8	9	10	11	12	13
SiO$_2$	48.4	46.5	52.98	50.37	44.31	46.79	49.18	47.4	44.2	49.48	46.28	45.5	47.5
TiO$_2$	1.06	2.51	1.24	1.02	.51	.71	3.50	.39	.66	2.40	1.24	.86	2.38
Al$_2$O$_3$	15.48	13.80	13.92	14.27	8.39	8.01	14.24	12.40	12.0	13.49	14.36	13.75	13.93
Fe$_2$O$_3$	4.02	8.32				5.55	2.10		3.2				
FeO	6.12	5.16	12.00	10.31	10.12	4.46	9.80	10.2	8.2	14.84	10.73	9.61	11.54
MnO	.16	.14	.20	.18	.17			.22	.18	.24	.20	.18	.20
MgO	8.11	5.91	7.21	8.52	24.4	22.81	6.48	17.6	15.9	6.01	9.55	12.85	7.20
CaO	12.27	9.71	8.68	12.40	7.13	9.60	9.28	10.7	10.1	8.80	1.56	12.20	9.60
Na$_2$O	1.53	2.22	3.72	2.16	.59	.36	3.07	1.16	1.13	2.54	1.54	1.60	3.11
K$_2$O	.08	1.90	.11	.16	.02	.07	.58		.02	.33	.54	.23	.24
P$_2$O$_5$	.08	.25	.10	.07	.04	.21	.21		.06	.23	.11	.18	.26
Cr	340	305	137	387	2468	1548	144	1250		118	346	910	170
Ni	113	106	80	109	1152	1076	111	720		53	120	365	105
Rb	.6	29.6		2	3			1		5	23	14	14
Sr	128	285	106	55	34	137	390	58		97	87	236	247
Y	22.9	33.1	26	19	12	13.7	31.3	14		44	18		
Zr	52	149	78	58	39	48.6	224	30		140	81	54.8	137.4
Nb			6	6.5	3	14.5	31.7		.5	9	5	13.7	20.1
Ba	11.4	37				18.5	98.1	3		41	260		
La	2.0	14.6	3.33	3.05	1.76	4.8	27.0			7.41	3.34		
Ce	5.8	35.4	10.0	7.18		10	63	.88		19.9	8.83		
Sm	1.59	5.65	2.42	2.18	1.09	1.4	9.6	.74		5.29	2.47		
Eu	.6	1.89	.82	.74	.37	.58	3.2	.41		1.72	.92		
Yb	1.67	2.32	2.63	1.97	1.13	.95	2.7	1.38		4.71	2.07		
Hf			1.65	1.22	.72								
Th	nil	2.19	.28	.22	.18								
U	.22	.91											

TABLE 1. (CONTINUED)

No.**	Primitive Island-arc Association									Cretaceous C A, Puerto Rico		
	Bonaire			Virgin I.					Tobago	Robles-Río Orocovis		
	14	15	16	17	18	19	20	21	22	23	24	25
SiO$_2$	55.18	71.69	70.28	74.7	75.0	70.3	46.1	40.6	51.8	57.3	50.8	50.2
TiO$_2$	1.28	.73	.55	.3	.3	.7	.56	.5	1.15	1.2	.7	.77
Al$_2$O$_3$	15.18	14.27	15.29	12.1	13.4	14.9	14.2	11.7	13.97	18.7	15.6	16.2
Fe$_2$O$_3$												
FeO	11.16	4.25	3.52	3.8	2.1	4.8	8.77	6.7	9.07	5.7	5.84	9.89
MnO	.15		.06			.18		.18			.19	.15
MgO	4.69	.89	.83	1.6	.7	7.71	3.1	7.11	2.6	4.8	3.15	3.49
CaO	8.75	.32	.92	3.5	.6	4.1	10.1	22.0	8.19	2.9	9.1	8.94
Na$_2$O	2.82	6.80	7.18	3.45	4.40	4.5	2.35	2.6	3.39	3.0	3.4	4.51
K$_2$O	.78	.87	1.22	.35	2.80	.3	.89	.3	.62	5.8	2.2	.40
P$_2$O$_5$	.20	.18	.16						.24			
Cr	37	4	4	4	2	5	130	38	150	27	430	15
Ni	21	1	1	4		5	54	21	20	19	133	8
Rb	7	11	15	2.8	25.6	2.6	12.6	3.4	18	128	56	38.6
Sr	269	72	136	124	128	176	157	102	416	493	419	1250
Y	28	32	63	23.4	23.8	34.2	13.5	14.4	24.1	23.4	19	28.6
Zr	78	102	264	85	108	54	24	29	65.5	124	81	74
Nb	4		6	.83	.96	.79	.16	.19	3.17	5		2.05
Ba				84	334	148	94	124	1860		1990	560
La	7.85	5.2	21.1	2.9	4.5	3.5	.84	1.32		16.1		9.6
Ce	17.0	13.1	43.8	7.0	10.1	9.1	2.7	4.2		33.1		20.6
Sm	3.81	3.3	9.09	1.66	1.76	2.4	.98	1.0		3.6		3.7
Eu	1.27	.94	2.59	.54	.45	.74	.42	.34		1.37		1.25
Yb	2.65	3.03	5.74	1.7	1.91	2.36	1.28	1.12		2.5		2.19
Hf	2.12	3.1	6.72							3.1		1.58
Th	1	1.46	2.4	.34	.95	.44	.16	.29		4.91	2.7	1.2
U					.3	.31	.23	.38		1.85	1.22	.62

TABLE 1. (CONTINUED)

	Cretaceous C A, Puerto Rico			Rift Assoc.		Lesser Antilles C A						
	post-Robles			Wagwater		Saba		St Kitts		Mart.	St Lucia	Mont.
No.**	26	27	28	29	30	31	32	33	34	35	36	37
SiO_2	50.6	49.2	56.5	46.56	70.72	51.0	60.05	51.1		61.9	62.8	50.9
TiO_2	.90	.90	.88	3.22	.31	.90	.59	1.02		.45	.5	.8
Al_2O_3	18.8	16.8	18.8	14.72	14.95	19.97	17.27	17.77		17.29	17.7	21.1
Fe_2O_3												
FeO	7.88	9.90	7.35	12.46	2.09	7.59	5.64	9.47		6.12	3.5	7.0
MnO	.22	.13	.07	.01	.15	.13	.19	.18				
MgO	6.09	2.77	9.82	.48	4.82	3.27	5.42	2.24		1.6		3.4
CaO	7.39	9.19	7.49	3.62	4.65	11.00	7.42	10.90		6.17	6.0	11.0
Na_2O	3.74	2.51	2.87	3.22	4.03	3.03	3.60	2.57		3.49	3.1	2.80
K_2O	3.33	1.19	.49	.62	1.15	.62	1.25	.39		1.00	1.7	.60
P_2O_5	;83	.31	.14	.22	.12	.05	.15	.09		.18		
Cr	24	26	24	187	24	33	40	71		8	25	4
Ni	22	20	19	132		40	54	38		6	5	10
Rb				8	30	12	24	7		28	74	
Sr	605	490	467	282	306	379	264			284	317	480
Y				23	11				22		19.5	
Zr	86	54	188	266	150			69			133	53
Nb	3.8	2.41	5.9					3		7.2	1.8	
Ba	1000	650	362	190	673	188	444	165		208	555	124
La	16.1		9.6	21.6	8.6	16.3				11.39	17.4	6.0
Ce	33.1		20.6	41.5	2.03	39.9			8.95	25.7	35.8	15.6
Sm	3.6		3.7	4.2	3.0	3.8			2.35	3.15	2.9	15.6
Eu	1.37		1.25	1.48	1.06	1.1			.94	1.04	.82	1.78
Yb	2.5		2.19	1.82	1.71	2.4			2.22	2.36	1.58	.7
Hf	1.58	1.0	3.3							2.75	3.5	1.35
Th	4.91	2.7	1.2	2.6	.43	3.8				2.9	7.71	
U	.9		1.5								2.29	1.82

TABLE 1. (CONTINUED)

	Lesser Antilles C A				Central America C A					
	St Luc.	St Vinc.	Grenada		Guatemala		El Sal.	Nic.	Costa Rica	BVF
No.**	38	39	40	41	42	43	44	45	46	47
SiO_2	70.32	53.87	52.08	47.52	52.10	63.86	51.60	47.4	54.64	52.3
TiO_2	.32	.95	1.02	.97	.92	.43	1.12	1.13	.61	.88
Al_2O_3	13.32	18.07	18.89	15.67	17.70	17.50	18.10	14.9	19.04	18.63
Fe_2O_3						1.81	3.74			
FeO	4.29	8.32	7.68	10.05	8.01	2.65	6.05	11.53	7.19	8.81
MnO	.15	.17	.15	.17		.14	.17	.18	.15	.16
MgO	.25	4.46	4.31	7.07	5.0	1.65	4.23	11.02	4.76	4.36
CaO	2.30	9.10	8.82	14.37	8.2	4.99	8.93	10.8	9.04	8.92
Na_2O	4.86	3.08	4.00	2.16	3.8	4.85	3.38	2.19	3.08	2.86
K_2O	1.91	.51	1.31	.63	.82	1.59	1.39	.14	.64	1.69
P_2O_5		.11	.41	.13	.17	.19	.29	.09	.18	.28
Cr			43.2	74.9	13	3	22	352	51	30
Ni		15.6	53.9	48.8	8		7	186	39	27
Rb	43	13.7	42.5	7.1	9	31	31	11	5	33
Sr	100	217	761	1016	609	518	454	280	755	696
Y	63	27.6	22.6	20.9	17		30.6	19.0	15.5	24.2
Zr	219	85	154	48.7	125	168	135		63	150
Nb	6	3.6	15.8	4.3						
Ba		124	541	256	580	946	501	89	569	947
La	15.4	35.5	8.41	9.08	45.66	12.0	2.87	13.2	37.4	
Ce	39.8		63.5	20.6	17.0	26.80	30.6	8.41	26.6	73.0
Sm	7.3		5.93	3.59	3.25	3.43	4.43	2.02	2.88	6.84
Eu	1.53		1.72	1.17	1.10	1.05	1.25	.92	.99	1.69
Yb	7.5		1.82	1.77			2.7	1.52	1.49	2.14
Hf					2.64	3.80				
Th	4.4				.59	1.99				
U			6.0	.68						

TABLE 1. (CONTINUED)

No.	Northwest Caribbean Alkaline and BVF						
	C. Rica	Dominican Republic				L. Yojoa	
	48	49	50	51	52	53	54
SiO_2	51.8	44.8	51.3	60.48	47.19	48.36	61.37
TiO_2	1.17	.77	.76	.52	2.43	2.60	.50
Al_2O_3	18.2	13.56	14.06	15.73	12.95	18.18	18.31
Fe_2O_3	2.3		5.09	2.67	7.40	1.95	1.74
FeO	7.2	8.77	3.35	2.04	2.80	8.80	4.28
MnO	.16	.16	.15	.11	.15	.18	.12
MgO	4.8	14.06	8.04	2.56	9.52	5.61	.37
CaO	8.2	12.43	8.28	5.66	11.03	8.64	1.33
Na_2O	3.64	1.06	1.85	4.83	2.01	3.60	5.93
K_2O	1.08	1.18	1.95	3.60	2.09	1.78	5.26
P_2O_5	.44	.36	.15	.256	.66	.53	0.6
Cr	39	440	428		239		
Ni	27	785	116		212	41	3
Rb	11	32				17	69
Sr	600	2771	829		1755	543	43
Y		16.6	20.6		24.3	33	232
Zr		92	92		319	235	748
Nb			4		69.7		
Ba	670	2863	2400		1690	307	448
La		64.4	19	82	157		
Ce		125.1	32	124	255		
Sm		7.53	3.9	6.8	16		
Eu		2.16	1.2	1.8	4.4		
Yb		1.67	1.6	1.4	1.7		
Hf			1.7	4.1	8		
Th			3.1	28	20		
U			.8	9.2	3.4		

*Key to column heads:

Cretaceous Basalt Association:
1. Basalt, Leg 15, DSDP site 146, 146-43R-1
2. Basalt, Leg 15, DSDP site 151, 151-15-1
3. Basalt, Aruba, 68BE71
4. Basalt, Curaçao, 79BE189
5. Picrite, Curaçao, 79KV018
6. Duarte metabasalt, Dominican Republic, OL78-106A
7. Duarte metabasalt, Dominican Republic, LB5-80
8. Komatiite, Isla Gorgona, 47
9. Komatiite, Isla Gorgona, 48
10. Basalt, lower Nicoya Complex, 33
11. Basalt, upper Nicoya Complex, 56
12. Basalt, southern Haiti, 4536
13. Basalt, southern Dominican Republic, 4732

Primitive island-arc association:
14. Mafic, Bonaire, 79KV475
15. Low-viscosity rhyolite, Bonaire, KV699
16. High-viscosity rhyolite, Bonaire, KV-751
17. Extrusive keratophyre, Virgin Is., 61-25D
18. Intrusive keratophyre, Virgin Is., 61-42
19. Dacite, Louisenhoj Fm., Virgin Is., 63-125X
20. Spilite, Virgin Islands, RH542
21. Andesite breccia, Louisenhoj Fm., Virgin Is., 63-79
22. Andesite breccia, Bacolet Fm., Tobago, GTO23

*Key to column heads, continued:

Cretaceous C A association, Puerto Rico
23. Shoshonite, Lapa Lava, WJ5B
24. Shoshonite, Lapa Lava, WJ16E
25. Pillow basalt, Las Tetas Lava, WJ60D
26. Basalt, Río de la Plata Fm., 500
27. Basalt, Alonso Fm. 532c
28. Andesitic basalt, Anon Fm. (Eocene), 711

Early Tertiary rifting association, Jamaica
29. Halberstadt basalt, JA170R
30. Newcastle dacite, JA101

Neogene Lesser Antilles C A association
31. Basalt, Saba, SA141
32. Andesite, Saba, SA155
33. Basalt pyroclastic, Mansion pyroclastics, St. Kitts, 14799
34. IAT, lithology unspecified, St. Kitts, K80
35. Andesitic pyroclastic, Mt. Pelee, 1902 eruption, Martinique, MT15Y
36. Dacite, St. Lucia, 65-5
37. Basalt, Montserrat, 64-28b

38. IAT rhyolite, St. Lucia, 70
39. Basalt, St. Vincent, 1979 eruption
40. "C-series" basalt, Grenada, 109
41. C-series basalt, Grenada, 454

Neogene Central American C A association:
42. Basalt, Santa Maria, Guatemala, SM124
43. Andesite, Santa Maria, Guatemala, S1129
44. Basalt, Santa Ana, El Salvador, SA204
45. Basalt, Nejapa, Nicaragua, Ne203
46. Andesitic basalt, Arenal, Costa Rica
47. Basalt Platanar, Costa Rica, CRPP3

Northwestern Caribbean alkaline and BVF associations:
48. BVF basalt, Guatemala, GUC-26
49. Costa Rica, PP7
50. Basalt, nr. Constanza, Dominican Republic, SAB
51. Andesite, nr. Constanza, Dominican Republic, LDHE-2
52. Alkalic basalt, Constanza, Dominican Republic, YB-1
53. Basalt, L. Yojoa, Honduras, LY-1
54. Trachyte, L. Yojoa, Honduras, LY-25

**Sources for analyses (parentheses indicate that analyses include contributions from multiple sources):

1, 2. Donnelly and others, 1973a
3, 4, 5, 14, 15, 16. Klaver, unpublished
6, 7. Lewis, unpublished
8. Echeverria, 1980
9. Dietrich and others, 1981
10, 11. Wildberg, 1984
12, 13, 22. Girard, 1981
17, 18, 19, (20, 21, 23, 24, 26, 27, 28, 30, 37). Donnelly, unpublished
(20, 26). Hekinian, 1969
(23, 24, 25). Jolly, 1970
(26, 27, 28). Lidiak, personal communication, 1972
29, 30. Jackson, unpublished
31, 32. A. Smith, unpublished
33. Baker and Holland 1973

34. Hawkesworth and Powell, 1950
35. Fichaut and others 1985
(36, 37). Donnelly and others, 1971
38. Le Guin de Kerneizon and others, 1982
39. Graham and Thirlwall, 1981
40, 41. Thirlwall and Graham, 1984
42, 43, (46, 47, 49). CENTAM (unpublished data file of M. J. Carr and W. Rose, Jr.)
(44). Carr and Pontier, 1981
(44, 45, 46, 47, 49). Feigenson and others, 1984
(45). Walker, 1984
48. Carr, unpublished
50, 51, 52. Vespucci, personal communication
53, 54. Mertzman, personal communication, 1986

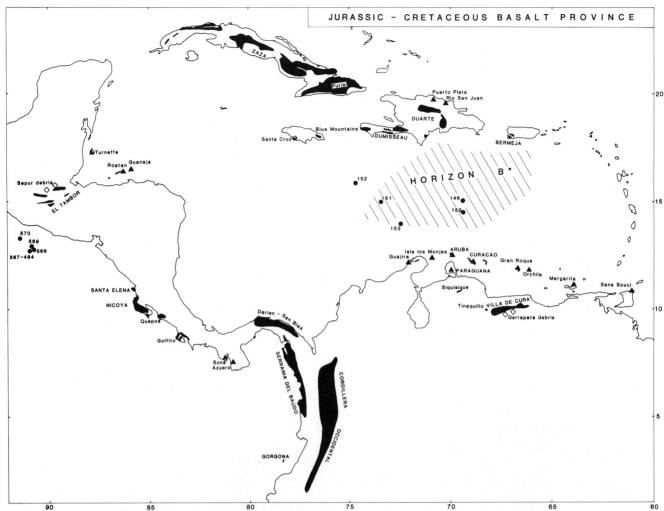

Figure 1. Map of the Caribbean region showing occurrences of the Mesozoic basalt province. Triangles = small occurrences; half-filled circles = occurrences in deep wells; open diamonds = clastic deposits containing mafic debris. Extent of horizon B" is indicated; possible continuations in the eastern Nicaraguan Rise and southeastern Venezuelan Basin are not shown.

in two major belts of basalt and ultramafic rocks in northern Venezuela: a coastal belt and a belt in the Serrania del Interior, approximately 50 km inland. Virtually all of the occurrences are highly tectonized and metamorphosed to low grade facies. In spite of intensive field studies, few fossils have been recovered. Previous descriptions of this area have lumped mafic rocks of the basalt-ultramafic assemblage and more siliceous rocks that are here assigned to the PIA series (see below).

Relatively few exposures of mafic rock are found in the Coast Ranges, and none have been dated satisfactorily. Vierbuchen (1984), Dengo (1953), and Morgan (1967) described metabasalts, amphibolites, and eclogites that are tectonically interlayered in the complexly deformed rocks of this cordillera.

In the Paraguaná Peninsula, Martin-Bellizia and de Arozena (1972) described a large (12 km greatest dimension) klippe of dunite, peridotite, gabbro, and finer grained mafic intrusive rocks. A K/Ar date (Santamaría and Schubert, 1974) places it within ages of the circum-Caribbean group.

In the Serranía del Interior and much of the Villa de Cura and smaller allochthons, there are several basaltic units which may be more or less correlative, but which are presently separated by thrust faults or cannot be otherwise stratigraphically placed. Units (and their ages, where established) include the Tiara lava (Smith, 1953; Shagam, 1960) and underlying Aptian or Albian radiolaria (Beck and others, 1984); the "Conoropa rocks" (Seiders, 1962); The Tiramuto, Las Placitas (Cenomanian to Coniacian), and Pilancones (Albian to Cenomanian) Formations (Menéndez, 1962); the Las Hermanas Formation, which was originally mapped as a southern part of the Tiara Lava (Beck, 1983); and the Los Naranjos Member of the Tucutunemo Formation (MacLachlan and others, 1960). The status of the last-named unit is in doubt because of recent information that the Tucutunemo Formation contains Permian fossils (Benjamini and Shagam, in prep.). The highly tectonized El Carmen lava of the Villa de Cura Group (Shagam, 1960; Navarro, 1983; Beets and others, 1984) is more magnesian than other mafic units and re-

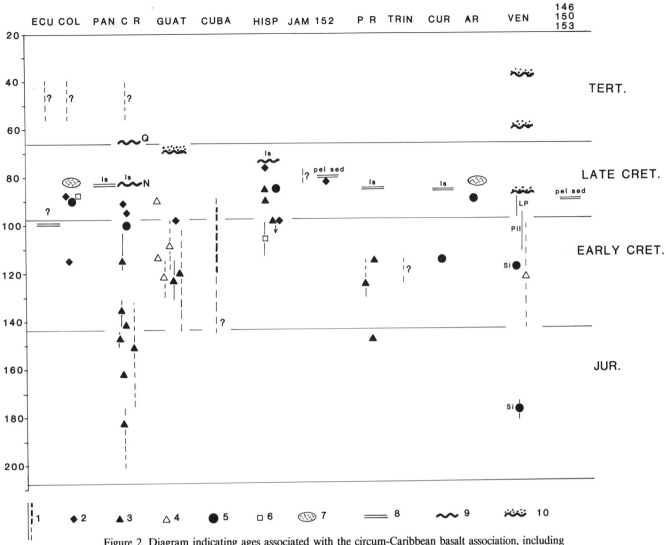

Figure 2. Diagram indicating ages associated with the circum-Caribbean basalt association, including DSDP sites 146, 150, 152, and 153. 1 = age range, dashed where less certain (heavy dashes for Cuba indicate consensus of major eruptive activity); 2 = foraminiferal ages; 3 = radiolarian age; 4 = radiolarian age in sedimentary rocks with uncertain relation to basalt; 5 = ammonite age; 6 = rudist or *Inoceramus* age; 7 = isotopic age of calc-alkaline pluton intruding basalt complex; 8 = sedimentary rocks overlying basalt (Q = Quepos and Osa Peninsula, Costa Rica; N = Nicoya Peninsula, Costa Rica); 9 = tectonic event; 10 = tectonic event providing ophiolitic debris to sedimentary deposit (LP = Las Placitas Formation; Pil = Pilancones Formation; Si = Siquisique; ls = limestone; pel = pelagic sediment.)

sembles picrites from Curaçao. Ultramafic units include the Tinaquillo peridotite (Mackenzie, 1960; Bellizia and López, 1972), the Loma de Hierro peridotite (Graterol, 1972), and the peridotites and gabbros of the Paraguaná Peninsula (Martin-Bellizia and de Arozena, 1972). A disjunct occurrence of tectonized mafic lithologies that occurs near Siquisique, Lara State, has been described by Bartok and others (1985), who listed Bajocian to Bathonian ammonites and noted an unpublished occurrence of Barremian ammonites by Stephan.

The Venezuelan mafic rocks are dominantly basalt (both pillowed and hyaloclastic or pyroclastic) but include widespread dolerites. The ultramafic units include cumulate mafic portions. Accompanying sedimentary rocks include cherts and other rocks

of pelagic aspect, as well as wackes. Graterol (1972) has noted the resemblance of one of the better exposed bodies, the Loma de Hierro peridotite and Tiara lava, to a typical ophiolite. Relatively few of these rocks have escaped the pervasive tectonism of northern Venezuela; however, the various igneous lithologies are very similar to mafic rocks exposed on Aruba and Curaçao.

The recognition that these rocks were emplaced in a major allochthonous event (Villa de Cura Nappe) is credited to Harry Hess (Menéndez, 1962). Since that time, additional allochthonous units have been recognized (see Stephan and others, 1980). The tectonic history of this obducted complex may span as much as 50 m.y. Mafic and ultramafic debris in Coniacian and Paleocene formations (Bell, 1967, 1971; Jarvis, 1964) suggest precur-

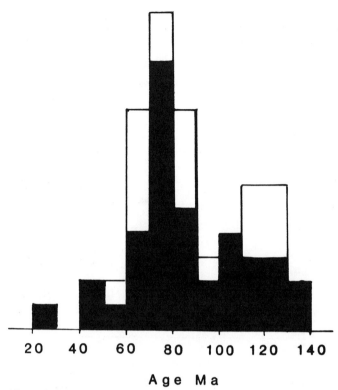

Figure 3. Histogram of individual reported K/Ar ages of basalts and gabbros (solid pattern) and amphibolites (open pattern) for circum-Caribbean basalt association.

sor uplift in the Cretaceous. The allochthonous massif locally overlies the Maastrichtian Paracotos Formation and is capped by a Paleocene limestone, which constrains an early Tertiary emplacement. There was a renewed, and possibly stronger, movement in the late Eocene and Oligocene, causing the shedding of thick sediment series to the south and also the deformation of earlier layered sedimentary units.

2. Curaçao. The island of Curaçao contains one of the best-exposed basalt series in the entire Caribbean region. Extensive studies (Beets, 1972; Beets and others, 1982, 1984) have established these rocks as among the petrologically best-known basalts in the Caribbean. An Albian ammonite was found within the sequence (Weidmann, 1978), and the basalts are overlain by late Santonian to early Campanian limestones.

The Curaçao basalt sequence is about 5 km thick. The lower part is dominantly pillowed and locally picritic; the upper pillow basalts are interbedded with reworked hyaloclastite and intruded by dolerite sills. The pillow basalt is dominantly a plagioclase-clinopyroxene phyric basalt whose original glassy mesostasis has largely been replaced by a fine-grained, low-grade metamorphic assemblage. The high-Mg (picritic) pillow basalts are olivine phyric and carry chrome spinel, but do not show the spinifex texture of flows of similar composition (komatiites), although the olivines are locally skeletal.

3. Aruba. The basaltic sequence on Aruba is about 3 km thick (Beets and others, 1984) and consists mainly of pillowed

and massive basalts with dolerite sills and pyroclastic and volcaniclastic sedimentary rock, intraformational conglomerate, and lapilli tuff. The formation is variably metamorphosed by the intrusion of a batholith. Turonian ammonites were reported by MacDonald (1968) and Beets and others (1984).

The Aruba basalts contrast with those of Curaçao in many ways. Pillow basalts are more scarce, and pyroclastic sedimentary rocks far more abundant. The lapilli tuff indicates that there was some subaerial eruption of basaltic material. The intraformational conglomerate indicates impressive relief. Finally, the age of the ammonites is very close to that indicated for the tonalitic batholith (80 to 85 Ma; Beets and others, 1984), indicating that basaltic magmatism preceded calc-alkaline magmatism by only a short time interval.

4. Venezuelan offshore islands. These islands contain local exposures of basaltic rock and minor mafic intrusions. Margarita has a highly metamorphosed mafic basal complex which has been considered to be Jurassic, but whose age is problematical (Beets and others, 1984). Gran Roque (Schubert and Motiska, 1972) consists of a greenschist facies metamorphosed fine-grained gabbro and a clinopyroxene-plagioclase rock. These rocks are both intruded by quartz diorites and aplites.

Small bodies of metamorphic mafic rock occur on Islas Los Monjes, Venezuela (Santamaría and Schubert, 1974). The composition of these rocks and the similarity of their radiometric ages with others in the Venezuelan coastal belt relates them to the larger basaltic province.

5. Trinidad. The Sans Souci volcanic rocks of northern Trinidad were first described by Barr (1963) and shown to consist of about 1,000 m of basalt and basaltic pyroclastic rock, with minor sedimentary rock. Although no fossils were found, the formation was considered to be approximately the same age or slightly younger than the Barremian to Aptian Toco Formation. Wadge and MacDonald (1985) have obtained a radiometric age (87 Ma) which places it within the age range of other circum-Caribbean basaltic rocks.

The basalt is dominantly pyroclastic, and contains minor lavas and a few gabbroic bodies. The interlayered sedimentary rocks consist of shales, conglomerate, and limestone, and are of terrigenous rather than pelagic facies. Wadge and MacDonald (1985) stated that the southern boundary of this series in Trinidad is a strike-slip fault, across which they postulated this series was transported from the oceanic realm to the north.

6. Northeastern Colombia. Small masses of possibly ophiolitic rock have been found in the Guajira Peninsula. MacDonald (1964) found serpentinite and metagabbro bodies in the Turonian or younger Parauinkrein Formation. Alvarez (1967) found serpentinite, with gabbro fragments, possibly within the Miocene Carpintero Formation, but the emplacement is clearly tectonic.

A subsurface occurrence of mafic igneous rocks described by Théry (1983) is enigmatic. These spilites are chemically unlike (high silica, low titanium) typical basalts. The K/Ar age is uncertain but appears to be earliest Cretaceous or Late Jurassic.

Lockwood's (1965, 1971) discovery of sedimentary features in some serpentinites suggests that these bodies represent, at least in part, a deposition of fragments from serpentinites which protruded through the sedimentary cover as the result of a tectonic process, either gravity slide or a high-angle fault.

The Lesser and Greater Antilles

Numerous bodies of serpentinite, basalt, and metabasaltic rocks are found on each of the Greater Antillean islands. A putative occurrence in the Lesser Antilles is here placed in the PIA series.

1. La Désirade. The small island of La Désirade in the outer part of the Lesser Antilles near Guadeloupe has an older rock sequence that consists of siliceous igneous rocks and pillow basalts, and whose mutual relationships are obscured by limited exposures. Mattinson and others (1980) considered these rocks to be an ophiolite; however, Donnelly and Rogers (1978), Le Guen de Kerneizon and others (1979), and Bouysse and others (1983) interpreted it as belonging to an orogenic series; we discuss it below with the PIA series.

2. Puerto Rico. The Bermeja Complex of southwestern Puerto Rico (Mattson, 1960; Tobisch, 1968; Lee and Mattson, 1976) consists dominantly of serpentinite and included blocks of amphibolite and chert. Less-metamorphosed igneous rocks are also present, including a large body of spilitic metabasalt near the city of Mayagüez. Mattson (1973) inferred that the Bermeja Complex formed a nappe which had moved northward, and which was subsequently overthrust by a higher nappe of younger age. The age of the movement is clearly older than Mayagüez Group sedimentary rocks of Campanian age.

Three radiolarian cherts yielded dates of early Tithonian, Hauterivian to late Aptian, and late Aptian (Mattson and Pessagno, 1979). Unfortunately, their stratigraphic context is not clear; the chert is not obviously interlayered within mafic igneous rocks, but is a mappable unit whose relation to the igneous rocks is not proven. Our conclusion is that the Bermeja Complex, containing igneous and metaigneous rocks and cherts, consists of a series of lithologically contrasting thrust sheets, and a prethrust arrangement that cannot be determined exactly.

3. Hispaniola. The island of Hispaniola has three belts of Cretaceous basaltic or metabasaltic rocks, each with differing characteristics. The southernmost consists of relatively unmetamorphosed basalts that occur along the southern margins of Haiti and the Dominican Republic. Originally described by Woodring and others (1924), this complex has become better known recently as the result of the work of Maurrasse and others (1979). Several French dissertations (Girard, 1981; Calmus, 1983; Van den Berghe, 1983) have provided additional data.

The Dumisseau Formation (Maurrasse and others, 1979) crops out south of Port-au-Prince and consists of 500 m of pillowed and massive basalts interlayered in places with thin sedimentary rocks, including both cherts and fine-grained, locally silicified, turbidites. Intrusive facies were not reported by them nor by later workers in this area, which led Wadge and others

(1984) to exclude this body from their list of northern Caribbean ophiolites. The formation is overlain by Maastrichtian limestones, and the highest basalts are interlayered with late Campanian sedimentary rocks. Sediments associated with lower basalts contain late Santonian to Cenomanian or Early Cretaceous (Maurrasse and others, 1979) faunas. Reeside (1947) found "approximately Santonian" ammonites in loose blocks, evidently from this unit. Woodring and others (1924) reported Albian rudists in beds intercalated with these basalts.

The tectonic environment of emplacement of the Dumisseau Formation is not clear. The area of exposure is highly faulted (Maurrasse and others, 1979; Mercier de Lepinay and others, 1979). The pelagic character of much of the later Cretaceous sedimentary rocks, including especially the series at Massif la Macaya, indicates a deep basinal origin and requires considerable vertical uplift. The Maastrichtian to Paleocene shallow-water limestones that are unconformable above this complex provide a minimal date for the emplacement. A Bouguer gravity anomaly of about 50 mg (Reblin, 1973) shows that the body must be several kilometers thick.

The Duarte Formation of the Cordillera Central of the Dominican Republic and northeastern Haiti (Bowin, 1966; Lewis, 1980b; Draper and Lewis, 1983) consists of schists and amphibolites, which were originally described as a monotonous tentatively series of metamorphosed mafic rocks. Later studies (Kesler and others, 1977c; Donnelly and Rogers, 1978) provided some radiometric and chemical data which appeared to confirm a Cretaceous age and an oceanic basaltic parentage. The latter paper also implied that the relatively unmetamorphosed Siete Cabezas Formation, a unit of basalt flows and hyaloclastic rocks and some intercalated cherts (with an unpublished Santonian radiolarian date), was an unmetamorphosed oceanic basalt. These rocks are here interpreted as a metamorphosed and tectonized allochthon of Caribbean Cretaceous basaltic rocks. This correlation is tentative and based largely on the occurrence of high-Ti metabasalts similar to unmetamorphosed examples from southern Haiti and DSDP site 151.

Ophiolitic rocks (mainly metamorphosed) have been known in the northern part of the Dominican Republic for some time. Some of these rocks form coherent mafic terranes (Samaná Peninsula, Joyce 1980; Cordillera Septentrional, Eberle and others, 1980), but other bodies occur as fragments within a thick olistostrome of middle Tertiary age (Nagle, 1966, 1971). The age of these basalts was given by Bourgois and others (1980) as Early Cretaceous, but sadly only as a brief note in the abstract of their article. There are no chemical or petrographic data for unmetamorphosed samples in this area.

4. Jamaica. There are two Cretaceous basaltic units in Jamaica that can be related to the circum-Caribbean event. The first is pre-Tertiary and was found in the Santa Cruz 1 well of western Jamaica. Contrary to Arden's (1975) suggestion that these are volcanic rocks, these rocks appear to be a layered mafic pluton whose composition (Donnelly and Rogers, 1978; Lewis, unpublished) places it in the basaltic association.

The Blue Mountains of eastern Jamaica contain a highly deformed and poorly exposed complex of basaltic rocks and their metamorphosed equivalents, interlayered with some sedimentary rocks, including fossiliferous limestones. These have been named the Bath-Dunrobin Formation, and were considered to be an ophiolite by Wadge and others (1982). The thickness was estimated at 2.5 km.

The oldest fossils reported from the inlier are Campanian. Overlying this formation is an early Maastrichtian limestone; structural complexities, however, raise the possibility that the relationship may be structural rather than stratigraphic. The recovery of early Campanian basalt at Site 152 (DSDP Leg 15), 300 km southeast of Jamaica, strengthens the possibility that the Jamaican basalt could be this age. Wadge and others (1982), however, suggested that this ophiolite originated north of Jamaica as Yucatan Basin crust and was thrust southward in the Maastrichtian, during opening of the Yucatan Basin.

5. Cuba. Perhaps the most extensive exposures of Cretaceous basaltic rocks in the Caribbean region occur in Cuba, where they crop out over most of the central part of the island. This basaltic complex is poorly understood because of the geological complexity of this terrane.

Stratigraphic information relating to the complex has been published sparingly (Meyerhoff, 1964; Meyerhoff and Hatten, 1968; Khudoley and Meyerhoff, 1971; Pardo, 1975; Brezsnyanszky and others, 1981; Pszczolkowski and de Albear, 1983); the consensus is that the bulk of the basaltic magmatism occurred in the interval Neocomian to Cenomanian or Turonian, and perhaps especially in the interval Aptian–Cenomanian. However, a minority opinion, unsupported by direct fossil evidence, is that basaltic magmatism was also abundant in the Jurassic.

The zone with abundant basaltic rocks (named variously "Santa Clara," "Zaza," and "Organos–Rosario" zones) is now recognized to be thrust over a carbonate-rich southern extension of the Bahama Platform, as well as over Jurassic–Cretaceous clastic sedimentary rocks. The stratigraphic thickness of the mafic rocks is unknown but given by Knipper and Cabrera (1974) and Pardo (1975) as up to about 6 km.

In all summaries, the stratigraphic sequence of igneous rock types places ultramafic and mafic plutonic rocks at the base, and the bulk of the basalts higher in the section and increasingly interlayered upward with turbiditic sedimentary rocks. Above the mafic unit is a sedimentary-volcanic sequence that contains andesitic volcanic rocks. The age and circumstances of the emplacement of this mafic unit are poorly known. Major thrusting and related metamorphism during the Eocene, especially in eastern Cuba, has drawn attention from the observation that earlier thrusting (Campanian) was widespread (Millan and Somin, 1981).

Central America and western Panamá

Serpentinites and mafic igneous rocks occur abundantly in Costa Rica and Guatemala, and sparingly in Belize (subsurface) and western Panamá.

1. Belize. A mafic complex in the subsurface of coastal Belize was encountered at Turneffe Cay during drilling by Royal Dutch Shell. The driller's log, examined in the office of the Government Geologist at Belmopan, describes the lower part of the well as Late Cretaceous wackes (correlative with the Sepur Group) underlain by altered mafic igneous rocks. The description closely resembles the outcropping Sepur Formation in the Sierra de Santa Cruz, Guatemala (Rosenfeld, 1981).

2. Guatemala. The mafic rocks of the Motagua Valley of eastern Guatemala were described briefly by Williams and others (1964) and were named the El Tambor Formation (now called Group) by McBirney and Bass (1969). Subsequent field-mapping studies from 1964 to 1979 (Bosc, 1971; Lawrence, 1975; Schwartz, 1976; Muller, 1979; and Rosenfeld, 1981) have considerably broadened our knowledge of this mafic association, provided numerous paleontological determinations, and have shown that this formation is more widespread than originally thought. Deep sea drilling (Legs 67 and 84; Bourgois and others, 1985) found that mafic rocks off the western coast of Guatemala, which were the lithic expressions of seismic reflectors, had the characteristics of this suite, though these authors compared them with the more distant Nicoya Complex. Several studies by Bertrand and co-workers (Bertrand and Vuagnat, 1975, 1976, 1977) provided a wealth of valuable petrographic detail, especially involving the mafic metamorphic rocks of the complex, as well as a K/Ar age (Bertrand and others, 1980) which has been found to be younger than a well-constrained paleontological age for its obduction (Rosenfeld, 1981).

Lawrence (1975) provided the first quasistratigraphic section of this highly deformed complex in its type area, and estimated its thickness as possibly between 6 and 9 km. A large body of monotonous, felted amphibolites (Sansare amphibolites) forms the structural base of the unit. The upper portion consists of phyllitic to schistose metawackes and interlayered metabasalt (commonly pillowed) units up to 100 m thick, which are relatively more abundant in the lower part of the unit. Minor radiolarian cherts (often red, with layering on a centimeter scale) have not yielded useful paleontological determinations. In its type area, the El Tambor Formation is pervasively metamorphosed to lower greenschist facies, and original igneous textures are scarce.

Although exposures to the north and to the east are more limited and weathering deeper, the rocks themselves are less deformed and metamorphosed. Igneous textures are better preserved, and co-occurring sedimentary rocks have yielded several paleontological age determinations. In the Los Amates area the mafic igneous rocks occur in juxtaposition with a series of wackes (lower El Pilar Group); the exact relationship is obscured by faulting (Muller, 1979). In the Oxec area, mafic rocks in a copper mine with Cyprus-like mineralization include most of the members of a typical ophiolite assemblage (Petersen and Zantop, 1980; Rosenfeld, 1981). In sum, the lithologies in the east (including the El Pilar wackes) and north are consistent with a less-metamorphosed equivalent of the type El Tambor. Rosenfeld also found abundant scattered fragments of gabbro (commonly mylonitized, evidently at high temperatures) and minor plagiogranite.

Ages within the El Tambor Group range from Berriasian to Albian to Cenomanian. Additional samples that are less-directly associated with the basalt but with apparently correlative wackes span the Aptian to Turonian, and may be as old as Hauterivian. Evidently the basaltic magmatism spanned a considerable time range in a geographically restricted area, and wackes were deposited during much of this magmatic interval.

Occurring with the serpentinites of the axial suture zone (the Motagua zone) are a variety of metamorphic rocks, including especially large amphibolite bodies near Morazán and Sansare. A complex of amphibolite and intimately interlayered marble near Los Amates was named the La Pita complex by Muller (1979) and interpreted as representing metamorphism of igneous and sedimentary materials at the base of a thickened, obducted ophiolite sheet. Eclogites are widespread (McBirney and others, 1967; Lawrence, 1975), but most have been retrogressively metamorphosed. Jadeites and albitites within serpentinite have been interpreted by Silva (1970) to represent a high-pressure metamorphism and metasomatism of fragments of granitic gneiss from the Chuacus series metamorphic rocks enveloped in serpentinite within a subduction zone dipping to the north. Of these metamorphic rocks, the amphibolites and eclogites have a protolith very similar to the basalt-dolerite-gabbro complex. Many of the mafic metamorphic rocks, however, have been extensively metasomatized (Lawrence, 1975; Donnelly, unpublished).

Rosenfeld (1981) found late Campanian pelagic foraminifera beneath the Sierra de Santa Cruz ophiolite. Sutter (see chapter by Donnelly and López Ramos, this volume) has shown that most of the metamorphic minerals of the Sierra de Chuacús dated by Ar 39/40 methods cluster tightly at 66 to 70 Ma. We believe that regional metamorphism and the emplacement of the ophiolite slide resulted from the collision of the Maya and Chortis blocks during the Maastrichtian.

3. Costa Rica and western Panamá. The Nicoya and Santa Elena complexes of Costa Rica are the most thoroughly studied of all Pacific-margin basalt associations. However, the numerous publications during the last decade are, to a person not directly acquainted with the area, difficult to comprehend, largely because rock units are defined in different manners. We believe the most useful papers to be those by Bourgois and others (1984), Baumgartner and others (1984), and Wildberg (1984).

The Nicoya complex consists of basalts and gabbros and intercalated radiolarian cherts and other sedimentary rocks. All workers agree on a distinction between a lower complex (dominantly masive basalt and small gabbroic and plagiogranite plutons, minor pillow basalts, and little sediment); and an upper complex (massive and pillowed basalt, intrusions, intercalated radiolarites, and minor tuffaceous sedimentary rocks and conglomerates). The Santa Elena complex is mainly serpentinized peridotite and associated minor basalts, amphibolites, and sedimentary rocks.

The first modern study was that of Dengo (1962) who interpreted the Nicoya complex as a "prototectonic" ophiolite formed in a volcanic island arc; both it and the Santa Elena peridotite were "emplaced along a major fracture." Weyl (1969; also Pichler and others, 1974; Weyl and Pichler, 1976) established these basalts as oceanic, and added analyses of an undoubtedly picritic basalt and of a plagiogranite.

The upper and lower portions of the Nicoya complex are defined differently by various authors, who provide correspondingly different interpretations of the complex. The most widely accepted nomenclature is that of Kuijpers (1980) who named the lower portion the Matapalo unit, and the upper the Esperanza unit. As further studied by Azéma and others (1979) and Baumgartner and others (1984), the age of the igneous portion of the Matapalo is established as older than a Callovian to Early Cretaceous chert, and the Esperanza as Albian to Santonian.

Schmidt-Effing (1979) subdivided the Nicoya into six basalt-bearing subunits (Brasilito, Tithonian to Valanginian; Junquillal, Cenomanian to Turonian; Murcielago, Santonian to Campanian; Golfito, Campanian; Garza, Maastrichtian; Quepos, early Tertiary). The Brasilito is placed now in the Matapalo, and the remaining five in the Esperanza or post-Nicoya units (Baumgartner and others, 1984). Schmidt-Effing's interpretation is the only one that does not emphasize a bipartite division of the complex, and it is not widely used.

Kuijpers (1980) emphasized that a major deformation terminated Nicoya magmatism at about the Santonian/Campanian boundary, and that the very minor post-Santonian igneous rocks should not be attributed to Nicoya magmatism. Kuijpers also pointed out that many of Schmidt-Effing's "xenoliths" of chert within basalt, which had been the major basis for the dating of the six subunits, were tectonically included fragments and did not give stratigraphic information. This last point has been very controversial: Wildberg (1984) illustrated radiolarites from the Junquillal Complex which are clearly contemporaneous with the basalt.

Kuijpers (1980) concluded that both the Esperanza and Matapalo represented oceanic crust, and that tectonism thrust younger Esperanza over older Matapalo. Bourgois and others (1984) retained the relative age determinations, but concluded that the Matapalo is thrust over the Esperanza. Overlying the Nicoya complex unconformably and dating the major deformation is a widespread Campanian limestone (Stibane and others, 1977) and a thick clastic, volcanogenic sedimentary series (Lundberg, 1982).

The Santa Elena complex consists of a widespread serpentinized peridotite and layered gabbroic and sheeted doleritic intrusions and amphibolitic inclusions (Bourgois and others, 1984). The complex is thrust from the north over radiolarites of Late Jurassic to Cenomanian age (Schmidt-Effing, 1980; de Wever and others, 1985) and pillow basalts. This lower unit cannot be correlated to either unit of the Nicoya complex. Bourgois and others (1985) have stressed the similarity between these rocks and the rocks recovered during DSDP Leg 84, off the coast of Guatemala. Lew (1984) has interpreted the Santa Elena complex as resulting from island-arc magmatism.

Small but important exposures of mafic igneous rocks are found along the mainland coast of Costa Rica near Quepos and Golfito. These are overlain by or interlayered with Paleocene limestones (Azéma and others, 1981; Lew, 1983; Baumgartner and others, 1984), but their age range has not been established. Kuijpers (1980) and Wildberg (1984) have pointed out that the compositions of these basaltic rocks differ from those of the true Nicoya complex, and a sastisfactory interpretation of their magmatic affinity has not been advanced.

Wildberg (1984) described basaltic rock in the Sona and Azuero peninsula of western Panamá. These rocks resemble Nicoya complex basalts but have not been studied thoroughly.

The Nicoya and Santa Elena complexes have been interpreted as oceanic crust with overlying, dominantly pelagic, sedimentary rock. Wildberg (1984) and Tournon (1984) have provided extensive petrological and chemical information, mainly on Nicoya mafic rocks. Unfortunately, Wildberg's "Unteren Komplex" and "Oberen Komplex" do not correspond completely with Tournon's "Matapalo" and "Esperanza" units, and thus their conclusions differ significantly.

Still unresolved are the affinities of small bodies of mafic rock found in the Santa Elena complex. Tournon (1984) found two alkali-rich intrusions of unknown age. Wildberg (1984) analyzed several basalts similar to those of the Nicoya complex. In addition, he presented analyses of several low-Ti basalts, which are high in magnesium, chromium, and nickel, and which he compared to boninites.

Wildberg (1984) called attention to several Nicoya basaltic rocks which he considered to represent island-arc tholeiites (IAT), rocks intimately comingled with his upper complex. Their locations are within both the Matapalo and Esperanze units, and their chemical distinction (higher potassium and more radiogenic Sr isotopes) might be alternatively explained by contemporaneous low-temperature, sea-floor alteration.

The Nicoya and Santa Elena complexes are the most varied and thoroughly studied of all the circum-Caribbean basaltic association. Whereas their chemical characteristics are oceanic (low-K), the many examples of iron- and titanium-rich rocks are not typical of known MORB, and their tectonic affinity is not clear. Their associated radiolarites are very similar to pelagic radiolarites, but Hein and others (1983) presented chemical characteristics which they interpreted as indicating formation near a continent. The Esperanza unit contains interlayered tuffaceous sedimentary rocks and conglomerates. Thus, although strongly indicative of oceanic origin, these complexes have no clear analogues among either MORB or OIB associations.

Eastern Panamá, western Colombia, and Ecuador

Widespread basaltic units from Ecuador to Costa Rica were recognized as belonging to a coherent group by Pichler and others

(1974) and Bourgois and others (1982a). To this group we add the Isla Gorgona komatiites described by Echeverría (1980).

Panamanian basaltic rocks form much of the basement of the Darien. Their gravity expression (Case, 1974) implies that they form the top of oceanic crust. Bandy and Casey (1973) constrained the younger age of this complex with a report of an overlying Campanian chert.

Basalts in western Colombia are found in two belts: the Serranía de Baudó along the Pacific coast, which is an extension of the Darién of Panamá, and the Cordillera Occidental. The oceanic affinities of these basalts are clear in the analyses presented by Goossens and Rose (1973), Goossens and others (1977), Barrero (1979), and Millward and others (1984). Mafic rocks of the Serranía de Baudó are largely unstudied, although Gansser (1950) stated that some are early Tertiary.

The bodies of the Cordillera Occidental occur as large tectonic slivers in dominantly serpentinite terrane. Barrero (1979) and Bourgois and others (1982b) have described many of the same rock units near Cali, but have assigned them different names and interpreted them somewhat differently. Both papers described thick pillow basalt units intruded by gabbro, interlayered with chert, and interlayered and overlain by wacke. Ages within the mafic complex are Albian (possibly as old as Barremian) to Coniacian and, in the wackes immediately above the igneous rocks, Coniacian to Santonian, and possibly older ages. The thickness of the mafic rocks was not given, but Barrero believed the pile exceeds 5 km, and gravity data presented by Case and others (1971, 1973) support this estimate.

The Isla Gorgona olivine-rich basalts were called "komatiites" by Echeverría (1980). Dupré and Echeverría (1984) stated that their age is about 90 Ma (technique unspecified), and Espinosa and others (1982) reported three Senonian K/Ar ages, which place them within the age span of the Cretaceous basaltic association. Their compositions are very similar to picrites from Curaçao (Beets and others, 1982). Younger basalts, whose age has been established only by stratigraphic position beneath early Tertiary sedimentary rocks, have differing Pb-isotopic characters (Dupré and Echeverría, 1984).

Basaltic rocks within the Caribbean basins

During the drilling of DSDP Leg 15 (in December 1970 and January 1971), basalt and fine-grained dolerite were recovered at five locations, two in the central Venezuelan Basin (sites 146, 150), one on the Beata Ridge (site 151), one on the eastern flank of the Nicaraguan Rise (site 152), and one in the Aruba Gap (site 153) between the Colombia and Venezuelan basins (Donnelly and others, 1973b). All these basalts appear to be shallow intrusives into limey and siliceous pelagic sediments. Because of limited penetration of the igneous rock (maximum 16 m), nothing is directly known of the total thickness of the igneous complex.

The seismic refraction data of Officer and others (1957) and the more elaborate seismic information from Diebold and others

(1981) are in agreement that the entire Venezuelan Basin crust is excessively thick (in places on the order of 10 km), in comparison with normal oceanic crustal sections. The top of the basalt section in the Venezuelan Basin is correlated with the widespread acoustic horizon B", and it has been mapped over most of this basin (except for the extreme southeastern corner) and much of the Colombian Basin (except for the central part, which is the site of thick turbidite accumulation). The age of this horizon is latest Turonian in the east (sites 146, 150, 153), indeterminate but possibly coeval at site 151, and early Campanian at site 152 on the Nicaraguan Rise. This nearly synchronous horizon is taken to correspond with the cessation of basinal basaltic magmatism over a vast area. It is considered as no coincidence that this age corresponds closely with the end of magmatism on most on-land occurrences where this age can be estimated. The slightly younger age of site 152, on the Nicaraguan Rise, in turn appears to correspond with some evidence that basaltic magmatism continued to slightly younger times in the west.

Chemical and mineralogical data were given by Donnelly and others (1973a, 1973b) and Bence and others (1975), both of whom compared these basalts to MORB, but noted that the site 151 basalt was higher in potassium, titanium, and light rare earth elements.

Summary of circum-Caribbean basalt and possible correlatives

Within and surrounding the Caribbean region, and extending south to Ecuador, is a basalt province of vast size (Donnelly, 1973a). In general, the association has the attributes of an ophiolite, and this term has been widely applied. Where its thickness can be estimated, its lithologic units appear to be thicker than normal oceanic crust. It contains fossils that suggest a considerable age range at restricted geographic localities. In southern Hispaniola and in western Costa Rica, the basalt composition varies somewhat with stratigraphic position; the difference is mainly in iron and titanium contents. The basalt unit locally contains scattered, thin pelagic sedimentary inclusions; in some places it includes impressive thicknesses of terrigenous sedimentary rock. In a few places, mainly along the northern margin of South America, basalt-clastic facies compose an impressive fraction of the complex. A few of these eruptions were demonstrably subaerial; the remainder appear to be subaqueous hyaloclastites. Whatever the exact environment, they represent a facies that is not recognized among numerous examples of drilled oceanic crust.

The total age span of the Caribbean basalts is unknown. Most fossils appear to indicate Aptian to Turonian, but there are three good (Costa Rica, Venezuela, and Puerto Rico) Jurassic dates on sedimentary rocks, none of which are demonstrably within the basalt themselves. In no locality is there impressive post-Santonian magmatism, but the Campanian age reports from site 152, southern Haiti, and Jamaica show somewhat younger activity there. Along the Pacific coast there is minor activity until perhaps the Eocene, but further study is needed to

clarify the magmatic affinity of this younger rock. Thus this basaltic association is oceanic, lacks the attributes of a typical ridge segment accreted at a linear ridge, is truly vast, and has apparently been obducted at numerous localities, following the beginnings of compressive tectonics that accompanied the Late Cretaceous shift in relative plate motions in the Atlantic world.

EARLY AND MIDDLE CRETACEOUS PRIMITIVE ISLAND-ARC VOLCANIC SUITE

The earliest volcanic rocks of the Caribbean island arc are well exposed in the Virgin Islands, Puerto Rico, Bonaire, and Tobago, and less well exposed elsewhere. They have not been positively recognized in Central America. They differ markedly from the more modern, calc-alkaline volcanics familiar in the Lesser Antilles and Central America. They are essentially coeval with the Cretaceous basalt province. Their importance lies in illuminating the early stages of the island-arc systems, and in this they are perhaps the best examples known in the world.

The primitive island-arc volcanic suite (PIA) was first recognized by Donnelly and Rogers (1967) on the basis of low thorium and U values and Th/U ratios in older volcanic rock units of the northeastern West Indies. The original rock unit placed in this category was the Water Island Formation (Donnelly, 1966) of the northern Virgin Islands, which is a thick, bimodal, Early Cretaceous series consisting mainly of lavas. The overlying Louisenhoj Formation of the Virgin Islands and the correlative pre-Robles rocks of Puerto Rico were later added to the PIA. Similar volcanic series placed in this category are the Washikemba Formation of Bonaire, their probable allochthonous correlatives in northern Venezuela, the volcanic and associated plutonic rocks of Tobago, the Los Ranchos Formation and possibly the Maimón Schist of the Dominican Republic, the older igneous rocks of La Désirade, and certain older volcanic rocks of Jamaica (Fig. 4). All of these series appear to be approximately Early Cretaceous in age, except that the Washikemba Formation extends into the Coniacian. A review of these occurrences is given in Donnelly and Rogers (1980).

The PIA series, as used here, has several distinctive characteristics. In addition to low thorium and uranium, all members have low total rare earth elements (REE) with flat spectra. The mafic members are low in titanium and show no enrichment of titanium with increasing Fe/Mg. Siliceous rocks are abundant, and the series can be either strikingly bimodal or unimodal, depending on the presence or absence of shallow differentiation prior to eruption. The potassium content is variable, but not necessarily very low. The Water Island Formation and the La Désirade trondjhemite (one sample) have also been found to have very nonradiogenic Pb isotopes (Armstrong and Cooper, 1971; Mattinson and others, 1980), but the Los Ranchos Formation of Hispaniola has somewhat more radiogenic Pb isotopes (Cumming and Kesler, 1981; Cumming and others, 1982).

These rocks have some of the attributes of the island-arc tholeiites (IAT) (Jakes and Gill, 1970), but differ in their higher

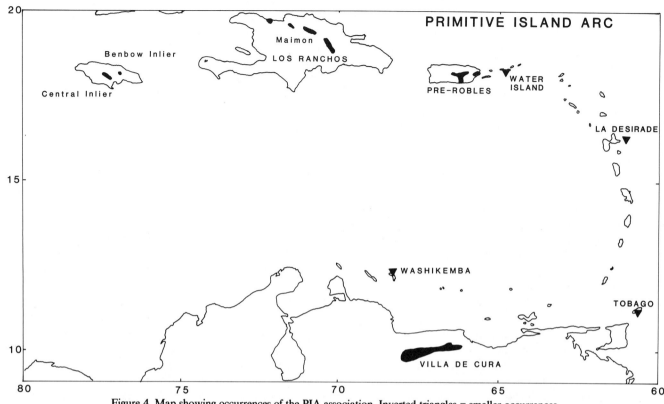

Figure 4. Map showing occurrences of the PIA association. Inverted triangles = smaller occurrences.

content of potassium and some other incompatible elements, and by the abundance in several places of highly siliceous rocks. Although there might be a demonstration in the future that both of these series merge or overlap in a meaningful tectono-magmatic sense, it seems preferable at present to note that there are differences between the PIA and IAT series in the Caribbean region. Probably neither group represents a distinct magma series, but instead may represent magmatic tendencies reflecting a min-imal amount of sedimentary material in the source, or a distinc-tive mode of generation or differentiation of magma. Possibly either series might be found commingled with the other or with normal CA volcanic rocks. In the Caribbean, however, there seems to be evidence that the series called PIA is old and is followed by a later diverse CA series, which includes examples of IAT rocks at various ages and stages. Thus, the recognition of the PIA is at least locally useful, although its significance is still not completely clear.

Greater Antilles

The original rock units of this association crop out widely on St. Thomas and St. John, Virgin Islands. Correlative rocks are found in east and central Puerto Rico, in central Hispaniola and, possibly, in Jamaica.

1. Virgin Islands. The Water Island Formation (Don-nelly, 1966, 1972) of St. Thomas and St. John consists of 3 km of interlayered mafic and siliceous lavas. Pyroclastic units are gener-ally scarce, except at the top of the unit, where they are abundant. The siliceous layers were estimated to make up about 80% of the outcropping formation; however, an 800-m drill hole spudded at a low level of the formation (Hekinian, 1971) drilled only about one third siliceous rocks.

The mafic rocks were called "spilite" by Donnelly (1966) and Hekinian (1971) to emphasize their dominantly albitic-chloritic mineralogy. The flows are nonpillowed, but commonly display an odd patchy texture best described as tiny amoeboid pillows (a few centimeters to about 20 cm in size) in an altered, hyaloclastic matrix. Only one true pillowed flow has been found in the formation (Fortberg Hill, St. John).

The siliceous rocks (kerotophyres) are mainly texturally monotonous flows (rarely streaky), brecciated flows, and nonex-plosive (subaqueous) pyroclastic rocks; explosive pyroclastic beds are confined to the uppermost part of the formation. The rocks are totally leucocratic, and contain quartz and sodic plagioclase phenocrysts in an aphanitic groundmass. The plagioclase is com-monly low- to intermediate-temperature albite; one convincing example of high-temperature sodic oligoclase has been found (Donnelly, 1963).

Donnelly (1972) summarized numerous mineralogical and textural criteria that indicate that these rocks do not result from the low-grade metamorphism of a basalt-rhyolite assemblage, but formed largely as the result of eruption of water-rich melts at a depth of water sufficient to retard the separation of the volatiles and to promote extensive deuteric reaction, including a sea-water–rock alkali exchange. The environment of eruption varied from very deep water in the lower part to shallow in the upper, and explosive separation of the volatiles is expressed in truly pyroclastic facies only at the very top.

A recent unpublished paleontological determination (radiolaria; E. Pessagno) places the top of the formation at "probably upper Aptian to lowermost Albian."

Overlying the Water Island Formation with a mild angular unconformity is an approximately 3-km-thick unit named the Louisenhoj Formation, which is composed dominantly of augite-andesite pyroclastics and their reworked epiclastic derivatives. The facies suggests accumulation in shallow water (perhaps partly subaerial) of explosively erupted volcanic materials. The Louisenhoj Formation has not been dated, but the immediately overlying wackes (Tutu Formation) contain late Albian ammonites (Young, 1972).

2. Puerto Rico. A series of poorly exposed and largely unstudied formations of central and eastern Puerto Rico have been known for several years by the semiformal name "Pre-Robles" (Briggs, 1969; M'Gonigle, 1977).

This group is estimated to be more than 5 km thick (Mattson, 1966) and consists dominantly of volcanic rocks, minor clastic sedimentary rocks, and a few limestones in the upper part. A few poorly exposed rock units resemble the Water Island Formation quartz keratophyres, but most of the group resembles the Louisenhoj Formation. Lavas are a minor component. The age range for the group is not known, but early Albian fossils are found near the top in several places.

3. Hispaniola. In the Dominican Republic, two volcanic units have been provisionally placed in the PIA assemblage: the Los Ranchos Formation and Maimón schists. The Los Ranchos Formation (Bowin, 1966) consists of about 1 km of dominantly volcanic rocks and intercalated clastic sedimentary rocks. The volcanic rocks are bimodal and consist of mafic and siliceous flows and dominantly siliceous pyroclastic units. The included sedimentary rocks are locally carbonaceous and contain plant fossils. Bowin found mid-Aptian to mid-Albian fossils within the formation and in the overlying Hatillo limestone.

Bourdon (1985) described a volcanic lower part of the El Seybo unit in the eastern Dominican Republic that contains metabasalts and dacite and rhyolite lava. These volcanic rocks are overlain by Aptian to Albian limestones. The basalts (which are pillowed in places) are not assignable to a magmatic category, but the siliceous rocks appear to belong to the PIA. The brief section was correlated with the Los Ranchos Formation.

The Maimón Formation (Bowin, 1966) is a group of undated siliceous and mafic schists that occupies the lowest apparent stratigraphic position in the central Dominican Republic. The Amina schists (Draper and Lewis, unpublished), which are found farther to the northwest, are similar and possibly correlative. Both units are apparently metavolcanic and compositionally bimodal. The attribution of these rocks to the PIA is provisional and is

based mainly on the sparse chemical data for Maimón samples (Donnelly and Rogers, 1978). Siliceous and mafic flows of northern Haiti (Soler and Cheilletz, 1985) are also possible correlatives of this unit.

4. Jamaica. Rocks from Jamaica attributed by Donnelly and Rogers (1978) to the PIA include a dacite flow from the Devil's Racecourse Formation (Barremian to Aptian of the Benbow inlier), the Arthur's Seat Formation (early Late Cretaceous?), and some probably middle Cretaceous flows from the Central inlier. Jackson and Smith (1980) placed the basalt flows of the Devil's Racecourse Formation in the IAT. The clear identification of these rocks as PIA (or, alternatively, as IAT) remains in doubt. REE patterns of some units are flat, and the uranium and thorium values, especially for the dacite, are appropriately low. However, the Devil's Racecourse basalts have higher titanium and lower potassium than is encountered in other PIA rocks. The association appears to be similar to the El Seybo unit of Hispaniola, described above. There seems no alternative but to leave these poorly exposed and highly altered Jamaican rocks in a state of petrological limbo for the present.

Lesser Antilles and northern South America

Occurrences of the PIA association in the Lesser Antilles are limited to La Désirade, which is just east of Guadeloupe, and Tobago. An extensive exposure of these rocks in Bonaire, and its putative allochthonous correlatives in Venezuela, are among the largest PIA exposures in the Caribbean region.

1. La Désirade. La Désirade has an extensive exposure of two types of volcanic rocks, both of which are intruded by mafic dikes. A Miocene limestone covers all these rocks, but exposures of the igneous rocks are extensive and spectacular along the sea shore.

This island has inspired argument as to its magmatic affinities far in excess of what might be expected from its small size (about 11 km long). The western end of the island is composed mainly of a shallow trondhjemite and associated minor siliceous and mafic lavas. The eastern end is a series of pillowed basalts and some minor siliceous intrusions. The relation between the igneous rocks of the two ends is not clear. The age of the trondhjemite was established at 145 Ma on the basis of Pb/U dating from separated zircons (Mattinson and others, 1980). Radiolarians from within the pillow-basalt complex are of Hauterivian to Barremian age (Bouysse and others, 1983). K/Ar ages of both units, and of still later minor siliceous intrusives into the pillow basalts, scatter widely to younger values (Dinkleman and Brown, 1977; Briden and others, 1979; discussion in Bouysse and others, 1983), suggesting serious limitations of this method for these rocks.

These rocks were originally placed by Fink (1972)—and later by Donnelly and Rogers (1978)—in an orogenic association correlative with the Water Island Formation of the Virgin Islands. Mattinson and others (1980) called them Jurassic oceanic crust, stating that siliceous rocks are found in other ophiolites. Le

Guen de Kerneizon and others (1979) called all the rocks orogenic on the basis of the composition of the clinopyroxenes of the pillow basalt. We conclude that this island is a tectonically detached fragment of the eastern Greater Antilles.

2. Tobago. The volcanic series of Tobago consist of thick, dominantly volcaniclastic igneous rocks (Maxwell, 1948; Girard, 1981). The thickness of the unit has not been specified, but Maxwell's map implies about 5 km, if no significant structural repetition is assumed. Lithologies are dominantly andesitic pyroclastic rocks and minor basalt and dacitic flows, the latter especially toward the top. A diorite batholith intrudes the lower levels of the volcanic complex.

Radiometric dates for the volcanic rocks, the diorite, and later dikes, yielded widely scattered results, including some that are clearly out of geological sequence (Rowley and Roobol, 1978). The pluton itself has yielded K/Ar ages of 127, 113, and 102 Ma.

The volcanic rocks were placed in the PIA provisionally by Donnelly and Rogers (1978). Girard (1981) and Girard and Maury (1983) greatly expanded the data, confirmed this placement, and showed that the diorite is consanguinous with the volcanic rocks. The diorite is the only large pluton of PIA affinity in the Caribbean.

3. Bonaire. The Washikemba Formation of Bonaire (Beets and Lodder, 1967; Beets and others, 1984) is a 5-km-thick series of dominantly volcanic rocks and minor pelagic sedimentary rocks, capped with coarse clastic sedimentary rocks. The volcanic rocks are bimodal, consisting of basalt, andesite, and dacite flows, and subaqueous pyroclastic deposits. The siliceous rocks compose slightly more than half the thickness of the formation.

A high original volatile content for these magmas is suggested by the high degree of vesicularity of the flows and by the thinness of some highly siliceous sills and flows (implying relatively low viscosity). Their eruption as flows rather than pyroclastic eruptives suggests subaqueous but not abyssal eruption; Beets and others (1984) found a shallowing from 3,500 m to 1,000 m during the eruptive history of this formation. This formation is dated as Albian in the lower part and Coniacian in the upper, which is the youngest known for Caribbean PIA.

4. Venezuela. The Villa de Cura Group of northern Venezuela is a 3- to 6-km-thick (Shagam, 1960; Piburn, 1967) series of mafic and siliceous metalavas and metatuffs. Shagam divided the group into four units: the El Caño, El Chino, El Carmen, and Santa Isabel Formations. The El Caño Formation consists of laminated metatuffs and minor lavas. The El Chino Formation is similar but has uniformly banded rather than finely laminated metatuffs. The El Carmen Formation consists of monotonous mafic metalavas, which we grouped with the basalt suite and discussed above. The Santa Isabel Formation consists of metasedimentary rocks and lesser amounts of metalava and chert. All these rocks consist dominantly of pervasively metamorphosed and deformed schists.

The entire Villa de Cura Group forms the bulk of the large Villa de Cura Nappe, discussed above.

Tectonic Significance of the Caribbean PIA Series

The Caribbean PIA series is exposed in a discontinuous arc from Jamaica to northern South America. It is poorly dated but appears to be coeval with the basaltic province. The evidence for a high intrinsic water content and abundance of siliceous differentiates argues for its generation in the presence of volatiles derived from subducted, hydrated crust. The two occurrences with nonradiogenic Pb isotopes (Virgin Islands, Le Désirade), however, indicate a minimal amount of sediment involvement in the locus of melting; the remaining minor elements support this. In two localities (Virgin Islands, Bonaire) the early rocks of the series appear to be abyssal, and grade upward to shallow-water eruptives; in no case is there abundant interlayered sediment. There are no proven cases of commingled basalt and PIA material; where they are geographically proximate (Puerto Rico, Netherlands Antilles, Hispaniola), the basalt appears to be allochthonous with respect to the PIA rocks. The PIA rocks are overlain by more normal CA rocks in Puerto Rico; in the other localities the transition cannot be seen. We cannot rule out the possibility that the PIA series and the remainder of the island arc above it are themselves allochthonous. The PIA seems to represent the earliest part of an island arc that is arguably autochthonous. The coincidence in age with the vast basalt series suggests that the two are related, but the nature of this relationship is enigmatic.

CRETACEOUS AND EARLY TERTIARY CALC-ALKALINE AND RELATED SUITES

Beginning in the Late Cretaceous, calc-alkaline (CA) and related igneous suites erupted widely in the Greater Antilles, Central America, and northern South America. This magmatism persists to the present day, but it is useful to note changing geographic position by dividing it into pre-Oligocene and post-Oligocene occurrences. We omit discussion of Jurassic and earlier CA occurrences of Central and northern South America, many of which may be related to Hercynian intercontinental suturing or its subsequent thermal imprint.

Classification of the calc-alkaline associations

We will not attempt an intricate classification of the orogenic volcanic and plutonic rocks of the Caribbean region. In this area the dominant rock types considered CA are andesites, with lesser amounts of basalt, and very minor rhyolite (except for the voluminous Miocene ignimbrites of Central America). The term "calc-alkaline" (CA) is used here in a broad sense that is close to Kuno's "hypersthenitic" rock series, but which grades broadly into his "pigeonitic" rock series. The definition is not strict but focuses on characteristics that are essentially constant: a continuous range of silica contents (most of the samples in the andesite range); the evidence for intrinsic high water content in the melt, resulting in an abundance of explosive eruptive products; and differentiation such that the titanium does not increase and commonly decreases with increasing Fe/Mg ratios.

The oldest Cretaceous CA rocks in the Caribbean region are notably enriched in potassium and have the attributes of shoshonites, which elsewhere have been considered to be a late phase of CA magmatism (Gill, 1970).

Rocks of the IAT association (in the strict sense; see above) include young basaltic centers of St. Kitts and Nicaragua and rhyolites of St. Lucia (data of Hawkesworth and Powell, 1980; Walker, 1984; Le Guen de Kerneizon and others, 1983).

Distribution and age range

Figure 5 shows the distribution of older CA plutons in the Caribbean region; volcanic units (not shown) are similarly distributed. The Dipilto pluton, which lies on the border of Honduras and Nicaragua (140 Ma; Horne, unpublished Rb/Sr isochron), a cluster of plutons in northern Colombia (around 165 to 178 Ma), and a series of volcanic and plutonic bodies of northern Colombia of latest Jurassic age (Tschanz and others, 1974) are the oldest CA examples that postdate the Jurassic split of North and South America.

Figure 6 shows the radiometrically determined ages of older circum-Caribbean CA plutons. Relatively few plutons are older than 90 Ma, and slightly more plutons are near the Cretaceous/ Tertiary boundary. Beginning at about Cenomanian time (overlapping only slightly with the basaltic magmatism), and increasing during the Senonian, CA igneous rocks, including both intrusive and extrusive varieties, were erupted extensively in the Greater Antilles and southern Central America. Some earlier plutons have lower values of potassium and are not distinct from the PIA series (Kesler and others, 1977a).

Plutonic and volcanic rocks are compositionally identical; the tendency of magmas to intrude rather than extrude depends in part on the availability of a cover of low-density sedimentary materials which an ascending higher density magma may be unable to penetrate. Plutonic rocks are volumetrically less important than volcanic in the latest Cretaceous of the Greater Antilles. In northern Central America and the coast ranges of Venezuela, volcanic rocks associated with widespread Cretaceous plutons are limited in volume, possibly because of Tertiary erosion.

Igneous activity continued to be vigorous in the Greater Antilles and Central America through the end of the Cretaceous. In the early Tertiary igneous material was subordinate to sedimentary; the activity in some places (see below) was chemically bimodal and not clearly CA in character. After the Eocene, the activity was reduced until a sharply defined recrudescence in Central America in the early Miocene, and a more gradual increase in the Lesser Antilles through the entire post-Eocene time.

Northern Central America and the Cayman Trough

Throughout Honduras, Guatemala, and along the northern boundary of the Cayman Trough, there are scattered Cretaceous plutons of CA mineralogy and character. These have been discussed briefly by Horne and others (1976a, 1976b), Ritchie and

McDowell (1979), Clemons and Long (1971), Williams (1960), Williams and others (1964), and Perfit and Heezen (1978). These bodies are concentrated along the Motagua zone—Cayman Trough plate boundary, but neither the distribution nor age patterns of these bodies fit any identifiable tectonic pattern.

Greater Antilles

Both plutonic and associated volcanic rocks of the CA association are abundantly exposed in Jamaica, Hispaniola, Puerto Rico, and the Virgin Islands. Cuban CA rocks are less thoroughly documented.

1. Puerto Rico and Virgin Islands. Numerous doctoral dissertations and extensive later investigations by the U.S. Geological Survey have provided us with a detailed stratigraphic and structural history of this area that far exceeds any comparable history elsewhere in the Greater Antilles. In the lower part of this stratigraphic interval, the dominant rock material is CA volcanic (with minor interstratified limestone) with an upward-increasing fraction of dominantly volcanogenic sedimentary rocks.

The transition between the PIA (pre-Robles) of Puerto Rico and the overlying CA series (Robles-Río Orocovis) is a well-defined boundary. The age of the youngest pre-Robles and the oldest of the overlying formations are both within the Albian, and the Robles–Río Orocovis may extend upward to the Turonian. The Robles–Río Orocovis interval is notable for the number of high-K (shoshonitic) members (Jolly, 1971).

Overlying this stratigraphic series (but possibly interfingering with its upper levels) are Turonian to Maastrichtian lavas and pyroclastic rocks. At higher levels, basalt is less conspicuous than porphyritic andesite flows; pyroclastic breccias and ignimbrites appear; and intercalated sedimentary material is coarser and more abundant. Intruding many of these units and consanguinous with them is the earlier part of the Utuado pluton and the San Lorenzo pluton.

The abundance of high-K units at the base of the CA series has led some authors (Donnelly and others, 1971; Kesler and Sutter, 1979) to suggest that K decreases with time in the igneous series. In fact, both high- and low-K series coexist throughout Late Cretaceous time, but the high-K series decreases in relative abundance upward.

In the early Tertiary, volcanic units are more restricted in thickness and dominantly andesitic and dacitic. The potassium contents of these and the accompanying Eocene phase of the Utuado pluton are distinctly lower than in the Late Cretaceous and are closer to the late Tertiary values seen in both Central America and the Lesser Antilles. Barabas (1982) noted that the copper mineralization of the Utuado pluton is related to this low-K event, and Kesler (1978) suggested that Caribbean island-arc porphyry copper deposits are in general related to less-K-rich intrusions than is the case for deposits within continental areas.

The Virgin Islands batholith (Longshore, 1965) was dated radiometrically as Oligocene (Cox and others, 1977; Kesler and Sutter, 1979). This large pluton has subunits ranging from olivine

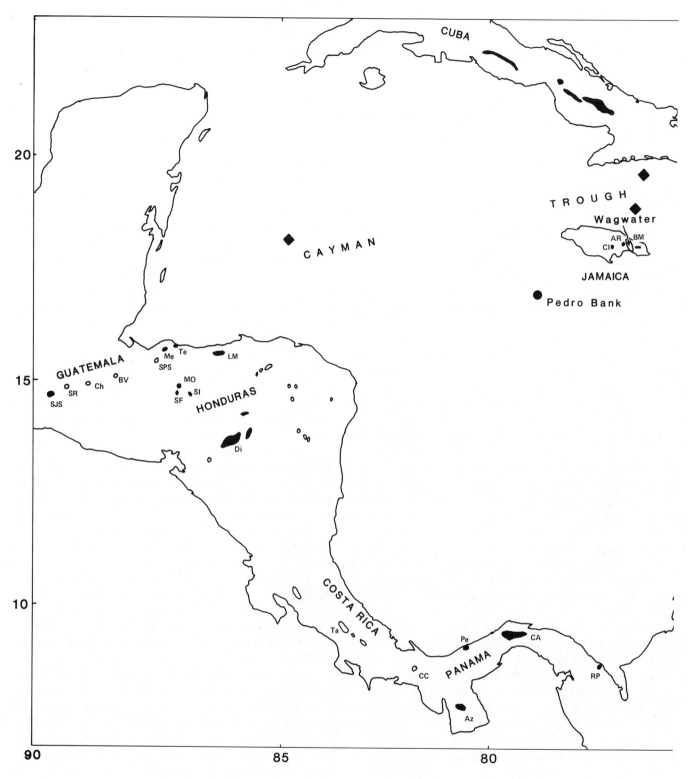

Figure 5. Map showing calc-alkaline plutons and locations of mid-Tertiary igneous suites associated with rifting tectonics. Solid patterns = pre-Eocene plutons; open squares = small pre-Eocene plutons; open circles = Eocene and younger plutons; solid diamonds = dredged rocks. The Pedro bank locality is in a deep well. Open ellipses = mid-Tertiary rifting associations. Symbols for Guatemala and Honduras as follows: SJS = San Juan Sacatepéquez; SR = Santa Rita; Ch = Chiquimula; BV = Buena Vista; SPS = San Pedro Sula; Me = Mezapa; Te = Tela; LM = Las Mangas; MO = Minas de Oro; SF = San Francisco; SI = San Ignacio; Di = Dipilto. Jamaica: CI = Central inlier; AR = Above Rocks; BM = Blue Mountains.

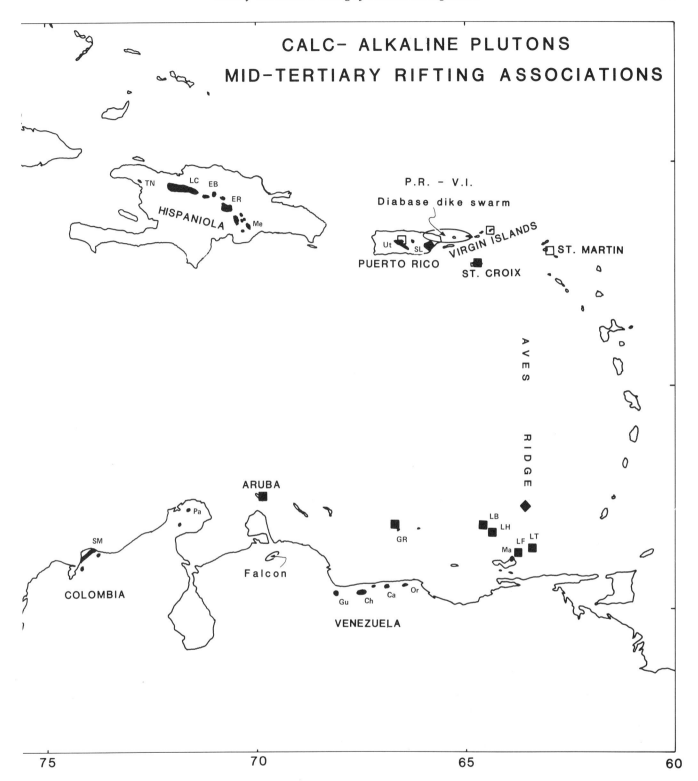

CALC- ALKALINE PLUTONS
MID-TERTIARY RIFTING ASSOCIATIONS

Hispaniola: TN = Terre Neuve; LC = Loma de Cabrera; EB = El Bao; ER = El Río; Me = Medina.
Puerto Rico: UT = Utuado (two ages shown); SL = San Lorenzo. Venezuelan offshore islands: GR =
Gran Roque; LB = La Blanquilla; LH = Los Hermanos; Ma = Margarita; LF = Los Frailes; LT = Los
Testigos. Venezuela onshore: Gu = Guaremal; Ch = Choroní; Ca = Caracas; Or = Oritapa. Northeast
Colombia: Pa = Parashi; SM = Santa Marta. Costa Rica and Panama: Ta = Talamanca; CC = Cerro
Colorado; Az = Azuero; Pe = Petaquilla; CA = Cerro Azul; RP = Río Pito.

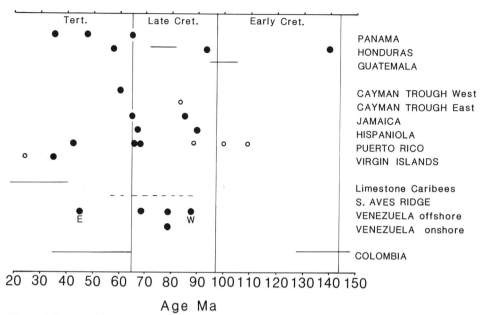

Figure 6. Diagram showing radiometrically determined ages of pre-Miocene CA plutons. Small open circles = single samples. Solid lines = range of ages. Dashed line for Aves Ridge = poorly established range of ages. W and E for the Venezuelan offshore islands show an age trend along the chain.

gabbro to granite and has a small mineralized zone with a notable molybdenite deposit. The chemistry of the pluton is parallel in the low content of potassium to that of the Eocene portion of the Utuado pluton of Puerto Rico (Chen, 1969; Donnelly and others, 1971).

2. Hispaniola. The stratigraphic information available for Hispaniola is far more limited than for Puerto Rico, and far more information is available for plutonic than volcanic examples (Kesler and others, 1977a; Jones and Kesler, 1980; Lewis, 1980a; Kesler, 1971).

The CA plutons of Hispaniola form an arcuate band oriented approximately northwest-southeast and stretching from northern Haiti to the south-central Dominican Republic. A 90 Ma Rb/Sr age for one of the largest (the Loma Cabrera batholith; Feigenson, 1977) is older than similar large plutons of Puerto Rico. The composition of the plutons is somewhat variable but, in general, much lower in potassium than Puerto Rican Cretaceous plutons or coeval volcanic rocks.

Some plutons from Hispaniola are of latest Cretaceous age. One of these bodies, the Terre Neuve pluton of northern Haiti (Kesler, 1971), has a high potassium content similar to that of the Utuado pluton of Puerto Rico (Chen, 1969).

3. Jamaica. The volcanic geology of Jamaica has been most thoroughly reviewed by Robinson and others (1970), Lewis and Gunn (1972), Roobol (1972), and Jackson and Smith (1980). The Cretaceous rocks of this island are confined to two large (Blue Mountain and Central) and several smaller inliers. The volcanic rocks can be grouped into three poorly defined stratigraphic groups. The oldest is the Early Cretaceous Devil's Racecourse Formation, mentioned above as a possible PIA unit.

The dominant Jamaican volcanic group of Cretaceous age

belongs to a poorly dated series of mafic pyroclastic deposits, minor flows, and generally unfossiliferous sedimentary rocks of the Central inlier. The older of these units may belong to the PIA (Donnelly and Rogers, 1978), and the younger may belong to the CA. Delong and others (1983) described a similar series of Santonian(?) to Campanian volcanic rocks from the small Lucea inlier in western Jamaica.

The late Campanian to Maastrichtian interval contains abundant CA ignimbrite debris. However, basaltic rocks within the Main Ridge group show striking tholeiitic tendencies and possibly belong to the basalt group. Whether they represent an intercalation of the very similar site 152 basalt, also of Campanian age, found on the Nicaraguan Rise southeast of Jamaica, or whether they represent magmatism of another origin remains to be established.

Some major granitoid bodies are essentially coeval with these volcanic rocks, including the well-studied Above Rocks granodiorite (Reed, 1968; Lewis and Gunn, 1972). The Jamaican Late Cretaceous igneous rocks are similar to many Puerto Rican volcanic rocks in that some units are rather potassium rich (Summerfield, Above Rocks), having values comparable to the lower potassium group of Late Cretaceous CA rocks from that island. The Blue Mountain granitoids and volcanic rocks, however, are distinctly less potassium rich.

4. Cuba. Younger (i.e., post-basalt) Cretaceous volcanic rocks have been described from many areas of central Cuba. However, relatively little has been published of their chemistry and mineralogy, and we simply record here that their published character is similar to that of coeval rocks of the remaining Greater Antilles. The Paleogene El Cobre Formation of southern Oriente Province consists of 4,000 to 6,000 m of dominantly volcanic rocks (Sokolova and others, 1974), having compositions that range from basalt to dacite.

Lesser Antilles

The northern Lesser Antilles contain Paleogene CA rock suites tht resemble the Virgin Islands batholith. They will be discussed below.

Northern South America

The Cretaceous and early Tertiary CA rocks of northern South America are represented dominantly by granitoid plutons on the offshore islands, in the coast ranges, and by some minor volcanic units. Much of the chemical and available radiometric information is from Santamaría and Schubert (1974); additional radiometric data for northeastern Colombia is from MacDonald and others (1971) and Tschanz and others, 1974).

1. Offshore islands. The offshore plutons are here interpreted to include the samples from the southernmost Aves Ridge that Fox and others (1971) interpreted as representative of the entire ridge. There is little doubt that the Aves Ridge contains CA rocks of early Tertiary or Late Cretaceous age, but the Fox and Heezen granitoid samples are closely related chemically to the island samples that are exposed on the continental platform (about 50 km to the south) (Donnelly and Rogers, 1978). Their radiometric ages (Fig. 6) are within the range of the islands in the center of this group (La Blanquilla, Los Roques, and Los Hermanos).

The age of the offshore plutons has been a subject of controversy, and lessons learned from the apparent age of the Aruba pluton (Priem and others, 1978; Beets and others, 1984) will serve as a warning against an overly eager acceptance of even well-clustered ages. The apparent ages decrease eastward from approximately Turonian (85 to 90 Ma) on Aruba to Eocene (about 45 Ma) on Los Testigos (Santamaría and Schubert, 1974). This apparent progression of ages mirrors the age progression seen in the Greater Antilles, an Eocene pluton in Puerto Rico, and Oligocene plutons in the Virgin Islands and Limestone Caribbees.

2. Northern onshore Venezuela and Colombia. The age of the onshore plutons is problematical. We take the age of a cluster of Venezuelan plutons (Oritapo, Choroní, and Guaremal) as probably the same (about 75 Ma) but having a reheating overprint at about 30 Ma (Martin-Bellizia, 1968; Morgan, 1967; Santamaría and Schubert, 1974). The younger age is suggestive of the Tertiary sliding episode for the Villa de Cura allochthon and might reflect a thermal disturbance at that time.

The Caribbean coast of northeastern Colombia has a small series of plutons. Radiometric studies by MacDonald and others (1971) and Tschanz and others (1974) showed a clustering of apparent dates at about 35 to 65 Ma, which places them approximately in the same range as the plutons farther east. However, there is no basis for guessing which of these K/Ar dates represent

magmatism and which represent reheating. Nothing has been published on the chemistry of these bodies, but their brief mineralogical descriptions place them in the CA group.

Tschanz and others (1974) listed a large cluster of Jurassic igneous dates from the Santa Marta area of northern Colombia. These include both volcanic rocks (largely rhyolite, many of which are ignimbrite) and small plutons. Their composition suggests an association with the La Quinta Formation of easternmost Venezuela, which is a rift-facies series of continental sandstones and other clastics, and locally prominent mafic and siliceous volcanic rocks.

CRETACEOUS AND CENOZOIC CALC-ALKALINE ASH IN DEEP-SEA SEDIMENTS

Although the analysis of volcanic activity through the study of widely dispersed ash in deep-sea sediments is a relatively new approach, ash recovered during legs of the DSDP Deep Sea Drilling Project has provided some valuable insights into both the timing of Caribbean volcanic activity and its character. Leg 15 provided an excellent opportunity to sample volcanic ash throughout Santonian to Holocene time in the central Caribbean sea (Donnelly, 1973b). Perhaps most significant is the occurrence at several sites of a Campanian and Maastrichtian subalkaline ash (containing conspicuous apatite, biotite, quartz, and alkali feldspar) found also in the same interval in Puerto Rico. The ash found farther west, on the other hand, has a more normal calc-alkalic mineralogy, and mirrors the observed volcanism of Jamaica.

During the Oligocene, rhyolitic ash beds a few centimeters in thickness are found in the Venezuelan Basin. These are interpreted as distal equivalents of thicker and more abundant correlative ash in the Gulf of Mexico (extending into the early Miocene). They evidently reflect the well-known rhyolitic volcanism of Mexico at this time. Occurrences of ash in Barbados may, in part, be of this same origin.

Several studies have focused on Neogene explosive ash distribution. East of the Lesser Antilles centers, Natland (1984) found that the late Pleistocene was an especially active period, but that there was also considerable early Pliocene activity.

Ash from sediments adjacent to Central America (Wilkens, 1977; Ledbetter, 1982; Cadet and others, 1982; Pouclet and others, 1985) has shown that Pleistocene activity was more vigorous than earlier, especially in northern Central America. An important find of Cadet and others was that the appearance of ash at the lower/middle Miocene boundary mirrors exactly the radiometric record for the onset of ignimbrites (discussed below).

The Los Chocoyos ash of central Guatemala (H tephra of Koch and Mclean, 1975) has been correlated with widespread marine tephra in both the Gulf of Mexico and Pacific Ocean (Drexler and others, 1980). Ledbetter (1985) summarized this correlation and the establishment of the age of the eruption at 84 ka. Ledbetter further established chemical criteria for the identification of 10 other ashes extending back to 300 ka.

CENOZOIC CALC-ALKALINE SERIES

The Cenozoic calc-alkaline (CA) igneous series are by far the best known and most actively investigated of all Caribbean igneous series. The study of these series sheds important light on Caribbean tectonic history and places substantial constraints on several tectonic hypotheses.

There are two major areas of Cenozoic CA igneous activity: the Central American volcanic area, which is further divided into a sharp line parallel to the mid-American trench (the volcanic front, or VF), and a more diffuse area of cinder cones farther from the trench (behind the volcanic front, or BVF) (Fig. 7) (which extends from the Guatemala-Mexican frontier to central Panamá; there has been Holocene activity over most of this range), and the Lesser Antilles belt (Fig. 8) (which extends from some recently surveyed seamounts near St. Croix south to Grenada). Minor areas of Neogene activity in the Greater Antilles, Central America, and northern South America that could be considered CA are sufficiently distinct to be discussed as a subgroup of alkaline volcanic rocks.

It should be noted at the outset that Neogene volcanism is very similar in Central America and the Lesser Antilles, and that both areas are highly representative of what is commonly called CA explosive volcanism of island arcs and continental margins. The rates of eruption in the two areas are, however, strikingly different. Wadge (1984) has recently summarized the rates of production of magma in the two arcs for the past 300 yr, and for the past 100,000 yr. He concluded that the relative rate was greater in Central America for the shorter interval by twelve times, and for the longer period by eight times. The subduction rate difference is about four times (based on magnetic lineation analysis), but levels of seismicity differ by about ten times.

Central American Cenozoic calc-alkaline history

The volcanoes of Central America are among the premier examples of their type in the entire world. Weyl's two books (1961a, 1980) are the starting point for this area. The Central American number of the Catalogue of Recent Volcanoes (Mooser and others, 1958) treated the Recent volcanic centers. Important general studies include those by Williams (1960), McBirney and Williams (1965), Williams and McBirney (1969), and Carr and others (1982). Reynolds (1980) outlined the stratigraphic framework of diverse volcanic series in northern Central America. Carr and others (1979) and Carr (1984) provided important regional comparative studies, especially with respect to seismicity and crustal character.

Early and mid-Tertiary igneous rocks of Central America.
The Cretaceous to early Tertiary CA rocks of Central America are relatively poorly known. Plutons of the Chortis block, some of which have Tertiary ages, were discussed above with Cretaceous CA rocks. Older volcanic series of Panamá, Costa Rica, Nicaragua, and (less widespread) Honduras and Guatemala consist of poorly dated and poorly exposed series of dominantly pyroclastic debris and intercalated sedimentary rocks and shallow, poorly exposed granitoid plutons.

Kesler and others (1977b) briefly described a series of granitoids in Panamá that range in age from Cretaceous to Pliocene and are chemically separated into two groups: an earlier low-K group and a later granodiorite suite. The younger group is locally associated with extensive porphyry copper mineralization, which reverses the relationship in Puerto Rico, where copper mineralization is associated with low-K granitoids.

The early Tertiary to Oligocene stratigraphy of Panamá to Nicaragua is dominated by clastic sedimentary rocks, minor limestones, and a constant, though minor content of pyroclastic volcanic debris, all set in an evolving convergent margin sedimentary-volcanic complex. The Matagalpa Formation of northern Nicaragua and western Honduras has been singled out for its high volcanic content (Williams and McBirney, 1965); its age is poorly known but is older than the overlying mid-Miocene ignimbrites. It reaches a maximum thickness of about 2,000 m in western Honduras, where it has a high fraction of pyroclastic igneous debris. Its age may be constrained by the finding of a low-K late Oligocene ash from DSDP Leg 84 (Pouclet and others, 1985). The Matagapla Formation is a high-K unit and thus may be only a little older than the equally high-K mid-Miocene ignimbrites found directly above it.

In Guatemala the Eocene Subinal Formation in extreme southeastern Guatemala is characterized by a high content of CA volcanic debris (Yang, 1976).

The Miocene was a period of extensive and thick rhyolitic ignimbrites (Weyl, 1961b) over much of Central America. Extensive and careful K/Ar dating (mainly unpublished; F. McDowell, University of Texas) has shown that there are two pulses of magmatic activity centered about at 18 and 14 Ma (Fig. 9). These ignimbrites were thickest in Honduras, but extend discontinuously to Guatemala, Nicaragua, northwestern Costa Rica, and central Panamá. Studies by Burkart (1965), Dupré (1970), Curran (1980), and Cox (1981) have found maximum thicknesses of 1400 m of ignimbrites. A limited age range throughout these sections attests to an immense rate of volcanic activity during the early and middle Miocene. Williams and McBirney (1969) estimated a volume of more than 5,000 km^3 for these beds. In several localities these ignimbrites are capped by basalts of a deceptively young morphology. Many of these "Quaternary" basalts have been shown (McDowell, unpublished data) to have ages only slightly younger than the ignimbrites themselves, and they evidently represent a late stage in the magmatic cycle.

The origin of the early and mid-Tertiary CA suite can be speculatively related to the subduction of the Farallon plate beneath Central America. According to Handschumacher (1976), the Farallon plate divided into the Nazca and Cocos plates about 26 Ma. The subsequent history of the Cocos plate shows a change from Miocene oblique impingement against Central America to more direct impingement from late Miocene on. The interaction of the obliquely subducting plate with the overriding crust may

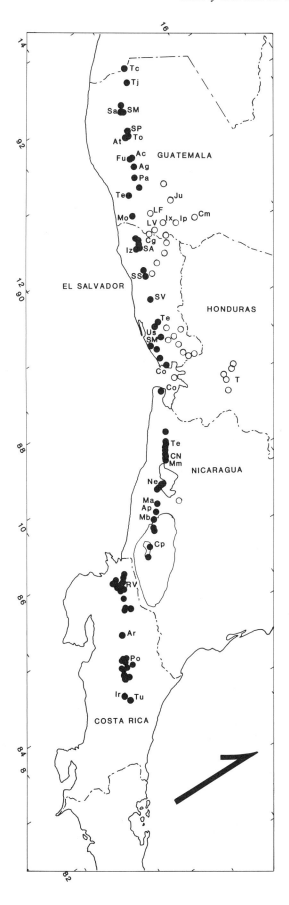

have caused buoyant extension such as that predicted by Wortel and Cloetingh (1981). In such a case, ascending melt might have invaded the continental crust at many locations scattered over a broad area, instead of being located along a narrow zone parallel to the trench axis. The ignimbrites, then, are the products of melting of the continental crust by this broadly distributed ascending melt, and the ignimbrite magmatism would appear to reflect interaction of the subducting Cocos Plate with the overlying Central American portion of the Caribbean plate. If this is the case, the radiometric dates for the inception of the ignimbrite event provide a more exact and slightly younger date for the division of the Farallon plate than was inferred by analyses of marine magnetic anomalies.

Pliocene to Holocene volcanism of Central America. The chain of Pleistocene to Holocene volcanic centers extends from Guatemala to central Costa Rica, and includes some inactive centers in western and central Panamá. The chain is not continuous, but divided into clusters reflecting the seismic segmentation of the subducted slab (Carr and others, 1979).

The magmas that erupted where the crust is of minimal thickness (central Nicaragua) are more mafic and have the lowest content of incompatible elements (Carr, 1984). They might represent the samples compositionally closest (least fractionated) to an original magma for the entire coastal belt; a similar magma fractionating at greater depth beneath a thicker continental crust could produce a series of more siliceous differentiates through the removal of olivine, oxides, plagioclase, and clinopyroxenes. The repeated identification of phenocrysts of the appropriate compositions for such a fractionation strengthens the hypothesis of fractionation from a single melt.

The scattered, dominantly basaltic, Pliocene to Holocene volcanic rocks of the western Chortis block are the most extensive of the behind-the-front (BVF) series in the Caribbean area (Walker, 1981). These volcanoes are aligned along a series of young, dominantly north-south grabens located 10 to 100 km behind the main CA front (VF). Whereas the VF volcanoes are large cones with a range of compositions centering on andesite, the BVF cones are much smaller, and consist of monotonous, nearly aphyric (minor olivine and plagioclase phenocrysts) basalt and subordinate local rhyolites. Their origin is similar to CA

Figure 7. Map showing location of active volcanic centers in Central America. Open circles: BVF centers. Named centers are as follows: Guatemala: Tc = Tacaná; Tj = Tajamulco; SM = Santa María; Sa = Santiaguito; SP = San Pedro; To = Tolimán; At = Atitlán; Ac = Acatenango; Fu = Fuego; Ag = Agua; Pa = Pacaya; Te = Tecuamburro; Mo = Moyuta; Ju = Jumay; Cm = Chiquimula; Ip = Ipala; Ix = Ixtepeque; LF = Las Flores; LV = Cerro Las Víboras. El Salvador: Cg = Chingo; Iz = Izalco; SA = Santa Ana; SS = San Salvador; Te = Tecapa; Us = Usulután; SM = San Miguel; Co = Conchagua. Honduras: T = Tegucigalpa. Nicaragua: Co = Cosegüina; Te = Telica; CN = Cerro Negro; Mm = Momotombo; Ne = Nejapa alignment; Ma = Masaya; Ap = Apoyo; Mb = Mombacho; Cp = Concepción. Costa Rica: RV = Rincón de las Viejas; Ar = Arenal; Po = Poas; Ir = Irazú; Tu = Turrialba.

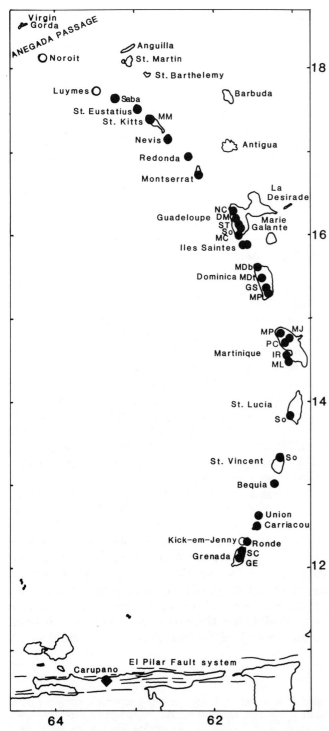

Figure 8. Map showing the location of active volcanic centers in the Lesser Antilles. Open circle = submarine volcano. Solid diamond = Carúpano rhyolite. Named centers are as follows: St. Kitts: MM = Mt. Misery. Guadeloupe: NC = Northern Center; DM = Les Deux Mamelles; ST = Sans Toucher; So = Soufriere; MC = Mt. Caraïbes. Dominica: MDb = Morne au Diable; MDt = Morne Diablotins; GS = Grand Soufrière; MP = Morne Patates. Matrinique: MF = Mt. Pelee; MJ = Morne Jacob; PC = Pitons du Carbet; IR = Ilet a Ramiers; ML = Morne Larcher-Diamont. St. Lucia: So = Soufrière. St. Vincent: So = Soufrière. Grenada: SC = St. Catherine; GE = Grand Etang.

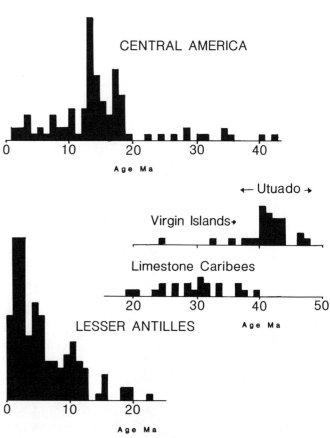

Figure 9. Histograms of individual K/Ar ages for Tertiary volcanism in Central America, Puerto Rico, Virgin Islands, Limestone Caribees, and young Lesser Antillean centers.

basalts, but they may originate at a greater depth, and their eruptive loci may be influenced by relatively young extensional tectonics that have provided an abundance of small north-south normal faults, along which these magmas appear to have risen.

Lesser Antillean calc-alkaline history

The history of Lesser Antillean petrology is as rich a chapter in petrologic history as that of Central America. The book by Weyl (1966) provides a comprehensive treatment, and the Catalogue of Recent Volcanoes (Robson and Tomblin, 1966) describes the Holocene centers. Whereas the Central American focus has been dominantly volcanological, recent studies in the Lesser Antilles have concentrated on minor element and isotopic evidence for the origins of magma series. In addition to the works cited above, summaries by Rea (1982), Maury and Westercamp (1985), Rea and Baker (1980), Lewis (1971), Smith and others (1980), Westercamp (1979), and Brown and others (1977) provide comparative data and outline petrological problems of this chain as seen through several points of view. A recent paper by Bouysse (1984) summarized tectonics, volcanology, and marine geology of the arc.

Middle Tertiary calc-alkaline rocks of the Lesser Antilles. The Lesser Antilles north of Guadeloupe is divided into two chains: an eastern, topographically lower chain ("limestone Caribbees"), and a western chain of small islands that have prominent young volcanic centers. The eastern chain consists dominantly of Miocene limestones which overlie Paleogene volcanic rocks and shallow plutonic rocks on several islands. The extrusive igneous rocks consist mainly of pyroclastic deposits of intermediate composition and minor flows. Their extensive alteration (or weathering) in most exposures has discouraged extensive study.

The shallow intrusives, especially of St. Martin and St. Barthelemy (Christman, 1953) are relatively unaltered and are very similar to the coeval Virgin Islands pluton (Donnelly and others, 1971). Volcanic rocks have been described from Antigua (Christman, 1972). The age of the volcanic rocks of the Limestone Caribbees is Paleocene to Oligocene.

From Guadeloupe southward, the earlier arc and later arc converge, so that south of this latitude older Tertiary volcanic rocks are largely hidden beneath deposits of the Pliocene to Holocene centers. Oligocene volcanic rocks are exposed in the northern Grenadines (Mustique, Petit Mustique, Savan, Chimney, and Canouan) as little-studied pyroclastic deposits and as volcaniclastic debris (Westercamp and others, 1985; Le Guen de Kerneizon and others, 1985). In Martinique (Westercamp, 1976, 1977) the "volcanic basal complex" of the eastern and southern part of the island consists of Oligocene and early Miocene basaltic, andesitic, and dacitic flows.

Miocene to Recent igneous rocks of the Lesser Antilles. Eruptive activity of the Lesser Antilles has been widespread during the latest Cretaceous, with several spectacular eruptions during this century. No part of the arc appears to be the special locus of activity, but the central islands (Guadeloupe to St. Vincent) have larger volumes of young volcanic material than those at the ends of the arc.

Radiometric dates (Nagle and others, 1976; Andreiff and others, 1976, 1981; Baubron and others, 1979; Bellon and Tournon, 1977; Briden and others, 1979; Bouysse and others, 1981; Le Guen de Kerneizon and others, 1982, 1983; Le Gall and others, 1983; Bellon and Maury, 1983) obtained for the younger centers have been summarized in Figure 9. In this figure, no attempt has been made to subdivide the data, and some centers are clearly overrepresented. The histogram shows an exponential form, in clear contrast to the Central American pattern of abrupt inception of volcanic activity in the early Miocene. The available radiometric age data do not support a sharp inception of volcanic activity during the middle Tertiary.

The igneous rocks associated with the younger volcanism of the Lesser Antilles arc are almost exclusively extrusive, and dominantly pyroclastic. The most widespread rock type is andesite, including one- or two-pyroxene andesites and hornblende andesites. In the southern part of the arc (especially St. Vincent), and

in the northern islands (especially St. Kitts), basalts are abundant. The island of St. Lucia has a particularly high abundance of dacite and rhyodacite.

The Grenadines and Grenada consist dominantly of alkali-rich CA basalts, which have been the foci of several recent studies. Sigurdsson and others (1973) noted that alkalic rocks dominated that island and were quite unlike rocks farther north in the arc. Arculus (1976, 1978) and Thirlwall and Graham (1984) have divided these rocks into two or three series; the latter have emphasized that the generation of the high-Sr subseries involves the presence of a component from subducted sediments in a magma derived mainly from the mantle above the subducted slab.

Tectonic significance of the calc-alkaline series

The CA series of the Caribbean region are without doubt an integral part of the subduction process, and their appearance at about 90 Ma signals the inception of widespread subduction. Although the series is typical of series in other orogenic areas, the Caribbean series show some special features. For instance, the early appearance of shoshonites effectively contradicts the supposed importance of these rocks in later stages of evolution of island-arc series (Gill, 1970). Most of the variations within the CA series (leaving aside for the moment the PIA series) concern the relation of various incompatible elements to silica during differentiation. Because rocks of similar composition are found in Central America and the Lesser Antilles, the role of crustal contamination seems to be minimized. Several lines of evidence point to the importance of sediment at the locus of fusion, the evidence of [10]Be (Brown and others, 1982) and Pb, Nd, and Sr isotopes (Dupre and others, 1985) being the most persuasive. The abrupt appearance of CA series at about the time the basalt-PIA event was ending signals a major change in plate movements, which must include the beginnings of persistent compression, subduction, and orogenic-zone formation.

TERTIARY IGNEOUS ACTIVITY ASSOCIATED WITH RIFTING TECTONICS

During the Cenozoic, several igneous associations putatively associated with rifting tectonics were erupted throughout the Caribbean area (Fig. 5). These include highly alkaline volcanic rocks in Venezuela and the northwestern Caribbean region, bimodal tholeiite-dacite volcanic associations of Jamaica, a dolerite dike swarm in the northeastern Caribbean region, a series of small granitoid plutons in Guatemala and Honduras, and a small rhyolite center in eastern Venezuela.

Early and middle Tertiary igneous associations

Jamaica. The Eocene Newcastle-Halberstadt volcanic association is well known stratigraphically from the work of Robinson and others (1970) and Green (1977). Jackson and Smith

(1979) have described the igneous rocks and discussed their significance. A bimodal lava series (2,000 m maximum) was erupted in the Wagwater Trough, a northwest-southeast–trending complex graben having more than 4,000 m of early Eocene continental (Wagwater) sedimentary rocks, and topped with a thinner (about 700 m) marine sequence (Richmond). The continental sedimentary rocks include a widespread gypsum-anhydrite unit.

The igneous rocks are dominantly dacitic (the Newcastle is the best-known unit, but there are two equally thick and several thinner units). These bodies had been considered sills, but are now interpreted as thick, massive, highly altered flows. The underlying Halberstadt basalts, which are locally altered, are about 350 m thick (maximum) and less widespread than the dacitic units. The mafic flows are tholeiitic; TiO_2 values reach more than 3%. The dacites are locally highly autometasomatized (Jackson and Smith, 1978). The bimodal pair is very similar to other suites associated with tensional tectonic regimes.

Venezuela. The Falcón volcanic rocks of Oligocene–Miocene age of northwestern Venezuela (Muessig, 1978, 1984) consist of a series of small, dominantly basaltic intrusives in the Falcón Basin. The rocks show varying degrees of alkalinity and were interpreted by Muessig as the igneous part of extensional tectonics associated with the movement of the Caribbean plate eastward during the early Tertiary. We note that this eruptive event is a younger tectono-magmatic mirror image of the Wagwater magmatism of Jamaica.

Puerto Rico and Virgin Islands. A series of dolerite dikes extending en echelon from San Juan through St. Thomas is included in this series (Donnelly and Rogers, 1980). The age of this series is placed in the Paleogene because it intrudes Paleocene strata and is found beneath the Oligocene coastal-plain series of Puerto Rico. In the eastern exposures the dike swarm has a characteristic northwest-southeast orientation, but to the west the orientation is more variable.

Guatemala and Honduras. Four small granitoid plutons located along a line parallel to the Motagua fault zone are of uncertain tectonic significance. Three western plutons (near El Progreso, Zacapa; part of the Chiquimula pluton; and Buena Vista) have Ar^{39}/Ar^{40} ages ranging from 34.7 to 35.0 Ma (J. Sutter, unpublished). The San Pedro Sula pluton has an age of 35.9 Ma (Horne and others, 1976b). Muller (1979) found the Buena Vista pluton to be a mildly alkalic granitoid. The tectonic significance of this sharply defined line of small plutons is unclear, but its parallelism with the northern Caribbean boundary fault zone strongly suggests that it represents magmatism accompanying the initial opening of the Cayman Trough.

Neogene alkalic series of the northwestern Caribbean region

The northwestern Caribbean region contains widespread, young alkalic and subalkalic volcanic rocks (mainly Quaternary age) in Honduras, Nicaragua, Costa Rica, Jamaica, Hispaniola, and Isla Providencia (Fig. 10). At numerous Central American localities, small alkaline basalt centers are aligned along apparently young, mainly north-south grabens. At other localities this series is represented by andesitic compositions, and high contents of incompatible elements. Wadge and Wooden (1982) summarized the occurrences in the western Caribbean region.

The distinction between the alkaline suite and the calc-alkaline BVF suite discussed above is not sharp, and the latter (even though grouped here with the CA series) share characteristics with both groups.

Hispaniola. Although the Haitian limburgites have been known since the work of Woodring and others (1924), Hispaniolan alkaline rocks have been studied extensively only very recently. MacDonald and Melson (1969) found a similar alkalic assemblage in the westernmost Dominican Republic. Donnelly and Rogers (1978) recognized a very young age for K-rich basalts, andesites, and dacites found in the central Dominican Republic, and which previous workers had considered Miocene or older. The Dominican Republic occurrences (Fig. 10) have been studied intensively by Vespucci (1980, 1983), Michael (1979), and Wertz (1985). The Hispaniolan alkalic rocks belong to two series: alkalic basalts, found mainly in the vicinity of the Enriquillo graben of Haiti, and in the parallel, more complex, downfaulted Valle de San Juan of the Dominican Republic; and K-rich andesites and dacites, exposed in the highlands northeast of these valleys and extending into the Cordillera Central of the Dominican Republic.

The eruptive mode of few of these rocks has been described. MacDonald and Melson (1969) noted that alkalic basalt flows about 200 m thick (in the aggregate) cap mesas. In the Constanza area, the rocks described by Donnelly and Rogers (1978) are mainly small flows of phlogopite-bearing basalt, diverse small andesite intrusions, and at least one very prominent dacite dome. The geomorphic inference of a very young age by these authors has been confirmed by radiometric dating (Wadge and Wooden, 1982). This dating has established ages of 1.1 Ma and less than 1 Ma in the Dominican Republic, and 1.8 Ma in Haiti. Unpublished K/Ar ages span the interval 2.9–0.3 Ma (Bureau de Recherches Géologiques et Minieres; Electro CONSULT).

The alkalic basalts range to nephelinite and limburgite; they have abundant olivine and augite and scarce feldspar. The andesitic group ranges over a wider silica content and varies from phlogopite-bearing olivine basalt to K-rich andesites and dacites; it can be considered a high-alkali CA group. The two groups are generally somewhat separated, but at some localities both rock series are commingled. The tectonic environment for these very young eruptives is not clear. Late Cenozoic tectonics of Hispaniola were dominated by strike-slip faulting having associated compressive or extensional vertical movements. Subduction from the northeast has been suggested for the eastern and central Dominican Republic (Bracey and Vogt, 1970), but Holocene seismicity does not extend beneath the young volcanic province.

Jamaica. At Low Layton, on the north coast of Jamaica, there is a small exposure of late Miocene alkalic basalt (Jackson and Smith, 1980). The Low Layton basalt has been dated at 9.5

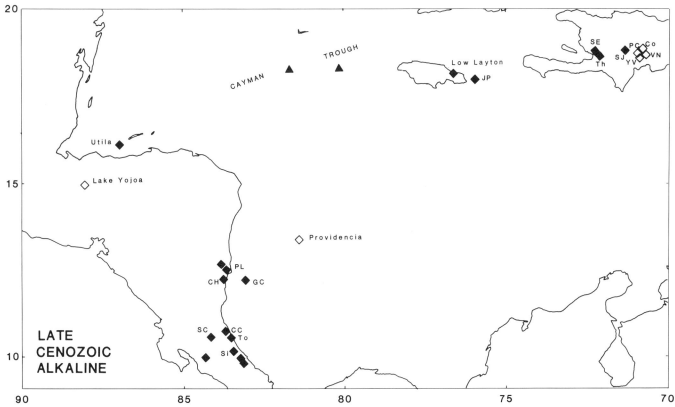

Figure 10. Map showing distribution of Neogene alkalic igneous associations in the northwest Caribbean region. Solid diamonds = basalts. Open diamonds = andesitic-dacitic rocks. Solid triangles = Cayman Trough spreading center. Named centers for Nicaragua and Costa Rica as follows: PL = Pearl Lagoon; CH = Cukra Hill; GC = Great Corn Island; CC = Cerro Coronel; SC = San Carlo; To = Tortuguero; Si = Siquirres. Hispaniola: SE = Saut d'Eau; Th = Thomaseau; SJ = San Juan Maguana; PC = Padre las Casas; YV = Yayas de Viajama; Co = Constanza; VN = Valle Nuevo. Jamaica: JP = Jamaica Passage dredged basalt.

Ma (Wadge and Wooden, 1982). A dredged sample of similar basalt has been recovered from shallow water about 20 km east of the island (Roobol and Horsfield, 1976).

Nicaragua and Costa Rica. Alkalic olivine basalts and minor basanites are found in small eruptive centers in southeastern Nicaragua and northeastern Costa Rica (McBirney and Williams, 1965; Tournon, 1972). Teschenites described from northern Costa Rica by Azambre and Tournon (1977) are the only intrusive alkalic rocks in Central America. Wadge and Wooden (1982) obtained an age of 1.2 Ma for a Costa Rican sample of alkalic basalt.

In the Costa Rica–Nicaragua area, these volcanic rocks are located along distinct north-south alignments, which prompted Robin and Tournon (1978) to compare this exposure with a similar alignment of young alkalic volcanic centers in eastern Mexico. Some of the alkaline centers in Costa Rica are located nearly within the major CA volcanic chain, but the alkalic alignment is distinctly oblique to that of the CA centers.

Isla Providencia. The island of Providencia is largely composed of a late Miocene–(?) Pleistocene lower series of alkalic basalt flows overlain by an upper series of andesitic and dacitic flows and breccias (Kerr, 1978). Mugearites, andesites, and da-

cites comprise the younger eruptive rocks and are intruded by a bimodal association of dikes. The island of Providencia is adjacent to a deep (more than 2,000 m) graben nearly 150 km long. Its north-south alignment is the same for the Costa Rica–Nicaragua alignments found about 200 km to the west, suggesting widespread young extensional tectonics for this part of the western Caribbean region.

Honduras. At Lake Yojoa, Honduras, cones of basalt, trachyandesite, and trachyte flows and cinders are aligned along young faults (northeast-southwest and northwest-southeast) that control the topography (Williams and McBirney, 1969). Wadge and Wooden (1982) reported K/Ar ages of 1.56 and 0.2 Ma for these rocks, confirming the young age suggested by Williams and McBirney. The rocks vary from alkalic basalt to trachyte and differ petrographically from the BVF basalts in their high phenocryst content. Plagioclase phenocrysts are conspicuous, and many of the basalts have abundant olivine and augite phenocrysts. Siliceous rocks have conspicuous anorthoclase or sanidine and smaller amounts of ferroaugite.

On Utila, the westernmost of the islands off the north shore of Honduras, two small cones have erupted alkalic basalt (Williams and McBirney, 1969) subsequent to the formation of coastal coral reefs. The basalt has olivine and titanaugite phenocrysts and inclusions of alkalic gabbro.

Cayman Trough. The Cayman Trough spreading center is located within this province and shares with it a very young age of eruption and north-south alignment of a graben. The observation that its basaltic magmas are indistinguishable from normal MORB (Perfit, 1977) basalts may reflect the superimposition of an extensional tectonic regime on very thin oceanic crust.

Venezuela. Small rhyolitic plutons near Carúpano in northeastern Venezuela (Schubert and Sifontes, 1983) pose a perplexing problem. Their age (5 Ma; early Pliocene) does not relate them to any obvious geologic event in this area. Their potassium content (about 5.5% K_2O) is far higher than for otherwise similar (but rare) Lesser Antillean rhyolites and dacites. The bodies are located along a northeast-southwest line forming an acute angle with the El Pilar fault system, and they are tentatively related here to extensional tectonics associated with movements on this system. Within the Caribbean area they most nearly resemble some highly siliceous rocks from the Hispaniolan alkalic assemblage, and their position nearly astride the El Pilar strike-slip fault zone mirrors the occurrence of the Hispaniolan alkalic rocks within the complex north Caribbean fault system.

Tectonic significance of igneous assemblages associated with rifting tectonics

The appearance in the early Tertiary of igneous associations related to rifting reflect both relaxation of Late Cretaceous inter-American compression and the initiation of movements on the northern (first) and southern (second) Caribbean transcurrent fault systems. The widespread late Neogene alkalic centers in the northwestern Caribbean region show that the Caribbean plate has deformed since the late Miocene by east-west extension; thus these centers emphasize dramatically the mutability of the Caribbean plate itself.

TECTONIC SIGNIFICANCE OF CARIBBEAN IGNEOUS ASSOCIATIONS

Within the Caribbean area, a varied and extensive assortment of igneous rocks has resulted from the complex tectonic activity accompanying the formation of this area during the Cretaceous and Cenozoic. Most of the rocks described here have counterparts in other young orogenic areas, but conclusions drawn for the Caribbean examples are not necessarily similar to conclusions that have been drawn for similar rock series in other areas. In particular, the Caribbean region lacks back-arc spreading accompanying the mid-Late Cretaceous to Holocene subduction and CA magmatism. Further, the early PIA rocks of the Caribbean region do not include boninites, although this series otherwise has counterparts in several places in the western Pacific. Shoshonites are abundant early in the Caribbean CA series, and IAT volcanic assemblages are included among the youngest volcanic centers. A consideration of the combined features of the

Caribbean region and western and northern Pacific may lead to important conclusions as to which features are fundamental and which are the result of special local conditions. The basalt association appears to be a special Caribbean feature, but further considerations of similar and coeval basalts in the southwest Pacific region may reveal common threads of great importance.

Plate motions and magmatic associations

The plate motions of the Caribbean region are controled dominantly by the relative motions of North and South America during the Mesozoic and Cenozoic; the relative importance of the Farallon (later the Cocos) plate is a significant unknown in the entire story. Postulated motions have been treated in some detail by Pindell and Dewey (1982); Donnelly (1985) reviewed seven solutions of plate movements and prepared a synthesis borrowing heavily from Pindell and Dewey.

First stage: Extension and basaltic volcanism. The first stage of Mesozoic Caribbean development was a rapid movement of South America away from North America (about 5 cm/yr) during the Jurassic. This was accompanied by the formation of oceanic crust, which may be represented by sub-B" reflectors and magnetic lineations in the Venezuelan Basin (Diebold and others, 1981; Ghosh and others, 1984); obducted Jurassic ophiolitic assemblages (Costa Rica, Venezuela, and possibly Puerto Rico) may be remnants of this crust.

In the early and middle Cretaceous (about 125 to 85 Ma), South America's relative motion slowed abruptly (to about 2 cm/yr) when it separated from Africa and the South Atlantic Ocean opened. At this time the magmatic activity became diffuse, resulting in a widespread "flood basalt," and local unusual variants (high-Ti and high-Mg basalts) showing the combined characteristics of MORB and OIB basalt.

The PIA series appears to have formed coevally with the basalt event. Although there are possible instances of a commingling of rocks from the two series, we suggest that the PIA formed as a subduction event around the periphery of a spreading, thickened, and elevated oceanic basaltic accumulation, and was a purely oceanic island-arc environment. The abundance of siliceous differentiates and the dominance of water-rich melts required subduction of altered crust but not necessarily sediment.

Second stage: Compression and the appearance of calc-alkaline magmatism. The basalt event continued until about 70–90 Ma, at which time South America moved eastward with a slight northward component, causing a compressional tectonic environment in Middle America. We cannot presently evaluate the contribution of the Farallon plate to this compression. At this time, island-arc tectonics (whose clearest record is sedimentological) and associated igneous activity were initiated around the margin of the Caribbean plate. The high potassium of some of the Cretaceous series (especially the spectacularly K-rich middle Cretaceous of Puerto Rico) remains perhaps the outstanding unsolved problem in the Caribbean region; the very high volume of this material seems, however, to have required substantial subduction, necessary to supply the large volume of the incompatible elements of this series.

Third stage: Initiation of North and South Caribbean transcurrent faulting, rift-associated magmatism, and young calc-alkaline volcanism. At the end of the Cretaceous, eastward movement of the Caribbean plate and southward movement of the South American plate was reflected in magmatic changes, such as igneous activity related to early Tertiary rifting in Jamaica and Puerto Rico and possibly northern Central America, and a distinct change in CA activity in Puerto Rico. Beginning in the Oligocene, the movement of South America was northwestward, but at about 0.5 cm/yr, creating the overall mild compressional tectonic environment that has persisted to the present day.

The eruption of a major siliceous ignimbrite in northern Central America is related here to the fragmentation of the Farallon plate into the Cocos and Nazca plates. The Neogene response to northwest-southeast compression has resulted in considerable internal deformation of the Caribbean plate, which in the west has resulted in the formation of a broad area of young grabens. A virtual epidemic of small alkalic eruptive centers along these grabens, and also along local rift zones associated with the complex transcurrent northern and southern boundary fault zones, reflects widespread production of small amounts of magma at fairly great depth. This alkalic volcanic activity emphasizes a diminished structural integrity of the Caribbean plate.

The late Cenozoic CA volcanism of Central America and the Lesser Antilles results from the subduction of the Cocos and Americas plates beneath the western and eastern Caribbean plate, respectively. The much higher rate of magmatism in Central America (Wadge, 1984) reflects the much higher relative convergence of the Cocos plate. The degree to which eastward movement of the Caribbean plate has contributed to the total convergence of the Americas plate beneath the Lesser Antilles is still debatable. A portion of this convergence may result from north-south convergence across the Caribbean plate and subsequent extension of the plate in an eastward direction.

CONCLUSION

The sensitivity of magmatism to changes in plate motion makes it potentially a very powerful tool in the unraveling of tectonic history, and especially in establishing the times of critical plate-motion changes. Many aspects of the origin and evolution of the Caribbean region are being debated today, but all workers agree that the Caribbean plate was a relatively helpless pawn in a global chess game, and no proposed evolutionary scheme will be acceptable without an account of changes of motions of the vast plates, between whose margins the Caribbean plate is a tortured and twisted minor fragment. This review concludes with the observation that the exceptionally well-displayed igneous history of the Caribbean region is an extraordinarily valuable and somewhat neglected source of information for deciphering the changes of plate motion that will be the necessary first step in any tectonic history.

REFERENCES CITED

Alvarez, W., 1967, Geology of the Simaru and Carpintero areas, Guajira Peninsula, Columbia [Ph.D thesis]: Princeton, New Jersey, Princeton University, 168 p.

Andreieff, P., Bellon, H., and Westercamp, D., 1976, Chronométrie et stratigraphie comparée des édifices volcaniques et formations sédimentaires de la Martinique (Antilles Françaises): Bulletin du Bureau de Recherches Géologiques et Minieres (2), Section IV, p. 345–356.

Andreieff, P., Bizon, G., Bouysse, P., 1981, Revision de l'age des formations sédimentaires de l'île de Saint-Martin; Implications sur la chronologie du volcanisme de l'arc insulaire des Petites Antilles: Comptes Rendus Sommaire, Societe Géologique de France (D), v. 292, p. 79–82.

Arculus, R. J., 1976, Geology and geochemistry of the alkali basalt-andesite association of Grenada, Lesser Antilles island arc: Geological Society of America Bulletin, v. 87, p. 612–624.

—— , 1978, Mineralogy and petrology of Grenada, Lesser Antilles island arc: Contributions to Mineralogy and Petrology, v. 65, p. 413–424.

Arden, D. D., Jr., 1975, Geology of Jamaica and Nicaragua Rise, in Nairn, A.E.M., and Stehli, F. G., eds., Ocean basins and margins, Volume 3: New York, Plenum Press, p. 617–661.

Armstrong, J. L., and Cooper, J. A., 1971, Lead isotopes in island arcs: Bulletin Volcanologique, v. 35, p. 27–63.

Azambre, B., and Tournon, J., 1977, Contribution de la géochronométrie K-Ar a l'etude du magmatisme de Costa Rica, Amérique Centrale: Geological Society of France Bulletin 7, v. 20, p. 955–959.

Azéma, J., Sornay, J., and Tournon, J., 1979, Découverte d'Albien supérieur à ammonites dans le matériel volcano-sédimentaire du "Complexe de Nicoya": Societe Géologique de France, Comptes Rendus Sommaire, fasc. 3, p. 129–131.

Azéma, J., Glaçon, G., and Tournon, J., 1981, Nouvelles données sur le Paleocène à Foraminifères planctoniques de la bordure pacifique du Costa Rica (Amérique centrale): Societe Géologique de France, Comptes Rendus Sommaire, fasc. 3, p. 85–88.

Baker, P. E., and Holland, J. G., 1973, Geochemical variations in a pyroclastic succession on St. Kitts, West Indies: Bulletin Volcanologique, v. 37, p. 472–490.

Bandy, O. L., and Casey, R. E., 1973, Reflector horizons and paleobathymetric history, eastern Panama: Geological Society of America Bulletin, v. 84, p. 3081–3086.

Barabas, A., 1982, Potassium-argon dating of magmatic events and hydrothermal activity associated with porphyry copper mineralization in west-central Puerto Rico: Economic Geology, v. 77, p. 109–126.

Barr, K. W., 1963, The geology of the Toco district, Trinidad, West Indies, pt. 2: London, Overseas Geological Surveys, 65 p. (reprinted and repaginated from Overseas Geology and Mineral Resources, v. 8, p. 379–415; v. 9, p. 1–29).

Barrero-Lozano, D., 1979, Geology of the central-western Cordillera, west of Buga and Roldanillo, Colombia: Publicaciones Geológicas Especiales del INGEOMINAS, no. 4, 75 p.

Bartok, P. E., Renz, O., and Westermann, G.E.E., 1985, The Siquisique ophiolites, northern Lara State, Venezuela; A discussion on their Middle Jurassic ammonites and tectonic implications: Geological Society of America Bulletin, v. 96, p. 1050–1055.

Baubron, J.-C., Bouysse, P., Maury, R. C., and Westercamp, D., 1979, L'îlot Redonda, un jalon de l'arc volcanique recent des Petites Antilles: Bulletin Bureau de Recherches Géologiques et Minieres (2), Section IV, p. 273–283.

Baumgartner, P. O., Mora, C. R., Butterlin, J., Sigal, J., Glacon, G., Azema, J., and Bourgois, J., 1984, Sedimentación y paleontología del Cretácico y Cenozóico del litoral Pacífico de Costa Rica: Revista Geológica de America Central, v. 1, p. 57–136.

Beck, C. M., 1983, Essai sur l' évolution géodynamique des Caraïbes sud-orientale: Bulletin de la Societe Géologique de France (7), v. 25, p. 169–183.

Beck, C. M., Girard, D., and DeWeber, P., 1964, Le "Volcano-sédimentaire du Rio Guare": Un élément de la nappe ophiolitique de Loma de Hierro, chaîne Caraïbe Vénézuélienne: Paris, Académie des Sciences, Comptes Rendus de Seances (D), v. 299, p. 337–342.

Beets, D. J., 1972, Lithology and stratigraphy of the Cretaceous and Danian succession of Curaçao: Natuurwetenschappelijk Studierkring voor Suriname en de Nederlandse Antillen, Uitgaven no. 70, 153 p.

Beets, D. J., and Lodder, W., 1967, Indication for the presence of ignimbrites in the Cretaceous Washikemba Formation of the Isle of Bonaire, Netherlands Antilles: Koninklijke Nederlandse Akademie van Wetenschappen, Proceedings (series B) v. 70, p. 63–67.

Beets, D. J., Klaver, G., Beunk, F. F., Kieft, C., and Maaskant, P., 1982, Picrites as parental magma of MORB-type tholeiites: Nature, v. 296, p. 341–343.

Beets, D. J., and 6 others, 1984, Magmatic rock series and high-pressure metamorphism as constraints on the tectonic history of the southern Caribbean, in Bonini, W. E., and others, eds., The Caribbean–South American plate boundary and regional tectonics: Geological Society of America Memoir 162, p. 95–130.

Bell, J. S., 1967, Geology of the Camatagua area, Estado Aragua, Venezuela [Ph.D. thesis]: Princeton, New Jersey, Princeton University, 282 p.

—— , 1971, Tectonic evolution of the central part of the Venezuelan coast range: Geological Society of America Memoir 130, p. 107–118.

Bellizia, A., and López Eyzaguirre, C., 1972, Gabro versus "pseudogabro" en el complejo ultramáfico de Tinaquilla: Boletín de Geología, Venezuela, Ministerio de Minas e Hidrocarburos, publicación especial no. 5, v. 4, p. 2139.

Bellon, H., and Maury, R. C., 1983, Les Petites Antilles de Saint-Kitts a Saint-Vincent; Bilan provisoire des données radiométriques K-Ar; Contraintes apportées a l'évolution géodynamique de l'archipel [abs.]: Seance Specialisée de la Societe Géologique de France, Brest, 1983, p. 16.

Bellon, H., and Tournon, J., 1977, Contribution de la géochronométrie K-Ar à l'étude du magmatisme de Costa Rica, Amérique Centrale: Bulletin de la Societe Géologique de France 7, v. 20, p. 955–959.

Bence, A. E., Papike, J. J., and Ayuso, R. A., 1975, Petrology of submarine basalts from the central Caribbean: Journal of Geophysical Research, v. 80, p. 4775–4804.

Bertrand, J., and Vuagnat, M., 1975, Sur la presence de basaltes en coussins dans la zone ophiolitique méridionale del la Cordillere centrale du Guatemala: Bulletin Suisse Minéralogie et Pétrologie, v. 55, p. 136–142.

—— , 1976, Étude pétrographique de diverses ultrabasites ophiolitiques du Guatémala et leur inclusions: Bulletin Suisse Minéralogie et Pétrologie, v. 56, p. 527–540.

—— , 1977, Données chimiques diverses sur des ophiolites du Guatémala: Bulletin Suisse Minéralogie et Pétrologie, v. 57, p. 466–483.

Bertrand, J., Delaloye, M., Fontignie, D., and Vuagnat, M., 1980, Ages (K-Ar) sur diverses ophiolites et roches associées de la Cordillère Centrale du Guatémala: Bulletin Suisse Minéralogie et Pétrologie, v. 60, p. 405–412.

Bosc, E., 1971, Geology of the San Agustín Acasaguastlán quadrangle and northeastern part of the El Progreso quadrangle [Ph.D. thesis]: Houston, Texas, Rice University, 131 p.

Bourdon, L., 1985, La Cordillère Orientale Dominicaine (Hispaniola, Grandes Antilles): un arc insulaire Crétacé polystructure [thesis]: Paris, Université Pierre et Marie Curie, 203 p.

Bourgois, J., Vila, J.-M., and Tavares, I., 1980, Datos geológicos nuevos acerca de la región de Puerto Plata (Republica Dominicana): Transactions, Caribbean Geological Conference, 9th, Santo Domingo, 1980, p. 633–636.

Bourgois, J., and 10 others, 1982a, Ages et structures des complexes basiques et ultrabasiques de la façade pacifique entre 3°N et 12°N (Colombie, Panamá, et Costa Rica): Bulletin de la Societe Géologique de France (7), v. 24, p. 545–554.

Bourgois, J., Calle, B., Tournon, J., and Toussaint, J.-F., 1982b, The Andean ophiolitic megastructures on the Buga-Buenaventura transverse (western Cordillera, Valle Colombie): Tectonophysics, v. 82, p. 207–229.

Bourgois, J., and 5 others, 1984, The geologic history of the Caribbean–Cocos plate boundary with special reference to the Nicoya ophiolite complex

(Costa Rica) and D.S.D.P. results (Legs 67 and 84 off Guatemala): A synthesis: Tectonophyiscs, v. 108, p. 1–32.

Bourgois, J., Desmet, A., Tournon, J., and Aubouin, J., 1985, Mafic and ultramafic rocks of Leg 84: Petrology and mineralogy, *in* von Huene, R., and Aubouin, J., Initial reports of the Deep Sea Drilling Project, Volume 84: Washington, D.C., U.S. Government Printing Office, v. 84, p. 642–663.

Bouysse, P., 1984, The Lesser Antilles island arc: Structure and geodynamic evolution, *in* Biju-Duval, B., and Moore, J. C., Initial reports of the Deep Sea Drilling Project, Volume 78A: Washington, D.C., U.S. Government Printing Office, p. 83–103.

Bouysse, P., and 5 others, 1981, Le Banc Luymes, terminaison septentrionale de l'arc recent des Petites Antilles: Bulletin de la Societe Géologique de France (7), v. 23, p. 185–194.

Bouysse, P., Schmidt-Effing, R., and Westercamp, D., 1983, La Désirade Island (Lesser Antilles) revisited: Lower Cretaceous radiolarian cherts and arguments against an ophiolitic origin for the basal complex: Geology, v. 11, p. 244–247.

Bowin, C. O., 1966, Geology of central Dominican Republic (Case history of part of an island arc), *in* Hess, H. H., ed., Caribbean geological studies: Geological Society of America Memoir 98, p. 11–84.

Bracey, D. R., and Vogt, P. R., 1970, Plate tectonics of the Hispaniola area: Geological Society of America Bulletin, v. 81, p. 2855–2860.

Brezsnyanszky, K., Coutin, D. P., and Jakus, P., 1981, Nuevos aspectos acerca del complejo basal en Cuba oriental: Ciencias de la Tierra y del Espacio (Cuba), v. 3, p. 23–29.

Briden, J. C., Rex, D. C., Faller, A. M., Tomblin, J. F., and Arculus, R. J., 1979, K-Ar geochronology and paleomagnetism of volcanic rocks in the Lesser Antilles island arc: Royal Society of London Philosophical Transactions, ser. A, v. 291, p. 485–528.

Briggs, R. P., 1969, Changes in stratigraphic nomenclature in the Cretaceous System, east-central Puerto Rico: U.S. Geological Survey Bulletin 1274-O, 31 p.

Brown, G. M., Holland, J. G., Sigurdsson, H., Tomblin, J. F., and Arculus, R. J., 1977, Geochemistry of the Lesser Antilles volcanic island arc: Geochimica et Cosmochimica Acta, v. 41, p. 785–801.

Brown, L., and 5 others, 1982, Beryllium-10 as a geochemical and geophysical probe: Carnegie Institute of Washington Yearbook, v. 81, p. 464–467.

Burkart, B., 1965, Geology of the Esquipulas, Chanmagua, and Cerro Montecristo quadrangles, southeastern Guatemala [Ph.D. thesis]: Houston, Texas, Rice University, 121 p.

Cadet, J.-P., Pouclet, A., Thisse, Y., Bardintzeff, J. M., and Azéma, J., 1982, Middle America Neogene explosive volcanism and ash layers: Evidence from the Middle America trench transect, Deep Sea Drilling Project Leg 67, *in* Aubouin, J., and von Huene, R., Initial reports of the Deep Sea Drilling Project Volume 67: Washington, D.C., U.S. Government Printing Office, p. 475–489.

Calmus, T., 1983, Contribution a l'étude géologique du massif de Macaya (sud-ouest d'Haïti, Grandes Antilles), sa place dans l'évolution de l'orogene nord-Caraïbe [Ph.D thesis]: Paris Université Pierre et Marie Curie.

Carr, M. J., 1984, Symmetrical and segmented variation of physical and geochemical characteristics of the Central American volcanic front: Journal of Volcanology and Geothermal Research, v. 20, p. 231–252.

Carr, M. J., and Pontier, N. K., 1981, Evolution of a young composite cone toward a mature central vent, Izalco and Santa Ana volcanoes in El Salvador, Central America: Journal of Volcanology and Geothermal Research, v. 11, p. 277–292.

Carr, M. J., Rose, W. I., Jr., and Mayfield, D. G., 1979, Potassium content of lavas and depth to seismic zone in Central America: Journal of Volcanology and Geothermal Research, v. 5, p. 387–401.

Carr, M. A., Rose, W. I., and Stoiber, R. E., 1982, Central America, *in* Thorpe, R. S., ed., Andesites: New York, John Wiley, p. 149–166.

Case, J. E., 1974, Oceanic crust forms basement of eastern Panama: Geological Society of America Bulletin, v. 85, p. 645–652.

Case, J. E., Durán, S., L. G., López, R., A., and Moore, W. R., 1971, Tectonic investigations in western Colombia and eastern Panama: Geological Society of America Bulletin, v. 82, p. 2685–2712.

Case, J. E., Barnes, J., Paris, Q., G., Gonzalez, I., H., and Viña, A., 1973, Trans-Andean geophysical profile, southern Colombia: Geological Society of America Bulletin, v. 4, p. 2895–2904.

Chen, J.-C., 1969, Petrological and chemical studies of Utuado pluton, Puerto Rico: Acta Geologica Taiwanica, v. 13, p. 21–41.

Christman, R. A., 1953, Geology of St. Bartholomew, St. Martin, and Anguilla, Lesser Antilles: Geological Society of America Bulletin, v. 64, p. 65–96.

—— , 1972, Volcanic geology of southwestern Antiqua, B.W.I.: Geological Society of America Memoir 132, p. 439–448.

Clemons, R. E., and Long, L. E., 1971, Petrologic and Rb-Sr isotopic study of the Chiquimula Pluton, southeastern Guatemala: Geological Society of America Bulletin, v. 82, p. 2729–2740.

Coleman, R. G., 1977, Ophiolites; ancient oceanic lithosphere?: Berlin, Springer-Verlag, 229 p.

Cox, D. P., Marvin, R. F., M'Gonigle, J. W., McIntyre, D. H., and Rogers, C. L., 1977, Potassium-argon geochronology of some metamorphic, igneous, and hydrothermal events in Puerto Rico and the Virgin Islands: U.S. Geological Survey Journal of Research, v. 5, p. 689–703.

Cox, M. L., 1981, A study of massive-bedded tuffs of the Padre Miguel Group, southeastern Guatemala, C. A. [M.Sc. thesis]: Arlington, Texas, University of Texas at Arlington, 105 p.

Cumming, G. L., and Kesler, S. E., 1981, Source of lead in Central American and Caribbean mineralization; II. Lead isotope provinces: Earth and Planetary Science Letters, v. 56, p. 199–209.

Cumming, G. L., Kesler, S. E., and Krstic, D., 1982, Source of lead in sulfide ore at the Pueblo Viejo gold-silver oxide deposit: Economic Geology, v. 77, p. 1939–1942.

Curran, D. W., 1980, Geology of the Siguatepeque quadrangle, Honduras, Central America [M.Sc. thesis]: Binghamton, New York, State University of New York at Binghamton, 194 p.

DeLong, S. E., Grippi, J., and Burke, K., 1983, Geochemistry of some igneous rocks from the Lucea inlier, western Jamaica: A preliminary report: Journal of the Geological Society of Jamaica, v. 22, p. 10–14.

Dengo, G., 1953, Geology of the Caracas region, Venezuela: Geological Society of America Bulletin, v. 64, p. 7–39.

—— , 1962, Tectonic-igneous sequence in Costa Rica, *in* Engel, A.E.J., James, H. L., and Leonard, B. F., eds., Petrologic studies: A volume to honor A. F. Buddington: Boulder, Colorado, Geological Society of America, p. 133–161.

De Wever, P., Azéma, J., Tournon, J., and Desmet, A., 1985, Découverte de matériel oceanique du Lias-Dogger inférieure dans la péninsule de Santa Elena (Costa Rica, Amérique Centrale): Paris, Académie de Science Comptes Rendus, v. 300, p. 759–764.

Diebold, J. B., Stoffa, P. L., Buhl, P., and Truchan, M., 1981, Venezuela Basin crustal structure: Journal of Geophysical Research, v. 86, p. 7901–7923.

Dietrich, V. J., Gansser, A., Sommerauer, J., and Cameron, W. E., 1981, Palaeogene komatiites from Gorgona Island, East Pacific—A primary magma for ocean-floor basalts?: Geochemical Journal, v. 15, p. 141–161.

Dinkleman, M. G., and Brown, J. F., 1977, K-Ar geochronology and its significance to the geological setting of La Désirade (Lesser Antilles) [abs.]: Caribbean Geological Conference, 8th, Curacao, 1977, p. 38–39.

Donnelly, T. W., 1963, Genesis of albite in early orogenic igneous rocks: American Journal of Science, v. 261, p. 957–972.

—— , 1966, Geology of St. Thomas and St. John, Virgin Islands, *in* Hess, H. H., ed., Caribbean geological studies: Geological Society of America Memoir 98, p. 85–176.

—— , 1972, Deep-water shallow-water, and subaerial island-arc volcanism: Example from the Virgin Islands, *in* Shagam, R., and others, eds., Studies in earth and space sciences: Geological Society of America Memoir 132, p. 401–414.

—— , 1973a, Late Cretaceous basalts from the Caribbean, a possible flood-basalt province of vast size [abs.]: EOS (American Geophysical Union Transactions), v. 54, p. 1004.

——— , 1973b, Circum-Caribbean explosive volcanic activity: Evidence from Leg 15 sediments, *in* Edgar, N. T., and Saunders, J., Initial reports of the Deep Sea Drilling Project, Volume 15: Washington, D.C., U.S. Government Printing Office, p. 969–988.

——— , 1985, Mesozoic and Cenozoic plate evolution of the Caribbean region, *in* Stehli, F. G., and Webb, S. D., eds., The great American biotic interchange: New York, Plenum Press, p. 89–121.

Donnelly, T. W., and Rogers, J.J.W., 1967, Crust vs. mantle derivation of eastern Antillean igneous rocks [abs.]: EOS (American Geophysical Union Transactions), v. 48, p. 253.

——— , 1978, The distribution of igneous rock suites around the Caribbean: Geologie en Mijnbouw, v. 57, p. 151–162.

——— , 1980, Igneous series in island arcs: The northeastern Caribbean compared with worldwide island-arc assemblages: Bulletin Volcanologique, v. 43, p. 347–382.

Donnelly, T. W., Rogers, J.J.W., Pushkar, P., and Armstrong, R. L., 1971, Chemical evolution of the igneous rocks of the eastern West Indies: An investigation of thorium, uranium, and potassium distributions and lead and strontium isotopic ratios, *in* Donnelly, T. W., ed., Caribbean geologic, tectonic, and petrologic studies: Geological Society of America Memoir 130, p. 181–224.

Donnelly, T. W., Kay, R., and Rogers, J.J.W., 1973a, Chemical petrology of Caribbean basalts and dolerites: EOS (American Geophysical Union Transactions), v. 54, p. 1002–1004.

Donnelly, T. W., Melson, K., Kay, R., and Rogers, J.J.W., 1973b, Basalts and dolerites of Late Cretaceous age from the central Caribbean, *in* Edgar, N. T., and Saunders, J. B., Initial reports of the Deep Sea Drilling Project, Volume 15: Washington, D.C., U.S. Government Printing Office, p. 989–1012.

Draper, G., and Lewis, J., 1983, Structural characteristics and tectonic implications of the Duarte Complex, Cordillera Central, Dominican Republic [abs.]: Caribbean Geological Conference, 10th, Cartagena, 1983, p. 34–35.

Drexler, J. W., Rose, W. I., Jr., Sparks, R.S.J., and Ledbetter, M. T., 1980, The Los Chocoyos ash, Guatemala: A major stratigraphic marker in Middle America and in three ocean basins: Quaternary Research, v. 13, p. 327–345.

Dupré, B., and Echeverría, L. M., 1984, Pb Isotopes of Gorgona Island (Colombia): Isotopic variations correlated with magma type: Earth and Planetary Science Letters, v. 67, p. 186–190.

Dupré, B., White, W. M., Vidal, P., and Maury, R. C., 1985, Utilisation des traceurs couples (Pb-Sr-Nd) pour déterminer le rôle des sédiments dans la genèse des basaltes de l'arc des Antilles, *in* Mascle, A., ed., Géodynamique des Caraïbes; Symposium, Paris 5-8 Fevrier 1985: Paris, Editions Technip, p. 91–97.

Dupré, W. R., 1970, Geology of the Zambrano quadrangle, Honduras [M.Sc. thesis]: Austin, University of Texas, 128 p.

Eberle, W., Hirdes, W., Muff, R., and Pelaez, M., 1980, The geology of the Cordillera Septentrional (Dominican Republic): Transactions, Caribbean Geological Conference, 9th, Santo Domingo, 1980, p. 619–632.

Echeverría, L. M., 1980, Tertiary or Mesozoic komatiites from Gorgona Island, Colombia: Field relations and geochemistry: Contributions to Mineralogy and Petrology, v. 73, p. 253–266.

Espinosa, A., Delaloye, M., and Wagner, J.-J., 1982, Radiometric ages of the Gorgona Island (Colombia) komatiitic ophiolite: Ofioliti, 1982 (2/3), p. 237–238.

Feigenson, M., 1977, The strontium-isotope geochemistry of a tonalite batholith of the Dominican Republic: Carnegie Institute of Washington Yearbook, v. 76, p. 870–878.

Fichaut, M., and 6 others, 1985, Magmatologie de la Montagne Pelée: Paris, Institut National d'Astronomie et de Géophysique, Centre Nacional de la Recherche Scientifique, Bulletin PIRPSEV, no. 101, 94 p.

Fink, L. K., Jr., 1972, Bathymetric and geologic studies of the Guadeloupe region, Lesser Antilles island arc: Marine Geology, v. 12, p. 267–288.

Fox, P. J., Schreiber, E., and Heezen, B. C., 1971, The geology of the Caribbean crust: Tertiary sediments, granitic, and basic rocks from the Aves Ridge: Tectonophysics, v. 12, p. 89–109.

Gansser, A., 1950, Geological and petrographical notes on Gorgona Island in relation to northwestern S. America: Schweizerische Mineralogische und Petrologische Mitteilungen, v. 30, p. 219–237.

Ghosh, N., Hall, S. A., and Casey, J. F., 1984, Seafloor spreading magnetic anomalies in the Venezuelan Basin, *in* Bonini, W. E., and others, eds., The Caribbean–South American plate boundary and regional tectonics: Geological Society of America Memoir 162, p. 65–80.

Gill, J. B., 1970, Geochemistry of the Viti Levu, Fiji, and its evolution as an island arc: Contributions to Mineralogy and Petrology, v. 27, p. 179–203.

Girard, D., 1981, Pétrologie de quelques séries spilitiques mésozoïques du domaine caraïbe at des ensembles magmatiques de l'île de Tobago: Implications and géodynamique [thesis]: Université de Bretagne Occidentale, 230 p.

Girard, D., and Maury, R. C., 1983, Pétologie d'un ensemble ophiolitique d'arc insulaire: le complexe volcanoplutonique crétacé de l'île de Tobago: Bulletin de la Societe Géologique de France (7), v. 25, p. 823–835.

Goossens, P. J., and Rose, W. I., Jr., 1973, Chemical composition and age determination of tholeiitic rocks in the basic igneous complex, Ecuador: Geological Society of America Bulletin, v. 84, p. 1043–1052.

Goossens, P. J., Rose, W. I., Jr., and Flores, D., 1977, Geochemistry of tholeiites of the basic igneous complex of northwestern South America: Geological Society of America Bulletin, v. 88, p. 1711–1720.

Graham, A. M., and Thirlwall, M. F., 1981, Petrology of the 1979 eruption of Soufrière Volcano, St. Vincent, Lesser Antilles: Contributions to Mineralogy and Petrology, v. 76, p. 336–342.

Graterol, M., 1972, Petrogenesis de la peridotita de Loma de Hierro, Estado Aragua: Transactions, Caribbean Geological Conference, 6th, Margarita, 1971, p. 329–336.

Green, G. W., 1977, Structure and stratigraphy of the Wagwater belt, Kingston, Jamaica: Institute of Geological Sciences, Overseas Geology and Mineral Resources, no. 48, 21 p.

Handschumacher, D. W., 1976, Post-Eocene plate tectonics of the eastern Pacific, *in* Sutton, G. H., Manghani, M. H., and Moberly, R., eds., The geophysics of the Pacific Ocean basin and its margin: American Geophysical Union Geophysical Monograph 19, p. 177–202.

Hawkesworth, C. J., and Powell, M., 1980, Magma genesis in the Lesser Antilles island arc: Earth and Planetary Science Letters, v. 51, p. 297–308.

Hein, J. R., Kuijpers, E. P., and Denyer, P., 1983, Paleogene and Cretaceous cherts of western Costa Rica, *in* Iijima, A., Siever, R., and Hein, J. R., eds., Second International Conference on Siliceous Deposits in the Pacific Region: Development in sedimentology: Amsterdam, Elsevier Press, p. 143–174.

Hekinian, R., 1969, Petrological and geochemical study of spilites and associated dike rocks from the Virgin Island core [Ph.D. thesis]: Binghamton, New York, State University of New York at Binghamton, 204 p.

——— , 1971, Petrological and geochemical study of spilites and associated rocks from St. John, U.S. Virgin Islands: Geological Society of America Bulletin, v. 82, p. 659–682.

Horne, G. S., Pushkar, P., and Shafiqullah, M., 1976a, Preliminary K-Ar age data from the Laramide Sierras of central Honduras: Publicaciones Geológicas ICAITI (Guatemala) no. 5, p. 91–98.

——— , 1976b, Laramide plutons on the landward continuation of the Bonacca Ridge, northern Honduras: Publicaciones Geológicas ICAITI (Guatemala) no. 5, p. 84–90.

Jackson, T. A., and Smith, T. E., 1978, Metasomatism in the Tertiary volcanics of the Wagwater Belt, Jamaica, W.I.: Geologie en Mijnbouw, v. 57, p. 213–220.

——— , 1979, The tectonic significance of basalts and dacites in the Wagwater Belt, Jamaica: Geological Magazine, v. 116, p. 365–374.

——— , 1980, Mesozoic and Cenozoic magma types of Jamaica and their tectonic setting: Transactions, Caribbean Geological Conference, 9th, Santo Domingo, 1980, p. 435–440.

Jakes, P., and Gill, J. B., 1970, Rare earth elements and the island-arc tholeiitic series: Earth and Planetary Science Letters, v. 9, p. 17–28.

Jarvis, H. A., Jr., 1964, Geology of the Río Pao-Río Tiznados area, Cojedes and

Guárico, Venezuela [Ph.D. thesis]: Houston, Texas, Rice University, 93 p.

Jolly, W. T., 1970, Petrologic studies of the Robles Formation, south central Puerto Rico [Ph.D. thesis]: Binghamton, New York, State University of New York at Binghamton, 150 p.

—— , 1971, Potassium-rich igneous rocks from Puerto Rico: Geological Society of America Bulletin, v. 82, p. 399–408.

Jones, L. M., and Kesler, S. E., 1980, Strontium isotope geochemistry of intrusive rocks, Puerto Rico, Greater Antilles: Earth and Planetary Science Letters, v. 50, p. 219–224.

Joyce, J., 1980, The lithology and structure of the eclogite and glaucophanite bearing rocks on the Samaná Peninsula: Transactions, Caribbean Geological Conference, 9th, Santo Domingo, 1980, p. 417–422.

Kerr, J. M., 1978, The volcanic and tectonic history of La Providencia Island, Colombia [M.Sc. thesis]: New Brunswick, New Jersey, Rutgers University, 52 p.

Kesler, S. E., 1971, Petrology of the Terre Neuve igneous province, northern Haiti, in Donnelly, T. W., ed., Caribbean geologic, tectonic, and petrologic studies: Geological Society of America Memoir 130, p. 119–137.

—— , 1978, Metallogenesis of the Caribbean region: Geological Society of London Journal, v. 135, p. 429–441.

Kesler, S. E., and Sutter, J. F., 1979, Compositional evolution of intrusive rocks in the eastern Greater Antilles: Geology, v. 7, p. 197–200.

Kesler, S. E., Lewis, J. F., Jones, L. M., and Walker, R. L., 1977a, Early island-arc intrusive activity, Cordillera Central, Dominican Republic: Contributions to Mineralogy and Petrology, v. 65, p. 91–99.

Kesler, S. E., Sutter, J. F., Issigonis, M. J., Jones, M. L., and Walker, R. L., 1977b, Evolution of porphyry copper mineralization in an oceanic island arc, Panama: Economic Geology, v. 72, p. 1142–1153.

Kesler, S. E., Sutter, J. F., Jones, L. M., and Walker, R. L., 1977c, Early Cretaceous basement rocks in Hispaniola: Geology, v. 5, p. 245–247.

Khudoley, K. M., and Meyerhoff, A. A., 1971, Paleogeography and geological history of Great Antilles: Geological Society of America Memoir 129, 199 p.

Knipper, A. L., and Cabrera, R., 1974, Tectónica y geología histórica de la zona de articulatión entre el mio- y eugeosynclinal y del cinturón hiperbásica de Cuba, in "Contribución a la Geología de Cuba: Academia de Ciencias de Cuba, Instituto de Geología y Paleontología, Publicación Especial 2, p. 15–78.

Koch, A. J., and McLean, H., 1975, Pleistocene tephra and ash-flow deposits in the volcanic highlands of Guatemala: Geological Socioety of America Bulletin, v. 86, p. 529–541.

Kuijpers, E. P., 1980, The geologic history of the Nicoya Ophiolite Complex, Costa Rica, and its geotectonic significance: Tectonophysics, v. 68, p. 233–255.

Lawrence, D. P., 1975, Petrology and structural geology of the Sanarate-El Progreso area, Guatemala [Ph.D. thesis]: Binghamton, New York, State University of New York at Binghamton, 255 p.

Ledbetter, M. T., 1982, Tephronchronology at sites 502 and 503, in Prell, W., and Gardner, J. V., eds., Initial reports of the Deep Sea Drilling Project Volume 68: Washington, D.C., U.S. Government Printing Office, p. 403–408.

—— , 1985, Tephrochronology of marine tephra adjacent to Central America: Geology, v. 13, p. 77–82.

Lee, V., and Mattson, P. H., 1976, Metamorphosed oceanic crust of early volcanic products in Puerto Rico basement rock association: Transactions, Caribbean Geological Conference, 7th, Guadeloupe, 1974, p. 263–270.

Le Gall, B., Bellon, H., Carron, J.-P., and Le Guen de Kerneizon, M., 1983, Données nouvelles sur le volcanisme de l'île de Montserrat (Petites Antilles): Bulletin de la Societe Géologique de France (7), v. 25, p. 837–843.

Le Guen de Kerneizon, M., Mascle, A., Maury, R. C., and Westercamp, D., 1979, Les laves de La Désirade (Petites Antilles), temoins d'un magmatisme de marge active: arguments minéralogiques: Bulletin Bureau de Recherches Géologiques ete Minieres (2), Section IV, p. 285–292.

Le Guen de Kerneizon, M., Carron, J. P., Maury, R. C., Bellon, H., and Dupuy, C., 1982, Les rhyolites a fayalite et ferroaugite de Sainte-Lucie (arc insulaire des Petites Antilles): Bulletin Minéralogique, v. 105, p. 203–211.

Le Guen de Kerneizon, M., Bellon, H., Carron, J. P., and Maury, R. C., 1983, L'île de Sainte-Lucie (Petites Antilles): distinction des principales séries magmatiques a partir des données pétrochimiques et géochronologiques: Bulletin de la Societe Géologique de France (7), v. 25, p. 845–853.

Le Guen De Kerneizon, M., Westercamp, D., and Bellon, H., 1985, The Grenadines, southern Lesser Antilles; Part II, Major petrochemical features of the volcanic rocks, in Géodynamique des Caraïbes, Symposium Paris: Paris, Editions Technip, p. 119–130.

Lew, L., 1983, The geology of the Osa Peninsula, Costa Rica: Observations and speculations about the evolution of part of the outer arc of the southern Central American orogen [M.Sc. thesis]: University Park, Pennsylvania State University, 128 p.

—— , 1984, The geology of the Santa Elena Peninsula, Costa Rica, and its implications for the tectonic evolution of the Central American-Caribbean region [Ph.D. thesis]: University Park, Pennsylvania State University, 382 p.

Lewis, J. F., 1971, Composition, origin, and differentiation of basalt magma in the Lesser Antilles, in Donnelly, T. W., ed., Caribbean geologic, tectonic, and petrologic studies: Geological Society of America Memoir 130, p. 159–179.

—— , 1980a, Granitoid rocks of Hispaniola: Transactions, Caribbean Geological Conference, 9th, Santo Domingo, 1980, p. 393–401.

—— , 1980b, Ultrabasic and associated rocks in Hispaniola: Transactions, Caribbean Geological Conference, 9th, Santo Domingo, 1980, p. 403–408.

Lewis, J. F., and Gunn, B. M., 1972, Aspects of island-arc evolution and magmatism in the Caribbean: Geochemistry of some West Indian plutonic and volcanic rocks: Transactions, Caribbean Geological Conference, 6th, Margarita, 1971, p. 171–177.

Lockwood, J. P., 1965, Geology of the Serranía de Jarara area, Guajira Peninsula, Colombia [Ph.D. thesis]: Princeton, New Jersey, Princeton University, 237 p.

—— , 1971, Detrital serpentinite from the Guajira Peninsula, Colombia, in Donnelly, T. W., ed., Caribbean geologic, tectonic, and petrologic studies: Geological Society of America Memoir 130, p. 55–75.

Longshore, J., 1965, Chemical and mineralogical variations in the Virgin Islands batholith and its associated wall rocks [Ph.D. thesis]: Houston, Texas, Rice University, 94 p.

Lundberg, N., 1982, Evolution of the slope landward of the Middle American Trench, Nicoya Peninsula, Costa Rica, in Leggett, J. K., ed., Trench-forearc geology: Sedimentation and tectonics on modern and ancient active plate margins: Geological Society of London Special Publication 10, p. 131–147.

MacDonald, W. D., 1964, Geology of the Serranía de Macuira area, Guajira Peninsula, Colombia [Ph.D. thesis]: Princeton, New Jersey, Princeton University, 167 p.

—— , 1968, Communication in status of geological research in the Caribbean: Mayagüez, University of Puerto Rico, no. 14, p. 40–41.

MacDonald, W. D., and Melson, W. G., 1969, A late Cenozoic volcanic province in Hispaniola: Caribbean Journal of Science, v. 9, p. 81–91.

MacDonald, W. D., Doolan, B. L. and Cordani, U. G., 1971, Cretaceous–early Tertiary metamorphic K–Ar age values from the south Caribbean: Geological Society of America Bulletin, v. 82, p. 1381–1388.

MacKenzie, D. B., 1960, High-temperature alpine-type peridotite from Venezuela: Geological Society of America Bulletin, v. 71, p. 303–318.

MacLachlan, J. C., Shagam, R., and Hess, H. H., 1960, Geology of the La Victoria area, Aragua, Venezuela: Geological Society of America Bulletin, v. 71, p. 241–248.

Martín-Bellizia, C., 1968, Edades isotópicas de rocas venezolanos: Boletín de Geología, Venezuela, Ministerio de Minas e Hidrocarburos, v. 10, p. 356–380.

Martín-Bellizia, C., and de Arozena, J. M., 1972, Complejo ultramáfico zonado de Tausabana-El Rodeo, gabro zonado de Siraba-Capuana y complejo sub-volcánico estratificado de Santa Ana, Paraguaná, Estado Falcón: Transactions, Caribbean Geological Conference, 6th, Margarita, 1971, p. 337–356.

Mattinson, J. M., Fink, L. K., Jr., and Hopson, C. A., 1980, Geochronologic and isotopic study of the La Désirade basement complex: Jurassic oceanic crust in the Lesser Antilles: Contributions to Mineralogy and Petrology, v. 71,

p. 237–245.

Mattson, P. H., 1960, Geology of the Mayagüez area, Puerto Rico: Geological Society of America Bulletin, v. 71, p. 319–362.

——, 1966, Geological characteristics of Puerto Rico, in Poole, W. H., ed., Continental Margins and Island Arcs: Geological Survey Canada Special Paper 66-15, p. 124–138.

——, 1973, Middle Cretaceous nappe structures in Puerto Rico ophiolites and their relation to the tectonic history of the Greater Antilles: Geological Society of America Bulletin, v. 84, p. 21–38.

Mattson, P. H., and Pessagno, E. A., Jr., 1979, Jurassic and Early Cretaceous radiolarians in Puerto Rican ophiolite—Tectonic implications: Geology, v. 7, p. 440–444.

Maurrasse, F., Husler, J., Georges, G., Schmitt, R., and Damond, P., 1979, Upraised Caribbean sea floor below acoustic reflector "B" at the southern peninsula of Haiti: Geologie en Mijnbouw, v. 58, p. 71–83.

Maury, R. C., and Westercamp, D., 1985, Variations chronologiques et spatiales des basaltes néogènes des Petites Antilles; Implications sur l'évolution del'arc, in Mascle, A., ed., Géodynamique des Caraïbes. Symposium, Paris 5-8 Fevrier 1985: Paris, Editions Technip, p. 77–89.

Maxwell, J. C., 1948, Geology of Tobago, British West Indies: Geological Society of America Bulletin, v. 59, p. 801–854.

McBirney, A. R., and Bass, M. N., 1969, Structural relations of pre-Mesozoic rocks of northern Central America, in McBirney, A. R., ed., Tectonic relations of northern Central America and the western Caribbean; The Bonacca Expedition: American Association of Petroleum Geologists Memoir 11, p. 269–280.

McBirney, A. R., and Williams, H., 1965, Volcanic history of Nicaragua: University of California Publications in Geology, v. 55, p. 1–66.

McBirney, A. R., Aoki, K.-I., and Bass, M., 1967, Eclogite and jadeite from the Motagua fault zone, Guatemala: American Mineralogist, v. 52, p. 908–918.

Mércier de Lepinay, B., Labesse, B., Sigal, J., and Vila, J.-M., 1979, Sédimentation chaotique et tectonique tangentielle maestrichtiennes dans la presqu'île sud d'Haïti (ile d'Hispaniola, Grandes Antilles): Paris, Académie de Sciences Comptes Rendus (D), v. 109, p. 887–890.

Menéndez, A., 1962, Geology of the Tinaco area, northcentral Cojedes, Venezuela [Ph.D. thesis]: Princeton, New Jersey, Princeton University, 238 p.

Meyerhoff, A. A., 1964, Review of Bermudez, P. J. (1961) Las Formaciones Geológicas de Cuba: International Geology Review, v. 6, p. 149–156.

Meyerhoff, A. A., and Hatten, C. W., 1968, Diapiric structures in central Cuba, in Braunstein, J., and O'Brien, G. D., eds., Diapirism and diapirs: American Association of Petroleum Geologists Memoir 8, p. 315–357.

M'Gonigle, J. W., 1977, The Rio Abajo, Pitahaya, and Daguao formations in eastern Puerto Rico: U.S. Geological Survey Bulletin 1435-B, 10 p.

Michael, R. C., 1979, Geology of the south-central flank of the Cordillera Central and the adjacent portions of the San Juan Valley between Río San Juan and Río Yacahueque, Dominican Republic [M.Sc. thesis]: Washington, D.C., George Washington University, 158 p.

Millan, G., and Somin, M. L., 1981, Litología, estratigrafía, tectónica, y metamorfismo del macizo de Escambray: Academía de Ciencias de Cuba, 104 p.

Millward, D., Marriner, G. F., and Saunders, A. D., 1984, Cretaceous tholeiitic volcanic rocks from the western Cordillera of Colombia: Geological Society of London Journal, v. 141, p. 847–860.

Mooser, F., Meyer-Abich, H., and McBirney, A. R., 1958, Catalogue of active volcanoes of the World; Part VI, Central America: Naples, International Association Volcanology, 146 p.

Morgan, B. A., 1967, Geology of the Valencia area, Carabobo, Venezuela [Ph.D. thesis]: Princeton, New Jersey, Princeton University, 220 p.

Muessig, K. W., 1978, The central Falcon igneous suite, Venezuela: Alkaline basaltic intrusions of Oligo–Miocene age: Geologie en Mijnbouw, v. 57, p. 261–266.

——, 1984, Structure and Cenozoic tectonics of the Falcon Basin, Venezuela, and adjacent areas: Geological Society of America Memoir 162, p. 217–230.

Muller, P. D., 1979, Geology of the Los Amates Quadrangle and vicinity, Guatemala, Central America [Ph.D. thesis]: Binghamton, New York, State University of New York at Binghamton, 326 p.

Nagle, F., 1966, Geology of the Puerto Plata area, Dominican Republic [Ph.D. thesis]: Princeton, New Jersey, Princeton University, 171 p.

——, 1971, Geology of the Puerto Plata area, Dominican Republic, relative to the Puerto Rico Trench: Transactions, Caribbean Geological Conference, 5th, St. Thomas, 1968: Queens College, Geological Bulletin, p. 79–84.

Nagle, F., Erlich, R. N., and Canovi, C. J., 1976, Caribbean dredge hauls: Geologie en Mijnbouw, v. 57, p. 267–270.

Natland, J. H., 1984, Occurrences of air-fall volcanic ash derived from the Lesser Antilles arc at Leg 78A drill sites, in Biju-Duval, B., and Moore, J. C., eds., Initial reports of the Deep Sea Drilling Project Volume 78A: Washington, D.C., U.S. Government Printing Office, p. 369–375.

Navarro F., E., 1983, Petrología y petrogenesis de las rocas metavolcánicas del Grupo Villa de Cura: Caracas, Escuela de Geología y Minas, Geos, no. 28, p. 170–317.

Officer, C. B., Ewing, J. I., Edwards, R. S., and Johnson, H. R., 1957, Geophysical investigations in the eastern Caribbean: Venezuelan Basin, Antilles island arc, and Puerto Rico outer trench: Geological Society of America Bulletin, v. 68, p. 359–378.

Pardo, G., 1975, Geology of Cuba, in Nairn, A.E.M., and Stehli, F. G., eds., Ocean basins and margins, Volume 3: New York, Plenum Press, p. 553–615.

Perfit, M., 1977, Petrology and geochemistry of mafic rocks from the Cayman Trench: Evidence for spreading: Geology, v. 5, p. 105–110.

Perfit, M., and Heezen, B. C., 1978, The geology and evolution of the Cayman Trough: Geological Society of America Bulletin, v. 89, p. 1155–1174.

Petersen, E. U., and Zantop, M., 1980, The Oxec deposit, Guatemala: An ophiolite copper occurrence: Economic Geology, v. 75, p. 1053–1065.

Piburn, M. D., 1967, Metamorphism and structure of the Villa de Cura Group, northern Venezuela [Ph.D. thesis]: Princeton, New Jersey, Princeton University, 134 p.

Pichler, H., Stibane, F. R., and Weyl, R., 1974, Basischer Magmatismus und Krustenbau in südlichen Mittelamerika, Kolumbien, und Ecuador: Neues Jahrbuch für Geologie und Paläontologie Monatschefte, 1974, no. 2, p. 102–126.

Pindell, J., and Dewey, J. P., 1982, Permo–Triassic reconstruction of western Pangea and the evolution of the Gulf of Mexico/Caribbean region: Tectonics, v. 1, p. 179–211.

Pouclet, A., Cadet, J. P., Fujioka, K., and Bourgois, J., 1985, Ash layers from Deep Sea Drilling Project Leg 84: Middle America Trench transect, in von Huene, R., and Aubouin, J., Initial reports of the Deep Sea Drilling Project, Volume 84: Washington, D.C., U.S. Government Printing Office, v. 84, p. 609–618.

Priem, H.N.A., Beets, D. J., Boelrijk, N.A.I.M., Hebeda, E. H., Verdurmen, E.A.T., and Verschure, R. H., 1978, Rb-Sr evidence for episodic intrusion of the Late Cretaceous tonalitic batholith of Aruba, Netherlands Antilles: Geologie en Mijnbouw, v. 57, p. 293–296.

Pszczolkowski, A., and de Albear, J. F., 1983, La secuencia vulcanógeno-sedimentaria de la Sierra del Rosario, Provincia de Pinar del Río, Cuba: Ciencias de la Tierra y del Espacio (Cuba), v. 6, p. 41–52.

Rea, W. J., 1982, The Lesser Antilles, in Thorpe, R. S., ed., Andesites: Orogenic andesites and related rocks: London, Wiley, p. 167–185.

Rea, W. J., and Baker, P. E., 1980, The geochemical characteristics and conditions of petrogenesis of the volcanic rocks of the northern Lesser Antilles—A review: Bulletin Volcanologique, v. 43, p. 325–336.

Reblin, M. T., 1973, Regional gravity survey of the Dominican Republic [M.Sc. thesis]: Salt Lake City, University of Utah, 129 p.

Reed, A. J., 1968, The Above Rocks granodiorite: Transactions, Caribbean Geological Conference, 4th, Trinidad and Tobago, 1965, p. 389–393.

Reeside, J. B., Jr., 1947, Upper Cretaceous ammonites from Haiti: U.S. Geological Survey Professional Paper 214A, 5 p.

Reynolds, J. H., 1980, Late Tertiary volcanic stratigraphy of northern Central America: Bulletin Volcanologique, v. 43, p. 601–608.

Ritchie, A. W., and McDowell, F. W., 1979, K-Ar ages of plutonic and volcanic rocks from the volcanic highlands of Guatemala northwest of Guatemala

City: Isochron/West no. 25, p. 3–4.

Robin, C., and Tournon, J., 1978, Spatial relations of andesite and alkaline provinces in Mexico and Central America: Canadian Journal of Earth Sciences, v. 15, p. 1633–1641.

Robinson, E., Lewis, J. F., and Cant, R. V., 1970, Field guide to aspects of the geology of Jamaica, *in* Donnelly, T. W., ed., Guidebook to the Caribbean island arc system: Washington, D.C., American Geological Institute, 47 p. (separate pagination).

Robson, G. R., and Tomblin, J. F., 1966, Catalogue of the active volcanoes of the World; Part XX, West Indies: Rome, International Association of Volcanology, 56 p.

Roobol, M. J., 1972, The volcanic geology of Jamaica: Transactions, Caribbean Geological Conference, 6th, Margarita, 1971, p. 100–107.

Roobol, M. J., and Horsfield, W. T., 1976, Sea floor lava outcrop in the Jamaica Passage: Journal of the Geological Society of Jamaica, v. 15, p. 7–10.

Rosenfeld, J. H., 1981, Geology of the western Sierra de Santa Cruz, Guatemala, Central America: An ophiolite sequence [Ph.D. thesis]: Binghamton, New York, State University of New York at Binghamton, 315 p.

Rowley, K. C., and Roobol, M. J., 1978, Geochemistry and age of the Tobago igneous rocks: Geologie en Mijnbouw, v. 57, p. 315–318.

Santamaría, F., and Schubert, C., 1974, Geochemistry and geochronology of the southern Caribbean-northern Venezuela plate boundary: Geological Society of America Bulletin, v. 85, p. 1085–1098.

Schmidt-Effing, R., 1979, Alter und genese des Nicoya-Komplexes, einer ozeanischen Paläokruste (Oberjura bis Eozän) im südlichen Zentralamerika: Geologische Rundschau, v. 68, p. 457–494.

—— , 1980, Radiolarien der Mittel-Kreide aus dem Santa Elena Massiv von Costa Rica: Neues Jahrbuch für Geologie und Paläontologie Abhandlungen, v. 160, p. 241–257.

Schubert, C., and Motiska, P., 1972, Reconocimiento geológico de las islas Venezolanos en el Mar Caribe, entre los Roques y Los Testigos (Dependencias Federales). Introducción y islas centrales: Acta Científica Venezolana, v. 23, p. 210–223.

Schubert, C., and Sifontes, R. S., 1983, La riolita pliocena tardia de Carúpano, Estado Sucre, Venezuela: ¿Extremo sur del arco volcánico de las Antillas Menores?: Acta Científica Venezolana, v. 34, p. 262–266.

Schwartz, D. P., 1976, Geology of the Zacapa quadrangle and vicinity, Guatemala [Ph.D. thesis]: Binghamton, New York, State University of New York at Binghamton, 179 p.

Seiders, V. M., 1962, Geology of central Miranda, Venezuela [Ph.D. thesis]: Princeton, New Jersey, Princeton University, 255 p.

Shagam, R., 1960, Geology of central Aragua, Venezuela: Geological Society of America Bulletin, v. 71, p. 249–302.

Sigurdsson, H., Tomblin, J. F., Brown, G. M., Holland, J. G., and Arculus, R. J., 1973, Strongly undersaturated magmas in the Lesser Antillean island arc: Earth and Planetary Science Letters, v. 18, p. 285–295.

Silva, Z.C.G., 1970, Origin of albitites from eastern Guatemala: Boletim dos Servicos Geologia e Minas (Brazil), no. 22, p. 23–32.

Smith, A. L., Roobol, M. J., and Gunn, B. M., 1980, The Lesser Antilles—A discussion of the island-arc magmatism: Bulletin Volcanologique, v. 43, p. 287–302.

Smith, R. J., 1953, Geology of the Los Teques-Cua region, Venezuela: Geological Society of America Bulletin, v. 64, p. 41–64.

Sokolova, E. A., Brito, A., and Coutin, D., 1974, La formación manganesífera El Cobre (Provincia de Oriente, Cuba), *in* Geología de los minerales utiles de Cuba: Instituto de Geología y Paleontología, Academia de Ciencias de Cuba, Publicación Especial No. 3, p. 92–124.

Soler, E., and Cheilletz, A., 1985, Caractéristiques du volcanisme du nord d'Haïti: Implications géotectoniques, *in* Mascle, A., ed., Geodynamique des Caraïbes: Symposium, Paris, 5–8 Fevrier 1985: Paris, Editions Technip, p. 353–362.

Stephan, J.-F., Beck, C., Bellizia, A., and Blanchet, R., 1980, Le chaîne Caraïbe du Pacifique à l'Atlantique: Bureau de Recherches Géologiques et Minieres Memoir 115, p. 38–59.

Stibane, F. R., Schmidt-Effing, R., and Madrigal, R., 1977, Zur stratigraphisch-

tektonischen Entwicklung der Halbinsel Nicoya (Costa Rica) in der Zeit von ober-Kreide bis unter-Tertiär: Giessener Geologischen Schriften, v. 12, Festschrift Richard Weyl, p. 315–358.

Théry, J. M., 1983, Découverte de spilites au sondage de los Manantiales l près de la Faille d'Oca (Basse Guajira, Colombie) implications géotectoniques régionales: Bulletin des Centres Recherches Exploration–Production, Elf-Aquataine, v. 7, p. 107–118.

Thirlwall, M. F., and Graham, A. M., 1984, Evolution of high-Ca, high-Sr C-series basalts from Grenada, Lesser Antilles: The effects of intra-crustal contamination: Geological Society of London Journal, v. 141, p. 427–445.

Tobisch, O. T., 1968, Gneissic amphibolite at Las Palmas, Puerto Rico, and its significance in the early history of the Greater Antilles island arc: Geological Society of America Bulletin, v. 79, p. 557–574.

Tournon, J., 1972, Présence de basaltes alcalins récents au Costa Rica (Amérique Centrale): Bulletin Volcanologique, v. 36, p. 140–147.

—— , 1984, Magmatismes du Mesozoïque a l'Actuel en Amérique Centrale: L'Exemple de Costa Rica, des ophiolites aux andesites [Ph.D. thesis]: Paris, Université Pierre et Marie Curie, 335 p.

Tschanz, C. M., Marvin, R. F., Cruz, B. J., Mehnert, H. H., and Cebula, G. T., 1974, Geologic evolution of the Sierra de Santa Marta, northeastern Colombia: Geological Society of America Bulletin, v. 85, p. 273–284.

Van den Berghe, B., 1983, Évolution et structurale depuis le Paleocene du secteur Massif de la Selle Haïti-'Baoruco" (Republique Dominicaine) au nord de la Ride de Beata, dans l'origene nord Caraïbe (Hispaniola–Grandes Antilles) [These, 3rd cycle]: Paris, Université Pierre et Marie Curie, 205 p.

Vespucci, P., 1980, Preliminary account of the petrology of the late Cenozoic volcanic province of Hispaniola: Transactions, Caribbean Geological Conference, 9th Santo Domingo, 1980, p. 379–389.

—— , 1983, Trace element and isotope geochemistry of the late Cenozoic volcanics of Hispaniola [abs.]: Caribbean Geological Conference, 10th, Cartagena, 1983, p. 70–71.

Vierbuchen, R. C., Jr., 1984, The geology of the El Pilar fault zone and adjacent areas in northeastern Venezuela, *in* Bonini, W. E., and others, eds., The Caribbean–South American plate boundary and regional tectonics: Geological Society of America Memoir 162, p. 189–212.

Wadge, G., 1984, Comparison of volcanic production rates and subduction rates in the Lesser Antilles and Central America: Geology, v. 12, p. 555–558.

Wadge, G., and MacDonald, R., 1985, Cretaceous tholeiites of the northern continental margin of South America: The Sans Souci Fm. of Trinidad: Geological Society of London Journal, v. 142, p. 297–308.

Wadge, G., and Wooden, J. L., 1982, Cenozoic alkaline volcanism in the northwestern Caribbean: Tectonic setting and Sr isotopic characteristics: Earth and Planetary Science Letters, v. 57, p. 35–46.

Wadge, G., Jackson, T. A., Isaacs, M. C., and Smith, T. E., 1982, The ophiolitic Bath-Dunrobin Formation, Jamaica: Significance for Cretaceous plate margin evolution in the northwestern Caribbean: Geological Society of London Journal, v. 139, p. 321–333.

Wadge, G., Draper, G., and Lewis, J. F., 1984, Ophiolites of the northern Caribbean: A reappraisal of their roles in the evolution of the Caribbean plate boundary, *in* Gass, I. G., Lippard, S. J., and Shelton, A. W., eds., Ophiolites and oceanic lithosphere: London, Geological Society of London, Blackwell, p. 367–380.

Walker, J. A., 1981, Petrogenesis of lavas from cinder cone fields behind the volcanic front of Central America: Journal of Geology, v. 89, p. 721–739.

—— , 1984, Volcanic rocks from the Nejapa and Granada cinder cone alignments, Nicaragua, Central America: Journal of Petrology, v. 25, p. 299–342.

Weidmann, J., 1978, Ammonites from the Curaçao Lava Formation, Curaçao, Caribbean: Geologie en Mijnbouw, v. 57, p. 361–364.

Wertz, W. K., 1985, The petrochemistry and genesis of late Cenozoic shoshonitic basalts, Dominican Republic, and their tectonic implications [M.S. thesis]: Gainesville, University of Florida, 196 p.

Westercamp, D., 1976, Petrology of the volcanic rocks of Martinique, West Indies: Bulletin Volcanologique, v. 39, p. 175–200.

—— , 1977, Évolution des séries volcaniques de Martinique (FWI) et des arcs insulaires des Petites Antilles dan leur contexte structurale [abs.]: Caribbean Geological Conference 8th, Curacao, 1977, p. 227–228.

——, 1979, Diversité contrôle structural et origines du volcanisme récent dans l'arc insulaire des Petites Antilles: Bulletin du Bureau de Recherches Géologiques et Minieres (2) Section IV, p. 211–226.

Westercamp, D., Andreiff, P., Bouysse, P., Mascle, A., and Baubron, J. C., 1985, The Grenadines, southern Lesser Antilles; Part 1. Stratigraphy and volcano-structural evolution, *in* Mascle, A., ed., Géodynamique des Caraïbes: Symposium, Paris, 5–8 Fevrier, 1985: Paris, Editions Technip, p. 109–118.

Weyl, R., 1961a, Die Geologie Mittelamerikas: Berlin, Gebrueder Borntraeger, 226 p.

——, 1961b, Mittelamerikanische Ignimbrite: Neues Jahrbuch für Geologie und Paläontologie Abhandlungen, v. 113, p. 23–46.

——, 1966, Geologie der Antillen: Berlin, Gebrueder Borntraeger, 410 p.

——, 1969, Magmatische förderphasen und Gesteinschemismus in Costa Rica (MIttelamerika): Neues Jahrbuch für Geologie und Paläontologie Monatshefte, no. 7, p. 423–446.

——, 1980, Geology of Central America: Berlin, Gebruder Borntraeger, 371 p.

Weyl, R., and Pichler, H., 1976, Magmatism and crustal evolution in Costa Rica, Central America: Publicaciones Geológicas ICAITI (Guatemala), v. 5, p. 56–70.

Wildberg, H., 1984, Der Nicoya-Komplex, Costa Rica, Zentralamerika: Magmatismus und Genese eines polygenetischen Ophiolith-Komplexes: Münstersche Forschungen zur Geologie und Paläontologie, v. 62, 123 p.

Wilkens, R. H., 1977, Windborne volcanic ash from DSDP Sites 84, 154A, and 158 [M.Sc. thesis]: Binghamton, New York, State University of New York at Binghamton, 87 p.

Williams, H., 1960, Volcanic history of the Guatemalan highlands: California University Publications in the Geological Sciences, v. 38, no. 1, p. 1–87.

Williams, H., McBirney, A. R., and Dengo, G., 1964, Geologic reconnaissance of southeastern Guatemala: University of California Publications in Geology, v. 50, 56 p.

Williams, H., and McBirney, A. R., 1969, Volcanic history of Honduras: University of California Publications in Geology, v. 85, 101 p.

Woodring, W. P., Brown, J. S., and Burbank, W. S., 1924, Geology of the Republic of Haiti: Baltimore, Lord Baltimore Press, 710 p.

Wortel, R. and Cloetingh, S., 1981, The origin of the Cocos-Nazca spreading center: Geology, v. 9, p. 425–430.

Yang, S.-R., 1976, Major chemical relationships in the volcanic and intrusive rocks of southeastern Guatemala abd their relationship to the tectonic model of an island arc [M.S. thesis]: Arlington, Texas, University of Texas, 62 p.

Young, K., 1972, Ammonites from Puerto Rico and the Virgin Islands: Transactions, 6th Caribbean Geological Conference, Margarita, p. 469.

ACKNOWLEDGMENTS

We are grateful to C. Schubert for the supply of copies of hard-to-find literature. F. McDowell and J. Sutter kindly provided extensive unpublished radiometric data. R. Krushensky provided a useful unpublished stratigraphic summary for Puerto Rico. Unpublished data were kindly supplied by E. Lidiak, H., Wildberg, J. Tournon, M. Lebrat, P. Vespucci, M. Perfit, G. Horne, J. Walker, J. Roobol and S. Mertzman. E. Pessagno has continued to supply highly appreciated microfossil ages. T. D. appreciates discussions with B. Mercier de Lepinay and R. Shagam on several matters. The data file CENTAM of M. Carr and W. Rose, Jr. was an especially useful source of Central American igneous data.

NOTE ADDED IN PROOF

Since the submission of this chapter in 1986, a number of interesting and pertinent papers have been published. The most significant references for understanding the tectonic history and associated magmatism of the entire Caribbean are several that pertain to the Cretaceous basaltic province.

A seismic reflection study of the Colombian Basin (Bowland and Rosencrantz, 1988) extends the plateau basalt of the Venezuelan Basin definitively into the western Caribbean. Previous to this information the basalt was largely inferred from on-land occurrences and the one drilled site (152, DSDP, Leg 15) in the northeastern Colombian Basin.

Two petrological studies (Sen and others, 1988; Berrangé and Thorpe, 1988) provide additional examples of the LIL-enriched facies of the basalt in southern Hispaniola and Costa Rica, respectively. This facies of basalt, first found on the Beata Ridge during Leg 15, is now recognized from several western localities and may represent a waning phase of the plateau basalt event.

A K-Ar study by Berrangé and others (1989) shows that the Costa Rican basaltic magmatism in one place (Osa Peninsula) occurred in three events, centered at about 44, 60, and 78 Ma. The confirmation of younger ages in Costa Rica reinforces the view that magmatism continued later in the west and renews the question as to whether it might have started later here also.

These studies add further insight into a major problem: whether the Caribbean Cretaceous basalt event is the beginning of a hot-spot trend culminating late in the Cenozoic in the Galapagos, an idea brought into focus by Richards and others (1989).

REFERENCES CITED

Berrangé, J. P., Bradley, D. R., and Snelling, N. J., 1989, K/Ar dating of the ophiolitic Nicoya Complex of the Osa Peninsula, southern Costa Rica: Journal of South American Earth Sciences, v. 2, p. 49–59.

Berrangé, J. P., and Thorpe, R. S., 1988, The geology, geochemistry, and emplacement of the Cretaceous-Tertiary ophiolitic Nicoya Complex of the Osa Peninsula, southern Costa Rica: Tectonophysics, v. 147, p. 193–220.

Bowland, C. L., and Rosencrantz, E., 1988, Upper crustal structure of the western Colombian Basin, Caribbean Sea: Geological Society of America Bulletin, v. 100, p. 534–546.

Richards, M. A., Duncan, R. A., and Courtillot, V. E., 1989, Flood basalts and hot-spot tracks; Plume heads and tails: Science, v. 246, p. 103–107.

Sen, G., Hickey-Vargas, R., Waggoner, D. G., and Maurrasse, F., 1988, Geochemistry of basalts from the Dumisseau Formation, southern Haiti; Implications for the origin of the Caribbean Sea crust: Earth and Planetary Science Letters, v. 87, p. 423–437.

The Geology of North America
Vol. H, The Caribbean Region
The Geological Society of America, 1990

Chapter 14

Volcanism

Michael J. Carr
Department of Geological Sciences, Rutgers University, New Brunswick, New Jersey 08903
Richard E. Stoiber
Department of Earth Sciences, Dartmouth College, Hanover, New Hampshire 03755

INTRODUCTION

Active volcanic belts mark the eastern and western margins of the Caribbean plate. The Lesser Antilles on the east form a classic island arc, but Central America on the west is a continental volcanic belt and not particularly arcuate. The Central American volcanic belt is slightly longer than that of the Lesser Antilles, 1,100 km versus 750 km, but Central America has 40 Neogene volcanic centers to only 12 for the Lesser Antilles. Central American volcanoes have produced 16 km³ of volcanic products since 1680, whereas the Antillean volcanoes have produced only 1 km³ in the same time period (Wadge, 1984). The contrast is between one of the most active circum-Pacific volcanic belts and one of the least active. Silicic tephra is the dominant volcanic product in the Lesser Antilles; whereas in Central America, basalts and andesites are more abundant. The southern end of the Antilles volcanic front, near Grenada, has a high proportion of alkaline volcanic rocks. The few alkaline lavas found near the volcanic front in Central America occur in Costa Rica, also near the southern end of the volcanic front. In addition to the real physical differences between the two volcanic belts, published descriptions differ because few volcanologists have worked in both areas.

The interdisciplinary nature of volcanology results in a wide range of research efforts, including detailed studies of fumarole minerals, geophysical measurements of many types, a full range of petrologic and geochemical studies, and various methods of measuring and estimating volcanic gas contents, to list but a few. Volcanic phenomena should be examined against a broad geologic and tectonic background. The adjacent chapters of this volume are all pertinent; the most important ones for understanding active volcanism are magmatism, crustal character, regional geology, seismicity, and neotectonics.

The regional geology of Central America is superbly summarized by Weyl (1980), who also provides the best introduction to the early literature and the pioneering studies of regional geology and volcanism by Howel Williams, A. R. McBirney, and their colleagues. Recent summaries of volcanic studies (Rose and

others, 1981; Carr and others, 1982; and Carr, 1984) have attempted to quantify regional variations in volcanic and geochemical parameters and relate them to variations in geologic and tectonic parameters.

The geologic and geophysical setting of West Indian volcanoes has been defined through well-planned, long-term research programs by British, West Indian, French, and United States universities and research institutions. Several excellent reviews of this work are available. Rea (1982) focused on andesitic volcanism and updated the comprehensive geologic and geophysical description of the Lesser Antilles by Tomblin (1975). The major and trace element geochemistry of the volcanic arc was summarized and interpreted by Brown and others (1977) and Smith and others (1980). A special issue of *Bulletin Volcanologique* (vol. 43, no. 2), edited by A. L. Smith, was devoted to volcanism in the Lesser Antilles. The history of Quaternary explosive volcanism was documented by Sigurdsson and Carey (1981). A comprehensive review of recent research was given in Lewis and others (1983). The review here relies primarily on these sources and on the excellent catalog of active volcanoes in the West Indies by Robson and Tomblin (1966).

VOLCANIC FRONTS AND PLATE BOUNDARIES

The Quaternary volcanic front of Central America extends for 1,100 km from the Mexico-Guatemala border to central Costa Rica and comprises 40 major volcanic centers (Fig. 1). These centers are regularly spaced along narrow discrete lineaments. The close spacing, approximately 26 km, provides one of the highest densities of active volcanic centers along any convergent plate margin.

The volcanic front stops abruptly at both ends. Beyond the northwesternmost volcano, Tacaná, the next volcano is El Chichón, 250 km to the northwest in Mexico. At the southeastern end of the front is the huge Irazú-Turrialba complex and the next volcano is Baru, 200 km farther southeast in Panamá. The vol-

Carr, M. J., and Stoiber, R. E., 1990, Volcanism, *in* Dengo, G., and Case, J. E., eds., The Caribbean region: Boulder, Colorado, Geological Society of America, The Geology of North America, v. H.

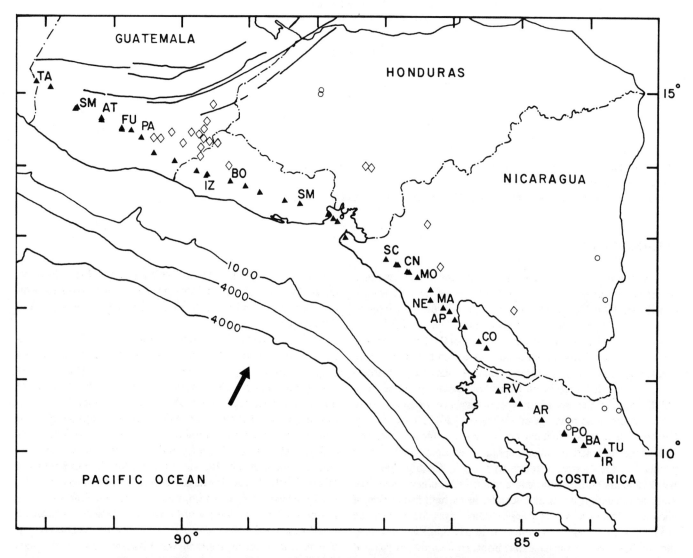

Figure 1. Location map for Central America. Arrow shows approximate direction of Cocos–Caribbean convergence. Triangles are volcanic centers of the volcanic front. Diamonds are regions of subalkaline BVF-volcanism. Circles are regions of alkaline volcanism. The solid lines in central Guatemala are faults marking the Caribbean–North America plate boundary. Middle America trench is outlined by bathymetric contours in meters. The unnamed country is El Salvador. From NW to SE the named volcanoes are: TA-Tacaná; SM-Santa María; AT-Atitlán; FU-Fuego; PA-Pacaya; IZ-Izalco; BO-Boqueron; SM-San Miguel; SC-San Cristóbal; CN-Cerro Negro; MO-Momotombo; NE-Nejapa; MA-Masaya; AP-Apoyo; CO-Conceptión; RV-Rincón de la Bieja; AR-Arenal; PO-Poás; BA-Barba; IR-Irazú; TU-Turrialba.

canic front is clearly the result of plate convergence between the Cocos and Caribbean plates along the Middle America trench (Molnar and Sykes, 1969; Dengo and others, 1970). The northwestern end of the front is near the Caribbean–North American plate boundary zone (Mann and others, this volume). The complexity of this boundary makes indentification of a specific North American–Caribbean–Cocos triple junction impossible, but from a volcanological perspective the pertinent observation is that the westernmost extension of the boundary passes approximately 30 km north of the last Central American volcano.

The southeastern end of the volcanic front, the Irazú–Turrialba complex, is located immediately onshore from where a nascent fracture zone at 85°W intersects the Middle America trench (van Andel and others, 1971). This developing fracture zone is redefining the Cocos–Nazca plate boundary which previously was located at the Panamá fracture zone at 83°W. This shift of the plate boundary appears to be a response to the resistence to subduction of the Cocos Ridge (Vogt and others, 1976), which enters the Middle America trench just between the two fracture zones. East of the Panamá fracture zone the Nazca plate converges against the Caribbean plate and active volcanism resumes in western Panamá with the volcano, Barú, which had a probable historic eruption in the middle of the sixteenth century (Simpkin and others, 1981). This is the only active volcano in Panamá and it is analogous to El Chichón in Mexico in that both are isolated explosive volcanoes separated from the highly active Central American volcanic front by plate boundaries and by volcanic gaps of a few hundred km.

The volcanic front of the Lesser Antilles is the result of underthrusting of the Americas plates beneath the eastern end of the Caribbean plate (Fig. 2). Because the pole of relative motion between the North American and South American plates is located between the Lesser Antilles and the Mid-Atlantic Ridge (Minster and Jordan, 1978) the relative motion of these two plates in the western Atlantic region is very low. As a result, the boundary between these plates and the triple junction they make with the Caribbean plate have been variously located. Stein and others (1982) found no compelling evidence for a boundary and treated the subducting plate as a single plate. For a complete discussion of this issue see Pindell and Barrett (this volume).

The active volcanic front does not extend all the way to the northern and southern margins of the zone of intermediate depth earthquakes (Tomblin, 1975). In the north the last active sub-aerial volcano is Saba. Two inactive and probably extinct submarine volcanoes extended the arc 110 km further northwest as recently as about 3 Ma (Bouysse and others, 1981). The convergent boundary was defined by Tomblin (1975) as the axis of negative gravity at the eastern base of the arc. The Barracuda Fracture Zone projects into this boundary with the correct orientation and location to coincide with the northern end of the active volcanic chain. Vogt and others (1976) have described the major effects that buoyant features have on convergent margins, and Stein and others (1982) and McCann and Sykes (1984) have described the unusual seismicity pattern resulting from the subduction of this feature. The southern end of the volcanic front is Grenada, which has unusually alkaline lavas (Arculus, 1976). Tomblin (1975) suggested that the hinge-type faulting postulated for the southeast corner of the convergence zone (Molnar and Sykes, 1969) extends as far north as the bend in the volcanic front between St. Lucia and Martinique.

DISTRIBUTION OF VOLCANOES AND VOLCANIC PRODUCTS

The subaerial volumes of active volcanoes in Central America and the Lesser Antilles were estimated from topographic maps and plotted in Figure 3. Central American volcanoes are generally larger and more closely spaced. In the Lesser Antilles, volumes are greatest near the center of the arc and progressively less toward the margins. Wadge (1984) attributed this fairly regular variation in size to changes in the angle of convergence. The plate model of Sykes and others (1982) gives essentially perpendicular convergence at the center of the Lesser Antilles and progressively more oblique convergence toward both ends. In the

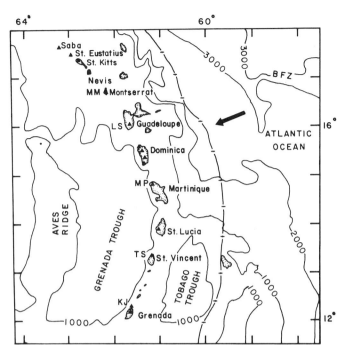

Figure 2. Location map for the Lesser Antilles. Arrow shows the approximate direction of Americas–Caribbean convergence. Triangles are active volcanoes. The line punctuated by minus signs is the negative gravity anomaly considered to be the plate boundary (Tomblin, 1975). From North to South the named volcanoes are: MM-Mt. Misery; LS-La Soufrière; MP-Mt. Pelée; TS-The Soufriere; KJ-Kick-ém-Jenny; .

Aleutians the sizes of volcanoes also decrease in conjunction with an increase in obliquity of convergence (Marsh, 1982). In Central America the angle of convergence is essentially constant along the arc, and the slight increase in rate of convergence toward the southeast does not affect the distribution of volumes (Wadge, 1984).

In Central America the young volcanoes with historic activity or slight degrees of erosion have been divided into four groups for convenience of description (Rose and others, 1981; Carr and others, 1982). Most of the large volcanic centers occur in lines that strike about N60W, parallel to the Middle America trench and coastline. Between these lines and the trench there are very few vents, most notably some maars and cinder cones near Cerro Negro in Nicaragua and some domes near Rincón de la Vieja in Costa Rica. Proceeding inland from the trench, the abrupt appearance of many closely spaced, large volcanic centers defines a distinct volcanic front. Several volcanic centers in Guatemala extend in transverse lines, striking N–S to NE. The Costa Rican volcanic center, Poás, includes seven vents in a transverse, N–S line about 15 km long. In general, the volcanic front is a 10–15-km-wide zone that has produced most of the volcanic products over the last 100,000 yr (Carr and others, 1982).

Quaternary silicic volcanism has occurred from several cal-

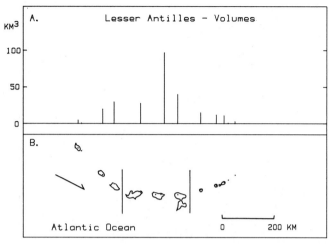

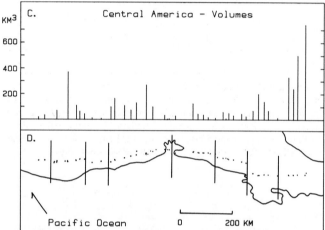

Figure 3. Distribution of volcanoes and volcanic products. Sketch maps of vents (B and D) are oriented with direction of convergence vertical. Arrows show North. The subaerial volumes of volcanic centers are represented by lines in A and C. Note the different scales.

deras along the length of the volcanic front but most of the volume has been produced in northern Central America, especially at the Atitlán caldera in Guatemala (Rose and others, 1981). The silicic centers are more widely spaced than the basaltic to dacitic centers that comprise the volcanic front; in northern Central America the calderas are north or behind the volcanic front (Rose and others, 1981). These silicic centers have produced a volume of tephra equivalent to at least 300–500 km³ of solid rock. There is considerable spatial overlap between these silicic centers and the volcanic front.

The third and fourth groups of young volcanoes occur northeastward or behind the volcanic front. Subalkaline basaltic cinder cones and shield volcanoes are abundant in southeastern Guatemala (Williams and others, 1964) and present in a few other areas (Fig. 1), including central Honduras (Williams and

McBirney, 1969). These small volcanoes, called BVF by Walker (1981), occur in areas of extensional faulting (Burkhart and Self, 1985) and are petrologically and geochemically distinct from the basalts of the volcanic front (Walker, 1981), even though they approach to within a few tens of km of the front. The fourth and smallest group is comprised of several alkaline basaltic cones that occur in the same structural-tectonic setting as the subalkaline BVF group. These small, alkaline volcanoes occur both near the volcanic front in Costa Rica and far behind it in Honduras and Nicaragua (Robin and Tournon, 1978; Pichler and Weyl, 1976).

The volcanic front of the Lesser Antilles is as well defined as that of Central America and has a similar width, about 10 km (Wadge, 1984). In contrast to Central America, there are no extensive areas of volcanism behind the volcanic front. In fact, the volcanic centers of the southern Lesser Antilles appear to have remained in nearly the same positions since the Oligocene (Rea, 1982). Seismic refraction studies by Boynton and others (1979) defined an upper crustal layer interpreted as mafic to intermediate intrusives, with some extrusives and sediments intermingled. Because this layer thickens beneath the volcanic islands and thins between them, they inferred that the volcanic centers are fairly permanent once established. Volcanic centers in Central America are not permanent on the time scale of millions of years, and tracking the past positions of the volcanic front remains an important problem (Reynolds, 1980; McBirney, 1985).

One common feature of the volcanic fronts on both ends of the Caribbean is that they comprise a few distinct lineaments (Fig. 3). The linearity of the Central American volcanic centers was described by Dollfus and Montserrat (1868) and Sapper (1897). Stoiber and Carr (1973) and Carr and Stoiber (1977) pointed out structural, geophysical, and geological features whose terminations coincided with the ends of the volcanic lines and proposed that the plate margin was divided into seven volcanic segments separated by zones of transverse faulting. Liaw and Matumoto (1980) added another segment by defining structural and seismological differences between western and central Costa Rica. Sigurdsson and Carey (1981) and Bouysse (1984) proposed three linear volcanic segments for the Lesser Antilles. The breaks between proposed segments are shown in Figure 3.

The origin of volcanic segments remains unresolved. Besides the volcanic lines, the most obvious surface features are volcano-tectonic depressions and active fault zones, which strike both parallel to the plate margin and transverse to it (Stoiber and Carr, 1973; Carr, 1976; Carr and Stoiber, 1977). Several hypotheses have been proposed to explain the Neogene fault pattern in Central America in terms of plate tectonics, usually in reference to the transform boundary in northern Central America between the Caribbean and North American plates. A major impediment in resolving this problem is the lack of firm constraints on the direction of plate convergence between the Cocos and Caribbean plates (Sykes and others, 1982). The contending hypotheses are reviewed in Mann and others (this volume).

Stoiber and Carr (1973) showed that the volcanic segments are not strictly parallel to or exactly coincident with any of the major fault zones at the surface. Instead, the volcanic lines cut across the structural grain, especially in El Salvador (Wiesemann, 1975), which has been most accurately mapped. Many vents are clearly associated with faults or dikes, but these are almost always oriented transverse to the volcanic front. Stoiber and Carr (1973) tried to explain the inconsistency of volcanic lines and major surface structures by suggesting that the subducted slab is segmented and that magma rises essentially vertically through the mantle.

There is no convincing evidence that the descending slab is segmented. Earthquakes relocated by joint hypocenter determination (JHD) provide the best control on the shape of the inclined seismic zone (Dewey and Algermissen, 1974; Carr, 1976). However, since relatively few earthquakes are large enough and widely recorded enough to provide precise JHD locations, these data sets are not sufficiently dense to define the nature of the observed changes in strike and dip of the inclined seismic zone. Carr (1976) and Carr and others (1979) showed that these most precise data sets are consistent with offsets and changes in strike and dip of the inclined seismic zone directly beneath breaks in the volcanic front. Tears in the slab are not required by these data, and most seismologists would agree with Burbach and others (1984), who infer a smooth, continuous, gently folded seismic zone.

Tomblin (1975) divided the seismic zone in the Lesser Antilles into three parts on the basis of differences in level of seismicity and in the dip and strike of the inclined seismic zone. There are few large, intermediate-depth earthquakes in the Lesser Antilles, so defining details of the zone's geometry is even more difficult than in Central America. Stein and others (1982) verified the changes in strike and dip proposed by Tomblin and interpreted the geometry of the zone as one continuous sheet with bends. Active transverse faulting appears to be occurring at intermediate depth between Dominica and Martinique; Stein and others (1982) interpreted this as reactivation of a subducted transform fault.

Major geologic transitions in the upper plate may influence the location of the volcanic segments, especially in Central America, which appears to be an assemblage of formerly disjunct terrains that have only recently been assembled (Dengo, 1969; de Boer, 1979; Gose, 1983). For example, the break between Nicaragua and Costa Rica coincides with the boundary between the Chortis and Chorotega blocks of Dengo (1985).

Oceanic transform faults that enter the trench parallel to the direction of plate convergence will have a stable position relative to the volcanic segments. Multichannel seismic reflection profiles (Crowe and Buffler, 1984) reveal such a transform fault entering the trench offshore from the proposed break separating central and western Costa Rica.

Marsh (1979) related the linearity of volcanic fronts and spacing of volcanic centers to diapiric rise of magma from a thin ribbon located along the upper surface of the inclined seismic zone. According to this model the volumes of volcanic centers should be positively correlated to their spacings in order to pre-

serve a uniform rate of magma production per length of arc. Large volcanoes should be widely separated and small volcanoes closer together. Central American data show this pattern (Carr, 1984) except that at the breaks between segments there are generally small volcanoes and several unusually wide spacings (Fig. 3). This suggests that the magma ribbon is pinched or cut at many of the breaks.

VOLCANIC ERUPTIONS AND EARTHQUAKES

In Central America, the Lesser Antilles and several other volcanic arcs (Kimura, 1976 and 1978; Carr, 1977), volcanic eruptions and great shallow earthquakes are closely associated in space and time, which suggests that changes in the regional stress field can influence volcanic activity. The temporal correlation differs in different areas, most probably because of the wide variation in the sizes, aspect ratios and orientations of the earthquake focal areas, as well as their distances from the volcanic fronts. Central American volcanoes adjacent to the focal area of a large, shallow-thrust earthquake have lower activity in the few years or decades prior to a great earthquake and markedly higher activity after the earthquake (Carr, 1977). For example, the largest historic eruption, Santa María in 1902, followed the largest recorded shallow-thrust earthquake in Central America by three months. the epicenter of this earthquake was located a few tens of km seaward of the volcano. Prolonged periods of low volcanic activity preceeded the large Central American earthquakes of 1850 and 1898 in Nicaragua, and 1902 in western Guatemala.

In the Lesser Antilles, volcanic activity and large, shallow earthquakes appear to be associated only in Guadeloupe. This region experienced destructive earthquakes in 1690, 1843, and 1897 and is now considered a gap of high seismic potential (McCann and Sykes, 1984; Dorel, 1981). Most of the volcanic activity on Guadeloupe occurred in association with these earthquakes. The 1843 earthquake was preceeded by a 50 year period of intermittent volcanic activity. All other eruptions, except those of the last few years, occurred within 10 years of a major earthquake. In other areas of the Lesser Antilles there is no relation between seismic and volcanic activity. The current volcanic activity in Guadeloupe may be a preseismic phenomenon.

In Central America, intermediate-depth earthquakes and volcanic eruptions have tended to cluster (Carr, 1983). The highest levels of intermediate-depth seismicity during 1963 to 1980 occurred adjacent to the volcanoes Santiaguito–Santa María, Fuego, and Pacaya, all of which were very active during that time. Clusters or nests of intermediate-depth earthquakes also occurred adjacent to Izalco and San Miguel in El Salvador and Masaya and Concepción in Nicaragua.

Swarms of small earthquakes occur at shallow depths beneath active volcanoes in both the Lesser Antilles and Central America. In addition, many destructive earthquakes occur along the volcanic belt of Central America, occasionally in conjunction with volcanic activity, but usually not (Carr and Stoiber, 1977). McNutt and Harlow (1983) clarified the high level of seismicity along the volcanic belt by summarizing microearthquake data collected by Central American seismic networks.

The historic record includes several examples of swarms of felt earthquakes preceeding eruptions. The most complete pre-instrumental record described the 1879–1880 eruption of Islas Quemadas in El Salvador in such detail that Golombek and Carr (1978) were able to show that the earthquake swarm was affected by the semidiurnal tide. Modern seismic networks are providing much new information about swarms of volcanic microearthquakes, which are far more common than the historic record indicates (Yuan and others, 1984). Small earthquakes, some as deep as 15 km, preceeded and accompanied eruptions of Fuego volcano during 1975–1977 (Yuan and others, 1984). A prolonged and unusually intense volcano-seismic crisis preceeded the recent eruption of Soufrière de Guadeloupe (Dorel and Feuillard, 1980). In contrast, the shallow seismicity prior to the recent eruptions of Soufriere, St. Vincent, was not intense and a station within two km of the vent was needed to record the premonitory earthquakes (Shepherd and Aspinall, 1982).

Volcanoes in the Lesser Antilles have long been known to suffer volcano-seismic crises that consist of swarms of subvolcanic earthquakes that are not followed by eruptions (e.g., Shepherd and Aspinall, 1982; Shepherd and others, 1971; Robson and others, 1962). This type of activity, which naturally leads to false expectations of eruptions, has begun to be observed in Central America as the quality of seismic networks has improved. Published reports include swarms at Momotombo in 1975 (Aburto, 1975), at Fuego in 1977 (Yuan and others, 1984), and at Irazú in 1982 (Güendel, 1985).

REGIONAL VARIATIONS IN PETROLOGY AND GEOLOGY

Valuable insights into the origin of volcanoes at convergent plate margins can be gained by comparison of volcanoes from different geologic environments. Because of the width of the volcanic belt, the large number of volcanoes, and the varied nature of the crust (Weyl, 1980), Central America is particularly well suited for this type of investigation.

Behind the Volcanic Front

The presence of several volcanic fields and isolated cones behind the Central American volcanic front has led to studies of the regional variation in alkali contents, and especially K_2O contents, of lavas. Pichler and Weyl (1973) emphasized the increasing alkalinity of young volcanic rocks with increasing distance inland from the volcanic front, in agreement with observations in many other convergent plate margins. Robin and Tournon (1978) summarized new information on alkaline volcanism in southern Central America, including Pliocene and Quaternary alkaline rocks erupted very close to the volcanic front in central Costa Rica. Because of their wide distribution across the western

end of the Caribbean plate, the Quaternary alkaline rocks have no simple tectonic setting (Robin and Tournon, 1978). Carr and others (1979) tested the hypothesis that K_2O contents are related to depth in the seismic zone and found that in Central America, at least, there is no statistically significant correlation. Wadge and Wooden (1982) measured Sr isotopes from alkaline volcanic centers across the northwestern Caribbean plate and found that the Costa Rican alkaline rocks had higher ratios (0.7036–0.7038) than the alkaline rocks in Nicaragua and Honduras (0.7026–0.7031). The high ratios in Costa Rica come from alkaline rocks that are found near the volcanic front and may have been influenced by a contribution of radiogenic Sr from the subducted slab (Wadge and Wooden, 1982).

Clusters of cinder cones, small shield volcanoes, and lava fields, located NE of or behind the volcanic front, are associated with extensional areas with abundant normal faults (Walker, 1981). Similar volcanic fields occur in other arcs, such as Mexico, the Cascades, Kamchatka, Chile, and New Zealand, so it is not the special result of faulting related to the complex triple junction in northern Central America, but instead is a typical component of arc volcanism, although a poorly described and often ignored one. Walker (1981) cited petrographic and geochemical characteristics of behind-the-front (BVF) lavas that distinguish this group from basalts erupted along the volcanic front. They have a simple mineralogy, being nearly aphyric with a few phenocrysts of olivine and plagioclase and no clinopyroxene or magnetite. They have considerably higher Ni and Cr contents than the basalts of the adjacent volcanic front. In contrast to observed petrography, geochemical variations require the removal of clinopyroxene as well as olivine and plagioclase. To resolve this contradiction, Walker (1981) proposed cotectic crystallization of clinopyroxene, olivine, and plagioclase at moderate pressure (5–10 kb) in the lower crust, followed by rapid ascent in an extensional environment. During eruption, just olivine and plagioclase crystalline because of the expansion of the primary phase volumes of olivine and plagioclase relative to clinopyroxene at low pressure. Walker concluded that there was no evidence for the addition of magma or hydrous flux escaping from the descending plate in the petrology and geochemistry of BVF lavas in Guatemala and Honduras.

Along the Volcanic Front in Central America

Several gradual variations in geochemical and volcanological parameters occur along the length of the Central American volcanic front. McBirney (1969) pointed out that rocks from different areas of the volcanic front plotted in bimodal or trimodal clusters. With distance southeastward from Guatemala the andesitic rocks become steadily more basic, and the felsic rocks become steadily less siliceous and more iron-rich. Carr and others (1982) showed that Na_2O contents of mafic lavas steadily decreased from Guatemala to Nicaragua. Kussmaul and others (1982) found that FeO_{tot}/MgO ratios increase in Costa Rican andesites from NW to SE and attributed this variation to increasing crustal thickness.

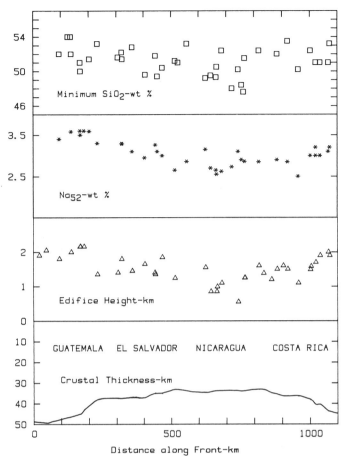

Figure 4. Regional variation in crustal thickness, edifice height, Na$_2$O content at 52% SiO$_2$, and silica content of most mafic lava. The cross section at the base is along the line of the volcanic front shown in Figure 1.

The regular variation in heights of Central American volcanoes is shown in Figure 4. McBirney (1969) suggested that this was caused by variations in depths of origin of magmas, and that heights were controlled by hydrostatic balance between the magma column and the solid rocks through which it rises. Rose and others (1977) also cited hydrostatic balance but suggested that the regional variation was in density of the primary magmas, rather than in depth of origin, and that smaller volcano heights were the result of more dense primary magmas. Carr (1984) proposed a hydrostatic model in which both height of volcano and density of the most mafic lavas extruded were related to depth of origin. The base of the crust was proposed as the depth of origin for most Central American volcanoes.

The regional variations along the volcanic front of Central America are summarized in Figure 4. Crustal thickness is estimated from regional elevation. The crust is thinnest in Nicaragua and thickens toward both Costa Rica and Guatemala. The other

parameters that vary smoothly along the volcanic front parallel this trend.

In addition to the regional variations shown in Figure 4, there are subtle variations in major elements. Most mafic Central American lavas have phenocrysts of magnetite, olivine, plagioclase, and augite; mass balance calculations demonstrate that observed major and trace element variations can be explained by fractional crystallization of these minerals (Carr and others, 1982). In pseudo-ternary phase diagrams, made by projecting from early crystallizing minerals onto planes within the system CMAS, suites of related lavas define narrow arrays that extend parallel to experimentally determined cotectics. Therefore, many Central American basalt and basaltic andesite lavas appear to be samples of magma evolving along multisaturated cotectics (Carr, 1984).

The projections used by Carr (1984) are isostructural diagrams. Elthon (1983) showed that these diagrams are very sensitive to small variations in alkalis and recommended the use of isomolar diagrams. Because there is a regional variation in Na$_2$O contents in Central America, Elthon's version of CMAS conversion is used in Figure 5. This figure includes all the data used by Carr (1984) and much new data from Costa Rican volcanoes. Cumulates and lavas lacking clinopyroxene, plagioclase, or a calcium-poor mafic mineral (olivine or orthopyroxene) were excluded. Analyses with greater than 60 wt.% SiO$_2$ were excluded.

Walker (1984) found unusual mafic tholeiitic basalts in central Nicaragua and separated them from other basalts by their high MgO and CaO and low Al$_2$O$_3$ contents. In central Nicaragua, four volcanic areas—Masaya, Granada, and parts of Nejapa and Apoyo—have these tholeiitic characteristics (Ui, 1972; Walker, 1984; Sussman, 1985). Masaya, the largest volcano in this area, has an active lava lake that for several periods of approximately 5–10 yr has degassed at a high rate, but from which no lava issued (McBirney, 1956). It currently emits a large plume with a flux of 1,000–3,000 tons of SO$_2$ gas per day (Williams, 1983) and appears to have a near-surface magma chamber. Other Central American volcanoes with tholeiitic affinities include Boqueron in El Salvador (Fairbrothers and others, 1978) and several volcanoes in central Costa Rica (Carr, unpublished). Except for Masaya, the volcanoes with some tholeiitic affinities comprise two or more batches of lavas, with at least one tholeiitic and one calc-alkaline batch. The lava suites with tholeiitic affinities are distinguished in Figure 5 by open boxes. In Nicaragua these suites plot near the 1 atm cotectics determined at 1 atmosphere, but show slight reductions of both the olivine field (Fig. 5a) and the plagioclase field (Fig. 5b). In Costa Rica the lavas with tholeiitic affinities are further displaced from the 1 atm cotectics. The data in Figure 5 suggest that the suites with tholeiitic affinities are produced by fractional crystallization in shallow, intracrustal magma chambers.

The calc-alkaline suites show progressive shrinkages of the olivine (Fig. 5a) and plagioclase (Fig. 5b) fields from Nicaragua northwestward to El Salvador and Guatemala and southeastward to Costa Rica. The extent of shrinkage of these primary phase

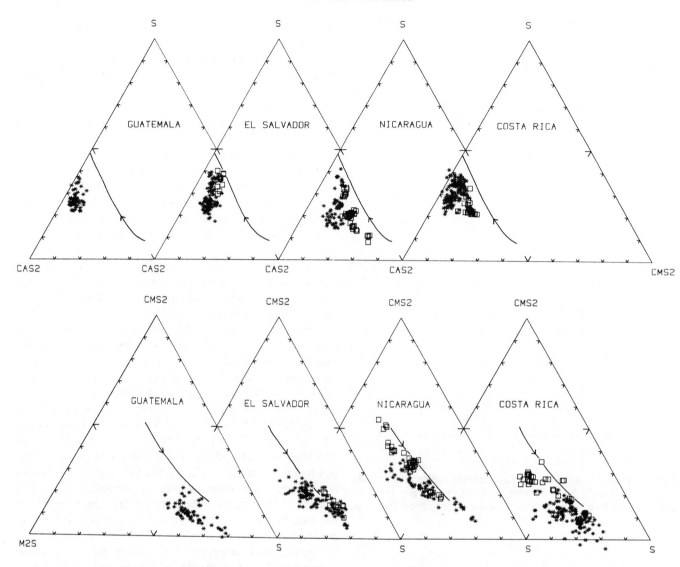

Figure 5. Bottom: Plagioclase (CAS2) projection onto diopside–olivine–quartz (CMS2-M2S-S). The line is the 1 atm pseudo-ternary cotectic determined from the data of Walker and others (1979) and Baker and Eggler (1983). Asterisks are calc-alkaline samples. Boxes are samples with tholeiitic affinities. Samples with SiO$_2$ >60 not plotted. Top: Olivine (M2S) projection onto diopside–plagioclase–quartz (CMS2-CAS2-Q). Symbols as in bottom.

volumes correlates with crustal thickness. The shifts away from the 1 atm cotectics are largest for the most mafic lavas. The more evolved lavas more closely approach the 1 atm cotectics, which suggests that their magmas fractionated at lower pressures during their rise (Baker and Eggler, 1983). It is not clear whether this polybaric fractionation occurs over a continuous depth range or in a few discrete upper-crustal magma chambers.

The regional variation along the volcanic front of Central America consists of several independent parameters: crustal thickness, edifice height, silica content of most mafic lava, and the pressure-sensitive primary phase volumes of olivine and plagioclase. The most probable mechanism for linking these parameters

is magma ponding by crustal layers. Because there is a sharp density gradient at the base of the crust between gabbro (3.0 gm/cc) and peridotite (3.3 gm/cc), this is a likely site for magma ponding. However, there is no detailed information about crustal thickness and crustal layering along the volcanic front; an intracrustal density gradient, such as between a lower gabbroic layer and an upper dioritic layer, could also trap magma. Martin and Rose (1981) have proposed an intracrustal magma chamber for Fuego volcano at about 15 km depth, and earthquakes accompanying recent eruptions of Fuego begin at about this depth (Yuan and others, 1984). Magma chambers at the Moho, within the crust and at very shallow depths, are all supported by Central

American data; some volcanoes may have magma chambers at more than one level.

Along the Volcanic Front of the Lesser Antilles

The primary regional petrologic variation observed in the Lesser Antilles is the alkaline character of some recent and older volcanic rocks in Grenada and the southern Grenadines (Brown and others, 1977; Smith and others, 1980). The alkalic rocks in this area are not isotopically uniform and have trace element abundances that require garnet and clinopyroxene in a residue from mantle melting (Arculus, 1976; Hoffman and Feigenson, 1983). The scattered cones and explosion craters of Grenada were probably produced by several separate melting episodes from a relatively fertile mantle source (Rea, 1982).

Smith and others (1980) reviewed the evidence for other regional variations and concluded that there were not differences that could be specifically related to position along the arc. K_2O does show a general decrease from north to south, and this will be discussed below.

There is much evidence that fractionation within the crust is an important process (Brown and others, 1977). Cognate cumulates are common, and Lewis (1973) showed that anorthite-bearing cumulates were the result of fractional crystallization occuring during the derivation of andesite from basalt. Powell (1978) suggested that the pressure of formation of cumulates decreased from north (9 kb) to south (3 kb), but that most were formed in the 5 to 9 kb range, or about 20 to 30 km depth. Arculus and Wills (1980) concluded that the pressure was in the 4 to 10 kb range and that there was no systematic regional variation. Dostal and others (1983) found evidence for complex multistage fractionation processes at Soufrière, St. Vincent.

Migration of Volcanic Fronts During the Tertiary

The volcanic islands of the Lesser Antilles south of Dominica consist of Quaternary and Pliocene volcanics overlying a basement of Miocene and in some cases Oligocene and possibly Eocene volcanic rocks. At Dominica and to the north, only Quaternary and Pliocene volcanics occur, and no pre-Pliocene basement is exposed. (Maury and others, this volume). In the northern islands the volcanic belt shifted westward sometime in late Miocene, but otherwise, volcanic centers in the Lesser Antilles have been relatively constant, both in location and overall geochemical characteristics (Rea, 1982).

Geochronological and stratigraphic studies have begun to clarify the Tertiary magmatic history of Central America. K-Ar dating has revealed pulses of magmatism spaced at about 5 m.y. intervals (McBirney and others, 1974). Two clear pulses occurred at 0–1 Ma (Quaternary) and 3–6 Ma (Pliocene). During 9–19 Ma, intense magmatic activity caused widespread and voluminous volcanic deposits, especially around 14 Ma (middle Miocene) and with smaller peaks at 9 Ma and 17–18 Ma (McBirney and others, 1974). Existing data do not show anything systematic about earlier periods.

Lithostratigraphic variations, correlated throughout northern Central America (Wiesemann, 1975; Reynolds, 1980), define four formations from middle Miocene to the present. The earlier rocks have not been adequately subdivided. The four formations are: Chalatenango, silicic, welded to unwelded tuffs and flows (middle to upper Miocene); Bálsamo, andesitic lavas (upper Miocene to Pliocene); Cuscatlán, a bimodal basalt–rhyolite suite (late Pliocene); and finally, the Quaternary volcanic rocks.

Since middle Miocene the main locus of volcanic activity has moved toward the Pacific coast, and the character of the extrusives has changed from dominantly silicic tuffs to andesitic flows to basaltic flows (Reynolds, 1980). From at least late Pliocene to the present, a secondary type of volcanism, composed of bimodal basalt–rhyolite suites, has persisted behind the volcanic front. The extensive flows and tuffs of the middle Miocene Chalatenango Formation occur inland of the present volcanic front and along the central and northern parts of the Tertiary volcanic belt. These extensive, predominantly silicic deposits represent a substantially more productive, broader, and longer-lasting volcanic front than has existed since. The next clearly defined pulse of volcanic activity occurred closer to the Pacific Coast along the southern part of the Tertiary volcanic belt and produced the andesitic lavas of the Pliocene Bálsamo formation. This volcanic front is similar to the current one in composition, breadth, and production rate of extrusives. The present volcanic front is coincident with or slightly closer to the Pacific coast than the Balsamo front, and geochemical data on Balsamo rocks are too few to determine if the present front is less silicic than the Balsamo andesites. The apparent shift of the volcanic fronts toward the Pacific is relatively small in Guatemala, slightly larger in El Salvador, and large in Nicaragua (McBirney, 1985). The Tertiary volcanic history of Costa Rica appears to be completely different than that of northern Central America.

VOLCANO SIZE AND INCOMPATIBLE ELEMENTS

Comparison of incompatible-element contents between volcanoes is complicated by the increase in incompatibles with crystal fractionation and the different rates of increase possible if the proportions of fractionating minerals are different (Rose and others, 1980). For calc-alkalic lavas, SiO_2 is a reasonable indicator of fractionation. In the subsequent discussion, all references to incompatible-element contents are in the context of values normalized to 52% SiO_2.

In the Central American volcanic front, incompatible elements are related to the size of a volcano; the larger the size, the greater the incompatible-element content. A positive correlation between normalized incompatible-element contents and $\log_{10}$ volume of volcano was observed in El Salvador (Carr and others, 1981). A similar correlation exists in Guatemala (Grant and others, 1984), Nicaragua (Carr, 1984) and Costa Rica (Fig. 6). Some large volcanic centers comprise two or more volcanoes that have different incompatible-element contents. At Barba, a large volcano in Costa Rica, batches of lava with distinctively different

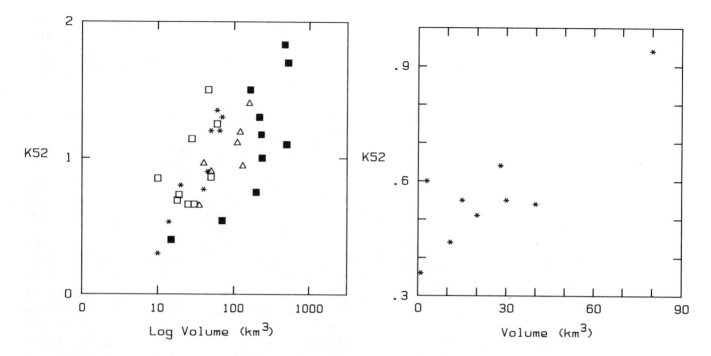

Figure 6. K$_2$O contents, normalized to 52% silica, versus log volume of Central American volcanoes. Symbols refer to different countries: Guatemala-asterisks, El Salvador—triangles, Nicaragua—open boxes, Costa Rica—filled boxes.

Figure 7. K$_2$O contents, normalized to 52% SiO$_2$, versus volume of Antillean volcanoes.

incompatible-element contents erupted from the same vent. Therefore, the geochemical complexity of volcanic centers increases with size. Small volcanoes have less variability as well as overall lower incompatible-element contents.

Volcanoes in the northern part of the Lesser Antilles have lower incompatible-element contents than those in the central part of the arc (Brown and others, 1977). A transition from island-arc tholeiite in the north to calc-alkaline toward the south was proposed (Brown and others, 1977). Smith and others (1980) showed that there was no strong trend in iron-enrichment in the northern volcanoes and that all Antillean volcanoes, except for the alkaline volcanoes at the south end of the arc, could be properly considered as having calc-alkaline fractionation trends. Gunn and others (1980) further showed that the Pliocene to recent volcanoes on Guadeloupe had a range of K$_2$O–SiO$_2$ trends that spanned the entire range found in the arc. The regional variation in incompatible elements proposed by Brown and others (1977) corresponds with the regional variation in size of the young volcanoes (Fig. 3). The K$_2$O contents of active Antillean volcanoes show a positive correlation with size of volcano, if the alkaline volcanism around Grenada is excluded (Fig. 7).

Whether small volcanoes evolve into large, incompatible-element–rich volcanoes is not known. There are no ideal stratigraphic sections that reveal the entire history of a volcano. In Central America most exposed stratigraphic sections reveal the

upper third or less of a volcano's history. Because much of the variation in incompatible elements takes place among small volcanoes, the innermost part of a large volcano may be the most critical for demonstrating changes during growth. The available evidence from stratigraphic sampling does not demonstrate incompatible-element enrichment during growth. At Izalco volcano there has been a progressive increase in incompatible-element contents during its 200-yr lifetime (Carr and Pontier, 1981). However, Izalco is a parasitic cone on Santa Ana volcano, and the most recent lavas from Santa Ana have higher incompatible-element contents than Izalco, so there has clearly been no increase if the whole volcanic center is considered. A traverse up the caldera wall at Santa María volcano in Guatemala (Rose and others, 1977) showed that SiO$_2$ increased with time, but incompatible elements, normalized to SiO$_2$, did not. The stratigraphic changes in lava compositions at Tolimán volcano (Rose and others, 1980b) show a slight decrease in incompatible elements with time. A stratigraphic sequence exposed on the ridge between Fuego and Acatenango volcanoes (Chesner and Rose, 1984) includes several magma batches identifiable by their Sr contents, and essentially constant in their normalized incompatible-element contents. In the crater of Boqueron volcano (Fairbrothers and others, 1978), the fractionation style of lavas changed from calc-alkaline to tholeiitic about half way up the crater wall, but there was no change in normalized incompatible elements. A tephra section that spans a brief interval at the beginning of volcanic activity at Nejapa (Walker, 1984) shows evidence of magma mixing but not incompatible-element enrichment.

The stratigraphic studies cited above, and work in preparation on Cerro Negro and Rincon de la Vieja volcanoes, provide no evidence for the progressive development of open-system magma chambers, a hypothesis called upon by Carr (1984) to explain the peculiar positive correlation between size of volcano and incompatible elements.

In the open-system model of O'Hara (1977), an incompatible element should increase, relative to major elements, with increasing cycles of magma replenishment until a steady state is reached. The steady-state level will be higher, the more incompatible an element is. Na_2O is less incompatible than K_2O, and the variation of Na_{52} values with K_{52} values (Fig. 8) is as the open-system model predicts. Na_{52} increases with K_{52} in small volcanoes and then reaches a plateau or possible steady-state level, which is lowest in Nicaragua, intermediate in El Salvador and Costa Rica, and highest in Guatemala. The regional variation in the apparent steady-state level, lowest in Nicaragua and highest in Guatemala, is consistent with increasing depth to a magma chamber, as pressure will shrink the plagioclase field and reduce the amount of plagioclase fractionation. This will lower the bulk partition coefficient for Na and thereby increase the steady-state level of Na.

EXPLOSIVE VOLCANISM

The intraoceanic setting of the Lesser Antilles results in contrasting volcanogenic sedimentation in the sedimentary basins to east and west of the arc and a high degree of preservation of volcanic history in the sedimentary record. This volcanic history was elucidated through tephrochronology by Sigurdsson and Carey (1981) and Wright and others (1984). The most productive volcanoes abut the Grenada Basin and produce about one third of the recent sediment in the basin. This high rate is caused by the influx of pyroclastic flows and ash turbidites directly into the basin (Sparks and others, 1980). The largest measured pyroclastic debris flow is the Roseau flow, which originated at Dominica and traveled 700 km south through the Grenada Basin. This submarine ignimbrite has a volume of about 30 km^3 and was erupted about 30,000 B.P. (Sigurdsson and Carey, 1981). On the Atlantic side of the arc, the percent of volcanogenic sedimentation is much less, and the volcanic deposits occur over a much wider area. These sediments are predominantly ash-fall, which was negligible in the Grenada Basin to the west. This pronounced asymmetry in ash-fall distribution is the result of the prevailing high-altitude westerly winds.

The ash-fall and ash-flow deposits have similar volumes, and together they have about four times the volume of the subaerial volcanic deposits. Lavas and dome rocks are a large proportion of the subaerial deposits and are generally more mafic. Consideration of the large volumes of submarine deposits demonstrates the

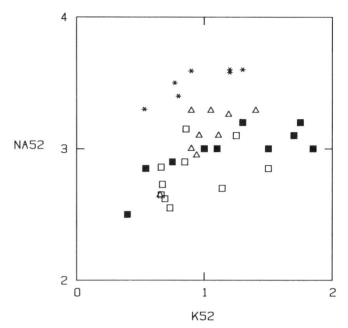

Figure 8. Na_{52} contents versus K_{52} contents for Central American volcanoes. Symbols refer to different countries (as in Figure 6).

overall silicic character of the Lesser Antilles volcanism (Brown and others, 1977; Sigurdsson and Carey, 1981).

Explosive andesitic to basaltic volcanism is typified by the recent eruptions of Mt. Pelée and Soufriere, St. Vincent (Roobol and Smith, 1975 and 1980). Less explosive Peléan eruptions generate nuées ardentes that leave a pyroclastic deposit composed of relatively dense basaltic andesite to andesite clasts in a poorly vesicular ash matrix. The more explosive Plinian eruptions generate air-falls and ash-flows that leave a pyroclastic deposit composed of vesicular andesitic pumice and ash. The pumiceous deposits can be further divided into air-fall lapilli, airfall-ash, crystal-pumice-surge, ash-pumice flow, and ash hurricane types. At several volcanoes the two types of deposits alternate regularly, and the Peléan-type deposits appear to grade upward into Plinian deposits (Roobol and Smith, 1980). Historically, only the less explosive nuée ardente type of eruption has occurred.

A regional synthesis of the tephra stratigraphy of Central America has not been completed, but much progress has been made in marine tephrochronology (Ledbetter, 1985) and in field studies in Guatemala and Nicaragua. Ledbetter used more than 300 piston cores from the oceans surrounding Central America to define eight tephra horizons that were produced by Central American eruptions over the last 300,000 yrs. One of these (Worzel D, 84,000 yr. B.P.) was firmly correlated to the Los Chocoyos ash, erupted from the Atitlán caldera. A second (I_2, 270,000 yr. B.P.) was tentatively correlated with the largest Plinian deposit produced by the Amatitlán caldera (Wunderman and Rose, 1984).

In Guatemala the stratigraphy of fall and flow deposits was defined by Koch and McLean (1975) on the basis of physical and petrographic characteristics. The most extensive unit is the H-tephra, which is the Plinian member of the Los Chocoyos ash. Hahn and others (1979) correlated this unit with the Worzel layer D in the Pacific. Drexler and others (1980) found that it also correlated with layer Y8 in the Gulf of Mexico. Rose and others (1981) made the first comprehensive stratigraphic correlation across Guatemala and western El Salvador. This stratigraphy was further updated by Wunderman and Rose (1984) during geological and geochemical investigation of the Amatitlán caldera adjacent to Pacaya volcano in Guatemala.

Bice (1985) has defined the tephra stratigraphy in the Managua, Nicaragua area. At the base of the stratigraphy is the thickest, most extensive deposit, the poorly understood Las Sierras group of lahars, ignimbrites, and air-fall tephras. The source and age of these volcanic rocks is not known. Above this unit there are seven principal air-fall tephra units, erupted during the last 36,000 years from four different source vents, all within 35 km of Managua. The most extensive of these are dacitic air-falls and ignimbrites erupted from the Apoyo caldera at about 23,000 yr. B.P. (Sussman, 1985). The most unusual are Plinian deposits of basaltic composition, erupted during the formation of the Masaya caldera (Williams, 1983).

MEASUREMENTS OF VOLCANIC GAS IN CENTRAL AMERICA

The high level of recent activity at Central American volcanoes has provided opportunities for a wide variety of volcanic gas studies. Direct quantitative measurements of gas flux are infrequently made, and only recently have sequences of repeated measurements been carried out. Most measurements are of SO_2 gas, a few are of other gasses. The primary analytical tool is a remote-sensing correlation spectrometer (Stoiber and Jepsen, 1973). The most notable results from this instrument are the documented increase in SO_2 flux preceeding and following the minor eruption of San Cristóbal in 1976 (Rose and others, 1982) and the high rate of gas emission from Masaya from Fall 1979 to the present (Stoiber and others, 1986). Masaya's activity is similar to previous gas crises that have occurred about every quarter century (McBirney, 1956). Measurements of SO_2 flux during active degassing have been reported for nine volcanoes: Santiaguito, Fuego, Pacaya, San Cristóbal, Telica, Momotombo, Masaya, Arenal, and Poás. SO_2 production varies from 20 metric tons per day at Santiaguito to more than 3,000 metric tons per day for some days at Masaya. Other estimates of the contents and flux of volcanic plumes were obtained by direct sampling using specially prepared aircraft (Cadle and others, 1979; Rose and others, 1980a).

Most SO_2 flux from volcanoes occurs during large eruptions, when direct measurement is unsafe. Several important indirect measurements have been developed. Microprobe analyses of glasses enclosed in phenocrysts showed that the pre-eruptive S

and Cl contents of the basaltic magma erupted at Fuego volcano in 1974 were 2,800 ppm. S and 800 ppm. Cl (Rose and others, 1978; Rose and others, 1982). Quantitative mapping of ash deposits, coupled with measurement of the soluble material adsorbed onto ash particles during transport in the eruption column, allow minimum estimates of the S and Cl flux during explosive eruptions (Taylor and Stoiber, 1973; Rose and others, 1973). The efficiency of ash particles in scavenging S and Cl from eruption clouds was directly measured by flying aircraft through some small eruption clouds (Lazrus and others, 1979) and found to be low—less than 7% for S, and 10% to 20% for Cl. A combination of indirect and direct measurements allowed Rose and others (1982) to determine a S and Cl budget for Fuego volcano during 1974–1977. They estimated that the 1974 eruption represented only about one sixth of the magma that was degassed during that period of activity.

It is important to measure the ratios of SO_2 concentration to the concentrations of other gasses because the SO_2 flux can be determined, and the fluxes of other gasses can be estimated from these ratios. By using filters to collect SO_2, HCl, and HF (Lazrus and others, 1979), and gold foil to collect Hg, the flux of these gases has been estimated at Fuego, Masaya, and Telica volcanoes.

During noneruptive periods, extensive sequences of fumarole temperature measurements have been made in conjunction with collections of fumarolic gas condensates and mineral sublimates. Stoiber and Rose (1970) summarized the data on gas condensates and showed that the S/Cl ratio varies directly with the intensity of volcanic activity. The mineral sublimates found around high-temperature fumaroles occur in a concentric zoning pattern that reflects the strong gradients in temperature and fO_2 at the mouths of fumaroles (Stoiber and Rose, 1974).

STUDIES OF VOLCANIC ERUPTIONS

Most of the recorded history of Central American volcanic activity can be found in three sources. The period from the Conquest (AD 1525) to 1965, is reported in the *Catalog of Active Volcanoes of the World,* Part VI (Mooser and others, 1958) and its update by Bohnenberger and others (1966). Recent activity was summarized by Weyl (1980). The third source is the continuing program by the Smithsonian Institution (SEAN—Scientific Event Alert Network). SEAN reports have been issued monthly since 1975. For the period 1975–1983 there have been 177 reports on activity of Central American volcanoes. The initial publication of this data file (Simkin and others, 1981) provides the best brief summary of Central American and Antillean volcanic activity.

The activity of Central American volcanoes since 1960 has been greater than the historic average. Beginning around 1960, marked changes occurred that cannot be ascribed to improved data gathering. In 1961, Pacaya resumed activity after over a century of dormancy. In 1966, Izalco ceased erupting after over a century of nearly continuous eruption. In 1968, Arenal erupted for the first time in more than 400 years, and in 1971, San Cristóbal erupted after a 286-yr period of dormancy.

The historic activity of volcanoes in the Lesser Antilles was reported by Robson and Tomblin (1966) and updated by Rea (1982). The prehistoric activity was summarized by Sigurdsson and Carey (1981). Three localities have been active since 1966. Eruptions occurred at Guadeloupe in 1976–1977 (Dorel and Feuillard, 1980; Tazieff, 1977); at St. Vincent in 1971–1972 (Tomblin and others, 1972) and in 1979 (Shepherd and others, 1979); and at Kick-'em-Jenny in 1972, 1974, and 1977 (Sigurdsson and Sparks, 1979). A supposed eruption, the Hodder event of 1902, was discredited (Bouysse and Sigurdsson, 1982).

Direct measurement of active volcanic processes depends on accessibility, hazard, and the tools at hand. Funding has a time constant far too long to allow rapid response, and local scientific groups are often without adequate funds and equipment. As a result, the volcanic activity in Central America and the Lesser Antilles during the last two decades has been inconsistently covered. Nevertheless, some eruptions have been examined in detail, and some novel approaches have been initiated. The following summary describes on a volcano-by-volcano basis several timely studies not included in the topics previously discussed.

Santiaguito. A compound dacite dome has been growing in the crater of the 1902 eruption of Santa María since 1922. Periods of pyroclastic activity and dome extrusion alternate with periods of lava extrusion. Lavas occur when the pyroclastic vent is plugged, allowing volatiles that formerly escaped to remain in the magma and make it fluid enough for lava flows (Rose, 1973a). Nuées ardentes have been observed erupting from the pyroclastic vent, the dome, and the foot of a lava flow (Rose, 1972 and 1973b; Rose and others, 1976). The 1902 eruption of Santa María produced a white silicic tephra, a black basaltic andesitic tephra, and various mixtures of the two end members (Williams and Self, 1983).

Fuego. Strong eruptions are common at Fuego. Major ones in 1971 and 1974 produced ash blankets with volumes estimated at 0.06 km³ and 0.20 km³, respectively. Nuées ardentes occurred in 1974 (Davies and others, 1978). Using the careful study of the 1974 eruption (Rose and others, 1978) as a starting point, Martin and Rose (1981) and Chesner and Rose (1984) have incorporated data on historic eruptions, geochemistry, petrology, and mineralogy into a model of the magmatic system feeding Fuego. Anderson (1984) correlated Ca–Na zoning patterns between plagioclase phenocrysts erupted in 1974. Because regions of supersaturation occur at about zones 25 and 50, Anderson proposed that the fine zones represented the semidiurnal tide, and the pattern of zones represented the fortnightly tide.

Pacaya. In 1961 a lava flow issued from the south flank, the first eruption since 1846 and possibly the first since 1775. In 1962 a collapse crater formed on the side of the main cone. This crater was filled by the growth of the Mackenny cone during 1965 to the present. Strombolian activity was common during this period, and lava flows were frequent from both the crater and the flanks. Eggers and Chavez (1979) and Eggers (1983) periodi-

cally reoccupied a network of gravity stations on the active cone and found temporal changes on the order of 1 milligal. The changes were attributed to vertical movements or changes in density of a shallow magma body undergoing vesiculation and degassing.

Izalco. In January 1959, after more or less continuous activity for 189 yr, Izalco paused. In October–November 1966 a small lava flow extruded from the flank (0.001 km³; Rose and Stoiber, 1969). Since 1966, fumaroles in the summit crater have cooled (Stoiber and others, 1975) and there has been no activity. New minerals have been described from the fumaroles, mostly unique occurrences of copper vanadates and a vanadium bronze (Birnie and Hughes, 1979; Hughes and Birnie, 1980; Hughes and Stoiber, 1985).

Arenal. A violent eruption occurred in July 1968, producing block and ash-flows and a directed blast (Melson and Sáenz, 1973). The last previous eruption was radiocarbon dated at AD 1530 ±20. Tephra stratigraphy indicates that the 1968 eruption was similar in style, but possibly smaller than a series of eight prehistoric eruptions (Melson, 1985). The major explosions of 1968 were followed by continuous lava effusion, producing a compound lava field of over 40 flows (Malavassi and Barquero, 1980). A much less explosive series of block and ash flows occurred in 1975. The growth of the lava field, detailed by Wadge (1983), indicates that the effusion rate decreased from 2–3 m³/sec in 1968 to 1 m³/sec in 1973. The site of effusion then moved 400 m higher and the rate was 0–3 m³/sec. Wadge (1983) suggested that measured downtilting of the western flank of the volcano is caused by the load of the compound lava flow field. The volume of lava to date is 0.317 km³, and the volume of the block and ash flows is only 0.031 km³ (Wadge, 1983). Borgia and others (1983) analyzed the dynamics of lava flow-fronts.

Poás. Small ash eruptions occurred in 1963, 1964, 1967, and 1977. Fumarole temperatures reached 700°C in 1983, but are now cooling. Fumaroles at the edge of a hot, acid crater lake continuously emit gas that has destroyed vegetation downwind. Unique pyroclastic sulfur eruptions occurred in 1977 (Bennett and Raccichini, 1978) and 1978 (Francis and others, 1980). Measurements of gravity suggest a cylindrical pipe of dense material extending vertically beneath the crater for several km (Thorpe and others, 1981). Periodic gravity changes occurred at the crater during April–May 1983, while the volcano was in a fumarolic stage of activity (Rhymer and Brown, 1984). The variation was interpreted as either small movements in a shallow magma body or changes in the extent of vesiculation. Casertano and others (1983) extensively updated the historic record of eruptions from Poás and mapped the structure of the summit region. Geologic mapping of the summit crater (Prosser, 1983) revealed two similar sequences of magmatic variation from felsic to mafic lava compositions over a period of about 10,000 yr.

Soufriere de la Guadeloupe. The 1975–1977 crisis of Soufrière consisted of more than 15,000 volcanic earthquakes, and 26 strong phreatic eruptions (Dorel and Feuillard, 1980). Nevertheless, juvenile magma did not reach the surface, most likely because the extensive hydrothermal system beneath the Soufrière dome inhibited the rise of magma by freezing it at shallow depths in the crust (Feuillard and others, 1983).

Mt. Pelée. Westercamp and Traineau (1983) defined 23 magmatic eruptions in the last 5,000 yr at Mt. Pelée. This stratigraphy, constrained by 75 radiocarbon dates, allowed a probabilistic approach to hazard prediction. If the 1929–1932 eruption was the last stage of the major eruption in 1902, then Mt. Pelée could remain dormant for another century.

Soufriere, St. Vincent. In 1971–1972 a lava island extruded into the existing crater lake. In 1979, phreatic eruptions demolished much of the lava island and caused the lake to dry out. After the lake was gone, a lava dome was quietly extruded.

Shepherd and Sigurdsson (1982) used heat and mass balance calculations to infer that part of the energy of the 1979 eruption came from hot lava extruded in 1971–1972 that was hydrofractured by the intrusion of the 1979 magma and then broken up by phreatic explosions. The growth of the lava dome can be physically modeled as the spread of a viscous fluid on a horizontal surface under its own hydrostatic pressure (Huppert and others, 1982). The volatile content of the 1979 magma was relatively high in glass inclusions found in early crystallizing olivine crystals, and much lower in later crystallizing crystals, indicating that the magma was substantially degassed before it erupted (Devine and Sigurdsson, 1983).

REFERENCES CITED

Aburto, Q. A., 1975, Reporte de los temblores occuridos in Nicaragua: Boletín del Instituto de Investigaciones Sísmicas, v. 1, 23 p.

Anderson, A. R., Jr., 1984, Probable relations between plagioclase zoning and magma dynamics, Fuego Volcano, Guatemala: American Mineralogist, v. 69, p. 660–676.

Arculus, R. J., 1976, Geology and geochemistry of the alkali basalt–andesite association of Grenada, Lesser Antilles island arc: Geological Society of America Bulletin, v. 87, p. 612–624.

Arculus, R. J., and Wills, K.J.A., 1980, Petrology of plutonic blocs and inclusions from the Lesser Antilles island arc: Journal of Petrology, v. 21, p. 743–799.

Baker, D. R., and Eggler, D. H., 1983, Fractionation paths of Atka (Aleutians) high alumina basalts; constraints from phase relations: Journal of Volcanology and Geothermal Research, v. 18, p. 387–404.

Bennett, F. D., and Raccichini, S. M., 1978, Subaqueous sulphur lake in Volcán Poás: Nature, v. 271, p. 342–344.

Bice, D. C., 1985, Quaternary volcanic stratigraphy in Managua, Nicaragua; Correlation and source assignment for multiple overlapping plinian deposits: Geological Society of America Bulletin, v. 96, p. 553–566.

Birnie, R. W., and Hughes, J. M., 1979, Stoiberite, $Cu_5V_2O_{10}$, a copper vanadate from the fumaroles of Izalco volcano, El Salvador, Central America: American Mineralogist, v. 64, p. 941–944.

Bohnenberger, O. H., and three others, 1966, Report on active volcanoes in Central America: Bulletin of Volcanic Eruptions, v. 9, p. 2–19.

Borgia, A., and four others, 1983, Dynamics of lava flow fronts, Arenal volcano, Costa Rica: Journal of Volcanology and Geothermal Research, v. 19, p. 303–330.

Bouysse, P., 1984, The Lesser Antilles island arc, structure and geodynamic evolution; Initial Reports Deep Sea Drilling Project Leg 78A: U.S. Government Printing Office, Washington, p. 79–103.

Bouysse, P., and Sigurdsson, H., 1982, The "Hodder" phenomenon of 1902; no active submarine volcano off St. Lucia (Lesser Antilles): Marine Geology, v. 50, p. M29–M36.

Bouysse, P., and five others, 1981, Le banc Luymes, terminaison septentrionale de l'arc recént des Petites Antilles: Bulletin de la Societe Geologique de France, v. XXIII, no. 2, p. 185–194.

Boynton, C. H., and three others, 1979, A seismic refraction investigation of crustal structure beneath the Lesser Antilles island arc: Geophysical Journal of the Royal Astronomical Society, v. 58, p. 371–393.

Brown, G. M., and four others, 1977, Geochemistry of the Lesser Antilles volcanic arc: Geochimica et Cosmochimica Acta, v. 41, p. 785–801.

Burbach, G. V., and three others, 1984, Seismicity and tectonics of the subducted Cocos plate: Journal of Geophysical Research, v. 89, p. 7719–7735.

Burkart, B., and Self, S., 1985, Extension and rotation of crustal blocks in northern Central America and effect on the volcanic arc: Geology, v. 13, p. 22–26.

Cadle, R. C., and nine others, 1979, Atmospheric implications of studies of Central American volcanic eruption clouds: Journal of Geophysical Research, v. 84, n. C11, p. 6961–6968.

Carr, M. J., 1976, Underthrusting and Quaternary faulting in northern Central America: Geological Society of America Bulletin, v. 88, p. 151–156.

——, 1977, Volcanic activity and great earthquakes at convergent plate boundaries: Science, v. 197, p. 655–657.

——, 1983, Nests of intermediate depth (70–160 km) earthquakes adjacent to active volcanoes during 1963–1982: Journal of Volcanology and Geothermal Research, v. 19, p. 349–365.

——, 1984, Symmetrical and segmented variation of physical and geochemical characteristics of the Central American volcanic front: Journal of Volcanology and Geothermal Research, v. 20, p. 231–252.

Carr, M. J., and Pontier, N. K., 1981, Evolution of a young parasitic cone toward a mature central vent; Izalco and Santa Ana volcanoes in El Salvador, Central America: Journal of Volcanology and Geothermal Research, v. 11, p. 277–292.

Carr, M. J., and Stoiber, R. E., 1977, Geologic setting of some destructive earthquakes in Central America: Geological Society of America Bulletin, v. 37, p. 326–337.

Carr, M. J., Rose, W. I., Jr., and Mayfield, D. G., 1979, Potassium content of lavas and depth to the seismic zone in Central America: Journal of Volcanology and Geothermal Research, v. 5, p. 387–401.

Carr, M. J., Mayfield, D. G., and Walker, J. A., 1981, Relation of lava compositions to volcano size and structure in El Salvador: Journal of Volcanology and Geothermal Research, v. 10, p. 35–48.

Carr, M. J., Rose, W. I. and Stoiber, R. E., 1982, Central America, in Thorpe, R. S., ed., Orogenic andesites and related rocks: New York, John Wiley, p. 149–166.

Casertano, L., Borgia, A., and Cigolini, C., 1983, El volcán Poás Costa Rica, Cronología y características de la actividad: Geofísica International,. v. 22-3, p. 215–236.

Chesner, C. A., and Rose, W. I., Jr., 1984, Geochemistry and evolution of the Fuego volcanic complex, Guatemala: Journal of Volcanology and Geothermal Research, v. 21, p. 25–44.

Crowe, J. C., and Buffler, R. T., 1984, Regional seismic reflection profiles across the Middle America trench and convergent margin of Costa Rica, in Bally, A. W., ed., Seismic expression of structural styles: American Association of Petroleum Geologists Studies in Geology #15, v. 3.4.2, p. 145–162.

Davies, D. K., Quearry, M. W., and Bonis, S. B., 1978, Glowing avalanches from the 1974 eruption of the volcano Fuego, Guatemala: Geological Society of America Bulletin, v. 89, p. 369–384.

de Boer, J., 1979, The outer arc of the Costa Rican orogen (oceanic basement complexes of the Nicoya and Santa Elena peninsulas): Tectonophysics, v. 56, p. 221–259.

Dengo, G., 1969, Problems of tectonic relations between Central America and the

Caribbean: Transactions of the Gulf Coast Association of Geologists Society, v. 19, p. 311–320.

——, 1985, Mid America, tectonic setting for the Pacific margin from southern Mexico to northwestern Columbia, *in* Nain, A.E.M., and Stehli, F. G., eds., The ocean basins and margins; Volume 7, The Pacific: New York, Plenum Publishing Company, p. 123–180.

Dengo, G., Bohnenberger, O. H., and Bonis, S., 1970, Tectonics and volcanism along the Pacific marginal zone of Central America: Geologishe Rundschau, v. 59, p. 1215–1232.

Devine, J. D., and Sigurdsson, H., 1983, The liquid composition and crystallization history of the 1979 Soufriere magma, St. Vincent, West Indies: Journal of Volcanology and Geothermal Research, v. 16, p. 1–31.

Dewey, J. W., and Algermissen, S. T., 1974, Seismicity of the Middle America arc-trench system near Managua, Nicaragua: Seismological Society of America Bulletin, v. 64, p. 1033–1048.

Dollfus, A., and Montserrat, E., 1868, Voyage géologique dans les républiques de Guatemala et de Salvador: France, Mission Scientifique au Mexique at dans l'Amerique centrale, Geologie, v. 9, Paris, Imprimerie impériale, 539 p.

Dorel, J., 1981, Seismicity and seismic gap in the Lesser Antilles: Annales de Geophysique, v. 30, p. 117–126.

Dorel, J., and Fuelliard, M., 1980, Note sur la crise sismo-volcanique a la Soufrière de la Guadeloupe 1975–1977: Bulletin Volcanologique, v. 43, p. 419–430.

Dostal, J., and four others, 1983, Partition coefficients of trace elements; application to volcanic rocks of St. Vincent, West Indies: Geochimica et Cosmochimica Acta, v. 47, p. 525–533.

Drexler, J. W., and three others, 1980, The Los Chocoyos Ash, Guatemala; A major stratigraphic marker in Middle America and in three ocean basins: Quaternary Research, v. 13, p. 327–345.

Eggers, A. A., 1983, Temporal gravity and elevation changes at Pacaya volcano, Guatemala: Journal of Volcanology and Geothermal Research, v. 19, p. 223–238.

Eggers, A. A., and Chavez, D., 1979, Temporal gravity variations at Pacaya Volcano, Guatemala: Journal of Volcanology and Geothermal Research, v. 6, p. 391–402.

Elthon, D., 1983, Isomolar and isostructural pseudo-liquidus phase diagrams for oceanic basalts: American Mineralogists, v. 68, p. 506–511.

Fairbrothers, G. E., Carr, M. J., and Mayfield, D. G., 1978, Temporal magmatic evolution at Boqueron volcano, El Salvador: Contributions to Mineralogy and Petrology, v. 67, p. 1–9.

Feuillard, M., and seven others, 1983, The 1975–1977 crisis of la Soufrière de Guadeloupe (West Indies); A still-born magmatic eruption: Journal of Volcanology and Geothermal Research, v. 16, p. 317–334.

Francis, P. W. and three others, 1980, Pyroclastic sulfur eruption at Poás Volcano, Costa Rica: Nature, v. 283, p. 754–756.

Golombek, M. P., and Carr, M. J., 1978, Tidal triggering of seismic and volcanic phenomena during the 1879–1880 eruption of Islas Quemadas Volcano in El Salvador, Central America: Journal of Volcanology and Geothermal Research, v. 3, p. 299–307.

Gose, W. A., 1983, Late Cretaceous–Early Tertiary tectonic history of southern Central America: Journal of Geophysical Research, v. 88, p. 10585–10592.

Grant, N. K., Rose, W. I., Jr., and Fultz, L. A., 1984, Correlated Sr isotope and geochemical variations in basalts and basaltic andesites from Guatemala, *in* Harmon, R. S., and Barreiro, B. A., eds., Andean magmatism; Chemical and isotopic constraints: American Geophysical Union, Shiva, Nantwich, England, p. 139–149.

Güendel, F., 1985, Enjambres sísmicos en el volcán Irazú: Catálogo de Temblores 1984, Heredia, Costa Rica, p. 100–104.

Gunn, B. M., Roobol, M. J., and Smith, A. L., 1980, Geochemistry of the volcanoes of Basse-Terre, Guadeloupe; an example of intraisland variation: Bulletin Volcanologique, v. 43, p. 403–412.

Hahn, G. A., Rose, W. I., Jr., and Meyers, T., 1979, Geochemical correlation of genetically related rhyolitic ash-flow and air-fall ashes, central and western Guatemala and the equatorial Pacific, *in* Chapin, C. E., ed., Ash-flow tuffs, Geological Society of America Special Paper 180, p. 101–112.

Hofmann, A. W., and Feigenson, M. D., 1983, Case studies on the origin of basalt; I. Theory and reassessment of Grenada Basalts: Contributions to Mineralogy and Petrology, v. 84, p. 382–389.

Hughes, J. M., and Birnie, R. W., 1980, Ziesite, B–$Cu_2V_2O_7$, a new copper vanadate and fumarole temperature indicator: American Mineralogist, v. 65, p. 1146–1149.

Hughes, J. M., and Stoiber, R. E., 1985, Vanadium sublimates from the fumaroles of Izalco volcano, El Salvador: Journal of Volcanology and Geothermal Research, v. 24, p. 283–291.

Huppert, J. E., and three others, 1982, On lava dome growth, with application to the 1979 lava extrusion of the Soufriere of St. Vincent: Journal of Volcanology and Geothermal Research, v. 14, p. 199–222.

Kimura, M., 1976, Major magmatic activity as a key to predicting large earthquakes along the Sagami trough, Japan: Nature, v. 260, p. 131–133.

——, 1978, Relation between great earthquakes and eruptive activity in the circum-Pacific area: Journal of Physics of the Earth, v. 26, p. 557–570.

Koch, A. J., and McLean, H., 1975, Pleistocene Tephra and ash-flow deposits in the volcanic high lands of Guatemala: Geological Society of America Bulletin, v. 86, p. 529–541.

Kussmaul, S., Paniagua, S., and Gainsa, J., 1982, Recopilación, clasificación e interpretación petroquímica de las rocas de Costa Rica: Informe Semestral del Instituto Geografico Nacional, San Jose, Costa Rica, v. 28, p. 17–79.

Lazrus, A. L., and five others, 1979, Sulfur and halogen chemistry of the stratosphere and of volcanic eruption plumes: Journal of Geophysical Research, v. 84, no. C12, p. 7869–7875.

Ledbetter, M. T., 1985, Tephrochronology of marine tephra adjacent to Central America: Geological Society of America Bulletin, v. 96, p. 77–82.

Lewis, J. F., 1973, Petrology of the ejected plutonic blocks of the Soufriere volcano, St. Vincent, West Indies: Journal of Petrology, v. 14, p. 81–112.

Lewis, J. F., and three others, 1983, Summary and bibliography of Caribbean Geodynamic investigators, *in* Cabre, R., ed., Geodynamics of the eastern Pacific region, Caribbean and Scotia arcs: Geodynamics Series, v. 9, p. 27–32.

Liaw, H. B., and Matumoto, T., 1980, Hinge faulting and its correlation with surface geology in northern Costa Rica: EOS, v. 61, p. 289–290.

Malavassi, R. E., and Barquero, H. J., 1980, Cronología de las coladas de lava del Vocán Arenal: Boletín de Vulcanología, v. 9, p. 5.

Marsh, B. D., 1979, Island arc development; some observations, experiments, and speculations: Journal of Geology, v. 87, p. 687–713.

——, 1982, The Aleutians, *in* Thorpe, R. S., ed., Andesites, orogenic andesites and related rocks: New York, John Wiley and Sons, p. 99–114.

Martin, D. P., and Rose, W. I., 1981, Behaviorial patterns of Fuego volcano, Guatemala: Journal of Volcanology and Geothermal Research, v. 10, p. 67–81.

McBirney, A. R., 1956, The Nicaraguan volcano Masaya and its caldera: American Geophysical Union Transactions, v. 37, p. 83–96.

——, 1969, Compositional variations in Cenozoic calc-alkaline suites of Central America: Oregon Department of Geology and Mineral Industries Bulletin 65, p. 185–189.

——, 1985, Volcanic evolution of Central America: Boletín de Vulcanologia, Heredia, Costa Rica, v. 14, p. 21–23.

McBirney, A. R., and four others, 1974, Episodic volcanism in the central Oregon Cascade range: Geology, v. 2, p. 585–589.

McCann, W. R., and Sykes, L. R., 1984, Subduction of aseismic ridges beneath the Caribbean plate and its implications for the tectonics and seismic potential of the northeastern Caribbean: Journal of Geophysical Research, v. 89, p. 4493–4519.

McNutt, S. R., and Harlow, D. H., 1983, Seismicity at Fuego, Pacaya, Izalco and San Cristobál volcanoes, Central America: Bulletin Volcanologique, v. 46, p. 283–298.

Melson, W. G., 1985, Alteration between acidic and basic magmas in major explosive eruptions of Arenal volcano, Costa Rica: Boletín de Vulcanología Heredia, Costa Rica, v. 14, p. 65–69.

Melson, W. G., and Sáenz, R., 1973, Volume, energy and cyclicity of eruptions of

Arenal volcano, Costa Rica: Bulletin Volcanologique, v. 37, p. 416–437.

Minster, J. B., and Jordan, T. H., 1978, Present day plate motions: Journal of Geophysical Research, v. 83, p. 5331–5354.

Molnar, P., and Sykes, L., 1969, Tectonics of the Caribbean and Middle America regions from focal mechanisms and seismicity: Geological Society of America Bulletin, v. 81, p. 1639–1684.

Mooser, F., Meyer-Abich, H., and McBirney, A. R., 1958, Catalogue of Active volcanoes of the World, Part VI, Central America: Naples, International Volcanological Association, p. 65–69.

O'Hara, M. J., 1977, Geochemical evolution during fractional crystallization of a periodically refilled magma chamber: Nature, v. 166, p. 503–507.

Pichler, H., and Weyl, R., 1973, Petrochemical aspects of Central American magmatism: Geologishe Rundschau, v. 62, p. 357–396.

—— , 1976, Quaternary alkaline volcanic rocks in eastern Mexico and Central America: Münster Forschungen in Geologie und Paläontologie, v. 38/39, p. 159–178.

Powell, M., 1978, Crystallization conditions of low-pressure cumulate nodules from the Lesser Antilles island arc: Earth and Planetary Science Letters, v. 39, p. 162–172.

Prosser, J. T., 1983, The geology of Poás Volcano, Costa Rica [M. S. Thesis]: Hanover, New Hampshire, Dartmouth College, 165 p.

Rea, W. J., 1982, The Lesser Antilles, in Thorpe, R. S., ed., Andesites; Orogenic andesites and related rocks: New York, John Wiley and Sons, p. 167–185.

Reynolds, J. H., 1980, Late Tertiary volcanic stratigraphy of northern Central America: Bulletin Volcanologique, v. 43, p. 601–607.

Rhymer, H., and Brown, G. C., 1984, Periodic gravity changes at Poás volcano, Costa Rica: Nature, v. 311, p. 243–245.

Robin, C., and Tournon, J., 1978, Spatial relations of andesitic and alkaline provinces in Mexico and Central America: Canadian Journal of Earth Science, v. 15, p. 1633–1641.

Robson, G. R., and Tomblin, J. F., 1966, Catalog of active volcanoes of the world, Part XX, West Indies: Rome, International Association of Volcanology, 56 p.

Robson, G. R., Barr, K. F., and Smith, G. W., 1962, Earthquake series in St. Kitts–Nevis 1961–62: Nature, v. 195, p. 972–974.

Roobol, M. J., and Smith, A. L., 1975, A comparison of the recent eruptions of Mt. Pelee, Martinique and Soufriere, St. Vincent: Bulletin Volcanologique, v. 39, n. 2, p. 214–140.

—— , 1980, Pumice eruptions of the Lesser Antilles: Bulletin Volcanologique, v. 43, p. 277–186.

Rose, W. I., Jr., 1972, Santiaguito Volcanic Dome, Guatemala: Geological Society of America Bulletin, v. 83, p. 1413–1434.

—— , 1973a, Pattern and mechanism of volcanic activity at the Santiaguito volcanic dome, Guatemala: Bulletin Volcanologique, v. 37, p. 73–94.

—— , 1973b, Nueé ardente from Santiaguito volcano, April, 1973: Bulletin Volcanologique, v. 37, p. 365–371.

Rose, W. I., Jr., and Stoiber, R. E., 1969, The 1966 eruption of Izalco volcano, El Salvador: Journal of Geophysical Research, v. 74, p. 3119–1434.

Rose, W. I., Jr., and four others, 1973, Studies of volcanic ash from two recent Central American eruptions: Bulletin Volcanologique, v. 37, p. 338–364.

Rose, W. I., Jr., and two others, 1976, Nueé ardente eruption from the foot of a dacite lava flow, Santiaguito, Guatemala: Bulletin Volcanologique, v. 40, p. 23–28.

Rose, W. I., Jr., and six others, 1977, The evolution of Santa María volcano, Guatemala: Journal of Geology, v. 85, p. 63–87.

Rose, W. I., Jr., and three others, 1978, The October 1974 basaltic tephra, Fuego volcano, Guatemala; Description and history of the magma body: Journal of Volcanology and Geothermal Research, v. 4, p. 3–53.

Rose, W. I., Jr., and three others, 1980a, Small particles in volcanic eruption clouds: American Journal of Science, v. 280, p. 671–696.

Rose, W. I., Jr., and three others, 1980b, Geochemistry of the andesite flank lavas of three composite cones within the Atitlán cauldron, Guatemala: Bulletin Volcanologique, v. 43, p. 131–153.

Rose, W. I., Jr., and five others, 1981, Quaternary tephra of northern Central

America, in Self, S., and Sparks, R.S.J., eds., Tephra Studies: Boston, Reidel Publishers, p. 193–212.

Rose, W. I., Jr., and two others, 1982, Eruptive gas compositions and fluxes of explosive volcanoes; Budget of S and Cl emitted from Fuego Volcano, Guatemala, in Thorpe, R. S., ed., Andesites; Orogenic andesites and related rocks: New York, John Wiley and Sons, p. 669–676.

Sapper, K., 1897, Uber die raumliche Anordnung der mittelamerikanischen Vulkane: Zeitschrift der Deutcher Geologishe Geschellsaft, v. 49, p. 672–682.

Shepherd, J. B., and Aspinall, W. P., 1982, Seismological studies of Soufriere St. Vincent, 1953–1979; Implications for volcanic surveillance in the Lesser Antilles: Journal of Volcanology and Geothermal Research, v. 12, p. 37–56.

Shepherd, J. B., and Sigurdsson, H., 1982, Mechanism of the 1979 explosive eruption of Soufriere volcano, St. Vincent: Journal of Volcanology and Geothermal Research, v. 12, p. 119–130.

Shepherd, J. B., Tomblin, J. F., and Wood, D. A., 1971, Volcano–Seismic Crisis in Montserrat, West Indies, 1966–67: Bulletin Volcanologique, v. 35, p. 143–163.

Shepherd, J. B., and six others, 1979, The eruption of Soufriere volcano, St. Vincent April–June 1979: Nature, v. 282, no. 5743, p. 24–28.

Sigurdsson, H., and Carey, S. N., 1981, Marine tephrochronology and Quaternary explosive volcanism in the Lesser Antilles arc, in Self, S., and Sparks, R.S.J., eds., Tephra Studies: Boston, Reidel Publishing Company, p. 255–280.

Sigurdsson, J., and Sparks, R.S.J., 1979, An active submarine volcano: Natural History, v. 88, p. 38–45.

Simkin, T., and five others, 1981, Volcanoes of the world: Stroudsburg, Pennsylvania, Hutchinson Ross Publishing company, 232 p.

Smith, A. L., Roobol, M. J., and Gunn, B. M., 1980, The Lesser Antilles; A discussion of the island arc magmatism: Bulletin Volcanologique, v. 80, p. 287–302.

Sparks, R.S.J., Sigurdsson, H., and Carey, S. N., 1980, The entrance of pyroclastic flows into the sea, I. Oceanographic and geologic evidence from Dominica, Lesser Antilles: Journal of Volcanology and Geothermal Research, v. 7, p. 87–96.

Stein, S., Engeln, J. F., and Wiens, D. A., 1982, Subduction, seismicity and tectonics in the Lesser Antilles: Journal of Geophysical Research, v. 87, p. 8642–8664.

Stoiber, R. E., and Carr, M. J., 1973, Quaternary volcanic and tectonic segmentation of Central America: Bulletin Volcanologique, v. 37, p. 304–325.

Stoiber, R. E., and Jepsen, A., 1973, Sulfur dioxide contribution to the atmosphere by volcanoes: Science, v. 182, p. 577–578.

Stoiber, R. E., and Rose, W. I., Jr., 1970, Geochemistry of Central American volcanic gas condensates: Geological Society of America Bulletin, v. 81, p. 2891–2912.

—— , 1974, Fumerole incrustations at active Central American volcanoes: Geochimica et Cosmochimica Acta, v. 38, p. 495–516.

Stoiber, R. E., and three others, 1975, The cooling of Izalco volcano (El Salvador): Geoogisches Jahrbuch, v. 13, p. 193–205.

Stoiber, R. E., and two others, 1986, Sulfur and halogen gases at Masaya caldera complex, Nicaragua; Total flux and variations with time: Journal of Geophysical Research, v. 91, p. 12, 215–12, 231.

Sussman, D., 1985, Apoyo Caldera, Nicaragua; a major Quaternary silicic eruptive center: Journal of Volcanology and Geothermal Research, v. 24, p. 249–282.

Sykes, L. R., McCann, W. R., and Kafka, A. L., 1982, Motion of Caribbean plate during last 7 million years and implications for earlier Cenozoic movements: Journal of Geophysical Research, v. 87, p. 10656–10676.

Taylor, P. S., and Stoiber, R. E., 1973, Soluble material on ash from active Central American volcanoes: Geological Society of America Bulletin, v. 84, p. 1031–1042.

Tazieff, H., 1977, La Soufrière, volcanology and forecasting: Nature, v. 269, p. 96–97.

Thorpe, R. S. and four others, 1981, Magma chamber below Poás volcano, Costa Rica: Journal of the Geological Society of London, v. 138, p. 367–373.

Tomblin, J. F., 1975, The Lesser Antilles and Aves ridge, in Nairn, A.E.M., and

Stehli, F. G., eds., The ocean basins and margins: New York, Plenum Publishing Company, v. 3, p. 467–500.

Tomblin, J. F., Sigurdsson, H., and Aspinall, W., 1972, Activity at the Soufrière volcano, St. Vincent, West Indies in October–November 1971: Nature, v. 235, p. 157–158.

Ui, T., 1972, Recent volcanism in the Masaya–Granada area, Nicaragua: Bulletin Volcanologique, v. 36, p. 174–190.

van Andel, T. H., and four others, 1971, Tectonics of the Panama basin, eastern equatorial Pacific: Geological Society of America Bulletin, v. 82, p. 1489–1508.

Vogt, P., and three others, 1976, Subduction of aseismic oceanic ridges; effects on shape, seismicity, and other characteristics of consuming plate margins: Geological Society of America Special Paper 172, 59 p.

Wadge, G., 1983, The magma budget of Volcan Arenal, Costa Rica, from 1968 to 1980: Journal of Volcanology and Geothermal Research, v. 19, p. 281–302.

—— , 1984, Comparison of volcanic production rates and subduction rates in the Lesser Antilles and Central America: Geology, v. 12, p. 555–558.

Wadge, G., and Wooden, J. L., 1982, Late Cenozoic alkaline volcanism in the northwestern Caribbean; tectonic setting and Sr isotopic characteristics: Earth and Planetary Science Letters, v. 57, p. 35–46.

Walker, D., Shibata, T., and DeLong, S. E., 1979, Abyssal tholeiites from the Oceanographer fracture zone, II-phase equilibria and mixing: Contributions to Mineralogy and Petrology, v. 70, p. 111–125.

Walker, J. A., 1981, Petrogenesis of lavas from cinder cone fields behind the volcanic front of Central America: Journal of Geology, v. 87, p. 721–739.

—— , 1984, Volcanic rocks from the Nejapa and Granada cinder cone alignments, Nicaragua, Central America: Journal of Petrology, v. 25, p. 299–342.

Westercamp, D., and Traineau, H., 1983, The past 5,000 years of volcanic activity at Mt. Pelée, Martinique, French West Indies; Implications for as-

sessment of volcanic hazards: Journal of Volcanology and Geothermal Research, v. 17, p. 159–186.

Weyl, R., 1980, Geology of Central America: Berlin, Gebruder Borntraeger, 371 p.

Wiesemann, G., 1975, Remarks on the geologic structure of the Republic of El Salvador: Mitteilungen des Geologische-Paläontologischen Institut der Universite Hamburg, v. 44, p. 557–574.

Williams, H., and McBirney, A. R., 1969, Volcanic history of Honduras: Berkeley, University of California Publications in the Geological Sciences, v. 85, p. 1–101.

Williams, H., McBirney, A. R., and Dengo, G., 1964, Geologic reconnaissance of southeastern Guatemala: Berkeley, University of California Publications in the Geological Sciences, v. 50, p. 1–56.

Williams, S. N., 1983, Plinian airfall deposits of basaltic composition: Geology, v. 11, p. 211–214.

Williams, S. N., and Self, S., 1983, The October, 1902, plinian eruption of Santa María volcano, Guatemala: Journal of Volcanology and Geothermal Research, v. 16, p. 33–56.

Wright, J. V., and six others, 1984, Late Quaternary explosive silicic volcanism on St. Lucia, West Indies: Geological Magazine, v. 121, p. 1–15.

Wunderman, R. L., and Rose, W. I., Jr., 1984, Amatitlan, an actively resurging cauldron 10 km south of Guatemala City: Journal of Geophysical Research, v. 89, p. 8525–8539.

Yuan, A.T.E., McNutt, S. R., and Harlow, D. H., 1984, Seismicity and eruptive activity at Fuego volcano, Guatemala: Journal of Volcanology and Geothermal Research, v. 21, p. 277–296.

MANUSCRIPT ACCEPTED BY THE SOCIETY JANUARY 22, 1987

NOTES ADDED IN PROOF

Subsequent to the completion of this manuscript the Smithsonian Institution published a valuable review of volcanic activity (McClelland and others, 1989). This book, *Global Volcanism 1975–1985,* is a great improvement over our attempt to summarize recent volcanic activity, both for Central America and the Lesser Antilles.

Volcanism in Central America was the subject of the August 1987 issue of the Journal of Volcanology and Geothermal Research (v. 33, no. 1–3). This special issue, completed by students of R. E. Stoiber to celebrate his 75th birthday, covers a wide range of volcanological topics and includes three papers on the Atitlan Caldera.

The regional variation in sodium contents of Central American volcanoes (Figure 4) has been related to crustal thickness and to the extent of partial melting by Plank and Langmuir (1988).

REFERENCES

McClelland, L., and four others, 1989, Global Volcanism 1975–1985: Englewood Cliffs, New Jersey, Prentice Hall, 655 p.

Plank, T., and Langmuir, C. T., 1988, An evaluation of the global variations in the major element chemistry of arc basalts: Earth and Planetary Science Letters, v. 90, p. 349–370.

Printed in U.S.A.

The Geology of North America
Vol. H, The Caribbean Region
The Geological Society of America, 1990

Chapter 15

Survey of Caribbean paleomagnetism

William D. MacDonald
Department of Geological Sciences, State University of New York at Binghamton, Binghamton, New York 13901

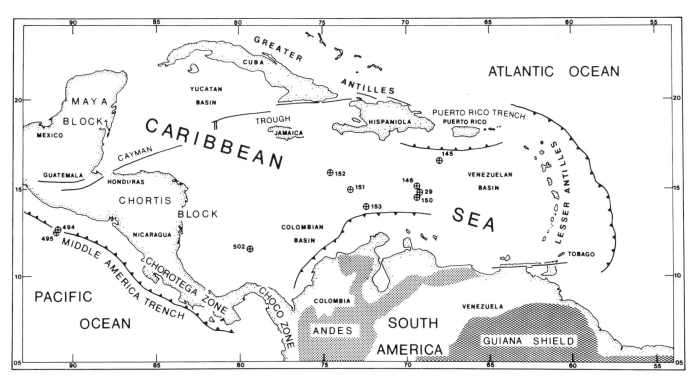

Figure 1. Index map shows Caribbean geographic localities, geologic provinces, major structures, and DSDP sites (circled crosses).

INTRODUCTION

Scope

The principal objective of this chapter is to present a compilation of original sources of paleomagnetic data for the Caribbean region, as published to the end of 1985. Secondarily, trends in the data and explanations for them are summarized, with emphasis on post-Paleozoic structural-tectonic rotations and paleogeographic implications.

Areal limits for this compilation coincide with the limits of the map of Case and Holcombe (1980): 05° to 24°N and 054° to 093°W (Fig. 1). A few studies overlap these boundaries. The focus is on paleomagnetic directional data; therefore, studies of regional continental and oceanic crustal magnetic anomaly trends

have been excluded. Some theses and a few abstracts have been included, but works in preparation or in press have been omitted. As the objective of this chapter is to summarize paleomagnetic information, no attempt has been made to evaluate the numerous tectonic scenarios proposed by many authors for the Caribbean. It is hoped that researchers of diverse interests will find the appendix and citations of original data sources useful. The appendix identifies data sources by region: Greater Antilles; Lesser Antilles; Central America; northern South America; and the Caribbean area oceanic basins.

Historical Aspects

Paleomagnetism was a slowly developing science until about 1960, when vigorous growth accompanied the plate tecton-

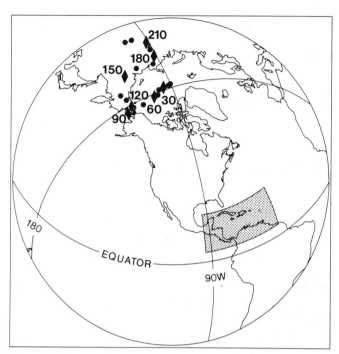

Figure 2. Reference paleomagnetic poles for cratonic North America are shown at 10 m.y. intervals and marked by diamonds at 30 m.y. intervals (after Irving and Irving, 1982). Area covered by this chapter is stippled.

CARIBBEAN PALEOMAGNETIC DATA: REGIONAL PATTERNS

General Remarks

Various paleogeographic reconstructions (Carey, 1958; Bullard and others, 1965; Ladd, 1976) make clear that prior to the mid-Mesozoic there was no room for the Caribbean plate between the Americas. The Caribbean plate evolved and/or was emplaced during the separation of the Atlantic continents in the Mesozoic and Cenozoic. The emphasis of this study, therefore, is on paleomagnetic results of that interval. For completeness, data sources for pre-Mesozoic rocks, mainly from northern South America, are included in the appendix and references but are not reviewed comprehensively.

Mesozoic–Cenozoic paleomagnetic poles are shown in Figure 3. The mean polar wander path for cratonic North America in Figure 2 (after Irving and Irving, 1982) shows mean poles computed at 10-m.y. intervals, using a 30-m.y. window; poles at 30-m.y. intervals are labeled and marked by diamonds. All paleomagnetic pole plots are Lambert azimuthal equivalent projections with center at 42°N, 110°W, for ease of comparison between figures. Where necessary to show all poles on the same hemisphere, antipodal poles have been plotted. Mesozoic poles are shown by circles and Cenozoic poles by squares. A single Paleozoic pole was plotted (diamond, pole 5, Fig. 3C). Pole numbers in Figure 3 are identified as to source in the caption. Many poles were computed from the directional data and site information of the source. This also is indicated in the caption to Figure 3.

More recent results have been given priority over earlier results for the same rock units. For example, poles of Gose (1985b) for the Chortis block of Central America have been plotted, whereas those of Gose and Swartz (1977) have not. Poles representing sparse sampling have generally not been plotted, with some exceptions like, for example, the Oligocene–Miocene poles for the Lesser Antilles (Briden, and others, 1979), which represent the only data available for this large area. Poles for the very young rock units of the Lesser Antilles were not plotted, as their mean is statistically indistinguishable from the present pole (Briden and others, 1979). Poles representing secondary magnetizations, undemagnetized samples, or erratic directions have not been plotted. Further details on the plots are given below.

Polar Arcs and Structural-Tectonic Rotations

Paleogmagnetic pole plots reflect the many diverse influences noted above. A dominant pattern in Caribbean paleomagnetic pole plots is one of diffuse polar arcs centered on the sampling regions (MacDonald and Opdyke, 1972, Fig. 7; MacDonald, 1976, Fig. 4; MacDonald, 1980b, Fig. 12). Diffuse polar arcs are evident in the detailed regional plots of Figure 3. Dispersion *along* the arcs can be attributed primarily to structural and tectonic rotations. Dispersion *across* the arcs especially reflects a

ics revolution globally. Caribbean paleomagnetic studies began with Creer (1962) who sampled Venezuelan and Colombian Andes localities in his regional survey of South America (Creer, 1970). With improvements in instruments and techniques, paleomagnetic studies expanded greatly. Many unexpected paleomagnetic directions were encountered in Caribbean samples. These directions were unusual in that they had not been predicted by prevailing assumptions of paleogeography and geomagnetic dipole fields. Eventually, many diverse phenomena were recognized as influencing the measured paleomagnetic directions. In the context of Caribbean locales, examples of these phenomena include unusual geomagnetic field behavior (Watkins and Cambray, 1970; Steinhauser and Vincenz, 1973a), structural and plate tectonic rotations (MacDonald and Opdyke, 1972; Vincenz and others, 1974; Gose and Swartz, 1977; Skerlec and Hargraves, 1980; Stearns and others, 1982), complex remagnetization (Hargraves and Shagam, 1969; Creer, 1970; Guja and Vincenz, 1978), and technical problems associated with thermal demagnetization (Gose and Testarmata, 1983). Recognition of these influences in Caribbean data was realized in parallel with similar developments elsewhere.

Patterns of Caribbean paleomagnetic polar distributions are discussed by region in the following section, followed by a discussion of the paleogeographic implications. To allow comparisons relative to North America, its Mesozoic and Cenozoic polar wander path is shown (Fig. 2).

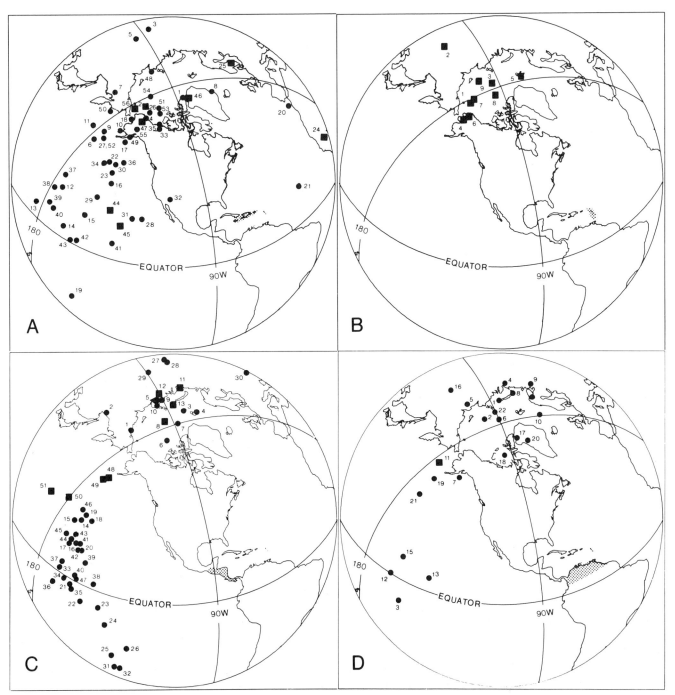

Figure 3. Caribbean paleomagnetic poles by region and age. Diffuse polar arcs have centers in sampling region (stipple). Circles = Mesozoic poles; squares = Cenozoic poles. Pole sources by region are: A. *Greater Antilles.* 1–15, Watkins and Cambray, 1970; 16, Fink and Harrison, 1972; 17–19, Steinhauser and Vincenz, 1973b; 20–23, Vincenz, and others, 1973; 24–25, Dasgupta and Vincenz, 1975; 26–43, Guja and Vincenz, 1978; 44–47, Vincenz and Dasgupta, 1978; 48–49, computed from Kent and Maurrasse, 1981; 50–56, Gose and Testarmata, 1983. B. *Lesser Antilles.* 1–9, Oligocene–Miocene poles, computed from Briden, and others, 1979. C. *Central America.* 1, Guerrero and Helsley, 1974, 1976; 2–4, computed from de Boer, 1979; 5, Gose and Sanchez-Barreda, 1981; 6–13, Gose, 1983; 14–51, Gose, 1985b. D. *South America.* 1, Creer, 1970; 2, Veldcamp and others, 1971; 3, MacDonald and Opdyke, 1972; 4–6, MacDonald and Opdyke, 1974; 7, MacDonald and Van Horn, 1977; 8–10, Hargraves, 1978; 11, MacDonald, 1980a; 12 (El Chacao), computed from Skerlec and Hargraves, 1980; 13–15, Stearns and others, 1982; 16, computed from Hargraves and others, 1984; 17–18, MacDonald and Opdyke, 1984; 19–21, computed from Maze and Hargraves, 1984; 22, Muessig, 1984.

shift of paleomagnetic latitude, associated with tectonic plate motion and polar wander. Many other factors contribute to scatter in the polar arcs, as noted earlier, creating patterns within patterns.

A clarification is perhaps necessary to distinguish between structural rotations and tectonic rotations. A structural deformation is a deformation of the crust. In structural deformation, the reorientation of any part of the crust involves a structural rotation. Movement of a lithospheric plate is a plate tectonic displacement, or more generally, a tectonic displacement. Relocation of a tectonic plate involves a plate tectonic rotation, or more simply, a tectonic rotation. Generally speaking, components of structural and tectonic rotations are recorded in the declination components of paleomagnetic vectors. The contributions of the structural rotation and of the tectonic rotation usually cannot be isolated from one another in the paleomagnetic declination at, for example, a site in an accretionary terrain.

Regionally, some trends within these patterns are evident. In the Greater Antilles, the dominant apparent rotation in Cretaceous rocks is counterclockwise (compare Figs. 3A and 2). For the Lesser Antilles, a clear trend is not evident (Fig. 3B). For the Cretaceous of Central America, large counterclockwise net rotations are evident in data from the Chortis block (compare Figs. 3C and 2). In the orogenic zones of northern South America, poles of Mesozoic rocks show large rotations of both senses, clockwise and counterclockwise (compare Figs. 3D and 2).

Greater Antilles

The bulk of the paleomagnetic data for the Greater Antilles (Fig. 3A) represents Cretaceous results from Jamaica. Few data are available from Hispaniola (Haiti and Dominican Republic), and very limited data are yet available for Puerto Rico. No data are known for Cuba, which now lies incorporated within the North America plate.

The Greater Antilles poles define a broad arc from northern Greenland to the Pacific equator near 170°W. Most results are from dikes and other intrusive rocks (Guja, 1970; Watkins and Cambray, 1970; Dasgupta, 1973; Dasgupta and Vincenz, 1975; Guja and Vincenz, 1978; Vincenz and Dasgupta, 1978). Studies emphasizing stratified rocks are by Robinson and Lamb (1970), Steinhauser and Vincenz (1973b), Vincenz and others (1973), Kent and Maurrasse (1981), and Gose and Testarmata (1983).

For Jamaica, Gose and Testarmata (1983) compare previous data with their results and conclude (1) that a limited 10° counterclockwise rotation has occurred relative to North America with no significant latitudinal shift, and (2) that the age of this rotation is post-Cretaceous, probably later than 10 Ma. Data from Jamaican Tertiary rocks is sparse. Both the Eocene Font Hill Formation and the Miocene Low Layton basalt lava give poles near the coeval North American poles. These are poles 56 and 26, respectively, in Figure 3A. Other Tertiary poles in that figure represent intrusive rocks. Robinson and Lamb (1970) presented preliminary polarity definitions for Plio-Pleistocene marine strata, encountering a predominance of rather steep paleomagnetic inclinations.

In Hispaniola, Cretaceous–Paleogene and Neogene paleomagnetic directions from intrusions (Vincenz and Dasgupta, 1978) do not agree with directions from Jamaica. The Hispaniolan results provide poles of low paleolatitude, and show declinations 60° to 70° west of north. Stratified Cretaceous volcanic and sedimentary rocks from south Haiti did not provide useful results (Kent and Maurrasse, 1981). The directions obtained are either well grouped near the present field direction, suggesting large components of secondary magnetization, or they show large intersite scatter, suggesting a complex magnetization history combined with structural effects.

Data are as yet sparse for Puerto Rico (Fink and Harrison, 1972), although several studies are in progress (D. Elston, personal communication, 1984; J. Channell, personal communication, 1985).

Lesser Antilles

From an area that otherwise has received little paleomagnetic attention, Briden and others (1979) report extensively on Lesser Antilles paleomagnetism and geochronology. They concluded that volcanic rock units in the Plio-Pleistocene age range have a mean paleomagnetic pole that is 1.5° from the present geographic pole and that is indistinguishable from the present geographic pole at the 95% confidence level. Nine of their rock units are in the Oligocene–Miocene age range, with ages from 23 to 8 Ma. Poles computed for these cluster around the Cenozoic of the polar wander path for North America (compare Figs. 3B and 2). They also report sparse and scattered results from Tobago, south of the Lesser Antilles volcanic arc.

Central America

Following the tectonic subdivisions of Central America of Dengo (1969, 1985), Central America is subdivided into four major regions (Fig. 1): the Maya and Chortis blocks, and the Chorotega and Choco zones. From a paleomagnetic perspective, the Chortis block has received the most attention. The Maya block and Chorotega zone have been investigated less, and the Choco zone not at all. Poles from this area (Fig. 3C) define a long polar arc with two nodal concentrations, one in the Arctic near the present geographic pole but slightly far-sided along 090°E, and the other in the Pacific equatorial region approximately in the area bounded by 0° to 30°N and 155° to 165°W. Geographically, the sampling areas corresponding to these nodes are the Chorotega zone and the Chortis block, respectively. Reviews of Central American paleomagnetism have been given by Gose and others (1980) and by Gose (1983; 1985a and b).

Most of Mexico lies outside of the defined area (see Fig. 1). Excellent reviews on paleomagnetism of Mexico are given by Pal (1978) and Urrutia-Fucugauchi (1984).

Maya block. The Maya block lies on the southern tip of the North America plate. From near the southwest limit of the Maya block, Permian carbonates of the Grupera and Paso Hondo formations yield declinations indicative of 22° of counterclockwise rotation relative to North America (Gose and Sanchez-Barreda, 1981). From the same sector of the Maya block, red beds of approximately Jurassic–Cretaceous age, and ascribed to the Todos Santos Formation or San Ricardo Formation (Guerrero, 1976; Guerrero and Helsley, 1974, 1979), suggest no relative motion between that area and North America. Elsewhere, in the southern sector of the Maya block, Recent lake sediments in Guatemala were studied for secular variation (Liddicoat and others, 1981).

Chortis block. Large plate tectonic rotations and related minor latitudinal shifts have been interpreted from Cretaceous strata of the Chortis block (Gose and Swartz, 1977; Gose and others, 1980; Gose, 1985, b). Comparison of the Cretaceous Pacific nodal concentration of poles (Fig. 3c) for the Chortis block with the Cretaceous of North America (Fig. 2) suggests that a net rotation of about 50° counterclockwise predominates. In evaluating the polar distribution for this region, the relative importance of structural versus tectonic rotations and of stratigraphic order have been debated (Gose and others, 1978; MacDonald, 1978, 1980b; Wilson and Meyerhoff, 1978). Gose (1985b) concluded that a large clockwise Early Cretaceous rotation was followed by yet a larger counterclockwise Late Cretaceous rotation, with concurrent latitudinal shifts, accompanying motions of the microplate carrying the Chortis block.

Chorotega zone. The cluster of poles in the Arctic area (Fig. 3C) is associated mainly with Cretaceous to Early Tertiary rock units in the Chorotega zone (deBoer, 1979; Gose and others, 1980; Gose, 1983). In situ directions give poles close to the present geographic pole, while structural tilt corrections displace some but not all poles about 15° to the far side of the geographic pole (Gose, 1983). Gose suggested some uncertainty exists here in the ages of the magnetizations. There is general agreement between the paleomagnetic directions for the Cretaceous and Paleogene stratified rocks studied by Gose (1983) and those obtained for the Late Cretaceous La Culebra intrusion by deBoer (1979).

Northern South America

The mostly Mesozoic paleomagnetic poles plotted for this area (Fig. 3D) define a diffuse polar arc that stretches from Scandinavia across the Arctic to the Pacific equator near 160W. The great span of this polar arc suggests large and variable structural rotations across a broad deformed area continuing from the northern Andes into the Caribbean Mountains and adjacent continental margin.

Paleomagnetic directions have been reported for many Precambrian rock units of the northern Guiana shield (Fig. 1; Hargraves, 1968, 1978; Veldcamp and others, 1971; Onstott, 1980; Onstott and Hargraves, 1980, 1981, 1982; Onstott and others, 1984; Caicedo, 1985; Perarnau, 1985b; Wong, 1985). Many of the units analyzed contain multicomponent magnetizations, with some uncertainty in their ages.

The few Paleozoic units analyzed, from the northern Andes, show strong evidence of remagnetization (Creer, 1970; Shagam and Hargraves, 1970). Remagnetization also affects some of the Mesozoic units (Creer, 1962, 1970; Hargraves and Shagam, 1969; Skerlec and Hargraves, 1980; Stearns and others, 1982; MacDonald and Ellwood, 1985; Perarnau, 1985c). Remagnetized directions are not always easily recognized because of similarities of some Mesozoic directions to those of the present field (MacDonald and Opdyke, 1984). Nevertheless, some remagnetized and some possibly remagnetized units show signs of large rotations (MacDonald and Van Horn, 1977; Hargraves and Skerlec, 1980; Skerlec and Hargraves, 1980; Stearns, and others, 1982).

Primary directions are evident from Triassic and Permo-Triassic dikes in the Guiana shield. The corresponding poles (2,8,9,10; fig. 3D) cluster in the Arctic region and are representative South American cratonic poles. Because of redefined age boundaries for the Triassic, now placed at 248 and 213 Ma (Harland and others, 1982), some poles previously assigned to the Triassic (MacDonald and Opdyke, 1974) are now considered early Jurassic. Similarly, improved radiometric dating has resulted in reassigning Mesozoic red-bed sequences such as the La Quinta (Venezuela) and Giron (Colombia) from the Triassic (Creer, 1962, 1970; Hargraves and Shagam, 1969; Shagam and Hargraves, 1977; Hargraves, 1978) to the Jurassic (Maze, 1983; MacDonald and Opdyke, 1984; Maze and Hargraves, 1984). Unlike the Triassic cratonic dike poles, the Jurassic poles, for sites in the orogenic zone, are spread along a polar arc suggestive of large rotations.

The many studies of Cretaceous rocks in northern South America have emphasized igneous intrusive and metamorphic rocks (Hargraves and Skerlec, 1980; Skerlec and Hargraves, 1980; Stearns and others, 1982; Hargraves and others, 1984) for which determination of paleohorizon and/or age of magnetization is difficult. Nevertheless, large rotations are apparent in the paleomagnetic directions. Creer (1970) obtained consistent natural remanent magnetization (NRM) directions from Cretaceous strata in this region but the samples were not demagnetized. Perarnau (1985c) found evidence of approximately 45° of clockwise rotation in Late Cretaceous to Paleogene sandstones of the San Juan Formation, with some variation in the inclinations.

Tertiary rock units in this region have been sparsely sampled. Folded Early and mid-Tertiary rock units of the Falcon Basin of northwestern Venezuela do not appear to have undergone large rotations about vertical axes (Muessig, 1979, 1984). Late Tertiary volcanic necks of the Cauca valley in the Andes of northern Colombia show northwesterly declinations, suggestive of small counterclockwise rotations, but the inclinations are curiously variable (MacDonald, 1980a).

Oceanic Basins

Directional data from the oceanic areas is scarce because of the difficulty of securing oriented samples from the deep sea floor.

Studies of paleomagnetic inclinations from Deep Sea Drilling Project (DSDP) cores have relevance mainly to paleogeographic studies and are discussed in a later section. At DSDP site 145, which was not drilled, Raff (1973) reported a reversed direction of magnetization deduced from a good fit to the magnetic anomaly of the associated seamount. The corresponding paleomagnetic pole is 73.6°N, 149.3°E. This has not been plotted, but lies near Novosibirsk Island in the Arctic, about midway between poles 1 and 10 of Figure 3C.

Latitudes of Origin and Paleogeography

A well-known expression in paleomagnetic studies relates paleomagnetic inclination i to the paleolatitude of origin l by tan $(i) = 2 \ tan \ (l)$. However, associated assumptions can lead to incorrect deductions of paleolatitudes. Examples include (1) magnetization in an unknown asymmetrical, canted, or non-dipolar magnetizing field, (2) overprinting by an unrecognized younger magnetization, and (3) an incorrect inference as to the orientation of the paleohorizon.

Although the Caribbean paleoinclination data are "noisy," some suggestive trends are apparent. In examining the patterns, it is helpful to refer to the paleomagnetic colatitude p, which is the distance from the sampling site to the corresponding paleomagnetic pole. The relationship between p and l is $p + l = 90°$, where l ranges from +90° at the north pole to –90° at the south pole, and p ranges from 0° at the north pole to 180° at the south pole. *Obviously, in polar arcs generated by structural rotations, the radius of the arc corresponds to the paleocolatitude of origin.*

Charts were prepared showing paleolatitudes relative to North America as reference (Figs. 4B, D, and 5D).

Circles of paleocolatitude are shown around North America cratonic poles of two different ages, Jurassic and Cretaceous, for the purposes of this discussion (Figs. 4B, D, and 5D). A mean Jurassic pole was computed for cratonic North America from poles 52, 54, and 60 of Irving and Irving (1982); the mean pole is 65°N, 103°E, N=3, A95=9°. This pole is weighted toward Early Jurassic, with an average age of 195 Ma. Although reasonably representative of Early Jurassic North America cratonic poles, this pole is less satisfactory for younger Jurassic poles, in the age interval from 160 to 135 Ma (see Fig. 2). For the Cretaceous cratonic pole of North America, the mean pole of Hagstrum and others (1985) was adopted; that pole is 67°N, 174°W, N=5, A95=3.4°. The rock units averaged range from 78 to 130 Ma, with a mean of 106 Ma.

Polar wander for North America seems to have been greater for the Jurassic than for the Cretaceous, especially in the interval 170 to 140 Ma. With this caveat in mind, paleogeographic possibilities can be explored with the help of histograms of paleocolatitudes (Fig. 6). A useful approximation to remember for this discussion is $l = |i|/2$ for latitudes from 0° to about 30°. That is, the paleolatitude of origin (l) corresponds approximately to one half of the absolute value of the measured paleomagnetic inclination (i).

Greater Antilles

Greater Antilles poles show considerable dispersion in paleocolatitudes (Fig. 6Aa). The scatter is greater for dike poles (Fig. 6Ab) than for stratified units (Fig. 6Ae). The maximum in the stratal colatitudes occurs in the 65° to 70° class, corresponding to paleolatitudes of 25° to 20°. Not much difference was noted between Early Cretaceous (Fig. 6Ac) and Late Cretaceous (Fig. 6Ad) stratal colatitudes.

When plotted separately, the stratal poles show two interesting features (Fig. 4A): (1) they cluster mainly near Alaska, slightly near-sided from the Cretaceous poles for North America (compare with poles for 65 to 135 Ma, Fig. 2); and (2) the maximum clustering of poles follows a small circle centered at the sampling area in the Greater Antilles and having a radius near 70°. This distribution suggests a latitude of origin of about 20° for the Greater Antilles sites (Fig. 4B). Recalling that these poles are mainly from Jamaica, it is noted that the Hispaniola and Puerto Rico colatitudes (x, Fig. 6Ad) tend to be greater, suggesting slightly lower latitudes of origin for the eastern Greater Antilles.

Paleogeographically speaking, a conservative minimum displacement hypothesis favors a north latitude of origin, perhaps nearly in situ (1, Fig. 4B), or perhaps from a Pacific longitude (2, Fig. 4B). An origin south of the Cretaceous equator (3, Fig. 4B) cannot yet be entirely discounted, but seems less likely.

The greater scatter of the Greater Antilles dike data, as compared to that for the stratified units, is consistent with the inference that because dikes cool quickly, they record virtual geomagnetic field (VGP) directions; i.e., they do not individually record the average geomagnetic field direction. The greater scatter in the dike poles can also be attributed to greater age uncertainty for the dikes, lack of paleohorizon control such as bedding, and the difficulty of recognizing secondary magnetizations. Some of these factors undoubtedly also account for erratic outlier poles for the stratified units, as might also polar wander or plate movement.

Insufficient data are available to define a clear history of paleolatitude change for the Tertiary strata of the Greater Antilles. A more complete record will be required to eliminate the possibility of a southerly latitude of origin (3, Fig. 4B).

Lesser Antilles

The available mid- to Late Tertiary poles (Fig. 3B) suggest paleolatitudes little different from present latitudes relative to the North America reference (Fig. 2).

Central America

Maya block. Although paleomagnetic data are scarce for the Maya block, Gose and Sánchez-Barreda (1981) note that post-Permian motion relative to North America is suggested by their results from Permian carbonates of the Grupera and Paso Hondo formations. An equatorial latitude is indicated, the sam-

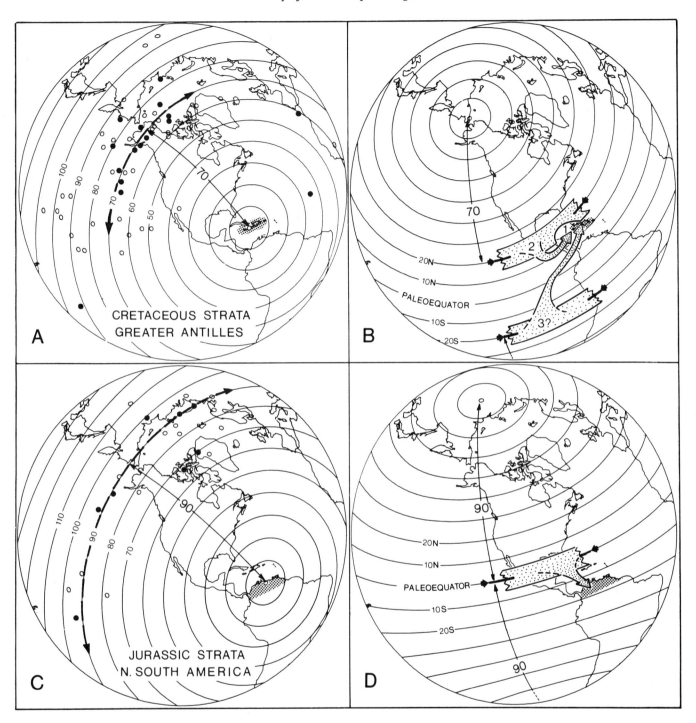

Figure 4. Paleomagnetic polar arcs (left) and latitudes of origin (right). A. Greater Antilles poles: Cretaceous strata = filled circles; all others = open circles; sampling area = stipple; radius of polar arc approximately 70°; B. Greater Antilles source possibilities: 1, in situ; 2, west of present location; 3, south of equator; all are 20° latitude; C. South America poles: Jurassic strata = filled circles; all others = open circles; sampling area = stipple; radius of polar arc approximately 90°; D. Northern South America Jurassic source possibilities: northern Caribbean and Gulf of Mexico region. See text for details.

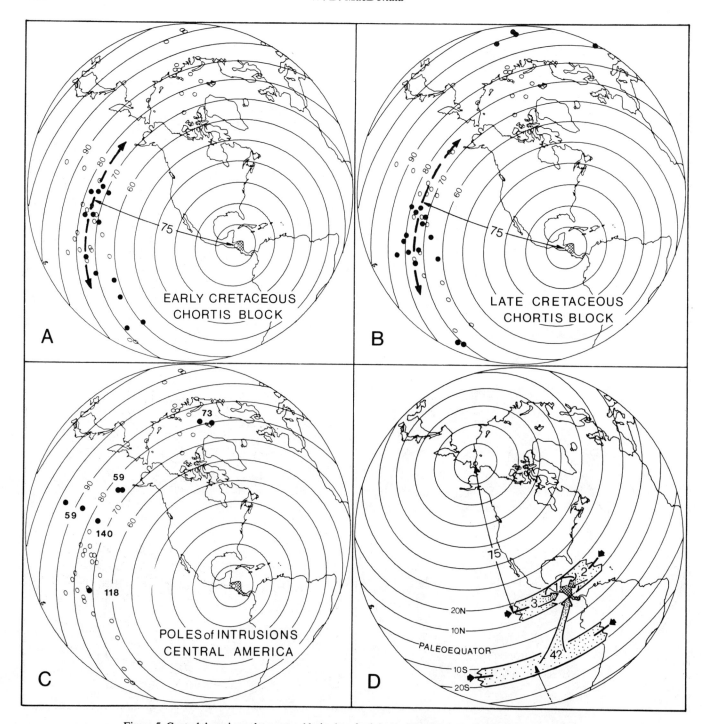

Figure 5. Central America polar arcs and latitudes of origin. A. Chortis block, Early Cretaceous poles = filled circles; all others = open circles; radius of polar arc approximately 75°; B. Chortis block, Late Cretaceous poles = filled circles; all others = open circles; radius of polar arc approximately 75°; C. Polar arc defined by poles of plutons = filled circles; all others = open circles; bold numerals give ages (Ma); D. Paleolatitudes of origin for Chortis block, with Cretaceous source alternatives: 1, in situ; 2, Caribbean source east of present location; 3, Pacific (north), west of present location; and 4, Pacific, south of equator. See text for details.

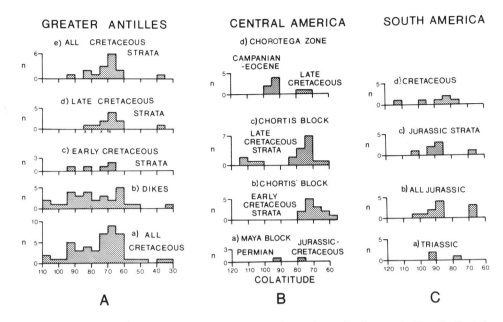

Figure 6. Caribbean paleocolatitudes of origin, by region and age: A. Greater Antilles; B. Central America; C. South America. Details in text.

pling area being about 90° from the pole (pole 5, diamond; Fig. 3C). This implies a post-Permian southward displacement of about 13° along the Pacific side relative to North America. The authors note that other interpretations are possible if the magnetization proves to be secondary.

Chortis block. The large rotations indicated for the Cretaceous of the Chortis block were accompanied by concurrent latitudinal displacements relative to North America reaching 15° to 20° (Gose and Swartz, 1977; Gose and others, 1980; Gose, 1985a, b). Separate plots show the pattern of Early Cretaceous versus Late Cretaceous poles (Figs. 5A, B) for the Chortis block. Both plots are consistent with paleocolatitudes of about 75°. This is supported by the histograms (Fig. 6Bb, Bc), which also show skewness in opposite senses for Early and Late Cretaceous paleocolatitudes. Cretaceous paleolatitudes of about 15° are thus indicated for the Chortis block. These paleolatitudes are nevertheless consistent with several conflicting tectonic paths for the Chortis block: (1) in situ or fixed relative to North America (1, Fig. 5D); (2) a Caribbean path (2, Fig. 5D); (3) a Pacific (north) path (3, Fig. 5D); and (4) a Pacific (south) path (4, Fig. 5D). For the latter locus, stronger evidence is known from the Chorotega zone, as discussed next.

Chorotega zone. From the Cretaceous rocks in the Nicoya region, de Boer (1979) notes southward declinations with positive inclinations and suggests magnetization south of the equator during a reversed interval. Slightly younger Late Cretaceous intrusions (La Culebra) show positive inclinations with northerly declinations, suggesting magnetization north of the equator. This pattern implies an equatorial crossing during the Cretaceous for rocks of the Nicoya area in the northern Chorotega zone

(de Boer, 1979, p. 240, 242). Data from Late Cretaceous to Early Tertiary formations elsewhere in the Chorotega zone are consistent with equatorial crossings in post-Eocene time (Gose, 1983). Gose (1983) favors a primary magnetization for the measured directions in this zone, but notes the clustering of Chorotega poles around the present geographic north pole, raising the possibility of young remagnetizations.

Finally, the polar arc tend is seen also in the poles of several plutons of Central America, with colatitudes generally consistent with those of the stratified rocks (Fig. 5C).

Northern South America

Permo-Triassic dikes from the Guiana shield indicate near-equatorial latitudes (Fig. 6Ca). Jurassic rocks in the orogenic zone have paleocolatitudes with an apparent bimodal distribution (Fig. 6Cb). However, an equatorial latitudinal maximum is clearly present for Jurassic stratified rocks (Fig. 6Cc; Fig. 4C). Relative to the cratonic Jurassic pole for North America cited earlier, a Jurassic latitude in the north Caribbean and Gulf of Mexico region is implied (Fig. 4D). Some Jurassic latitudinal uncertainty exists because of the age uncertainty for the Jurassic South American strata and because of less control on the Middle to Late Jurassic polar wander path for North America.

Cretaceous units with primary magnetization, good age control, and prominent paleohorizon references are scarce in the literature for this region. Nevertheless, a paleocolatitude near 85° is suggested (Fig. 6Cd) by results from diverse rock types.

Tertiary paleolatitudinal data are as yet too sparse for comment.

Oceanic Basins

   Caribbean basins. Three paleomagnetic studies of Caribbean DSDP cores have been published. Henry and Opdyke (1970) found shallow but variable inclinations at sites 29, 30, and 31. Owing to instrumental difficulties, the results are not very informative. Lowrie and Opdyke (1973) examined 34 specimens from five DSDP sites: 146, 150, 151, 152, and 153. Sites 151 and 152 lie in the north central Colombian basin (Fig. 1). The others are in the Venezuelan Basin. The Cretaceous limestone and diabase samples revealed low magnetic latitudes of origin, 3° to 17°. Their maximum inclination cluster (Fig. 7) is in the 5° to 10° class, corresponding to a paleolatitude of 3° to 5°. Because the cores are not oriented, the sense of the latitude, north or south, is ambiguous. Raff (1973) deduced a 03°N latitude of origin for the seamount at DSDP site 145 (x, Fig. 7).

   A secondary maximum (Fig. 7), for the 25° to 30° class, is due to a single site, DSDP 152, on the southeast side of the Nicaragua rise. This steeper inclination argues for a younger age for the magnetization here, or for a more northerly (or southerly) latitude of origin than for other Caribbean DSDP sites.

   The paleomagnetic reversal stratigraphy of DSDP site 502 was determined by Kent and Spariosu (1982, 1983), back to about 5.5 Ma. They noted a decrease of paleomagnetic inclination back into Late Miocene strata, and favored a compaction explanation. A post-Miocene 5° north latitudinal shift is an alternative they regard as less likely (Kent and Spariosu, 1982).

   Pacific basin. On the Pacific side of Central America, DSDP sites straddling the Middle America trench were analyzed by Gose (1982). Only sites 494 and 495, on opposite sides of the trench, provided useful data. For site 495, on the Cocos plate, Gose concluded that an equatorial crossing is recorded by shallow paleomagnetic inclinations from basalt and overlying Miocene chalk. For site 494, on the lower trench slope off Guatemala, three Cretaceous sedimentary rock samples indicated paleolatitudes of 28°, 21°, and 17°. An Oligocene limestone clast indicated paleolatitudes of 12° and 7°. Gose concluded that deposition occurred at, or nearby northward of, the present location.

CONCLUSIONS

   Caribbean paleomagnetic data reveal patterns amid much scatter. Paleomagnetic poles define polar arcs probably resulting mainly from structural and tectonic rotations. Paleomagnetic inclinations have trends possibly useful for paleogeographic interpretation. For example, Late Cretaceous latitudes of origin cluster as follows: Caribbean basins, about 05°; Greater Antilles, about 20°; and Chortis block, Central America, about 15°. Ambiguity exists in many cases as to the north or south latitude. Nevertheless, the data are encouraging. Expanded sampling, especially of Cretaceous and Tertiary strata, may resolve the latitudinal ambiguities and will undoubtedly yield a clearer understanding of Caribbean structure, tectonic evolution, and paleogeography.

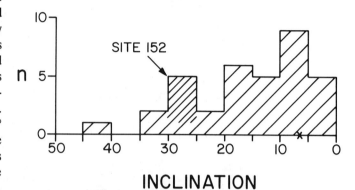

CARIBBEAN BASINS
LATE CRETACEOUS DSDP

INCLINATION

Figure 7. Caribbean Late Cretaceous paleomagnetic inclinations for DSDP sites favor low latitudes of origin. 'x' marks paleomagnetic inclination for DSDP site 145 inferred by Raff (1973). Site 152, on lower Nicaragua rise, shows steeper inclinations, consistent with either younger magnetizations or higher latitudes of origin relative to other Caribbean DSDP sites.

APPENDIX

Caribbean Paleomagnetic Data: Original Sources

   Lesser Antilles.
   Briden, and others, 1979.
   Greater Antilles.
   Dasgupta, 1973; Dasgupta and Vincenz, 1975; Fink and Harrison, 1972; Gose and Testarmata, 1983; Guja, 1970; Guja and Vincenz, 1978; Kent and Maurrasse, 1981; Robinson and Lamb, 1970; Steinhauser and Vincenz, 1973a, b; Vincenz and Dasgupta, 1978; Vincenz, and others, 1973, 1974; Watkins and Cambray, 1970.
   Central America.
   de Boer, 1979; Gose, 1982, 1983, 1985a, b; Gose and Sanchez-Barreda, 1981; Gose and Swartz, 1977; Liddicoat, and others, 1981.
   Northern South America.
   Caicedo, 1985; Creer, 1962, 1970; Hargraves, 1968, 1978; Hargraves and Shagam, 1969; Hargraves and Skerlec, 1980; Hargraves, and others, 1984; MacDonald, 1980a; MacDonald and Ellwood, 1985; MacDonald and Opdyke, 1972, 1974, 1984; MacDonald and VanHorn, 1977; Maze and Hargraves, 1984; Muessig, 1979, 1984; Onstott, 1980; Onstott and Hargraves, 1980, 1981, 1982, 1984; Perarnau, 1985a, b, c; Shagam and Hargraves, 1970, 1977; Skerlec and Hargraves, 1980; Stearns, and others, 1982; Veldcamp, and others, 1971; Wong, 1985.
   Caribbean area, oceanic basins.
   Gose, 1982; Henry and Opdyke, 1970; Kent and Spariosu, 1982, 1983; Lowrie and Opdyke, 1973; Raff, 1973.

REFERENCES CITED

Briden, J. C., Rex, D. C., Faller, A. M., and Tomblin, J. F., 1979, K–Ar geochronology and paleomagnetism of volcanic rocks in the Lesser Antilles island arc: Philosophical Transactions of the Royal Society of London, v. 291A, p. 485–528.

Bullard, E., Everett, J. E., and Smith, A. G., 1965, The fit of the continents around the Atlantic: Transactions of the Royal Society of London, v. 258A, p. 41–51.

Caicedo, M. I., 1985, Mediciones paleomagnéticas y de anisotropía de la suceptibilidad magnética en areniscas de Roraima, *in* Memoria, Congreso Geólogico Venezolano, VI, Caracas, 1985, v. 8: Sociedad Venezolana de Geólogos, p. 4969–5005.

Carey, S. W., 1958, A tectonic approach to continental drift, *in* Carey, S. W., ed., Continental drift, a symposium: Hobart, University of Tasmania, p. 177–355.

Case, J. E., and Holcombe, T. L., 1980, Geologic-tectonic map of the Caribbean region: U.S. Geological Survey Miscellaneous Investigations Map I–1100, scale 1:2,500,000.

Creer, K. M., 1962, Palaeomagnetic data from South America: Tokyo, Japan, Journal of Geomagnetism and Geoelectricity, v. 13, p. 154–165.

—— , 1970, A palaeomagnetic survey of South American rock formations: Philosophical Transactions of the Royal Society of London, v. 267A, p. 457–558.

Dasgupta, S. N., 1973, Paleomagnetism of a Paleocene pluton on Jamaica [M.S. thesis]: St. Louis, St. Louis University, 91 p.

Dasgupta, S. N., and Vincenz, S. A., 1975, Paleomagnetism of a Paleocene pluton on Jamaica: Earth and Planetary Science Letters, v. 25, p. 49–56.

de Boer, J., 1979, The outer arc of the Costa Rican orogen (oceanic basement complexes of the Nicoya and Santa Elena peninsulas): Tectonophysics, v. 56, p. 221–259.

Dengo, G., 1969, Problems of tectonic relations between Central America and the Caribbean: Gulf Coast Association of Geological Societies Transactions, v. 19, p. 311–320.

—— , 1985, Mid–America; Tectonic setting for the Pacific margin from southern Mexico to northwestern Colombia, *in* Nairn, A.E.M., Stehli, F. G., and Uyeda, S., eds., The ocean basins and margins, v. 7A: New York, Plenum Press, p. 123–180.

Fink, L. K., and Harrison, C.G.A., 1972, Paleomagnetic investigations of selected lava units on Puerto Rico [abs.]: Caribbean Geological Conference Transactions, no. 6, p. 379.

Gose, W. A., 1982, Some paleomagnetic results from Deep Sea Drilling Project Leg 67 off Guatemala, *in* Aubouin, J., and others, eds., Initial Reports of the Deep Sea Drilling Project: Washington, D.C., U.S. Government Printing Office, v. 67, p. 669–673.

—— , 1983, Late Cretaceous-Early Tertiary tectonic history of southern Central America: Journal of Geophysical Research, v. 88, p. 10585–10592.

—— , 1985a, Caribbean tectonics from a paleomagnetic perspective, *in* Stehli, F. G., and Webb, S. D., eds., The great American biotic interchange: New York, Plenum Publishing Company, p. 285–301.

—— , 1985b, Paleomagnetic results from Honduras and their bearing on Caribbean tectonics: Tectonics, v. 4, p. 565–585.

Gose, W. A., and Sánchez-Barreda, L. A., 1981, Paleomagnetic results from southern Mexico: Mexico City, Geofisica Internacional, Union Geofisica Mexicana, v. 20, p. 163–175.

Gose, W. A., and Swartz, D. K., 1977, Paleomagnetic results from Cretaceous sediments in Honduras; Tectonic implications: Geology, v. 5, p. 505–508.

Gose, W. A., and Testarmata, M. M., 1983, Paleomagnetic results from sedimentary rocks in Jamaica; Initial results: Journal of the Geological Society of Jamaica, v. 22, p. 16–24.

Gose, W. A., Finch, R. C., and Horne, G. S., 1978, Reply *to* Comment *on* 'Paleomagnetic results from Cretaceous sediments in Honduras; Tectonic implications': Geology, v. 6, p. 444–447.

Gose, W. A., Scott, G. R., and Swartz, D. K., 1980, The aggregation of Meso-America; Paleomagnetic evidence, *in* Pilger, R., ed., The origin of the Gulf of Mexico and the early opening of the central North Atlantic: Baton Rouge, Louisiana State University, Department of Geology, p. 51–54.

Guerrero, J. C., 1976, Contributions to paleomagnetism and Rb–Sr geochronology [Ph.D. thesis]: Dallas, University of Texas, 139 p.

Guerrero, J. C., and Helsley, C. E., 1974, Paleomagnetic evidence for post–Jurassic tectonic stability of southeastern Mexico [abs.]: EOS American Geophysical Union Transactions, v. 56, p. 1110.

—— , 1976, Paleomagnetismo y evolucion tectonica post–Jurasica de la Peninsula de Yucatan, Mexico: Acapulco, Congreso Latinoamericano de Geologia, III, Resumenes, p. 56.

Guja, N. H., 1970, Paleomagnetic investigations of Jamaican rocks [Ph.D. thesis]: St. Louis, St. Louis University, 326 p.

Guja, N. H., and Vincenz, S. A., 1978, Paleomagnetism of some Late Cretaceous and Miocene igneous rocks on Jamaica: Royal Astronomical Society Geophysical Journal, v. 52, p. 97–115.

Hagstrum, J. T., McWilliams, M. O., Howell, D. G., and Gromme, S., 1985, Mesozoic paleomagnetism and northward translation of the Baja California Peninsula: Geological Society of America Bulletin, v. 96, p. 1077–1090.

Hargraves, R. B., 1968, Palaeomagnetism of the Roraima dolerites: Royal Astronomical Society Geophysical Journal, v. 16, p. 147–160.

—— , 1978, Problems in palaeomagnetic synthesis illustrated by results from Permo–Triassic dolerites in Guyana: Physics of the Earth and Planetary Interiors, v. 16, p. 277–284.

Hargraves, R. B., and Shagam, R., 1969, Paleomagnetic study of La Quinta formation, Venezuela: American Association of Petroleum Geologists Bulletin, v. 53, p. 537–552.

Hargraves, R. B., and Skerlec, G. M., 1980, Paleomagnetism of some Cretaceous–Tertiary igneous rocks on Venezuelan offshore islands, Netherlands Antilles, Trinidad and Tobago, *in* Caribbean Geological Conference Transactions, no. 9, p. 509–517.

Hargraves, R. B., Shagam, R., Vargas, R., and Rodríguez, G. I., 1984, Paleomagnetic results from rhyolites (Early Cretaceous?) and andesite dikes from two localities in the Ocana area, northern Santander Massif, Colombia: Geological Society of America Memoir 162, p. 299–302.

Harland, W. B., Cox, A. V., Llewellyn, P. G., Pickton, C.A.G., Smith, A. G., and Walters, R., 1982, A geologic time scale: Cambridge, England, Cambridge University Press, 131 p.

Henry, K. W., and Opdyke, N. D., 1970, Preliminary report on paleomagnetism of Deep Sea Drilling Project Leg 4 specimens: Initial Reports, Deep Sea Drilling Project, v. 4, p. 439–454.

Irving, E., and Irving, G. A., 1982, Apparent polar wander paths Carboniferous through Cenozoic and the assembly of Gondwana: Geophysical Surveys, v. 5, p. 141–188.

Kent, D. V., and Maurrasse, F. J.–M. R., 1981, Paleomagnetic results from the Cretaceous Dumisseau formation of Haiti, *in* Transactions, Premier Colloque sur la Geologie d'Haiti, Port au Prince, 1980: L'Universite d'Etat d'Haiti, p. 236–244.

Kent, D. V., and Spariosu, D. J., 1982, Magnetostratigraphy of Caribbean Site 502 hydraulic piston cores, *in* Press, W. L., and others, ed., Initial reports of the Deep Sea Drilling Project: Washington, D.C., U.S. Government Printing Office, v. 68, p. 435–440.

—— , 1983, High resolution magnetostratigraphy of Caribbean Plio–Pleistocene deep-sea sediments: Palaeogeography, Palaeoclimatology, and Palaeoecology, v. 42, p. 47–64.

Ladd, J. W., 1976, Relative motion of South America with respect to North America and Caribbean tectonics: Geological Society of America Bulletin, v. 87, p. 969–976.

Liddicoat, J. C., Denham, C. R., and Paull, C. K., 1981, Paleomagnetism of cored sediment from Late Atitlan, Guatemala; A preliminary study: Geofisica Internacional, Union Geofisica Mexicana (Mexico City), v. 20, p. 263–270.

Lowrie, W., and Opdyke, N. D., 1973, Paleomagnetism of igneous and sedimentary samples; *in* Initial Reports, Deep Sea Drilling Project, v. 15: Washington, D.C., National Science Foundation, p. 1017–1022.

MacDonald, W. D., 1976, Cretaceous-Tertiary evolution of the Caribbean, *in* Transactions, Caribbean Geological Conference, VII, Guadeloupe, 1974: Ministere de l'Industrie et de la Recherche, Pointe-a-Pitre, French Antilles, p. 69–78.

——, 1978, Comment *on* 'Paleomagnetic results from Cretaceous sediments in Honduras: tectonic implications': Geology, v. 6, p. 443–444.

——, 1980a, Anomalous paleomagnetic directions in late Tertiary andesitic intrusions of the Cauca depression, Colombian Andes: Tectonophysics, v. 68, p. 339–348.

——, 1980b, Net tectonic rotation, apparent tectonic rotation, and the structural tilt correction in paleomagnetic studies: Journal of Geophysical Research, v. 85, p. 3659–3669.

MacDonald, W. D., and Ellwood, B., 1985, Magnetic fabric and petrofabric of the Tinaquillo peridotite, *in* Memoria, Congreso Geologico Venezolano, VI, Caracas, 1985, v. 4: Sociedad Venezolana de Geologos, p. 2470–2482.

MacDonald, W. D., and Opdyke, N. D., 1972, Tectonic rotations suggested by paleomagnetic results from northern Colombia, South America: Journal of Geophysical Research, v. 77, p. 5720–5730.

——, 1974, Triassic paleomagnetism of northern South America: Bulletin, American Association of Petroleum Geologists, v. 58, p. 208–215.

——, 1984, Preliminary paleomagnetic results from Jurassic rocks of the Santa Marta massif, Colombia: Geological Society of America, Memoir 162, p. 295–298.

MacDonald, W. D., and Van Horn, J., 1977, Paleomagnetism of the Hawk's Bill Formation, Tobago, *in* Memoria, Congreso Geológico Venezolano, V, Caracas, 1977, v. 2: Venezuela, Ministerio de Energía y Minas, p. 817–834.

Maze, W. B., 1983, Jurassic LaQuinta Formation in the Sierra de Perija, northwestern Venezuela: Geology, tectonic environment, paleomagnetic data, and copper mineralization of red beds and volcanics [Ph.D. thesis]: Princeton, New Jersey, Princeton University, 371 p.

Maze, W. B., and Hargraves, R. B., 1984, Paleomagnetic results from the Jurassic LaQuinta Formation in the Perija Range, Venezuela and their tectonic significance: Geological Society of America, Memoir 162, p. 287–293.

Muessig, K. W., 1979, The central Falcon igneous rocks, northwestern Venezuela: Their origin, petrology, and tectonic significance [Ph.D. thesis]: Princeton, New Jersey, Princeton University, 252 p.

——, 1984, Paleomagnetic data on the basic igneous intrusions of the central Falcon Basin, Venezuela: Geological society of America, Memoir 162, p. 231–237.

Onstott, T. C., 1980, Paleomagnetism of Guayana shield, Venezuela, and its implication concerning Proterozoic tectonics of South America and Africa [Ph.D. thesis]: Princeton, New Jersey, Princeton University, 272 p.

Onstott, T. C., and Hargraves, R. B., 1980, Paleomagnetism of the Precambrian rocks of the Guayana shield, Venezuela: International Geological Correlation Project, Newsletter no. 4-5, p. 20–22.

——, 1981, Proterozoic transcurrent tectonics: Paleomagnetic evidence from Venezuela and Africa: Nature, v. 289, p. 131–136.

——, 1982, Paleomagnetic data and the Proterozoic apparent polar wander curve for the Venezuelan Guayana shield: *in* Transactions, Caribbean Geological Conference, IX, Santo Dominto, Dominican Republic, 1980, p. 475–508.

Onstott, T. C., Hargraves, R. B., York, D., and Hall, C., 1984, Constraints on the motions of South American and African shields during the Proterozoic: I; 40Ar/39Ar and paleomagnetic correlations between Venezuela and Liberia: Geological Society of America, Bulletin, v. 95, p. 1045–1054.

Pal, S., 1978, A survey of paleomagnetic data on Mexico: Journal of Physics of the Earth, v. 26, supplement, p. S203–S219.

Perarnau, A., 1985a, Paleomagnetic studies of some Venezuelan rocks [Ph.D. thesis]: University of Newcastle upon Tyne, 273 p.

Perarnau, A., 1985b, Resultados paleomagneticos del Grupo Roraima en el sitio de La Escalera, *in* Memoria, Congreso Geologico Venezolano, VI, Caracas,

v. 8: Sociedad Venezolana de Geólogos, p. 5218–5243.

Perarnau, A., 1985c, Resultados paleomagnéticos preliminares de la Fm. San Juan a lo largo de la falla de San Francisco, *in* Memoria, Congreso Geologico Venezolano, VI, Caracas, v. 8: Sociedad Venezolana de Geologos, p. 5244–5257.

Raff, A., 1973, Site 145; *in* Initial Reports, Deep Sea Drilling Project, v. 15; Washington, D.C., National Science Foundation, p. 1063–1066.

Robinson, E., and Lamb, J. L., 1970, Preliminary paleomagnetic data from the Plio-Pleistocene of Jamaica: Nature, v. 227, p. 1236–1237.

Shagam, R., and Hargraves, R. B., 1970, Geologic and paleomagnetic study of Permo–Carboniferous red beds (Sabaneta and Merida facies), Venezuelan Andes: Bulletin, American Association of Petroleum Geologists, v. 54, p. 2336–2348.

——, 1977, Paleomagnetism of tuffaceous volcanics at the base of the La Quinta Formation, Venezuela: *in* Memoria, Congreso Latinoamericano de Geologia, II, Caracas, 1973: Venezuela Ministerio de Minas e Hidrocarburos, Boletin de Geologia, Publicacion Especial, no. 7, v. 4, p. 3055–3057.

Skerlec, G. M., and Hargraves, R. B., 1980, Tectonic significance of paleomagnetic data from northern Venezuela: Journal of Geophysical Research, v. 85, p. 5303–5315.

Stearns, C., Mauk, F. J., and Van der Voo, R., 1982, Late Cretaceous–early Tertiary paleomagnetism of Aruba and Bonaire (Netherlands Leeward Antilles): Journal of Geophysical Research, v. 87, p. 1127–1141.

Steinhauser, P., and Vincenz, S. A., 1973a, Equatorial paleopoles and behavior of the dipole field during polarity transitions, Earth and Planetary Science Letters, v. 19, p. 113–119.

——, 1973b, Paleomagnetism of Lower Cretaceous lavas on Jamaica: Arch. Met. Geophys. Biokl., series A, v. 22, p. 325–336.

Urrutia-Fucugauchi, J., 1984, On the tectonic evolution of Mexico: paleomagnetic constraints, *in* Van der Voo, R., Scotese, C. R., and Bonhommet, N., eds., Plate reconstructions from Paleozoic paleomagnetism: American Geophysical Union, Geodynamics Series, v. 12, p. 29–47.

Veldcamp, J., Mulder, F. G., and Zijderveld, J.D.A., 1971, Palaeomagnetism of Suriname dolerites: Physics of the Earth and Planetary Interiors, v. 4, p. 370–380.

Vincenz, S. A., and Dasgupta, S. N., 1978, Paleomagnetic study of some Cretaceous and Tertiary rocks on Hispaniola: Pure and Applied Geophysics, v. 116, p. 1200–1210.

Vincenz, S. A., Steinhauser, P., and Dasgupta, S. N., 1973, Paleomagnetism of Upper Cretaceous ignimbrites on Jamaica: Zeitschrift fur Geophysik, v. 39, p. 727–737.

Vincenz, S., Steinhauser, P., and Dasgupta, S., 1974, Die Bewegung der Karibishen Platte nach den Ergebnissen von palaomagnetischen Messungen: Jahrestagung der Deutsch Geophysikalischen Gesellschaft, v. 34, p. 5–33.

Watkins, N. D., and Cambray, F. W., 1970, Paleomagnetism of Cretaceous dikes from Jamaica: Geophysical Journal, Royal Astronomical Society, v. 212, p. 163–179.

Wilson, H. H., and Meyerhoff, A. A., 1978, Comment *on* 'Paleomagnetic results from Cretaceous sediments in Honduras: Tectonic implications': Geology, v. 6, p. 440–442.

Wong, J. M., 1985, Estudios paleomagneticos de unidades Precambricas del escudo de Guayana y su contribucion a la curva de deriva polar suramericana, *in* Memoria, Congreso Geologico Venezolano, VI, Caracas, v. 8: Sociedad Venezolana de Geologos, p. 5417–5465.

Manuscript Accepted by the Society January 22, 1987

ACKNOWLEDGMENTS

Among the many individuals who contributed to this compilation, I thank especially S. Vincenz, R. Hargraves, T. Onstott, and W. Gose. I am grateful to G. Dengo, S. Gromme, and A. R. Palmer for comments. Thanks also go to all those who provided reprints and preprints.

The Geology of North America
Vol. H, The Caribbean Region
The Geological Society of America, 1990

Chapter 16

Geological evolution of the Caribbean region;
A plate-tectonic perspective

James L. Pindell
Department of Earth Sciences, Dartmouth College, Hanover, New Hampshire 03755
Stephen F. Barrett
Amoco Production Company, Box 3092, 501 West Lake Boulevard, Houston, Texas 77253

INTRODUCTION

This chapter examines the geologic evolution of the Caribbean region from a plate-tectonic perspective, and is composed of three major parts. First, some primary tectonic constraints on plate-tectonic models of Caribbean evolution are defined and reviewed. These constraints include: (1) the plate-kinematic framework: the spatial relationships of the plates through time, derived from an initial reconstruction and the subsequent relative motions of the North American, African, South American, and Farallon plates, which encompass the Caribbean area; and (2) the following plate-tectonic elements: (a) the polarity and timing of subduction (magmatic activity) of arcs (arcs = magmatic belts), (b) the age of formation (magmatic crystallization) and of emplacement of pieces of oceanic crust preserved in thrust belts, (c) the timing and vergence of thrusting within known Caribbean collision zones, (d) the paleogeographic significance of the Yucatán Basin, Grenada Basin, and Cayman Trough, and (e) the development of the northern and southern Caribbean plate boundary zones.

Second, in tabular form, twelve published models of the plate-tectonic evolution of the Gulf of Mexico and Caribbean are examined by outlining the implications of each for seventeen subregions, by highlighting alternate interpretations of the geologic history of each subregion, and by presenting arguments for choosing among the alternatives. Third, a new model of Caribbean evolution is developed by integrating the Caribbean plate-tectonic elements, defined earlier, into an accurate plate-kinematic framework. The new model is presented on eight plate-boundary maps with accompanying descriptions (see accompanying plate).

THE CARIBBEAN: AN INTERPLATE REALM

The present boundaries of the Caribbean plate (Fig. 1) are defined roughly by the distribution of seismic activity (Sykes and Ewing, 1965; Molnar and Sykes, 1969; Aggarwal, 1983). The boundaries in the west and east, respectively, are the Middle America and Lesser Antilles subduction zones. In the north and south, the boundaries are less well defined. These "plate boundary zones" are broad zones dominated by strike-slip motion (Burke and others, 1978), from central Guatemala to the Puerto Rico Trench in the north, and from Colombia to Trinidad in the south. At present the Caribbean plate is moving eastward relative to North and South America at rates between 2 to 4 cm/yr (Ross and others, 1986; Sykes and others, 1982); therefore, the present-day Caribbean plate is allochthonous with respect to North and South America (Case and others, 1984).

Former plate boundaries in the Caribbean area evolved within the framework of the changing relative positions of North and South America following the Late Triassic–Jurassic breakup of Pangea; most Pangean reconstructions eliminate the area presently occupied by the Caribbean plate. Consequently, the present plate-boundary configuration only hints at earlier configurations, which included plate boundaries in the Gulf of Mexico, Yucatán Basin, and Pacific. Therefore, it is appropriate to think of Caribbean evolution in terms of the development and evolution of plate boundaries in a complex "interplate realm."

Plate-tectonic analysis of interplate realms requires the kinematic-geologic approach (Atwater, 1970; Dewey and others, 1973; Ladd, 1976). Plate-tectonic/geologic elements of the region in question must be defined, and these then must be integrated into the kinematic/geometric framework provided by the paleopositions and relative motions through time of the major encompassing plates. In the following sections, this approach is taken to assess the evolution of the Caribbean region.

PLATE-KINEMATIC FRAMEWORK
FOR THE CARIBBEAN

Unlike many ocean basins, the Caribbean is not a simple Atlantic-type ocean basin in which the paleogeography of the bordering continents can be determined by realigning pairs of

Pindell, J. L., and Barrett, S. F., 1990, Geological evolution of the Caribbean region: A plate-tectonic perspective, *in* Dengo, G., and Case, J. E., eds., The Caribbean region: Boulder, Colorado, Geological Society of America, The Geology of North America, v. H.

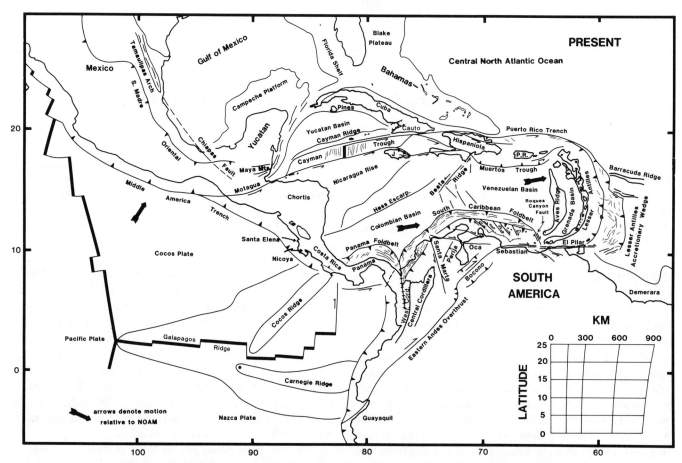

Figure 1. Geography and present plate boundaries of the Caribbean region. Plate boundaries and major faults denoted by thrust (teeth on overriding plate) and strike-slip arrow symbols. Heavy arrows indicate directions of plate motions relative to North America. J, Jamaica; PR, Puerto Rico. Modified from Case and Holcombe (1980).

coeval magnetic anomalies along fracture-zone traces. This is because of the strong evidence for large-scale shear displacements at the boundaries between the Caribbean Plate and North and South America. The Caribbean Plate is allochthonous to its neighbors, which implies that the Americas are not the rifted margins of the present-day Caribbean ocean basin, and also that marine magnetic anomalies in the Caribbean plate cannot be used to establish the separation history of North and South America.

Rather, the relative paleopositions of North and South America can be determined by finite-difference solutions for the three-plate system of North America, Africa, and South America (Ladd, 1976). In this method, finite plate rotations that fit equivalent magnetic anomaly pairs are used to reconstruct the paleopositions of Africa with respect to North America, and of South America with respect to Africa. The paleopositions of South America with respect to North America can then be calculated by completion of the finite difference circuit (small-circle vector addition) for various times. The post-breakup history of relative

motion can be displayed as a flow line connecting points representing the paleopositions of South America relative to North America, or vice versa (Pindell and Dewey, 1982).

Initial circum-Atlantic reconstructions

The early portion of the relative-motion history of North and South America is critically constrained by the initial prerift continental reconstruction, derived by closing the central North Atlantic and South Atlantic Oceans. Three different approaches to deriving the initial fits are shown in Figure 2: (1) least-error fitting of the 1,000-fathom (2,000 m) isobaths (Bullard and others, 1965); (2) realignment of marginal offsets and fracture zones from opposing continental margins (Le Pichon and Fox, 1971); and (3) least-error fitting of paleomagnetic poles of Permian age for each of the three continents (Van der Voo and others, 1976). The least-error fitting of present-day margins does not recognize the blanketing effects of postbreakup sedimentation, or emplace-

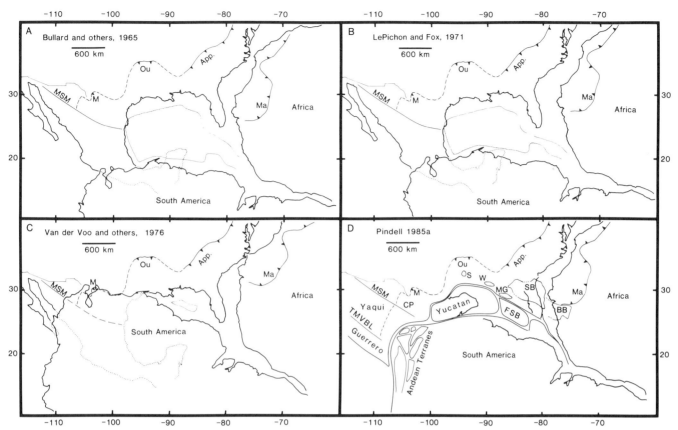

Figure 2. Four Permo-Triassic reconstructions of circum-Atlantic continents (Mercator projection, North American reference frame) commonly used as starting points in models of Gulf/Caribbean evolution. Shaded areas indicate noncontinental gaps within the reconstructions. MSM, Mojave-Sonora Megashear; App, Appalachians; Ou, Ouachitas; M, Marathons; Ma, Mauritanides; TMVBL, Trans-Mexican Volcanic Belt Lineament; FSB, Florida Straits Block; CP, Coahuila Peninsula; S, Sabine Uplift; W, Wiggins Arch; MG, Florida Middle Grounds Arch; SB, Suwannee Basin; BB, Bove Basin.

ment of allochthonous blocks from elsewhere, on the original configuration of the rifted continental basement, and the fit suggested by paleomagnetic data does not provide, on its own, a satisfactory reassembly of the late Paleozoic foldbelt in the Gulf of Mexico area. The realignment of marginal offsets and fracture zones, however, is a requirement of the reconstruction at the commencement of continental breakup.

All of these reconstructions use the South Atlantic fit of Bullard and others (1965), which contains significant error because the 1,000 fathom isobath along the Amazon portion of the Brazilian shelf does not coincide with the continental limit (Rabinowitz and LaBrecque, 1979; Pindell, 1985a; Pindell and Dewey, 1982). A better coincidence of these margins comes from restoring the intracontinental extension that occurred during continental separation, and then aligning the prerift shapes of the margins. This suggests a tighter reconstructed fit between the north Brazilian and Guinea margins, relative to the fit of Bullard and others (1965). The adverse effects of this tighter Equatorial

Atlantic fit on the southern South Atlantic fit can be reconciled by considering that Africa behaved as two separate plates during the Early Cretaceous (for a discussion of that problem, see Burke and Dewey, 1974; Pindell and Dewey, 1982; Pindell, 1985a; Klitgord and others, 1984). The proper reassembly of the Equatorial Atlantic margins is important to the early paleogeography of the Caribbean, because a tighter fit, relative to that of Bullard and others (1965), places South America several hundred kilometers closer to North America when Africa is reconstructed with North America to form a Pangean reconstruction.

The initial reconstruction between North and South America can be improved further by identifying and incorporating all areas of pre-Mesozoic continental crust, and by restoring synrift lithospheric attenuation, and postrift strikeslip offsets and shortening, within all rifted margins. Figure 2D, after Pindell (1985a), incorporates these additional considerations as well as a tighter Equatorial Atlantic reconstruction, and juxtaposes Africa and North America approximately along marginal fracture zone

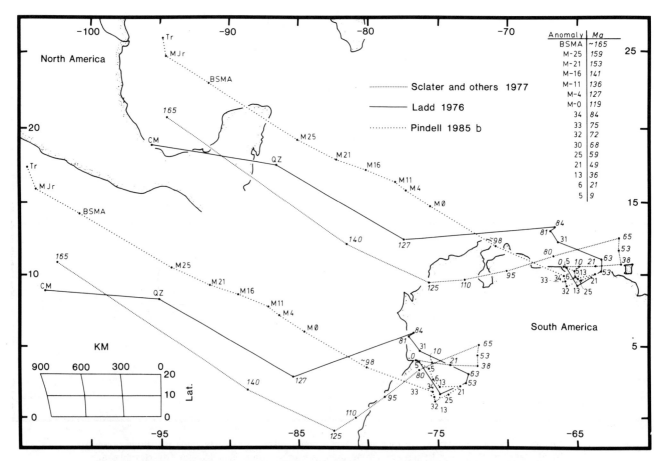

Figure 3. Post-Triassic relative-motion histories, or flow lines, determined for two points (10.5N, 66W and 4N, 77W) along South America, with respect to North America, from three data sets. Mercator projection. For the vectors of Ladd (1976) and Pindell (1985b), upright numerals identify positions computed from vector addition of the Central and South Atlantic rotation parameters in the three-plate system of North America–Africa–South America. Inclined numerals indicate age in millions of years and were interpolated between positions picked by anomaly identification. The vector of Sclater and others (1977) is based on rotation parameters defined by the age-depth curve in the ocean basins, and its points are defined by age in millions of years. CM, continental margin; QZ, quiet zone; BSMA, Blake Spur magnetic anomaly; Tr, Late Triassic; MJr, Middle Jurassic.

traces in the central North Atlantic. Because it satisfies these important aspects, Figure 2D serves as the starting point for the model of Caribbean evolution developed later.

Relative motion vectors of the major plates

Figure 3 shows relative motion vectors, or flow lines, of South America with respect to North America, for three different data sets that define finite-difference solutions for the three-plate system of South America–Africa–North America. The paleopositions of the major plates constrain models of Caribbean evolution by defining the geographic size and shape of the interplate region through time. The relative-motion vector constrains the nature of the North America–South America plate boundary through time.

Differences between the vectors in Figure 3 are due to: (1) differing initial reconstructions of North America, South America, and Africa, and (2) differences in identification of marine magnetic anomalies and fracture zone traces, and consequent differences in total finite-rotation parameters for each ocean. The vector of Pindell (1985b) is derived from a recent data set (Lamont-Doherty Geological Observatory, 1985, for Campanian to Present anomalies; and Klitgord and Schouten, 1987, for the Keathley Sequence in the central North Atlantic) and incorporates the initial reconstruction of Figure 2D. Therefore, the paleopositions derived from the vector of Pindell (1985b) form the framework for the evolutionary model proposed later. Briefly, this vector describes the motion of South America as it (1) migrated from North America during Late Triassic through early

Campanian time (DNAG time scale); (2) remained essentially fixed relative to North America during Campanian through middle Eocene time, except for possible minor north-south compression (100 km) and sinistral shear during the early Paleogene; and (3) converged with North America by 250 to 300 km in a north-northwestly direction since the middle Eocene. All post-Campanian displacements probably have occurred by extensional and compressional strike-slip motions at the Barracuda, Tiburon, and other fracture zones east of the Lesser Antilles.

Motions through time of the Farallon Plate of the Pacific realm are also important to understanding the evolution of the Caribbean. The theoretical direction and rate of convergence of the Farallon Plate, shown relative to North America for two points near the western Caribbean area in Figure 4, may have controlled the style of subduction beneath, and possible microplate migrations along, the Pacific subduction systems of the Americas and the Caribbean. Further, this convergence may have affected the rate at which the Caribbean Plate entered the proto-Caribbean realm in the Late Cretaceous.

PLATE-TECTONIC INTERPRETATION OF CARIBBEAN GEOLOGICAL FEATURES

In this section we define a set of plate-tectonic elements that are critical parts of any model of the Caribbean region's evolution. These elements are subduction-related magmatic arcs ("island arcs" or "volcanic arcs"), ultramafic-mafic complexes representing oceanic crust, and orogenic collision zones, including metamorphic belts. Other important considerations discussed here are the paleogeographic significance of the Yucatán Basin, Grenada Basin, and Cayman Trough, and the development of the northern and southern Caribbean plate boundary zones.

Magmatic arcs and occurrences of oceanic crust: Keys to the timing and polarity of subduction in the Caribbean

General significance of arcs. Subduction-related rocks in the Caribbean (Jurassic to Recent intermediate magmatic rocks) can be grouped into eight separate magmatic arcs or magmatic-arc pieces (Fig. 5): Greater Antilles, Aves Ridge, Lesser Antilles, Leeward Antilles, Costa Rica–Panamá, Chortis (southern Guatemala, Honduras, northern Nicaragua, western Nicaraguan Rise), eastern Nicaraguan Rise–Jamaica, and the arc(s) of northwestern South America. In addition, the Neogene Middle American magmatic belt has developed upon the western portion of the Chortis arc and upon the Costa Rica–Panamá arc. We treat this activity simply as continuations of the activity of the primary arcs that form the basement of the Middle American belt.

The eight arcs have different histories, although some may be genetically related. Criteria for identifying and distinguishing between arcs include (1) the record of subduction-related magmatism, (2) history of volcanogenic sedimentation, and (3) evidence for deciphering arc polarity. Some of these arc terranes

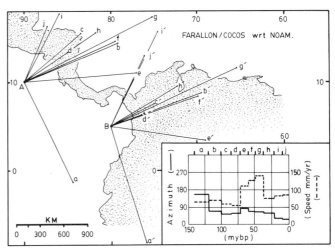

Figure 4. Stage-pole motion vectors of the Farallon/Cocos Plate relative to North America, determined for two points (A, 10N, 90W) and (B, 5N, 80W). In the Early Miocene, the Cocos Plate decoupled from the Farallon Plate, developing independent motion relative to North America. Data for increments a through h from Engebretson (1982). For increments i and j, Cocos motion relative to North America was computed through the three-plate system North America–Pacific-Cocos, and includes data from Engebretson (1982), Mammerickx and Klitgord (1982), and Klitgord and Mammerickx (1982).

have been dissected by transcurrent plate motions and thrusting during and following their formation and, therefore, no longer possess their original arc geometry. We use the terms "continental" and "intraoceanic" to refer to subduction-related magmatic arcs that have developed upon preexisting continental and oceanic crust, respectively.

The nature of the basement in some of the intraoceanic arcs is disputed as to whether it is oceanic crust or "primitive arc" material. We regard as indicative of subduction, only those magmas that are truly intermediate and calc-alkaline. We refer to the direction from the arc plutons to the forearc and accretionary prism as the "facing" direction (e.g., an east-facing arc overlies a west-dipping Benioff Zone).

The subduction-related igneous activity for each of the arc systems in the Caribbean (plutons, lavas, tuffs) is summarized in Figure 6; the period over which each was volcanically or magmatically active correlates approximately with the period of active subduction. Radiometric ages on metamorphic, mafic, and silicic rocks are also shown; these lend additional information on each arc. Most radiometric dates on plutons are K-Ar dates, which may indicate time of uplift rather than emplacement; nevertheless, K-Ar dates on plutons place a minimum on the age of arc activity. Furthermore, general correlation exists between stratigraphic and radiometric ages for arcs where data from both methods are available. Emplacement of subduction-related plutons (and the oldest K-Ar dates on them) may postdate initiation of

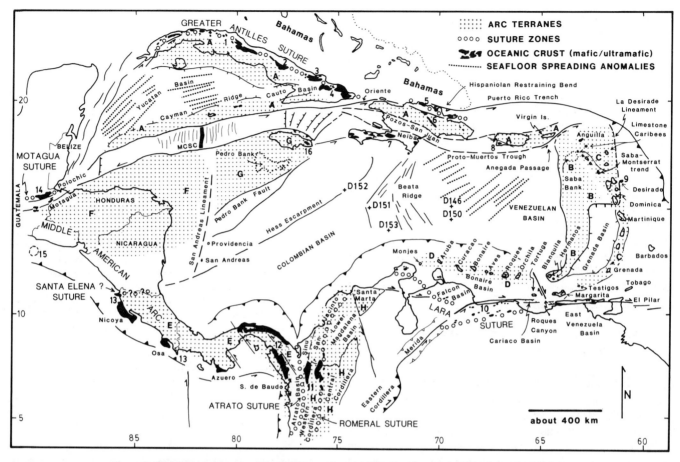

Figure 5. General tectonic map of the Caribbean, features described in text. A to H refer to the following arcs: A, Greater Antilles; B, Aves Ridge; C, Lesser Antilles; D, Leeward Antilles; E, Costa Rica–Panamá; F, Chortis; G, Nicaragua Rise–Jamaica; H, Central and Western Cordillera. Numbers 1 through 16 are occurrences of oceanic crust, keyed to and described in Table 1. D146 and D150 to D153 are DSDP holes (Leg XV) that reached medial Cretaceous basalts of the B″ seismic horizon (Edgar and others, 1971). In our interpretation, the Lara Suture (northern Venezuela) has been dextrally offset since the late Miocene by transcurrent motions along the Merida Andes. MCSC, Mid-Cayman Spreading Center, with flanking structural trends. Oceanic portion of Cayman Trough bounded by first normal-fault symbol at each end.

subduction by 2 to 10 m.y., depending on subduction rate and angle.

General significance of occurrences of oceanic crust. Ultramafic-mafic complexes are another primary source of information for plate-tectonic syntheses; they commonly are fragments of oceanic crust (ophiolites) representing now-vanished oceans in accretionary complexes or forearc nappes (Burke and others, 1977). In intraoceanic arc terranes, they may also represent basement brought to the surface by strike-slip faulting or thrusting. Ultramafic-mafic bodies representing oceanic crust (Fig. 5) occur throughout the Caribbean region (Case, 1980; Burke and others, 1984; Wadge and others, 1984). The important aspects of these occurrences for tectonic syntheses are the age of

formation (magmatic crystallization) and the timing and style of emplacement into their present tectonic settings (Table 1).

In accretionary complexes, the age of formation of ophiolitic rocks indicates the age or age range of at least some of the crust that was subducted at that margin. In collision zones, ultramafic-mafic rocks may have been accreted from the downgoing plate prior to collision, or may represent the basement of the forearc. In the first case, the age of formation indicates the age of subducted crust in the ocean prior to closure, and in the second case, the age of basement of the arc complex. In thrust belts or flower structures in intraoceanic arcs, formation ages indicate the age of basement upon which the arc developed.

Emplacement ages in accretionary complexes (obduction

TABLE 1. OCCURRENCES OF SEA-FLOOR CRUST IN THE CARIBBEAN

Name/location (Keyed to Fig. 5) and Tectonic Significance	Age of Formation	Age and Modes of Emplacement	Selected References
1. Central Cuba, A or C	Pre-Albian	Paleocene to mid-Eocene, E	Wadge and others, 1984; Gealey, 1980; Soto, 1978; Mossakovskiy and Albear, 1978
2. Las Villas, Camaguäy, Cuba, A or C	Pre-Aptian	Early or mid-Eocene, E	Wadge and others, 1984; Thayer and Guild, 1947; Mossakovskiy and Albear, 1978; Pardo, 1975; Flint and others, 1948; Meyerhoff and Hatten, 1968
3. Holguín, Cuba, A or C	Pre-Aptian	Mid-Eocene, E	Kozary, 1968; Knipper and Cabrera, 1974; Wadge and others, 1984; Brezsnyansky and Korpas, 1973
4. Nipe-Purial, Cuba, A or C	unknown	Maastrichtian-Paleocene, E?	Boiteau and Michard, 1976; Cobiella and others, 1977; Cobiella, 1978; Lewis and Straczek, 1955; Wadge and others, 1984; Boiteau and others, 1972
5. Northern Hispaniola, A or C	Pre-Aptian	Paleocene-mid Eocene, E. post-mid-Miocene, F	Nagle, 1966; Pindell, 1985b; Bourgois and others, 1980; Eberle and others, 1980; Wadge and others, 1980; Wadge and others, 1984; Bowin and Nagle, 1980
6. Central Hispaniola, B or C	Early Cretaceous	Albian?, D. Oligo-Miocene, F	Bowin, 1960; Palmer, 1963; Haldemann and others, 1980; Draper and Lewis, 1983; Theyer, 1983
7. Southern Hispaniola, B and C	Cenomanian to Campanian	Pre-Paleocene, D. Neogene, F	Maurrasse and others, 1979; Mercier de Lepinay and others, 1979
8. Bermeja, Puerto Rico, C	Tithonian	Pre-Turonian, D	Mattson, 1973; Mattson and Pessagno, 1979
9. La Désirade, C*	Late Jurassic-Early Cretaceous	Pre-Eocene, D	Mattinson and others, 1980, 1973; Briden and others, 1979; Fink, 1970
10. Villa de Cura, Venezuela, A	Hauterivian-Albian	Paleocene to Miocene, E	Gealey, 1980; Maresch, 1974; Stephan and others, 1980; Beck, 1978; Santamaria and Schubert, 1974; Beets and others, 1984
11. Western Cordillera, Colombia, C†	Pre-Cenomanian	Campanian to Maastrichtian, D	Barrero, 1979; Shagam, 1975; Henderson, 1979; Irving, 1975; Bourgois and others, 1982; Mooney, 1980
12. Eastern Panamá, B	Cenomanian? to Campanian	Neogene, E	Case and others, 1971; Bandy and Casey, 1973; Bandy, 1970; Bourgois and others, 1982; Case, 1974b
13. Nicoya, Santa Elena, C	Late Jurassic to Late Cretaceous	Campanian to Paleogene, D	Bourgois and others, 1982; Azema and Tournon, 1980; de Boer, 1979; Galli-Olivier, 1979; Lundberg, 1983; Gursky and others, 1983; Schmidt-Effing, 1979
14. Santa Cruz, others, Guatemala, A	Late Valanginian-Early Cenomanian	Campanian-Maastrichtian, E. Cenozoic, F	Williams, 1975; Rosenfeld, 1981; Bertrand and others, 1978
15. Pacific margin, DSDP Leg 84, C	Pre-Cenomanian	Paleocene, D	Auboin and others, 1982
16. Blue Mountains, Jamaica, C	Campanian?	Maastrichtian to Paleocene?, D	Wadge and others, 1984; Wadge and others, 1982

A: Basement of forearc of associated magmatic arc.
B: Basement of arc or local terrane.
C: In accretionary complex, clipped from downgoing plate at associated trench.
D: Accreted to subduction complex by obduction.
E: Arc/continent collision and obduction of forearc/accretionary prism.
F: flower structure or diapir in compressional strike-slip domain.
*Possibly basement of Lesser Antilles, initially accreted to Aves Ridge arc.
†Cenozoic arc developed upon ophiolitic basement after the latter was obducted/accreted to Central Cordillera.

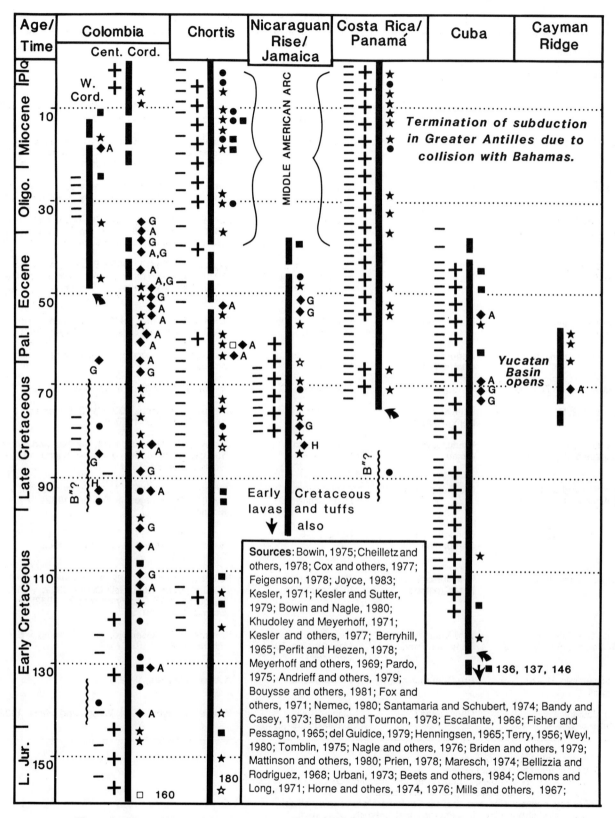

Figure 6. Igneous history of Caribbean arcs defined in text and Figure 5. Radiometric age symbols represent one or more ages, from one or more igneous bodies, at a 2 m.y. sampling interval. All constants are those of the International Union of Geological Sciences, either in the original work or by recalculation. Greater Antilles arc includes Cuba, Cayman Ridge, Hispaniola, Puerto Rico, Virgin

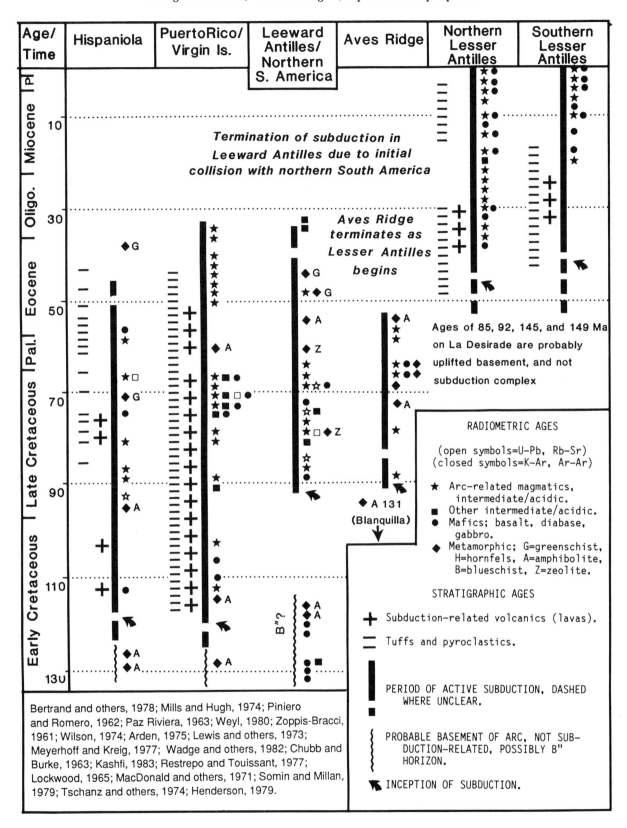

Islands. Boundary of the northern and southern Lesser Antilles is between Martinique and St. Lucia. Aves Ridge includes La Blanquilla, Los Hermanos, and Saba Bank. Leeward Antilles and northern South America are treated together due to uncertain genetic relationship.

from the downgoing plate) may span the entire period of subduction. The age of emplacement in collision zones records the time of collision, although field relations defining older emplacement ages from the accretionary stage may be preserved. Emplacement ages in flower structures or thrusts are, obviously, coeval with development of the thrust systems.

Magmatic belt (arc) systems in the Caribbean. Greater Antilles arc. The Cretaceous-Paleogene histories of island arc development in Cuba, the Cayman Ridge, Hispaniola, Puerto Rico, and the Virgin Islands are similar (Fig. 6, Table 1), suggesting that these islands belonged originally to the same arc system (White and Burke, 1980; Sykes and others, 1982; Pindell and Dewey, 1982; Coney, 1983). The present-day geographic discontinuity of these arc components can be explained by intra-arc spreading in Yucatán Basin, which separated Cuba from the Cayman Ridge in the Paleogene (Gealey, 1980; Hall and Yeung, 1980), and by large-scale strike-slip offsets along splays of the Cayman Transform System through Hispaniola, Puerto Rico, and Aves Ridge (Sykes and others, 1982; Pindell and Dewey, 1982). Westernmost Cuba, west of the Pinar Fault, and north-central Cuba along the Old Bahamas Channel, however, appear to be continental (Pszczolkowski, 1978) and unrelated to the Greater Antilles magmatic arc.

In Cuba and Hispaniola, subduction-related magmatism began in the Early Cretaceous, increased during the Late Cretaceous, and ceased in the middle Eocene (Fig. 6). In western and central Cuba, Maastrichtian and Paleogene plutons are absent. However, the onshore portions of the island are too close to the paleotrench (ophiolite complexes) for the plutons (if any were produced in the Maastrichtian or Paleocene) to be exposed. In Puerto Rico and the Virgin Islands, magmatism started in the latest Early Cretaceous or early Late Cretaceous and persisted into the Late Eocene (Puerto Rico) and Oligocene (Virgin Islands). However, the young magmatism in the Virgin Islands may relate to subduction beneath the adjacent, but younger, Lesser Antilles arc, rather than to subduction beneath the Greater Antilles arc. The Greater Antilles arc probably was built on oceanic crust; the metamorphosed mafic Duarte Formation of Hispaniola (Bowin, 1975) and the Domingo Belt of Cuba (Pardo, 1975) are probable examples of such basement. The possibility of continental crust in central Cuba is not proved, and possible continental blocks may be allochthonous, as is the rest of the volcanic part of the island south of the ophiolite belt (Case and others, 1984).

The early polarity of the arc is unknown; the ultramafic-bearing Bermeja Complex of Puerto Rico may be oceanic crust accreted to the south side prior to the Campanian (Mattson, 1973; Mattson and Pessagno, 1979), suggesting south-facing polarity. After the Santonian or Campanian, the arc was definitely north facing, as indicated by the Late Cretaceous to Eocene ultramafic-bearing subduction complexes along the northern side of the arc (Case and others, 1984) that overthrust the Jurassic to early Paleogene shelf carbonates of the Bahamas (Pardo, 1975; Wadge and others, 1984) in the early Paleogene.

The Aves Ridge arc. Included with the Aves Ridge are Saba Bank to the north and, probably, La Blanquilla and Los Hermanos to the south (Fig. 5). Dredging on this largely submarine ridge has produced basalts and granodioritic rocks indicative of arc magmatism (Fox and others, 1971; Fox and Heezen, 1975). Gravimetric and seismic studies (Kearey, 1974) suggest that the crustal structure of Aves Ridge is similar to that of an island arc.

Subduction-related magmatism occurred at least during the Late Cretaceous through early Paleogene (Fig. 6). Nothing is known of this arc's pre–Late Cretaceous history; Eocene to Recent shallow- and deep-water limestones form the bulk of the known sediment. The slight eastward convexity of the ridge and the magnetic expression of plutons in Aves Ridge (Speed and Westbrook, 1984) are the only indications of arc polarity; it was probably an east-facing arcuate continuation of the Greater Antilles arc during Late Cretaceous–Eocene time.

The Lesser Antilles arc. This arc comprises Anguilla to Grenada (including Saba Island and the Limestone Caribbees). The bathymetric ridge upon which the arc is built extends to Los Testigos and Margarita, but those islands are far removed from the primary belt of Lesser Antillean volcanism.

Initial magmatism in the present Lesser Antilles arc is difficult to date. The Lesser Antilles frontal arc may have been built upon older volcanic rocks, possibly associated with the pre-Paleocene Aves Ridge arc. Paleogene intra-arc spreading may have dissected the original Aves Ridge arc complex and created the Grenada Basin (Tomblin, 1975). Subduction-related arc magmatism has been continuous in the northern Lesser Antilles arc since the Eocene, but magmatism in the southern Lesser Antilles may have started only in the Oligocene (Fig. 6; Briden and others, 1979; Bouysse and others, 1980).

The Lesser Antilles arc is east-facing; Barbados is a subaerially exposed portion of the Lesser Antilles accretionary ridge. Mafic rocks on La Desirade Island appear to be a piece of oceanic crust with isotopic ages of 149 to 85 Ma and Late Jurassic fauna (Mattinson and others, 1980; Briden and others, 1979; Bouysse and others, 1983), probably accreted to the Lesser Antilles from the Atlantic, or uplifted from the forearc. However, an island arc origin cannot be ruled out (Le Guen de Kerneizon and others, 1979; Bouysse and others, 1983).

The Leeward Antilles arc and northern South America. The islands of Los Monjes, Aruba, Curaçao, Bonaire, Aves, Los Roques, and Orchila are exposures of a largely submarine ridge whose pre–middle Eocene rocks consist of weakly metamorphosed mafic (Bonaire and Curaçao) and intermediate igneous rocks suggestive of an island arc (Case, 1974a; Maresch, 1974; Beets and others, 1984). Similar plutonic and volcanic rocks occur on the islands of the southeastern Caribbean and onshore northern South America from the Guajira Peninsula to Trinidad and Tobago. The number of arcs and the effects of Cenozoic strike-slip offsets on the original geography are unclear; therefore, these rocks are portrayed collectively in Figure 6 as a single arc system.

Radiometric age determinations on intermediate-composition

plutons are as old as 88 Ma, but on the offshore islands the plutons intrude a basement of Early Cretaceous mafic rocks with K-Ar dates of 135 to 115 Ma (Fig. 6; Gonzalez de Juana and others, 1980; Santamaria and Schubert, 1974). Both igneous series have been ascribed to island arc volcanism (Maresch, 1974), but the age and petrological differences between the plutons and the older mafic rocks suggest that a Late Cretaceous arc developed upon preexisting Early Cretaceous oceanic crust (Pindell and Dewey, 1982; Beets and others, 1984). This suggestion is corroborated by deep-water pelagic sediments of Albian age from Curaçao and Bonaire (Beets, 1975); volcanogenic sediments were not deposited until the Late Cretaceous.

The origin and polarity of this arc are not clear. The ultramafic- and blueschist-bearing Villa de Cura klippe in northern Venezuela (Beets and others, 1984; Stephan and others, 1980; Maresch, 1974) may be part of the forearc of the Leeward Antilles arc, as several authors have proposed (Maresch, 1974; Gealey, 1980). The Paleogene emplacement of the nappe followed the termination of magmatism and uplift of the arc; this history fits temporally and geometrically with the scenario of a south-facing arc colliding with continental crust of South America.

Another possibility is that the Leeward Antilles magmatic arc was part of the Aves Ridge arc, emplaced onto northern South America over an extended period. In this scheme, convergence between the Caribbean and South American plates, possibly resulting from north-south opening of the Grenada Basin by right-lateral shear, caused emplacement of fragments of the arc as the Caribbean Plate migrated eastward. In this case, polarity would also be east- or southeast-facing prior to obduction and rotation.

Arcs along northwest South America. Magmatic activity indicative of subduction has occurred since at least Jurassic time within the central, and locally within the western, Cordillera of Colombia and the main Cordillera of Ecuador, whose basements consist of a variety of pre-Mesozoic continental rock types (Fig. 6; Shagam, 1975). Mesozoic and Cenozoic plutons are also located in the Santa Marta Massif. Rocks of the Santa Marta Massif are very similar to those of Cordillera Central; basement is probably continuous beneath the Lower Magdelena Basin, but strike-slip faulting during the Late Cretaceous or Paleogene may have offset the two massifs.

Arc plutonism and volcanism also has occurred within the Western Cordillera of Colombia since the Late Cretaceous, but mainly during the middle Cenozoic (Irving, 1975; Restrepo and Toussaint, 1977). Basement of the Western Cordillera of Colombia is Cretaceous oceanic crust that was accreted to the Central Cordillera in the Late Cretaceous along the Romeral fault (Case and others, 1971; Barrero, 1979; Mooney, 1980; Bourgois and others, 1982). Accretion and subduction zone step-out probably was caused by choking of an east-dipping subduction zone beneath the Central Cordillera by abnormally thick and buoyant crust (relative to "normal oceanic crust") now seen in the Western Cordillera and the rest of the Caribbean Plate.

The magmatic arc of the Central (and Eastern) Cordillera

and Santa Marta Block developed mainly on South American continental crust, and the Western Cordillera had already been accreted at the time it began to receive arc-related magmatism. Since the Jurassic, the Cordilleras have been magmatically active only to the east of known or inferred subduction zones. Therefore, the arc probably has been continuously west-facing.

The Costa Rica–Panamá arc. This intraoceanic arc includes the Central American isthmus from northern Costa Rica (Santa Elena Peninsula) to the western border of the Western Cordillera of Colombia. The arc was built on Upper Jurassic(?) to Late Cretaceous oceanic crust (Case, 1974b); Campanian tuffs, shallow-water limestones, and volcanic sandstones in Costa Rica mark the initiation of subduction and uplift of the forearc (Lundberg, 1983; Galli-Olivier, 1979; Schmidt-Effing, 1979). The oldest subduction-related pluton, in the Azuero Peninsula of Panamá, has yielded a radiometric age of 71 Ma (Kesler and others, 1977). Paleogene shallow-water sediments are common from central Panamá to southeast Costa Rica, indicating a well-developed arc foundation by that time. However, in eastern Panamá, deep-water sediments were deposited upon oceanic crust into the Neogene (Bandy and Casey, 1973). The eastern end of the arc, therefore, seems less well-developed than the rest.

Northwest of the Azuero Peninsula, the arc has been west-facing since its inception; the Nicoya forearc developed in the Late Cretaceous (Lundberg, 1983; Galli-Olivier, 1979). However, since Miocene time the Panamanian portion of the arc has had mixed polarity (Lowrie, 1978), and may be in the process of reversing polarity from south-facing to north-facing. The arc's present northward convexity in Panamá is probably the result of sinistral displacements on several northwest- to north-trending faults crossing Panamá (Fig. 5; Case and Holcombe, 1980). Offshore seismic sections across the Panamanian foldbelt show that the arc is overriding the southwestern Colombian Basin (Lu and McMillan, 1983).

Since the Eocene, the Costa Rica–Panamá arc and the western part of the Chortis arc (see below) have composed the Middle America arc system (Weyl, 1980; Carr and Stoiber, this volume). However, prior to that time the two may have had separate histories.

The Chortis arc of southern Guatemala, Honduras, northern Nicaragua, and western Nicaraguan Rise. This "continental" arc was built upon pre-Mesozoic continental crust. A boundary with the Nicaraguan Rise–Jamaica arc (see below) is unclear but may occur at the San Andres Trough (Fig. 5; Christofferson, 1983; Case and Holcombe, 1980). Volcanogenic sediments and radiometric ages on intermediate plutons suggest that subduction-related magmatism had begun by the Late Jurassic (Fig. 6). Most plutons yield Cretaceous and Paleocene ages, and arc magmatism ceased in the Eocene in central and eastern Honduras (Horne and others, 1976b).

Polarity of the Chortis arc is uncertain; polarity indicators within the arc itself are absent. However, in southern Yucatán, across the Motagua-Polochic fault system, the Santa Cruz ophiolite and other ultramafic bodies representative of a forearc were emplaced from the south during the Late Cretaceous (Rosenfeld, 1981; Donnelly, 1977). It has been suggested that the emplacement of the forearc thrusts was caused by collision of a north-facing Chortis arc, originating from the Pacific (Donnelly, 1977; White and Burke, 1980). This scenario is compatible with estimates of sinistral offset for the Cayman Trough system of 0 to 850 km (estimates of offset range from 0 to 1,400 km; see below). Larger, and in our opinion, more realistic estimates of Cayman offset since the Eocene (1,100 km) place the arc west of the forearc thrusts and into the realm of the Mexican Cordillera. This amount of offset suggests that Chortis has been adjacent to Cordilleran Mexico since the Jurassic or Early Cretaceous, always with south-facing polarity (Pindell and Dewey, 1982; Wadge and Burke, 1983; Duncan and Hargraves, 1984).

The demise of the Chortis arc was concomitant with the initiation of the Middle America arc, which is superposed upon the western part of the Chortis arc and includes the Costa Rica–Panama arc. The Cretaceous-Paleogene Chortis arc and the Costa Rica–Panama arc are geographically distinct; they were probably separated by a plate boundary (trench?) prior to the Eocene. The development of the Middle American arc in the Eocene suggests that the volcanic axes became aligned in the west at that time, possibly by oblique collision of the Costa Rica–Panamá arc with the western part of the Chortis arc. The boundary between the two arcs may be the Santa Elena Peninsula of northern Costa Rica, which aligns to the east with the Hess Escarpment.

Nicaraguan Rise–Jamaica Arc. This arc includes Jamaica and the shallow banks and intervening deeps of the eastern Nicaraguan Rise, and is bounded on the north by the Cayman Trough. The southern boundary is poorly defined, but is probably the Pedro Escarpment, a prominent bathymetric break. The arc presently is aligned with the Chortis arc, but former relationships may have been different. The arc may be intraoceanic, as pre-Cretaceous continental crust is apparently absent there and in Jamaica, but existing seismic velocity data do not distinguish between continental and oceanic crust (Arden, 1975; Perfit and Heezen, 1978). A boundary may exist between this intraoceanic(?) arc and the Chortis arc (founded on continental crust), possibly at the longitude of the San Andres Trough (Fig. 5; Christofferson, 1983; Case and Holcombe, 1980). The boundary may have been a plate boundary, such as a transform, or may be a transition within a single Chortis–Nicaraguan Rise–Jamaica arc with continental basement on the west and oceanic basement on the east.

Volcanogenic sedimentation in Jamaica indicates that arc activity was underway by the Early Cretaceous. On the Nicaraguan Rise east of 81.5°W, the oldest arc-related igneous rocks (recovered from drilling) are Paleocene or latest Cretaceous (Arden, 1975; Holcombe and others, this volume). Radiometric ages and stratigraphic studies (Fig. 6) indicate that magmatism continued in the arc until the Eocene (Kashfi, 1983; Chubb and Burke, 1963; Meyerhoff and Kreig, 1977). The eastern Nicaraguan Rise has no known pre-Paleocene volcanic or sedimentary history, but the broad development of the rise and its apparent

continuity between Jamaica and the Chortis Block suggest that it too comprises arc-related rocks, and may be as old as Early Cretaceous.

No obvious forearc or accretionary prism exists for the Nicaragua Rise–Jamaica arc; its polarity is uncertain and may have varied through time. North-facing polarity would be suggested by: (1) the concept that restoring the offset on the Cayman Trough realigns Jamaica and the Santa Cruz and related ophiolites of central Guatemala, which could be interpreted as Jamaica's forearc; (2) the interpretation that the Cayman Trough developed on a former south-dipping subduction zone (Perfit and Heezen, 1978). South-facing polarity is suggested by the presence of blueschists in the Blue Mountain inlier to the south of arc plutons in Jamaica (Draper, 1987; Burke and others, 1978). However, the blueschists lie much closer to the arc plutons than expected for a normal arc-trench gap, raising the possibility of Late Cretaceous or Cenozoic tectonic juxtaposition. Another alternative is that Jamaica originated with the Chortis Block in the Cordilleran domain of southwestern Mexico. Restoration of an assumed total post-Campanian Chortis–North America offset of 1,650 km places Jamaica west of the Guatemalan ophiolites. In this case, emplacement of the Santa Cruz ophiolite may have been related to the passage of the Greater Antilles magmatic arc as it migrated into the proto-Caribbean (see "Collision zones").

Collision zones

In this section we distinguish between long-lived compressional deformation related to subduction, common throughout Caribbean evolution, and orogenic "events" caused by collision between buoyant masses such as arcs or continents. At least five such collisions can be identified: (1) the Greater Antilles arc with the southern Bahamas Platform in the early Paleogene; (2) an unknown terrane possessing an ophiolitic forearc against the southern part of the Yucatán block (or Maya block in other chapters of this volume) in the Late Cretaceous (Motagua suture zone); (3) the North Venezuelan nappes with northern South America throughout the Cenozoic; (4) the Western Cordillera oceanic complex with the Central Cordillera of Colombia (Romeral suture zone) in the Late Cretaceous; and (5) the eastern part of the Costa Rica–Panamá arc with the Western Cordillera in the late Neogene. We briefly review the timing and the vergence (direction of motion and emplacement in the orogenic zones) of each of these collisions, because these elements further constrain the spatial and temporal motions of plates during Caribbean evolution. Locations of various geologic features mentioned herein may be found in other chapters of this volume.

Paleogene collision of Greater Antilles arc with Bahamas Platform. The effects of this Paleogene collision are most pronounced in Cuba, where the edge of the Bahamas carbonate bank was incorporated into thrust sheets that include rocks of the Greater Antilles forearc and, possibly, the arc (for localities, see Lewis and others, this volume). An uplifted subduction complex exists in northern Hispaniola (Bowin and Nagle, 1980), but evidence for large-scale compression due to collision is lacking.

Northern Puerto Rico has no evidence for collision at all, although marbles and gneisses have been dredged from the Puerto Rico Trench (Heezen and others, 1975).

In northern Cuba, three important tectonostratigraphic assemblages are, from south to north: (1) a Cretaceous to Eocene arc and forearc, (2) an intermediate zone of Late Jurassic to Eocene deep-water strata (continental slope/rise, abyssal plain), and (3) a carbonate platform (Bahamas) of Late Jurassic through middle Eocene age (Pardo, 1975; Mossakovskiy and Albear, 1978; Meyerhoff and Hatten, 1974; Mattson, 1979).

Rocks of the forearc, and possibly the arc, were thrust northward over the carbonate platform by as much as 90 km (Shein and Kleschev, 1977). Paleocene–upper Eocene olistostromes and nappes formed during this Paleogene thrusting. Rocks of the allochthonous arc/forearc and the autochthonous carbonate platform all were folded and overlapped unconformably by little-deformed late Eocene and younger sediments (Pardo, 1975). Development of northeast-trending left-lateral strike-slip tear faults across Cuba accompanied the folding (Shein and Kleschev, 1977).

The structure and stratigraphy suggest the following sequence of tectonic events during Late Cretaceous–Paleogene time: (1) the Cuban part of the north-facing Greater Antilles arc approached the edge of the Bahamas Platform, and the forearc region began to override first the carbonate-bank edge and then the bank itself; (2) the forearc was squeezed into a north-vergent nappe before compression ceased, (3) subsequently the whole package was folded and sinistrally tear faulted; (4) late Eocene and younger sediment unconformably transgressed the collision zone.

The Cauto Basin seems to be a fundamental structural break along the strike of the arc terrane in Cuba. To the west of this break, the Bahamas Platform is involved in the thrusting whereas to the east, obducted ophiolites and mélanges occur but the carbonate-platform sediments apparently are not thrust significantly. A more positive gravity field in the east (Bowin, 1976; Case, 1980) also indicates less involvement of Bahamian sediments. The difference in response to collision may be due to the original shape of the Bahamas Platform or the arc, or to differing degrees of compression.

In Hispaniola, the effects of collision are much diminished relative to those in Cuba. The structure of the original arc-trench system is well preserved: volcanic arc (Cordillera Central), forearc basin (Cibao Basin, basement of Cordillera Septentrional), and subduction complex (north coast). The Eocene collision apparently did not progress to the point where the subduction complex was thrust onto the Bahamas Platform. The collision in Hispaniola is marked by an Eocene tectonic mélange containing ophiolitic debris and Cretaceous to Paleocene rocks, which is unconformably overlain by relatively undeformed late Eocene shallow-water sandstones (Luperon Formation) along the north coast (Nagle, 1966, 1979; Bowin and Nagle, 1980). Magmatic-arc volcanism ceased in Hispaniola in middle Eocene time, coeval with collision.

Seismic reflection and seismological studies, however, indicate compression between Hispaniola and the Bahamas during the Neogene to Recent (Austin, 1983; Bracey and Vogt, 1970; Sykes and others, 1982). This compression is due to transpressional motion along the Oriente fault between Cuba and Hispaniola, parallel to Cayman Trough flow lines.

In Puerto Rico, a forearc region and subduction complex are not exposed north of the arc. Consequently, the end of arc-continent convergence is identifiable only by the mid-to-late Eocene unconformity (Meyerhoff and others, 1983; Glover, 1971) and by the termination of arc magmatism (Cox and others, 1977). Oligocene dates on granodiorites and quartz diorites in the Virgin Islands (Kesler and Sutter, 1979; Cox and others, 1977) may represent the final Greater Antillean magmatism, or may relate to initial subduction along the Lesser Antilles.

In summary, the collision between the Greater Antilles and the Bahamas Platform occurred in the late Paleocene to mid-Eocene, and the effects of collision decrease eastward. Most thrusts are north-vergent, which supports the concept of south-dipping subduction of the proto-Caribbean beneath the Greater Antilles arc prior to collision. There is no strong diachroneity of the time of collision along strike, although the sinistral tear faults in Cuba (Skvor, 1969; Case and Holcombe, 1980) may indicate slightly oblique, eastward-progressive suturing.

An arc terrane with southern Yucatán (Motagua Zone). This Late Cretaceous collision occurred between a volcanic arc possessing a blueschist-bearing ophiolitic forearc, and the continental crust and carbonate shelf of southern Mexico and southern Yucatán (Rosenfeld, 1980; Donnelly, 1977). During the Campanian to early Maastrichtian, the Neocomian to Santonian carbonate shelf (Campur and Coban Formations; Vinson, 1962) was depressed and buried by up to 2,500 m of turbiditic, serpentinite-bearing flysch from a southern source (Chemal and Sepur Formations; Rosenfeld, 1981).

The Early Cretaceous Santa Cruz ophiolite appears to be a true forearc complex rather than a block within an accretionary prism, and was thrust (or slid) northward onto the Sepur foredeep (Williams, 1975; Rosenfeld, 1980, 1981). Overlying the ophiolite are deep-water deposits of the Aptian-Albian Tzumuy Formation (Rosenfeld, 1981), which grade from pelagic strata to increasingly coarse and proximal turbidites with ash and volcanic debris of andesitic composition. These deposits suggest a volcanic arc as the source area. The timing of emplacement of the ophiolite, which dates the collision, is Campanian and Maastrichtian; the ophiolite was initially thrust onto Campanian Sepur sediments, and the Sepur depocenter migrated northward during the Maastrichtian, presumably as thrust loading progressed. Subsequently, uplift and large-scale transform motion has occurred along the Polochic and Motagua faults (Burkart, 1983).

The amount of Cenozoic offset along the Cayman Trough and Polochic-Motagua transform is uncertain; therefore, the arc terrane that collided with southern Yucatán is unknown. Sediments derived from the unknown terrane indicate that it was a volcanic arc. Southern Yucatán was a stable shelf up to the time of collision, and the vergence of the collision is thought to be northward (south-dipping subduction). That the Santa Cruz is a true ophiolitic forearc suggests that the colliding mass was an intraoceanic arc rather than a continental-type arc. The likely candidate for this intra-oceanic arc is Cuba.

North Venezuelan nappes with northern Venezuela. The northern margin of Venezuela (and northeasternmost Colombia) from the Guajira Peninsula to Trinidad has been overthrust from the north or northwest during Cenozoic time (Lara Suture of Fig. 5). The thrust sheets comprise mainly Cretaceous to Paleogene variously metamorphosed volcanic rocks, ultramafic rocks, and volcanogenic sandstones and shales, with minor limestones. These rocks collectively form an assemblage typical of accretionary wedges at subduction zones. Shallow-water rocks deposited on the Venezuelan shelf are sometimes incorporated in the thrusting.

The assemblage crops out in the northern Guajira and Paraguana peninsulas (MacDonald, 1964; Lockwood, 1965; Martin-Bellizzia and Arozena, 1972), and occurs in the Falcón Basin mainly in the subsurface (except along the basin's southern margin; Muessig, 1984; Bellizzia and others, 1972). In the Caribbean Mountain system of north-central Venezuela these rocks comprise the Lara Nappe of metasedimentary rocks and the Villa de Cura Klippe of mafic metavolcanic rocks of blueschist facies, metasedimentary rocks, and ultramafic rocks; metamorphism is medial to Late Cretaceous in age (Stephan and others, 1980; Maresch, 1974; Gealey, 1980; Beets and others, 1984). Similar assemblages of rocks occur in the Araya and Paria peninsulas, Margarita, and in the coastal ranges of northern Trinidad and Tobago.

Two major problems must be considered before attempts are made to interpret the apparent arc-continent collision: (1) the amount of deformation of northwestern South America during the late Miocene to Recent Andean orogeny; and (2) timing and diachroneity of emplacement of the thrust sheets of oceanic rocks onto the Venezuelan continental margin. The key to the first problem is determining the amount of strike-slip offset along the Merida Andes. The Bocónó Fault offsets the Paleogene thrust belt by about 100 km (Stephan, 1985), which probably is a good estimate. Other offsets in northwest South America have been assessed by Dewey and Pindell (1986). The key to the second problem is differentiating the sediments of the accretionary wedge, and their deformation during subduction, from the foredeep sediments and the deformation resulting from the actual emplacement of the accretionary wedge onto the margin. In the case of northern South America, this differentiation is difficult because both the accretionary wedge and the foredeep basin are composed of similar terrigenous sediments.

The best evidence for the timing of collision comes from the subsidence history of the autochthon, the Venezuelan shelf to the south of the thrust sheets. Subsidence pertaining to collision in the Maracaibo Basin area is Paleocene–lower Eocene (Zambrano and others, 1972; Gonzalez de Juana and others, 1980); subsidence south of the central Venezuelan Andes (Piedmont Province

of Beck, 1978) is Oligocene-Miocene (Beck, 1978), although Beck did not relate this subsidence to thrusting; initiation of subsidence in the East Venezuela Basin is Miocene-Pliocene (I. Rodríguez, personal communication, 1983; Vierbuchen, 1984). This evidence suggests that emplacement of the North Venezuelan Nappes was diachronous, growing younger to the east. Much of the Paleocene–lower Eocene flysch in front of the entire thrust belt (such as the Piemontine Nappe of central Venezuela; Beck, 1978), commonly referred to as the foredeep facies, probably formed in the accretionary complex, prior to the actual emplacement onto the margin.

Assuming the Caribbean Plate has migrated eastward with respect to North and South America since the Eocene, interaction between the Caribbean and northern South America should become younger to the east (see section on "South Caribbean Plate Boundary Zone"). A close correlation exists between the estimated position of the leading edge of the Caribbean Plate and the emplacement age of the North Venezuelan Nappes at various points along the margin. The North Venezuelan Nappes were emplaced progressively during the Cenozoic as a result of a compressional component of the predominantly transcurrent relative motion. This time-transgressive emplacement history provides an indirect check on the predicted motion history of the Caribbean Plate relative to South America. This model is in contrast to the interpretations of some previous geologic-kinematic Caribbean evolutionary models (White and Burke, 1980; Pindell and Dewey, 1982), which attributed nappe emplacement to Late Cretaceous–Paleogene convergence between North and South America, rather than to interaction with the Caribbean Plate. The revised relative motion vector for North and South America, however, indicates no such Late Cretaceous to Paleogene convergence between North and South America.

The arc complex that collided with northern South America is difficult to identify with certainty because of postcollisional strike-slip offsets within the system. However, the Leeward Antilles probably formed at least a part of the arc complex. Assuming that the diachronous collision was related to interaction between the Caribbean and South American Plates, the Leeward Antilles arc represents a portion of the leading edge of the Caribbean Plate. As shown later in a more complete model for the development of northern South America, the Leeward Antilles arc, forearc, and accretionary wedge probably formed a southern extension of the Aves Ridge arc that was progressively clipped off and accreted to northern South America during the Cenozoic. The metamorphic rocks of the Lara Nappes were metamorphosed during the accretionary prism stage, prior to their Cenozoic emplacement. The apparent geochemical affinity between the basalts defining the seismic horizon B″ of the Caribbean Plate and the tholeiitic units (basement) of the Leeward Antilles (T. Donnelly, personal communication, 1985) is further evidence for this model of arc-continent collision.

Western Cordillera/San Jacinto Belt with Cordillera Central, Colombia and Ecuador (Romeral Suture). In Colombia and Ecuador, the Romeral Suture (Fig. 5)—a major fault zone along which occur ultramafic rocks, mélanges, and blueschists—separates two distinct geologic provinces. To the east occur Precambrian through Cenozoic continental rocks of the Cordillera Central and Santa Marta Massif, whereas directly to the west, rocks include Cretaceous oceanic crust, highly deformed Late Cretaceous through Paleogene deep-water sediments, and Cenozoic magmatic rocks of the Western Cordillera and San Jacinto Belt (Case and others, 1971; Case and MacDonald, 1973; Irving, 1975; Duque-Caro, 1979, 1984; Barrero, 1979). Oceanic basement crops out in only a few places in the San Jacinto Belt, but it is inferred to exist at depth along strike of the Western Cordillera. Structural and facies relations indicate that the Western Cordillera and San Jacinto terranes were accreted to Cordillera Central during Late Cretaceous–Paleogene time; suturing was completed by the Eocene.

The predominantly mid-Cenozoic magmatism within the Western Cordillera postdates the accretion to Cordillera Central. The Western Cordillera's brief history as a magmatic arc, therefore, bears no relationship to subduction geometries prior to collision. The only subduction-related magmatism prior to the Late Cretaceous collision occurred in the Cordillera Central/Santa Marta arc, suggesting east-dipping subduction beneath the Central Cordillera prior to accretion.

Accretion probably occurred as the result of a nonsubductible oceanic crustal block (Western Cordillera) arriving at and choking the Cordillera Central subduction zone during Late Cretaceous–Paleogene time. Subduction then stepped outboard of the Western Cordillera for the remainder of the Cenozoic. It is possible that oceanic crust in the San Jacinto Belt and Western Cordillera is related to the abnormally thick crust of the Caribbean Plate (basalts and sediments below seismic horizon B″ in the Colombian and Venezuelan basins, above oceanic crust; Duque-Caro, 1979). After the westward stepping out of the subduction zone in the Late Cretaceous, the locus of arc magmatism shifted to the Western Cordillera primarily during the early to middle Cenozoic; subsequently, magmatism has returned primarily to the Central Cordillera in the Neogene.

Eastern Panamá with western Colombia (Atrato Suture). If the Caribbean Plate, with Costa Rica–Panamá forming its western edge, has moved eastward with respect to South America, then the southwestern portion of the Caribbean must have converged with South America. Hundreds of kilometers of relative motion implies that the Costa Rica–Panamá Arc was formerly distant from Colombia and, therefore, that the two have collided at some time during the period of migration.

Structural and lithologic trends continue from eastern Panamá into the Serranía de Baudó, and a suture may lie along the east flank of the Atrato–San Juan Basin, which separates the Serranía de Baudó from the formerly accreted Western Cordillera (Case and others, 1971). Post-Eocene sediment accretion is known to the north in the Sinu Belt, and is due to subduction of, and sediment offscraping from, the Colombian Basin beneath northern Colombia throughout that period (Duque-Caro, 1979, 1984).

Collision appears to have begun in the Miocene (Early to Middle?), as suggested indirectly by (1) uplift and deformation within the Panamanian forearc, Serranía de Baudó, and the Atrato Basin in middle to late Miocene (Bandy and Casey, 1973; Bandy, 1970; Bourgois and others, 1982; Duque-Caro, 1972); (2) termination of chert deposition in the Caribbean during Miocene time, implying deep-water circulation was interrupted (Keller and Barron, 1983); (3) differentiation between planktonic species in the Pacific and Caribbean in the early Pliocene (Keigwin, 1978); and (4) initiation of major faunal exchange between North and South America during the Plio-Pleistocene (Webb, 1976).

Accompanying this collision is the northward escape of blocks of the eastern part of the Panamá arc along north- to northwest-trending sinistral faults (Case and Holcombe, 1980). The escape is probably within the upper crust only (deep-seated décollement). This motion has given the arc its northward convexity. The body of the arc itself has been converging onto the Colombian Basin, as evidenced by the Panamanian Foldbelt of recently accreted sediment overriding the Colombian Basin (Lu and McMillen, 1983). This eastern part of the arc appears to be reversing polarity in response to subduction zone choking at the Atrato trench/suture.

Paleogeographic significance of the Yucatán Basin, Grenada Basin, and Cayman Trough

Yucatán Basin. Models for the origin of the Yucatán Basin include (1) Mesozoic ocean crust formed by rotation of Chortis from the eastern Yucatán margin (Dillon and Vedder, 1973), (2) Cretaceous ocean crust rafted in from the Pacific (White and Burke, 1980), or (3) an intra-arc basin formed by separation between Cuba and the Cayman Ridge during the Paleogene (Gealey, 1980). Seismic reflection and heat-flow data, and age-depth relationships, suggest an early Paleogene (55 to 65 Ma) age for a sea-floor–spreading origin (Rosencrantz and others, 1989), consistent with Gealey's (1980) model of intra-arc spreading. Northeast-trending magnetic anomalies, possibly related to sea-floor spreading, suggest a northwest-southeast direction of spreading (Hall and Yeung, 1980).

Assuming that the Yucatán Basin is an intra-arc basin between Cuba and the Cayman Ridge, then the arc-related portion (south of ophiolite belt) of Cuba must have migrated northeastward along a transform, the eastern Yucatán margin. However, the trend of the eastern Yucatán margin is discordant with the trend of opening of the Yucatán Basin suggested by magnetic anomalies. Hence, a three-plate model is required, involving North America, Cuba, and the Cayman Ridge, shown in Figure 7. This model suggests that the Caribbean Plate (Cayman Ridge) migrated about 377 km east-northeast with respect to North America during the formation of the Yucatán Basin, while at the same time, Cuba migrated north-northwestward relative to the Caribbean, about a pole near the Cauto Basin.

The Grenada Basin. The Grenada Basin appears to be an

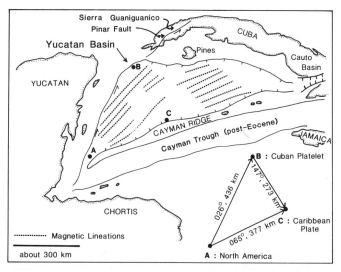

Figure 7. Magnetic anomaly lineations in Yucatán Basin, after Hall and Yeung (1980). In our interpretation of the three-plate system of North America, Cuba, and the Caribbean (Cayman Ridge), Cuba migrated from point A to point B with respect to North America, as defined by the trend and length of the eastern Yucatán sheared margin. The Cayman Ridge migrated, with respect to Cuba, from point B to point C, as defined by the perpendicular to the mean trend of the magnetic anomalies and the width of the basin. Connecting the vector triangle from point A to point C gives the motion of the Caribbean relative to North America during the period of back-arc spreading in the basin (Maastrichtian to mid-Eocene, a duration of 15 to 20 m.y.), assuming no subduction at any margins of the basin. Vector triangle defines trends and magnitudes of these apparent motions. Pinar fault in western Cuba separates the Cuban arc to the east from continental crust of the northeastern Yucatán block to the west.

intra-arc basin formed by the separation of the Lesser Antilles basement foundation from the Aves Ridge arc. In the north, the subsided edifice of the Cretaceous arc is block faulted (Nemec, 1980), and extension did not create oceanic crust. In the south, however, basement lies beneath 4,000 m of undisturbed deposits (Biju-Duval and others, 1978) and is probably oceanic. The age of formation is probably early Paleogene; seismic reflectors representing Eocene strata are undisturbed (Speed and Westbrook, 1984). Further, plutonism probably ceased in Aves Ridge and began in the Lesser Antilles arc in the Eocene (Fig. 6). Heat-flow measurements in the deep southern portion (G. Westbrook, personal communication, 1984) also suggest a Paleocene-Eocene age of formation. A simple east-west extensional origin for the basin has been proposed (Tomblin, 1975), but magnetic lineations run generally east–west across the basin (Speed and Westbrook, 1984). If these are, in fact, sea-floor–spreading anomalies, an oblique opening for the basin is indicated. Such a model is outlined in Figure 8.

The Cayman Trough. This long, deep basin (100 by 1,400 km) forms the North America–Caribbean plate boundary

in the northwest Caribbean (Perfit and Heezen, 1978; Sykes and others, 1982). Much of the basin is floored by oceanic crust produced at the north-trending Mid-Cayman Spreading Center (Holcombe and others, 1973), a short mid-ocean ridge segment that links the sinistral Swan and Oriente transform faults (Fig. 5). The Cayman Trough is critical in unraveling the plate-tectonic history of the Caribbean, because the amount of oceanic crust created at the Mid-Cayman Spreading Center defines the minimum amount of motion between the Caribbean and North American Plates since sea-floor spreading began.

The Oligocene age of the oldest deep-water sediments obtained from the trough, in conjunction with coeval strike-slip faulting in the Tavera Basin of Hispaniola, suggests a minimum age of initial trough opening of Oligocene (Wadge and Burke, 1983). However, eastward migration of the Caribbean Plate by the Eocene is indicated by arc volcanism in Lesser Antilles (Fig. 6). MacDonald and Holcombe (1978) interpreted magnetic anomalies flanking the Mid-Cayman ridge axis to suggest at least 284 km of spreading occurred since the late Miocene (anomaly 4'), with a decrease in spreading rate from 4 cm/yr to 2 cm/yr over the last 2.4 m.y. Anomalies beyond anomaly 4' were not identified by them in the trough, but basement bathymetric lineations attributable to east-west sea-floor spreading suggest an offset of at least 560 km (Holcombe and Sharman, 1983). The magnetic anomalies have been reexamined, however. Ross and others (1986) suggested that the spreading rate appears to be more on the order of 15 to 20 mm/yr, with spreading having begun sometime in the Eocene, consistent with the indication from the Lesser Antilles phase of volcanism.

Estimates of east-west offset across the trough range from 180 km, based on displacement of similar metamorphic belts (subduction complex and magmatic arc) of Cuba and Hispaniola (Meyerhoff, 1966), to 1,400 km, based on the assumption that the entire bathymetric expression of the trough is due to spreading at the Mid-Cayman Spreading Center (Sykes and others, 1982; MacDonald, 1974). However, that portion with depths typical of true oceanic crust is only 980 km. The western and eastern ends of the trough (420 km) are floored by block-faulted, probably nonoceanic basement (arc-related igneous rocks, as shown by dredging; Perfit and Heezen, 1978). These ends probably formed by the stretching of arc-related or continental crust during initial basin formation. We estimate that 70 to 100 km of basement extension is sufficient to have produced the 420 km of subsided, yet nonoceanic, ends of the trough. Hence, if one accepts a pull-apart model of formation, total extension across the Cayman Trough is about 1,050 to 1,100 km. Therefore, Meyerhoff's (1966) suggested 180 km offset of the Cuban and Hispaniolan metamorphic belts is probably not the total amount of east-west offset across the Cayman Trough. Two alternatives for this discrepancy are (1) that much of the motion could have occurred along faults that pass south of the Central Cordillera arc of Hispaniola (Pindell and Dewey, 1982), or (2) that all of Hispaniola lay to the west of Cuba prior to the development of the Cayman Trough (MacDonald, 1974).

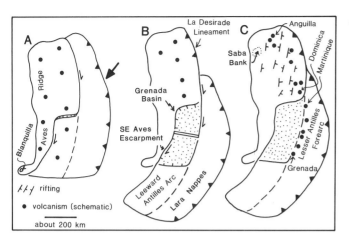

Figure 8. Model suggested here for the formation of Grenada Basin. A, Late Cretaceous; B and C, early Paleogene. Oblique subduction (convergence) (indicated by heavy arrow) induced a dextral shear stress that mobilized the southeastern Aves Ridge arc and subduction complex and opened the Grenada Basin (stippled area). Southern protrusion of the original arc and forearc system consisted of the Leeward Antilles Islands and the Lara nappes of northern Venezuela. La Desirade and the southeast Aves lineaments are speculated remnants of transforms offset by a seafloor–spreading ridge in Grenada Basin. The pull-apart opening of the basin was accompanied by extensional adjustments in the north during the Eocene-Oligocene (Nemec, 1980). Young volcanism in the southern Lesser Antilles relative to that in the north (see Fig. 6) possibly was due to a lag in subduction as the Lesser Antilles forearc remained essentially fixed to the South American Plate during opening of the Grenada Basin.

In light of (1) Oligocene deep-water sedimentation in portions of Cayman Trough, (2) east-west Caribbean–North America relative motion since the late Eocene, (3) the alignment of Cuban and Hispaniolan metamorphic belts bearing no constraint upon total offset across the trough, and (4) the position of the Mid-Cayman Spreading Center halfway between the ends of the trough, we conclude that plate accretion at the Mid-Cayman Spreading Center has produced the entire oceanic portion of the trough. Hence, the Cayman Trough appears to be an exceptionally extended pull-apart basin that records a sinistral offset of 1,050 to 1,100 km between the Caribbean and North American plates since the Eocene.

A large amount of offset along the Cayman Trough (more than 800 km) is especially important in constraining models for the evolution of the Caribbean. The concept of the Caribbean Plate originating within the Pacific realm and entering the North–South American gap prior to the Eocene depends on this interpretation. If smaller estimates of offset are assumed, an in situ formation of the Caribbean Plate (between North and South America) is required.

Caribbean plate boundary zones

Middle Eocene time separated two phases of development in the northern and southern Caribbean: (1) an Early Cretaceous-

early Eocene phase of arc volcanism and compressional tectonism that culminated in arc-continent collision in the north and cessation of volcanism in the south, and (2) a subsequent phase of predominantly transcurrent faulting (with more than 100 km of southeastward thrusting in the southern Caribbean) associated with more than 1,000 km of eastward migration of the Caribbean Plate relative to the Americas. The latter phase has produced complicated northern and southern plate boundary zones (PBZ) with anastomosing faults and a diffuse pattern of seismicity (Burke and others, 1980). In this section the locations of fault zones pertaining to this migration, and the timing of movement along them, are defined.

Northern Caribbean Plate Boundary Zone.

The northern PBZ extends from central Guatemala, through Jamaica, Hispaniola, and Puerto Rico, to the northern Lesser Antilles, and includes the Cayman Trough. Cuba, which had been a part of the Caribbean Plate through the Paleocene, remained fixed to the North American Plate for the rest of the Cenozoic. The Cayman Trough records a minimum of 1,050 km of North America/Caribbean transcurrent motion. At the eastern end of the trough, the Oriente fault (Fig. 5) presently separates Cuba from Hispaniola. However, the Oriente splays into the Bahamas Channel, Camu, and Septentrional faults in northern Hispaniola; these faults probably coalesce into the Puerto Rican Trench transform fault farther east. Motions within southern Hispaniola are largely compressional at present, although minor strike-slip motion is occurring there as well (Mann and others, 1984).

Figure 9 shows a reconstruction of Cuba and northern Hispaniola, which realigns the arc, forearc basin, and subduction complexes of both. Total offset in this reconstruction is 400 km. Most of the 400 km of sinistral offset has occurred offshore between the two islands (Bahamas Channel), but the Tavera, Camu, and Septentrional faults account for some of the displacement (see Lewis and others, this volume, for locations). If 400 km of motion occurred to the north of Hispaniola's arc complex, then the fault systems responsible for the remaining 650 km of the Cayman Trough's 1,050 km offset must pass to the south of the Cordillera Central–Massif du Nord of Hispaniola. Because the southern peninsula of Hispaniola lies south of the eastern end of Cayman Trough (Fig. 5), it appears that the motion must have passed between the Cordillera Central and the southern peninsula.

Southwestern Hispaniola consists of subparallel physiographic highs separated by the San Juan–Plateau Central and the Enriquillo–Cul de Sac sedimentary basins (see Lewis and others, this volume). The late Miocene to Recent history of southwest Hispaniola is dominated by north-south compression, with thrusts verging south (Biju-Duval and others, 1983a; Bourgois and others, 1979a, 1979b).

If an Oligocene to middle Miocene strike-slip phase preceded the late Miocene to Recent south-vergent thrusting, then it might be expected that thrusting nucleated upon the preexisting transcurrent fault zones. Following this logic, the northern boundaries of the San Juan/Plateau Central and Enriquillo/Cul de

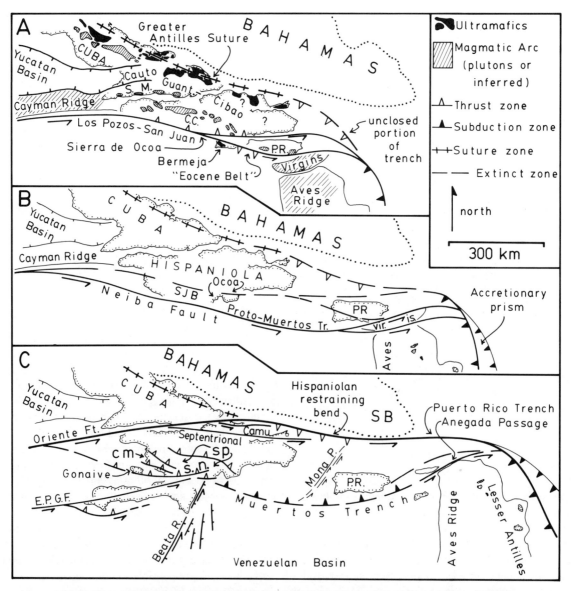

Figure 9. Proposed primary development of the northern Caribbean PBZ. A: Eocene time, following Greater Antilles-Bahamas collision. The magmatic arc (S.M., Sierra Maestra; C.C., Cordillera Central), the Guantánamo-Cibao forearc basin, and the subduction complexes (ultramafic and blueschist-facies rocks) are intact and aligned. Eocene–early Miocene motion on Los Pozos–San Juan transform system separated Puerto Rico (P.R.) from Hispaniola and juxtaposed the San Juan block (SJB, to the west of the area depicted on Figure 9A) and the Hispaniolan arc. B: Possible early Miocene reconstruction, showing San Juan block juxtaposed to main Hispaniolan arc complex, and southern peninsula of Hispaniola still to the west. Transcurrent motion on Sierra Neiba–Proto Muertos Trough–Anegada system may have juxtaposed the southern peninsula of Hispaniola with the San Juan block by the middle Miocene, and separated the Aves Ridge from Puerto Rico. C: Alternative early Miocene reconstruction, showing *all* of southern Hispaniola juxtaposed to the main arc. Difference in B and C depends on estimated offset along the Los Pozos–San Juan Fault Zone. Since middle? Miocene time, primary zone of transcurrent motion jumped to the Oriente–North Hispaniolan system between Hispaniola and Cuba. Compressional tectonism has since dominated strike-slip faulting in southern Hispaniola; most previous transforms became thrusts. Hispaniola converged upon and overthrust the southern flank of Silver Bank (SB, eastern Bahamas) in the Pliocene, producing the Hispaniolan Restraining Bend. Cordillera Septentrional has been, or is becoming, docked against the Bahamas, as the Septentrional fault has become an important transform fault between the North American and Caribbean plates. The Puerto Rico Trench is a compressional transform with lithospheric underthrusting (Schell and Tarr, 1978) of late Miocene to Recent age (Monroe, 1968). cm, Chaines de Matheux; s.n., Sierra Neiba; sp, San Juan–Plateau Central Basin; E.P.G.F., El Plantain Garden Fault.

Sac basins are the likely locations to find evidence for large-scale strike-slip offset.

Along the northern margin of San Juan Basin and Plateau Central, the Los Pozos–San Juan boundary fault (Figs. 5, 9) separates two very different terranes: (1) on the north, metamorphosed Cretaceous to Paleogene arc-related rocks and volcanogenic sands of the Cordillera Central and Massif du Nord; (2) on the south, Paleogene deep-water micrites, which possess no arc-derived volcanic debris (Michael, 1979; Bown, 1975). This relationship holds for a distance of at least 350 km in western and central Hispaniola (Michael, 1979; Bowin, 1975). Only in Sierra El Numero southeast of the San Juan Basin do the expected Eocene-Oligocene arc-flank volcaniclastics and conglomerates occur (Biju-Duval and others, 1983a; Bourgois and others, 1979b). Not until the Miocene did significant amounts of sand enter the San Juan Basin (Michael, 1979), suggesting that the basin had begun to arrive in proximity to the arc terrane by that time. Thus, the facies discrepancy across the northern San Juan Basin suggests that at least 350 km of transcurrent motion occurred along the Los Pozos–San Juan boundary fault. As the Los Pozos extends west to the Cayman Trough for another 350 km, the total motion could be as much as 700 km. The timing of the motion could be early Eocene through early Miocene.

In the Enriquillo/Cul de Sac Basin, the first proximal, arc-derived volcanogenic sediments are of late Miocene age (Trinchera Formation; Cooper, 1983). Thrusting in Sierra Neiba is post–lower Tortonian (about 10 Ma; Bourgois and others, 1979a), as indicated by Eocene rocks overthrusting Tortonian rocks, and by the late Miocene–Pliocene subsidence of the Fondo Negro foredeep basin to the south, an exposed part of the Enriquillo Basin (Cooper, 1983). Some of the strike-slip displacement could have occurred along the Sierra Neiba, but the arrival of clastics only just postdates that in the San Juan Basin, and no large-scale strike-slip offset is required to explain the facies change: the southern portion of the island could have come in from the west *with* the San Juan Basin, in which case the total motion along the Los Pozos–San Juan fault may approach 700 km. However, large strike-slip offsets could have occurred at both the Los Pozos–San Juan and Sierra Neiba fault systems, as shown in Figure 9.

In Figure 9, Puerto Rico is shown against the southeastern flank of the Dominican Republic during the Eocene (as shown in Sykes and others, 1982). This reconstruction, which is speculative, restores 350 km of offset between Hispaniola and Puerto Rico, and aligns the Late Cretaceous–Paleogene arc plutons of the two islands, placing the Bermeja ultramafic complex on the south side of the arc. The Bermeja Complex probably was accreted from the south prior to the middle Cretaceous (Burke and others, 1978).

An eastward continuation of the San Juan fault system probably passed to the north of Puerto Rico, with motion on the fault translating Puerto Rico 350 km eastward from its initial position. This postulated displacement agrees well with the suggested minimum offset for the San Juan fault system. Additional

motion along the Los Pozos–San Juan (or Neiba) passed south of Puerto Rico, probably along a proto–Muertos Trench transform system that has since become compressional with southward vergence, like southern Cordillera Central and Sierra Neiba (Biju-Duval and others, 1983a). Farther east, this fault probably passed through the sinistral Anegada Passage (Murphy and McCann, 1979) to the Lesser Antilles Trench.

In early Miocene time, transcurrent motion began along the Oriente fault and related splays in northern Hispaniola. This motion was accompanied by a gradual change from strike-slip to compression in southern Hispaniola. The eastward motion of Hispaniola from Cuba has led to convergence between northeastern Hispaniola and the southeastern Bahamas (Hispaniolan Restraining Bend, Fig. 9). Compression at this restraining bend is responsible for much of central and western Hispaniola's rugged relief.

Southern Caribbean Plate Boundary Zone. The southern Caribbean Plate Boundary Zone (PBZ) is a complex zone of thrusting, transcurrent motion, and rifting that has developed throughout the Cenozoic (Stephan and others, 1980; Biju-Duval and others, 1983b; Schubert, 1984; Mann and Burke, 1984; Case, 1974a). The presumed Cenozoic offset between South America and the Caribbean Plate is as much as 1,400 km, derived by summing (1) the Cayman Trough's offset between North America and the Caribbean (1,050 km), (2) possible offset along the southeast Cayman margin for the last 2.4 m.y. (48 km, Sykes and others, 1982), and (3) North America–South America dextral displacement along the Barracuda and related fracture zones (300 km, Fig. 3). However, because the Caribbean has migrated across the northern margin of South America, actual offset diminishes progressively, from 1,400 km in the west, to zero at the Barbados accretionary complex in the east.

Some models for the evolution of northern South America (e.g., Maresch, 1974) speculate that the North Venezuelan nappes were thrust onto the margin in the Late Cretaceous to Paleogene, and that the strike-slip boundary zone developed subsequently. However, the subsidence history of the Venezuelan foreland basins (Maracaibo Basin to Eastern Venezuela Basin) suggests that the North Venezuelan nappes were emplaced onto the Venezuelan margin diachronously (younging to the east), from the Paleocene to the Pliocene. This emplacement was in close association with the Cenozoic eastward advance of the Caribbean Plate (see section on collision zones). Emplacement of the North Venezuelan nappes and the development of an associated flysch-bearing foredeep occurred in the Maracaibo Basin area (Misoa and Trujillo Formations) during the Paleocene–early Eocene (Zambrano and others, 1972), in the Caribbean Mountain System (Lara nappes) during the Oligocene-Miocene, and in the East Venezuela Basin area during the late Miocene–Pliocene (Vierbuchen, 1984). Thus, nappe emplacement and Caribbean–South American Plate interaction, and hence PBZ development, appear to be closely related.

In addition to the emplacement history of the North Venezuelan nappes, the following points are important. (1) Eastward-dipping subduction of the Caribbean Plate has occurred at the Sinu Trench of western Colombia since the Eocene (Duque-Caro, 1979, 1984). (2) Oligocene subsidence within the Falcón Basin, and possibly the Bonaire Basin, was caused by dextral strike-slip motions and attendant pull-apart basin development (Biju-Duval and others, 1983b; Muessig, 1984). The total east-west offset across the Falcón Basin due to pull-apart opening is unknown, but the occurrence of Paleogene metamorphosed deposits at depth and a sedimentary section of 6 km that is intruded by alkaline rather than tholeiitic basalts (Muessig, 1984) suggests an origin by continental stretching, rather than by formation of oceanic crust as in the Cayman Trough. Alkaline basalts are typically associated with lithosperic thinning to about 50 percent of normal (Dewey, 1982); therefore, if the Falcón Basin is estimated to be about 200 km long, strike-slip offset associated with the basin's formation may be as much as 100 km. (3) Paleomagnetic studies suggest that certain blocks within the southern Caribbean PBZ have been rotated clockwise in association with dextral shear (Hargraves and Skerlec, 1980; Skerlec and Hargraves, 1980; Maze, 1984; Maze and Hargraves, 1984; Hargraves and others, 1984). (4) The Late Miocene to Recent Andean orogeny has mobilized several blocks in the Venezuelan Borderland, primarily by strike-slip motions along the intervening Oca, Santa Marta, Boconó, and other faults. Schubert (1984) reported up to 100 km of dextral offset along the Boconó fault, and the northeast migration of the Andean terranes has led to convergence between them and the Caribbean Plate; the Venezuelan Borderland has overridden the Caribbean Plate and flexurally depressed the Venezuelan Basin to the west of La Blanquilla Island, thereby producing the marked negative gravity anomaly (Bowin, 1976) associated with the South Caribbean Foldbelt (Fig. 1).

To the southwest, in Colombia and Ecuador, convergence and uplift dominates the southern Caribbean PBZ. Strike-slip motions probably occur, but assessment of these is as yet incomplete. The three Cordilleras of Colombia are being uplifted relative to the intervening valleys, the cause of which is compression from the west, due primarily to the Miocene Panamá collision with the Western Cordillera.

In Figure 10, these considerations are integrated into a model for the development of the southern Caribbean PBZ, the early history of which is closely associated with the opening of the Grenada Basin (see Fig. 8). Until the Late Miocene, a Caribbean–South American transcurrent plate boundary to the north of the Leeward Antilles Islands accommodated most of the strike-slip relative motion, but this transform has been overthrust since that time, leading to the development of the South Caribbean accretionary foldbelt (Dewey and Pindell, 1985; Ladd and Watkins, 1978; Biju-Duval and others, 1983b). This overthrusting may evolve into subduction in the future, but it is as yet amagmatic.

REVIEW OF MOBILIST MODELS OF CARIBBEAN EVOLUTION

Twelve published models of the plate tectonic evolution of all or part of the Gulf of Mexico/Caribbean region are analyzed

in Table 2 on Plate 12. In this analysis, the region is divided into 17 subregions, and the original authors' viewpoints on each subregion are summarized. Additional published studies consider parts or aspects of the Gulf/Caribbean, such as those by Burke and others (1984), McCann and Sykes (1984), Mattson (1979), Maresch (1974), Speed (1985), Gealey (1980), Pilger (1978), Perfit and Heezen (1978), Maurrasse (1981), Wadge and others (1984), and Burkart (1983), but these are not included in Table 2 because of their limited geographic coverage or because their ideas are well represented by one of the included models. Entries for the twelve models in Table 2 are explicit in the authors' texts or diagrams, or can be inferred from their texts or diagrams.

The purpose of this review, besides summarizing the twelve models, is to point out various possible interpretations of the development of each subregion. Included as well is a summary of the model proposed here (below). The alternatives for the development of each subregion are listed, as are geological facts that assist in choosing the best interpretation. Points of contention, or unresolved problems, for each subregion then are listed to suggest topics needing further research in order to clarify the evolution of the various subregions.

PROPOSED MODEL OF CARIBBEAN EVOLUTION

In eight sequential reconstructions with accompanying text, Plate 12 outlines a plate-tectonic model of Caribbean evolution that incorporates the plate tectonic elements and interpretations defined above. We begin with the Permo-Triassic reconstruction of Figure 2D and develop a geologic-kinematic model using the relative motions of the North American, South American, and Farallon Plates (Figs. 3, 4).

The shape of northern South America has changed during Caribbean evolution. Throughout the reconstructions, we have restored Neogene transcurrent fault offsets related to the Andean orogeny using the assumptions of Dewey and Pindell (1985, 1986), and we have excluded the area occupied by the Western Cordillera of Colombia, the eastern Costa Rica–Panamá Arc, and the Leeward Antilles until the times of their respective creation and accretion to South America.

DISCUSSION AND SUMMARY

This chapter illustrates the kinematic-geologic approach to paleogeographic analysis, integrating plate-tectonic/geologic elements with paleopositions and relative motions of plates through time. Like the Mediterranean, the Caribbean is a region where this approach is essential.

Although it cannot be directly proved, the following several lines of evidence point to a Pacific origin for the Caribbean Plate.

1. Present motion of the Caribbean Plate is eastward relative to North America. Extrapolating this motion into the past implies an origin farther to the west.

2. The present plate boundary configuration and magnetic anomalies produced by sea-floor spreading in the Cayman

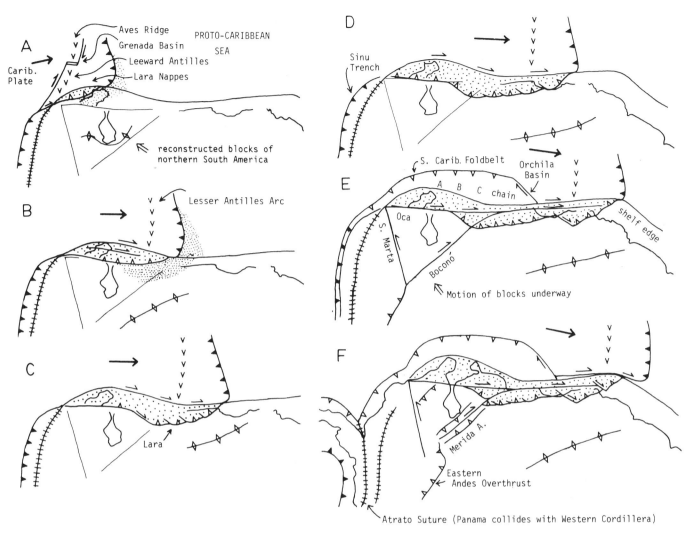

Figure 10. Six-staged Cenozoic development of northern South America, after Dewey and Pindell (1986). A: Paleocene. Opening of Grenada Basin by north-south intra-arc spreading. Arc system along Cordilleran Colombia fed turbiditic clastics into the Maracaibo Basin and trench offshore, which were depressed by the advancing Caribbean Plate. 100 km, 150 km, and 65 km of strike-slip offset has been restored along the Boconó, the Santa Marta, and the Oca faults, respectively, which became mobile in the Miocene. B and C: Eocene and Oligocene. The turbidites were accreted to the already metamorphosed Lara nappes of the advancing Caribbean Plate. Continued eastward motion of the Caribbean progressively emplaced the nappes and accretionary complex onto the Venezuelan margin throughout the Cenozoic, accompanied by dextral shear and clockwise rotation of rock assemblages within the nappes. D and E: Early and Late Miocene. The onset of the Andean orogeny in the west mobilized blocks of the Cordilleran terranes. The Caribbean–South America transform boundary became convergent, and the Leeward Antilles Islands, originally part of the Caribbean Plate, have been thrust northward onto the more oceanic portion of the Caribbean Plate. F: Present. The Panamanian arc has collided with the western Cordillera along the Atrato Suture, and continued convergence has produced the rugged Andean topography. Heavy stipple pattern, continental crust overthrust by oceanic terranes. Light stipple, flysch of the Scotland Formation of Barbados. V's denote island arc volcanism. Heavy arrows denote relative motion of Caribbean and South American plates. Anticlinal symbols represent foreland flexural bulge of the advancing thrust load of the oceanic terranes.

Trough suggest eastward migration of the Caribbean Plate relative to North America (MacDonald and Holcombe, 1978; Ross and others, 1986). A similar mode of formation for the entire trough would imply more than 1,000 km of offset since the Eocene, placing the Caribbean Plate into the Pacific realm.

3. Subduction-related magmatism in the Lesser Antilles arc has been continuous since the Eocene, suggesting Caribbean motion relative to the Americas since at least that time.

4. Two genetically unrelated suites of rocks exist throughout the Caribbean: (1) passive margin carbonate or terrigenous shelf sequences of Jurassic to Late Cretaceous or early Tertiary age (such as the Bahamas, Yucatán, and Venezuela), and (2) magmatic-arc and ultramafic assemblages of Upper Jurassic to Cenozoic age. Contacts between the two suites are tectonic; the arcs are allochthonous to, but coeval with, the passive margins. Tectonic juxtaposition between the two occurred later toward the east; Late Cretaceous in southern Yucatán (emplacement of Santa Cruz ophiolite) and Colombia (accretion of Western Cordillera against the Andean magmatic arc), Eocene in the central Bahamas and west Venezuela, and Miocene in eastern Venezuela and the eastern Bahamas. This diachronous juxtaposition documents the eastward advance of the Caribbean Plate relative to the Americas.

5. Marine magnetic anomalies of the Caribbean Plate do not easily fit the spreading history between North and South America. Magnetic anomalies thought to be [M21–M11] in the Venezuelan Basin trend northeast (Ghosh and others, 1984), but the gap between North and South America at that time was too small to have accommodated the Caribbean Plate.

Most plate-tectonic models of Caribbean evolution differ not so much about the origin of the plate itself, but as to how and when the Caribbean entered the gap between the Americas. These differences are highlighted in the "Unresolved Problems" column of Table 2 (Plate 1).

Assuming a Pacific provenance for the Caribbean Plate, the following phases of evolution can be recognized:

1. Middle to Late Jurassic rifting and initial separation between North America, the Bahamas, the Yucatán block, and northern South America.

2. Late Jurassic through Late Cretaceous or Early Tertiary passive margins in the Bahamas, Yucatán, and northern South America during drift between the Americas and the widening of the proto-Caribbean Basin.

3. Eastward-progressing, time-transgressive (Late Cretaceous to Recent) orogeny around the Caribbean, caused by the tectonic interaction (collision or transpression) of the eastward migrating Caribbean Plate and the stable margins of the proto-Caribbean.

4. Eocene to Recent development of complex strike-slip boundary zones in the northern and southern Caribbean, associated with the eastward migration of the Caribbean Plate.

5. A Miocene to Recent period of deformation across the entire Caribbean, referred to here as the Neo-Caribbean phase of deformation. The deformation results from interaction between the Caribbean and the American plates, specifically (1) compression caused by convergence between North and South America, (2) northeastward migration of the Andean Terranes of northwest South America, and (3) convergence at the Hispaniolan Restraining Bend along the Oriente–Puerto Rico Trench transform fault, northeast of the Dominican Republic.

Because the Caribbean region is composed largely of a collection of allochthonous terranes (Case and others, 1984) whose exact relative motions are poorly known, models of Caribbean evolution should attempt to reconcile existing geological data with known or inferred plate motions. Improvement in the understanding of Caribbean evolution will come from the continued integration of geological and geophysical studies, and further refinement of the plate-kinematic framework.

REFERENCES CITED

Aggarwal, Y., 1983, Present-day boundary and the motion of the Caribbean Plate relative to South America [abs.]: Caribbean Geological Conference, 10th, Abstracts with Programs, Cartegena, Colombia, p. 16.

Anderson, T. H., and Schmidt, V. A., 1983, The evolution of Middle America and the Gulf of Mexico–Caribbean Sea region during Mesozoic time: Geological Society of America Bulletin, v. 94, p. 941–966.

Andrieff, P., Bouysse, P., and Westercamp, D., 1979, Reconnaissance geologique de l'arc insulaire des Petites Antilles; Resultats d'une campagne a la mer de prelevements de roches entre Sainte-Lucie et Anguilla: (ARCANTE 1): Bulletin du Bureau Recherches Geologiques et Mineres (Deuxieme Serie), Sec. IV, nos. 3–4, p. 227–270.

Arden, D. D., 1975, Geology of Jamaica and the Nicaragua Rise, *in* Nairn, A.E.M., and Stehli, F. G., eds., The ocean basins and margins; Vol. 3, The Gulf of Mexico and the Caribbean: New York, Plenum, p. 617–661.

Atwater, T., 1970, Implications of plate tectonics for the Cenozoic tectonic evolution of western North America: Geological Society of America Bulletin, v. 81, p. 3513–3536.

Auboin, J., van Heune, R., and others, 1982, Leg 84 of the Deep Sea Drilling Project: Nature, v. 297, p. 458–460.

Austin, J. A., 1983, Thrusting in a deep-water carbonate terrane, *in* Bally, A. B., ed., Seismic expression of structural styles, Vol. III: American Association of Petroleum Geologists Studies in Geology 15, p. 167–172.

Azema, J., and Tournon, J., 1980, La peninsule de Santa Elena, Costa Rica; Un massif ultrabasique charrié en marge Pacific de l'Amerique centrale: Comptes Rendues de l'Academie des Sciences, ser. D, v. 290, p. 9–12.

Bandy, O. L., 1970, Upper Cretaceous–Cenozoic paleobathymetric cycles, eastern Panamá and northern Colombia: Gulf Coast Association of Geological Societies Transactions, v. 20, p. 181–193.

Bandy, O. L., and Casey, R. E., 1973, Reflector horizons and paleobathymetric history, eastern Panamá: Geological Society of America Bulletin, v. 84, p. 3081–3086.

Barrero, L. D., 1979, Geology of the central Western Cordillera, west of Buga and Roldanillo, Colombia: Publicaciones Geológicas Especiales del Ingeominas (Bogotá), no. 4, 75 p.

Beck, C. M., 1978, Polyphasic Tertiary tectonics of the interior range in the central part of the western Caribbean chain, northern Venezuela: Geologie en Mijnbouw, v. 57, p. 99–104.

Beets, D. J., 1975, Superimposed island arcs along the southern margin of the

Caribbean, *in* Borrodaile, G. J., and others, eds., Progress in geodynamics, Scientific Report 13: Amsterdam, North Holland Publishing Company, p. 218–228.

Beets, D. J., Maresch, W. V., Klaver, G. Th., Mottana, A., Bocchio, R., Beunk, F. F., and Monen, H. P., 1984, Magnetic rock series and high-pressure metamorphism as constraints on the tectonic history of the southern Caribbean, *in* Bonini, W. E., Hargraves, R. B., and Shagam, R., eds., The Caribbean–South American Plate Boundary and Regional Tectonics: Geological Society of America Memoir 162, p. 95–130.

Bellizzia, G., Alirio, and Rogríguez, G., Domingo, 1968, Consideraciones sobre la estratigrafía de los Estados Lara, Yaracuy, Cojedes, y Carabobo: Venezuela, Ministério de Minas e Hidrocárburos, Boletín de Geología, v. 9, no. 18, p. 515–563.

Bellizzia, G., Alirio, Rodríguez, G., Domingo, and Graterol, M., 1972, Ofiolitas de Siquisique y Río Tocuyo y sus relaciones con la falla de Oca: Caribbean Geological Conference, 7th, Transactions, Isla de Margarita, Venezuela, p. 182–183.

Bellon, H., and Tournon, J., 1978, Contribution de la geochronometrie K-Ar a l'étude magmatisme de Costa Rica, Amerique Centrale: Bulletin de la Societé Geologique de France, v. 20, p. 955–959.

Berryhill, H. L., Jr., 1965, Geology of the Ciales Quadrangle, Puerto Rico: U.S. Geological Survey Bulletin 1184, 116 p.

Bertrand, J., Delaloye, M., Fontaignie, O., and Vaugnat, M., 1978, Ages (K-Ar) sur diverses ophiolites et roches associées de la Cordillere Centrale du Guatemala: Schweizerische Mineralogische und Petrographische Mitteilungen, v. 58, p. 405–413.

Biju-Duval, B., Mascle, A., Montadert, L., and Wanneson, J., 1978, Seismic investigations in the Colombia, Venezuela, and Grenada basins, and on the Barbados Ridge, for future IPOD drilling: Geologie en Mijnbouw, v. 57, p. 105–116.

Biju-Duval, B., Bizon, G., Mascle, A., and Muller, C., 1983a, Active margin processes; Field observations in southern Hispaniola: American Association of Petroleum Geologists Memoir 34, p. 325–344.

Biju-Duval, B., Mascle, A., Rosales, H., and Young, G., 1983b, Episutural Oligo–Miocene basins along the north Venezuelan margin: American Association of Petroleum Geologists Memoir 34, p. 347–358.

Boiteau, A., and Michard, A., 1976, Données nouvelles sur le socle metamorphique de Cuba; Problèmes d'application de la tectoniques des plaques: Caribbean Geological Conference, 7th, Transactions, p. 221–226.

Bourgois, J., Glacon, G., Tavares, I., and Vila, J.-M., 1979a, Decouverte d'une tectonique tangentielle recente a vergence Sud dans las sierra de Neiba (île d'Hispaniola, Republique Dominicaine, Grandes Antilles): Paris, Comptes Rendues de l'Academie des Sciences, v. 289, p. 258–260.

Bourgois, J., Rosa, N. G., Tavares, I., and Vila, J.-M., 1979b, L'Eocene a blocs d'Ocoa (Republique Dominicaine, Grandes Antilles); Temoin d'une tectonique tangentielle a vergence sud dans l'île d'Hispaniola: Bulletin de la Societé Geologique de France, v. 6, p. 759–764.

Bourgois, J., Vila, J.-M., Llinas, R., and Tavares, I., 1980, Datos geológicos nuevos acerca de la región de Puerto Plata. (República Dominicana): Caribbean Geological Conference, 9th, Transactions, Santo Domingo, Dominican Republic, p. 35–38.

Bourgois, J., Calle, B., Tournon, J., and Toussaint, J. F., 1982, The Andean ophiolitic megasutures on the Buga–Buenaventura traverse (Western Cordillera–Valle Colombia): Tectonophysics, v. 82, p. 207–230.

Bouysse, P., Andrieff, P., and Westercamp, D., 1980, Evolution of the Lesser Antilles Island Arc; New data from the submarine geology: Caribbean Geological Conference, 9th, Transactions, Santo Domingo, Dominican Republic, p. 75–88.

Bouysse, P., Maury, R. C., and Westercamp, D., 1981, Le Banc Luymes, terminaison suptentrionale de l'arc recent des Petites Antilles: Bulletin de la Societé Geologique de France, v. 23, p. 185–194.

Bouysse, P., Schmidt-Effing, R., and Westercamp, D., 1983, La Desirade Island (Lesser Antilles) revisited; Lower Cretaceous radiolarian cherts and arguments against an ophiolitic origin for the basal complex: Geology, v. 11,

p. 244–247.

Bowin, C., 1960, Geology of central Dominican Republic; A case history of part of an island arc: Geological Society of America Bulletin, v. 98, p. 11–84.

——— , 1975, The geology of Hispaniola, *in* Nairn, A.E.M., and Stehli, F. G., eds., The Ocean Basins and Margins; Vol. 3, The Gulf of Mexico and the Caribbean: New York, Plenum, p. 501–552.

——— , 1976, Caribbean gravity field and plate tectonics: Geological Society of America Special Paper 169, 79 p.

Bowin, C., and Nagle, F., 1980, Igneous and metamorphic rocks of northern Dominican Republic; An uplifted subduction zone complex: Caribbean Geological Conference, 9th, Transactions, p. 39–50.

Bracey, D. R., and Vogt, P. R., 1970, Plate tectonics in the Hispaniola area: Geological Society of America Bulletin, v. 81, p. 2855–2860.

Brezsnyansky, K., and Korpas, L., 1973, Esquema geológico de la sedimentación orogénica: Actas del Instituto Geológico, Academia de Ciencias de Cuba, v. 3, p. 75–78.

Briden, J. C., Rex, D. C., Faller, A. M., and Tomblin, J. R., 1979, K-Ar geochronology and paleomagnetism of volcanic rocks in the Lesser Antilles Island arc: Philosophical Transactions of the Royal Society of London, v. 291, p. 485–528.

Bullard, E. C., Everett, J. E., and Smith, A. G., 1965, The fit of the continents around the Atlantic; A symposium on continental drift: Philosophical Transactions of the Royal Society of London, series A, v. 258, p. 41–51.

——— , 1983, Neogene North American–Caribbean plate boundary across northern Central America; Offset along the Polochic fault: Tectonophysics, v. 99, p. 251–270.

Burke, K., and Dewey, J. F., 1974, Two plates in Africa during the Cretaceous?: Nature, v. 249, p. 313–316.

Burke, K., Dewey, J. F., and Kidd, W.S.F., 1977, World distribution of sutures; The sites of former oceans: Tectonophysics, v. 40, p. 69–99.

Burke, K., Fox, P. J., and Sengor, A.M.C., 1978, Buoyant ocean floor and the evolution of the Caribbean: Journal of Geophysical Research, v. 83, p. 3949–3954.

Burke, K., Grippi, J., and Sengor, A.M.C., 1980, Neogene structures in Jamaica and the tectonic style of the northern Caribbean plate boundary zone: Journal of Geology, v. 88, p. 375–386.

Burke, K., Cooper, C., Dewey, J. F., Mann, J. P., and Pindell, J., 1984, Caribbean tectonics and relative plate motions, *in* Bonini, W. E., Hargraves, R. B., and Shagam, R., eds., The Caribbean–South American Plate Boundary and Regional Tectonics: Geological Society of America Memoir 162, p. 31–64.

Case, J. E., 1974a, Major basins along the continental margin of northern South America, *in* Burk, C. A., and Drake, C. L., eds., The geology of continental margins: New York, Springer-Verlag, p. 733–742.

——— , 1974b, Oceanic crust forms basement in eastern Panama: Geological Society of America Bulletin, v. 85, p. 645–652.

——— , 1980, Crustal setting of mafic and ultramafic rocks and associated ore deposits of the Caribbean region: U.S. Geological Survey Open-File Report 80-304, 94 p.

Case, J. E., and Holcombe, T. L., 1980, Geologic-tectonic map of the Caribbean region: U.S. Geological Survey Miscellaneous Investigations Series Map I-100, scale 1:2,500,000.

Case, J. E., and MacDonald, W. J., 1973, Regional gravity anomalies and crustal structure in northern Colombia: Geological Society of America Bulletin, v. 84, p. 2905–2916.

Case, J. E., Durán, L. G., Alfonso López, R. A., and Moore, W. R., 1971, Tectonic investigations in western Colombia and eastern Panama: Geological Society of America Bulletin, v. 82, p. 2685–2712.

Case, J. E., Holcombe, T. L., and Martin, R. G., 1984, Map of geologic provinces in the Caribbean region, *in* Bonini, W. E., Hargraves, R. B., and Shagam, R., eds., The Caribbean–South American Plate Boundary and Regional Tectonics: Geological Society of America Memoir 162, p. 1–30.

Cheilletz, A., Kachrillo, J. T., Sonet, J., and Zimmerman, J. J., 1978, Petrographie et geochronologie de deux complexes intrusifs a porphyres cupriferes d'Haiti: Bulletin de la Societé Geologique de France, v. 20, p. 907–914.

Christofferson, E., 1983, Plate model of the collapsing Caribbean continental slope of Nicaragua and the adjacent San Andres Island trough [abs.]: Caribbean Geological Conference, 10th, Abstracts with Programs, Cartagena, Colombia, p. 32.

Chubb, L. J., and Burke, K., 1963, Age of the Jamaican granodiorite: Geological Magazine, v. 100, p. 524–532.

Clemons, R. E., and Long, L. E., 1971, Petrologic and isotopic study of the Chiquimula Pluton, southeastern Guatemala: Geological Society of America Bulletin, v. 82, p. 2729–2740.

Cobiella, J. L., 1978, Una mélange en Cuba Oriental: Minería en Cuba, v. 4, p. 46–51.

Cobiella, J. L., Campos, M., Boiteau, A., and Quintas, F., 1977, Geología del flanco sur de la sierra del Purial: Minería en Cuba, v. 3, p. 54–62.

Coney, P. J., 1983, Un modelo tectónico de Mexico y sus relaciones con América del Norte, América del Sur y el Caribe: Revista del Instituto Mexicano del Petróleo, v. 15, p. 6–15.

Cooper, J. C., 1983, Geology of the Fondo Negro Basin and adjacent areas, Dominican Republic [M.S. thesis]: State University of New York at Albany, 145 p.

Cox, D. P., Marvin, R. F., McGonigle, J. W., McIntyre, D. H., and Rogers, C. L., 1977, Potassium-argon geochronology of some metamorphic, igneous, and hydrothermal events in Puerto Rico and the Virgin Islands: U.S. Geological Survey Journal of Research, v. 5, p. 689–703.

de Boer, J., 1979, The outer arc of the Costa Rican orogen (ocean basement complexes of the Nicoya and Santa Elena peninsula): Tectonophysics, v. 56, p. 221–254.

del Guidice, D., 1979, Características geológicas de la República de Panamá: Universidad Nacional Autónoma de Mexico Boletín, v. 101, p. 4–25.

Dewey, J. F., 1982, Plate tectonic evolution of the British Isles: Journal of the Geological Society of London, v. 139, p. 371–412.

Dewey, J. F., and Pindell, J. L., 1985, Neogene block tectonics of Turkey and northern South America; Continental applications of the finite difference method: Tectonics, v. 4, p. 71–83.

——, 1986, Neogene block tectonics of Turkey and northern South America; Continental applications of the finite difference method; Reply: Tectonics, v. 5, p. 703–705.

Dewey, J. F., Pitman, W. C., III, Ryan, W.B.F., and Bonnin, J., 1973, Plate tectonics and the evolution of the Alpine System: Geological Society of America Bulletin, v. 84, p. 3137–3180.

Dietz, R. S., and Holden, J. C., 1970, Reconstruction of Pangea; Breakup and dispersion of continents, Permian to present: Journal of Geophysical Research, v. 75, p. 4939–4956.

Dillon, W. P., and Vedder, J. G., 1973, Structure and development of the continental margin of British Honduras: Geological Society of America Bulletin, v. 84, p. 2713–2732.

Donnelly, T. W., 1977, Metamorphic rocks and structural history of the Motagua suture zone, eastern Guatemala [abs.]: Caribbean Geological Conference, 8th, Abstracts with Programs, Curacao, p. 40–41.

Draper, G., 1987, A revised tectonic model for the evolution of Jamaica, in Ahmad, R., ed., Proceedings of a workshop on the status of Jamaican geology, Kingston, Jamaica, March, 1984: Journal of the Geological Society of Jamaica, Special Issue, p. 151–169.

Draper, G., and Lewis, J. F., 1983, Petrology and structural development of the Duarte Complex, central Dominican Republic; A preliminary account and some tectonic implications [abs.]: Caribbean Geological Conference, 10th, Abstracts with Programs, Cartagena, Colombia, p. 34–35.

Duncan, R. A., and Hargraves, R. B., 1984, Plate tectonic evolution of the Caribbean region in the mantle reference frame, in Bonini, W. E., Hargraves, R. B., and Shagam, R., eds., The Caribbean–South American Plate Boundary and Regional Tectonics: Geological Society of America Memoir 162, p. 81–84.

Duque-Caro, H., 1972, Relaciones entre le bioestratigrafía y la cronestratigrafía en el Llamado Geosinclinal de Bolívar: INGEOMINAS, Boletín Geológico, v. 19, p. 25–68.

——, 1979, Major structural elements and evolution of northwest Colombia: American Association of Petroleum Geologists Memoir 29, p. 329–351.

——, 1984, Structural style, diapirism, and accretionary episodes of the Sinu-San Jacinto terrane, southwestern Caribbean borderland, in Bonini, W. E., Hargraves, R. B., and Shagam, R., eds., The Caribbean–South American Plate Boundary and Regional Tectonics: Geological Society of America Memoir 162, p. 303–316.

Eberle, W., Hirdes, W., Muff, R., and Palaez, M., 1980, The geology of the Cordillera Septentrional (Dominican Republic): Caribbean Geological Conference, 9th, Transactions, p. 619–632.

Edgar, N. T., Ewing, M. I., and Hennion, J., 1971, Seismic refraction and reflection in the Caribbean Sea: American Association of Petroleum Geologists Bulletin, v. 55, p. 833–870.

Engebretson, D. C., 1982, Relative motions between oceanic and continental plates in the Pacific basin: [Ph.D. thesis]: Stanford, California, Stanford University, 211 p.

Escalante, G., 1966, Geología de la cuenca superior del Río Reventazón, Costa Rica, in Trabajos técnicos presentados en la primera reunión de geológos de America Central: Publicaciones Geológicas del ICAITI, no. 1, p. 59–70.

Feigenson, M., 1978, The strontium-isotope geochemistry of a tonalite batholith of the Dominican Republic: Annual Report of the Director, Department of Terrestrial Magnetism, Carnegie Institute, p. 870–878.

Fink, L. J., Jr., 1970, Field guide to the island of La Desirade with notes on the regional history and development of the Lesser Antilles Island arc: American Geological Institute International Field Institute Guidebook, p. 17.

Fisher, S. P., and Pessagno, E. A., 1965, Upper Cretaceous strata of northwest Panamá: American Association of Petroleum Geologists Bulletin, v. 49, p. 433–444.

Flint, D. E., Albear, J. F., and Guild, P. W., 1948, Geology and chromite deposits of the Camagüey Province, Cuba: U.S. Geological Survey Bulletin, v. 954eB, p. 39–63.

Fox, P. J., and Heezen, B. C., 1975, Geology of the Caribbean crust, in Nairn, A.E.M., and Stehli, F. G., eds., The ocean basins and margins; Vol. 3, The Gulf of Mexico and the Caribbean: New York, Plenum, p. 421–465.

Fox, P. J., Schreiber, J., and Heezen, B. C., 1971, The geology of the Caribbean crust; Aves Ridge: Tectonophysics, v. 12, p. 89–109.

Freeland, G. L., and Dietz, R. S., 1972, Plate tectonic evolution of the Caribbean-Gulf of Mexico region: Nature, v. 232, p. 20–23.

Galli-Olivier, C., 1979, Ophiolitic and island-arc volcanism in Costa Rica: Geological Society of America Bulletin, v. 90, p. 444–452.

Gealey, W. K., 1980, Ophiolite obduction mechanism, in Panayiotou, A., ed., Ophiolites; Proceedings of the International Ophiolite Symposium: Nicosia, Cyprus Geological Survey Department, p. 228–243.

Ghosh, N., Hall, S. A., and Casey, J. F., 1984, Seafloor spreading magnetic anomalies in the Venezuelan Basin, in Bonini, W. E., Hargraves, R. B., and Shagam, R., eds., The Caribbean–South American Plate Boundary and Regional Tectonics: Geological Society of America Memoir 162, p. 65–80.

Glover, L., III, 1971, Geology of the Coamo area, Puerto Rico, and its relation to the volcanic arc-trench association: U.S. Geological Survey, Professional Paper 636, 102 p.

Gonzalez de Juana, C., Arozena, J. A., and Picard Cadillat, X., 1980, Geología de Venezuela y sus cuencas petrolíferas: Caracas, Venezuela, Ediciones Foninves, 1031 p.

Gursky, H., Schmidt-Effing, J. R., Strebin, M., and Wildbert, H., 1983, The geologic development of the ophiolitic basement in southern Central America [abs.]: Caribbean Geological Conference, 10th, Abstracts with Programs, Cartagena, Colombia, p. 39.

Haldemann, E. G., Brouwer, S. B., Blowes, J. H., and Snow, W. E., 1980, Lateritic nickel deposits at Bonao: Caribbean Geological Conference, 9th, Field Guide, Santo Domingo, Dominican Republic, p. 69–80.

Hall, S. A., and Yeung, T., 1980, A study of magnetic anomalies in the Yucatán Basin: Caribbean Geological Conference, 9th, Santo Domingo, Dominican Republic Transactions, p. 519–526.

Hargraves, R. B., and Skerlec, G. M., 1980, Paleomagnetism of some Cretaceous-

Tertiary igneous rocks on Venezuelan offshore islands, Netherland Antilles, Trinidad, and Tobago: Caribbean Geological Conference, 9th, Transactions, Santo Domingo, Dominican Republic, p. 509–517.

Hargraves, R. B., Shagam, R., Vargas, R., and Rodriguez, G. I., 1984, Paleomagnetic results from rhyolites (Early Cretaceous?) and andesite dikes from two localities in the Ocana area, northern Santander Massif, Colombia, *in* Bonini, W. E., Hargraves, R. B., and Shagam, R., eds., The Caribbean–South American Plate Boundary and Regional Tectonics: Geological Society of America Memoir 162, p. 299–302.

Heezen, B. C., Catalano, R., and Rawson, M., 1975, Geological map of the Puerto Rico Trench and adjacent margins: Geological Society of America Abstracts with Programs, v. 7, p. 1108.

Henderson, W. G., 1979, Cretaceous to Eocene volcanic arc activity in the Andes of northern Ecuador: Journal of the Geological Society of London, v. 136, p. 367–378.

Henningsen, D., 1965, Stratigraphy and paleogeography of Upper Cretaceous and Tertiary sediments in southern Costa Rica: Publicaciones Geologicas de Instituto Centroamericano de Investigacion y Tecnología Indusrial, no. 1, p. 53–57.

Holcombe, T. L., and Sharman, G. F., 1983, Post-Miocene Cayman Trough evolution; A speculative model: Geology, v. 11, p. 714–717.

Holcombe, T. L., Vogt, P. R., Matthews, J. E., and Murchison, R. R., 1973, Evidence for seafloor spreading in the Cayman Trough: Earth and Planetary Science Letters, v. 20, p. 357–371.

Horne, G. S., Pushkar, P., and Shafiquallah, M., 1974, Laramide plutons on the landward continuation of the Bonacca ridge, northern Honduras: Caribbean Geological Conference, 7th, Transactions, p. 583–588.

Horne, G. S., Pushkar, P., and Shafiquallah, M., 1976, Preliminary K-Ar age data from the Laramide Sierras of central Honduras, *in* Informe y Trabajos Técnicos, IV, Reunion de Geologos de America Central: Guatemala, C. A., Publicaciones Geologicas de ICAITI, no. V, p. 91–98.

Irving, E. M., 1975, Structural evolution of the northernmost Andes, Colombia: U.S. Geological Survey Professional Paper 846, p. 1–47.

Joyce, J., 1983, K-Ar ages for blueschist metamorphism on the Samana Peninsula, Dominican Republic [abs.]: Caribbean Geological Conference, 10th, Abstracts with Programs, Cartagena, Colombia, p. 44.

Kashfi, M. S., 1983, Geology and hydrocarbon prospects of Jamaica: American Association of Petroleum Geologists Bulletin, v. 67, p. 2117–2124.

Kearey, P., 1974, Gravity and seismic reflection investigation into the crustal structure of the Aves Ridge, eastern Caribbean: Caribbean Geological Conference, 7th, Transactions, p. 311–320.

Keigwin, L. D., Jr., 1978, Pliocene closing of the Isthmus of Panamá, based on biostratigraphic evidence from nearby Pacific Ocean and Caribbean Sea cores: Geology, v. 6, p. 630–634.

Keller, G., and Barron, J. A., Paleoceanographic implications of Miocene deep-sea hiatuses: Geological Society of America Bulletin, v. 94, p. 590–613.

Kesler, S. E., 1971, Petrology of the Terre-Nueve igneous province, northern Haiti: Geological Society of America Memoir 130, p. 119–137.

Kesler, S. E., and Sutter, J. F., 1979, Compositional evolution of intrusive rocks in the eastern Greater Antilles Island arc: Geology, v. 7, p. 197–200.

Kesler, S. E., Sutter, J. F., Jones, L. M., and Walker, R. L., 1977, Early Cretaceous basement rocks in Hispaniola: Geology, v. 5, p. 245–247.

Khudoley, K. M., and Meyerhoff, A. A., 1971, Paleogeographic and geologic history of the greater Antilles: Geological Society of America Memoir 129, 199 p.

Klitgord, K. D., and Mammerickx, J., 1982, Northern East Pacific Rise; Magnetic anomaly and bathymetric framework: Journal of Geophysical Research, v. 87, p. 6725–6750.

Klitgord, K., and Schouten, H., 1987, Plate kinematics of the Central Atlantic, *in* Vogt, P. R., and Tucholke, B. E., eds., The Western North Atlantic Region: Boulder, Colorado, Geological Society of America, The Geology of North America, v. M, p. 351–378.

Klitgord, K. D., Popenoe, P., and Schouten, H., 1984, Florida; A Jurassic transform plate boundary: Journal of Geophysical Research, v. 89, p. 7753–7772.

Knipper, A. L., and Cabrera, R., 1974, Tectónica y geología histórica de la zona de articulacion entre el mio- y eugeosynclinal y del cinturón hiperbasico de Cuba, *in* Contribución a la geología de Cuba: Instituto de Geología y Paleontología, Publicación Especial 2, p. 15–77.

Kozary, M. T., 1968, Ultramafic rocks in the thrust zones of northwestern Oriente Province, Cuba: American Association of Petroleum Geologists Bulletin, v. 52, p. 2298–2317.

Ladd, J. W., 1976, Relative motion of South America with respect to North America and Caribbean tectonics: Geological Society of America Bulletin, v. 87, p. 969–976.

Ladd, J. W., and Watkins, J. S., 1978, Tectonic development of trench-arc complexes on the northern and southern margins of the Venezuelan Basin, *in* Watkins, J. S., Montadert, L., and Dickerson, P. W., eds., Geological and geophysical investigations of continental margins: American Association of Petroleum Geologists Memoir 29, p. 363–371.

Le Guen de Kerneizon, M., Mascle, A., Maury, R. C., and Westercamp, D., 1979, Les laves de la Desirade (Petites Antilles) temoins d'un magmatisme de marge actives; Arguments mineralogique: Bulletin B. R. G. M., v. 2, section 4, (deuxieme series), p. 285–292.

Le Pichon, X., and Fox, P. J., 1971, Marginal offsets, fracture zones, and the early opening of the North Atlantic: Journal of Geophysical Research, v. 76, p. 6294–6308.

Lewis, G. E., and Straczek, J. A., 1955, Geology of south-central Oriente, Cuba: U.S. Geological Survey Bulletin, v. 975-D, p. 171–336.

Lewis, J. F., Harper, C. T., Kemp, A. W., and Stripp, J. J., 1973, Potassium-argon retention ages for some Cretaceous rocks from Jamaica: Geological Society of America Bulletin, v. 84, p. 335–340.

Lockwood, J. P., 1965, Geology of the Serranía de Jarara area, Guajira Peninsula, Colombia: [Ph.D. thesis]: Princeton, New Jersey, Princeton University, 237 p.

Lowrie, A., 1978, Buried trench south of the Gulf of Panamá, Geology: v. 6, p. 434–436.

Lu, R. S., and McMillen, K. J., 1983, Multichannel seismic survey of the Colombia Basin and adjacent margin, *in* Watkins, J. S., and Drake, C. L., eds., Studies in continental margin geology: American Association of Petroleum Geologists Memoir 34, p. 395–410.

Ludwig, W. J., Houtz, R. E., and Ewing, J. I., 1975, Profiler-sonobuoy measurements in the Colombia and Venezuela basins, Caribbean Sea: American Association of Petroleum Geologists Bulletin, v. 59, p. 115–123.

Lundberg, N., 1983, Development of forearcs of intraoceanic subduction zones: Tectonics, v. 2, p. 51–61.

MacDonald, W. D., 1964, Geology of the Serranía de Macuira area, Guajira Peninsula, Colombia [Ph.D. thesis]: Princeton, New Jersey, Princeton University, 167 p.

—— , 1974, Cretaceous-Tertiary evolution of the Caribbean: Caribbean Geological Conference, 7th, Transactions, p. 69–78.

MacDonald, K. C., and Holcombe, T. L., 1978, Inversion of magnetic anomalies and sea-floor spreading in the Cayman Trough: Earth and Planetary Science Letters, v. 40, p. 407–414.

MacDonald, W. D., Doolan, B. L., and Cordani, U. G., 1971, Cretaceous-Early Tertiary metamorphic K-Ar age values from the south Caribbean: Geological Society of America Bulletin, v. 82, p. 1381–1388.

Malfait, B. T., and Dinkelman, M. G., 1972, Circum-Caribbean tectonic and igneous activity and the evolution of the Caribbean Plate: Geological Society of America Bulletin, v. 83, p. 251–272.

Mammerickx, J., and Klitgord, K. D., 1982, Northern East-Pacific Rise; Evolution from 25 m.y.B.P. to the present: Journal of Geophysical Research, v. 87, p. 6751–6759.

Mann, P., and Burke, K., 1984, Neotectonics of the Caribbean: Reviews of Geophysics and Space Physics, v. 22, p. 309–362.

Mann, P., Burke, K., and Matumoto, T., 1984, Neotectonics of Hispaniola; Plate motion, sedimentation, and seismicity at a restraining bend: Earth and Planetary Science Letters, v. 70, p. 311–324.

Maresch, W. V., 1974, Plate tectonics origin of the Caribbean mountain system of

northern South America; Discussion and proposal: Geological Society of
    America Bulletin, v. 85, p. 669–682.
Martín-Bellizzia, C., and de Arozena, J.M.T., 1972, Complejo ultramáfico zonado
    de Tausabana-El Rodeo, gabro zonado de Siraba-Capuana, y complejo
    subvolcánico estratificado de Santa Ana, Paraguaná, Estado Falcón:
    Transactions Caribbean Geological Conference, 6th, Isla de Margarita,
    Venezuela, p. 337–356.
Mattinson, J. M., Fink, L. K., Jr., and Hopson, C. A., 1973, Age and origin of
    ophiolitic rocks on La Desirade Island, Lesser Antilles Island arc: Carnegie
    Institute of Washington Yearbook, v. 72, p. 616–623.
——— , 1980, Geochronologic and isotopic study of the La Desirade Island base-
    ment complex; Jurassic oceanic crust in the Lesser Antilles?: Contributions
    to Mineralogy and Petrology, v. 71, p. 237–245.
Mattson, P. H., 1973, Middle Cretaceous nappe structures in Puerto Rican ophio-
    lites and their relation to the tectonic history of the Greater Antilles: Geo-
    logical Society of America Bulletin, v. 84, p. 21–37.
——— , 1979, Subduction, buoyant braking, flipping, and strike-slip faulting in the
    northern Caribbean: Journal of Geology, v. 87, p. 293–304.
Mattson, P. H., and Pessagno, E. A., Jr., 1979, Jurassic and Early Cretaceous
    radiolarians in Puerto Rican ophiolite; Tectonic implications: Geology, v. 7,
    p. 440–444.
Maurrasse, F. J-M. R., 1981, Relations between the geologic setting of Hispaniola
    and the origin and evolution of the Caribbean, in Maurrasse, F. J-M. R., ed.,
    1er Colloque sue la geologie d'Haiti, Presentations et Transactions: Port-au-
    Prince, Haiti, Imprimerie Le Natal, p. 246–264.
Maurrasse, F. J-M. R., Husler, J., Georges, G., Schmitt, R., and Damond, P.,
    1979, Upraised Caribbean sea-floor below acoustic reflector "B" at the
    southern peninsula of Haiti: Geologie en Mijnbouw, v. 58, p. 71–83.
Maze, W. B., 1984, Jurassic La Quinta Formation in the Sierra de Perijá, north-
    west Venezuela; Geology and tectonic movement of red beds and volcanic
    rocks, in Bonini, W. E., Hargraves, R. B., and Shagam, R., eds., The Carib-
    bean–South American Plate Boundary and Regional Tectonics: Geological
    Society of America Memoir 162, p. 263–282.
Maze, W. B., and Hargraves, R. B., 1984, Paleomagnetic results from the Jurassic
    La Quinta Formation in the Perijá Range, Venezuela, and their tectonic
    significance, in Bonini, W. E., Hargraves, R. B., and Shagam, R., eds., The
    Caribbean–South American Plate Boundary and Regional Tectonics: Geo-
    logical Society of America Memoir 162, p. 287–294.
McCann, W. R., and Sykes, L. R., 1984, Subduction of aseismic ridges beneath
    the Caribbean Plate; Implications for the tectonic and seismic potential of
    the northeastern Caribbean: Journal of Geophysical Research, v. 89,
    p. 4493–4519.
Mercier de Lepinay, B., Labesse, B., Sigal, J., and Vila, J.-M., 1979, Sedimenta-
    tion chaotique et tectonique tangentielle Maestrichtiennes dans la presque-île
    du sud d'Haiti, (île d'Hispaniola, Grandes Antilles): Comptes Rendues de
    l'Academie des Sciences, ser. D, v. 289, p. 887–890.
Meyerhoff, A. A., 1966, Bartlett fault system; age and offset: Caribbean
    Geological Conference, 3rd, Transactions, p. 1–9.
Meyerhoff, A. A., and Hatten, C. W., 1968, Diapiric structures in central Cuba:
    American Association of Petroleum Geologists Memoir, v. 8, p. 315–357.
——— , 1974, Bahamas salient of North America; Tectonic framework, stratig-
    raphy, and petroleum potential: American Association of Petroleum Geolo-
    gists Bulletin, v. 58, p. 1201–1239.
Meyerhoff, A. A., and Kreig, E. A., 1977, Five major cycles make up Jamaican
    tectonic and structural history: Oil and Gas Journal, v. 75, p. 141–146.
Meyerhoff, A. A., Khudoley, K. M., and Hatten, C. W., 1969, Geologic signifi-
    cance of radiometric dates from Cuba: American Association of Petroleum
    Geologists Bulletin, v. 53, p. 2494–2500.
Meyerhoff, A. A., Krieg, E. A., Cloos, J. D., and Taner, I., 1983, Petroleum
    potential of Puerto Rico: Oil and Gas Journal, v. 81, p. 113–120.
Michael, R. C., 1979, Geology of the south-central flank of the Cordillera Central
    and the adjacent portions of the San Juan Valley between Río San Juan and
    Río Yacahueque, Dominican Republic [M.S. thesis]: Washington, D.C.,
    George Washington University, 162 p.

Mills, R. A., and Hugh, K. E., 1974, Reconnaissance geologic map of Mosquitia
    region, Honduras and Nicaragura Caribbean coast: American Association of
    Petroleum Geologists Bulletin, v. 58, p. 189–207.
Mills, R. A., Hugh, K. E., Feray, D. E., and Swolfs, H. C., 1967, Mesozoic
    stratigraphy of Honduras: American Association of Petroleum Geologists
    Bulletin, v. 51, p. 1711–1786.
Molnar, P., and Sykes, L. R., 1969, Tectonics of the Caribbean and Middle
    America regions from focal mechanisms and seismicity: Geological Society
    of America Bulletin, v. 80, p. 1639–1684.
Monroe, W. H., 1968, The age of the Puerto Rico Trench: Geological Society of
    America Bulletin, v. 79, p. 487–494.
Mooney, W. D., 1980, An east Pacific-Caribbean ridge during the Jurassic and
    Cretaceous and the evolution of western Colombia, in Pilger, R. H., ed., The
    Origin of the Gulf of Mexico and the Early Opening of the Central North
    Atlantic: Baton Rouge, Louisiana State University, p. 55–73.
Mossakovskiy, A. A., and Albear, J. F., 1978, Nappe structure of western and
    northern Cuba and history of its emplacement in the light of a study of
    olistostromes and molasse: Geotectonics, v. 12, p. 225–236.
Muessig, K. W., 1984, Structure and Cenozoic tectonics of the Falcón Basin,
    Venezuela and adjacent areas, in Bonini, W. E., Hargraves, R. B., and
    Shagam, R., eds., The Caribbean–South American Plate Boundary and Re-
    gional Tectonics: Geological Society of America Memoir 162, p. 217–230.
Murphy, A. J., and McCann, W. R., 1979, Preliminary results from a new seismic
    network in the northeastern Caribbean: Seismological Society of America
    Bulletin, v. 69, p. 1497–1513.
Nagle, F., 1966, Geology of the Puerto Plata area, Dominican Republic [Ph.D.
    thesis]: Princeton, New Jersey, Princeton University, 171 p.
——— , 1979, Geology of the Puerto Plata area, Dominican Republic, in Hispani-
    ola, tectonic focal point of the Caribbean, three tectonic studies in the
    Dominican Republic: Miami, Florida, Miami Geological Society, p. 1–28.
Nagle, F., Stipp, J. J., and Fisher, D. E., 1976, K-Ar geochronology of the
    Limestone Caribbees and Martinique, Lesser Antilles, West Indies: Earth
    and Planetary Science Letters, v. 29, p. 401–412.
Nemec, M. C., 1980, A two-phase model for the tectonic evolution of the
    Caribbean: Caribbean Geological Conference, 9th, Transactions, p. 23–24.
Palmer, H. C., 1963, Geology of the Moncion-Jarabacoa area, Dominican Re-
    public [Ph.D. thesis]: Princeton, New Jersey, Princeton University, p. 256.
Pardo, G., 1975, Geology of Cuba, in Nairn, A.E.M., and Stehli, F. G., eds., The
    Ocean Basins and Margins; v. 3, The Gulf of Mexico and the Caribbean:
    New York, Plenum, p. 553–615.
Paz Rivera, N., 1963, Reconocimiento geológico de la costa Pacífico de Nica-
    ragua: Boletín Servício Geológico Nacional (Nicaragua), v. 8, p. 69–87.
Perfit, M. R., and Heezen, B. C., 1978, The geology and evolution of the Cayman
    Trench: Geological Society of America Bulletin, v. 89, p. 1155–1174.
Pilger, R. H., Jr., 1978, A closed Gulf of Mexico, pre-Atlantic Ocean plate
    reconstruction and the early rift history of the Gulf and North Atlantic: Gulf
    Coast Association of Geological Societies Transactions, v. 28, p. 385–393.
Pindell, J. L., 1985a, Alleghenian reconstruction and the subsequent evolution of
    the Gulf of Mexico, Bahamas and Proto-Caribbean Sea: Tectonics, v. 4,
    p. 1–39.
——— , 1985b, Plate-tectonic evolution of the Gulf of Mexico and Caribbean
    Region [Ph.D. thesis]: England, Durham University, 287 p.
Pindell, J. L., and Dewey, J. F., 1982, Permo-Triassic reconstruction of western
    Pangea and the evolution of the Gulf of Mexico/Caribbean region: Tec-
    tonics, v. 1, p. 179–212.
Piniero, R. F., and Romero, R. S., 1962, Reconocimiento geológico minero de la
    porción noreste de la República de Nicaragua: Boletín Servico Geológico
    Nacional (Nicaragua), v. 6, p. 51–91.
Priem, H.N.A., 1978, First progress report on the isotopic dating project in
    Colombia (Proradam) Amsterdam (Cited in Huguett and others, 1979):
    Huguett, A., Galvis, J., and Ruge, P., 1979, Geologia, in La Amazona
    Colombiana y sus recursos: Proyecto Radargrametrico del Amazonas,
    Bogota, chapter 2, p. 29–92.
Pszczolkowski, A., 1978, Geosynclinal sequences of the Cordillera de Guani-

guanico in western Cuba; Their lithostratigraphy, facies development, and paleogeography: Acta Geologica Polonica, v. 28, p. 1–96.

Rabinowitz, P. D., and LaBrecque, J., 1979, The Mesozoic South Atlantic Ocean and evolution of its continental margins: Journal of Geophysical Research, v. 84, p. 5973–6002.

Restrepo, J. J., and Touissant, J. R., 1977, Recopilación de dataciones radiométricas en el occidente Colombiano: Departamento de Ciencias de la Tierra, Universidad Nacional de Colombia, Medellin, 5 p.

Rosencrantz, E., Sclater, J. G., and Boerner, S. T., 1989, Basement depths and heat flow in the Yucatan Basin and Cayman Trough, northwestern Caribbean; Implications for basin ages, *in* Wright, J. A., and Laudon, K. E., eds., CRC Handbook of sea floor heat flow: Boca Raton, Florida, CRC Press Incorporated, p. 257–276.

Rosenfeld, J. H., 1980, The Santa Cruz ophiolite, Guatemala, Central America: Caribbean Geological Conference, 9th, Transactions, Santo Domingo, Dominican Republic, p. 451–452.

—— , 1981, Geology of the western Sierra de Santa Cruz, Guatemala, Central America, an ophiolite sequence [Ph.D. thesis]: State University of New York at Binghamton, 313 p.

Ross, M. I., Rosencrantz, E., Scotese, C., and Barrett, S. F., 1986, Caribbean plate reconstructions; new interpretation of data in the Cayman Trough, *in* Sager, W., and Scotese, C., eds., Mesozoic and Cenozoic Plate Reconstructions, abstracts: 1986 Geodynamics Symposium, College Station, Texas, Texas A&M University, p. 117–118.

Salvador, A., and Green, A. G., 1980, Opening of the Caribbean Tethys, in Auboin, J., coordinator, Geology of the Alpine chains born of the Tethys: France, Bureau de Recherches Géologiques et Minières Memoire 115, p. 224–229.

Santamaría, F., and Schubert, C., 1974, Chemistry and geochronology of the southern Caribbean–Northern Venezuelan plate boundary: Geological Society of America Bulletin, v. 85, p. 1085–1098.

Schell, B. A., and Tarr, A. C., 1978, Plate tectonics of the northeastern Caribbean Sea region: Geologie en Mijnbouw, v. 57, p. 319–324.

Schlager, W., and 16 others, 1984, Deep Sea Drilling Project, Leg 77, southeastern Gulf of Mexico: Geological Society of America Bulletin, v. 95, p. 226–236.

Schmidt-Effing, R., 1979, Geodynamic history of oceanic crust in southern Central America: Latin American Geological Congress, 4th, Geologische Rundschau, v. 68, p. 457–494.

Schubert, C., 1984, Basin formation along the Boconó-Morón–El Pilar Fault System, Venezuela: Journal of Geophysical Research, v. 89, p. 5711–5718.

Sclater, J. G., Hellinger, S., and Tapscott, C., 1977, The paleobathymetry of the Atlantic Ocean from the Jurassic to the present: Journal of Geology, v. 85, p. 509–522.

Shagam, R., 1975, The northern termination of the Andes, *in* Nairn, A.E.M., and Stehli, F. G., eds., The ocean basins and margins; Vol. 3, The Gulf of Mexico and the Caribbean: New York, Plenum, p. 325–420.

Shein, V. S., and Kleschev, K. A., 1977, Structure and genesis of thrust sheets of the Greater Antilles: Doklady Akademii Nauk SSSR, v. 234, p. 104–105.

Shepherd, A., Hall, S., and Snow, R., 1982, Magnetic and gravity anomaly fields of the eastern Gulf of Mexico: Geological Society of America Abstracts with Programs, v. 14, p. 615.

Skerlec, G. M., and Hargraves, R. B., 1980, Tectonic significance of paleomagnetic data from northern Venezuela: Journal of Geophysical Research, v. 85, p. 5303–5315.

Skvor, V., 1969, The Caribbean area; A case of destruction and regeneration of a continent: Geological Society of America Bulletin, v. 80, p. 961–968.

Somin, R. L., and Millan, G., 1977, Sobre la edad de las rocas metamórficas Cubanas: Academia de Ciencias de Cuba, Informe Científico-Técnico no. 2, p. 1–11.

Soto, R. S., 1978, La secuencia espilítico diabásica perforada por el pozo "Mercedes 2": Geologie en Mijnbouw, v. 57, p. 382.

Speed, R. C., 1985, Cenozoic collision of the Lesser Antilles arc and continental South America and origin of the El Pilar fault: Tectonics, v. 4, p. 40–70.

Speed, R. C., and Westbrook, G. K., eds., 1984, Lesser Antilles arc and adjacent terranes, Ocean Margin Drilling Program, Regional Atlas Series, Atlas 10: Woods Hole Massachusetts Marine Science International, 27 plates.

Stephan, J. F., 1985, Andes et chain Caraïbes sur la transversale de Barquisimeto (Venezuela); Evolution geodynamique, *in* Mascle, A., ed., Geodynamiques des Caraïbes: Editions Technip, p. 505–531.

Stephen, J. F., Beck, C. M., Bellizzia, A., and Blanchet, R., 1980, La chaine caraïbe du Pacifique a l'Atlantique: International Geological Conference, 26th, v. C-5, Paris, p. 38–59.

Sykes, L. R., and Ewing, M., 1965, The seismicity of the Caribbean region: Journal of Geophysical Research, v. 70, p. 5065–5074.

Sykes, L. R., McCann, W. R., and Kafka, A. L., 1982, Motion of Caribbean Plate during last 7 million years and implications for earlier movements: Journal of Geophysical Research, v. 87, p. 10656–10676.

Terry, R. A., 1956, A geological reconnaissance of Panamá: California Academy of Science Occasional Paper 23, 91 p.

Thayer, T. P., and Guild, P. W., 1947, Thrust faults and related structures in eastern Cuba: EOS American Geophysical Union Transactions, v. 28, p. 919–930.

Theyer, P., 1983, An obducted ophiolite complex in the Cordillera Central of the Dominican Republic: Geological Society of America Bulletin, v. 94, p. 1438–1441.

Tomblin, J. F., 1975, The Lesser Antilles and Aves Ridge, *in* Nairn, A.E.M., and Stehli, F. G., eds., The ocean basins and margins; Vol. 3, The Gulf of Mexico and the Caribbean: New York, Plenum, p. 467–500.

Tschanz, C. M., Marvin, R. F., Cruz, B. J., Mehnert, H., and Cebula, G. T., 1974, Geological evolution of the Sierra Nevada de Santa Marta, northeastern Colombia: Geological Society of America Bulletin, v. 85, p. 273–284.

Van der Voo, R., Mauk, F. J., French, R. B., 1976, Permian-Triassic continental configurations and the origin of the Gulf of Mexico: Geology, v. 4, p. 177–180.

Vierbuchen, R. C., 1984, The geology of the El Pilar fault zone and adjacent areas in northeastern Venezuela, *in* Bonini, W. E., Hargraves, R. B., and Shagam, R., eds., The Caribbean–South American Plate Boundary and Regional Tectonics: Geological Society of America Memoir 162, p. 189–212.

Vinson, G. L., 1962, Upper Cretaceous and Tertiary stratigraphy of Guatemala: American Association of Petroleum Geologists Bulletin, v. 46, p. 425–456.

Wadge, G., and Burke, K., 1983, Neogene Caribbean Plate rotation and associated Central American tectonic evolution: Tectonics, v. 2, p. 633–643.

Wadge, G., Jackson, T. A., and Isaacs, M. C., 1982, The Bath-Dunrobin Formation, Jamaica; Recognition of another ophiolite in the northwestern Caribbean: Journal of the Geological Society of London, v. 139, p. 321–333.

Wadge, G., Draper, G., and Lewis, J. F., 1984, Ophiolites of the northern Caribbean; A reappraisal of their roles in the evolution of the Caribbean plate boundary, *in* Gass, I. G., Lippard, S. J., and Shelton, A. W., eds., Ophiolites and Oceanic Lithosphere: Geological Society of London, p. 367–380.

Walper, J. L., 1980, The tectonic-sedimentary history of Caribbean basins and their hydrocarbon potential: Canadian Society of Petroleum Geologists Memoir 6, p. 887–911.

Webb, S. D., 1976, Mammalian faunal dynamics of the great American interchange: Paleobiology, v. 2, p. 220–234.

Weyl, R., 1980, Geology of Central America: Berlin, Gebrüder Borntrager, 371 p.

White, G. W., and Burke, K., 1980, Outline of the tectonic evolution of the Gulf of Mexico and the Caribbean region: Houston Geological Society Bulletin, v. 22, p. 8–13.

Williams, M. D., 1975, Emplacement of Sierra de Santa Cruz, eastern Guatamala: American Association of Petroleum Geologists Bulletin, v. 59, p. 1211–1216.

Wilson, H. H., 1974, Cretaceous sedimentation and orogeny in nuclear Central America: American Association of Petroleum Geologists Bulletin, v. 58, p. 1348–1396.

Zambrano, E., Vásquez, E., Duval, B., Latreille, M., and Coffinieres, B., 1972, Paleogeographic and petroleum synthesis of western Venezuela: Editions Technip, 42 p.

Zoppis, Bracci, L., 1961, Reconocimiento geológico-minero para el fosfato en en Departamento de Rivas: Boletín del Servicio Geológico Nacional (Nicaragua), v. 4, p. 85–117.

MANUSCRIPT ACCEPTED BY THE SOCIETY JUNE 26, 1987

ACKNOWLEDGMENTS

The authors thank Kevin Burke, Jim Case, Cal Cooper, Gabriel Dengo, John Dewey, Grenville Draper, Bob Erlich, Kent Johnson, Carol Kazmer, Paul Mann, Fred Nagle, Edward Robinson, Norm Rosen, George Tappan, Graham Westbrook, and Stan White for valuable discussions on Gulf and Caribbean geology and evolution. We also thank Thomas Anderson, Jim Case, Garry Karner, Carol Kazmer, Warren Hamilton, Amos Salvador, and James Kellogg for reviewing and improving early drafts of the manuscript. We are indebted to Kim Klitgord and Hans Schouten for providing rotation parameters for the Keathley Sequence in the central North Atlantic, and to Walter Pitman, John LaBrecque, and Steve Cande of Lamont-Doherty Geological Observatory for assisting with the derivation of the post-Jurassic relative motions of South America relative to North America.

NOTE ADDED IN PROOF

We have not significantly changed our view of the evolution of the Caribbean since our 1986 submission, but we wish to highlight some recent results and discussions that we feel clarify or strengthen the model of Plate 12. One of our main arguments that is gaining popularity is that the Caribbean Plate (including allochthonous parts of Cuba) originated in the eastern Pacific and has migrated relatively eastward since the Cretaceous, progressively overthrusting from west to east the formerly passive margins of southern Yucatan, the Bahamas, and northern South America during its journey (mainly westward drift of the Americas in a mantle reference frame). We have treated the internal Caribbean lithosphere between fault zones as torsionally rigid, following the tenets of plate tectonics. The geometric viability of our model was corroborated by Ross and Scotese (1988) in spherical coordinates. However, some authors, most recently Donnelly (1989), believe in a unique, plastic behavior for the Caribbean lithosphere through time (massive north-south compression and east-west extension), allowing Caribbean/American relative motion in some areas but not in others. We firmly stand by our methodology for assessing the region's development and on a regional scale we are confident in the use of rigid portions of lithosphere separated by fault zones, and we see no way around the concept of a Pacific origin (see Pindell, in press). On the scale of individual fault systems and basins, we look forward to continuing studies that will help to refine, alter, or support the general model.

Our first note concerns the relative motion history vector between North and South America. Assumptions used in the vector of Pindell (1985b) and results of further data refinement are fully presented in Pindell and others (1988). Their refined vector shows Late Triassic(?) to Late Cretaceous separation, little or no motion from Campanian to Eocene, and very slow Eocene to Present north-south convergence that lessens eastward to zero near the mid-Atlantic Ridge east of the Lesser Antilles (Euler pole). It is predicted that no significant post-Campanian deformations of the Caribbean region can be attributed to North/South American relative motions; rather, such deformations must have resulted from interactions between elements of the Caribbean Plate and a "greater" American Plate. Rotation parameters of Pindell and others (1988) *were* used in Plate 12.

Our second note concerns the Cenozoic strike-slip history of the northern Caribbean Plate Boundary Zone. Despite direct evidence in the Cayman Trough for 1,000 km of Eocene to Recent relative motion (Rosencrantz and others, 1989), some authors refuse to accept such a motion history. However, such a history explains many other independent lines of evidence. First, Eocene to Recent intermediate volcanism in the Lesser Antilles (Fig. 6) indicates subduction and relative eastward migration for that entire interval. Second, assessments of basin development and deformation in Hispaniola and Puerto Rico indicate strike-slip tectonics since the Eocene: in Hispaniola, the Eocene/Oligocene of the San Juan basin (J. Dolan, personal communication; arguments in this chapter), the Oligocene of the Tabera basin (Mann and others, 1984), and the Neogene of northern Hispaniola (Pindell and Draper, in press); and in Puerto Rico, the Eocene/early Oligocene of the "Eocene Belt" (Erikson, 1988). Third, the delay until the Neogene for the inception of magmatism in the Trans-Mexican Volcanic Belt is probably due to the former presence of Chortis along southwestern Mexico until strike-slip carried Chortis east, progressively exposing southwestern Mexico to Pacific subduction and coastal fore-arc uplift for the first time. Finally, concerning magnitude, Figure 9 shows a plausible Eocene reconstruction of the Greater Antilles Arc with about 900 km of strike-slip offset removed from between the several presented segmented parts of an original, north-facing, probably curvilinear, magmatic axis.

This history implies a similar offset along mainly the Motagua Fault in Guatemala. However, Donnelly (1989) claims that the occurrence of serpentinite/amphibolite (El Tambor) locally across the Motagua Valley proves that little offset has occurred since his suggested Cretaceous collision between the unrelated basement terranes of the Yucatan (Maya) and Chortis blocks (Motagua suture zone). We point out that a strike-slip offset of 1,000 km places Chortis well west of Yucatan (along southwestern Mexico) prior to the Eocene; thus, Chortis may never have collided with Yucatan in the late Cretaceous at all. We interpret the Motagua suture as resulting from a Late Cretaceous island arc collision with Yucatan, followed by convergent strike-slip motion within the suture zone that has replaced the arc with Chortis. Emplacement of El Tambor onto Chortis could be a Cenozoic extrusion (flower structure) during strike-slip, prior to most Neogene motion through Guatemala on the Polochic fault (Burkart, 1983). In cross-section only, the resulting orogen appears as a collision between Yucatan and Chortis.

Our third note concerns the metamorphic basements of at least Tobago (Snoke and Frost, and others, in preparation), the Villa de Cura complex of Venezuela (Beets and others, 1984), and various Greater Antillean basement complexes. In each, metamorphism occurred during or before Albian/Cenomanian time, followed in most by Upper Cretaceous magmatism and volcanigenic sedimentation. In Plate 12, sketch c (Cenomanian) suggests a flip of subduction polarity that allowed Caribbean crust of Pacific provenance to enter the proto-Caribbean seaway. It is possible that orogenesis related to such a flip caused the metamorphism, and that the flip was caused by the arrival of thick, buoyant crust (Caribbean) at originally west-facing arcs between Chortis and Colombia. The resulting metamorphosed arc complex, composed possibly of multiple arcs and closed back-arc basins, subsequently received magmatism during relative eastward migration ahead of the Caribbean Plate, before cold emplacement (oblique collision) onto various proto-Caribbean margins.

Our fourth note concerns the Precambrian of Cuba (Renne and others, 1989). We favor the Rio Cana Complex representing Bahamian rocks beneath Cuban arc thrust sheets, but an allochthonous arrival *with* the Cuban arc from western North America is compatible with Plate 12.

To summarize, since the Late Cretaceous the Caribbean Plate has migrated relatively eastward between North and South America, and Caribbean oceanic/arc rocks have overthrust the proto-Caribbean passive margins, creating foredeep basins upon the latter. Rapid subsidence and synorogenic flysch deposits date the initial arrival of the Caribbean Plate at each basin (Pindell and others, 1988). The Early Cretaceous history of the proto-Caribbean margins is one of thermal subsidence and passive sedimentation, whereas that of the Caribbean Plate is unknown. Unfortunately, drilling has failed to reach Caribbean sediments older than Coniacian; probably the best record of the Early Cretaceous eastern Pacific ocean lies below the Caribbean seismic reflector B".

ADDITIONAL REFERENCES CITED

Donnelly, T. W., 1989, Geologic history of the Caribbean and Central America, in Bally, A. W., and Palmer, A. R., eds., The Geology of North America—An overview: Boulder, Colorado, Geological Society of America, Geology of North America, v. A, p. 299–321.

Erikson, J. P., 1988, Structural study of the Paleogene deformation in and around the Southern Puerto Rico Fault Zone [M.S. Thesis]: Stanford University, Stanford, California, 74 p.

Pindell, J. L., 1990, Arguments for a Pacific origin for the Caribbean Plate: Christianstadt, St. Croix, 12th Caribbean Geological Conference Transactions (in press).

Pindell, J. L., Cande, S. C., and Pitman III, W. C., Rowley, D. B., Dewey, J. F., LaBrecque, J., and Haxby, W., 1988, A plate-kinematic framework for models of Caribbean evolution: Tectonophysics, v. 155, p. 121–138.

Renne, P. R., Mattinson, M., Hatten, C. W., Somin, M., Onstott, T. C., Millan, G., and Linares, E., 1989, $^{40}Ar/^{39}Ar$ and U-Pb evidence for Late Proterozoic (Grenville-age) continental crust in north-central Cuba and regional tectonic implications: Precambrian Research, v. 42, p. 325–341.

Rosencrantz, E., Ross, M., and Sclater, G., 1988, Age and spreading history of the Cayman Trough as determined from depth, heat flow, and magnetic anomalies: Journal of Geophysical Research, v. 93, p. 2141–2157.

Ross, M., and Scotese, C. R., 1988, Hierarchical tectonic analysis of the Gulf of Mexico and Caribbean region: Tectonophysics, v. 155, p. 139–160.

The Geology of North America
Vol. H, The Caribbean Region
The Geological Society of America, 1990

Chapter 17

Tectonic evolution of the Caribbean region; Alternative hypothesis

Anthony E. L. Morris
Morris Petroleum, Inc., P.O. Box 64610, Los Angeles, California 90064
Irfan Taner
3625 South Florence Place, Tulsa, Oklahoma 74105
Howard A. Meyerhoff*
3625 South Florence Place, Tulsa, Oklahoma 74105
Arthur A. Meyerhoff
P.O. Box 4602, Tulsa, Oklahoma 74159

INTRODUCTION

Frederick Nagle (1972b, p. 782) wrote, "Probably many Caribbean geologists (myself included) are suffering from varying degrees of geologic schizophrenia, torn between the general popularity of the plate tectonic concept and the knowledge that to date the Caribbean region has not been satisfactorily integrated into this new world scheme. If plate tectonics cannot incorporate key areas such as the Caribbean, the hypothesis will require some major overhauling." Nagle's words are in a sense prophetic, because the Caribbean region still defies every attempt to incorporate it into plate tectonics. As a result, we developed an alternative hypothesis.

To present the hypothesis as it applies to the Caribbean, numerous place names had to be used. Many of these appear on Figure 1. Those that do not may be found on Plate 1.

PREVIOUS HYPOTHESES

General

The great Austrian geologist and parliamentarian, Eduard Suess, published the first geological synthesis of the Caribbean region (Suess, 1885, p. 700–710; 1909, p. 524–529). Among many original observations, Suess recognized Barbados as part of the South American continent. Then, as bathymetric data became more abundant, Robert T. Hill (1905) recognized the Aves Ridge as a major structural element. Yet it was not until the late 1920s that a comprehensive tectonic hypothesis of the Caribbean appeared. This, by Wendell P. Woodring (1928), opened the door to two successive, partly overlapping "waves" of hypotheses.

Pre-plate tectonic hypotheses

Woodring's hypothesis was followed by those of *Schuchert (1932)*[1] and *Willis (1932)*. By the 1960s, reconstructions of the Caribbean had become notable for their diversity. Mechanisms espoused included (1) contraction (*Schuchert, 1932, 1935; Willis, 1932; Waters and Hedberg, 1939*; Senn, 1940; H. A. Meyerhoff, *1946*, 1954; *Meyerhoff and Meyerhoff, 1972a*); (2) mantle convection with or without a tectogene (*Vening Meinesz and others, 1934; Rutten, 1935; Hess, 1938; Hess and Maxwell, 1953; Eardley, 1954; Barr, 1963; MacGillavry, 1970*); (3) earth expansion (*Carey, 1958*); (4) continental drift (*Corral, 1940*; North, 1965); and (5) oceanization (*Judoley and Furrazola, 1971*).

Still other aspects of tectonic evolution were considered. Some authors postulated that the Caribbean once was occupied by a landmass, since foundered or basaltified (Woodring, 1928, *1954*; Bucher, 1947, *1952; Eardley, 1954; Butterlin, 1956; Škvor, 1969; Judoley and Furrazola, 1971; Pushcharovskiy and others, 1979*). Most favored an oceanic origin for the Caribbean crust. A few suggested progressive west-to-east development of the region through time (H. A. Meyerhoff, *1946*, 1954; Bucher, 1947, *1952; Hess and Maxwell, 1953; Eardley, 1954; Woodring, 1954*; North, 1965; *Meyerhoff and Meyerhoff, 1972a*). *Butterlin (1956, 1977)* published comprehensive summaries of these diverse views.

Plate-tectonic era hypotheses

Morgan (1968) was the first to portray the Caribbean as a discrete plate, although he used the term "block." "Plate" is an

---

*Deceased, March 24, 1982

[1]References in italics may be found in "Supplemental References Cited," in the microfiche accompanying this volume.

Morris, A.E.L., Taner, I., Meyerhoff, H. A., and Meyerhoff, A. A., 1990, Tectonic evolution of the Caribbean region; Alternative hypothesis, *in* Dengo, G., and Case, J. E., eds., The Caribbean Region: Boulder, Colorado, Geological Society of America, The Geology of North America, v. H.

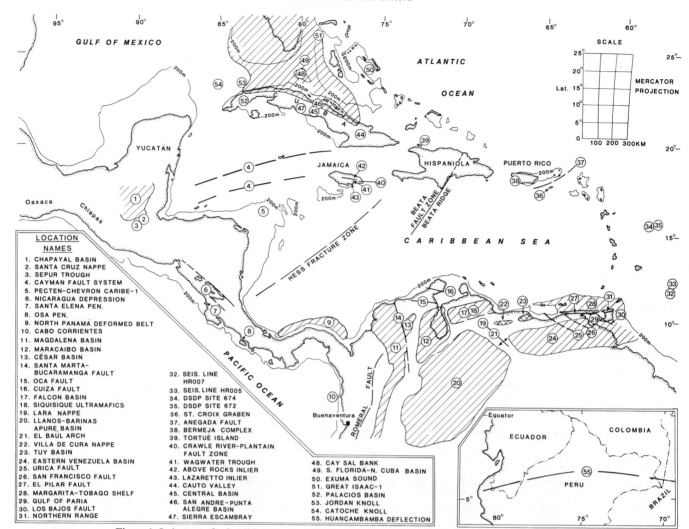

Figure 1. Index map for localities mentioned in text. The names that do not appear here may be found on Plate 1.

older term that was used by Bucher (1947, p. 113), H. A. Meyerhoff (1954, p. 154), and North (1965, p. 81), each of whom recognized this region to be a unique segment of the earth's surface. Today, the spectrum of plate-tectonic postulates is vast, diverse, and repetitive.

Although classification of the existing plate-tectonic hypotheses may differ among individuals, there are six basic plate models:

1. The Caribbean plate predates the onset of sea-floor spreading in Jurassic time (*Nafe and Drake, 1969*).

2. The Caribbean plate formed in situ. It is of Tethyan origin according to Aubouin and others (1982a, p. 755), who concluded, "The Caribbean is not of Pacific origin; all available evidence indicates its Tethys affinity." *Ball and Harrison (1969)* earlier published an in situ model involving north-south extension accompanied by sinistral shear and a migrating Mid-Atlantic Ridge spreading center.

3. *Mattson (1969)* proposed that the Caribbean plate was inserted from the Pacific. The best-known version of this model is

that by *Malfait and Dinkelman (1972)*. Later versions, generally with a spreading center extending from the East Pacific Rise to the Mid-Atlantic Ridge until Late Cretaceous time, include *Walper and Rowett (1972), Sclater and others (1977), Mattson (1979, 1984), Dickinson and Coney (1980), Pindell and Dewey (1982), Burke and others (1984), Duncan and Hargraves (1984), Ghosh and others (1984), Leclere and Stéphan (1985), and Pindell (1985)*. Most of the conflicts within the Pacific-insertion model involve (a) the timing of events, (b) locations of spreading centers, (c) locations of plate boundaries, (d) orientations of spreading centers, and (e) derivation of component blocks (e.g., Chortís, Yucatán, Cuba, etc.).

4. *Mooney (1980)* proposed a somewhat similar model, except that, after 80 Ma, a northeast-striking Venezuela Basin spreading center remained. Between 65 and 55 Ma, South America overrode that spreading center. The magnetic anomalies in the Venezuela Basin today were interpreted to be remnant on the northern flank of that postulated spreading center.

5. *Salvador and Green (1980)* took issue with all existing

models, noting, correctly, that most of them violated important field-geological data (Salvador, 1986). They presented another model of Pacific insertion, but it differs from all others. And like the others, the Salvador and Green model is contradicted by many field data, especially outside of South America.

6. *Anderson and Schmidt (1983)* published a radically different spreading model for the region. Their proposed pattern of megashears, however, violates numerous data from the field.

The foregoing generalizations mask the many contradictory interpretations of the same geologic phenomena, even of whole geologic provinces (e.g., Nicaragua Rise). Also, not one major tectonic feature seems to have been interpreted uniquely. Examples range from Trinidad's Northern Range (two interpretations) to the Nicaragua Rise (four). Even major fault zones are shown differently in each interpretation. Such important variants cannot be explained solely as a consequence of having insufficient data; they suggest, instead, that something is wrong with the models proposed. We list some of the problems about which there is either major disagreement or almost no mention:

1. The positions of more than 50 percent of both the northern and southern Caribbean plate boundary zones are disputed, and clear geological-geophysical evidence for positioning them is lacking.

2. The amounts of movement along the northern and southern plate boundaries are questioned. Plate-tectonic models require a cumulative offset of about 1,400 km along these two boundaries; field evidence permits only a fraction of this amount—15 to 20 percent.

3. The origin and age of the Cayman Trough are unknown.

4. The presence of Paleozoic and older rocks, at least in Cuba, is now proved (Hatten and others, 1986). One late Paleozoic locality may have been found in Hispaniola (Joyce and Aronson, 1983).

5. The sources of the Caribbean crust are contested.

6. The origin and role of the Nicaragua Rise are not understood.

7. The genesis of the Barbados Ridge is disputed.

8. Why, east of the Lesser Antilles and the Barbados Ridge, do east-west trends in the magnetic anomalies predominate over north-south trends?

9. No two chronologies of the geologic history match.

10. Morphotectonic units such as the Puerto Rico–Virgin Islands platform, the Barbados Ridge, and the Nicaragua Rise have crustal thicknesses similar to that of many continental areas, 22 to 30 km, yet are said by some workers to be oceanic, apparently so as to fit an existing geophysical crustal model (e.g., eastern Bahama Islands). (We point out that the results of the approximately 12-km-deep borehole on the Kola Peninsula already have disproved all conventional concepts of the structure of the continental crust [Kozlovsky, 1986].)

Nevertheless, three hypotheses—all mobilist but not plate-tectonic—are in accord with most of the facts known in the Caribbean. These are the hypotheses of H. A. Meyerhoff (*1946*, 1954), Bucher (1947, *1952*), and North (1965). Meyerhoff postu-

lated clockwise rotation of South America against the Caribbean region, causing a buckling of mobile belts around its margins, accompanied by eastward growth. Bucher postulated an eastward-directed glacierlike lithospheric flow to produce the deformed belts and furrows around the margins of the Caribbean. North postulated the "squeezing out" of the Caribbean crust and subcrust between a clockwise-rotating South America and a counterclockwise-rotating North Pacific basin, and even foretold the origin of the Nicaragua Rise. We consider Kenneth North's interpretation to be the most satisfactory, partly because his chronology of events is accurate—as far as it goes—and partly because this chronology fits closely the hypothesis that we summarize at the end of this chapter.

GEOLOGIC HISTORY

Pennsylvanian-Permian

The data base for reconstructing Caribbean geologic history effectively commences in Pennsylvanian-Permian times. Older data are sparse and confined to the northern, northwestern, and southern boundaries.

Continental cratonic massifs. During Pennsylvanian-Permian times, continental massifs surrounded large areas of the modern Caribbean Sea (hachured areas, Fig. 2). In the north and northwest, the Florida-Bahamas block extended southwestward toward Yucatán, southward beneath Cuba, and eastward beneath northern Hispaniola, probably passing beneath the northern flank of the Puerto Rico–Virgin Islands platform. Radiometric dates from Cuba (*Khudoley, 1967*; *Meyerhoff and others, 1969*) and Florida (*Milton, 1972*) range from 138 to 945 Ma, the oldest being in Cuba. Until recently, the only Paleozoic fossils known were from central and northern Florida. However, Carboniferous-Permian faunas, including fusulinids, recently were found in clasts of the Jurassic San Cayetano Group (Cuba), and are now being studied (A. Pszczółkowski, written communication, Feb. 6, 1988).

The Yucatán block flanks the western Caribbean. Basement ages range from 206 to 420 Ma (*Dengo, 1969*; *Viniegra, 1971*; *Bateson, 1972*). The block probably connects with the Florida-Bahamas block in the north and with the Chortís-Nicaragua-Jamaica block in the south. The Catoche Knoll, between Yucatán and Florida, has yielded basement ages of 449 to 501 Ma (*Schlager and others, 1984a*).

The Chortís-Nicaragua-Jamaica block underlies Middle America south of the Motagua fault zone, and appears to continue beneath the Nicaragua Rise to Jamaica. We refer to this block as the "paleoisthmus," because it may once have joined Central America to Colombia. Radiometric dates range from 275 to 1,075 Ma (*Gomberg and others, 1968*; Horne and others, 1976).

The Guayana block, the largest craton in the region, is a Precambrian massif that extends from the Atlantic coast of Brazil through Venezuela to the present Cordillera Central (Colombia).

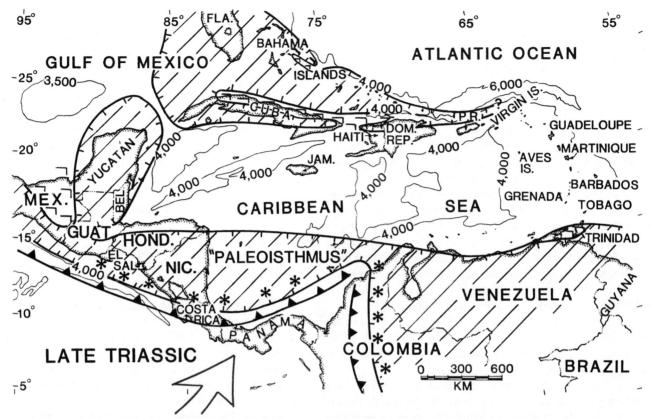

Figure 2. Major tectonic elements, Caribbean region, Late Triassic time. Land masses (continental) are shown by diagonal lines. Trace of edge of active magmatic arcs are shown by lines of solid triangles. Volcanoes are shown by stars. Red arrow indicates the direction of asthenosphere surge.

Radiometric dates and fossil localities confirm the widespread occurrence of Paleozoic rocks in the Cordillera Central, the Guajira Peninsula, and northern Venezuela (*Martín-Bellizia, 1968; Martín-Bellizia and others, 1968; Goldsmith and others, 1971; MacDonald, 1972; Mendoza, 1977; Restrepo and Toussaint, 1978*; González de Juana and others, 1980; *Alvarez, 1981; Kroonenberg, 1982; Alvarez and Linares, 1983, 1984; Feo-Codecido and others, 1984*).

Paleozoic platform sequences are widespread on the Chortís and Guayana blocks. All sections have warm-water faunas, mostly in carbonates and shale. About 90 Pennsylvanian-Permian marine genera have been found in northwestern South America, and 46 genera in Central America (*Dunbar, 1939; Thompson and Miller, 1944; Dixon, 1956; Compañía Shell-Creole, 1964; Arnold, 1966; Forero, 1970; Stehli and Grant, 1970; Hoover, 1981*). Of these, at least 22 genera and several species are common to both areas.

Mobile belts. Four Paleozoic orogens have been identified in the region; one each in Middle America, Colombia, and Cuba; a fourth possibly occupied northern Venezuela.

The Middle America belt extends from west of Oaxaca (Mexico) to the Nicaragua Rise, presumably to Jamaica. Pre-Mesozoic metamorphic rocks of eugeosynclinal origin are present in the Chiapas massif and the Chortís block (*Dengo, 1969*;

McBirney and Bass, 1969a; Horne and others, 1976; López-Ramos, 1983; *González-Hervert and others, 1984; Ortega-Gutiérrez, 1984; Ramírez-Espinosa, 1984*). At least two tectonic cycles, one Pennsylvanian-Permian and the other older, are recorded (*Meyerhoff, 1967; McBirney and Bass, 1969a*; Horne and others, 1976). Granitic intrusives have a 279 to 345 Ma range.

We believe that the Middle America and Colombia mobile-belt segments are parts of a single Paleozoic magmatic arc complex that once was connected via the paleoisthmus (now the Nicaragua Rise) mentioned above (Fig. 2). The rise, in our opinion, is underlain by a thick granitic crustal layer (seismic velocities and gravity anomalies can be interpreted in more than one way); depths to the Mohorovičić discontinuity are greater than 28 km (Ewing and others, 1960; Case and others, 1984). This "old" crust crops out in the Lazaretto Inlier of southeastern Jamaica (Meyerhoff and Krieg, 1977, *1977*) as the Green Bay metamorphic assemblage, which is wholly unlike other Jamaican rocks, but which resembles closely the metamorphosed Paleozoic (and older?) rocks of Honduras (Horne and others, 1976).

A second mobile belt segment occupied the region of the present Cordillera Central of Colombia. Here, as in Middle America, a magmatic arc lies Pacificward from the equivalent platform section, and two tectonic cycles appear to be present: Devonian and older and Pennsylvanian-Permian (Irving, *1971*,

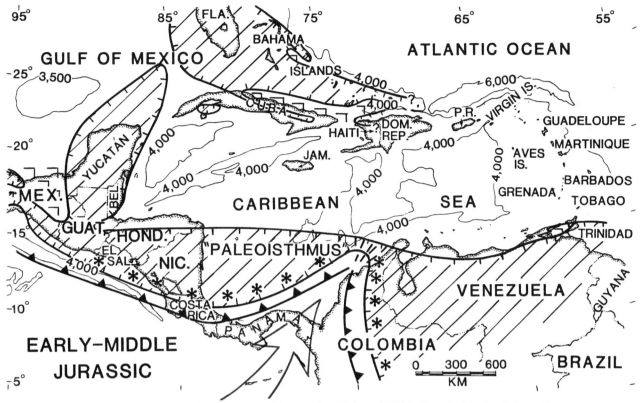

Figure 3. Major tectonic elements, Caribbean region, Early and Middle Jurassic time. Symbols are the same as before. Paleoisthmus is beginning to rupture where it joins northwestern South America.

1975; *Forero, 1973; Shagam, 1975; Restrepo and Toussaint, 1978; París and Marín, 1979; Bogotá and Aluja, 1981; INIGM, 1983; McCourt and others, 1984*).

The third mobile belt is exposed in the Sierra de Escambray of southern Cuba (Millán and Somin, 1981), and presumably was adjacent to the platform facies represented by the late Paleozoic faunas recovered recently from San Cayetano clasts in Pinar del Río Province. This largely eugeosynclinal sequence (relict magmatic arc) has long been thought to be Paleozoic, but until recently without proof (*Lewis, 1932; Schuchert, 1935; Waters and Hedberg, 1939; Hatten and others, 1958; Meyerhoff, 1966, 1967; Hatten, 1967; Meyerhoff and Hatten, 1968;* Meyerhoff, *in* Khudoley and Meyerhoff, 1971). During 1972, Robert J. McCorkell of the chemistry department at Carleton University, Ottawa, dated samples of metamorphic rocks at 174 to 346 Ma, mostly clustering at 250 Ma. Hatten and others (1986) dated samples from the same localities in the 247 to 255 Ma range, confirming the presence of a Cuban Paleozoic orogenic belt that may overlie a Proterozoic basement (945 Ma; Somin and Millán, *1977,* 1981). The 900+ Ma age of this basement has yet to be verified.

This Paleozoic magmatic arc probably strikes eastward beneath Tortué Island (*Nagle and others, 1982*), northern Hispaniola, and the southern slope of the Puerto Rico Trench (*Alonso and others, 1988*). A 250-Ma date was obtained from the Sa-

maná Peninsula by Joyce and Aronson (1983). Although these authors question the validity of the date, they wrote that, "Lithologically the Samaná rocks most closely resemble the Escambray rocks of Cuba. . . ," a statement since corroborated in the field by C. W. Hatten (personal communication, May 1987). Some of the Escambray rocks are now known to be Permian.

A fourth magmatic arc probably occupied both northern Colombia and Venezuela where pre-Mesozoic radiometric dates have been recorded (*MacDonald, 1972;* González de Juana and others, 1980; *Feo-Codecido and others, 1984*).

Triassic-Middle Jurassic (Figs. 2 and 3)

The Paleozoic mobile belts were deformed and intruded during Late Permian time, the continental areas were uplifted and exposed, taphrogenic conditions prevailed, the seas withdrew, and red beds—locally with volcanics—were deposited in grabens and other depressions. A seaway occupied the site of the present Cordillera Central of Colombia, where a new magmatic arc formed west of the late Paleozoic arc (Fig. 2; *Stéphan and others, 1980*). The principal marine Triassic sections were described by *Bürgl (1961a, 1964, 1973), Geyer (1973, 1982),* and *Cediel and others (1981).* Data published by Bartok and others (1985) suggest that rupture of the eastern end of the paleoisthmus began during Bajocian time, permitting the diapiric emplacement of the

Siquisique ultramafic rocks, pillow basalt, and chert along northeast-trending fractures. These fractures appear to continue into the Venezuela Basin where we believe they permitted the intrusion of the igneous bodies that produce the northeast-trending magnetic lineations that characterize that basin (*Watkins and Cavanaugh, 1976*; *Ghosh and others, 1984*).

Tschanz and others (1974) also postulated an extensional environment in the region to accommodate the large northeast-striking granitic intrusions of the Sierra Nevada de Santa Marta. They noted that such extension during Jurassic time conflicts with plate-tectonic models; we mention this because extension here is required by our hypothesis.

Marine conditions also prevailed in western Mexico but, except locally, were limited to the eugeosynclinal zone adjacent to the Pacific (*Silva-Pineda, 1979*; López-Ramos, 1983, *1984*). As in Colombia, the magmatic arc "jumped" about 100 km toward the Pacific during Triassic time.

Taphrogeny was widespread during Triassic and Jurassic times in North and South America; it was accompanied by intrusions of intermediate to mafic dikes and sills, which have K-Ar dates of 137 to 210 Ma (150–190 Ma in the Bahamas Great Isaac well and Catoche Knoll; 137–196 Ma in Cuba; 150–210 Ma in Mexico, Middle America, and Colombia's Cordillera Central).

Marine incursions increased in frequency and area during Jurassic time; Tethyan faunas are abundant. Marine sections have been described from southern Mexico (*Erben, 1956*; *Cortés-Obregón and others, 1957*; López-Ramos, 1983, *1984*); western Cuba (Khudoley and Meyerhoff, 1971; *Haczewski, 1976*; *Myczyński and Pszczółkowski, 1976*), southern Cuba (*Millán and Myczyński, 1978, 1979*), southeastern Cuba (K. M. Khudoley, personal communication, 1986), Central America (*Carpenter, 1954*; *Sprechmann, 1984*), Colombia (*Bürgl, 1973*; *Geyer, 1973, 1980*), and Venezuela (González de Juana and others, 1980).

Rugged highlands occupied parts of the continental blocks. Within them, subsiding fault-bounded depressions were filled with red beds and intermediate to silicic volcanic rocks (e.g., *Burkart and Clemons, 1972*). The red-bed/volcanic section is known by a variety of names, such as La Quinta in Venezuela and the Todos Santos in Central America.

A probable equivalent of the Todos Santos crops out on Jamaica, the Mount Charles and Border Formations of the Above Rocks Inlier (Meyerhoff and Krieg, 1977, *1977*). These two formations, unaffected by compression, include red beds, arkosic conglomerate and sandstone, andesite, andesitic tuff, and dikes (A. J. Reed, *in* Geological Survey Department, 1967). Although separated from the overlying submarine volcanics of the Neocomian Devil's Racecourse Formation by normal faults, the field relations suggest that the two are separated also by a gentle angular unconformity.

Two Todos Santos equivalents that do not contain red beds are El Plan Formation of Honduras (*Carpenter, 1954*) and the San Cayetano Group of Cuba (*Pszczółkowski, 1978*). Both units are thick continental-margin accumulations with marine tongues. In Cuba, the marine tongues are of Bajocian-Bathonian,

Callovian, and early-middle Oxfordian ages (Khudoley and Meyerhoff, 1971; *Myczyński and Pszczółkowski, 1976*). *Haczewski (1976)* wrote that the provenance was a continental area south or southwest of Cuba. The source probably included uplifted parts of the Cuban Paleozoic geosyncline and the Yucatán platform (*Pyle and others, 1973*). In Honduras, the El Plan is Late Triassic–Early Jurassic, based on plant assemblages (*Azéma and others, 1985*).

This time interval is represented by lagoonal evaporite facies (Figs. 2, 3) in the U.S. Gulf Coast, southern Mexico, and parts of the interior Gulf of Mexico. Smaller salt basins include the Gulf of Paria (*Bray and Eva, 1983*), Exuma Sound (*Ball and others, 1968*), the San Andrés–Punta Allegre basin of Cuba (*Ducloz, 1960*; *Meyerhoff and Hatten, 1968*; *Iturralde and Roque, 1982*; *Piotrowski and de Albear, 1986*), and the Old Bahama Channel north of Haiti (*Bally, 1983*).

The age of the salt is widely assumed to be Middle to Late Jurassic (*Imlay, 1952*; *Jux, 1961*), although ages from Permian to Cretaceous have been proposed (*Schuchert, 1943*). A Jurassic age for much of the salt is certain, but some of it is Late Triassic (or older). A well in southeastern Chiapas penetrated Early Cretaceous–Late Jurassic salt underlain by partly marine Late Triassic shale, which is underlain by a second salt sequence (F. Viniegra, written communications, 1979, 1986, 1987; *Bishop, 1980, p. 25–26*; López-Ramos, 1983, p. 263). Also, Norian salt is present in northern Colombia (*Cediel and others, 1981*).

Other than North (1965)—a structural geologist—and numerous paleontologists, there has been little acceptance of a paleoisthmus between North and South America from early Carboniferous (or earlier) time onward. The many similarities between Triassic tetrapods of North and South America (Charig, 1971, *1973*; Cox, 1973; Clemens and others, 1979; Kalandadze and Rautian, 1983) are explained as a consequence of the predrift fit of the continents proposed by *Bullard and others (1965)*. A paleoisthmus *also* was present during all of Jurassic and parts of Cretaceous times, as shown unequivocally by Kauffman (1973), Aubouin and others (1977, 1982a), and Rémane (1980). Its presence is demonstrated by the fact that Jurassic planktonic calpionellids are widespread in the Caribbean, but are absent in coeval strata in the Pacific (Rémane, 1980).

Callovian-Tithonian (Fig. 3)

The Triassic–Middle Jurassic taphrogenic regime was replaced during late Tithonian time by the present orogenic cycle. Evaporitic carbonate banks gradually covered the site of the modern Bahamas (*Tator and Hatfield, 1975*; *Jacobs, 1977*), and overlie older, gently folded strata unconformably (*Ladd and Sheridan, 1987*). In Cuba and Florida, however, marine transgressions were limited to marginal areas.

Callovian and Oxfordian marine units overlie the Bajocian-Bathonian tongues of western Cuba. Terrigenous clastic deposits with Oxfordian ammonites crop out in the Sierra de Escambray; a similar fauna is present in easternmost Cuba (*Millán and Myczyński, 1978, 1979*; K. M. Khudoley, personal communication,

1986). Basement in central Cuba includes, in addition to the older rocks already mentioned, 160-Ma gabbro intruded by troctolite (Somin and Millán, 1981; Millán and Somin, 1981) and pink orthoclase granites that yield K-Ar dates ranging from 139 to 150 Ma (R. E. Denison, personal communication, 1976; Somin and Millán, *1977, 1981*).

In Yucatán, marine incursions were limited to the western side of the platform (Viniegra, 1981), and to the axis of the future Chapayal basin (*Bishop, 1980*). Both the eastern and western ends of the paleoisthmus were exposed (*Carpenter, 1954; Roberts and Irving, 1957; Vinson and Brineman, 1963; Mills and others, 1967; Clemons and Burkart, 1971; Burkart and others, 1973; Wilson, 1974*; Meyerhoff and Krieg, 1977; *Meyerhoff and Morris, 1977; Bishop, 1980*; Weyl, 1980; *Finch, 1981; Kashfi, 1983*). Red-bed deposition continued in the existing continental basins, while marine sections of terrigenous clastics, carbonates, and minor evaporites accumulated in northern South America and Trinidad (*Kugler, 1956; Bürgl, 1960; Renz, 1960; Rollins, 1965*; González de Juana and others, 1980; *Stéphan and others, 1980*).

A deep sea separated the paleoisthmus from the Florida-Bahamas block, as shown by the abundance of pelagic carbonates in the many Cuban surface and subsurface nappes (*Furrazola and others, 1964, 1978; Weyl, 1966; Meyerhoff and Hatten, 1968, 1974*; Pszczółkowski, *1971, 1978, 1981*, 1982, *1983, 1986*; Khudoley and Meyerhoff, 1971; Knipper and Cabrera, 1974; Kuznetsov and others, *1977, 1985; Mossakovsky and de Albear, 1978, 1979; Shopov, 1982; Pszczółkowski and de Albear, 1983; Rodríguez, 1983; Segura and others, 1985*). Deep-sea conditions also prevailed in the Venezuela Basin, as shown by the presence of Jurassic deep-water facies in the Bermeja Complex of Puerto Rico that were thrust from the south (*Mattson and Pessagno, 1979*). Deep-sea conditions also are shown by the presence of deep-water deposits at various localities in northern South America (*Rowley and Roobol, 1978*; Beets and others, 1984; *Beck, 1985; Rowe and Snoke, 1986*).

Obducted oceanic deposits crop out on the Santa Elena, Nicoya, and Osa Peninsulas of western Costa Rica. Mafic and ultramafic rocks, chert, and radiolarite contain Pliensbachian through early Santonian fossils (*Rivier, 1983; De Wever and others, 1985*). The cherts—Pliensbachian and younger—accumulated close to the continent (Hein and Karl, 1983; Hein and others, 1983).

The formation of the east-west Guajira trough, which has a Kimmeridgian marine fauna, and the continuing emplacement of granitic plutons in the Sierra Nevada de Santa Marta probably reflect the continuance of the tensile stress field in northwestern South America (*MacDonald, 1968*). Oxfordian, Kimmeridgian, and Tithonian marine strata are exposed on the Paraguaná Peninsula; Kimmeridgian deep-water limestone is present in the Lara nappe farther southeast (*Stéphan and others, 1980*).

Berriasian–early Albian (Fig. 4)

The orogenic cycle which began with the breakup between South America and the paleoisthmus accelerated steadily until

middle Eocene time; it continues, albeit weakly, today. The land connection between North and South America was breached, producing a shallow-water passage between the Pacific and Caribbean. We suspect that the shear zone along which the continents separated evolved into the Beata fracture zone (Figs. 4, 5), which has the proper strike. Creation of this shallow-water passage permitted some mingling of Atlantic and Pacific faunas, which had not been possible for much of Jurassic time (Aubouin and others, 1977, 1982a). Even during parts of the Cretaceous, communication between the oceans was severed repeatedly (Kauffman, 1973).

The influx of cool Pacific water into the warm Caribbean and adjacent Atlantic induced an abrupt change in Caribbean and Atlantic sedimentation. Large amounts of carbonaceous matter began to accumulate in both the Caribbean and Atlantic (*Ewing and Hollister, 1972; Bernoulli and Jenkyns, 1974; Sheridan and others, 1978; Arthur and Natland, 1979; Tissot and others, 1979*). Reducing conditions persisted almost everywhere through Albian time, and lasted until the late Santonian in the Caribbean and parts of the adjacent Atlantic. Saunders and others (1973, p. 1098) wrote that " . . . the absence of carbonaceous sediment in Pacific cores of the same age demands a barrier between the Pacific and Caribbean separating the bottom water regime of the two basins." Not until late Santonian time were oxidizing conditions restored to most of the Caribbean and Atlantic.

During this time, major tectonic and depositional changes accompanied the formation of four new magmatic arcs, the modification of the Middle America magmatic arc, and the continuing activity of the Colombia magmatic arc (Fig. 4). The four new arcs are (1) the Venezuela arc, (2) the Cuba arc, (3) the Main Antilles arc south of it (including the Aves Ridge or its precursor, and (4) the Paleoisthmus arc along the leading edge of the rotating paleoisthmus.

Two magmatic arcs occupied what now are the Greater Antilles (Fig. 4). The Cuba arc extended from east of the Yucatán platform to the present Cauto Valley. The second, the Main Antilles magmatic arc, extended from the western end of the Cayman Ridge to the southern end of the Aves Ridge. We recognize now that La Désirade Island is not a part of this arc as proposed by *Meyerhoff and Hatten (1974)* and by *Bouysse and others (1983)*.

The Cayman Ridge is included in the Main Antilles arc because of its continuity with southeastern Cuba, whose geologic history resembles that of northern Haiti far more than that of the rest of Cuba. The Lower and Upper Cretaceous of the Sierra Maestra are unmetamorphosed and much less deformed than coeval strata north of the Cauto Valley. Similarly, Jamaica belongs to the Paleoisthmus magmatic arc because its geology, especially the tectonic style, resembles that of Honduras but is very unlike that of southeastern Cuba (*Cobiella and others, 1984*).

The four arcs appeared at nearly the same time. In the Cuba arc, the oldest paleontologically dated volcanic deposits are Tithonian (Khudoley and Meyerhoff, 1971; *Piotrowski, 1976; Itur-*

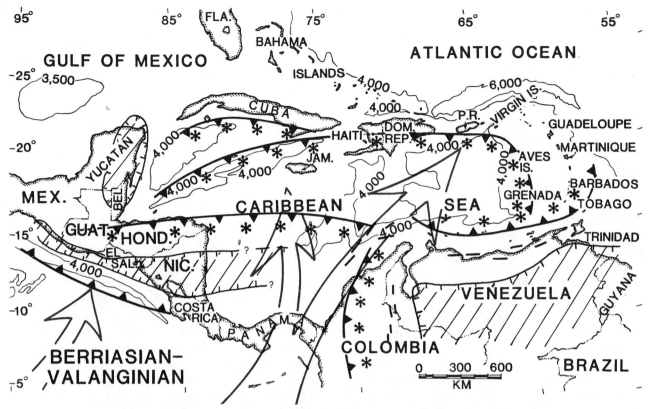

Figure 4. Shows island-arc development of Berriasian-Valanginian time. Middle America and Colombia magmatic arcs are now separated. In the western Caribbean, the magmatic arcs are, from north to south, the Cuba, Main Antilles, and Paleoisthmus arcs. In the eastern Caribbean, the arcs are the Main Antilles in the north and east, and the Venezuela in the southeast.

ralde and Marí, 1984). In the Main Antilles arc, the oldest dated volcanic rocks (Hauterivian) are in Puerto Rico; they overlie deep-sea chert of early Tithonian age (*Mattson and Pessagno, 1979*). In the Paleoisthmus arc, late Tithonian to early Neocomian volcanic deposits of the back-arc basin are present below 2,400 m in the Pecten-Chevron Caribe-1 well east of Honduras (Fig. 3; L. W. Funkhouser and L. Gordon, personal communications, 1984). In Guatemala, *Rosenfeld (1981, 1982)* found Valanginian through early Campanian deep-water pelagic carbonate strata in the Santa Cruz ophiolite nappe. On Jamaica, late Neocomian to Barremian volcanogenic rocks overlie the Mt. Charles–Border red beds (*Montadert and others, 1985*). The oldest paleontologically dated beds of the Venezuela volcanic arc are Barremian, although most workers believe that the oldest volcanic rocks are Tithonian (*Stéphan and others, 1980; Beck, 1985*).

Marine encroachment onto continental areas surrounding the Caribbean accelerated notably during Tithonian-Neocomian time. Downwarps next to some of the arcs became major sedimentary basins during Cretaceous-Tertiary time. The principal of these basins are the Chapayal, the South Florida–North Cuba, the Eastern Venezuela, and the Llanos-Barinas-Apure. Carbonate and evaporite deposition was predominant in the first two;

terrigenous-clastic sedimentation dominated in the last two. By Aptian time, shallow carbonate-shelf deposition commenced in the western part of the Chortís-Nicaragua-Jamaica block (*Mills and others, 1967; Bonis, 1969b; Wilson, 1974; Finch, 1981*).

Beginning in middle to late Oxfordian time, terrigenous clastics deposited on the Bahamas platform (northwestern Cuba) were derived exclusively from sialic areas north and west of modern Cuba (Pszczółkowski, *1978,* 1982; *Segura and others, 1985*). Of the 136 measured paleocurrent directions mentioned—but still unpublished—by Pszczółkowski (1982), one can see clearly that almost all terrigenous material is concentrated in northwestern Cuba or, in the case of the older terrigenous San Cayetano Group, coarsens in the same direction.

Deep wells along Cuba's northern coast penetrate one or more nappes. The deepest wells bottom in autochthonous platform carbonates and evaporites (with interbedded terrigenous clastics in the west; Kuznetsov and others, 1985). Except for the quartzose sediments, this is the Bahamas facies described by *Holser and Kaplan (1966), Spencer (1967), Meyerhoff and Hatten (1968, 1974), Tator and Hatfield (1975), Jacobs (1977), Sheridan and others (1981), Schlager and others (1984b),* and *Ball and others (1985).* In southern Cuba, the few wells that penetrated the serpentinite nappes bottomed in Escambray-type

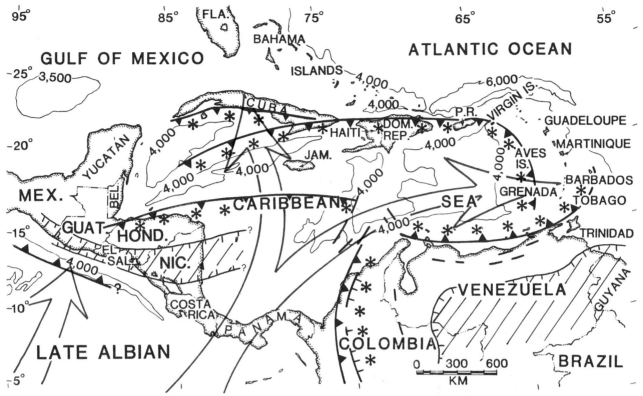

Figure 5. Positions of magmatic arcs, Caribbean region, late Albian time.

metamorphic rocks (Khudoley and Meyerhoff, 1971). Thus, Cuba's geologic foundation is the southern part of the Florida-Bahamas block.

Late Albian–Santonian (Fig. 5)

During this period, tectonism and granitic intrusion almost continuously affected some part, or parts, of the Caribbean. Granitic intrusions of 103 to 85 Ma are common in Cuba (Somin and Millán, *1977,* 1981), Hispaniola (*Bowin, 1966; Kesler and others, 1977;* Joyce and Aronson, 1983), Puerto Rico (*Tobisch, 1968;* Khudoley and Meyerhoff, 1971; *Cox and others, 1977*), the Aves Ridge (*Fox and others, 1971;* J. R. Curray and others, *in Meyerhoff and Meyerhoff, 1972a*), Venezuela (*Santamaría and Schubert, 1974; Rowley and Roobol, 1978;* González de Juana and others, 1980; *Stéphan and others, 1980;* Beets and others, 1984; *Hebeda and others, 1984; Loubet and others, 1985*), and Middle America (Horne and others, 1976; López-Ramos, 1983; *Pantoja-Alor, 1983*).

Manifestations of tectonism also include: (1) metamorphism of the Caracas Group and its equivalents during early Albian, possibly earlier, time (*MacDonald and others, 1971; Stéphan and others, 1980;* Talukdar and Loureiro, 1982); (2) unconformity development in northern South America during Aptian-Albian times (*Stéphan and others, 1980*); (3) absence, in the Bahamas, of much of the Cenomanian (e.g., Cay Sal Bank; Great Isaac area);

(4) segmentation of the Bahamas platform (Khudoley and Meyerhoff, 1971; *Meyerhoff and Hatten, 1974; Sheridan and others, 1981; Schlager and others, 1984b; Ball and others, 1985*); (5) drowning of the Jordan Knoll off northwestern Cuba (*Bryant and others, 1969; Schlager and others, 1984a*); (6) abrupt change from carbonate bank deposition to red-bed deposition in Honduras (*Carpenter, 1954; Finch, 1981*); (7) shrinking of the Yucatán evaporite pan (López-Ramos, *1975,* 1983); (8) repeated extrusive magmatic events in Jamaica (Meyerhoff and Krieg, 1977, *1977; Wadge and Draper, 1978*); (9) westward shift of the Colombia magmatic arc (*McCourt and others, 1984*); and (10) similar events in Middle America (*Carfantan, 1977, 1984*).

In the Caribbean Sea, flood basalts covered large areas (*Donnelly, 1975*). As the paleoisthmus rotated toward its present position, the trailing sea floor of the Colombia Basin was fractured deeply. Fracturing presumably began when rotation started, so that the oldest basalts could be late Tithonian. Deep-sea Albian tholeiites on Haiti's Southern Peninsula may have been a part of the flood-basalt episode (*Bellon and others, 1985*). In the Venezuela Basin, the youngest basalts are late Turonian or older; in the Colombia Basin, they are Coniacian or older (*Premoli Silva and Bolli, 1973*).

Late Santonian–Maastrichtian (Fig. 6)

By the end of Santonian time, the intrusion of a whole new generation of granitic plutons had immobilized the existing mag-

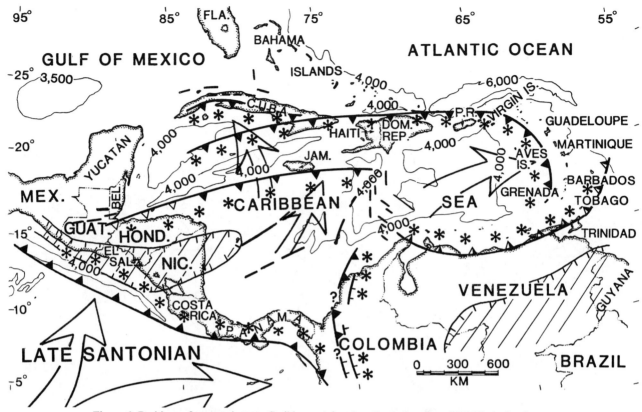

Figure 6. Positions of magmatic arcs, Caribbean region, late Santonian time. Half-filled triangles are
dying arcs; open triangles are dead arcs, or parts of arcs.

matic arcs, forcing renewed "jumps." New arcs, however, were
unable to form in three places because of collisions with continental massifs. Thus, the Cuba and Venezuela magmatic arcs, plus
what remained of the Middle America arc, died. The Main Antilles, Paleoisthmus, and Colombia magmatic arcs remained
active.

The northwestern branch of the Middle America magmatic
arc was extinct by late Santonian time; the Cuba and Venezuela
magmatic arcs were extinct by late Maastrichtian time. The
deaths of the three arcs focused tectonic stresses into the three
remaining magmatic arcs and into the narrowed space between
them (Figs. 6, 7). Stresses that would have been relieved within
the extinct arcs were relieved, instead, by the crushing of the
rocks against the adjacent continental massifs during the "Laramide" orogeny.

In the Cuba arc, northward nappe movements began in
Campanian-Maastrichtian time, followed by nappe entrainment
and the shattering of the nappe trains against the Bahamas
(Khudoley and Meyerhoff, 1971; Knipper and Cabrera, 1974;
Pardo, 1975; Pszczółkowski and Flores, 1986). Volcanism died
gradually; flysch troughs formed in front of the advancing nappes,
and tectonically undisturbed successor basins formed on their
backs (e.g., Palacios and Central basins). Details of these Cretaceous events were published by Rigassi-Studer (1961), Kozary
(1968), Meyerhoff and Hatten (1968, 1974), Khudoley and

Meyerhoff (1971), Knipper and Cabrera (1974), Piotrowska,
1978, Pszczółkowski (1982, 1986), and Shopov (1982).

Similar events took place in the former Venezuela magmatic
arc. Southward nappe movements were underway by Maastrichtian time (e.g., Villa de Cura nappe). Seas withdrew from parts of
the craton. Linear welts rose above sea level on the site of the
former Paleozoic geosynclinal zone, creating multiple internal
source areas for terrigenous clastics. As in Cuba, all volcanism
stopped (Liddle, 1946; Hedberg, 1950; Kugler, 1953, 1961a; H.
Renz and others, 1958; Mencher, 1963; Bell, 1971, 1974; Bellizia, 1972; Shagam, 1972; Gansser, 1973; Potter, 1973; Maresch,
1974; Saunders, 1974; Beck, 1977, 1985; Stéphan, 1977, 1985;
González de Juana and others, 1980; Stéphan and others, 1980;
Talukdar and Loureiro, 1982; Beets and others, 1984).

The active northwestern branch of the Middle America magmatic arc died, with strong orogeny beginning in Santonian time
(Carfantan, 1977, 1984; Pedrazzini and others, 1982). Farther
south, northward-directed compressive stresses folded and
thrusted in pre-Campanian time what is now the Santa Elena
Peninsula (Azéma and Tournon, 1979, 1980; Rivier, 1983; De
Wever and others, 1985).

Tectonic-magmatic activity at the western end of the Paleoisthmus magmatic arc slowed (Vinson and Brineman, 1963;
Bonis, 1969b; Dengo, 1969, 1975; Dengo and Bohnenberger,
1969; McBirney and Bass, 1969b; Kesler and others, 1970;

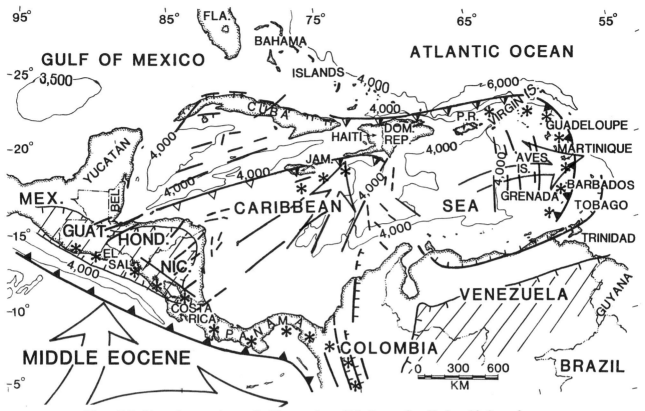

Figure 7. Positions of magmatic arcs, Caribbean region, middle Eocene time. Hachured faults are former volcanic arc margins. Active magmatic arcs are the Colombia and Middle America arcs, now reconstituted and joined; part of the Paleoisthmus arc; and the Lesser Antilles arc in the eastern Caribbean.

Clemons and Burkart, 1971; *Burkart and others, 1973*; *Wilson, 1974*; Weyl, 1980; *Rosenfeld, 1981*). The Sepur trough at the southern edge of the Chapayal basin filled with angular sedimentary debris. East of the Bay Islands, the Paleoisthmus arc remained active (*Robinson and others, 1970*; *Kemp, 1971*; Meyerhoff and Krieg, 1977, *1977*; *Krijnen and Lee Chin, 1978*; *Jackson and Smith, 1982*; *Kashfi, 1983*; *Wadge and others, 1984*; *Draper, 1986*). As it was not folded against a continental mass, its structural style is one of normal faults and tilted fault blocks (*Rezak and others, 1972*).

Farther south, between Nicaragua and Colombia, a new magmatic arc segment formed, extending northward to the Guatemala-Mexico frontier along the western coast of Central America, replacing the former arc (*Dengo, 1962*; *Henningsen, 1966*; *Henningsen and Weyl, 1968*; *Case and others, 1971*; Weyl, 1980; *Aubouin and others, 1982*; *Bourgois and others, 1982a, 1984*; *Azéma and others, 1985*). It also extended southward to the Colombia arc, which had remained active without interruption (*Feininger and others, 1972*; *Hall and others, 1972*; *Case and others, 1973*; Gansser, 1973; *Campbell, 1974*; *Goosens and others, 1977*; *Barrero, 1979*; *Duque-Caro, 1979, 1980, 1984*; Geyer, 1980; *Bourgois and others, 1982a, 1982b, 1985*; *Feininger, 1982*; *Alvarez, 1983*; *Ramírez and others, 1983*; Marriner and Millward, 1984; *Millward and others, 1984*; *McCourt*

and others, 1984). Marriner and Millward (1984) found abundant continental detritus in the Cretaceous arc section, from which they deduced that (1) the arc was close to South America during Cretaceous time and (2) the arc magmatism was not necessarily subduction related.

In the Main Antilles magmatic arc, thrusting took place in the present mountainous areas of southeastern Cuba. Reliably dated submarine Maastrichtian nappes are present (*Cobiella and others, 1977*; *Cobiella, 1978, 1983*), and the structural history is very complex (*Pushcharovskiy and others, 1967*; *Boiteau and Michard, 1976*; *Bovenko and others, 1980*). Extreme complexity also is seen in Hispaniola and the Puerto Rico–Virgin Islands platform (*Tobisch, 1968*; Bowin, 1975).

In Hispaniola, only the northern and central parts belong to the Main Antilles magmatic arc. These areas have been described partially by several workers, among them *Butterlin (1960)*, Bowin (*1966*, 1975), *Nagle (1972a, 1974, 1979)*, *Kesler and others (1977)*, *Palmer (1979)*, *Lewis (1980, 1982)*, Maurrasse (*1981b*, 1982), *Bowin and Nagle (1982)*, *Eberle and others (1982)*, *Biju-Duval and others (1983a)*, *Nemec (1982)*, *Theyer (1983)*, *Bellon and others (1985)*, and Bourdon and others (1985). Southern Hispaniola's history is related to that of the Paleoisthmus arc. Although southern Hispaniola was thrust from the south, much of northern Hispaniola shows thrusting from the north. Recent work, including our own, shows that (1) overall regional compression was from south to north and (2) many southward-directed thrusts are compensatory back-thrusts (e.g., Kesler and others, 1981; Bourgois and others, 1982c, 1982d; Maurrasse, 1982; Bourdon and others, 1985). In fact, the regional geology requires overall northward vergence of Hispaniola.

Similar events characterized the Puerto Rico–Virgin Islands platform *(Meyerhoff, 1933; Berryhill and others, 1960; Pessagno, 1960, 1962; Donnelly, 1964, 1966; Tobisch, 1968; Helsley, 1971; Meyerhoff and others, 1983a, 1983b; Kerdraon and others, 1985).* Thrusting probably was later than in southeastern Cuba—possibly latest Maastrichtian or Paleocene *(Mattson, 1973).*

Farther southeast, the Aves Ridge is underlain by Cretaceous through middle Eocene volcanic and volcanogenic rocks *(Fox and others, 1971; Nagle, 1972a;* Fox and Heezen, 1975; *Pinet and others, 1985),* and is intruded by granitic plutons *(Fox and others, 1971;* J. R. Curray and others, *in Meyerhoff and Meyerhoff, 1972a; Bouysse and others, 1985).* Upper Cretaceous volcaniclastic rocks, marls, and weathered limestone on several Lesser Antilles islands (Fox and Heezen, 1975; *Bouysse and others, 1985; Westercamp and others, 1985)* indicate proximity to the Aves segment of the Main Antilles arc. At the same time, activity along the Barbados branch of the Venezuela arc began to die *(Persad, 1984).*

Paleocene–middle Eocene (Fig. 7)

The paroxysmal phase *(sensu* Tercier, 1948) of the Cretaceous-Eocene orogenic cycle took place throughout the Caribbean region about middle Eocene time. The total length of the six circum-Caribbean arcs exceeds 10,000 km, and a pronounced angular unconformity is everywhere present. In those arcs that were crushed against adjacent continental massifs, the unconformity has a high angle, and some true flysch-wildflysch troughs developed (Kugler, 1953; *Brönnimann and Rigassi, 1963; Hatten, 1967; Green, 1977; Stéphan and others, 1980).* However, where continental massifs were not adjacent to an arc, deformation was less and the unconformities less pronounced. Deep-water troughs with turbidites developed in the Eastern Venezuela and Falcón basins, Colombia arc, Wagwater trough (Jamaica), Hispaniola, and Puerto Rico.

The Cuba of today appeared for the first time. The Cuba magmatic arc lay south of the Bahamas platform. As the arc and platform collided, huge nappes of deepwater fore-arc carbonates, followed by volcanic nappes, were obducted onto the platform. The collisions of the Cuba and Main Antilles arcs with the Bahamas sealed off all sites for new arc development; both arcs ceased to be active magmatically.

It was during the middle Eocene orogeny that the northeast-striking magnetic anomalies of the Yucatán Basin appear to have formed *(Hall and Yeung, 1982).* Their age is demonstrated by the fact that seismic reflectors A" (middle Eocene) and B" (Late Cretaceous) are absent in this basin, presumably buried by middle Eocene flood basalts.

The Bahamas block extended to the eastern end of the Puerto Rico–Virgin Islands platform as shown by the following facts (Moussa and others, 1987): (1) a nonmagnetic 17- to 25-km crust strikes west along the southern slope of the Puerto Rico Trench to within a short distance of the Samaná Peninsula/Navidad Bank area (Talwani and others, 1959; Geddes and Dennis, 1964); (2) this crust is overlain by Cretaceous-Pliocene bank carbonates (Fox and Heezen, 1975; Perfit and others, 1980); (3) the 250-Ma rocks on the Samaná Peninsula (Joyce and Aronson, 1983) are on strike with the projected platform; (4) west of, and on trend with, the Samaná locality, Soler and Cheilletz (1985) described thick silicic Cretaceous lava flows contaminated with continental crust; (5) the pre–late Eocene structures of Puerto Rico and the Virgin Islands have the same tectonic style as those of Hispaniola; and (6) the presence of northeast-striking folds in the northern Lesser Antilles also implies the presence farther north of a rigid massif (Bonneton, 1983).

The eastern end of the Paleoisthmus magmatic arc collided with Hispaniola; this had four immediate effects: (1) further rotation of the Paleoisthmus arc was impossible, so that magmatism ceased along the arc; (2) the Haitian Southern Peninsula first appeared, pushed northward from the Caribbean oceanic floor by the Paleoisthmus arc *(Maurrasse and others, 1979, 1982;* Maurrasse, *1981a, 1981b,* 1982; *Biju-Duval and others, 1983a),* thereby destroying the deep-water trough that previously existed between the eastern Paleoisthmus arc and the Main Antilles arc *(Bowin, 1968);* (3) the Beata Ridge rose as a consequence of dextral shear along the Beata fracture zone; and (4) strong south-to-north compression occurred with both south-and-north-verging thrusts (Bourgois and others, 1982c, 1982d; *Llinas and Rodríguez, 1982).* The Beata fracture zone extended farther north at this time, dividing the Main Antilles arc. Hence, the post–early Eocene histories of the two arc segments of the Main Antilles differ greatly.

The appearance of the Lesser Antilles magmatic arc in middle Eocene time may be related in part to the sudden reduction in magmatism and tectonism along the Barbados branch of the Venezuela arc. Here the youngest igneous rocks are 62 to 69 m.y. old *(Rowley and Roobol, 1978; Persad, 1984).* Eastward-directed stresses were concentrated increasingly along the newly forming Lesser Antilles arc that lay east of it, thereby creating a depocenter on the site of the present Barbados Ridge. Abundant terrigenous clastics (Scotland Group) were stripped from raised welts in the preexisting arc and deposited in northeast-trending furrows between them from Trinidad to north of Barbados, as shown by the fact that the Scotland is petrographically nearly identical with the partly coeval Point-à-Pierre Formation of Trinidad (Kugler, 1953, *1956).* The raised welts exposed Mesozoic, Paleozoic, and possibly, Precambrian terranes (Senn, 1940, *1947; Velbel, 1985; Baldwin and others, 1986; Kaspar and Larue, 1986).* The Scotland carries quartz, metamorphic minerals, Cretaceous limestone clasts, and grains of whole *Orbitolina* of Albian age (H. D. Hedberg, *in* Senn, 1940; *Senn, 1947; Douglass, 1961;* Pudsey and Reading, 1982; *Biju-Duval and others, 1985).* These clasts could not have come directly from the Guyana shield, because the area between the Barbados Ridge and the shield was a large epeiric sea (Weeks, 1947; Harrington, 1962).

Other origins for the Barbados Ridge have been postulated. Suggestions include: (1) Barbados is part of a giant gravity slide (*Daviess, 1971*); (2) it is part of a sedimentary pile originally deposited far to the west and later brought eastward along the El Pilar or related faults (*Dickey, 1982*); or (3) it is part of the Lesser Antilles "accretionary complex" widely referred to in recent literature. None of these concepts is supported by field data. The first two are not supported by either geological or geophysical data (*Ewing and others, 1957; Bassinger and others, 1971; Lattimore and others, 1971; Weeks and others, 1971; Kearey and others, 1975; Westbrook, 1975, 1982; Bowin, 1976; Bonini, 1978*). We interpret the refraction and gravity data to indicate that the crust is continental. With respect to the "accretionary complex," our seismic interpretation is compatible with the field data, but at variance with recent published interpretations (e.g., Biju-Duval and others, 1982; *Speed and Larue, 1982; Speed, 1983; Larue and Speed, 1984; Brown and Westbrook, 1987*).

The concept of a chaotic gravity slide is negated by the facts that (1) structural trends have an average strike of N55°E, the approximate trend of all middle Eocene and older strata in the fold belts of the region (Senn, 1940, *1947; Hedberg, 1950;* Kugler, 1953, *1956, 1961a, 1961b; Baadsgaard, 1960;* Biju-Duval and others, 1985; *Speed and Larue, 1985; Valery and others, 1985*); and (2) paleocurrent directions in the Scotland Group, measured in the field, uniformly show southwest to northeast flow (Pudsey and Reading, 1982).

The possibility of the Barbados Ridge being translated from a distant western source is discussed in the succeeding section on wrench faults.

In the "accretionary complex" concept, the Scotland Group should have been deposited from 700 to 1,100 km farther east as required by calculated spreading rates (*Minster and Jordan, 1978;* Westbrook and others, 1984). Space permits mention of only a very few of the formidable problems raised by such a concept. These include:

1. The conglomerate layers in the Scotland Group have sizable pebbles whose source is local (Pudsey and Reading, 1982, p. 300).

2. Middle and late Eocene sandstones, containing large amounts of Jurassic-Precambrian quartz, are present in the Scotland Group at site 674 behind the "deformation front," and at DSDP site 672 on the abyssal plain (Pudsey and Reading, 1982; *Biju-Duval and others, 1985; Baldwin and others, 1986; Scientific Drilling Party, 1987*). Hence, the three sites had nearly the same geographic relations with one another in Eocene time as today.

3. Other minerals, such as the clays, show the same, or nearly the same abundances, whether from Scotland outcrops or the abyssal plain (*Latouche and Maillet, 1984; Biju-Duval and others, 1985*).

4. Of the many seismic lines available, east-west lines show

thickening of all units at the same longitude into the Barbados Ridge; north-south lines show north-to-south thickening (e.g., Biju-Duval and others, 1982; Westbrook and others, 1984), thus defining an in situ depocenter, not one that shifted with time.

5. Angular unconformities are present in the middle Miocene and Eocene; clasts in the Scotland Group indicate the presence of a pre-Scotland unconformity. Thus, only the present site of the ridge has been deformed repeatedly.

6. Seismic lines published by Biju-Duval and others (1982; lines HR005, HR007) show excellent correlations between all strata on the ridge and equivalent sections of the Atlantic floor east of the ridge.

The above facts indicate that at least two processes molded the Barbados Ridge into its present form: (1) in situ uplift, accompanied by mild compression of the Cenozoic depocenter that occupied the position of the ridge; and (2) gravity sliding on the unstable ridge flanks, a process noted in other oceanic arc systems (e.g., von Huene, 1972). Hence, Case and Holcombe's (1980) term "deformed belt" is more appropriate than "accretionary complex."

Middle Eocene–middle Miocene (Fig. 8)

The post-paroxysmal phase of the Cretaceous-Recent tectonic cycle had begun everywhere in the Caribbean region by late Eocene time. Three magmatic arcs were active: Middle America, Colombia, and Lesser Antilles. Tangential compression, now much reduced, expressed itself by wrench faulting and, during the middle Miocene orogeny, by moderate folding and thrusting. Vertical movements became important in the region's morphotectonic evolution. Granitic plutons intruded folded areas and active Benioff zones. Large basins were segmented into smaller ones typified by molasse-type deposition. The carbonate banks of the northwestern Caribbean and Yucatán were further reduced in size. In fact, the overall sedimentary history from middle Eocene time to the present is one of regression.

Arc magmatism became increasingly silicic. For a while (late Eocene–Oligocene), some arc magmatism extended along the Puerto Rico–Virgin Islands segment of the Main Antilles arc (*Cox and others, 1977*). Plateau volcanism became important for the first time since the pre-Cretaceous tectonic cycle. The most outstanding example is in the pivot zone of the Paleoisthmus arc. The Yucatán block was the fulcrum about which the Paleoisthmus pivoted and moved counterclockwise from South America to its present position. Just east of the pivot zone, plateau volcanism took place from middle Eocene to middle Miocene time, covering several tens of thousands of square kilometers along the trailing edge of the paleoisthmus block (*McBirney and Williams, 1965; Williams and McBirney, 1969;* Weyl, 1980).

Tectogenesis during middle Miocene time folded the unstable tectonic areas around the Caribbean, but without the intensity of the middle Eocene orogeny (*Ellis, 1982; Redmond, 1982; Saunders and others, 1982*). Folding and thrusting, much of it southward backthrusting, took place in Hispaniola where the

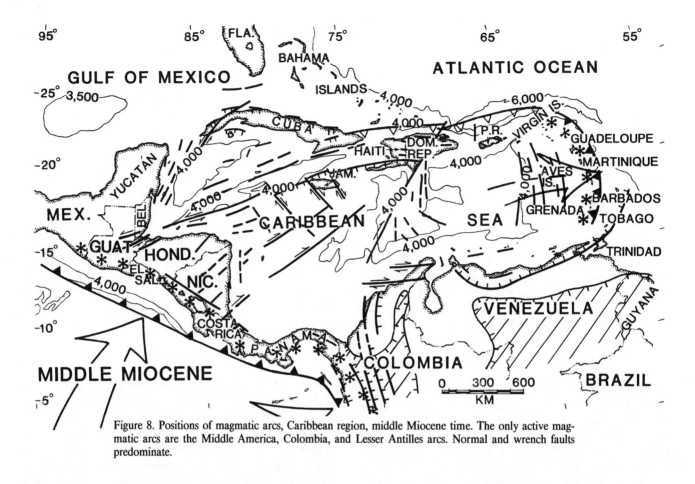

Figure 8. Positions of magmatic arcs, Caribbean region, middle Miocene time. The only active magmatic arcs are the Middle America, Colombia, and Lesser Antilles arcs. Normal and wrench faults predominate.

northeastern end of the paleoisthmus block acted as a "battering ram." The paleoisthmus, as a result of squeezing between Middle America and the Bahamas, was broken up by a myriad of Cenozoic faults that impart a "shattered glass" appearance to the Nicaragua Rise from the Chixoy-Polochic fault on the west to the northern shores of Jamaica on the east (*Woodring and others, 1924; Bermúdez, 1949; Hoylman and Chilingar, 1965; Rezak and others, 1972; Wright and Robinson, 1974; McFarlane, 1977;* Meyerhoff and Krieg, 1977; Weyl, 1980). The modern Cayman fault system also may have formed at this time. Southeastern Cuba was folded only gently (*Lewis and Straczek, 1955*), because this segment of the Main Antilles, unlike Hispaniola, was pressed against the more pliant sedimentary-volcanic pile of the former Cuba arc. Along the Cayman Ridge, deformation was negligible because this part of the Main Antilles arc had no rigid massif along its northern margin. Gentle arching occurred on the Bahamas block, including Cuba (*Meyerhoff and Hatten, 1974; Ball and others, 1985*).

Mild deformation also characterized the Main Antilles arc east of the Beata fracture zone. Eastern Hispaniola was very gently folded (*Weyl, 1966;* Bourdon and others, 1985); Puerto Rico and the Virgin Islands were tilted slightly northward (*Seiglie, 1973; H. A. Meyerhoff, 1975; Moussa and Seiglie, 1975; Seiglie and Moussa, 1976, 1984; Monroe, 1980*); and the north-

south Mona fault developed (Weaver and others, 1975; *Heezen and others, 1985*).

The Anegada fracture zone—interpreted to be a dextral fault zone—also originated in Miocene time (*Houlgatte and others, in Stéphan and others, 1985*). We postulate dextral motion, because such motion along both the Anegada and Mona fault zones together would explain (1) the apparent counterclockwise rotation of the Puerto Rico–Virgin Islands platform, (2) the opening of the St. Croix graben (*Whetten, 1966; Todd and Low, 1976*), and (3) a *westward* jump of the Lesser Antilles magmatic arc from the Limestone Caribbees to its present location in the Volcanic Caribbees (*Tomblin, 1975; Lewis and Robinson, 1976; Bouysse and others, 1982; Bouysse and Guennoc, 1983*).

Folding and thrusting occurred in Trinidad and in northern Venezuela east of the Barquisimeto transverse zone (Kugler, 1953; *Barr and others, 1958; Renz, 1959; Mencher, 1963; Bell, 1971; Bellizia, 1972;* Gansser, 1973; *Maresch, 1974; Saunders, 1974;* Aubouin, 1975; Stéphan, 1977, 1985; *Beck, 1978;* González de Juana and others, 1980). Similar tectonic events accompanied the middle Miocene orogeny in Middle America (Weyl, 1980) and Colombia (*Morales and others, 1958; Bürgl, 1961a; Campbell, 1974;* Irving, 1975), where granitic intrusions were emplaced and the Benioff zones shifted westward. In contrast, folding was very gentle in the northern part of the Lesser Antilles,

Figure 9. Present tectonic framework of the Caribbean. Note that the Middle America magmatic arc has died from Panamá southeastward, and that the active Colombia magmatic arc today is south of the area shown in the figure.

paralleling the northeast-striking middle Eocene fold axes (Bonneton, 1983). The main uplift of the Barbados Ridge occurred during the middle Miocene orogeny.

Uplift of the Hispaniola, Guatemala, and northwestern South America regions began during Oligocene time (Weyl, *1966*, 1980; *Kohn and others, 1984a, 1984b; Shagam and others, 1984*), increased through the middle Miocene orogeny, and probably continues today.

Middle Miocene to present (Fig. 9)

In general, the events that began during late Eocene time continued. Magmatic-arc magmatism was limited to the Lesser Antilles, Middle America, and Colombia arcs, although it ceased between the Coiba Ridge area of southern Panamá and Cabo Corrientes in western Colombia (*Lonsdale and Klitgord, 1978*).

On the southwestern part of the Nicaragua Rise (the former paleoisthmus), plateau volcanism continued (Weyl, 1980). Volcanoes appeared along a fault zone connecting San Andrés and Providencia Islands (*Bürgl, 1961b; Pagnacco and Radelli, 1962; Milliman and Supko, 1968*). Farther east, volcanism occurred in northeastern Jamaica (*Robinson, 1958*) and offshore, east of Jamaica (*Roobol and Horsfield, 1976*). The Plio-Pleistocene vol-

canic rocks of central Haiti (*Butterlin, 1960*) and the adjacent Dominican Republic (*MacDonald and Melson, 1969*) also are part of this late Tertiary–Quaternary volcanic trend. Mafic volcanic activity also characterized the Cayman Trough (*Ballard and others, 1979*).

The sinistral Cayman and dextral Hess (*Burke and others, 1984, Fig. 9*) fracture zones continued to form along the northern and southern flanks, respectively, of the Nicaragua Rise. The age of these faults is indicated by three phenomena. (1) Rocks that had been overridden and folded previously by the advancing Paleoisthmus arc have been sliced from the rise into isolated fault blocks. One is now capped by Swan Island, where deformed Oligocene–early Miocene deep-sea turbidites are overlain unconformably by undisturbed late Miocene and younger carbonates (*U.S. Geological Survey, 1967; Perfit and Heezen, 1978*). Fault separation allowed the block to rise isostatically in middle Miocene time. (2) The Nicaragua depression, a northwest-southeast–trending graben, formed in late Miocene time as the rise was translated east-northeast between these two faults. This activity further supports the concept of dextral motion along the Hess fracture zone. (3) Pliocene and younger strata on Hispaniola are steeply folded both inside and outside of areas of Miocene salt, thereby indicating continued east-northeast movement of the rise.

Also, the west-northwest–trending grabens of Hispaniola continued to sink rapidly, as combined reverse and sinistral movements along their boundary faults, together with folding, alleviated the stresses generated by the east-northeast motion of the paleoisthmus.

North of the Huancabamba deflection (*Ham and Herrera, 1963; de Loczy, 1970*), South America began to rotate clockwise (H. A. Meyerhoff, 1954), establishing a regime of compression west of a line joining the El Baúl uplift and the Paraguaná Peninsula ("Barquisimeto Transverse Zone" of Aubouin, 1975, and Stéphan, 1977) and a tensional regime east of the line.

Much of present northern South America and the southern Caribbean developed from this rotation. West of the El Baúl–Paraguaná line, effects of the rotation included (1) establishment of a compressive-stress regime, (2) strong uplift of the Andean ranges, (3) reverse faulting and partial displacement of several of these ranges, (4) fragmentation of the greater Cretaceous-Miocene basin into smaller basins (Cesar, Magdalena, Maracaibo, Llanos-Barinas-Apure), (5) limited wrench movements on the Romeral and other faults, (6) compression of the South Caribbean deformed belt, and (7) acquisition by the Panamanian isthmus of its sigmoid shape (as northwestern South America encroached on Middle America). The bending of Panamá shattered the isthmus into a complex structural mosaic, faulted it along northwest-striking sinistral wrench faults, caused near cessation of volcanism along the Panamá segment of the Middle America arc, and created compressional structures in the North Panamá deformed belt (*Lloyd, 1963; Dengo, 1969*; Case and Holcombe, 1980; *Lu and McMillen, 1983; Vitali and others, 1985*).

East of the El Baúl–Paraguaná line, tensile stress affected northeastern Venezuela and the Venezuela Basin as far north as Puerto Rico. This tension, coupled with eastward-directed stress from the Pacific, produced many tectonic phenomena. (1) Northwest-southeast dextral wrench faults with complimentary normal faults became active, forming new basins as a result of movements along these faults (e.g., Tuy, Cariaco, Margarita-Tobago shelf; *Biju-Duval and others, 1983b*). (2) Similar movements on parallel faults enlarged preexisting basins (e.g., Bonaire, Gulf of Paria). (3) These northwest-southeast faults (e.g., Urica, San Francisco, Los Bajos) offset almost all east-west structural trends in northern South America, including the El Pilar fault (Munro and Smith, 1984). (4) Numerous normal, down-to-the-north growth faults developed in the Tertiary basins cited above, as well as in the South Caribbean deformed belt and on the southern margins of the Grenada and Tobago basins; down-to-the-south growth faults are found along the northern flanks of these basins (M. A. Furrer, personal communication, 1982; *Despretz and others, 1985*). (5) South-dipping growth faults are numerous in the North Caribbean deformed belt. (6) Finally, the Aves and Beata Ridges subsided, and deep-water deposition was dominant there during Tertiary time (*Fox and others, 1970, 1971; Bouysse and others, 1985*).

We are aware that the North and South Caribbean de-

formed belts have been interpreted as subduction zones (e.g., *Ladd and Watkins, 1979*). However, clean seismic lines show clearly the Gulf Coast–type of structure, with down-to-the-north growth faults on the south and the opposite in the north. *Stéphan and others (1985)* listed reasons why the two deformed belts are not subduction zones, and coined the term "pseudosubduction zone" to describe them.

The Puerto Rico Trench formed during this period (*Monroe, 1968*). It acquired its present form after deposition of the early Pliocene Quebradillas Limestone (*Meyerhoff and others, 1983a; Alonzo and others, 1988*). This formation was deposited across a shelf and carbonate bank that occupied at least 4,000 km^2 on the southern slope of the present trench. The water depth was moderate and nearly constant (Moussa and others, 1987). Subsequent to Quebradillas deposition, the carbonate bank was tilted northward, and today the northern edge of the former shelf is deeper than 5,200 m.

On the Atlantic and Pacific abyssal plains close to the continental margins, late Miocene–Recent sections as well as the Late Cretaceous–middle Miocene sequences below them, indicate deposition at or close to their present locations. These conditions have been discussed for the area east of the Barbados Ridge. A similar situation is found in the Pacific where, 20 km west of the Middle America Trench axis, the Miocene in a DSDP core hole is a hemipelagic section with abundant sand- and silt-size quartz grains. *Von Huene and Aubouin (1982, p. 784–785*; Auboin and Von Huene, 1985) acknowledged the incongruity of this section, which, according to plate tectonics, was deposited some 900 km west of the trench beyond the reach of any ancestral detrital source.

WRENCH FAULTS (FIG. 9)

Most wrench faults in the Caribbean developed during Cenozoic time, although several occupy older zones of weakness (e.g., *Meyerhoff, 1966; Donnelly and others, 1968; Bonis, 1969a*). Most show no evidence for lateral movements greater than 15 km, in a region where the plate-tectonic hypothesis requires approximately 1,400 km of offset. We know of no well-documented offset greater than 110 km (Santa Marta–Bucaramanga fault zone; Irving, *1971*, 1975); even this figure has been challenged as being too high (*Polson and Henao, 1968*). Our concern, however, is with the faults that supposedly form the northern and southern Caribbean plate boundary zones.

The first problem, in both the northern and southern Caribbean, is that through-going faults do not exist. Unequivocal field evidence from Guatemala shows that neither the Motagua nor the Chixoy-Polochic faults continue into the Pacific (Muehlberger and Ritchie, 1975), despite assertions to the contrary (*Burkart, 1978, 1983; Burkart and Self, 1985*). *Anderson and others (1973, 1985)* demonstrated that offsets on the Chixoy-Polochic system do not exceed a few kilometers since Late Cretaceous time.

Farther east, the Cayman fault zone (Miocene and younger)

has been called a spreading center (*Ballard and others, 1979*). In actual fact, the ridges that are claimed to be a part of the spreading center lie on faults oriented at 70° to the Cayman boundary faults. This relationship suggests strongly that these faults are not associated with a spreading center, but that they are horsts and grabens of a complementary shear zone of the same order as the Cayman faults (*Moody and Hill, 1956, p. 1233*). Moreover, the mechanics and geometry of such a spreading center create apparently insoluble problems of physics (Jaeger, 1962).

The Cayman fault zone intersects the west-northwest–trending faults of Hispaniola at an angle. The bathymetry shows no gradation from one fault direction to the other. In fact, the Hispaniola faults appear to be older than the Cayman faults, as pointed out by *Bizon and others (1985)*. Farther east, these faults are cut off by the north-northeast–trending Beata fault zone. East of the Beata fault zone, the Puerto Rico Trench shows an even different trend—N85°E (*Savit and others, 1964*). Both the Cayman and Puerto Rico Trench faults are cut by north-south dextral wrench faults (*Meyerhoff, 1966*; Maley and others, 1974; Weaver and others, 1975).

Burke and others (1980) suggested that the east-west Crawle River–Plantain Garden fault zone of central and eastern Jamaica might have been a part of the northern Caribbean plate boundary. *McFarlane (1977)* and *Kashfi (1985),* however, demonstrated that no post–middle Eocene wrench movements have taken place, although up to 10 or 15 km of pre–late Eocene movement can be inferred (Meyerhoff and Krieg, 1977).

In summary, a reasonable boundary for the northern Caribbean plate margin can be postulated only for the zone between the Chiapas massif and Hispaniola. Elsewhere, a continuous boundary is absent.

In the southern Caribbean, the problem is more severe. A fault zone is not present for more than half of the distance from the Atlantic to the Pacific. The El Pilar fault is not through-going; in fact, it disappears or is cut off by the Urica fault west of the Araya Peninsula (Munro and Smith, 1984) and may not continue eastward through Trinidad (*Speed, 1985*). Field data show that the fault is not continuous and exhibits little or no lateral displacement (Saunders, 1977; *Pérez and Aggarwal, 1981*; Schubert, 1981; *Speed, 1985*). Schubert (1981) proposed that the 1,400-km displacement required by plate-tectonic hypotheses was adsorbed along the northern plate boundary as there was no evidence for significant movement in the south. Very substantial gaps in continuity also are demonstrated by the seismicity (*Sykes and Ewing, 1965; Molnar and Sykes, 1969*). *Burke and others (1984)* suggested that the southern plate boundary fault lies offshore, but neither the seismicity nor the seismic-reflection records provide substance for this idea.

In western Venezuela and Colombia, east-west faults (e.g., Cuiza, Oca) are all but inactive. Hence, the boundary has been postulated to be along the Boconó and associated faults (*Pennington, 1981*). However, there has been little or no lateral movement along the Boconó, as demonstrated by Schubert (1981, *1984*), *Giegengack (1984)*, and Salvador (1986). Moreover, the sub-

stantial change in strike between the Boconó and El Pilar directions raises a physically insoluble mechanical problem (Inglis, 1913; Anderson, 1951; Brace, 1960; Jaeger, 1962; *Brace and Bombolakis, 1963*; Walsh and Brace, 1964), involving friction.

We conclude that neither a northern nor southern Caribbean plate boundary, as predicted by plate-tectonic models, has been identified to date. Consequently, we have reviewed fundamental concepts of global-tectonic mechanisms and, from a mechanism that operates on a worldwide scale, we have developed an alternative hypothesis for the evolution of the Caribbean region.

ALTERNATIVE HYPOTHESIS: SURGE TECTONICS

Contraction and mantle surge

General. To interpret the tectonic history of the Caribbean region, we combined two hypotheses proposed previously to explain the tectonic evolution of the Earth. The combined hypothesis created a dynamic model of the Earth's interior, which in a development we did not anticipate, almost exactly mirrors Dziewonski and Woodhouse's (1987) seismotomographic model of the Earth above 670 km, specifically, their U84L85/SH model. The first of the two hypotheses is the *contraction* hypothesis of Jeffreys (1970), renamed the *fracture-contraction* hypothesis by Meyerhoff and others (1972). The second hypothesis is the *mantle surge* hypothesis of H. A. and A. A. Meyerhoff (1977). The two mechanisms are interdependent: both trigger episodic (as opposed to periodic) orogeny. The two processes act in tandem: first, a contractive pulse takes place; and second, each such pulse sets the mantle-surge mechanism in motion. Surges of low-viscosity mantle (asthenosphere) generally follow channels predicted by Meyerhoff and Meyerhoff (1977). What is remarkable is that these surge channels show up most clearly on the seismotomographic models of Adam M. Dziewonski and various colleagues (e.g., Dziewonski and Anderson, 1984; *Woodhouse and Dziewonski, 1984*; Dziewonski and Woodhouse, 1987). No other published tectonic hypothesis fits these seismotomography images. We elaborate this in a separate paper (Meyerhoff and others, unpublished manuscript).

Contraction. In recent years, several physicists and geophysicists have concluded that the Earth is contracting (e.g., Stacey, 1981; Lyttleton, 1982). G.J.F. MacDonald (1963, 1965), in two classic papers on upper mantle and continental structure, presents the basic contraction case, for which compelling evidence has since been adduced from many sources (e.g., Elder, 1965; Stacey, 1981; Lyttleton, 1982). The mechanics of contraction are explained by Jeffreys (1970) and, in a variant of the hypothesis, by Lyttleton (1982).

According to the hypothesis, the hard mantle directly below the asthenosphere—called the stereosphere by Bucher (1956)—contracts, causing the lithosphere to buckle and fracture. The contracting stereosphere and the compressing lithosphere must therefore be separated by a level of no strain in the upper mantle. The level of no strain is a zone that is generally called the asthenosphere or low-velocity zone (cf., Wilson, 1954; Jeffreys, 1970; Meyerhoff and others, 1972). Contraction (cooling) of a sphere, and therefore tectogenesis or orogeny, takes place most efficiently along great circles (Jeffreys, 1970), which today are represented by the Circum-Pacific and Mediterranean orogenic systems. These are the only remnants of several deforming great-circle zones of orogenesis that existed before Mesozoic time.

Contraction presumably takes place steadily in the stereosphere. As the stereosphere cools, the lithosphere must readjust by tangential compression along the great-circle fracture zones to fit itself to the decreasing Earth radius. In contrast to the steady contraction within the stereosphere, stresses that build up in the lithosphere probably are relieved abruptly in an episodic, not a periodic, manner. Although such tectogenesis can be worldwide (e.g., the middle Eocene orogeny), it is more likely to be localized in large regions (e.g., Indosinian orogeny).

Granitic intrusion is a nearly continuous process during each orogenic cycle. This is shown by the great age ranges within batholithic complexes, and the composite nature of most batholiths. Thus, radiometric dates of granites cannot be used to date orogeny. Also, granitic intrusion into mobile belts effectively welds them to the adjacent continent, and thus is the principal mechanism of accretion. Because granitic intrusions do invade magmatic arcs so pervasively, the positions of the arcs "jump" episodically to new, subparallel zones of weakness.

Reduction of the Earth's radius is a continuous process. Even so, many workers have stated that total radial shortening through geologic time has been too small to account for the observed shortening in mobile belts (e.g., *Bott, 1971*). Bucher (1956), in a dramatic scale-model laboratory experiment, demonstrated otherwise. He found that, for example, 20 km of tangential shortening can, because of near-surface gravitational adjustments, produce the illusion of 80 to 100 km of true shortening. As substantial amounts of radial shortening are now known to be possible (MacDonald, 1963; Lyttleton, 1982), hundreds of kilometers of measured (both apparent and real) tangential shortening in the forms of thrusting and folding can be accounted for. Then, if the mechanism of mantle surge is added to the effects of contraction, thousands of kilometers of measured shortening in foldbelts can be accommodated (Meyerhoff and Meyerhoff, 1977).

Most of the reasons for invoking contraction were enumerated by Meyerhoff and others (1972). One of their points is critical to *all* tectonic hypotheses. This is the long-known fact that the ocean basins are antipodal to continents (Arldt, 1907; Hobbs, 1921; *Bucher, 1933*; Wilson, 1954; Harrison, 1966; *Dietz and others, 1970*). Plate-tectonic hypotheses attach little improtance to this fact, which if it is unimportant, is one of the most remarkable coincidences in physical science. The antipodal relationship indicates that continental shields are fixed (Meyerhoff and others, 1972), although the more recently accreted margins of the continental masses may still be very mobile. Lowman (1985, 1986) summarized the large volume of data showing that the asthenosphere is absent beneath the oldest shields, a finding which, as

Lowman wrote (1985, 1986), renders the Archean parts of shields immobile.

Although contraction is able to account for all measurable shortening in mobile belts, at least one more mechanism is required to explain all field evidence for substantial foreshortening in mobile belts. In our hypothesis, the low-velocity zone is very mobile. Movement of matter in it is triggered by contractive spasms (orogeny) as the stereosphere cools. Rotation of the earth, acting in concert with contractive spasms, causes the asthenosphere to surge episodically (Meyerhoff and Meyerhoff, 1977), thus providing the mechanism of *mantle surge.*

Mantle surge. *Meyerhoff and Meyerhoff (1972b)* noted that many large-scale tectonic features of the Pacific basin indicate that eastward-flowing subcrustal currents are active beneath this region. These include the eastward-facing arcs of the western Pacific and other features. *Roeder and Nelson (1971)* had made a similar observation one year earlier. Their ideas were expressed by the term *mainstream mantle convection,* the details of which were explained by Nelson and Temple (1972). The Roeder-Nelson-Temple concept was tied closely to the plate-tectonics postulate, and especially to hypothetical convection cells, the movements of which were supposed to drive the plates. The Meyerhoffs' concept does not involve convection or any other hypothetical mechanism; it utilizes mechanisms already active within the upper mantle.

Mantle surge takes place in the asthenosphere (see Nelson and Temple, 1972). The surge, or movement, is caused by contraction acting in concert with rotation. The asthenosphere is thickest beneath the ocean basins (>100 km), thinnest under the continental margins, and is absent beneath the oldest parts of the shields (Lowman, 1985, 1986). We suggest that the following sequence of events takes place (basically a pressure-volume-temperature relationship).

(1) The stereosphere contracts, probably rather steadily. (2) A time delay ensues before the overlying lithosphere and asthenosphere adjust to the decreasing stereosphere radius. (3) During the time delay, asthenosphere volume increases slowly, thereby sustaining the lithosphere dynamically. Consequently, asthenospheric decompression occurs. (4) The decompression is accompanied by rising temperature, generation of new magma, and, therefore, lowered viscosity. (5) The viscosity is reduced to some critical value, the lithosphere collapses, buckles, fractures, and founders, as the circumference readjusts to that of the shrinking stereosphere. (6) Following the laws that govern the cooling of spherical bodies (Jeffreys, 1970), the lithosphere fractures along the Earth's great circle fracture zones, as predicted by theory (Jeffreys, 1970), demonstrated in the laboratory (Bucher, 1956), and recorded in earthquake patterns (*Lowman and Frey, 1979*). (7) The critical viscosity value at which lithosphere collapse takes place may be the value at which the asthenosphere becomes sufficiently mobile to flow.

(8) Tectogenesis then occurs, accompanied by the beginning of mantle surge. The collapsing lithosphere propels the asthenosphere both tangentially and radially upward (the resistant

stereosphere prevents downward movement). (9) The surge fractures the overlying lithosphere and applies stress against the subcontinental mantle in its path. (10) After lithosphere collapse, tectogenesis, and surge, the whole lithosphere begins to fill once again, preparatory to the next collapse, tectogenesis, and surge (i.e., the next tectonic cycle). Differential lag between the lithosphere and the stereosphere is accentuated, thus contributing to the building of the magmatic arcs.

In this hypothesis, moving asthenosphere and contraction provide the means of folding and thrusting thick rock prisms at the earth's surface, generally following the mechanics proposed by H. A. and A. A. Meyerhoff (1977). Bruce D. Martin (personal communication, May 1987) has coined the term *surge tectonics* to describe this combined mechanism (H. A. Meyerhoff, just before his death, suggested the term *asthenosphere tectonics*). A detailed exposition of this hypothesis will appear elsewhere (Meyerhoff and others, 1989a-d–see note added in proof).

We interpret the midocean ridges to be the surface expressions of the principal paths (conduits) used by the mobilized asthenosphere. The median positions, with respect to continents, of these ridges in the Arctic, Atlantic, Indian, and Southern Oceans are related directly to contraction, which causes gentle arching midway between fixed continental massifs (Menard, 1958). The East Pacific Rise, however, is not truly median, because it is offset eastward from a truly median position. This is true because the distance across that ocean basin is too great for a median ridge to be sustained dynamically. Instead, the East Pacific Rise is sustained by mantle surge that has offset it 1,200 km eastward. As a result, the East Pacific Rise is genetically somewhat different from other midocean ridges, although all of these ridges can be conduits for surging asthenosphere.

The net eastward movement of the asthenosphere that results from contraction and rotation involves centrifugal force, as well as differential lag between the stereosphere and the lithosphere. The friction between the asthenosphere and the lithosphere fractures the ocean floors, during asthenosphere surges. This is especially true beneath the median ridges, which are (1) underlain by the most mobile part of the asthenosphere and (2) overlain by the thinnest lithosphere. Volcanism is greatest at ridge crests because the lithosphere is the thinnest here (to see how this thinning is accomplished, see Perry and others, 1987).

Tectogenesis, or orogeny, is strongest during the paroxysmal phase of a tectonic cycle when the volume of mobile asthenosphere is largest and the pressure exerted by it during flow is greatest. As the volume and surge decrease, tangential compression (at the surface) decreases, ultimately ceasing altogether. During anorogenic phases, the friction between the asthenosphere and the lithosphere produces only tension fractures in the lithosphere. Hence, tectogenesis and taphrogenesis alternate, together composing a full tectonic cycle.

Because continents are underlain by thick lithosphere, and the asthenosphere beneath them is greatly thinned or nonexistent (Lowman, 1985, 1986), asthenosphere flow is impeded severely, and the mobile parts of the asthenosphere are diverted around such obstacles. The American continents, for example, form major obstacles to asthenosphere flow eastward from the Pacific. Consequently, the major fracture zones of the Pacific basin are concentrated in the eastern Pacific, where island arcs are absent except in the Caribbean and Scotia Seas—where eastward-flowing asthenosphere can flow almost unimpeded beneath Atlantic lithosphere. Because the American continents are asthenosphere barriers, trench systems here are pressed against the continental massifs, and back-arc basins are not developed. Therefore, island arcs with back-arc basins (marginal seas) are necessarily developed best in the western Pacific.

Similar fault zones and arcs are absent in the other ocean basins because eastward flow beneath those basins is unimpeded by a great-circle orogenic belt. Such a belt (e.g., Circum-Pacific belt) must be present for arc-trench formation.

Seismotomographic studies. Dramatic evidence portraying the parts of the asthenosphere that flow was published by Dziewonski and Anderson (1984), *Woodhouse and Dziewonski* (*1984*), and Dziewonski and Woodhouse (1987). The figures showing most graphically the exact locations of the surge channels along the western margins of the American continents and passing beneath the Caribbean Sea are Plates 2 and 3a of *Woodhouse and Dziewonski* (*1984,* model M84C, p. 6296–6297), Figures 5 and 10 of Dziewonski and Anderson (1984, p. 488, 493), and Figures 6 and 12 of Dziewonski and Woodhouse (1987, Model U84L85/SH, p. 42, 46). Plate 3a of *Woodhouse and Dziewonski* (*1984*) and Figure 10 of Dziewonski and Anderson (1984) even show the surge channels that dip eastward from Asia beneath the western Pacific, as predicted by Meyerhoff and Meyerhoff (1977), and the rise of these surge channels toward the east in the eastern Pacific and beneath the Caribbean, as required by the model, as well as by the data presented in this paper. We point out that the illustrations by Dziewonski and his colleagues give no hint of the presence of convection cells; in fact, asthenosphere surge would eliminate convective motions.

Summary. In summary, eastward asthenospheric flow across the Pacific basin is known by the presence of (1) trenches, magmatic arcs, back-arc basins, and deformed belt (western Pacific); (2) trenches parallel with and at the continental margins (eastern Pacific); (3) eastward-facing arcs in the Caribbean and Scotia Seas, the only place where Pacific-to-Atlantic flow is possible; (4) the concentration of east-striking fracture zones in the eastern Pacific (*Meyerhoff and Meyerhoff, 1972b*); and (5) the distribution of asthenospheric surge channels in the upper mantle as revealed by seismotomography (*Woodhouse and Dziewonski, 1984*). A sixth phenomenon produced by eastward flow is the position of the East Pacific Rise.

Magnetic lineations

The magnetic lineations on mid-ocean ridges are a cornerstone of plate tectonics, yet to this day, with the sole exception of the axial anomaly, not a single anomaly source has been dated by samples. Axis-parallel anomalies, in fact, are absent from many parts of the mid-ocean ridge system, and the symmetry of magnetic anomalies claimed by plate-tectonic adherents is largely illusory, as van Andel (1968, p. 154) once observed.

The magnetic lineations in the Caribbean have different strikes in each basin (Yucatán, Colombia, Venezuela); we interpret them to be tension fractures filled by intrusions of mafic lavas having magnetic susceptibilities different from those of the surrounding crust. We believe that van Andel's nonspreading Model 2 (1968, p. 154–158) most closely resembles the actual structural conditions known to prevail over the ridges. The van Andel Model 2, moreover, is a direct consequence of compression accompanied by asthenosphere surges. Meyerhoff and others (1989a-d–see note added in proof) have demonstrated quantitatively that a nonspreading model fits the observed geological and geophysical data far better than the popular *Vine and Matthews (1963)* and *Morley and Larochelle (1964)* model.

Summary of contraction-mantle surge hypothesis in the Caribbean (Figs. 2–9)

The following is our interpretation of the sequence of tectonic events in the Caribbean that were produced by contraction coupled with a surging, partly eastward-flowing asthenosphere.

1. Extensive Indosinian (Triassic-Middle Jurassic) orogeny in Asia is believed to have triggered a massive asthenospheric surge from west to east across the Pacific because of earth rotation. The surge exerted pressure against the western side of the Americas, as the taphrogenic effects of the Paleozoic–Middle Jurassic orogenic cycle began to dissipate.

2. The pressure against the Americas caused the rupture, during Middle Jurassic time, of the paleoisthmus that connected North and South America, and formed the Nicaragua Rise. A prominent surge channel extends toward the Atlantic beneath the Caribbean, and shows clearly on seismotomographic cross sections through the Caribbean. (An even more dramatic surge channel passes beneath the Scotia Sea between South America and Antarctica.)

3. The resulting surge of Pacific asthenosphere beneath the Caribbean toward the Atlantic rotated the paleoisthmus counterclockwise northward and produced the succession of magmatic arcs observed there: (a) the Cuba arc, which shifted episodically northward until its Maastrichtian collision with the Florida-Bahamas block; (b) the Main Antilles arc, which collided in middle Eocene time with the Florida-Bahamas block; (c) the Aves branch of the Main Antilles arc, which moved successively eastward, ultimately to create the Lesser Antilles arc in middle Eocene time; (d) the Paleoisthmus arc, which formed in front of the rotating mass that evolved into the Nicaragua Rise, colliding in Maastrichtian time with the Yucatán block in the west and in late Eocene–Oligocene time with the Main Antilles arc in the east; (e) the Venezuela arc and its Barbados Ridge extension, which shifted repeatedly southward and eastward until its collision with the Guayana shield; and (f) the Middle America–Colombia magmatic arcs that face the Pacific. The Middle America magmatic arc was selectively destroyed from early Berriasian through late Santonian time, ultimately being replaced by the

reconstituted Panamá magmatic arc and the Middle America Trench system; the Colombia magmatic arc shifted successively westward through time. Thus, the surge model explains both the eastward growth of the Caribbean region and the westward accretionary growth of Mexico and Colombia.

4. Repeated orogeny during Cretaceous–early Tertiary time, culminating in the middle Eocene paroxsymal phase, created a tectonic "logjam" in the Caribbean of dead arcs, segments of arcs, and newly created ridges. The Lesser Antilles, Middle America, and Colombia arcs are the sole survivors of this history of magmatic arcs, and these too are gradually becoming extinct. Wrench-fault, tear-fault, and vertical movements began to predominate, with vertical movements by far the most spectacular (e.g., the Hispaniola and Guatemala syntaxes; the Santa Marta massif; the Puerto Rico Trench; and so on). The surges, with the resulting "logjam" in the Caribbean, tilted the region eastward; both the topography and bathymetry sink eastward across the whole region. East of the Lesser Antilles, surges of the asthenosphere probably ruptured the thin Atlantic lithosphere and produced the east-west magnetic anomalies that are so prominent east of the Lesser Antilles and Barbados Ridge. The Caribbean today is entering a taphrogenic phase similar to that which terminated the preceding Paleozoic–Middle Jurassic orogenic cycle.

This hypothesis appears to explain best the chronological order of recorded events in the region, and the Pacific insertion of the Colombia Basin part of the Caribbean plate. The mechanical advantages of the model presented here require no additional explanation, for the surge-tectonic model provides much more flexibility than the plate-tectonic model that deals with highly rigid plates delimited by unnecessarily restrictive plate boundaries. We hope that the increased degrees of freedom provided by surge tectonics will eliminate the need to invoke new ad hoc postulates every time a new scientific discovery is made that does not fit the various plate-tectonic models. The surge hypothesis is presented in detail by Meyerhoff and others (1989a-d–see note added in proof).

ACKNOWLEDGMENTS

The authors thank M. Ismail Bhat, Arthur J. Boucot, Arthur L. Bowsher, Richard E. Chapman, Dong R. Choi, Ashok K. Dubey, Charles W. Hatten, Maurice Kamen-Kaye, Frank E. Kottlowski, Konrad B. Krauskopf, Wallace D. Lowry, Bruce D. Martin, W. W. Olive, John F. Spangler, Curt Teichert, George A. Thompson, Francisco Viniegra-Osorio, and Charles W. Whiting for their whole-hearted and enthusiastic support and for their continuous encouragement during the writing of this paper. All of these scientists reviewed at least some part of the paper—particularly the surge-tectonic concept—and offered constructive criticisms; all strongly pushed for its prompt publication. We thank A. R. Palmer for his incredible patience, and James E. Case and Gabriel Dengo for guidance. Finally, we are grateful to Kay Meyerhoff for drafting the figures, and to Ernestine R. Voyles for repeated typing and retyping.

REFERENCES CITED

(Text references in *italics* will be found only on the accompanying microfiche.)

Anderson, E. M., 1951, The dynamics of faulting and dyke formation with applications to Britain (2nd ed.): Edinburgh, Oliver and Boyd, 206 p.

Arldt, Th., 1907, Die entwicklung der kontinente und ihrer Lebewelt: Leipzig, Christian Hermann Tauchnitz, 729 p.

Aubouin, J., 1975, Réflexion sur les bordures pacifiques; L'exemple des cordillères sud-américaines: Comptes Rendus, t. 280, ser. D, p. 2633–2636.

Aubouin, J., Blanchet, R., Stéphan, J.-F., and Tardy, M., 1977, Téthys (Mésogée) et Atlantique; Données de la géologie: Comptes Rendus, t. 280, ser. D., p. 1025–1028.

Aubouin, J., Azéma, J., Carfantan, J.-C., Demant, A., Rangin, C., Tardy, M., and Tournon, J., 1982a, The Middle America Trench in the geological framework of Central America, *in* von Huene and others, eds., Initial reports of the Deep Sea Drilling Project: Washington, D.C., U.S. Government Printing Office, v. 67, p. 747–755.

Bartok, P. E., Renz, O., and Westerman, G.E.G., 1985, Siquisique ophiolites, northern Lara State, Venezuela; A discussion on their Middle Jurassic ammonites and tectonic implications: Geological Society of America Bulletin, v. 96, p. 1050–1055.

Beets, D. J., Maresch, W. V., Klaver, G. Th., Mottana, A., Bocchio, R., Beunk, F. F., and Monen, H. P., 1984, Magmatic rock series and high-pressure metamorphism as constraints on the tectonic history of the southern Caribbean, *in* Bonini, W. E., Hargraves, R. B., and Shagam, R., eds., The Caribbean–South America plate boundary and regional tectonics: Geological Society of America Memoir 162, p. 95–130.

Biju-Duval, B., Le Quellec, P., Mascle, A., Rénard, V., and Valery, P., 1982, Multibeam bathymetric survey and high resolution seismic investigations on the Barbados Ridge complex (eastern Caribbean); A key to the knowledge and interpretation of an accretionary wedge: Tectonophysics, v. 86, p. 275–304.

Bonneton, J. R., 1983, Folding and faulting to the north of the Lesser Antilles island arc; St. Martin, *in* 10th Caribbean Geological Conference, Cartagena 1983, Programs and Abstracts of Papers: Bogotá, Ingeominas, p. 25.

Bourdon, L., Mercier de Lepinay, B., and Vila, J. M., 1985, Étude géologique de la Cordillère Orientale dominicaine (Hispaniola, Grandes Antilles), *in* Caribbean geodynamics: Paris, Éditions Technip, p. 317–328.

Bourgois, J., Vila, J. M., Llinas, R., and Tavares, I., 1982c, Tectónicas sobrepuestas en La Española (Antillas Mayores), *in* Transactions, 9th Caribbean Geological Conference, Santo Domingo (Dominican Republic), 1980: Santo Domingo, Amigo del Hogar, v. 1, p. 35–38.

Bourgois, J., Vila, J. M., and Tavares, I., 1982d, Datos nuevos acerca de la región de Puerto Plata, *in* Transactions, 9th Caribbean Geological Conference, Santo Domingo (Dominican Republic), v. 2, 633–636.

Bowin, C. O., 1975, The geology of Hispaniola, *in* Nairn, A.E.M., and Stehli, F. G., eds., The ocean basins and margins; v. 3, The Gulf of Mexico and the Caribbean: New York, Plenum Press, p. 501–552.

Brace, W. F., 1960, An extension of the Griffith theory of fracture to rocks: Journal of Geophysical Research, v. 65, p. 3477–3480.

Bucher, W. H., 1947, Problems of earth deformation illustrated by the Caribbean Sea basin: New York Academy of Sciences Transactions, ser. II, v. 9, no. 3, p. 98–116.

—— , 1956, Role of gravity in orogenesis: Geological Society of America Bulletin, v. 67, p. 1295–1318.

Case, J. E., and Holcombe, T. L., 1980, Geologic-tectonic map of the Caribbean region: U.S. Geological Survey Miscellaneous Investigation Series Map I–1100, scale 1:2,500,000.

Case, J. E., Holcombe, T. L., and Martin, R. L., 1984, Map of geologic provinces in the Caribbean region, *in* Bonini, W. E., Hargraves, R. B., and Shagam, R., eds., South American plate boundary and regional tectonics: Geological Society of America Memoir 162, p. 1–30.

Charig, A. J., 1971, Faunal provinces on land; Evidence based on the distribution of fossil tetrapods, with especial reference to the reptiles of the Permian and Mesozoic, *in* Middlemiss, F. A., and Rawson, P. F., eds., Faunal provinces in space and time: Liverpool, U.K., Seel House Press, p. 111–128.

Clemens, W. A., Lillegraven, J. A., Lindsay, A. H., and Simpson, G. G., 1979, When, where, and what; A survey of known Mesozoic mammal distribution, *in* Lillegraven, J. A., Kielan-Jaworowska, Z., and Clemens, W. A., eds., Mesozoic mammals; The first two-thirds of mammalian history: Berkeley, University of California Press, p. 7–58.

Cox, C. B., 1973, Triassic tetrapods, *in* Hallam, A., ed., Atlas of palaeobiogeography: New York, Elsevier Scientific Publishing Company, p. 213–223.

Dziewonski, A. M., and Anderson, D. L., 1984, Seismic tomography of the Earth's interior: American Scientist, v. 72, no. 5, p. 484–494.

Dziewonski, A. M., and Woodhouse, J. M., 1987, Global images of the Earth's interior: Science, v. 236, no. 4797, p. 37–48.

Elder, J. W., 1965, Physical processes in geothermal areas, *in* Lee, W.H.K., ed., Terrestrial heat flow: American Geophysical Union Geophysical Monograph 8, p. 211–239.

Ewing, J., Antoine, J., and Ewing, M., 1960, Geophysical measurements in the western Caribbean Sea and in the Gulf of Mexico: Journal of Geophysical Research, v. 65, p. 4087–4126.

Fox, P. J., and Heezen, B. C., 1975, Geology of the Caribbean crust, *in* Nairn, A.E.M., and Stehli, F. G., eds., The ocean basins and margins; v. 3, The Gulf of Mexico and the Caribbean: New York, Plenum Press, p. 421–466.

Gansser, A., 1973, Facts and theories on the Andes: Journal of The Geological Society of London, v. 129, pt. 2, p. 93–131.

Geddes, W. H., and Dennis, L. S., 1964, Preliminary report on a special aeromagnetic survey of the Puerto Rico Trench, *in* Burk, C., ed., A study of serpentinite, the AMSOC hole near Mayagüez, Puerto Rico: Washington, D.C., National Academy of Science/National Research Council, Publication 1188, 185 p.

Geological Survey Department, 1967, Annual report for the year ended 31st March 1967: Kingston, Jamaica, Government Printer, 16 p.

González de Juana, C., Iturralde de Arozena, J. M., and Picard-Cadillat, X., 1980, Geología de Venezuela y de sus cuencas petrolíferas: Caracas, Ediciones Foninves, t. 1, p. 1–407; t. II, p. 409–1031.

Harrington, H. J., 1962, Paleogeographic development of South America: American Association of Petroleum Geologists Bulletin, v. 46, no. 10, p. 1773–1814.

Harrison, C.G.A., 1966, Antipodal location of continents and ocean basins: Science, v. 133, p. 1246–1248.

Hatten, C. W., Somin, M., Millán, G., Renne, P., Kistler, R. W., and Mattinson, J. W., 1986, Tectonostratigraphic units of central Cuba: 9th Caribbean Geological Conference, Barbados 1986, 32 p. (preprint).

Hein, J. R., and Karl, S. H., 1983, Comparisons between open-ocean and continental margin chert sequences, *in* Iijima, A., Hein, J. R., and Siever, R., eds., Siliceous deposits in the Pacific region: New York, Elsevier Scientific Publishing Company, p. 25–44.

Hein, J. R., Kuijpers, E. P., Denyer, P., and Sliney, R. E., 1983, Petrology and geochemistry of Cretaceous and Paleogene cherts from western Costa Rica, *in* Iijima, A., Hein, J. R., and Siever, R., eds., Siliceous deposits in the Pacific region: New York, Elsevier Scientific Publishing Company, p. 143–174.

Hill, R. T., 1905, Pelé and the evolution of the Windward Archipelago: Geological Society of America Bulletin, v. 16, p. 243–288.

Hobbs, W. H., 1921, The earth and its facial expression: New York, the Macmillan Company, 178 p.

Horne, G. S., Clark, G. S., and Pushkar, P., 1976, Pre-Cretaceous rocks of northwestern Honduras; Basement terrane in Sierra de Omoa: American Association of Petroleum Geologists Bulletin, v. 60, no. 4, p. 566–583.

Inglis, C. E., 1913, Stresses in a plate due to the presence of cracks and sharp corners: London, Transactions of the Institute of Naval Architecture, v. 55,

p. 219–230.

Irving, E. M., 1975, Structural evolution of the northernmost Andes, Colombia: U.S. Geological Survey Professional Paper 846, 47 p.

Jaeger, J. C., 1962, Elasticity, fracture, and flow with engineering and geological applications (2nd ed.): London, Methuen and Company, Ltd., 208 p.

Jeffreys, H., 1970, The Earth (5th ed.): Cambridge University Press, 420 p.

Joyce, J., and Aronson, J., 1983, K-Ar age dates for blueschist metamorphism on the Samaná Peninsula, Dominican Republic: 10th Caribbean Geological Conference, Cartagena, 1983, 8 p. (preprint).

Kalandadze, N. N., and Rautian, A. S., 1980, The role of central Asia in the zoogeographical history of the Mesozoic, *in* Barsbold, R. and 6 others, eds., Fossil reptiles of Mongolia: Moscow, Sovmestnaya Sovetsko-Mongol'skaya Paleontologischeskaya Expeditsiya, Izdatel'stvo Nauka, v. 24, p. 6–44. (in Russian)

Kauffman, E. G., 1973, Cretaceous Bivalvia, *in* Hallam, A., ed., Atlas of palaeobiogeography: New York, Elsevier Scientific Publishing Company, p. 353–383.

Kesler, S. E., Russell, N., Seaward, M., Rivera, J., McCurdy, K., Cumming, G. L., and Sutter, J. F., 1981, Geology and geochemistry of sulfide mineralization underlying the Pueblo Viejo gold-silver oxide deposit, Dominican Republic: Economic Geology, v. 76, p. 1096–1117.

Khudoley, K. M., and Meyerhoff, A. A., 1971, Paleogeography and geological history of Greater Antilles: Geological Society of America Memoir 129, 199 p.

Knipper, A. L., and Cabrera, R., 1974, Tectónica y geología histórica de la zona de articulación entre el mio- y eugeosinclinal y del cinturón hiperbásico de Cuba, *in* Contributción a la geología de Cuba: Academia de cincias de Cuba, Instituto de Geología y Paleontología, Publicación Especial no. 2, p. 15–17.

Kozlovsky, Ye. A., ed., 1986, The superdeep well of the Kola Peninsula: New York, Springer-Verlag, 558 p.

Kugler, H. G., 1953, Jurassic to Recent sedimentary environments in Trinidad: Association Suisse des Géologues et Ingénieures du Pétrole, Bulletin, v. 20, no. 59, p. 27–60.

Kuznetsov, V. I., Sánchez-Arango, J. R., Furrazola-Bermúdez, G., and García-Sánchez, R., 1985, Nuevos datos sobre la estratigrafía de los mantos tectónicos de la costa norte de Cuba: Ministerio de Industria Básica (La Habana), Série Geológica, no. 2, p. 106–118.

López-Ramos, E., 1983, Geología de México, t. III (3rd ed.): Published privately by the author; obtainable from Biblioteca, Instituto de Geología, Universidad Nacional Autónoma de México, Mexico City, 453 p.

Lowman, P. D., Jr., 1985, Plate tectonics with fixed continents; A testable hypothesis, I: Journal of Petroleum Geology, v. 8, no. 4, p. 373–388.

——, 1986, Plate tectonics with fixed continents—a testable hypothesis, II: Journal of Petroleum Geology, v. 9, p. 71–87.

Lyttleton, R. A., 1982, The Earth and its mountains: New York, John Wiley and Sons, 206 p.

MacDonald, G.J.F., 1963, The deep structure of continents: Reviews of Geophysics, v. 1, p. 585–665.

——, 1965, Geophysical deductions from observations of heat flow, *in* Lee, W.H.K., ed., Terrestrial heat flow: American Geophysical Union, Geophysical Monograph 8, p. 191–210.

Maley, T. S., Sieber, F. D., and Johnson, G. L., 1974, Topography and structure of the western Puerto Rico Trench: Geological Society of America Bulletin, v. 85, p. 513–518.

Marriner, G. F., and Millward, D., 1984, The petrology and geochemistry of Cretaceous to recent volcanism in Colombia; The magmatic history of an accretionary plate margin: Journal of The Geological Society of London, v. 141, pt. 3, p. 474–486.

Maurrasse, F.J.-M.R., 1982, Survey of the geology of Haiti; Guide to the field excursion in Haiti: Miami, Florida, Miami Geological Society, 103 p.

Menard, H. W., 1958, Development of median elevations in ocean basins: Geological Society of America Bulletin, v. 69, p. 1179–1185.

Meyerhoff, A. A., and Krieg, E. A., 1977, Petroleum potential of Jamaica: Kingston, Ministry of Mines and Natural Resources, Mines and Geology Division Special Report, 131 p.

Meyerhoff, A. A., Meyerhoff, H. A., and Briggs, R. S., Jr., 1972, Continental drift; V, Proposed hypothesis of Earth tectonics: Journal of Geology, v. 80, p. 663–692.

Meyerhoff, H. A., 1954, Antillean tectonics: New York Academy of Sciences Transactions, Series 2, v. 16, no. 3, p. 149–155.

Meyerhoff, H. A., and Meyerhoff, A. A., 1977, Genesis of island arcs, *in* Géodynamique du sud-ouest Pacifique, Symposium international, Noumea, Nouvelle-Calédonie, 27 Août-2 Septembre, 1976: Paris, Éditions Technip, 413 p.

Millán, G., and Somin, M. L., 1981, Litología, estratigrafía, tectónica, y metamorfismo del macizo de Escambray: La Habana, Cuba, Editorial Academia, 104 p.

Morgan, W. J., 1968, Rises, trenches, great faults, and crustal blocks: Journal of Geophysical Research, v. 73, p. 1959–1982.

Moussa, M. T., Seiglie, G. A., Meyerhoff, A. A., and Taner, I., 1987, The Quebradillas Limestone (Miocene–Pliocene), northern Puerto Rico, and tectonics of the northeastern Caribbean margin: Geological Society of America Bulletin, v. 99, p. 427–439.

Muehlberger, W. R., and Ritchie, A. W., 1975, Caribbean–Americas plate boundary in Guatemala and southern Mexico as seen on Skylab IV orbital photography: Geology, v. 3, p. 232–235.

Munro, S. E., and Smith, F. D., Jr., 1984, The Urica fault zone, northeastern Venezuela, *in* Bonini, W. E., Hargraves, R. B., and Shagam, R., eds., The Caribbean–South American plate boundary and regional tectonics: Geological Society of America Memoir 162, p. 213–215.

Nagle, F., 1972b, Caribbean geology: Science, v. 177, p. 782.

Nelson, T. H., and Temple, P. G., 1972, Mainstream mantle convection; A geologic analysis of plate motion: American Association of Petroleum Geologists Bulletin, v. 56, p. 226–246.

North, F. K., 1965, The curvature of the Antilles: Geologie en Mijnbouw, v. 44, no. 3, p. 73–86.

Pardo, G., 1975, Geology of Cuba, *in* Nairn, A.E.M., and Stehli, F. G., eds., The ocean basins and margins; v. 3, The Gulf of Mexico and the Caribbean: New York, Plenum Press, p. 553–616.

Perfit, M. R., Heezen, B. C., Rawson, M., and Donnelly, T. W., 1980, Chemistry, origin, and tectonic significance of metamorphic rocks from the Puerto Rico Trench: Marine Geology, v. 34, p. 125–156.

Perry, F. V., Baldridge, W. S., and DePaolo, D. J., 1987, Role of asthenosphere and lithosphere in the genesis of late Cenozoic basaltic rocks from the Rio Grande Rift and adjacent regions of the southwestern United States: Journal of Geophysical Research, v. 92, no. B9, p. 9193–9213.

Pszczółkowski, A., 1982, Cretaceous sediments and paleogeography in the western part of the Cuban miogeosyncline: Acta Geologica Polonica, v. 32, p. 135–161.

Pudsey, C. J., and Reading, H. G., 1982, Sedimentology and structure of the Scotland Group, Barbados, *in* Leggett, J. K., ed., Trench-forearc geology; Sedimentation and tectonics on modern and active plate margins: The Geological Society of London Special Publication 10, p. 291–308.

Rémane, R., 1980, Calpionellids, *in* Haq, B. V., and Boersma, A., eds., Introduction to marine micropaleontology: New York, Elsevier Publishing Company, p. 161–170.

Salvador, A., 1986, Comments *on* "Neogene block tectonics of eastern Turkey and northern South America; Continental applications of the finite difference method" by J. F. Dewey and L. L. Pindell: Tectonics, v. 5, p. 697–701.

Saunders, J. B., 1977, A review of models for the geological development of the southeast corner of the Caribbean region, *in* 8th Caribbean Geological Conference, Curaçao, Program and Abstracts: Geologische Universitet van Amsterdam Papers of Geology, Ser. 1, no. 9–1977, Amsterdam, Geologisch Instituut, p. 170.

Saunders, J. B., Edgar, N. T., Donnelly, T. W., and Hay, W. W., 1973, Cruise synthesis, *in* Edgar, N. T., and others, eds., Initial reports of the Deep Sea Drilling Project: Washington, D.C., U.S. Government Printing Office, v. 15, p. 1077–1111.

Schubert, C., 1981, Are the Venezuelan fault systems part of the southern Caribbean plate boundary?: Geologische Rundschau, Bd. 70, Heft 2, p. 542–551.

Senn, A., 1940, Paleocene of Barbados and its bearing on history and structure of Antillean–Caribbean region: American Association of Petroleum Geologists Bulletin, v. 24, p. 1548–1610.

Soler, E., and Cheilletz, A., 1985, Caractéristiques du volcanisme du nord d'Haïti; Implications géotectoniques, *in* Mascle, A., ed., Caribbean geodynamics: Paris, Éditions Technip, p. 961–968.

Somin, M. L., and Millán, G., 1981, Geologiya metamorfischeskikh kimpleksov Kuby: Moscow, Nauka, 220 p.

Stacey, F. D., 1981, Cooling of the Earth—A constraint on paleotectonic hypotheses, *in* O'Connell, R. J., and Fyfe, W. S., eds., Evolution of the Earth: American Geophysical Union, Geodynamics Series, v. 5, p. 272–276.

Stéphan, J.-F., 1977, El contacto cadena Caribe–Andes Merideños entre Carora y El Tocuyo (Estada Lara); Observaciones sobre el estilo y la edad de las deformaciones cenozóicas en el occidente venezolano, *in* Memoria, 5th Congreso Geológico Venezolano, t. II, Geodinámica: Caracas, Ministerio de Energía y Minas y Sociedad Venezolana de Geología, p. 789–815.

Suess, E., 1885, Das Antlitz der Erde, Band I: Wien (Vienna), F. Tempsky, 729 p.

—— , 1909, Das Antlitz der Erde, Band 3, erste Hälfte: Wien (Vienna), F. Tempsky, 789 p.

Talukdar, S., and Loureiro, D., 1982, Geología de una zona ubicada en el segmento norcentral de la Cordillera de la Costa, Venezuela; Metamorfismo y deformación; Evolución del margen septentrional de Suramérica en el marco de la tectónica de placas: Caracas, Geos, v. 27, p. 15–76.

Talwani, M., Sutton, G. H., and Ewing, W. M., 1959, A crustal section across the Puerto Rico Trench: Journal of Geophysical Research, v. 64, p. 1545–1555.

Tercier, J., 1948, Le flysch dans la sédimentation alpine: Eclogae Geologicae Helvetiae, v. 40, no. 2, p. 163–198.

Tschantz, C. M., Marvin, R. F., Cruz-B., J., Mehnert, H. H., and Cebula, G. T.,

1974, Geologic evolution of the Sierra Nevada de Santa Marta, northwestern Colombia: Geological Society of America Bulletin, v. 85, p. 273–284.

van Andel, Tj., 1968, The structure and development of rifted mid-oceanic rises: Journal of Marine Research, v. 26, no. 2, p. 144–161.

Viniegra-O., F., 1981, Great carbonate bank of Yucatán: Journal of Petroleum Geology, v. 3, no. 3, p. 247–278.

von Huene, R., 1972, Structure of the continental margin and tectonism at the eastern Aleutian Trench: Geological Society of America Bulletin, v. 83, p. 3613–3626.

Walsh, J. B., and Brace, W. F., 1964, A fracture criterion for brittle anisotropic rock: Journal of Geophysical Research, v. 69, p. 3449–3456.

Weaver, J. D., Smith, A. L., and Seiglie, G. A., 1975, Geology and tectonics of Mona Passage [abs.]: EOS American Geophysical Union Transactions, v. 56, no. 6, p. 451–452.

Weeks, L. G., 1947, Paleogeography of South America: American Association of Petroleum Geologists Bulletin, v. 31, p. 1194–1241.

Westbrook, G. K., Mascle, A., and Biju-Duval, B., 1984, Geophysics and the structure of the Lesser Antilles forearc, *in* Biju-Duval, B., and others, eds., Initial reports of the Deep Sea Drilling Project: Washington, D.C., U.S. Government Printing Office, v. 78A, p. 23–38.

Weyl, R., 1980, Geology of Central America: Berlin, Gebrüder Borntraeger, 371 p.

Wilson, J. T., 1954, The development and structure of the crust, *in* Kuiper, G. P., ed., The Earth as a planet: The University of Chicago Press, p. 138–214.

Woodring, W. P., 1928, Tectonic features of the Caribbean region: Proceedings, 3rd Pan-Pacific Science Congress, Tokyo 1926, v. 1, p. 401–431.

MANUSCRIPT ACCEPTED BY THE SOCIETY JULY 12, 1988

NOTES ADDED IN PROOF

(Italicized references are on microfiche accompanying this volume.)

General. Research subsequent to acceptance of this paper has enabled us to refine considerably the concept of surge tectonics and apply it on a global scale. We summarize this research briefly as it affects the Caribbean region.

The principal drawback of the hypothesis proposed in the preceding pages is that we provide no mechanism for the thin-skinned alpinotype tectogenesis that typifies the Caribbean region. Movements in the asthenosphere take place at depths that probably are too great to affect the surface directly. Thus, a shallower, more active mechanism within the lithosphere is required. We have found such a mechanism.

Origin of Midocean Ridges. In plate tectonics, the 65,000-km-long network of midocean ridges and associated structures is assumed to be a manifestation of plate separation, or sea-floor spreading, which commenced in Middle Jurassic time with the breakup of Pangea. Thus, all motions beneath midocean ridges are assumed to be orthogonal to the ridges. This assumption can no longer be sustained.

During the last 14 years, high-resolution sonographs (side-scanning sonar) have been acquired from much of the midocean ridge systems. All of them reveal the presence across the full width of each ridge of linear, ridge-parallel fissures, fractures, and faults, some 100 km or more long (Macdonald and others, 1984). Many of these fissure, fracture, and fault systems form en echelon structures and flowlines similar to those observed in glaciers. En echelon and flowline structures of these types are produced only by ridge-parallel flow, and provide a clear manifestation of Stokes's Law (Sears and others, 1974; Blatt, 1983). Thus the most fundamental assumption of plate tectonics—flow at right angles to and away from the midocean ridges—is contradicted by the structures on the ridges.

Geophysical studies of the midocean ridges have revealed the presence at shallow depths of at least one low-velocity zone (Talwani and others, 1965;

Pavlenkova, 1989). This zone, some 10 to 20 km thick and several hundred kilometers across, resembles a lens in cross section. It was first identified by Ewing and Ewing (1959) and by Talwani and others (1965). The zone is associated with what commonly is called "anomalous upper mantle" and "crust-mantle mix" (Ewing and Ewing, 1959; Talwani and others, 1965; Vogt and others, 1969). "Anomalous upper mantle" is so called because it has P-wave velocities of 7.0 to 7.8 km/s (Revelle, 1958), intermediate between the velocities of the underlying mantle (8.1 km/s) and the overlying crust (6.1–6.8 km/s).

We then concentrated on these "anomalous" lens-like bodies, and soon found that nearly identically shaped (the main differences are of size) lenses of rock with a 7.0- to 7.8-km/s P-wave velocity underlie every major structure on Earth, whether continental or oceanic. Such structures include all foldbelts (Taylor and others, 1980), wrench-fault systems (Brune, 1969; Blümling and Prodehl, 1983), and rift systems (Mooney and others, 1983), in addition to midocean ridges. Marillier and others (1989) have reached a similar conclusion. We found further that, in addition to zones of low velocity inside the lens-like bodies, low-velocity zones commonly overlie the lenses, as on the East Pacific Rise (Harding and others, 1989).

We call these "anomalous" lenses, and their associated low-velocity zones *surge channels* (Meyerhoff and others, 1989a). This expression takes precedence over the same phrase used in a broader sense in the text and which should no longer be used. Thus the midocean ridges are underlain by large surge channels. Their near-median positions are a consequence of earth contraction (Meyerhoff and others, 1989b, 1989c).

Surge tectonics. Further investigation revealed that surge channels form an interconnected worldwide network that resembles, in some respects, the body's vascular system. The existence of such an interconnected network has been demonstrated under Southeast Asia (Liu Futian and others, 1989). Because of Earth contraction, this network—which lies wholly in the lithosphere—is constantly being compressed. When magma and void space are available, the compression causes the magma in the channels to surge.

As we stated in the original text, the intensity of compressive stress changes during the geotectonic cycle, from a maximum just before tectonogenesis to a minimum at the end of tectogenesis. Tectogenesis begins when the pressure exerted by the magma on the surge-channel walls exceeds the ability of the walls to contain it, and causes rupture. If, as we believe, collapse of the lithosphere into the asthenosphere is the trigger for tectogenesis, then tectogenesis can affect millions of square kilometers at a time, because the surge channels are interconnected. When lithosphere collapse takes place, the sudden compression of the asthnosphere drives all available magma upward toward the surge channels. When full, the channels burst, because the fractures in the surge-channel roof extend to the Earth's surface. Thus, lithosphere collapse into the asthenosphere is very much like stamping one's foot on a full tube of toothpaste—an example of Pascal's Law—and the Earth's asthenosphere–lithosphere–surge channel system may be likened to a giant hydraulic press.

The manner of bursting (i.e., the style of tectogenesis) is controlled largely by the thickness of lithosphere above the surge channels. Where this thickness is of the order fo 30 km, the channel simply inflates, distending the upper surface. Here, mainly horsts and grabens form, and plateau basalts may extrude. In contrast, along the midocean ridges where the lithosphere is thinnest, rupture may be near total, with great basalt floods engulfing the ocean floor, drastically altering sea-water temperatures and destroying the deep-water biota.

In the transition zone between the extremes of oceanic and continental lithosphere, the mafic-ultramafic contents of the surge channel, together with the overlying lithosphere and sedimentary/volcanic column, are thrust bilaterally away from the channel axis, forming alpinotype foldbelts with ophiolites and mélange, as Kober (1921) noted long ago. Alpinotype foldbelts are universally bivergent, as we demonstrate elsewhere (Meyerhoff and others, 1989c). Examples include the Appalachians (Rodgers, 1987), the Alps (Frei and others, 1989), and many more.

The Caribbean foldbelts are no exception to the bivergency rule. In the northern and western Caribbean, bivergent foldbelts of Campanian-Cenozoic age are proved in Guatemala (Weyl, 1980), Cuba (Iturralde, 1981), Hispaniola (*Nemec, 1982*; Bourdon and others, 1985), and Puerto Rico (*Kerdraon and others, 1985*). In the southern and eastern Caribbean, bivergency of the same age is established in Colombia (Mégard, 1987), Venezuela (Biju-Duval and others, 1982), Trinidad (*Saunders, 1974*), and the Barbados Ridge (*Westbrook, 1982*). Bivergency also characterizes the Panamanian Isthmus (*Lu and McMillen, 1982*).

These bivergent foldbelts fall into three surge-channel systems: the Antilles system in the north, the approximately parallel Venezuela system in the south, and the Colombia-Ecuador system along South America's northwestern coast. All three systems originate in the East Pacific Rise. The Antilles and Venezuela surge-channel systems enter North America via the Tehuantepec Ridge (at least as old as early Paleozoic). The Colombia-Ecuador system enters South America via the Galapagos rift west of Ecuador. A branch of the Galapagos rift, the Panama fracture zone, is a small surge channel linking that rift with the Panama Isthmus (*Lonsdale and Klitgord, 1978*).

The Antilles and Venezuela surge-channel systems are at least as old as the Carboniferous, which is the age of the oldest magmatic-arc rocks now known from either channel. The two systems very likely date to the late Proterozoic. We have not begun our study of the Colombia-Ecuador surge-channel system, and know only that it was in existence by Triassic time.

We have confirmed that the paleoisthmus broke away from South America no later than Middle Jurassic time, so that this important aspect of our origin hypothesis is valid. We have determined the probable mechanism, which is eddy-like turbulence caused by interaction among two surge channels and the upper asthenosphere.

The surge-tectonics concept, as developed beyond the original submittal date of this chapter, has so far been able to explain every major feature of Caribbean geology, including those that have baffled plate tectonics. These include the locations and amounts of plate-boundary offsets, the double thickness of the Colombia Basin, the source of the Caribbean crust, origin of the Nicaragua Rise, the Beata Ridge, and the mechanical problems involved in juxtaposing (and replacing)

tensional and compressional regimes. Our results are soon to be published (Meyerhoff and others, 1989d), and we hope that they will stimulate new approaches to this very complex area.

ADDITIONAL REFERENCES CITED

Blatt, F. J., 1983, Principles of physics: Boston, Allyn and Bacon, Inc., 815 p.

Blümling, P., and Prodehl, C., 1983, Crustal structure beneath the eastern part of the Coast Ranges (Diablo Range) of central California from explosion seismic and near earthquake data: Physics of the Earth and Planetary Interiors, v. 31, p. 313–326.

Brune, J. N., 1969, Surface waves and crustal structure, *in* Hart, P. J., ed., The Earth's crust and upper mantle: American Geophysical Union, Geophysical Monograph 13, p. 231–242.

Ewing, J., and Ewing, M., 1959, Seismic-refraction measurements in the Atlantic Ocean basins, in the Mediterranean Sea, on the Mid-Atlantic Ridge, and in the Norwegian Sea: Geological Society of America Bulletin, v. 70, no. 3, p. 291–316.

Frei, W., Heitzmann, Lehner, P., and Valasek, P., 1989, Die drei Alpentraversen von NFP 20: Swiss Association of Petroleum Geologists and Engineers Bulletin, v. 55, no. 128, p. 13–43.

Harding, A. J., Orcutt, J. A., Kappus, M. E., Vera, E. E., Mutter, J. C., Buhl, P., Detrick, R. S., and Brocher, T. M., 1989, Structure of young oceanic crust at 13°N on the East Pacific Rise from expanding spread profiles: Journal of Geophysical Research, v. 94, no. B9, p. 12163–12196.

Iturralde-Vinent, M. A., 1981, An expanding Earth model explanation of the origin and evolution of Cuba, *in* Carey, S. W., ed., The expanding Earth, a symposium: Hobart, University of Tasmania, Geology Department Symposia, p. 215–218.

Kober, L., 1921, Der Bau der Erde: Berlin, Gebrüder Borntraeger, 324 p.

Liu Futian, Qu Kexin, Wu Hua, Li Qiang, Liu Jianhua, and Hu Ge, 1989, Seismic tomography of the Chinese continent and adjacent regions: Acta Geophysica Sinica, v. 32, no. 3, p. 281–291.

Macdonald, K., Sempère, J.-C., and Fox, P. J., 1984, East Pacific Rise from Siquieros to Orozco fracture zones; Along-strike continuity of axial neovolcanic zone and structure and evolution of overlapping spreading centers: Journal of Geophysical Research, v. 89, no. B7, p. 6049–6069, 6301–6305.

Marillier, F., Keen, C. E., and Stockmal, G. S., 1989, Laterally persistent seismic characteristics of the lower crust; Examples from the northern Appalachians, *in* Mereu, R. F., Mueller, S., and Fountain, D. M., eds., Properties and processes of Earth's lower crust: American Geophysical Union, Geophysical Monograph 51, p. 45–52.

Mégard, F., 1987, Cordilleran Andes and marginal Andes; A review of Andean geology north of the Arica elbow (18°S), *in* Monger, J.W.H., and Francheteau, J., eds., Circum-Pacific orogenic belts and evolution of the Pacific Ocean basin: American Geological Institute and Geological Society of America, Geodynamics Series 18, p. 71–95.

Meyerhoff, A. A., Taner, I., Morris, A.E.L., and Martin, B. D., 1989a, Surge tectonics, *in* Chatterjee, S., and Hotton, N., III, eds., New concepts in global tectonics, abstracts volume, Smithsonian Institution, Washington, D.C., 20–21 July, 1989: Lubbock, Texas Tech University Press, p. 25–26.

Meyerhoff, A. A., Agocs, W. B., Taner, I., Morris, A.E.L., and Martin, B. D., 1989b, Origin of the midocean ridges, *in* Chatterjee, S., and Hotton, N., III, eds., New concepts in global tectonics: Lubbock, Texas Tech University Press (in press).

Meyerhoff, A. A., Taner, I., Morris, A.E.L., Martin, B. D., Agocs, W. B., and Meyerhoff, H. A., 1989c, Surge tectonics, *in* Chatterjee, S., and Hotton, N., III, eds., New Concepts in global tectonics: Lubbock, Texas Tech University Press (in press).

Meyerhoff, A. A. Morris, A.E.L., and Taner, I., 1989d, Tectonic evolution of the Caribbean region, *in* Chatterjee, S., and Hotton, N., III, eds., New concepts in global tectonics: Lubbock, Texas Tech University Press, (in press).

Mooney, W. D., Andrews, M. C., Ginzburg, A., Peters, D. A., and Hamilton,

R. M., 1983, Crustal structures of the northern Mississippi embayment and a comparison with other continental rift zones: Tectonophysics, v. 94, no. 1–4, p. 327–348.

Pavlenkova, N. I., 1989, Struktura zemnoy kory i verkhney mantii i tektonika plit, *in* Beloussov, V. V., eds., Tektonosfera; yeye stroyeniye i razvitiye: Akademiya Nauk SSR, Mezhduvedomstvennyy Geofizicheskiy Komitet, Geodinamicheskiye Issledovaniya 13, p. 36–45.

Revelle, R., 1958, The *Downwind* Expedition to the southeast Pacific [abs.]: American Geophysical Union Transactions, v. 39, no. 3, p. 528–529.

Rodgers, J., 1987, The Appalachian geosyncline, *in* Schaer, J.-C., and Rodgers, J., eds., The anatomy of mountain ranges: Princeton University Press, p. 241–258.

Sears, F. W., Zemansky, M. W., and Young, H. D., 1974, College physics, 4th ed.: Reading, MA, Addison-Wesley Publishing Company, 751 p.

Talwani, M., Le Pichon, X., and Ewing, M., 1965, Crustal structure of the mid-ocean ridges, 2; Computed model from gravity and seismic refraction data: Journal of Geophysical Research, v. 70, no. 2, p. 341–352.

Taylor, S. R., Toksöz, M. N., and Chaplin, M. P., 1980, Crustal structure of the northeastern United States; Contrasts between Grenville and Appalachian provinces: Science, v. 208, no. 4444, p. 595–597.

Vogt, P. R., Schneider, E. D., and Johnson, G. L., 1969, The crust and upper mantle beneath the sea, *in* Hart, P. J., ed., The earth's crust and upper mantle: American Geophysical Union, Geophysical Monograph 13, p. 556–617.

The Geology of North America
Vol. H, The Caribbean Region
The Geological Society of America, 1990

Chapter 18

Metallogenic evolution of the Caribbean region

Stephen E. Kesler
Department of Geological Sciences, University of Michigan, Ann Arbor, Michigan 48109
Enrique Levy
25 Calle "A" 12-03, Zona 11, Guatemala, Guatemala
Cecilia Martín F.
Avenida Principal de Cumbres de Curumo, Residencia 680 PH, Caracas 1080, Venezuela

INTRODUCTION

Application of metallogenesis to regional geologic and tectonic analyses of the Caribbean area

The principal objective of this review is to illustrate the relation between the mineral deposits of the Caribbean region (Fig. 1, Plate 13) and their geologic and tectonic environment. In areas such as the Caribbean, where regional geological data are scarce, the distribution and composition of mineral deposits provides important information on the location and offset of large-scale faults and the continuity and relations between dissected terranes. In addition, because the hydrothermal systems that form many mineral deposits scavenge metals from large volumes of surrounding crust, their metal and isotopic compositions can provide useful insights into the characteristics and sources of these rocks, including deeper, unexposed parts of the crust.

To illustrate the relation between mineral deposits and their geologic framework, it is necessary to use a genetic (or model-based) classification of mineral deposits rather than simply a commodity or element-based system. Readers unfamiliar with the deposit models used here should consult Guilbert and Park (1986) or Jensen and Bateman (1979). Caribbean mineral deposits fit easily into commonly used models, with a few exceptions. The most important of these exceptions are the deposits found in the Cobre Formation of eastern Cuba and the Wagwater belt of Jamaica, which exhibit a close relation to the tectonic evolution of the region, as discussed below. In preparing this review, a strong effort was made to incorporate Cuban mineral deposits, although much of the literature on these deposits lack observations of the type needed to classify the deposits.

Historic and economic importance of Caribbean mineral deposits

The Caribbean region was the site of the first mining in the New World and continues to produce more than its share of world mineral supplies. The large gold mine at Pueblo Viejo (Fig. 1) in the Dominican Republic was first operated by the Spanish at least as early as 1505 and might have been mined by the indigenous population before that (Russell and others, 1981). The El Cobre mine in eastern Cuba, which began operation in about 1544, was the first copper mine in the New World and a major source of metal to Spain throughout the period of colonization (Lawrence, 1910). The Espíritu Santo gold mine in the Darién Peninsula of Panamá was worked intermittently during the 1600s by a succession of French, English, and Spanish adventurers and pirates (Woakes, 1923).

More recent mining efforts in the region are equally impressive. Cuba has produced 4 to 9 percent of world nickel supplies annually for several decades, and the U.S. Bureau of Mines estimates that it contains more than 20 percent of world nickel reserves. Jamaica has yielded 7 to 11 percent of world bauxite production and contains almost 10 percent of world reserves. Pueblo Viejo has produced about 1 percent of world gold production annually since 1976. Haiti, Honduras, Jamaica, and Nicaragua also have strong mining industries that have contributed to their economies, and the region contains many world-class mineral deposits (Table 1). Several of these deposits, including the Cerro Colorado (Panamá) and Río Viví-Tanamá (Puerto Rico) porphyry copper deposits, remain undeveloped because government and foreign interests cannot agree on the division of equity, investment, and dividends (Anonymous, 1977). Regrettably, it is this factor, rather than geologic constraints, that is principally responsible for the relatively low level of mineral exploration and development in the Caribbean region.

METALLOGENIC EVOLUTION IN THE CARIBBEAN REGION

The Caribbean region, as discussed in this review, includes the complex volcanic arcs of Central America, the Greater Antilles, Lesser Antilles, and northern South America (Fig. 1). The geology of these areas is not discussed here, except where it is directly relevant to specific mineral deposit types, and the reader

Kesler, S. E., Levy, E., and Martín F., C., 1990, Metallogenic evolution of the Caribbean region, *in* Dengo, G., and Case, J. E., eds., The Caribbean Region: Boulder, Colorado, Geological Society of America, The Geology of North America, v. H.

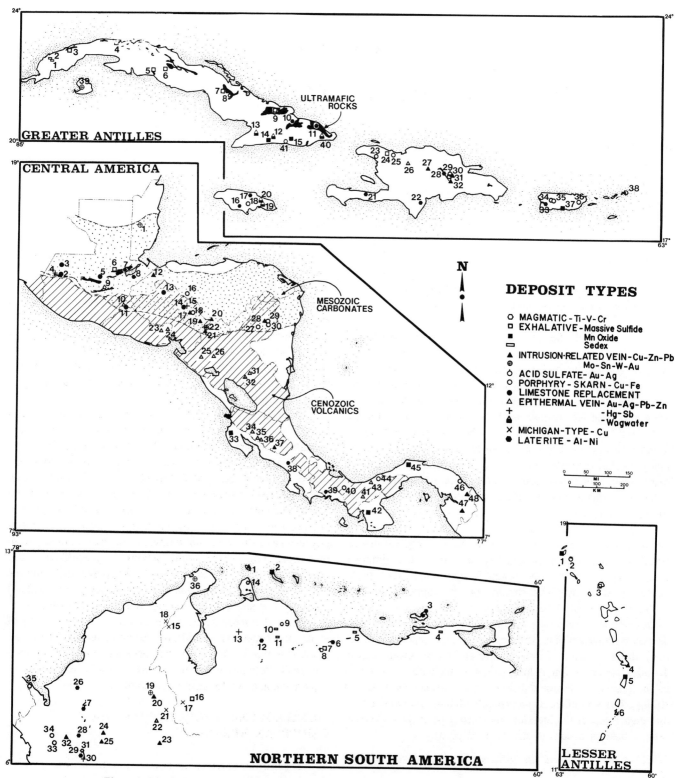

Figure 1. Distribution of mineral deposits in the Caribbean region. Individual deposits are identified by number in Table 1 and are divided into genetic classes that are discussed in the text. This map shows only those deposits or districts discussed in the text. Smaller deposits not shown on the map can be found in reports by Levy (1970), Barrero Lozano (1976), Levy and others (1977), Kesler (1978), Martín (1983), Loubet and others (1985), and other regional reports referred to in the text.

should consult other chapters in this volume for this information and related maps. The metallogenic evolution of individual Caribbean arcs closely reflects the type of underlying crust and the interaction of this crust with arc volcanism. Caribbean crust can be divided roughly into oceanic and continental. Areas thought to be underlain largely by oceanic crust include most of southern Central America, the Cordillera de la Costa and Western Cordillera in northern South America, the Lesser Antilles, and the central and eastern Greater Antilles. Areas underlain by older continental crustal fragments include northern (nuclear) Central America, eastern Colombia, and southern and western Venezuela. Obducted ophiolite is present locally, such as in northern Central America where the El Tambor terrane has been wedged between the Maya block and Americas plates.

Caribbean arcs exhibit a systematic metallogenic evolution through geologic time, as shown in Figure 2 for the Greater Antilles and Central America. The metallogenic evolution can be divided into deposits that formed in the oceanic or continental basement prior to commencement of arc volcanism and deposits that resulted from actual arc volcanism and tectonism.

In arcs that formed on *oceanic basement* (and in obducted fragments associated with the continental arcs) pre-arc deposits include sedimentary exhalative (sedex) deposits in western Cuba and ophiolite-related chromite, manganese, and (Cyprus-type) volcanogenic massive sulfide deposits, all of which formed prior to emplacement of the host rocks in their present location. Submarine-arc volcanism on this oceanic basement in the Greater Antilles and northern South America formed Kuroko-type volcanogenic massive sulfide deposits. As these volcanic piles grew, they became large enough to host high-level intermediate intrusions, which formed mesothermal(?) gold-base metal veins, porphyry copper deposits, and acid-sulfate precious metal deposits. Late-stage silicic, subaerial volcanism was limited in abundance in most oceanic arcs, and related epithermal deposits are correspondingly scarce, although the Wagwater-Cobre epithermal and exhalative deposits of the Greater Antilles are their approximate metallogenic equivalent, as discussed below.

Central America, western Venezuela, and eastern Colombia, which are underlain by *continental basement,* contain pre-arc mineralization that formed during earlier tectonic cycles, such as the Paleozoic-age Bailadores massive sulfide deposit in Venezuela (Carlson, 1977). The earliest mineralization related to the Caribbean tectonic cycle are Keweenaw-type copper deposits that formed in grabens that cut the continental basement rocks. Submarine volcanism was largely absent in these arcs, and massive sulfide deposits are lacking except where oceanic island arcs have been accreted onto the continental arcs, as in the case of the Villa de Cura Group of Venezuela. Instead, most volcanism was subaerial and intermediate to silicic in composition and is associated with hydrothermal systems that deposited porphyry copper, vein, and lead-zinc-silver limestone replacement deposits. The absence of widespread late-stage subaerial volcanism of this type in arcs underlain by oceanic basement is one of the dominant features in the metallogenic evolution of the Caribbean area.

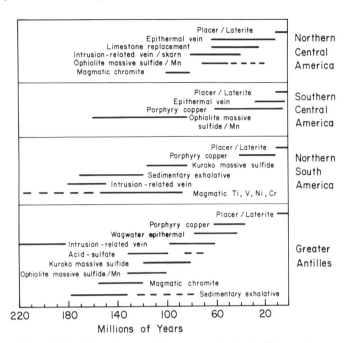

Figure 2. Evolution of mineral-deposit types in the Caribbean region.

The final phase in the metallogenic evolution of both types of arcs was the formation of nickel and aluminum laterites and gold and platinum placer deposits.

DISTRIBUTION AND CHARACTERISTICS OF CARIBBEAN MINERAL DEPOSITS

Magmatic deposits

Chromite deposits. The large ophiolite belt on the north side of Cuba contains several chromite districts (Fig. 1; Thayer, 1942; Flint and others, 1948; Ukhana and others, 1985), including the well-described Cayaguan and Narciso districts in the Moa complex (Guild, 1947). The chromite in these deposits ranges from massive to disseminated and exhibits cumulate textures locally. The deposits are hosted by serpentinized dunite, with associated gabbro, troctolite, and anorthosite, and are thought to have formed in the mantle and been tectonically emplaced at their present location (Guild, 1947). Similar, but smaller, deposits are present in the Trapiche Grande area of central Guatemala (Roberts and Irving, 1957) and in the Paraguaná Peninsula (El Rodeo) of Venezuela (Martín and Arozena, 1972).

Titanium-vanadium deposits. Deposits of this type are found only in pre-arc, continental basement rocks of Venezuela. Here, the Yumare metamorphic complex hosts anorthosites, which contain the San Quintín ilmenite-hematite deposit (Bellizzia and others, 1981). The Yumare complex is tentatively correlated with similar rocks in the Santa Marta massif of northern Colombia, which also contains anorthosite with ilmenite (Tschanz and others, 1974). In Colombia these rocks have radiometric ages of 750 to 1,400 Ma (Irving, 1975).

TABLE 1. MAJOR MINERAL DEPOSITS AND DISTRICTS IN THE CARIBBEAN REGION *

Deposit/District	Country	Metals	Type of deposit
Central America			
1. Mountain Pine Ridge	BZ	Sn	Intrusion-related vein
2. Chiántla	GU	Pb-Zn	Limestone replacement
3. San Miguel	GU	Pb-Zn-Ag	Limestone replacement
4. Ixtahuacán	GU	W-Sb	Sediment hosted vein
5. Cobán	Gu	Pb-Zn	Limestone replacement
6. Oxec	GU	Cu	Massive sulfide
7. Exmibal (Niquegua)	GU	Ni(Co)	Laterite
8. Buena Vista	GU	Ni(Co)	Laterite
9. Trapiche Grande	GU	Cr	Magmatic
10. San Pantaleón	GU	Ag-Au	Epithermal vein
11. Conc. las Minas/Metapan	GU/ES	Au-Ag-Pb-Zn	Mesothermal(?) vein
12. Camalote	HO	Au-Ag	Mesothermal(?) vein
13. Mochito	HO	Ag-Pb-Zn(Cu)	Limestone replacement
14. Agalteca	HO	Fe	Contact/skarn
15. Victoria del Oriente	HO	Hg	Vein/limestone replacement
16. Minas de Oro	HO	Cu(Au)	Contact/skarn
17. San Juancito	HO	Au-Ag	Mesothermal(?) vein
18. Las Animas	HO	Ag-Pb-Zn	Limestone replacement
19. Yuscarán	HO	Ag-Au	Mesothermal(?) vein
20. Agua Fria	HO	Au-Ag	Vein
21. Dipilto	NU	Ag-Pb-Zn	Intrusion-related vein
22. Macuelizo	NU	W-Mo	Mesothermal vein
23. Montecristo	ES	Ag-Au	Epithermal vein
24. San Sebastián	ES	Au	Epithermal vein
25. El Limón	NU	Au-Ag	Epithermal vein
26. La India	NU	Au-Ag	Epithermal vein
27. La Luz	NU	Au-Cu	Contact/skarn
28. Bonanza	NU	Au-Ag-Pb-Zn	Mesothermal vein
29. Monte Carmelo	NU	Fe	Contact/skarn
30. Rosita	NU	Cu-Au	Contact/skarn
31. Santo Domingo	NU	Au-Ag	Epithermal vein
32. La Libertad	NU	Au-Ag	Epithermal vein
33. Nicoya	CS	Mn	Exhalative
34. Abangares	CS	Au-Ag	Epithermal vein
35. Miramar	CS	Au-Ag	Epithermal vein
36. Esparta	CS	Au-Ag	Epithermal vein
37. Aguacate	CS	Au-Ag-Pb-Zn	Mesothermal(?) vein
38. San Isidro del General	CS	Al	Laterite
39. David	PN	Al	Laterite
40. Cerro Colorado	PN	Cu-Mo	Porphyry copper
41. Remance/Alto la Mina	PN	Au-Ag	Epithermal vein
42. Azuero (Bahia Honda)	PN	Mn	Exhalative
43. Margaja	PN	Au(Cu)	Epithermal(?) vein
44. Petaquilla	PN	Cu-Mo	Porphyry copper
45. Mandinga/Boquerón	PN	Mn	Exhalative
46. Río Pito	PN	Cu-Au	Porphyry copper
47. Caná	PN	Au-Ag-Pb-Zn	Vein/breccia pipe
48. Tuquesa	PN	Au-Cu	Vein

TABLE 1. MAJOR MINERAL DEPOSITS AND DISTRICTS IN THE CARIBBEAN REGION * (continued)

Deposit/District	Country	Metals	Type of deposit
Greater Antilles			
1. Matahambre	CB	Cu	Exhalative/vein
2. Sta. Lucia–Castellanos	CB	Pb-Zn	Sedimentary exhalative
3. Bahia Honda	CB	Cu	Massive sulfide
4. Minas	CB	Cu	Massive sulfide
5. Caroltta	CB	S-(Cu)	Massive sulfide
6. Fernando–Antonio	CB	Cu	Massive sulfide
7. Camagüey	CB	Cu	Massive sulfide
8. Cayaguan-Narciso	CB	Cr	Magmatic
9. Holguín	CB	Cu	Massive sulfide
10. Moa	CB	Ni-Co	Laterite
11. Nicaro	CB	Ni-Co	Laterite
12. Guisa–Los Negros	CB	Mn	Exhalative
13. Eureka	CB	Cu	Epithermal vein
14. Cobre	CB	Cu	Epithermal vein
15. Abundancia–Sigua	CB	Mn	Exhalative
16. Mandeville	JA	Al	Laterite
17. Claremont	JA	Al	Laterite
18. Connors	JA	Cu(Au)	Porphyry copper
19. Hope	JA	Pb-Zn(Ag)	Epithermal replacement
20. Orchard Hill	JA	Fe-Cu	Contact/skarn
21. Miragoane	HA	Al	Laterite
22. Barahona	DR	Al	Laterite
23. Memé/Casseus	HA	Cu(Au-Ag)	Contact/skarn
24. Camp Coq-Milot	HA	Cu-Pb-Zn-Au	Massive sulfide
25. Blondin–Douvray	HA	Cu	Porphyry copper
26. Restauracion	DR	Au-Ag	Epith. vein/hot spring
27. Matá Grande	DR	Cu	Mesothermal(?) vein
28. Loma Caribe	DR	Ni(Co-Fe)	Laterite
29. Maimon–Hatillo	DR	Fe	Contact/skarn
30. Pueblo Viejo	DR	Au-Ag(Hg)	Acid sulfate - vein
31. Cerro Maimon/Barbuito	DR	Cu(Zn-Au)	Massive sulfide
32. Altagracia	DR	Au	Vein/placer
33. Guanajibo/Las Mesas	PR	Ni	Laterite
34. Tanamá	PR	Cu(Au)	Porphyry copper
35. Río Viví	PR	Cu(Au)	Porphyry copper
36. Keystone	PR	Fe(Cu)	Contact/skarn
37. Coamo Springs	PR	Mn	Exhalative
38. Copper Mine Point	VI	Cu-Mo	Porphyry-related veins
39. Siguanea	CB	W	Mesothermal(?) vein
40. Eleccion	CB	Cu	Epithermal(?) vein
41. Daiquiri–Firmeza	CB	Fe-(Cu)	Contact/skarn
Northern South America			
1. Alto Vista, Calabas	AR	Au	Mesothermal(?) vein
2. Groot Sint Martha	CU	Mn-Cu	Exhalative-massive sulfide
3. Espiritu Santo	VZ	Ni	Laterite
4. Canchunchu	VZ	Pb-Ag	Vein (Sedex?)
5. Capaya	VZ	Fe	Sedimentary exhalative
6. Loma de Hierro	VZ	Ni	Laterite/magmatic
7. Sta Isabel–Providencia	VZ	Zn-Pb-Cu-Ba	Massive sulfide
8. Chacao	VZ	V-Fe-Ti	Magmatic
9. San Quintín	VZ	Ti	Magmatic
10. Aroa	VZ	Cu-Fe	Sedimentary exhalative

TABLE 1. MAJOR MINERAL DEPOSITS AND DISTRICTS IN THE CARIBBEAN REGION* (continued)

Deposit/District	Country	Metals	Type of deposit
Northern South America (continued)			
11. Cocuaima	VZ	Pb-Sb-Ag	Vein (sedex?)
12. Carorita–Bobare	VZ	Al (Pyroph)	Sedimentary-laterite
13. San Jacinto	VZ	Hg	Epith. vein/hot spring
14. El Rodeo	VZ	Cr	Magmatic
15. Cano Tigre	VZ	Cu	Volcanic/red bed copper
16. Bailadores	VZ	Zn-Pb-Cu-Ag	Massive sulfide
17. Seboruco–El Cobre	VZ	Cu	Volcanic/red bed copper
18. El Rincón	CO	Cu-(Ag)	Volcanic/red bed copper
19. Ocana–La Playa–Aspasica	CO	Sn	Mesothermal(?) vein
20. Hacarí–Abrego	CO	Pb-Ba-F	Mesothermal(?) vein
21. El Tuto–Cascajalas	CO	Cu	Volcanic/red bed copper
22. California–Veta	CO	Au-(Cu-Pb-Zn)	Mesothermal(?) vein
23. El Minto	CO	F-Pb	Mesothermal(?) vein
24. Segovia–Remedios	CO	Au-Pb-Zn	Mesothermal(?) vein
25. Guadalupe y Gómez Plata	CO	Au	Mesothermal(?) vein
26. Planeta Rica	CO	Ni	Laterite
27. Cerromatoso-Uré	CO	Ni	Laterite
28. Ituango–Morropelón	CO	Ni	Laterite
29. Medellíon	CO	Ni	Laterite
30. Retiro	CO	Hg	Epith. vein/hot spring
31. Santa Helena	CO	Cr	Magmatic
32. Frontino	CO	Au	Mesothermal(?) vein
33. Pantanos–Pegadorcito	CO	Cu-Mo	Porphyry copper
34. Murindó	CO	Cu-Mo	Porphyry copper
35. Acandí	CO	Cu-Mo	Porphyry copper
36. Serrandía Carpintero	CO	Sn	Mesothermal(?) vein
Lesser Antilles			
1. Kay Bay–Groote Zoutpan	SB	Mn	Exhalative
2. Saint Martin	SM	Cu-Au	Porphyry copper
3. Belmont Est.–Sugar Loaf	AU	Ba-Cu-Au	Massive sulfide (?)
4. Caravelle	MR	Zn-Ba	Vein
5. Comorette Point	SL	Mn	Vein/exhalative
6. Mustique	SV	Au-Hg	Epithermal stockwork

*Locations of these deposits are shown by corresponding number in Figure 1.
Country code modified from U.S. Geological Survey Circular 858-B.
AR = Aruba, AU = Antigua, BH = Belice, CU = Curaçao, CO = Colombia, CS = Costa Rica, CB = Cuba, DR = Dominican Republic, ES = El Salvador, GL = Guatemala, HA = Haiti, HO = Honduras, JM = Jamaica, MR = Martinique, NU = Nicaragua, PN = Panamá, RQ = Puerto Rico, SB = St. Bartholomew, SL = Santa Lucia, SM = St. Martin, SV = Saint Vincent, VI = Virgin Islands, VZ = Venezuela.

Exhalative deposits

Cyprus-type massive sulfide deposits. Clearly identifiable Cyprus-type massive sulfide deposits are widespread in the Caribbean region, but are of economic importance only in the belt that borders the northern part of the region (Fig. 1). The Oxec district (Peterson and Zantop, 1980) at the western end of this belt, in the Sierra de Santa Cruz of Guatemala, contains small pyrrhotite-pyrite-chalcopyrite lenses in a sequence of pillow lavas on the northern margin of a large ultramafic complex that also hosts the Exmibal nickel laterite deposits. The ages of this ophiolite and the mineralization are limited by the appearance of serpentinite detritus in nearby pre–Late Cretaceous sedimentary units (Bonis, 1968). Ore at Oxec differs from the classical Cyprus-type deposits in its higher pyrrhotite/pyrite ratio and in being extensively diluted by post-ore diabase dikes. Related ophiolites extend eastward into Cuba (Case and others, 1984) and host similar copper deposits in the Encrucijada (Bahia Honda) belt on the northern side of the Pinar del Río province (Feoktostov and others, 1983) and possibly in the Minas district east of Havana

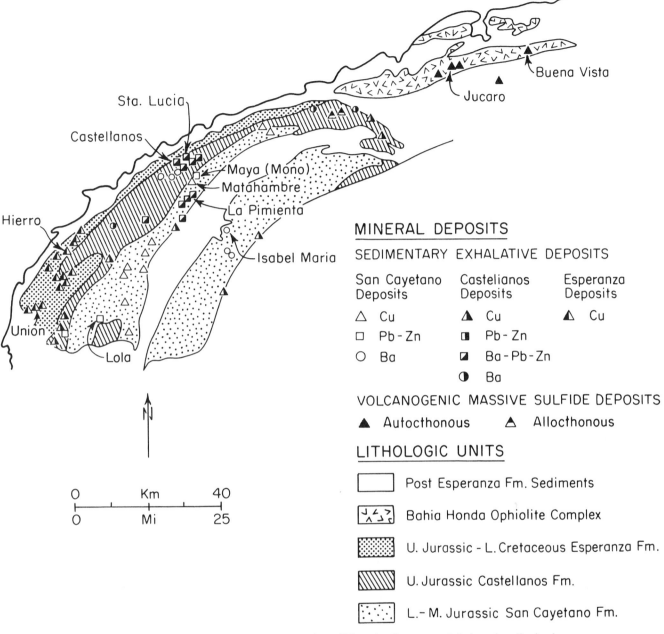

Figure 3. Geologic setting of Cyprus-type massive sulfide and sedimentary exhalative mineralization in the Cayateno basin and Bahia Honda ophiolite complex of western Cuba (after Feoktistov and others, 1983).

(Weed, 1905). Several deposits in the Bahia Honda area are thought to have been displaced southward by thrusting (Fig. 3). Farther to the east in central and western Cuba, probable Cyprus-type massive sulfide deposits are found south of Santa Clara (Fernando, Antonio) (Vaughn, 1901; Bogdanov and others, 1966; Cabrera and Tolkunov, 1979), east of Camagüey, and between Holguín and Gibara (Taylor, 1837). South of this belt, in the Trinidad Mountains of Las Villas province, massive sulfide lenses consisting largely of pyrite are found in apparently older metavolcanic rocks of the Carlotta district (Hill, 1958, 1959).

Manganese oxide deposits. Ophiolite-related manganese deposits are widespread in the Caribbean region, but are not of major economic importance. The best characterized deposits of this type are in the Nicoya Peninsula on the west coast of Costa Rica (Fig. 1), where manganese oxide is found in siliceous (jasper) pipes and in stratiform jasper and radiolarite lenses in basalts (Roberts, 1944; Kuypers and Denyer, 1979). Similar deposits are present in the Azuero Peninsula (Bahia Honda) and eastern Darien (Mandingo-Boquerón) areas of Panamá (Woodring, 1957).

A distinct type of manganese deposit is found in the Upper Cretaceous(?)–middle Eocene Cobre Formation in eastern Cuba, which consists largely of water-laid pyroclastic material of basaltic, andesitic, and dacitic composition (Lewis and Straczek, 1958). The largest manganese deposits in the Cobre Formation are stratiform oxide lenses in tuff (Fig. 4), which are commonly associated with jasper, known as bayate, or similar stratiform lenses in limestone (Woodring and Daviess, 1944; Simons and Straczek, 1958). They are found at and just below the lower contact of the middle Eocene Charco Redondo limestone-tuff, the uppermost unit of the Cobre Formation (Park, 1942). Similar deposits are found in Haiti (Butterlin, 1960) and Puerto Rico (Cox and Briggs, 1974). Closely related copper mineralization, in the form of vein and stockwork deposits associated with subvolcanic intrusions, is abundant in the lower part of the Cobre Formation in Cuba. These deposits, which include Eureka (Bogdanov and others, 1966) and the historic El Cobre mine mentioned above (Ansted, 1856; Lawrence, 1910), are probably coeval with the manganese and could occupy the deeper parts of the manganese depositing systems. Probably related hot spring, epithermal vein, and replacement base and precious-metal mineralization is also found in the Wagwater trough of Jamaica, as discussed in a later section.

The Cobre-type manganese deposits clearly formed from submarine hydrothermal activity rather than as hydrogenous sediments, but they differ significantly from the ophiolite-related manganese deposits in both depth of formation and composition. Whereas most submarine manganese deposits are associated with pillow basalt and abundant radiolarian and chemical cherts, the Cobre deposits are closely associated with pyroclastic rocks and shallow-water limestone (Lewis and Straczek, 1958). Secondly, the Cobre-type deposits plot in conflicting fields on the main chemical diagrams used to classify submarine manganese deposits (Fig. 5). In particular, they have too much Al and Si, and their Mn:Fe ratio is too low (Sokolova, 1977). The abundance of Al and Si is likely due to the location of these deposits in a region where relatively large amounts of detrital sediments contaminated the manganese lenses as they formed, and the relative abundance of Fe could reflect shallower, more oxidizing waters into which the solutions exhaled.

Kuroko-type volcanogenic massive sulfide deposits. Kuroko-type massive sulfide deposits are best developed in several areas on Hispaniola. The largest group of deposits is in the Maimon belt of the Dominican Republic, a metavolcanic unit that makes up part of the Cordillera Central (Bowin, 1966). Recent mapping here has delineated large areas of pillowed, spilitized basalt, dacite, and fragmental dacite with local zones of siliceous to graphitic sedimentary rocks that host massive sulfide prospects (Fig. 1). On the west side of the complex, the rocks have been strongly deformed and are essentially schists, whereas relict volcanic textures are common on the east. Massive sulfide prospects in the Maimon Formation include Loma la Mina (Koschmann and Gordon, 1950), Barbuito (Russell and others, 1982), and Cerro Maimon, all of which are pyrite-rich bodies

Figure 4. Schematic illustration of types of primary manganese deposits in the Cobre Formation of eastern Cuba (modified from Woodring and Daviess, 1944). 1, bedded ore in limestone; 2, bedded ore in tuff (not associated with bayate); 3, bedded ore in tuff (associated with bayate); 4, nonbedded ore in limestone; 5, nonbedded ore in tuff.

with small lenses of massive chalcopyrite and sphalerite and local zones of copper-rich secondary enrichment. Similar, but probably younger, mineralization is known in the Rivière Mapou and Camp Coq areas of Haiti to the west (Nicolini, 1982) and in the Santa Isabel and La Providencia areas of the Villa de Cura Group in the Cordillera de la Costa of Venezuela (Rogríguez, 1980; Bellizzia and others, 1981).

Several Kuroko-type deposits and prospects are present in the pre-arc continental basement that underlies nuclear Central America and northern South America. The largest of these is Bailadores, in the southern part of the Cordillera de los Andes of Venezuela, which is closely associated with a silicic pyroclastic facies of the late Paleozoic Mucuchachí Formation (Carlson, 1977).

Sedimentary exhalative deposits. Sedimentary exhalative deposits are best developed in western Cuba and Venezuela, where sizable sedimentary basins were present prior to arc volcanism (Pardo, 1975; Feoktistov and others, 1983). The largest of these is in Pinar del Río province in western Cuba, where a long-lived sedimentary exhalative province formed in the Middle Jurassic to Late Cretaceous Cayetano basin. Sediments in this basin reach a total thickness of about 3,000 m and consist largely of sandstone and shale, with carbonate units near the top of the sequence. Stratigraphically controlled mineralization is found throughout the sequence. In the San Cayetano Formation, the basal unit in the basin (Fig. 3), the large Matahambre copper mine consists largely of veins (Benês and Hanus, 1967), which are overlain by stratiform Pb-Zn mineralization that extends discontinuously along strike to the Maya (Mono) mine 3 km to the northeast (Fig. 3). Similarly, the Nieves deposit, which is a few kilometers south of Matahambre, consists of pyrite-pyrrhotite-chalcopyrite veinlets overlain by stratiform galena-sphalerite-pyrite zones in carbonaceous shale of the overlying Castellanos Formation. Elsewhere, the Castellanos Formation contains the Castellanos and Santa Lucía stratiform lead-zinc-barite-pyrite

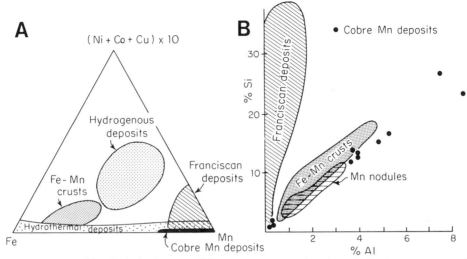

Figure 5. Compositional relation between Cobre-type manganese deposits and other important types of manganese deposits for: (A) Mn, Fe and Cu+Co+Ni; and (B) Si and Al. Note that the Cobre-type deposits fall in conflicting fields in these diagrams. Diagrams from Bonatti and others (1972).

deposits (Shadlun, 1982), which have underlying chalcopyrite-pyrite feeder zones(?). In the Esperanza Formation, the uppermost of the three main units of the Cayetano basin, pyrite-pyrrhotite(?)-chalcopyrite lenses, including the Hierro and Union deposits, form part of a stratiform mineral zone that can be traced for 30 km.

Descriptions of the Cayetano deposits, including those that host the Matahambre deposit, emphasize their sandy nature, complete with ripple marks suggesting deposition in shallow water. However, the lead-zinc ores that overlie Matahambre, as well as the associated Maya (Mono) deposit and the Castellanos–Santa Lucia deposits are in carbonaceous shale (Zhidkov and others, 1975). These observations are best interpreted to indicate that the copper vein systems were feeder zones for the stratiform lead-zinc-barite ore (Feoktistov and others, 1983), which was deposited in locally starved, anoxic basins in the San Cayetano and overlying units. The fact that mineralization extends over large vertical intervals that span formation boundaries, such as the Matahambre-Nieves deposits, suggests that individual vent systems were relatively long lived. Sedimentary exhalative deposits form when solutions with temperatures of at least 200° C vent onto the sea floor. Pressures of 50 to 75 bars, corresponding to water depths of about 500 m, are required to prevent boiling of such solutions, which indicates that the San Cayetano basin was quite deep, at least during the intervals of metal deposition. This suggests, in turn, that the Cayetano basin underwent rapid deepening after deposition of the sandy beds with ripple marks.

The Barquisimeto area of Venezuela hosts smaller, but generally similar, mineralization such as the Aroa pyrite-pyrrhotite-chalcopyrite deposit, which is hosted by graphitic, calcareous schists of probable Mesozoic age (Rodríguez, 1980; Martín, 1983). Anderson and Schmidt (1983) have proposed that the Cayetano basin originated on the northern flank of the South American continent. If so, the Cayetano and Aroa Formations could have been deposited in a single basin, although paleomagnetic data are needed to evaluate this possibility.

Hydrothermal deposits closely associated with intrusive rocks

Intrusion-related vein deposits and pegmatite deposits. Intrusion-related pegmatite and vein deposits, which are widespread in the Caribbean region, formed in two stages. The earliest deposits formed around Paleozoic and possibly older intrusions and contain tin and tungsten. For instance, the quartz-ferberite-tourmaline veins of the Siguanea district on the Isle of Pines, Cuba (Page and McAllister, 1944), are associated with quartz porphyry dikes that cut metamorphic rocks of probable Paleozoic age, and the deposits are thought to be of similar age. The cassiterite-bearing veins of the Maya Mountains (Bateson and Hall, 1970) are associated with true granites, also of late Paleozoic age (Kesler and others, 1974). Possibly related stibnite-scheelite veins are found in the Ixtahuacán district in western Guatemala (Collins and Kesler, 1969), although these veins are not directly associated with intrusive rocks. Small tin and tungsten vein systems that are probably the same age are known in the Santander area of eastern Colombia (Angulo Carmona, 1978; Hodges and others, 1984).

Larger gold-bearing vein (and pegmatite) systems of this type formed in northern South America and Central America during Mesozoic time. In Venezuela, gold-quartz vein systems cut the lower part of the Caracas Group in the Baruta area, and in Colombia, the Segovia, California, Remedios, Guadalupe y Gómez Plata, and Frontino gold-base metal districts are closely associated with Jurassic-age plutons (Sillitoe and others, 1982). The Late Cretaceous Dipilto batholith and related stocks at the Honduran-Nicaraguan border are surrounded on the north and east by gold-quartz veins in the Alhambra, Azabache, La Virgen, and Conchagua districts of Honduras and the San Juan Telpaneca, San Albino, and Murra districts of Nicaragua (Levy, 1970), most of which are hosted by Paleozoic(?) metasediments. The southwest end of the batholith is bordered by the Macuelizo district tungsten-molybdenum pegmatites. Other smaller, but similar vein systems are associated with Late Cretaceous plutons in the Sierra de Omoa in Honduras and the Chiquimula area of Guatemala.

Elsewhere in the Caribbean region, gold-quartz veins surround quartz diorite batholiths in Aruba and the Dominican Republic (Bowin, 1966). Also in the Dominican Republic, the small Matá Grande copper vein (Palmer, 1963) is at the north border of the El Bao batholith (Kesler and others, 1977).

Porphyry copper and contact/skarn deposits. Porphyry copper deposits and prospects, which are found throughout the Caribbean area, appear to become larger with decreasing age. The largest deposits are found in Panamá, Puerto Rico, and Colombia (Fig. 1), in areas underlain largely by oceanic crust. Smaller deposits are present in areas underlain by continental crust in northern Central America and the Cordillera Central of Colombia (Martín, 1980, 1983).

The Panamanian deposits can be divided into a northern group, including Cerro Colorado and Petaquilla (Fig. 1), that includes the prospects of the Talamanca Range in Costa Rica, and a southern group that extends along the eastern coast of Panamá through the Río Pito–Acandí area into the Murindo and Pantanos-Pegadorcito deposits of Colombia (Sillitoe and others, 1982). Available age dates indicate that porphyry-related magmatism is Eocene in age in the southern belt and Oligocene to Pliocene in age in the northern belt (Sillitoe and others, 1982; Kesler and others, 1977; Clark and others, 1977). During this interval there were distinct increases in the potassium content of the intrusive rocks and the size of the associated porphyry copper deposits (Fig. 6). A similar age pattern prevailed in the Greater Antilles. Late Cretaceous porphyry copper prospects are known in Jamaica, Hispaniola, and Puerto Rico (Kesler and others, 1975; Watanabe, 1974; Cheilletz and others, 1978; Fenton, 1979), but none have been shown to be large or high grade. In contrast, the large Eocene-age Tanamá and Río Viví porphyry copper deposits in Puerto Rico (Cox and others, 1975, 1977; Barabas, 1982; Cox, 1985) are associated with dacitic intrusions, which are lower in potassium. Cox (1973) proposed that these deposits formed when north-directed subduction under the Greater Antilles gave way to west-directed subduction beneath the Lesser Antilles.

The variation in composition of intrusive rocks associated with the porphyry copper deposits is reflected in the alteration and ore mineralogy of the deposits. At Cerro Colorado, for instance, where the intrusion is granodioritic, the original core alteration assemblage is thought to have consisted of K-feldspar, quartz, and anhydrite (Issignis, 1973). This core zone is hosted largely by the porphyry stock and contains abundant biotite only where it cuts mafic volcanic wall rocks, making Cerro Colorado anomalously low in biotite. The deposit has undergone several

phyllic overprints that have formed various assemblages containing unusually fine-grained sericite and illite. Highest Cu grades are closely associated with these overprints, and in particular with sericite. Even later, advanced argillic overprints containing pyrophyllite have been recognized locally above the core at Cerro Colorado. At Tanamá, in Puerto Rico, in contrast, the core zone contains amphibole and magnetite, with very low copper values. This core has been overprinted by an intermediate zone with chlorite, biotite, and K-feldspar and an outer zone with sericite, clay, and calcite (Cox, 1985). Ore is associated with this overprint where chalcopyrite replaces magnetite.

In contrast to the steady increase in size of porphyry copper mineralization with time throughout the Caribbean region, the most important contact-related skarn deposits formed at the close of Cretaceous time. These deposits are associated with granodiorite and diorite and consist largely of chalcopyrite with variable amounts of magnetite in garnet-pyroxene skarns. The Fe:Cu ratio in these deposits appears to be related to the mafic content of the related intrusion. For instance, skarn deposits in the Daiquiri district of Cuba (whence the well-known rum drink), which are associated with diorite to quartz diorite, produced important amounts of iron (Lindgren and Ross, 1916). In contrast, the Memé (Haiti), Minas del Oro (Honduras), and Rosita (Nicaragua) skarn deposits, which are associated with granodioritic intrusions, are largely copper deposits (Kesler, 1968; Atwood, 1972; Bevan, 1973; Simonson, 1976). The Agalteca and Monte Carmelo districts in Central America (Roberts and Irving, 1957;

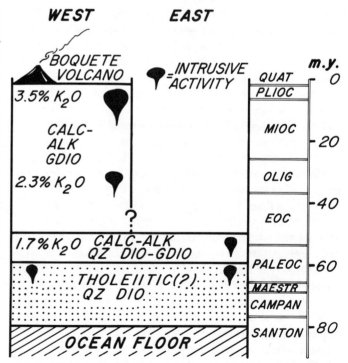

Figure 6. Schematic illustration of the evolution of magmatism and porphyry copper mineralization in the Panamanian part of the southern Central American arc (Kesler and others, 1977).

Levy, 1970) are probably part of this group, although they contain only iron mineralization.

A completely distinct group of Fe-rich contact deposits formed in the eastern Greater Antilles, at least partly during Eocene time (Bowin, 1966). These deposits consist essentially of magnetite and hematite with small amounts of pyrite, and are localized at or very near the contact of diorite intrusions. Skarn, though present, is not widespread in these deposits. Important deposits of this type are in the Juncos belt in Puerto Rico (Broedel, 1961) and the Maimon-Hatillo district in the Dominican Republic (Koschmann and Gordon, 1950).

Acid-sulfate precious-metal deposits. Acid-sulfate-type vein and stockwork deposits (Hayba and others, 1985) are found largely in the Greater Antilles, where they form a belt extending from the Virgin Islands possibly as far as Cuba. These deposits appear to have formed above porphyry-type deposits, possibly where magmatic vapor plumes mixed with meteoric water (Brimhall and Ghiorso, 1983). Pueblo Viejo, which is one of the largest open-pit gold-silver mines in the world, is the only one of these to have been explored in detail. Mineralization at Pueblo Viejo is found in a maar or caldera at the top of the Early Cretaceous Los Ranchos Formation, which consists largely of keratophyre and spilite and related volcaniclastic debris (Kesler and others, 1981). The ore is hosted by funnel-shaped alteration zones consisting of alunite, pyrophyllite, kaolinite, and massive quartz, which contain small veins filled by pyrite, sphalerite, barite, enargite, and precious metals. Weathering of the upper part of this system produced a large oxide ore body consisting of quartz, limonite, and gold (Russell and others, 1981).

Apparently correlative rocks in Puerto Rico contain similar advanced argillic alteration zones that extend discontinuously across the east-central part of the island (Hildebrand, 1961). These zones are hosted by volcanic rocks similar in age to the Los Ranchos Formation, but they are also concentrated along the northern margin of the San Lorenzo batholith and the Caguas stock (Cox and Briggs, 1974; Kesler and others, 1977) and could be related to hydrothermal systems developed above these intrusions, depending on their age. In the U.S. Virgin Islands, advanced argillic alteration zones are associated with quartz porphyry plugs that appear to be part of the Water Island volcanic pile (Donnelly, 1966), which is correlative with the Los Ranchos Formation (Cumming and Kesler, 1986). Alminas and Tucker (1987) have described precious-metal mineralization associated with these rocks in St. Thomas and St. John, and Tucker (1987) has reported whole-rock K-Ar ages of 66 to 31 Ma for this mineralization. The older of these ages agrees with the ^{40}Ar/^{39}Ar age of 69 Ma reported by Kesler and others (1981) for alunite at Pueblo Viejo, raising the possibility that, either these deposits are not genetically associated with the Los Ranchos, Water Island, and related formations, or these formations are younger than previously thought.

Velnikov and others (1983) have described advanced argillic alteration zones containing alunite in the Zaza volcanic arc in Camagüey province, Cuba (Fig. 1). Pyrite is not noted as a part of the assemblage in these deposits, making it possible that these advanced argillic alteration zones are related to shallow oxidation of pyrite or H_2S, although the volcanic host is approximately the same age as the Los Ranchos Formation. Younger advanced argillic alteration assemblages that are more clearly the result of high-level oxidation are present in the Restauración area of the Cordillera Central in the Dominican Republic, on Nevis (Martin-Kaye, 1959) and possibly other islands of the Lesser Antilles (Sillitoe, 1986), and in the Cordillera de la Costa of Venezuela, where the Early Cretaceous Bobare Formation contains pyrophyllite deposits of uncertain origin (Bellizzia and others, 1981).

Hydrothermal deposits not closely associated with intrusive rocks

Limestone-replacement deposits. Limestone-replacement deposits are widespread in the Caribbean region and range from deposits directly at an intrusive contact to more distal chimney-manto deposits. As can be seen in Figure 1, these deposits are confined to the area of northern Central America that is underlain by thick sequences of the Cretaceous Atima and Cobán Limestones, where they were cut by Cenozoic magmatic activity. Chimney-manto limestone replacement deposits range from well-developed, cylindrical ore bodies hundreds of meters in length, to smaller vein-like pods and lenses. The main ore minerals are pyrite, galena, and sphalerite, and the gangue ranges from hedenbergite-andradite-magnetite-quartz skarn in the larger deposits to calcite and silica in the smaller ones. Silver values in these deposits are found largely in tetrahedrite and related sulfosalts. The largest of these deposits, Mochito (Fig. 7), consists of large skarn-sulfide chimneys with high Ag values (Seaward and Warner, 1971; Dilles, 1982; Schultz and Hamaan, 1985). Smaller skarn deposits in the Concepción–Las Minas district (Fig. 1) consist largely of sphalerite, galena, and pyrite associated with garnet-epidote-calcite skarn close to intrusive contacts (Roberts and Irving, 1957). In Guatemala, deposits of this type with low Ag contents include the Cobán, Chiantla, and San Miguel districts, all of which are north of the Polochic fault zone. These deposits consist largely of sulfides and calcite without large volumes of skarn (Kesler and Ascarrunz-K, 1973).

Epithermal precious-metal and base-metal vein deposits. Epithermal vein deposits of the adularia-sericite type (Hayba and others, 1985) are found largely along the western margin of Central America (Fig. 1) where they are hosted by intermediate to silicic volcanic rocks of Miocene to Pliocene age (Weyl, 1980). The largest group of these veins extends from the Gulf of Fonseca region in El Salvador through most of western Nicaragua. A second group of veins is in the Tilarán volcanic province of Costa Rica (Roberts and Irving, 1957; Anonymous, 1987), and a third and smaller group is present north of Santiago in western Panamá (Low, 1931; Ferencic, 1971). Silver:gold ratios of these vein systems range from 0.1 to more than 100; most Ag-rich deposits are in areas of northern Central America that are underlain by continental crust (Kesler, 1978).

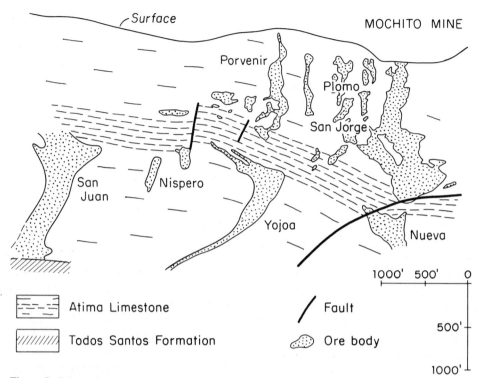

Figure 7. Schematic cross section of the Mochito limestone-replacement Ag-Pb-Zn-Cu deposit in Honduras showing the extensive ore-skarn chimneys partly deflected by a thick shale interbed in the Atima Limestone (after White, 1977).

The epithermal precious-metal veins consist almost entirely of quartz with electrum, argentite and sulfosalts, and smaller amounts of base-metal sulfides (Müller-Kahle, 1962; Anonymous, 1987). In the largest of these deposits, Limón, veins extend to depths of as much as 300 m locally and reach maximum lengths of 2 km and widths of more than 5 m (Malone, 1987). Alteration surrounding the veins is largely clay, sericite, and adularia. In El Salvador, vein systems on the west side of the Gulf of Fonseca are hosted by rhyolitic to andesitic flows and pyroclastic deposits of the Oligocene Morazán Formation, as well as silicic flows, domes, and ignimbrites of the overlying Miocene(?) Chalatenango Formation (Weber and Weissemann, 1978). In Costa Rica, the veins are hosted by the Miocene-Pliocene Aguacate Formation, which consists of andesites and volcanoclastic sedimentary rocks (Roberts and Irving, 1957; Levy and others, 1978; Laguna-Morales, 1983; Anonymous, 1987).

Base metal–rich, possibly mesothermal, veins are found to the east of the Au-Ag vein deposits in northern Central America, where the Cenozoic volcanic cover is thinner and Mesozoic and older basement is exposed in windows (Fig. 1). Most of the veins are found at and near the sedimentary-volcanic contact and are hosted by either rock type. The veins consist largely of pyrite, base-metal sulfides, sulfosalts, and electrum in quartz. The largest of these districts are San Juancito (Rosario) in Honduras, which produced 746,000 oz of Au and 129,000,000 oz of Ag between 1880 and 1954 (Carpenter, 1954), and Bonanza in eastern Nicaragua, which has produced at least 9 million tons of ore contain-

ing 0.3 oz/t Au and another million tons of sulfide ore averaging about 1.8 percent Pb, 10 percent Zn, 0.5 percent Cu, 0.6 oz/t Ag, and 0.09 oz/t Au since 1901 (Stonehouse, 1976). The veins at San Juancito occupied an area of about 2 by 4 km centered around a dacitic plug that intruded Mesozoic sedimentary rocks; the largest vein was 2 km long, and maximum vein widths were 1 to 2 m. The Bonanza system covers an area 20 by 3 km and contains individual veins as much as 4 km long with ore shoots as wide as 15 m (Fig. 8). Veins were mined to depths of about 500 m in both districts. Base metals were not recovered at San Juancito, but are an important part of the Bonanza system. With the exception of an early stage of hematite deposition at Bonanza, mineral paragenesis was similar in the two districts, but Bonanza is zoned more strongly than San Juancito. Burn (1969) reported fluid inclusion temperatures of 250° to 350° C on the early stages of vein material at Bonanza. Although no data are available for San Juancito, the relative absence of base metals indicates that temperatures were probably lower. Presently available information is not adequate to determine whether there is a systematic difference between the ages of the epithermal Au-Ag and the base-metal vein systems in Central America.

The San Sebastián mine in El Salvador does not fall conveniently into either of the above mentioned vein types. This deposit had a silver:gold ratio of about 0.1 and was mined largely for gold and copper (Wuensch, 1917; Levy, 1970). Mineralization at San Sebastián is in quartz gash veins with sericitic alteration that are found along the margins of a diorite dike that cuts a

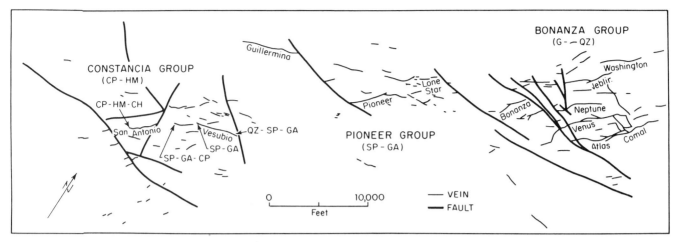

Figure 8. Schematic illustration of veins and major faults in the Bonanza district, Nicaragua, showing the zonation from chalcopyrite-hematite on the west, through galena-sphalerite in the center, to quartz-gold-chlorite on the east. Detailed zoning in the San Antonio–Vesubio system is also shown (Burn, 1969). Stonehouse (1976) has suggested that this pattern probably reflects a vertical zoning from deep chalcopyrite-hematite to intermediate galena-sphalerite to shallow gold-quartz-chlorite and that different levels of the system are exposed in the district due to vertical faulting. Minerals are: CP, chalcopyrite; HM, hematite; CH, chlorite; SP, sphalerite; GA, galena; QZ, quartz; G, gold.

Morazán andesitic volcanic center (Weber and Weissemann, 1978). In addition to gold, the veins contained pyrite, barite, and local tetrahedrite, chalcopyrite, bornite, calaverite, and molybdenite, as well as chalcocite, pyrolusite, and numerous secondary copper minerals. The close association with a dike, as well as the increase in Cu and Mo downward in the vein suggest that San Sebastián is the upper extension of a shallow intrusive system and that it could be related to acid-sulfate or porphyry copper mineralization at depth.

Wagwater-type epithermal deposits. A wide variety of epithermal to hot spring–type hydrothermal mineralization is found in the Wagwater trough in Jamaica, a graben that was filled by over 5,000 m of terrestrial conglomerates, marine shales, and volcanic rocks during Paleocene to early Eocene time (Arden, 1975; Green, 1977; Jackson and Smith, 1978). Hydrothermal systems at and near the contact between sedimentary rocks and dacite in the trough (Fenton, 1979) formed the galena-sphalerite-carbonate lens at the Hope mine (Fig. 9), chalcopyrite-bornite-chalcocite veins at the Barbecue River prospect (Carby, 1978; Black and Bailey, 1968), and other Cu and Fe prospects. None of these deposits appears to have formed by direct exhalative processes; instead, they appear to be largely shallow vein or replacement deposits. They are closely related in time and genesis to the previously mentioned manganese and copper deposits of the Cobre Formation in Cuba, as well as to precious metal–bearing hydrothermal systems, such as those in the Wenatchee district of Washington (Ott and others, 1986). Support for this latter association comes from recent geochemical surveys in Jamaica, which have indicated widespread anomalous values of Au, As, Sb, and Te in both the Wagwater trough and older intrusive rocks (Bondar-Clegg and Company, 1988; Simpson and others, 1988).

Keweenaw-type copper deposits. Deposits of this type are in grabens that probably represent the early stages of the rifting that separated North and South America. The Sierra de Perijá, the northern extension of the Andes that separates Colombia and Venezuela, hosts the most important examples of these deposits in the Caribbean region. Mineralization is observed discontinuously over a distance of 200 km and is found largely in the Jurassic La Quinta Formation, which consists of continental deposits with interbedded basaltic andesite flows and some felsic intrusions (Viteri, 1978, 1980). Maze (1980, 1984) has divided the mineralization into native copper in mafic flow tops, copper sulfides with

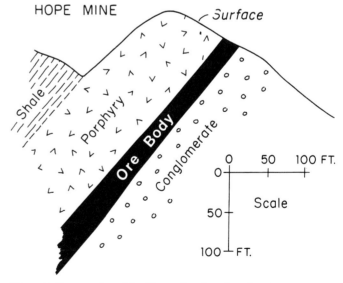

Figure 9. Cross section of the Hope mine, Jamaica, showing concentration of mineralization at the lower contact of the Newcastle volcanic rocks (after Carby, 1978).

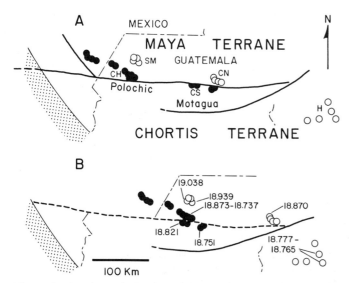

Figure 10. A. Present distribution of lead-zinc deposits of northern Central America in relation to the Polochic fault zone, which separates the Maya and Chortis terranes. B. Proposed reconstruction of the Chiantla and southern Cobán districts after correction for about 130 km of left-lateral offset along the fault, showing gradational change in ^{206}Pb/^{204}Pb ratios produced by this reconstruction (modified from Kesler and Ascarrunz-K. 1973; Burkart, 1983). CH, Chiantla district; CS, southern Cobán district; CN, northern Cobán district; SM, San Miguel district; H, Honduran deposits in Chortis terrane.

local petroleum filling porosity in sedimentary rocks, and copper-iron sulfides in felsic volcanic rocks or at the contacts of mafic dikes. Silver values have been observed locally. Possibly similar copper mineralization is found in red beds of the Totogalpa Formation at Yalagüina, Nicaragua (Roberts and Irving, 1957).

Deposits associated with surface processes

Placer deposits. Placer gold deposits are widespread in the Caribbean area and have not been shown on Figure 1. During his voyages of exploration, Columbus obtained placer gold, including some large nuggets, from Indians in Cuba, Hispaniola, and southern Central America, in particular. The largest deposits are apparently in eastern Nicaragua, although significant production has come from numerous areas of Honduras, the Osa peninsula of Costa Rica, the Margaja area of northern Panamá, the Belén area and Darién Peninsula of Panamá and its extension into the Western Cordillera of Colombia, and the Cordillera Central of Hispaniola. With the possible exception of Panamá, the source for this gold is reasonably well known (Levy, 1970). The Miches area of the Dominican Republic contains residual (colluvial) gold deposits for which no bedrock source has been identified (Kulstad, 1980). Placer platinum deposits, which are widespread in the Western Cordillera of Colombia (Singewald, 1950), are thought to have been derived from zoned ultramafic intrusions in the area (Hodges and others, 1984; Angulo Carmona, 1978).

Laterite deposits. Laterite deposits are unusually abundant in the Caribbean region and have accounted for a large proportion of mineral production from the area. Present interest focuses on the bauxite and nickel deposits, although ferruginous laterites, largely developed on serpentinite in eastern Cuba, were major sources of iron in the early part of this century (Kuhn, 1926). The largest bauxite mines in the Caribbean region are in Jamaica and Hispaniola, with smaller prospects in Costa Rica (Fig. 1). The bauxite deposits are developed on limestone in Jamaica and Hispaniola (Goldich and Berquist, 1948) and on mafic to intermediate volcanic and volcaniclastic rocks in Costa Rica (Castillo and others, 1970). Studies in Jamaica indicate that the higher grade plateau bauxites there formed by weathering of Miocene-age volcanic ash that accumulated on the limestones, whereas the lower grade graben bauxites and terrarosa soils formed from alluvial deposits derived from older Late Cretaceous to Eocene volcanic and intrusive rocks (Comer, 1974; Comer and others, 1980).

The large nickel laterite deposits and prospects in the region, which are in Hispaniola, Cuba, Guatemala, Venezuela, and Colombia, formed on serpentinized peridotite (Haldemann and others, 1979; Harju, 1979; Cortina, 1978; Patterson, 1967; Angulo Carmona, 1978; Bellizzia and others, 1981). Most of the nickel in these deposits is in solid solution or adsorbed on limonite, or is in asbolite, rather than garnierite (Golightly, 1979).

RELATION BETWEEN MINERAL DEPOSITS AND TECTONIC EVOLUTION OF THE CARIBBEAN REGION

Characterization of large-scale fault systems using mineral deposits

The northern margin of the Caribbean plate in Central America is marked by the Motagua-Polochic-Chixoy fault system (Fig. 10). The magnitude of offset along this fault system has been a focus of controversy, with large-scale basement rock patterns indicating an offset of about 130 km (Kesler, 1971; Burkart, 1983) and smaller scale features indicating less (Anderson and others, 1985). As suggested by Burkart (1983), the Pb-Zn deposits of northern Guatemala appear to confirm the larger amount of offset. In their present setting, the deposits have been divided into the San Miguel and Chiantla districts on the north side of the fault and the Cobán district, which is bisected by the fault (Fig. 10). Restoration of approximately 130 km of left-lateral offset suggests that the southern Cobán district represents the southern continuation of the Chiantla district (Fig. 10). The resulting pattern is a series of deposits on the southwest (Chiántla and southern Cobán districts) in which mineralization is dominantly in Paleozoic rocks and a second series on the northeast (the San Miguel and northern Cobán districts), in which mineralization is largely in younger, Cretaceous limestones. This reconstruction also places the northern Cobán district adjacent to the limestone replacement deposits of central Honduras across the Motagua fault to the south (Fig. 10), suggesting a relation between these

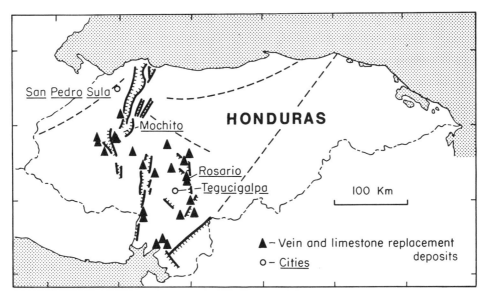

Figure 11. Relation between distribution of grabens and late Cenozoic vein and limestone replacement mineralization in Honduras (distribution of faults modified from Mann and Burke, 1984).

deposits. Support for the first of these interpretations is seen in the fact that the lead isotopic composition of the deposits becomes less radiogenic toward the southeast (Fig. 10, Table 2). This suggests, in turn, that the age and/or volume of basement rock underlying the limestone replacement deposits decreases to the southeast, although other, more complex processes, involving contamination of possible basin-related fluids (Kesler and Ascarrunz, 1973), could also produce the observed trend. The lead isotopic data do not support the suggested correlation between the northern Cobán district and the Honduran limestone replacement deposits, as seen by the distinct difference in their isotopic compositions (Fig. 10, Table 2).

The manganese deposits of Panamá provide similar control on the probable offset of the Azuero and eastern Darién areas along faults that cut the isthmus along the Canal Zone (Case and others, 1984). Kesler and others (1977) have shown that the ages of intrusive rocks in the two areas are similar, thereby providing support for the apparent correlation of the two areas. Manganese deposits and prospects are abundant along the northern margin of both areas (Fig. 1), and reconstruction of faulting to place these deposits in a single zone suggests a left-lateral offset of about 110 km.

Tectonic control of mineral deposits

Large-scale structural and tectonic features have had a strong control on Caribbean mineral deposits. For instance, the most important features controlling mineral deposits along the northwestern margin of the Caribbean region are grabens. These grabens range in age from Oligocene on the east to Recent on the west and are thought to have formed as a result of the eastward movement of the Caribbean plate past the Americas plate (Mann and Burke, 1984). The abundant igneous activity and increased structural ground preparation associated with these grabens appears to have enhanced the size and abundance of hydrothermal systems along the grabens.

The type of mineral deposits that developed in the grabens depended on whether they formed in submarine or subaerial settings and on the timing of intrusion with respect to sedimentation in the grabens. In Jamaica and Cuba, these troughs hosted shallow submarine volcanism that formed the Wagwater-Cobre–type deposits. In Honduras, where these grabens are much younger and entirely continental, the major limestone replacement and vein districts appear to concentrate along their margins (Fig. 11). Most of the important epithermal precious-metal vein systems in northern Central America are on the margins of the Nicaragua depression, a large graben that parallels the Pacific coast of Nicaragua behind the present volcanic arc. Although the porphyry copper deposits of Puerto Rico formed before this graben system developed, the porphyritic plugs and fractures in their host rocks are aligned in northeast-trending zones that could represent the earliest effects of this stress regime (Cox, 1985).

The distribution of laterite deposits in the Greater Antilles appears to be controlled by more recent tectonic processes. The weathering that formed these deposits probably extended over much of the late Cenozoic, but final stages of weathering and the ultimate preservation of the deposits must have been closely controlled by the extensive uplift that affected most of the Caribbean region in Pleistocene time. Horsefield (1975) has shown that Quaternary marine terraces in the Greater Antilles have been uplifted as much as 400 m in an east-west elongated domal zone centering on two areas, one over western Cuba and northwestern Haiti, and another over the Barahona Peninsula of the Dominican Republic. As can be seen in Figure 12, the larger producing laterite deposits in the region are found within zones with greater than 100 m of Quaternary uplift, and only the subeconomic

TABLE 2. LEAD ISOTOPE COMPOSITION OF CARIBBEAN MINERAL DEPOSITS*

Country-District/Mine	Sample Identification	$^{205}Pb/^{204}Pb$	$^{207}Pb/^{204}Pb$	$^{208}Pb/^{204}Pb$
Greater Antilles				
CB Pinar del Río/Santa Lucia	CBA-SL	18.693	15.685	38.828
CB Pinar del Río/Castillanos	CBA-CAST	18.714	15.712	38.892
HA Camp Coq	H-K-1	19.048	15.621	38.849
HA Camp Coq	H-K-2	19.062	15.630	38.959
PR Loc. 20-3. USGS Map 1-721	PR-72-GA	18.877	15.606	38.646
JA Hope	J-72-HM	18.722	15.593	38.476
DR Pueblo Viejo	DDH162-171-GV	18.457	15.590	38.290
DR Puablo Visjo	DDH100-16-PYL	18.482	15.601	38.406
DR Pueblo Viejo	T-6-2-PYV	18.485	15.608	38.356
DR Pueblo Viejo	DD71-107-PYL	18.486	15.597	38.355
DR Pueblo Viejo	T-2-5-PYL	18.490	15.498	38.337
DR Pueblo Viejo	DDH92-46-GV	18.500	15.607	38.340
DR Pueblo Viejo	DDH174-56-PYV	18.509	15.598	38.341
DR Pueblo Viejo	DDH162-83-PYL	18.614	15.605	38.420
DR Pueblo Viejo	DDH-101-21-PYL	18.635	15.611	38.544
DR Pueblo Viejo	DDH163-83-ENV	18.821	15.617	38.477
DR Pueblo Viejo	DDH-161-123-EN	18.858	15.625	38.588
Central America				
CR Abangares/Boston	CR-AB	18.901	15.599	38.710
PA Cerro Colorado	78-722	19.054	15.627	38.804
PA Cerro Colorado	P-CC	19.106	15.605	38.812
GU Cuchumatanes/Villa Linda	VL-SJ	18.939	15.668	38.867
GU Cuchumatanes/Rosario	RB-GA	19.038	15.693	39.085
GU Cuchumatanes/Santo Domingo	A-27	18.816	15.653	38.774
GU Cuchumatanes/Santo Domingo	SD-3	18.831	15.668	38.790
GU Cuchumatanes/Torlón	A-143	18.870	15.670	38.855
GU Cuchumatanes/Torlón	A-195	18.873	15.678	38.871
GU Cuchumatanes/Tziminas	TZ-3	18.737	15.642	38.685
GU Cobán/Suquinay	A-490	18.751	15.647	38.676
GU Cobán/San Joaquin	A-467	18.821	15.652	38.693
GU Cobán/Capiquec	A-486	18.870	15.659	38.789
GU Concepción las Minas/Peñasco	PNCO-4-8	18.771	15.637	38.661
GU Concepción las Minas/Montenegro	NTNG-MTO	18.801	15.654	38.714
HO San Juancito/Las Animas	H-R	18.765	15.654	38.716
HO San Juancito/Las Animas	H-LA	18.766	15.639	38.678
HO Mochito	H-LV	18.776	15.634	38.650
HO Mochito	ML-1225SJ	18.777	15.649	38.703
NU Bonanza/Neptune	N-VS-1	18.762	15.652	38.729
NU Bonanza/Neptune	N-VS-2	18.748	15.637	38.663
NU Bonanza/Blag	BLAG	18.760	15.638	38.654
ES Montecristo	LL-1-ES	18.663	15.617	38.481
ES Montecristo	ES-2-MC	18.665	15.621	38.535

*From Cumming and others, 1981, 1982.
Key to country abbreviations is given in Table 1.

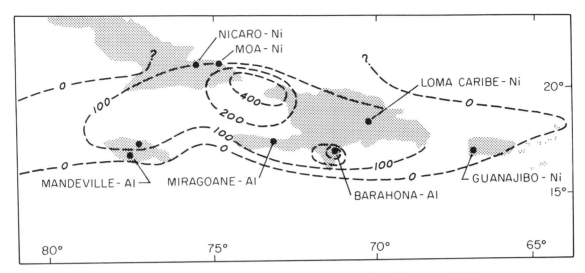

Figure 12. Distribution of laterite deposits in the Greater Antilles in relation to uplift of Quaternary wave-cut terraces in the region (uplift data from Horsefield, 1975).

Guanajibo nickel laterite deposits are in the zone of little or no uplift.

Mineral deposits and Caribbean terranes

The distribution and lead isotopic composition (Table 2) of mineral deposits in the Caribbean region provide useful information on the borders and sources of Caribbean terranes. The most convincing illustration of this is seen in northern Central America, where the lead isotopic compositions of ore deposits in the Maya terrane (Campa and Coney, 1983) fall along a linear array that extends to relatively high $^{206}Pb/^{204}Pb$ ratios, whereas isotopic data for deposits in the Chortis terrane, south of the Motagua-Chixoy-Polochic fault zone, form a more restricted cluster (Cumming and others, 1981). The Chortis terrane isotopic cluster falls within a larger, but generally similar, cluster of lead isotopic compositions that characterize the extensive ore deposits of central Mexico (Fig. 13), supporting suggestions from paleomagnetic data (Burke and others, 1984; Gose, 1985) that the Chortis terrane is a fragment of the Mexican subcontinent. The lead isotopic data suggest further that the original position of the Chortis terrane with respect to Mexico was near Acapulco, as indicated by the fact that deposits in that area, at Angangueo, Etzatlan, and Taxco, show the greatest similarity to the Chortis terrane deposits (Fig. 13). Finally, the significant difference between isotopic compositions of ore leads in the Chortis terrane and in Costa Rica and Panamá (Figs. 13 and 14) suggests that the thickened crust underlying Costa Rica (and possibly western Panamá) is not simply a sliver of the Chortis terrane. The lower $^{207}Pb/^{204}Pb$ ratios of the Costa Rican lead, which are similar to available data from Panamá and the Greater Antilles (Table 2), suggests further that the crust underlying this area is probably of younger age.

The isotopic composition of the lead-bearing exhalative deposits of the Cayetano basin in Cuba provide insights into the probable source of this terrane as well. It has been suggested that the Cayetano basin is a fragment from either the El Plan sediments in Honduras (Iturralde-Vinent, 1975) or the Caracas and Juan Griego Groups in Venezuela (Anderson and Schmidt, 1983). The unusually high ^{207}Pb content of the Cayetano deposits differs greatly from deposits such as San Juancito, which is partly hosted by the El Plan Formation (Fig. 13, Table 2) and probably contains lead leached from these rocks. No directly comparable data are available from the Venezuelan sedimentary rocks (or from the possibly related Aroa deposits), but the high ^{207}Pb content of the lead in the Cayetano deposits indicates a continental origin for these strata. This provides support, in turn, for the previously mentioned possibility that the Cayetano sediments were derived from the Guyana shield (Anderson and Schmidt, 1983).

The distribution of acid-sulfate deposits in the eastern Greater Antilles also provides insights into the separate terranes that make up this complex arc. These deposits extend from Cuba through the central Dominican Republic to the Virgin Islands (Fig. 1), and at least east of the Dominican Republic, they are hosted by volcanic piles of similar age and Pb isotopic composition (Cumming and Kesler, 1986). Similar deposits and volcanic rocks are not known to the southwest of the Cordillera Central of the Dominican Republic, supporting the view that this is an important suture zone separating an arc consisting of southern Haiti and Jamaica from the remainder of the Greater Antilles (Donnelly, 1975; Burke and others, 1984).

Several other tectonic provinces appear to be indicated by their mineral deposits, as follows:

1. The Western Cordillera of Colombia and adjacent Panamá contains generally similar Eocene-age porphyry copper deposits extending from Río Píto, Panamá, on the north to Río Andagueda in central, western Colombia (Kesler and others,

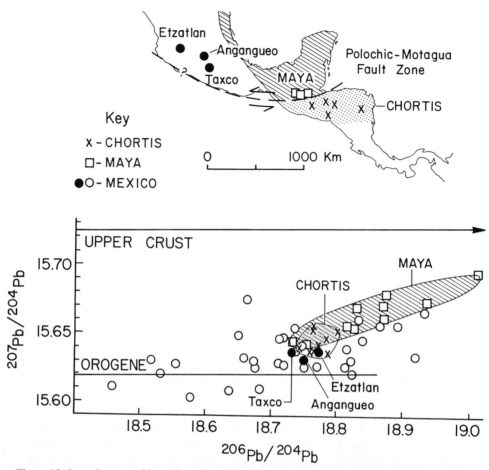

Figure 13. Isotopic composition of uranium-derived lead in mineral deposits from northern Central America and Cuba (modified from Cumming and others, 1981, 1982), showing the difference between isotopic compositions of ore leads in the Chortis and Maya terranes, and confirming that these two terranes contain basement rocks of different types (Campa and Coney, 1983; Case and others, 1984). The close similarity between Chortis terrane leads and those from the Etzatlan, Angangueo, and Taxco deposits in central Mexico suggests that the Chortis terrane was derived from this area of the Mexican subcontinent.

1977; Sillitoe and others, 1982). These deposits probably mark the eroded remnants of a volcanic arc of that age.

2. Precambrian anorthosite-bearing crustal fragments in Colombia and Venezuela characterized by ilmenite mineralization (San Quintín, Santa Marta area) could be pieces of the much larger Oaxaca terrane in Mexico, which hosts the similar, anorthositic Pluma Hidalgo ilmenite deposit (Paulson, 1964). The Oaxaca terrane is of Grenville age (Patchett and Ruiz, 1987), and paleomagnetic data allow for the possibility that it was adjacent to the Grenville province of eastern Canada at about 950 Ma (Ballard and others, 1989); the Grenville province also contains similar ilmenite deposits.

3. The Keweenaw-type copper deposits of the Sierra de Perijá in Colombia (Maze, 1980) indicate the location and extent of rifting associated with disruption of the South American craton during late Mesozoic time.

Relation between mineral deposits and crustal type

As noted at the outset of this summary, the type of mineral deposits found in individual Caribbean arcs depends on whether the arcs are underlain by oceanic or continental crust. The metals found in these deposits also appear to be related to crustal characteristics. Arcs with crust thicker than about 30 km, which includes all areas of known continental crust in the Caribbean region, contain essentially all lead mineralization, as well as most of the mercury, antimony, tungsten, and tin deposits (Fig. 14). Belice and the Isle of Pines (Cuba), which host tin and tungsten mineralization, fall outside the 30-km contour (Fig. 14), but the highly granitic composition of intrusive rocks in this area (Page and McAllister, 1944; Kesler and others, 1974), along with the well-known association of tin deposits with continental environments (Jones and others, 1977), suggest that this is due to a lack

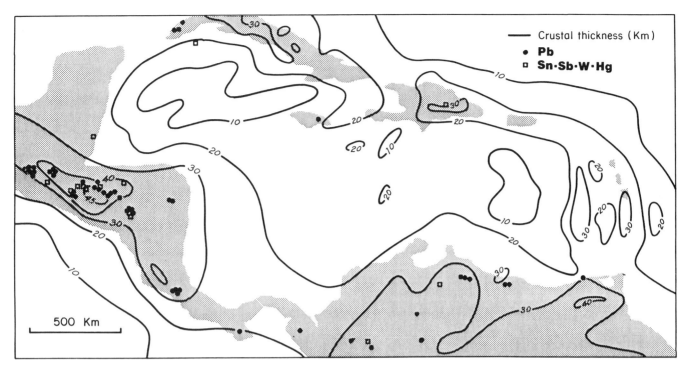

Figure 14. Distribution of Pb and Sn-Sb-W-Hg deposits in the Caribbean region in relation to thickness of crust (crustal thickness from Case, 1980).

of crustal thickness measurements in Belize and the Isle of Pines (see Plate 3, Case and others, this volume).

Two occurrences of these "continental" metals, at Pueblo Viejo, Dominican Republic, and from prospects in the Virgin Islands, are in areas of relatively thin crust of oceanic affinity (Case, 1980; Case and others, 1984). The metals in these deposits do not appear to be strongly concentrated, however. Mercury is a by-product of gold at Pueblo Viejo only because it follows gold through the hydrometallurgical process. Average mercury grades at Pueblo Viejo are about 0.0003 percent versus 0.5 percent and higher in the Central American deposits, indicating that the element is not strongly enriched here. Tin metal, tin chlorides, and poorly crystallized cassiterite have been found associated with Pb-Cu-Sb-Bi-Ag-Au mineralization in the Virgin Islands (Alminas and Tucker, 1987; Tucker, 1987). These tin concentrations are thought to be related to subcropping intrusive centers and to be at least partly exhalative in origin (Alminas and Tucker, 1987). Tin is a relatively common trace constituent of many older massive sulfide deposits where it is thought to have been leached from the host volcanic rocks by circulating seawater (Petersen, 1986). Thus, the Virgin Island tin mineralization might have formed from a submarine exhalative system that was unable to precipitate base-metal sulfides, perhaps because of the lack of reduced sulfur or boiling in the feeder zone, but which was able to deposit tin, possibly in more oxidizing shallower waters. It seems unlikely, therefore, that these deposits represent important exceptions to the generalization that significant tin and mercury concentrations are found in areas underlain by continental crust.

Epithermal precious-metal deposits in the Caribbean area are also associated with thickened crust. All known deposits are found in areas thicker than about 30 km, with the exception of Panamá where crustal thickness data are scarce and thicker crust could be present, as noted above. This correlation is also seen in the Lesser Antilles, where islands with abundant hot-spring activity, silicic volcanism and precious metal potential are underlain by the thickest crust (although no economic deposits are yet known in these rocks). Areas with similar 30-km crustal thicknesses in central Hispaniola also contain the previously mentioned epithermal, acid sulfate precious-metal mineralization in the Restauración area.

It is a logical extension of these observations to ask whether lead, tin, gold, and related mineralization are present in areas of thickened crust because their host rocks are enriched in these elements or whether these crustal blocks simply provide more suitable tectonic environments in which to form hydrothermal systems of the composition necessary to leach and deposit these elements. Average compositions of continental and oceanic crust given by Taylor and McLennan (1985) indicate that continental crust is enriched in lead and gold by an order of magnitude, and tin is enriched by about two times. Similarly, Cumming and Kesler (1976) have reported that intermediate intrusive rocks in northern Central America are richer in lead than those in southern Central America or the Greater Antilles. Thus, whatever the tectonic-hydrothermal setting, continental crust provides a more enriched background from which to form this type of mineralization in the Caribbean region.

It is less easy to determine whether specific areas of continental crust are more enriched than others. A rough estimate of the degree of lead enrichment might be gained from the relative abundance of [207]Pb in an ore or rock in view of the fact that this isotope is derived from the relatively fast-decaying [235]U, which has made a significant contribution of lead to older, continental-type crust through geologic time. Thus, blocks of crust that contain relatively large amounts of lead, whether derived from in situ decay of uranium or addition from underlying crust through magmatic processes, might be expected to exhibit high [207]Pb/[204]Pb ratios. This generalization is supported by the relations shown in Figures 13 and 15 where the lead-rich Caribbean deposits, which are in areas of the Maya and Chortis terranes that are underlain by continental crust, have the highest [207]Pb/[204]Pb ratios. Within areas of the Caribbean that are underlain by oceanic crust, the isotopic compositions do not indicate that such lead enrichment is important, however. Note that deposits in these areas fall along linear arrays that extend above the MORB field (Fig. 15), but the lead-bearing deposits do not fall at the [207]Pb-enriched end of the arrays. Thus, it appears that lead deposits in areas of oceanic crust are not derived *only,* or perhaps even largely, from rocks that are anomalously enriched in lead. Conversely, areas such as Martinique in the Lesser Antilles, where extreme crustal(?) contamination has occurred (Davidson, 1987), do not host more lead mineralization than other Caribbean oceanic island arcs.

The Caribbean lead isotopic data suggest further that anomalous metal abundances are also not needed to form precious metal deposits. The most likely control on the distribution of precious metal deposits, in fact, is the relatively high solubility of gold in low-salinity, reducing, meteoric hydrothermal systems such as form in continental volcanic rocks (Barnes, 1979). The formation of such mineralization is necessarily a late phase in the evolution of volcanic arcs because of the need for a sufficiently thick crust to produce an emergent land mass in which meteoric hydrothermal systems can function. In arcs underlain by continental crust, such as northern Central America, or in those with

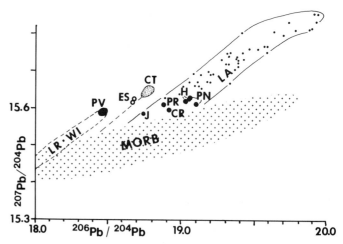

Figure 15. Relation between uranium-derived lead isotopic compositions of Caribbean volcanic rocks and ores (after Cumming and others, 1981; Cumming and Kesler, 1986; Davidson, 1987; White and Dupre, 1986). Pueblo Viejo (PV) and Los Ranchos–Water Island (LR–WI) linear array from Cumming and others (1981) and Cumming and Kesler (1986). Lesser Antilles (LA) and mid-ocean ridge basalt (MORB) fields from Davidson (1987) and White and Dupre (1986). Deposit data from El Salvador (ES), Jamaica (J), Puerto Rico (PR), Haiti (H), Costa Rica (CR), Panama (PN), and Chortis Terrane (CT) from Cumming and others (1981).

significant sialic sedimentary(?) contamination such as southern Central America and possibly the Lesser Antilles, silicic volcanic rocks are relatively abundant late-stage products. In others, such as the Greater Antilles, subaerial volcanic rocks of the appropriate composition did not form widely, possibly because a change in plate-motion directions stopped volcanism before significant sialic melts could form by melting of the arc crust, and epithermal vein mineralization is correspondingly scarce. The lack of epithermal vein deposits in otherwise favorable areas such as northern South America, which is underlain by continental crust, is probably attributable to a similar premature cessation in subduction.

REFERENCES

Alminas, H. V. and Tucker, R. E., 1987, Lead, tin, and precious-metal mineralization in the U.S. Virgin Islands: Society of Mining Engineers Preprint 87-108, 24 p.

Anderson, T. H. and Schmidt, V. A., 1983, The evolution of Middle America and the Gulf of Mexico–Caribbean Sea region during Mesozoic time: Geological Society of America Bulletin, v. 94, p. 941–966.

Anderson, T. H., Erdlac, R.J., Jr., and Sandstrom, M. A., 1985, Late Cretaceous allochthons and post-Cretaceous strike-slip displacement along the Cuilco–Chixoy–Polochic fault, Guatemala: Tectonics, v. 4, p. 453–476.

Angulo Carmona, R., 1978, Recursos minerales de Colombia: Ministerio de Minas y Energía, Instituto Nacional de Investigaciones de Geologia y Minas Publicación Especial 1, 544 p.

Anonymous, 1977, The Caribbean; New faces in a mixed mining scene: Engineering and Mining Journal, November, p. 55–198.

Anonymous, 1987, Mineral resource assessment of the Republic of Costa Rica: U.S. Geological Survey Miscellaneous Investigations Map I–1865, 75 p.

Ansted, D. T., 1856, The Cobre (copper) of Santiágo de Cuba: Proceedings of the Geological Society of London, v. 12, p. 145–153.

Arden, D. D., 1975, Geology of Jamaica and the Nicaraguan Rise, *in* Nairn, A.E.A., and Stehli, F. G., eds., The Ocean Basins and Margins; v. 3, The Gulf of Mexico and Caribbean: New York, Plenum Press, p. 617–662.

Atwood, M. G., 1972, Geology of the Minas de Oro Quadrangle, Honduras, Central America [M.A. thesis]: Middletown, Connecticut, Wesleyan University, 88 p.

Ballard, M. M., Van der Voo, R., and Urrutia-Fucugauchi, J., 1989, Paleomagnetic results from Grenvillian-aged rocks from Oaxaca, Mexico; Evidence for a displaced terrane: Precambrian Research, v. 42, p. 343–352.

Barabas, A. H., 1982, Potassium-argon dating of magmatic events and hydrothermal activity associated with porphyry copper mineralization in west-central Puerto Rico: Economic Geology, v. 77, p. 109–126.

Barnes, H. L., 1979, Solubilities of ore minerals, *in* Barnes, H. K., ed., Geochemistry of Hydrothermal Ore Deposits (2nd edition): New York, Wiley-

Interscience, p. 404–460.

Barrero Lozano, D., 1976, Mapa metalogénico de Colombia: Ministerio de Minas y Energía, Instituto Nacional de Investigaciones de Geología y Minas, Bogotá. Scale, 1:5,000,000.

Bateson, J. H., and Hall, I.H.S., 1970, Reconnaissance geochemical and geological investigation of the Maya Mountains of southern British Honduras: Institute of Geological Science Overseas Division Report 16, 41 p.

Bellizzia G., A., Pimentel de Bellizzia, N., and Rodríguez, S., 1981, Recursos minerales de Venezuela y su relación a la metalogénesis: Minerales de Venezuela, Ministerio de Energía y Minas, Caracas, p. 6–77.

Benês, K., and Hanus, V., 1967, Structural control and history of origin of hydrothermal metallogeny in western Cuba: Mineralium Deposita, v. 2, p. 318–338.

Bevan, P. A., 1973, Rosita mine; A brief history and geological description: Canadian Institute of Mining and Metallurgy Bulletin, August, p. 80–84.

Black, C.D.G., and Bailey, B. V., 1968, Investigations of the Barbecue copper prospect: Jamaican Geological Survey Economic Geology Report no. 2, 11 p.

Bogdanov, Y. V., Gur'yanova, V. N., and Mirayes, M., 1966, Outline and metallogeny of copper deposits of Cuba: International Geology Review, v. 8, no. 10, p. 1218–1225.

Bonatti, E., Kraemer, T., and Rydell, H., 1972, Classification and genesis of submarine iron-manganese deposits, *in* Horn, D., ed., Ferromanganese deposits of the ocean floor: National Science Foundation, p. 149–165.

Bondar-Clegg and Company, 1988, Jamaica metallic mineral survey; Phase I, Geochemical survey: Ottawa, Ontario, Canadian International Development Agency Project no. 504/0012280, 1,218 p.

Bonis, S. B., 1968, Age of the Guatemalan serpentinite [abs.]: *in* Abstracts for 1967: Geological Society of America Special Paper 115, p. 18.

Bowin, C. O., 1966, Geology of the central Dominican Republic: Geological Society of America Memoir 98, p. 11–84.

Brimhall, G. H., and Chiorso, M.S ., 1983, Origin and ore-forming consequences of the advanced argillic alteration process in hypogene environments by magmatic gas contamination of meteoric fluids: Economic Geology, v. 78, p. 73–90.

Broedel, C. H., 1961, Preliminary geologic map showing iron and copper prospects in the Juncos Quadrangle, Puerto Rico: U.S. Geological Survey Miscellaneous Investigations I-326, scale 1:20,000.

Burkart, B., 1983, Neogene North American–Caribbean plate boundary across northern Central America; Offset along the Polochic fault: Tectonophysics, v. 99, p. 251–270.

Burke, K., Cooper, C., Dewey, J. F., Mann, P., and Pindell, J. L., 1984, Caribbean tectonics and relative plate motions: Geological Society of America Memoir 162, p. 31–64.

Burn, R. G., 1969, The Pis-pis gold mining district of N.E. Nicaragua: Mining Magazine, v. 120, no. 3, p. 169–175.

Butterlin, J., 1960, Geologie general et regional de la Republique d'Haiti: Paris, Institut des Hautes Etudes de l'Amerique Latine IV, 194 p.

Cabrera, R., and Tolkunov, A. E., 1979, Tipos y condiciones geologicas de localizacion de los yacimientos de oro de las zona mineral septentrional de la antigua Provincia de Las Villa: Ciencias de la Tierra y del Espacio, v. 1, p. 51–68.

Campa, M. F. and Coney, P. J., 1983, Tectono-stratigraphic terranes and mineral resource distributions in Mexico: Canadian Journal of Earth Science, v. 20, p. 1040–1051.

Carby, B. E., 1978, The dispersion of Na, K, Ca, and Mg along the footwall of a Pb-Zn ore body, Hope Mine, Jamaica, 8th Caribbean Conference: Geologie Mijnbouw, v. 57, p. 135–138.

Carlson, G. G., 1977, Geology of the Bailadores, Venezuela, massive sulfide deposit: Economic Geology, v. 72, p. 1131–1141.

Carpenter, R. H., 1954, Geology and ore deposits of the Rosario mining district and the San Juancito Mountains, Honduras: Geological Society of America Bulletin, v. 65, p. 23–38.

Case, J. E., 1980, Crustal setting of mafic and ultramafic rocks and associated ore deposits of the Caribbean region: U.S. Geological Survey Open-File Report 80-3041, 95 p.

Case, J. E., Holcombe, T. L., and Martin, R. G., 1984, Map of geologic provinces in the Caribbean region: Geological Society of America Memoir 162, p. 1–30.

Castillo M., R., Madrigal G., R., and Sandoval M., F., 1970, Nota geotécnica sobre el yacimiento de laterita bauxita del Valle de el General: Costa Rica, Ciudad Universitaria, Dirección de Geología, Minas y Petróleo, Informe Técnico Geológico 34, p. 1–22.

Cheilletz, A., Kachrillo, J. J., Sonct, J., Zimmerman, J. L., 1978, Petrographie et geochronologie de deux complexes intrusifs a porphyres cupriferes d'Haiti: Societe Geologie de France Bulletin, v. 20, no. 6, p. 107–114.

Clark, A. H., Farrar, E., and Kents, P., 1977, Potassium-argon age of the Cerro Colorado porphyry copper deposit, Panamá: Economic Geology, v. 72, p. 1154–1158.

Collins, E. M., and Kesler, S. E., 1969, High-temperature, telescoped tungsten-antimony mineralization, Guatemala: Mineralium Deposita, v. 4, p. 65–71.

Comer, J. B., 1974, Genesis of Jamaican bauxite: Economic Geology, v. 689, p. 1251–1264.

Comer, J. B., Naeser, C. W., and McDowell, F. W., 1980, Fission track ages from Jamaican bauxite and terrosa: Economic Geology, v. 75, p. 117–121.

Cortina, F., 1978, Clasificación morfogénetica de las cortezas de intemperismo nickelíferas sobre las rocas ultrabásicas de Cuba: Ciencias Terra Espacio, v. 1, p. 33–49.

Cox, D. P., 1973, Porphyry copper deposits in Puerto Rico and their relation to arc-trench tectonics: U.S. Geological Survey Open-File Report 73–51, 9 p.

—— , 1985, Geology of the Tanama and Helecho porphyry copper deposits and vicinity, Puerto Rico: U.S. Geological Survey Professional Paper 1327, 59 p.

Cox, D. P., and Briggs, R. P., 1974, Metallogenic map of Puerto Rico: U.S. Geological Survey Miscellaneous Investigations Map I-721, scale 1:240,000.

Cox, D. P., Gonzalez, I. P., and Nash, J. T., 1975, Geology, geochemistry, and fluid inclusion petrography of the Sapo Allegre porphyry copper deposit: U.S. Geological Survey Journal of Research, v. 3, p. 313–327.

Cox, D. P., Marvin, R. F., McGonigle, J. W., McIntyre, D. H., and Rogers, C. L., 1977, Potassium-argon geochronology of some metamorphic, igneous, and hydrothermal events in Puerto Rico and the Virgin Islands: U.S. Geological Survey Journal of Research, v. 5, p. 689–703.

Cumming, G. L., and Kesler, S. E., 1976, Source of lead in Central American and Caribbean mineralization: Earth and Planetary Science Letters, v. 31, p. 262–268.

—— , 1986, Lead isotopic composition of the oldest volcanic rocks of the eastern Greater Antilles island arc: Isotope Geoscience, v. 65, p. 15–23.

Cumming, G. L., Kesler, S. E. and Krstic, D., 1981, Source of lead in Central American and Caribbean mineralization; II, Lead isotope provinces: Earth and Planetary Science Letters, v. 56, p. 199–209.

Cumming, G. L., Kesler, S. E., and Krstic, D., 1982, Source of lead in sulfide ore at the Pueblo Viejo gold-silver oxide deposit, Dominican Republic: Economic Geology, v. 77, p. 1939–1942.

Davidson, J. P., 1987, Crustal contamination versus subduction zone enrichment; Examples from the Lesser Antilles and implications for mantle source compositions of island arc volcanic rocks: Geochimica et Cosmochimica Acta, v. 51, p. 2185–2198.

Dilles, P. A., 1982, Skarn formation and mineralization within the Lower Cretaceous Cantarranas Formation, El Mochito mine, Honduras [M.Sc. thesis]: Anchorage, University of Alaska, 97 p.

Donnelly, T. W., 1966, Geology of St. Thomas and St. John, U.S. Virgin Islands: Geological Society of America Memoir 98, p. 85–176.

—— , 1975, The geological evolution of the Caribbean and Gulf of Mexico; Some critical problems and areas, *in* Nairn, A.E.M., and Stehli, R. G., eds., The ocean basins and margins; v. 3, The Gulf of Mexico and the Caribbean: New York, Plenum Press, p. 663–690.

Fenton, A. D., 1979, Copper deposits of Jamaica; A geological review: Jamaican Geological Survey Report no. 9, 225 p.

Feoktistov, V. P., Aniyatov, I. A., and Norman, A., 1983, Metallogeny of western

Cuba: International Geology Review, v. 25, p. 309–318.

Ferencic, A., 1971, Metallogenic provinces and epochs in southern Central America: Mineralium Deposita, v. 6, p. 77–78.

Flint, D. E., Albear, J. F. and Guild, P. W., 1948, Geology and chromite deposits of Camagüey district, Camagüey province, Cuba: U.S. Geological Survey Bulletin 954–B, p. 39–63.

Goldich, S. S., and Berquist, H. R., 1948, Aluminous lateritic soil of the Republic of Haiti, W.I.: U.S. Geological Survey Bulletin 959–C, p. 63–112.

Golightly, J. P., 1979, Nickeliferous laterites; A general description, *in* Evans, D.J.I., Shoemaker, R. S., and Veltman, H., eds., International Laterite Symposium: Society of Mining Engineers, p. 3–23.

Gose, W. A., 1985, Paleomagnetic results from Honduras and their bearing on Caribbean tectonics: Tectonics, v. 4, p. 565–585.

Green, G. W., 1977, Structure and stratigraphy of the Wagwater Belt, Kingston, Jamaica: Institute of Geological Science (London) Overseas Geology and Mineral Resources, no. 48, 21 p.

Guilbert, J. A., and Park, C. F., 1986, Geology of ore deposits: San Francisco, California, W. H. Freeman, 987 p.

Guild, P. W., 1947, Petrology and structure of the Moa district, Oriente Province, Cuba: EOS Transactions of the American Geophysical Union, v. 28, p. 218–246.

Haldemann, E. G., Buchan, R., Blowes, J. H., and Chandler, T., 1979, Geology of the lateritic nickel deposits, Dominican Republic, *in* Evans, D.J.I., ed., International Laterite Symposium: Society of Mining Engineers, p. 57–84.

Harju, H. O., 1979, Exploration of Exmibal's nickel laterite deposits in Guatemala, *in* Evans, D.J.I., ed., International Laterite Symposium: Society of Mining Engineers, p. 245–251.

Hayba, D. O., Bethke, P. M., Heald, P., and Foley, N., 1985, Geologic, mineralogic and geochemical characteristics of volcanic-hosted epithermal precious metal deposits: Society of Economic Geologists Reviews in Economic Geology, v. 2, p. 129–168.

Hildebrand, F. A., 1961, Hydrothermally altered rocks in eastern Puerto Rico: U.S. Geological Survey Professional Paper 424–B, p. 219–221.

Hill, P. J., 1958, Banded pyrite deposits of Minas Carlota, Cuba: Economic Geology, v. 53, p. 966–1003.

——, 1959, Geology and structure of the northwest Trinidad Mountains, Las Villas Province, Cuba: Geological Society of America Bulletin, v. 70, p. 1459–1478.

Hodges, C. A., and 26 others, 1984, U.S. Geological Survey–INGEOMINAS mineral resource assessment of Colombia: U.S. Geological Survey Open-File Report 84–345, 348 p.

Horsefield, W. T., 1975, Quaternary vertical movements in the Greater Antilles: Geological Society of America Bulletin, v. 86, p. 933–938.

Irving, E. M., 1975, Structural evolution of the northernmost Andes, Colombia: U.S. Geological Survey Professional Paper 846, 47 p.

Issignonis, M. J., 1973, The geology and geochemistry of the porphyry-type copper and molybdenum mineralization at Cerro Colorado, Panama [M.Sc. thesis]: Ontario, University of Toronto, 207 p.

Iturralde-Vinent, M. A., 1975, Problems in application of modern tectonic hypotheses to Cuba and Caribbean region: American Association of Petroleum Geologists Bulletin, v. 59, p. 2369–2379.

Jackson, T. A., and Smith, T. E., 1978, Metasomatism in the Tertiary volcanic rocks of the Wagwater Belt: Geologie Mijnbouw, v. 57, p. 213–220.

Jensen, M. L., and Bateman, A. M., 1979, Economic mineral deposits (3rd edition): New York, John Wiley, 593 p.

Jones, M. T., Reed, B. L., Doe, B. R., and Lanphere, M. A., 1977, Age of tin mineralization and plumbotectonics, Belitung, Indonesia: Economic Geology, v. 72, p. 745–752.

Kesler, S. E., 1968, Contact-localized ore formation at the Memé mine, Haiti: Economic Geology, v. 63, p. 541–552.

——, 1971, Nature of the ancestral orogenic zone in nuclear Central America: American Association of Petroleum Geologists Bulletin, v. 55, p. 2116–2129.

——, 1978, Metallogenesis of the Caribbean region: Journal of the Geological

Society of London, v. 135, p. 429–441.

Kesler, S. E., and Ascarrunz-K., R. O., 1973, Lead-zinc mineralization in carbonate rocks, central Guatemala: Economic Geology, v. 68, p. 1268–1274.

Kesler, S. E., and Sutter, J. F., 1977, Compositional evolution of intrusive rocks in the eastern Greater Antilles island arc: Geology, v. 7, p. 197–200.

Kesler, S. E., Kienle, C. F., and Bateson, J. H., 1974, Tectonic significance of intrusive rocks in the Maya Mountains, British Honduras: Geological Society of America Bulletin, v. 85, p. 549–552.

Kesler, S. E., Jones, L. M., and Walker, R. M., 1975, Intrusive rocks associated with porphyry copper mineralization in island arc areas: Economic Geology, v. 70, p. 515–526.

Kesler, S. E., Sutter, J. F., Issigonis, M. J., Jones, L. M., and Walker, R. L., 1977, Evolution of porphyry copper mineralization in an oceanic island arc: Economic Geology, v. 72, p. 1142–1153.

Kesler, S. E., Russell, N., Seaward, M., Rivera, J. A., McCurdy, K., Cumming, G. L., and Sutter, J. F., 1981, Geology and geochemistry of sulfide mineralization underlying the Pueblo Viejo gold-silver oxide deposit, Dominican Republic: Economic Geology, v. 76, p. 1096–1117.

Koschmann, A. H., and Gordon, M., 1950, Geology and mineral resources of the Maimon–Hatillo district, Dominican Republic: U.S. Geological Survey Bulletin 964–D, p. 307–360.

Kuhn, O. R., 1926, Iron-ore deposits of Cuba: Engineering and Mining Journal, v. 121, no. 15, p. 607–612.

Kulstad, R., 1980, Investigacion geológica preliminar del sector Miches, Cordillera Oriental, República Dominicana: 9th Caribbean Geological Conference Transactions, Santo Domingo, p. 663–668.

Kuypers, E. P., and Denyer Ch., P., 1979, Volcanic exhalative manganese deposits of the Nicoya ophiolite complex, Costa Rica: Economic Geology, v. 74, p. 672–678.

Laguna-Morales, J., 1983, Hydrothermale Veranderung and Verwitterungseffekte in Vulkaniten der Aguacate-Formation (Miozan–Pliozan), Costa Rica: Zentralblatt für Geologie und Palaeontologie, teil I, h. 3/4, p. 223–233.

Lawrence, B. B., 1910, Two Cuban mines: Journal of the Canadian Mining Institute, v. 13, p. 91–106.

Levy, E., 1970, La metalogenesis in America Central: Publicaciones Geologicas, Instituto Centroamericano de Investigacion Tecnologica y Industria, III, p. 17–57.

Levy, E., Morales, A., Varela, A., and Valdevellano, F., 1977, Diagnóstico del sector minero de la República Dominicana: Washington, D.C., Organizacion de Estados Americanos, 125 p.

Levy, E., Morales, A., and Varela, A., 1978, Diagnóstico del sector minero de Costa Rica: Washington, D.C., Organizacion de Estados Americanos, 76 p.

Lewis, G. E., and Straczek, J. A., 1958, Geology of south-central Oriente Cuba: U.S. Geological Survey Bulletin 975–D, p. 171–335.

Lindgren, W., and Ross, C. P., 1916, The iron deposits of Daiquiri, Cuba: Transactions of American Institute of Mining Engineers, v. 53, p. 40–66.

Loubet, M., Mountigny, R., Chachati, B., Durate, N., Lambert, B., Martín, F. C., and Thuizat, R., 1985, Geochemical and geochronological constraints on the geodynamical development of the Caribbean chain of Venezuela, *in* Symposium on Geodynamiqe des Caraibes, Edit. Techanip, Paris, p. 553–566.

Low, V.F.S., 1931, Panama: Mining Magazine, v. 23, p. 201–209 and 273–279.

Malone, G. B., 1987, Caldera-related gold mineralization of the El Limon mining district, western Nicaragua: Journal of Volcanology and Geothermal Research, v. 33, p. 217–222.

Mann, P., and Burke, K., 1984, Cenozoic rift formation in the northern Caribbean: Geology, v. 12, p. 732–736.

Martín, C., 1980, Metalogénesis en America del Sur, *in* Simposio Internacional sobre Metalogénesis en Latino América: México, International Union of Geological Scientists Publication 5, p. 223–248.

——, 1983, Metallogenic Map of South America: Caracas, Venezuela, Ministerio de Energía y Minas, Dirección de Geología, scale, 1:5,000,000.

Martín, C., and Arozena, J., 1972, Complejo ultramafico zonado de Tausabana–El Rodeo, gabro zonado de Siraba–Capuana y complejo subvolcánico estratificado de Santa Ana, Paraguaná, Edo. de Falcón, Venezuela:

6th Caribbean Geological Conference Transactions, Porlamar, Venezuela, p. 337–357.

Martin-Kaye, P.H.A., 1959, Geology of the Leeward and British Virgin Islands: St. Lucia, Voice Publication Co., 117 p.

Maze, W. B., 1980, Geology and copper mineralization of the Jurassic La Quinta Formation in the Sierra de Perijá, northwestern Venezuela: Transactions of the 9th Caribbean Conference, Santo Domingo, p. 283–294.

——, 1984, Jurassic La Quinta Formation in the Sierra de Perijá, northwestern Venezuela; Geology and tectonic environment of redbeds and volcanic rocks: Geological Society of America Memoir 162, p. 263–282.

Müller-Kahle, E., 1962, Die Lagerstätte der Grube Montecristo, El Salvador, und ihr geologischer Rahman: Neues Jahrbuch Für Geologie und Palaontologie Abhandlungen, v. 115, p. 289–334.

Nicolini, P., 1982, Gitologie Haitienne, *in* Maurrasse, F., ed., Transactions der ler collegue sur la geologie d'Haiti, Port-au-Prince, p. 105–111.

Ott, L. E., Groody, D., Follis, E. L., and Siems, P. L., 1986, Stratigraphy, structural geology, ore mineralogy, and hydrothermal alteration and the Cannon Mine, Chelan County, Washington, U.S.A.: Toronto, Gold '86 Proceedings, p. 425–435.

Page, L. R., and McAllister, J. F., 1944, Tungsten deposits, Isla de Pinos, Cuba: U.S. Geological Survey Bulletin 935–D, p. 177–246.

Palmer, H. C., 1963, Geology of the Moncion–Jarabacoa area, Dominican Republic [Ph.D. thesis]: Princeton, New Jersey, Princeton University, 256 p.

Pardo, G., 1975, Geology of Cuba, *in* Nairn, A.E.M., and Stehli, F. G., eds., The ocean basins and margins; v. 3, The Gulf of Mexico and Caribbean: New York, Plenum Press, p. 553–615.

Park, C. F., 1942, Manganese deposits of Cuba: U.S. Geological Survey Bulletin 935–B, 97 p.

Patchett, P. J., and Ruiz, J., 1987, Nd isotopic ages of crust formation and metamorphism in the Precambrian of eastern and southern Mexico: Contributions to Mineralogy and Petrology, v. 96, p. 523–528.

Patterson, S. H., 1967, Bauxite reserves and potential aluminum resources of the world: U.S. Geological Survey Bulletin 1228, 175 p.

Paulson, E. G., 1964, Mineralization and origin of the titaniferrous deposits at Pluma Hidalgo, Oaxaca, Mexico: Economic Geology, v. 59, p. 753–767.

Petersen, E. U., 1986, Tin in volcanogenic massive sulfide deposits; An example from the Geco mine, Manitouwadge district, Ontario, Canada: Economic Geology, v. 81, p. 323–342.

Petersen, E. U., and Zantop, H., 1980, The Oxec deposit, Guatemala; An ophiolite copper occurrence: Economic Geology, v. 75, p. 1053–1065.

Roberts, R. H., 1944, Manganese deposits in Costa Rica: U.S. Geological Survey Bulletin 935–H, p. 387–408.

Roberts, R. J., and Irving, E. M., 1957, Mineral deposits of Central America: U.S. Geological Survey Bulletin 1034, 205 p.

Rodríguez, S. E., 1980, Nuevas ideas concernientes a metalogénesis y tectónica de placas en Sur América Septentrional: 9th Caribbean Geological Conference Transactions, Santo Domingo, Dominican Republic, p. 295–302.

Russell, N., Seaward, M., Rivera, J. A., McCurdy, K., Kesler, S. E., and Cloke, P. L., 1981, Geology and geochemistry of the Pueblo Viejo gold-silver oxide ore deposit, Dominican Republic: Institute of Mining and Metallurgy Transactions, Sect. B, v. 90, p. B153–B162.

Russell, N., Brouwer, S., and Kesler, S. E., 1982, Economic geology of the central Dominican Republic: Santo Domingo, Dominican Republic, Rosario Dominicana, S.A., 95 p.

Schultz, J., and Hamaan, R. J., 1985, The Mochito mine, Honduras: Society of Mining Engineers Annual Meeting Program, p. 16.

Seaward, M., and Warner, T. G., 1971, How Mochito cuts dilution by sampling and grade control: World Mining, February, p. 30–33.

Shadlun, T. N., 1982, Ore textures as indicators of formation conditions of mineral paragenesis in different types of stratiform lead-zinc deposits, *in* Amstutz, G. C. and others, eds., Ore genesis: New York, Springer-Verlag, p. 607–624.

Sillitoe, R. H., 1986, Gold potential of the Lesser Antilles: unpublished United Nations report, 48 p.

Sillitoe, R. H., Jaramillo, L., Damon, P. E., Shafiqullah, M., and Escobar, R., 1982, Setting, characteristics, and age of the Andean porphyry copper belt in Colombia: Economic Geology, v. 77, p. 1837–1850.

Simons, F. S., and Straczek, J. A., 1958, Geology of the manganese deposits of Cuba: U.S. Geological Survey Bulletin 1057, 233 p.

Simonson, B. M., 1976, Igneous petrology of the Minas de Oro Quadrangle, central Honduras: Guatemala City, Publicaciones Geologicas del Instituto Centroamericano de Investigación y Tecnología Industrial (ICAITI) 5, p. 78–83.

Singewald, Q. D., 1950, Mineral resources of Colombia: U.S. Geological Survey Bulletin 964–B, 204 p.

Simpson, P. R., and 6 others, 1988, New evidence of epithermal gold potential in andesitic volcanics of the Central Inlier, Jamaica: Transactions, Institution of Mining and metallurgy, v. 97, p. B88–B92.

Sokolova, E. A., 1977, Origin of stratiform ore deposits (the manganese deposits of Cuba): Lithology and Ore Deposits, v. 15, p. 223–237.

Stonehouse, J. M., 1976, Movement of mineralizing fluids, Bononza mining district, Nicaragua [M.Sc. thesis]: Hanover, New Hampshire, Dartmouth University, 64 p.

Taylor, R. C., 1837, Notes relative to the geology of a portion of the district of Holguín in the island of Cuba: London Philosophical Magazine, v. 11, ser. 3), p. 17–33.

Taylor, S. R., and McLennan, S. M., 1985, The continental crust; Its composition and evolution: Palo Alto, California, Blackwell Scientific Publishers, 385 p.

Thayer, T. P., 1942, Chrome resources of Cuba: U.S. Geological Survey Bulletin 935A, p. 1–47.

Tschanz, C. M., Marvin, R. F., Cruz B., J., Mehnert, H. H., and Cebula, G. T., 1974, Geologic evolution of the Sierra Nevada de Santa Marta, northeastern Colombia: Geological Society of America Bulletin, v. 85, p. 273–284.

Tucker, R. E., 1987, A geochemical study of St. John, U.S. Virgin Islands [Ph.D. thesis]: Golden, Colorado School of Mines, 405 p.

Ukhana, A. V., Kogarko, L. N., Kononkova, N. N., Krigman, L. D., Merigno, H., and Norman, A., 1985, The origin of chromite ores at peridotite-gabbroid contacts; The example of the Mercedita deposit, Cuba: Geochemistry International, v. 22, p. 114–122.

Vaughn, T. W., 1901, The copper mines of Santa Clara province, Cuba: Engineering and Mining Journal, v. 62, p. 814–816.

Velnikov, I., Gorova, M., Tcholakov, P., Tchounev, D., and Ianeva, I., 1983, Secondary quartzites developed after Cretaceous volcanics from Zaza zone, Cuba: Geolica Balcanica, v. 13, no. 6, p. 53–68.

Viteri, A. E., 1978, Genesis del cobre nativo asociado a rocas de la Formación La Quinta en la Sierra de Perijá, Venezuela: Ministerio de Energía y Minas Boletin Geologico 13, p. 17–82.

——, 1980, Aspectos geologicos de las exploraciones cupriferas en la Sierra de Perijas, Venezuela: 9th Caribbean Geological Conference Transactions, Santo Domingo, Dominican Republic, p. 281–282.

Watanabe, J., 1974, Geology and copper mineralization of the Cordillera of Hispaniola: Mining Geology (Japan), v. 24, p. 323–333.

Weber, H. S., and Weisseman, G., 1978, Geologische Karte der Republik El Salvador/Mittelamerika; San Miguel sheet: Hannover, Bundesanstalt für Geowissenschaften und Rohstoffe, scale 1:100,000.

Weed, W. H., 1905, Copper mines near Havana, Cuba: Engineering and Mining Journal, v. 79, p. 176–177.

Weyl, R., 1980, Geology of Central America (2nd edition): Berlin, Gebrüder Borntrager, 370 p.

White, E. M., and Dupre, B., 1986, Sediment subduction and magma genesis in the Lesser Antilles; Isotopic and trace element constraints: Journal of Geophysical Research, v. 91, p. 5927–5941.

White, L., 1977, Central America: diverse mineralization provides targets for exploration: Engineering Mining Journal, v. 178, p. 159–198.

Woakes, E. R., 1923, The Darien gold mine, Panama: Mining Magazine, p. 270–278.

Woodring, W. P., 1957, Geology and paleontology of Canal Zone and adjoining parts of Panama: U.S. Geological Survey Professional Paper 306–A, 145 p.

Woodring, W. P., and Daviess, S. N., 1944, Geology and manganese deposits of Guisa–Los Negros area Oriente Province, Cuba: U.S. Geological Survey Bulletin 935–G, p. 357–385.

Wuensch, C. E., 1917, Geology of the San Sebastián mine, Salvador: Mining Science Press, p. 345–350.

Zhidkov, A., Ovsiannikov, V., and del Pino, J., 1975, Papel de la materia organica en la formacion del yacimiento Santa Lucía: Revista Minera Cuba, v. 2, p. 12–18.

Manuscript Accepted by the Society September 19, 1988

ACKNOWLEDGMENTS

Field and laboratory work on Caribbean ore deposits has been supported by numerous organizations, including the United Nations, Organization of American States, Instituto Centro-Americano de Investigacion y Technología Industrial, Instituto Geografico Nacional (Guatemala), Ministerio de Energía y Minas (Venezuela), National Science Foundation (U.S.), National Research Council (Canada), Forestry Division (Belize), Division of Mines and Geology (Jamaica), Exxon, Utah Mines, Canadian Javelin, and Rosario Resources (Amax). Conversations, correspondence, or field work with H. V. Alminas, R. J. Arculus, W. C. Bagby, S. L. Bolivar, S. B. Bonis, B. Burkart, J. E. Case, D. P. Cox, C. G. Cunningham, Jr., J. Davidson, G. Dengo, R. G. Garrett, E. Hoffman, J. F. Lewis, N. Russell, and M. Seaward have been particularly helpful in clarifying aspects of the geology of Caribbean mineral deposits. We are grateful to D. P. Cox, F. M. Haynes, R. M. Kettler, and R. R. Seal for helpful reviews of this paper, and to Jim Case and Gabriel Dengo for their dedication to the task of compiling this volume.

The Geology of North America
Vol. H, The Caribbean Region
The Geological Society of America, 1990

Chapter 19

Energy resources of the Caribbean region

Anthony E. L. Morris
Morris Petroleum, Inc., P.O. Box 64610, Los Angeles, California 90064
Arthur A. Meyerhoff
P.O. Box 4602, Tulsa, Oklahoma 74159
Irfan Taner
3625 South Florence Place, Tulsa, Oklahoma 74105
Rafael Bueno-Salazar
Empresa Colombiana de Petroleos, Apartado Aereo 5938-6813, Bogotá, Colombia
Gordon A. Young
Petroleos de Venezuela S.A., Apartado 169, Caracas, 1010A, Venezuela

INTRODUCTION

The Caribbean region comprises all of Central America, much of Colombia and Venezuela, and the Greater and Lesser Antilles, including their Atlantic shelves and slopes. Peripherally, it encompasses the Yucatán Peninsula, interior basins of Colombia and Venezuela, and the Bahamas and southern Florida. The Caribbean Sea constitutes almost half of the 8.5 million km² area.

Petroleum is by far the principal energy resource of the region. Colombia, Venezuela, Trinidad, Cuba, Guatemala, and Barbados produce petroleum commercially, but only the first three are self sufficient and net exporters. There is minor potential in the Bahamas, Honduras, Nicaragua, Costa Rica, and Panamá.

Commercial deposits of coal are known only in Colombia, Venezuela, and Costa Rica. Other resources, in order of utilization, are hydropower, geothermal, biomass, wind, and solar. There is minor potential for uranium-thorium deposits in Venezuela, Colombia, and Nuclear Central America. Ocean temperature gradients offer unlimited energy to islands, particularly those with near-shore deep water. A distant-future potential major resource is gas hydrates on the Pacific continental slopes of Guatemala, Nicaragua, and Panamá and the continental borderlands of Colombia and Venezuela.

CARIBBEAN ENERGY IN THE GEOLOGIC FRAMEWORK

For the purpose of this chapter the geologic framework of the region is reported in its present physical state without reference to geologic evolution, which is covered elsewhere in this volume (Morris and others, ch. 17; Pindell and Barrett).

In general terms, the Caribbean region is bordered by two Precambrian-Paleozoic igneous and metamorphic crystalline massifs—North and Central America on the north and west; and South America on the south. North and Central America extend from the eastern end of the Bahamas through part of Cuba, the western Bahamas and southern Florida, thence through Yucatán to northern Nacaragua. South America extends from the Santa Marta massif to the shelf east of Trinidad and Venezuela. Connecting these two "old lands" are the isthmus of southern Central America on the southwest, and the Aves Ridge, Lesser Antilles, and part of the Greater Antilles on the east and northeast (Fig. 1).

These generalities are pertinent to the consideration of the loci of optimum petroleum accumulation in the region. The main requisites for petroleum accumulation—abundant source rocks, clean reservoirs, secure seals, and large traps—are present commonly in or adjacent to geologically mature, tectonically stable areas. A wide age range of objectives is likely to be present in such environments. Conversely, petroleum is less likely to be present in commercial volumes in tectonically immature or mobile areas, and the age range of objectives is severely curtailed (e.g., active volcanic arcs). The same environmental conditions apply to other hydrocarbons, such as tar sands, oil shale, and coal, as well as uranium and thorium deposits.

In contrast, geothermal resources are associated with tectonically active areas, and especially with volcanic arcs. Hydropower, too, requires a mountain-building environment in addition to moisture-laden air currents.

The foregoing axioms require petroleum and coal deposits in Colombia, Venezuela, and Trinidad on the south and in Nuclear Central America, Yucatán, Cuba, and the Bahamas on the north. This is spectacularly true as to the southern region where production through 1986 has been 45,200 million barrels (MMbbl) of oil and 58,600 billion ft³ (bcf) of gas. Reserves are

Morris, A.E.L., Meyerhoff, A. A., Taner, I., Bueno-Salazar, R., and Young, G. A., 1990, Energy resources of the Caribbean region, *in* Dengo, G., and Case, J. E., eds., The Caribbean region: Boulder, Colorado, Geological Society of America, The Geology of North America.

estimated at 27,400 MMbbl and 73,700 bcf, and future potential resources in the ranges of 53,500 to 109,500 MMbbl and 137,000 to 214,000 bcf. The oil reserves do not include a recent reclassification of Orinoco Oil Belt reserves. Coal reserves are placed at 6,230 million metric tons (mt) and future potential resources at 28,000 million mt.

The northern area, although productive, has yielded only approximately 64 MMbbl and 35 bcf through 1986 (exclusive of minor production in southern Florida). This scarcity is attributable to widespread regional fragmentation at the edge of the craton: autochthonous rocks are buried deeply by thrust sheets in northern Cuba, only carbonate-evaporate sequences are present in eastern Yucatán and the Bahamas, and potential areas of Nuclear Central America have to a great extent been destroyed by repeated tectonic events. Basins are summarized in Table 1 and drilling statistics in Table 2 (Plate 14).

SEDIMENTARY BASINS AND PETROLEUM POTENTIAL

Central America

Geologic framework. One minor and six major morphotectonic provinces make up the geologic framework of Central America (Figs. 2 and 3): (1) the Paleozoic (250 to 500 Ma radiometric dates) and possibly older Yucatán platform, covered by relatively undeformed Cretaceous and Tertiary rocks overlying a wedge of Jurassic rocks, which thickens westward and southward; (2) the Northern Central American Orogen (Meyerhoff, 1967), a geosynclinal-type fold belt that extends from the Isthmus of Tehuantepec through Guatemala and Honduras; (3) a stable Precambrian and early Paleozoic platform that extends from Nuclear Central America northeastward toward Jamaica as the Nicaragua Rise; (4) the middle Cretaceous and younger Southern Central American orogen (Dengo, 1962), a eugeosynclinal belt that extends from western Ecuador to northwestern Costa Rica (Meyerhoff, 1967), and, according to offshore well and gravity data, may continue northwestward beneath the Pacific shelf and continental slope to the Isthmus of Tehuantepec; (5) the deep offshore Middle America Trench, considered by many to be an active subduction zone, and its associated chain of active volcanoes bordering the narrow Pacific coastal plain; and (6) the linear Cayman Trough, a pull-apart according to many, parallel to the northern edge of the Nicaragua Rise. The small, seventh province is the late Cenozoic San Andrés–Providencia volcanic belt east of central and southern Nicaragua (Fig. 1).

The Middle America Trench and associated volcanic arc terminate abruptly where the northeast-trending Cocos Ridge and the north-striking Panamá Fracture Zone abut western Panamá. Panamá on- and offshore east of this junction could be interpreted to be a separate morphotectonic province.

Sixteen sedimentary regions are known within this geologic framework (Fig. 2; Plate 5B). Only those that have or may have hydrocarbon potential are discussed. Table 1 (Plate 14) describes their principal characteristics; also see Dengo (1969).

Chapayal basin. The Chapayal basin (Vinson, 1962; the Petén basin of Lloyd and Dengo, 1960), with 5,000+ m of Pennsylvanian, Permian, Mesozoic, and Tertiary strata, occupies central and northern Guatemala. It is 290 km long and 100 km wide at its widest part in the west, the third largest in Central America, the only productive one, and the most attractive for petroleum. Although exploration began in 1921, the first commercial discovery was not made until 1972. Five small fields have been found; many more should be discoverd. All produce from Lower to middle Cretaceous carbonates.

The basin's eastern limit is the Maya Mountains, except in the south where it extends eastward into the Caribbean Sea between the Maya Mountains and the southern margin, the Sierra Madre overthrust belt. The western edge is the Chiapas massif and Villahermosa horst (Viniegra-O, 1981). It continues northwestward into Mexico, and its northeastern border is the southwestward-dipping Yucatán platform. The La Libertad arch has been cited as the northern limit of the basin (Vinson, 1962; Vinson and Brineman, 1963), but this is illusory as two wells were drilled into Jurassic sediments below 5,000 m, one on and the other north of the western end of the arch.

The Pennsylvanian and Permian marine section of the Maya Mountains is strongly deformed. Structural complexity decreases westward so that the upper Paleozoic is a potential deep drilling objective in the western half of the basin. The section in Guatemala wedges out northward near 18° N lat.

The principal objective sequence, of Late Jurassic(?), Cretaceous, and early Tertiary ages, is thickest in the west (5,000+ m) near the Mexican frontier. It thins eastward south of the Maya Mountains and again thickens eastward to more than 4,000 m offshore where it becomes part of the Amatique basin.

The basin was deformed repeatedly from middle Paleozoic through Miocene times. Stresses were directed toward the north. The competent Yucatán platform acted as a buttress, and its position is the principal reason for the concave-northward shape of the basin structures. Large folds in the southern part of the basin die out to gentle folds near the La Libertad arch (Fig. 2). Along the Usumacinta River on the western border with Mexico, décollement (box-type) folds are common.

The 1974 and 1977 discoveries of the Rubelsanto and West Chinaja fields on the Rubelsanto anticline, close to the Mexican frontier, led to the construction of a pipeline to the Caribbean coast. Production, which commenced in 1976, reached a maximum of 8,450 bopd in September 1982. Since then it has ranged from 3,760 bopd in 1985 to 6,850 bopd in 1986 (Table 3, Plate 14).

Amatique basin and Belize borderland. These two areas, geographically contiguous, differ structurally. South of the Maya Mountains the strata of the Chapayal basin continue eastward beneath Amatique Bay and the Gulf of Honduras at least to the head of the Cayman Trough. The Motagua fault is the southern limit of the basin. In 1976, an offshore well penetrated Tertiary mixed carbonates and clastics, Cretaceous carbonates, and Upper Jurassic red beds before reaching a total depth of 4,230 m in a

Permian(?) limestone. The Lower Cretaceous and Permian(?) carbonates are a backreef facies so there is a potential for reef development nearby.

The northeast-striking Chixoy-Polochic and Motagua faults dominate the basin and set the structural pattern. Numerous parallel, lesser faults further disturb the region so that potential traps are likely to be small and discontinuous. The basin has very limited potential for commercial petroleum deposits.

The Belize borderland is characterized by a series of north-northeast–striking horsts and grabens that step down progressively to the floor of the Yucatán Basin (Bishop, 1980). They may represent the foundered eastern edge of the Yucatán platform (Fahlquist and others, 1972; Dillon and Vedder, 1973) associated with Tertiary subsidence of the Yucatán Basin. Other origins suggested are sphenochasmic rifting and a left-lateral transform margin (Case and others, 1984).

The troughs are relatively sediment starved and, although the ridges are crowned with carbonates that may have good reservoir properties, they appear to lack adequate seals; the shal-low depth of burial probably precludes thermal maturity of potential source rocks. The stratigraphic column has a maximum thickness of 2,000 m.

Through 1986, 14 dry holes have been drilled in the Amatique basin, and 12 in the Belize borderland. Only minor shows of oil and gas have been logged.

Tela and Ulúa basins. The Tela basin is a Teritary half-graben, possibly a pull-apart, with 1,500 to 4,000 m of section in the offshore where diapirs of unknown composition (evaporite, mud, or serpentine) are present (Pinet, 1972; Meyerhoff, 1973; Case and others, 1984). Onshore, eight wells have been reported; seven shallow ones on the west and one on the east. Four wells have been drilled offshore at the eastern end of the basin. The faults bounding this basin are related to the Motagua and Chamelecón faults. The offshore extent of the basin is uncertain, but it may extend farther east than shown on Figure 2 and possibly connect with Mosquitia basin.

The Ulúa is not a sedimentary basin in a tectonic sense as much of the sequence is exposed in anticlinoria that strike gener-

Figure 1 (following two pages). Location map for localities and some geologic features mentioned in the text.

Number	Locality of Phenomenon	Number	Locality of Phenomenon
1	La Libertad arch	38	Bolívar Coastal field
2	Rubelsanto field	39	Mene Grande field
3	Lago Izabal	40	Golfo de Vela
4	Villahermosa horst	41	Barquisimeto transverse zone
5	Sierra Madre Overthrust Belt of Guatemala	42	Golfo Triste
6	Xan heavy oil deposit	43	Caribbean Coastal Ranges (Cordillera de la Costa)
7	Isabella arch	44	Cariaco deep, Venezuela
8	Chixoy-Polochic fault	45	Serranía del Interior (Interior Coastal Ranges)
9	Motagua fault	46	Orinoco delta-fan
10	Chamelecón fault	47	Guanoco field
11	Amatique Gulf	48	Point Fortin field, Pitch Lake, Trinidad
12	Maya Mountains	49	Teak field, east of Trinidad
13	Ahuanchapán geothermal field, El Salvador	50	Barbados Ridge
14	Momotombo geothermal field, Nicaragua	51	Turner's Hall field
15	Caratasca Lagoon	52	Limestone Caribbees
16	San Andrés-Providencia volcanic belt	53	Volcanic Caribbees
17	Río San Carolos (NW Costa Rica)	54	Locations of Saba Bank 1, 2 wells,
18	Miravalles volcano, Costa Rica	55	Puerto Rico - Virgin Is. platform
19	Diablo field	56	Mona fault
20	Cocoles-2 well	57	Beata fault
21	Río Sixaola	58	Maleno anticline
22	Bocas del Toro	59	Cordillera Central (Dominican Republic)
23	Cordillera Occidental (Colombia)	60	Navidad Bank
24	Cocorna, Nare heavy oil deposits	61	Cordillera Septentrional (Dominican Republic)
25	Vaupes swell	62	Central Plateau (Central Plain), Haiti
26	Cordillera Oriental (Colombia)	63	Sierra de Purial (Cuba)
27	Cordillera Central (Colombia)	64	Sierra Maestra (Cuba)
28	La Cira-Infantas field	65	Cauto fault
29	Arauca field	66	Motembo field
30	Caño Limón field	67	Varadero field
31	Cordillera de Mérida	68	Boca de Jaruco field
32	Río Zulia field	69	Martín Mesa field
33	Petrólea and Tibú-Socuavó anticlines	70	Pinar fault
34	Santa Marta Massif (Sierra de Santa Marta)	71	Dubloon-Saxon-1 well
35	Sierra de Perijá	72	Andros-1 well
36	Mara field	73	Sunniland field area, Florida
37	La Paz field		

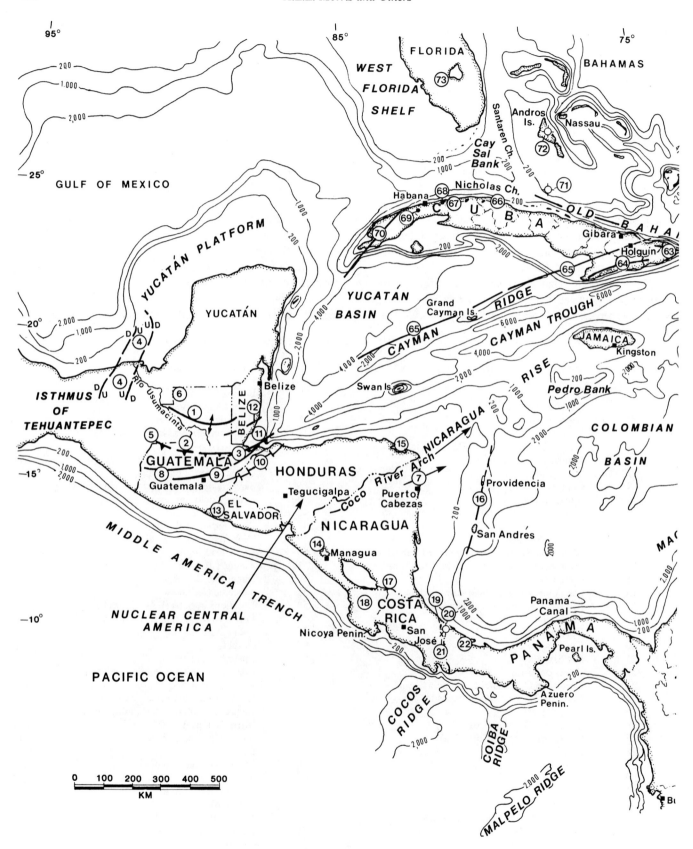

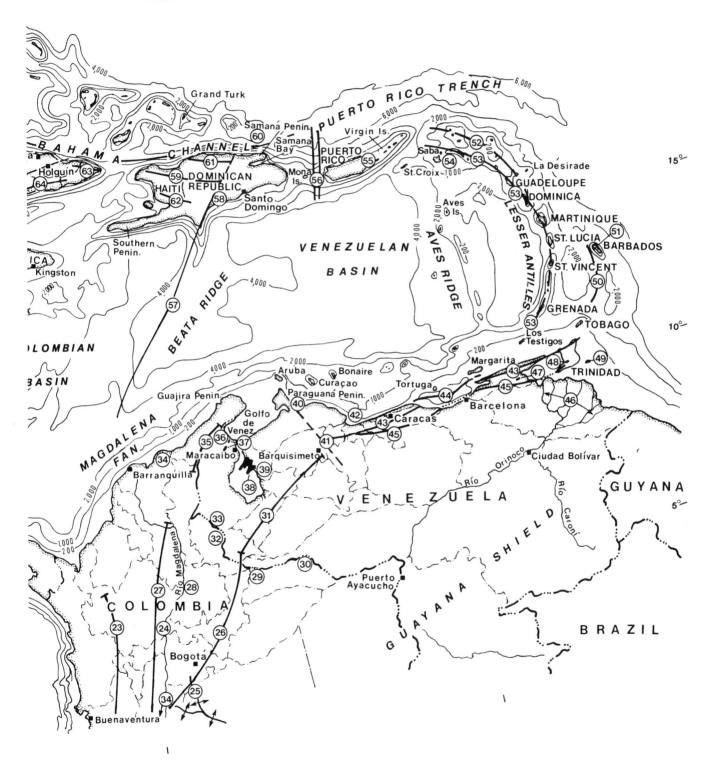

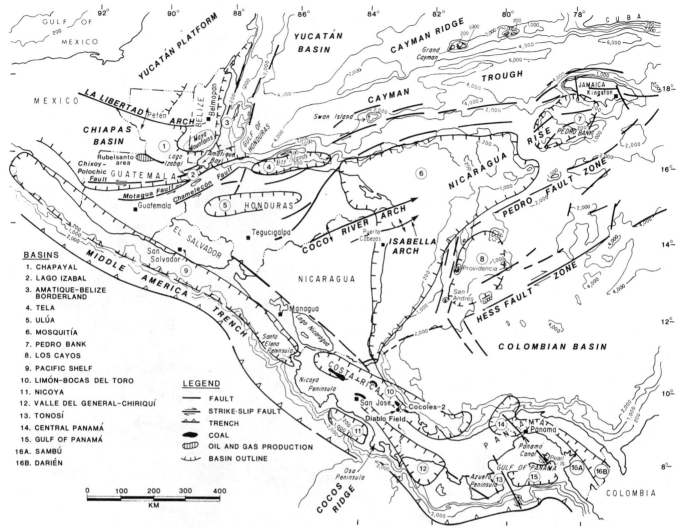

Figure 2. Central America: basins that produce petroleum or have the potential for so doing; petroleum-producing areas; coal fields; major structural elements. For strike-slip sense of motion on Hess fault zone see Bonini and others (1984, p. 53, Fig. 9).

ally northeast. The exposed strata, largely of Cretaceous age, are intensely folded and faulted. This complexity has led to wide disagreement over the age and correlation of many formations.

Although four oil seeps are known and rocks with good reservoir characteristics abound, the likelihood of commercial petroleum accumulations is remote because of the largely exposed objective section and the extensive structural disruption.

A midbasin narrowing owing to partial uplift of Paleozoic metamorphics has led some workers to consider the eastern half of the area a separate basin, the Olancho (Deal, 1983; Cáceres-Avila and others, 1984). Three core holes and two exploratory wells were drilled in the western part of the basin in the period 1957 to 1963 and another in 1983. A shallow well was drilled in the Olancho area in 1921.

Mosquitía basin. Except for a narrow coastal fringe in Honduras and Nicaragua, this is an offshore basin complex on the western Nicaragua Rise; the largest in Central America.

Cretaceous and Tertiary rocks are the principal objectives. Onshore, thick Cretaceous carbonates overlie a Triassic-Jurassic red-bed sequence. The Cretaceous Yojoa Group is favorable for the generation and accumulation of oil and gas. It is a complex of lagoonal backreef, reef, forereef, and deep-water carbonate rocks (Mills and others, 1967; Wilson, 1974). The depositional axis strikes offshore onto the Nicaragua Rise. The overlying Tertiary section is a mixture of carbonates, red beds, and volcaniclastics.

Offshore, except on the north, the nature and age of the oldest sediments are unknown for lack of penetration. Up to 2,000 m of beds of Early and early Late Cretaceous ages were drilled in three wells near the northern shelf break. Unlike the equivalent-age onshore facies, the sequence is a mixed deep-neritic terrigenous and volcanic-arc type (L. Gordon, personal communication, 1984). Shallower water facies similar to onshore may be present in the central and southern parts of the basin. Lower Tertiary rocks generally are marine, but the section becomes progressively more terrigenous upward as material eroded from Nuclear Central America pushed coeval carbonate deposits eastward.

Onshore major structural trends are directed east-northeast. The Coco River arch is a prominent feature; it dates from the Paleozoic, with Laramide and middle Tertiary rejuvenations. Depositional axes both north and south of the arch parallel it, and a second ridge to the south, the Isabella, is of Tertiary age. Subsequent Tertiary faults, trending north-northwest, have broken the continuity of the older features, particularly offshore where horsts and grabens are the main structural pattern.

Many of the larger grabens are conspicuous depocenters. The deepest, just seaward from the mouth of the Coco River, may contain up to 10,000 m of Cretaceous and Tertiary sediments (Cáceres-Avila and others, 1984). A second (or possible extension of the first) depocenter may be present onshore just south of Caratasca Lagoon where a well penetrated a thick section of red clastics and evaporites before reaching total depth of 4,236 m in a volcanic breccia. This sequence has been identified both as lower Tertiary (Mills and Hugh, 1974) and undifferentiated Cretaceous (Pinet, 1972). A third depocenter may be present on the eastward projection of the Isabella arch where a well was halted at 4,571 m in thin-bedded, predominantly marine clastics of Eocene (Mills and Hugh, 1974), or Paleocene (Hoylman and Chilinger, 1965) or possibly uppermost Cretaceous age (Sawyer, 1975, p. 993).

Through 1986, 36 wells (4 onshore) were drilled in the Mosquitia basin. Six offshore wells had shows of oil and gas, mostly in Eocene carbonates. One well had oil in a Miocene sandstone and a lower Eocene limestone (H. Wories, personal communication, 1985). Two wells tested gas, one (40 percent CO_2) at a rate of 10,000 Mcfd. The central portion of the offshore area appears to be most promising.

East of the basin, two wells have been drilled on Pedro Bank and nine on Jamaica, all unsuccessful.

Pacific Shelf. This on- and offshore forearc basin has been widely studied in connection with the Deep Sea Drilling Project (DSDP) (Seely, 1979; Von Huene and others, 1980, 1985; Aubouin and others, 1982). Up to 6,000 m of strata range from Turonian to Recent in age (Pedrazzini and others, 1982). The sequence contains igneous, metamorphic, and carbonate debris derived from Nuclear Central America. Basement on the north is K/Ar-dated Early Permian granite; elsewhere it is eugeosynclinal. The basin is seaward from a magmatic arc (Pedrazzini and others, 1982).

Turonian–early Santonian rocks are mildly deformed, but Campanian and younger strata are nearly flat lying. Structures are broad and gentle. Source rocks and seeps are unknown, and potential reservoirs probably are tight owing to their volcaniclastic origin. Hence, the basin probably has little or no potential (Pedrazzini and others, 1982). Three wells were drilled off Mexico in the 1970s, one off Guatemala in 1972, and four off Nicaragua between 1967 and 1974.

Limón-Bocas del Toro basin. Best exposures of sediments of this basin straddle the Costa Rica–Panamá border. Approximately 1,200 m (base not exposed) of Cretaceous carbonate has been measured, together with an aggregate thickness of up to 6,000 m of Paleocene, Eocene, and Oligocene mainly deep-water terrigenous-clastic rocks with some volcanics and limestone. Locally, there are thick organic-rich black shales and shallow-water lagoonal and reefal limestones. The Miocene-Pliocene section consists of moderately to poorly sorted sandstone, siltstone, shale, and carbonate deposited in a shallow-marine to continental environment.

Sedimentary and structural trends parallel the northwest-southeast basin axis. They include a number of large anticlinal folds, some associated with thrust faults, generally verging and decreasing in intensity northeastward.

Since the first well (Costa Rica) was drilled in 1916, 32 wells, including three offshore, have been drilled. Many were near the abundant oil seeps in the Río Sixaola area. Several wells had good shows, and one, Cocoles-2 on the northwestern plunge of a major anticline, initially produced 1,800 bopd but went to water after producing approximately 8,000 bbl from a fractured andesite within a deep-water Oligocene limestone (H. Wories, personal communication, 1985). In 1984 an unknown number of core holes 10 to 300 m deep were drilled on the Diablo structure. Some 45° API oil was recovered, but the project was abandoned.

The region has poor to fair potential for future oil and gas discoveries. Further exploration is warranted, particularly in the north and offshore.

Gulf of Panamá. The outer half of the Gulf of Panamá is underlain by a sedimentary sequence up to 3,000 m thick. The strata thin northward, are bounded on the east and west by northwest-trending faults, and are truncated southward by the continental slope. Seismic data show velocity contrasts that may indicate variable lithologies or basalt flows, which are numerous. Two dry holes were drilled in 1974.

The petroleum potential is considered to be very poor because of immature source rocks and extensive volcaniclastic debris in potential reservoirs.

Sambú and Darién basins. These two basins are squeezed tightly between the precipitous, fault-bounded ranges of eastern Panamá. The Darién widens and deepens southeastward. The Sambú basin may have been once part of the Darién but now is separate as a result of post-deposition uplift.

An approximately 3,000-m Cretaceous (and possibly older) section is composed of interbedded mafic volcanics with minor abyssal sedimentary rocks. The Tertiary thickness is estimated to be 7,000 m. Oligocene rocks are largely marine shale, with some thin tuffaceous beds and a persistent limestone up to 700 m thick. Miocene rocks were deposited in shallow water—marine to deltaic and paludal. Shale, sandstone, and sandy carbonates predominate; some beds are very carbonaceous, lignitic, or bituminous.

Major northwest-striking faults characterize the region, imparting a basin-range tectonic style. Large anticlines and synclines parallel the major faults. Subsurface structure, according to sparse well data, is complex.

Petroleum seeps are known in the Sambú basin, and gas

shows have been found in wells of both basins. A shallow well drilled in 1924 in the Sambú basin reportedly had oil seeping from the casing (Johnson and Headington, 1971). Petroleum potential is poor to fair. The basins were nearly closed during the times of deposition. Thick marine shales are reportedly rich in organic matter, but known reservoir properties are poor.

Northern South America

Geologic framework. Cratonic Precambrian basement crops out in eastern Colombia and southern Venezuela. Rimming this Guayana Shield in a great arc from western Colombia to Trinidad is a nearly complete geologic sequence commencing with a nearshore fringe of sediments grading laterally westward and northward into an epeirogenic shelf, then into a thrust- and wrench-faulted miogeosynclinal sequence, and lastly into a faulted, folded, and elevated eugeosynclinal complex (Fig. 3).

Nearshore and shelf sediments occupy the Eastern Llanos, the Barinas-Apure, and the Eastern Venezuela basins as a great wedge that thickens to the west and north as basement deepens.

Steep, basinward-dipping reverse faults generally mark the change to Phanerozoic miogeosynclinal suites, except in eastern Venezuela and Trinidad where eugeosyncline rocks abut the shelf and slope sediments.

These folded, faulted, and partly metamorphosed rocks crop out in the mountains of northern Colombia and western Venezuela. Major faults bound all of these ranges: most are reverse but many also exhibit significant lateral displacement. Productive or potential Late Cretaceous and Tertiary basins occupy the intermontane valleys.

The regional arcuate pattern is broken in northeastern Colombia and northwestern Venezuela by a great, south-pointed triangular block bounded by the Santa Marta–Bucaramanga, Oca, and Boconó faults. The Sierra de Perijá and the Cordillera de Mérida almost encircle the Maracaibo basin.

In the outermost arc, eugeosynclinal terranes are exposed in the western ranges of Colombia and along the Caribbean coast from the Santa Marta massif to Trinidad and Tobago. Major faults separate the continental and oceanic terranes. In western Colombia the boundary has been identified as the Romeral fault (Case and others, 1984, p. 7). Prominent faults also are boundaries in the Sierra Nevada de Santa Marta and Guajira Peninsula. Allochthonous oceanic rocks that make up much of the Cordillera de la Costa have been thrust south over the epeirogenic sediments of the Eastern Venezuela basin. The Tertiary basins between the coast and the Netherland and Venezuelan Antilles exhibit both extensional and compressional tectonics (Biju-Duval and others, 1983). Farther east, the El Pilar fault separates Mesozoic eugeosynclinal strata on the north from the Tertiary sedimentary basins of easternmost Venezuela and southern Trinidad (Rod, 1956, p. 468; Vierbuchen, 1984). For additional data see de Cizancourt (1933), Schuchert (1935), Weeks (1947), Mencher and others (1953), Kugler (1956), López and others (1956), Olsson (1956), Bürgl (1967, 1973), Gansser (1973), Sha-

gam (1975), Stephan and others (1980), and Bonini and others (1984).

Pacific Coastal basin. A major north-south basin in western Colombia, known by a variety of names (Atrato–San Juan, Bolívar geosyncline), is called the Pacific Coastal by Colombian geologists (Bueno and Govea, 1976). It is seldom more than 50 km wide. The Cordillera Occidental overrides the basin on the east along the east-dipping reverse Atrato fault, which also may have left-lateral strike-slip movement (Irving, 1975). Desultory, unsuccessful exploration has been undertaken since 1953.

An estimated 6 to 10 km of Tertiary, largely clastic, sediments is present in several subbasins separated by cross-basin highs. The section ranges from pelagic and turbiditic (lower Tertiary) to neritic and paralic (upper Tertiary). Reservoir quality is likely to be poor because of the graywacke character of sandstones and low porosity in the occasional limestones.

Structures in the basin trend north-south, except near Buenaventura where a cross-basin high is characterized by northeast-southwest structural trends.

Upper Magdalena basin. This basin straddles the Magdalena River for 380 km but is seldom more than 50 km wide. It is relatively small but important because of its production— 46,000 bopd in 1986. A major arch and the Cambao fault, both trending northeast, subdivide the basin (Corrigan, 1967; Van Houten and Travis, 1968). It is a complex tectonic valley that has been deformed by several Cenozoic episodes of reverse faulting and folding. The Cambao and associated faults on the east separate it from the Cordillera Oriental, while to the west the sediments either wedge out on (northern area), or are in fault contact with, the Cordillera Central. The north end of the basin is arbitrary as the sedimentary wedge continues into the Middle Magdalena basin.

Transgressive marine Cretaceous sediments (Aptian and younger) range in thickness from 3,700 m on the northeast to 2,200 m on the southwest. They are overlain by a nearly complete Cenozoic nonmarine section up to 12,000 m thick, which was deposited in four major cycles (Van Houten and Travis, 1968).

Oil exploration has been undertaken since 1918 but significant production has only been achieved since 1962 in the southern subbasin, mainly from Cretaceous sandstones in complex, thrust-faulted anticlines (H. Wories, personal communication, 1986). The northern subbasin has only one operating field, which produced approximately 400 bopd in 1985. Source rocks are organically rich Cretaceous shales. The basin has modest potential.

Middle Magdalena basin. This 400-km-long, vaguely elliptical, basin varies in width from 30 km at its ends to 80 km at its central, deepest part. It resembles a half-graben in that sediments, which lap onto pre-Cretaceous rocks of the Cordillera Central, thicken eastward to be terminated by the reverse faults of the Cambao–La Salina system and the left-lateral Santa Marta–Bucaramanga fault (Morales and others, 1958).

The Cretaceous-Tertiary wedge is unconformable on Jurassic red beds. Except in its lowest formation the Cretaceous is marine, comprising massive limestones and marls, and black, thin-bedded shales, some soft, others calcareous. In contrast, most of the Tertiary sediments were deposited as a mixture of deltaic, fluviatile, paludal, and lacustrine deposits, which accounts for abrupt lateral stratigraphic changes. Maximum thicknesses are found along the central eastern edge of the basin and beneath the reverse faults; the Cretaceous exceeds 4,000 m and the Tertiary 8,000 m. The section wedges out on the west and north but persists southward into the Upper Magdalena basin (Morales and others, 1958).

A system of northeast-trending normal faults is prominent in the west-side outcrop. They continue into the basin and are frequently associated with anticlinal features with similar orientations. The combination provides traps in the Buturama, Totumal, and Casabe fields, among others. Occasionally, secondary southeast-trending normal faults, in association with a prominent northeast-trending fault, provide entrapment, as in the Cantagallo field. Close to the eastern mountain-front secondary, north-south reverse faults have induced folding to form traps, as in the giant La Cira–Infantas field (Taborda, 1965; Sawyer, 1975, p. 1111).

This basin produced 62 percent of the country's cumulative oil through 1986. In 1985 it yielded 48 percent of production, but this ratio dwindled to 27 percent by the end of 1986 owing to the start of Llanos production. Half of the cumulative gas has come from this basin, but it only accounted for 33 percent of 1986 gas, being overshadowed by the major dry gas fields of the Guajira basin. The La Cira–Infantas field has yielded nearly 700 million barrels and will produce much more through enhanced recovery programs in progress. Almost all production is from sandstones of Eocene and Oligocene ages. Only very minor amounts of oil have been recovered (less than 100 bopd in 1986) from Cretaceous fractured limestones in the northern end of the basin. Twenty-six fields produced approximately 95,000 bopd during 1986. The potential for additional discoveries is good, particularly in unexplored overthrust structures.

Lower Magdalena basin. This area includes the entire Colombian Coastal Plain north of the Cordilleras Occidental and Central and west of the Santa Marta–Bucaramanga fault and the offshore platform. It is a complex region with three distinct subdivisions. The eastern half is a faulted cratonic basin underlain by continental crust. A north-northeast–trending anticlinorium of highly deformed and contorted strata occupies the central region from the northern end of the Cordillera Occidental through Barranquilla into the Caribbean. The western portion of the region is occupied by a deep basin filled with moderate to gently folded strata. Shale diapirs are common, particularly along the crest of the anticlinorium where they and mud volcanoes are prominent. The eastern half of the area is generally considered the Lower Magdalena basin; the two western subareas are identified as the Sinú–San Jacinto terrane by Duque-Caro (1984, p. 304).

The Lower Magdalena basin is filled primarily with middle and late Tertiary near-shore sediment up to 3,000 m in thickness. The Sinú–San Jacinto terrane consists of 6,000 m of pelagic and hemipelagic facies of Late Cretaceous–early Tertiary age overlain by 3,000 m of turbidites, in turn overlain by 3,000 m of late Pliocene to Pleistocene terrestrial deposits (Duque-Caro, 1984, p. 309).

Oil exploration has been undertaken since 1910 (Bueno S., 1970). Gas and minor amounts of oil are produced only from the eastern area, although the Sinú–San Jacinto region has had numerous shows in the dozens of wells drilled. Production in 1986 amounted to only 1,300 bopd of oil and condensate and 37,000 Mcfd of gas. Source rocks are the thick, early Tertiary–Late Cretaceous shale sequences. Large structures are not known at present. The turbidite sequences could contain good reservoirs. The future potential of the region, including offshore where only 16 wells have been drilled, is deemed to be only fair.

Guajira basin. This basin occupies the southern half of the Guajira Peninsula between the Cuiza and Oca faults and continues offshore to the west. It deepens from north to south and east to west, reaching more than 5 km just north of the Santa Marta Massif. The basin is only moderately deformed, probably as a secondary response to the forces involved in the Oca fault and the right-lateral Cuiza fault.

Basin fill consists of Eocene and Oligocene limestones and sandy limestones, Miocene sandstones and shales (the thickest sequence), and Pliocene and younger terrigenous clastic sediments. The area is established as gas prone, probably because of the depth of sediment burial and type of organic matter.

Only 23 wildcats have been drilled through 1986 since the first well in 1949. However, major gas reserves (Table 3, Plate 14) were discovered in 1973 (onshore) in Miocene sandstones grading westward into limestones (Franco, 1975). The gas is 98 percent methane. There is fair potential for additional dry-gas discoveries.

Eastern Llanos basin. The Llanos, the largest basin of Colombia, lies between the Cordillera Oriental and the Guayana Shield; the southern and northern limits are the Vaupes swell and Arauca arch, respectively, both spurs of the shield. The basin has three principal structural elements: (1) the folded and faulted foothills zone on the west (overthrust); (2) the central or antithetic fault-belt with prominent northeast and northwest trends; and (3) the stable area or heavy oil province to the south and east near the basin margin.

A Cretaceous and Tertiary clastic sedimentary wedge occupies the basin. It thickens westward to more than 6,000 m near the overthrust belt. Paleozoic and early Mesozoic beds probably are present in the westernmost part and beneath the thrusts (Campbell and Bürgl, 1965, Plate 1) (Fig. 4). The Cretaceous-lower Tertiary sequence is of shallow marine, deltaic, and fluvial origin. The Neogene is represented by terrestrial deposits (Fig. 4). The Guadalupe, Mirador, and Carbonera Formations are the principal reservoirs. The Mirador is widespread, with massive sands, and contains approximately 60 percent of known reserves.

Exploration activity is currently the most intense of Colombia's history as a result of recent major discoveries. Exploration has been cyclical, commencing in the period 1944 to 1948 when

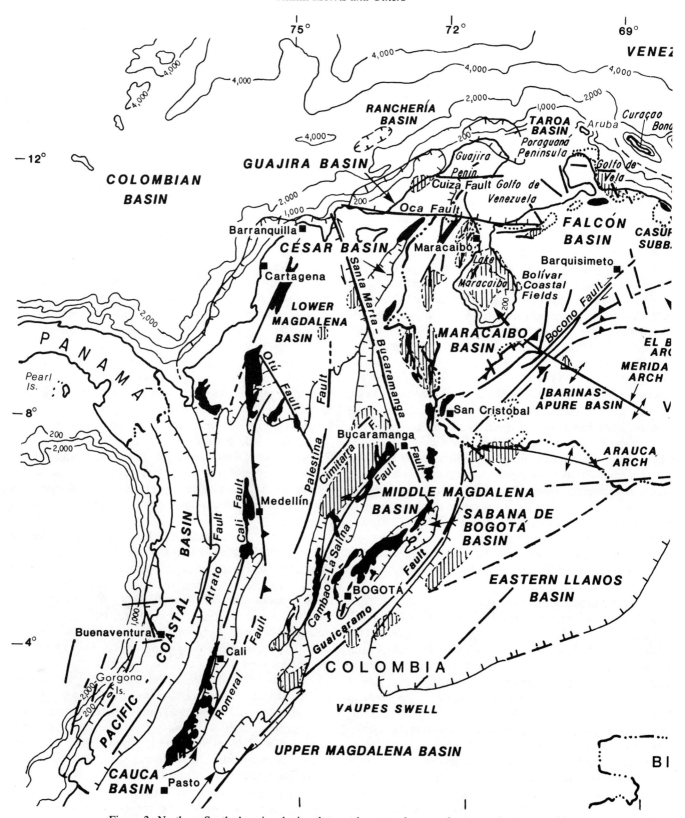

Figure 3. Northern South America: basins that produce petroleum or have petroleum potential; petroleum-producing areas; petroleum-prospective areas; coal fields; major structural elements.

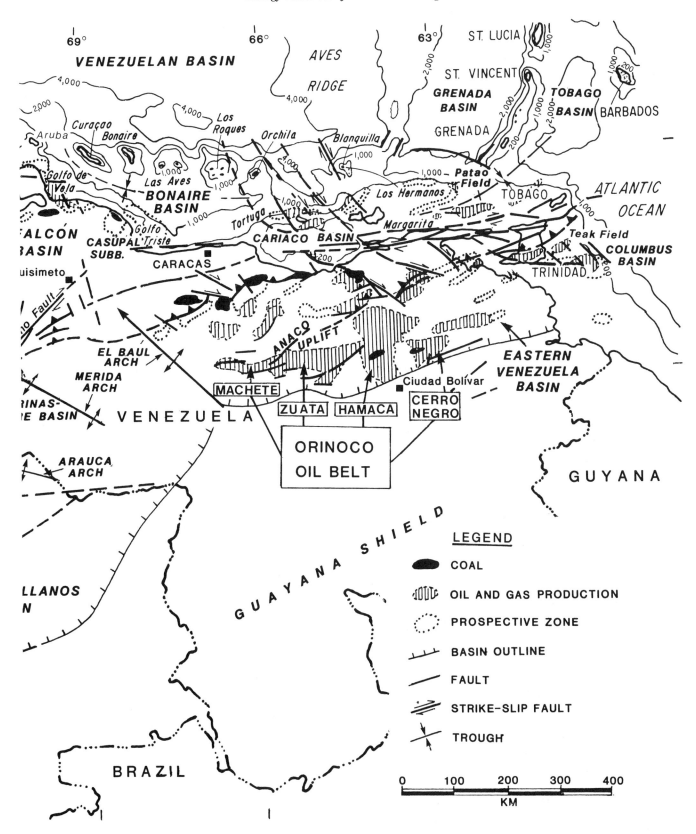

LEGEND

COAL

OIL AND GAS PRODUCTION

PROSPECTIVE ZONE

BASIN OUTLINE

FAULT

STRIKE-SLIP FAULT

TROUGH

0   100   200   300   400
KM

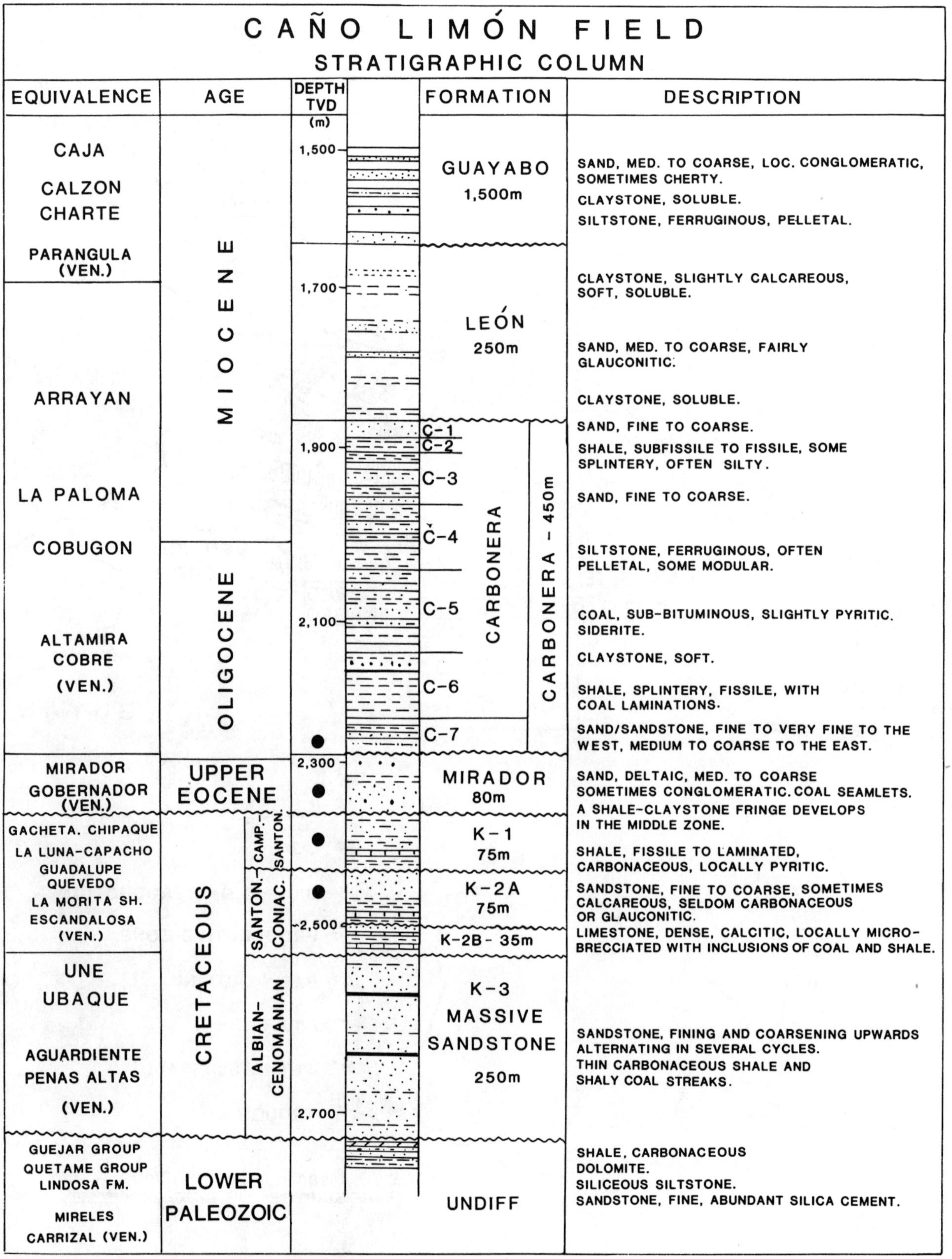

CAÑO LIMÓN FIELD
STRATIGRAPHIC COLUMN

EQUIVALENCE	AGE	DEPTH TVD (m)		FORMATION	DESCRIPTION
CAJA CALZON CHARTE	MIOCENE	1,500		GUAYABO 1,500m	SAND, MED. TO COARSE, LOC. CONGLOMERATIC, SOMETIMES CHERTY. CLAYSTONE, SOLUBLE. SILTSTONE, FERRUGINOUS, PELLETAL.
PARANGULA (VEN.)		1,700		LEÓN 250m	CLAYSTONE, SLIGHTLY CALCAREOUS, SOFT, SOLUBLE. SAND, MED. TO COARSE, FAIRLY GLAUCONITIC.
ARRAYAN					CLAYSTONE, SOLUBLE. SAND, FINE TO COARSE.
LA PALOMA	OLIGOCENE	1,900	C-1 C-2 C-3 C-4	CARBONERA – 450m	SHALE, SUBFISSILE TO FISSILE, SOME SPLINTERY, OFTEN SILTY. SAND, FINE TO COARSE. SILTSTONE, FERRUGINOUS, OFTEN PELLETAL, SOME MODULAR.
COBUGON					
ALTAMIRA COBRE (VEN.)		2,100	C-5 C-6 C-7		COAL, SUB-BITUMINOUS, SLIGHTLY PYRITIC. SIDERITE. CLAYSTONE, SOFT. SHALE, SPLINTERY, FISSILE, WITH COAL LAMINATIONS. SAND/SANDSTONE, FINE TO VERY FINE TO THE WEST, MEDIUM TO COARSE TO THE EAST.
MIRADOR GOBERNADOR (VEN.)	UPPER EOCENE	2,300		MIRADOR 80m	SAND, DELTAIC, MED. TO COARSE SOMETIMES CONGLOMERATIC. COAL SEAMLETS. A SHALE-CLAYSTONE FRINGE DEVELOPS IN THE MIDDLE ZONE.
GACHETA. CHIPAQUE LA LUNA-CAPACHO GUADALUPE QUEVEDO LA MORITA SH. ESCANDALOSA (VEN.)	CRETACEOUS (SANTON.-CAMP.-SANTON.) (CONIAC.)			K-1 75m K-2A 75m K-2B- 35m	SHALE, FISSILE TO LAMINATED, CARBONACEOUS, LOCALLY PYRITIC. SANDSTONE, FINE TO COARSE, SOMETIMES CALCAREOUS, SELDOM CARBONACEOUS OR GLAUCONITIC. LIMESTONE, DENSE, CALCITIC, LOCALLY MICRO-BRECCIATED WITH INCLUSIONS OF COAL AND SHALE.
UNE UBAQUE AGUARDIENTE PENAS ALTAS (VEN.)	(ALBIAN-CENOMANIAN)	2,500 2,700		K-3 MASSIVE SANDSTONE 250m	SANDSTONE, FINING AND COARSENING UPWARDS ALTERNATING IN SEVERAL CYCLES. THIN CARBONACEOUS SHALE AND SHALY COAL STREAKS.
GUEJAR GROUP QUETAME GROUP LINDOSA FM. MIRELES CARRIZAL (VEN.)	LOWER PALEOZOIC			UNDIFF	SHALE, CARBONACEOUS DOLOMITE. SILICEOUS SILTSTONE. SANDSTONE, FINE, ABUNDANT SILICA CEMENT.

Figure 4. Stratigraphic column, Caño Limón area, eastern Llanos, Colombia.

six unsuccessful wells were drilled. Between 1958 and 1968, approximately 20 additional wells were drilled in the east-central part of the basin and foothill belts; many had significant shows. A 1969 discovery of 14° API oil in the south has subsequently become the Castilla field. In 1974, exploration moved into the central basin with the discovery of 32° API oil in the Trinidad field. The Caño field was discovered in 1978, followed by Arauca in 1980, and Apiay in 1981. The giant Caño Limón–La Yuca–Matanegra complex (Fig. 5), discovered during 1983 to 1984 on the Arauca arch, is now estimated to have proved 1.8 billion barrels of oil in place. Oil shipments began in December 1985 at 30,000 bopd; by the end of 1986 the rate had increased to 176,186 bopd (Wiman, 1987).

Other Colombian basins. There are four additional Colombian basins germane to this chapter, but they have little or no potential for oil and gas: the Sabena de Bogotá, César, Taroa, and Ranchería (Fig. 3).

The Sabana de Bogotá is an elevated basin in the central Cordillera Oriental. Up to 11 km of Cretaceous marine clastic (largely shale) sediments are moderately folded into long anticlines separated by broad synclines filled with the remnants of marine Tertiary cover (Campbell and Bürgl, 1965). Movement of underlying Jurassic salt, known from plugs and brine springs, probably has influenced structural patterns.

The northeast-trending César basin contains up to 5,500 m of Cretaceous-Tertiary sediments with affinities to both the Middle Magdalena and the Maracaibo basins. It has been interpreted as the offset northern end of the Middle Magdalena basin (Campbell, 1968; Alvarez, 1971). Shows have been recorded in some of the 13 wells drilled.

The Taroa (Franco, 1975), largely offshore north of the tip of the Guajira Peninsula, contains up to 5,000 m of Tertiary sediments; the deepest of seven wells (2 onshore) reached a total depth of 4,630 m.

The tiny (2,500 km²) Ranchería basin, partially filled (1,500 m) with turbidites, is perched on the continental slope at the 2,600-m isobath northwest of the Guajira Peninsula (Krause, 1971). It has no petroleum potential.

Maracaibo-Falcón petroleum province. The Maracaibo basin, between the Sierra de Perijá and Cordillera de Mérida, deepens to a maximum of 11,000 m at the base of the Cordillera de Mérida. The Colombian portion of the basin on the southwest is the Catatumbo area.

Basement consists of igneous and metamorphic rocks on which pre-Cretaceous rocks are thinly and erratically distributed, except in a deep graben in the western part of the lake (Kellogg, 1984). Lower and middle Cretaceous strata are a transgressive sequence that culminated in Turonian-Coniacian times (La Luna Formation). Open-sea, shallow-water limestones were deposited in the north, sandstones in the Catatumbo area, and mixed clastics to the west. Upper Cretaceous rocks display a regressive cycle terminating in the deposition of coal-bearing sequences at the close of Cretaceous time. Brackish-water deposits are thickest in the west and south where up to 1,000 m of sediment was depos-

ited. Restricted marine, paralic, and fresh-water deposition continued during the Paleocene and Eocene, except on the northeast where up to 7,500 m of open-marine shales and sandstones were deposited. The uplift of the surrounding ranges during the late Tertiary Andean orogeny caused the isolation of the basin and provided the source of up to 7,500 m of brackish-water Oligocene-Miocene sediments in the southern part of the basin.

Structural features of the basin generally reflect patterns exposed in the surrounding mountains but are more subdued. In most of the basin the principal structural grain is north-south but may deviate as much as 30°. Thus structural grain near the Cordillera de Mérida has an east-northeast trend. On the north, approaching the Oca fault, patterns turn eastward, and on the western margin, north-northeast folds parallel the Sierra de Perijá. The lack of intense folding and faulting, except near the basin edges, is probably related to the generally rigid basement. Three hinge-belts are intimately associated with major petroleum accumulation; a Cretaceous hinge line trends north-south along the western edge of the basin, an Eocene belt is present in the northeast portion, and an Oligocene-Miocene cross-basin high is beneath Lake Maracaibo.

For additional information, see Sutton (1946), Staff of Caribbean Petroleum Company (1948), Young and others (1956), Miller and others (1958), Rubio (1961), Martinez (1970), and Sutherland (1972).

The Maracaibo basin is one of the world's most prolific; among other large fields it contains the giant, 30-billion-barrel Bolívar Coastal field (Carmalt and St. John, 1986), the world's fifth largest, discovered in 1917. The field produces from Eocene, Oligocene, and Miocene fluvial and deltaic sandstones. Gently tilted strata dip generally southwest as a homocline. Entrapment is provided by lateral and updip stratigraphic variations, unconformities both with and without asphalt seals, and a system of north-to-northwest–trending normal faults (Staff of Caribbean Petroleum Company, 1948). To the west, the Mara and La Paz anticlines produce high-gravity oil from shallow-marine Eocene sandstones, deeper Cretaceous euxinic limestones, and pre-Jurassic fractured crystalline basement (Guariguata and Richardson, 1960).

In the Catatumbo area, sharp anticlinal features have produced more than 150 million bbl of oil from fractured Aptian limestone and sandstone (Tibú anticline) and the "sparkling" sandstones of the Paleocene Barco Formation in the Petrólea and Tibú-Socuavó anticlines (Notestein and others, 1944; Roberts and others, 1959, Fig. 1). In the Río Zulia fields, Eocene continental sandstones, the Mirador Formation, are oil productive (Preston, 1975). Other discoveries in the folded zone have yielded gas.

Deep Eocene and Cretaceous potential in the southern part of the basin is substantiated by the 1987 discovery of 4,500 bopd from Cretaceous rocks at 5,485 m (Oil & Gas Journal, 1987). Also the foothills belt along the Sierra de Perijá has been only lightly explored, and the region southeast of the Bolívar Coastal field deserves additional exploration.

The Falcón basin, including the Casupal subbasin and the

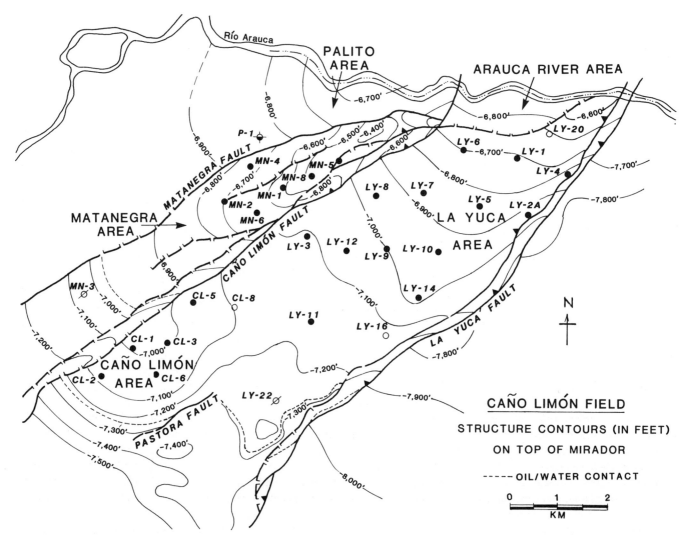

Figure 5. Structure contour map, top of Mirador Formation, Caño Limón area, Colombia.

Bonaire basin, an eastward offshore extension east of the Maracaibo platform, is floored, at least in part, by eugeosynclinal rocks overlain by Eocene flysch but is essentially an Oligocene-Miocene sedimentary trough. Postdepositional compression gave rise to tight folds and thrusting (Muessig, 1984). Minor oil and gas production from Miocene paralic sandstones has been established since 1921. Traps are closures against faults or anticlines, but also are partly stratigraphic because of sandstone lenticularity.

The Gulf of Venezuela basin, between the Guajira and Paraguaná Peninsulas, is unexplored. Hence, the geology is unknown except through geophysical data. It is probably a subbasin, as the sedimentary column is thickest (up to 7,000 m) in the southeast adjacent to the Falcón basin and thins northwestward over a rising basement. González de Juana and others (1980) suggested stratigraphic affinities with the Maracaibo basin. Major fault trends are northwest and northeast. The primary physical requirements for petroleum generation and accumulation appear to be present, so the basin should have fair potential.

The Golfo de Vela is offshore east of the Paraguaná Peninsula. An east-west high separates it from the Falcón basin. Mafic igneous and metamorphic basement is overlain by red beds (up to 300 m) followed by as much as 3,700 m of upper Tertiary limestone, thick shale, and mixed sandstones, shale, and calcarenite. A major anticlinal nose plunges northwest, parallel to principal fault strikes (González de Juana and others, 1980).

Exploration began in 1972 with an oil discovery (Vasquez, 1975). At the end of 1986, six oil wells and one gas well had been established out of a total of 19 wells. Substantial flow rates were confirmed on the productive wells, and official reserves have been estimated at 150 to 500 million bbl of liquids, 1,000 bcf of associated gas, and 300 bcf of free gas.

In the Casupal area a thick sequence of upper Tertiary shale with minor thin sandstones is tightly folded in an east-west trend. Minor production has been obtained from the sandstones. The sequence continues eastward into the Golfo Triste where three unsuccessful wells have been drilled.

Barinas-Apure petroleum province. Geographically, this province is a northeast continuation of the eastern Llanos. Geologically, it is circumscribed by the Cordillera de Mérida, the Río Orinoco, and the Arauca and El Baúl arches.

In general, the sedimentary fill of the region thickens westward and northwestward to a maximum of 7,500 m. Early Paleozoic unmetamorphosed rocks are present, but the thickness and areal extent are unknown for lack of drilling. Marine Cretaceous rocks rest with profound unconformity on basement and older sedimentary formations. In turn they are overlain by marine Eocene formations. Mostly nonmarine upper Oligocene and Miocene sediments unconformably overlie older strata and lap onto the Guayana Shield. On the west, the Cretaceous–early Tertiary strata thicken dramatically and become more marine and complete toward the mountain front. The basin was contiguous with the Maracaibo basin from Cretaceous to mid-Tertiary time, when uplift associated with the Andean orogeny isolated the area.

The province is bimodal, with the basement surface dipping westward in both modes, which are separated by the east-west Apure fault (Feo-Codecido and others, 1984). It is a significant tectonic feature as it appears to separate metamorphosed mid-Paleozoic rocks on the north from unmetamorphosed lower Paleozoic sediments on the south. The southern basin segment is the deeper and has many grabenlike features. Displacement on the Apure fault is greatest on the west; it appears to die out eastward.

Above the pre-Cretaceous unconformity, structure is confined to mild block faulting and sediment drape over basement fault blocks. The Mérida arch, a gentle northwest-southeast swell, separates the province into the Barinas (north) and the Apure (south) basin. The latter also is known as the Uribante.

Source rocks are relatively sparse and probably are confined to the more marine western area. The stratigraphic equivalent of La Luna and Colón Formations is present but not in the facies that is the prolific source rock of the Magdalena and Maracaibo basins. Reservoir rocks abound as channel and fluviatile sandstones. Basin potential is generally only fair but is good in the deep southwestern area, a fact established by recent discoveries along the Arauca arch.

The first well was drilled in 1930, and the first significant discovery was Silvestre in 1948 on the Mérida arch. Discoveries were confined to the Mérida arch until 1984 when the Guafita field, offsetting the Caño Limón field, was discovered. The cluster of fields on the Mérida arch has produced 550 million bbls, and two fields have been accorded "giant" status (Martinez, 1970); a third is likely to achieve it. Press reports suggest that 500 million bbls has been proved along the Venezuelan side of the Arauca arch.

Eastern Venezuela petroleum province. Most of the Venezuelan Llanos is underlain by widely diverse sedimentary and structural regimes (Mencher and others, 1953; Lopez and others, 1956; Renz and others, 1958). The region extends from the El Baúl arch to beyond the shelf break of the Atlantic platform and from the Guayana Shield to the Caribbean mountains and the Central Range of Trinidad. There are seven major centers

of conventional oil and gas fields and a vast concentration of heavy oil, the Orinoco Oil Belt. The province is frequently divided into two basins; the Gúarico on the west and the Maturín on the east, separated by the northeast-trending Anaco uplift and its southwestward projection.

Unmetamorphosed sedimentary rocks of Paleozoic and pre-Cretaceous Mesozoic ages have been identified in the Guárico basin; Cretaceous sediments rest directly on Precambrian basement in the Maturín basin. Cretaceous-Tertiary terrigenous clastics are the most widespread and important sediments in the province. They were deposited in three successive cycles of transgression (and regression) from the north and east. Hence, depositional environments range from continental through paralic on the south and west to deep-water turbidites on the north and northeast.

The sedimentary wedge thickens northward and eastward as the basement surface deepens. Total thickness in the northeast is 12,000 m or more. This deepening is relatively constant in the Maturín basin, but northwest of the Anaco uplift, a major deep graben occupies part of the Guárico basin (Feo-Codecido and others, 1984). The north-dipping sedimentary wedge is terminated by the southward-thrust Caribbean Mountains. Folds are present only in the central and northern parts of the basin where they increase in amplitude and steepness northward. The southern shelf is characterized by widespread normal faults. Fault and fold trends are generally northeast and northwest. Several prominent northwest-striking right-lateral faults disrupt the Caribbean Mountains.

The seven areas of major accumulation are, from west to east: Las Mercedes, Anaco, Oficina, Jusepín, Temblador, Southern basin, and Columbus basin. The Orinoco Oil Belt is discussed in a subsequent section.

The Las Mercedes and associated fields, in the central Guárico basin, produce from both Cretaceous and Oligocene rocks in traps formed by conjugate systems of normal faults. The Anaco fields are located on the structural high that separates the Guárico and Maturín basins. Reservoirs are Eocene and Oligocene-Miocene deltaic and fluviatile sandstones draped over older anticlinal closures, frequently thrust faulted.

In the Maturín basin, the Oficina area is the largest locus of accumulation (Hedberg and others, 1947). Oil is produced from Oligocene-Miocene deltaic, channel-bar, and other paralic deposits. All of the fields have multiple reservoirs. Traps are formed by conjugate sets of normal faults, many up-to-the-basin. Similar stratigraphic and structural conditions exist in the Temblador area where the main production is from lower Miocene sandstones. Fields frequently have a high gas-oil ratio.

Accumulations in the Jusepín area are largely in sandstone pinchouts of overlapping Oligocene-Miocene flyschlike strata on northeast-striking thrust-faulted folds. At the northeastern end of the trend, the Quiriquire field produces from Pliocene beds (Borger, 1952). Minor production is also obtained from some Cretaceous rocks. The Pedernales field, on the shores of the Gulf of Paria, is an anticline with an axial mud diapir. This is approximately the western limit of a diapir field that extends eastward into the Southern and Columbus basins.

Major accumulations in the Southern basin of Trinidad occur in Miocene and Pliocene deltaic sandstones, which are in overturned and thrust-faulted en échelon folds and against antithetic strike-slip faults associated with the Los Bajos fault zone (Barr and others, 1958). Others are in anticlines on both flanks of the onshore synclinal basin, several with diapiric shale cores. Still other accumulations are found in lower Miocene turbidites.

Prograded deltaic strata of Pliocene and Pleistocene ages occupy depocenters in the Columbus basin: the Pleistocene depocenter is farther east. The Pliocene depocenter features an eastward-striking Pliocene-Pleistocene wrench system with associated east-northeast–striking anticlines that, in combination with north-northwest–striking down-to-the-northeast growth and other normal faults, form major traps (Leonard, 1983). Clay ridges and swells and antithetic, down-to-the-southwest growth faults are associated with the north-northwest faults (Bane and Chanpong, 1980) (see Fig. 7).

Source beds are believed to be Miocene shales. The overlying Pliocene to Quaternary section is estimated to be 5,500 to 6,000 m thick; the total Tertiary section has not been penetrated but is estimated at 9,000 m. Production is typically high-gravity oil with a high gas-oil ratio.

Sediments in the Pleistocene depocenter are much finer grained, being farther removed from source material. The sand-shale ratio is much lower than in the Pliocene area; consequently, reservoir productivity is less. Faults are generally listric and associated in places with rollover anticlines. The region is gas prone; major deposits have been tapped, but several discoveries are undeveloped.

Although oil and tar seeps have been known since the sixteenth century, modern exploration in Trinidad began in 1857 with the commencement of mining the Pitch Lake and the drilling of an 85-m well nearby. The first successful well (8 bopd) was completed in 1867, and the first commercial well in 1908 near the Pitch Lake (Frampton and Birchwood, 1979).

In Venezuela the earliest drilling was near oil seeps associated with Pedernales field in 1890, and the first commercial well was Quiriquire-1 in 1928 (Borger, 1952). In the 1920s, exploration was centered near the seeps along the thrust-faulted northern edge of the basin in the Jusepín area. The 1930s saw major discoveries in the La Mercedes, Anaco, Oficina, and Temblador areas and the Southern basin. From 1937 to 1960, giant oil fields were found in eastern Venezuela at the rate of one every eight months, and through 1970, 29 giant oil fields with aggregate reserves of 6.0 billion bbls had been discovered (Martinez, 1970). Additional large finds were made in the 1970s and early 1980s. In the Jusepín area, 1.0 billion bbl and 3,700 bcf of gas were reported discovered (Oil & Gas Journal, 1986). Cumulative oil production in this province is 11,100 million bbl, including 2,333 million bbl in Trinidad (Table 3, Plate 14).

Offshore exploration began in the Gulf of Paria in the early 1950s, and the first discovery was in 1955. In the Columbus basin, exploration commenced in 1961, and within a decade four discoveries had been confirmed. The province potential remains good to excellent despite all the discoveries; it is probably best in the deep eastern part of the Maturín basin, which includes the Orinoco Delta and Columbus basin.

Margarita-Tobago petroleum province. A 100-km-wide continental shelf extends from the island of Tortuga 500 km eastward to Tobago. Seven depocenters have been identified on the shelf and the presence of hydrocarbons established in nine separate areas. Sedimentary fill is generally Tertiary and younger; early Tertiary rocks are frequently highly disturbed and, at least locally, they can be considered economic basement.

The western half of the province, the Testigos platform, is a horst and graben region with pre-Tertiary metamorphics either exposed or covered with a thin veneer of lower Tertiary strata on the horsts and younger sediments in the grabens. The eastern half of the shelf is underlain by a major sedimentary basin that widens and deepens, first eastward, then gradually turning northeastward across the continental shelf to continue as the deep-water Tobago Basin. Aside from geological summaries (González de Juana and others, 1980; Biju-Duval and others, 1983), little has been published regarding the petroleum geology of the region.

The five depocenters in the western half of the province have common stratigraphy: Miocene and younger terrigenous clastics with sandstones as reservoirs or potential reservoirs. Block faulting is the common structural style. Three principal fault trends are apparent: east-west, east-northeast, and northwest. Hence, the opportunities for fault traps are numerous.

Such a fault trap is found in the Barcelona area in the acute angle formed by the intersection of the El Pilar and Urica faults. A well, drilled in 1981 to a total depth of 1,426 m, tested 350 bopd of light oil and 50 MMcfpd of gas from Miocene basal sandstones on Cretaceous metasediments.

Tortuga Island is a horst flanked by depocenters. The South Tortuga slope contains more than 4,000 m of Neogene sediments, as determined by geophysical measurement and drilling. The presence of hydrocarbons was established in 1979 by a well drilled to 3,686 m that tested high-gravity oil at a rate of 691 bopd from Miocene sandstones and gas at 36.3 MMcfpd from Pliocene-Pleistocene sandstones. The North Tortuga slope, with a similar geologic setting, has up to 5,000 m of prospective sediments. A well drilled to that depth in 1980 tested light oil at the rate of 200 bopd.

Two depocenters northwest of Margarita Island contain at least 4,000 m of sediment and trend east-northeast. A well drilled in 1980 to 3,765 m recovered gas flows at the rate of 11.0 MMcfpd with 250 bopd of condensate from thin Miocene sandstones overlying Oligocene and Eocene sediments.

The major sedimentary area on the east, Carúpano basin of local usage, contains 6,000 m or more of sediments in its northeastern end. The basin is more or less symmetrical, with the axis trending east and curving to the northeast. Four productive areas have been established on the southeast flank and one discovery on the northwest flank. The first discovery was 15 km northwest of Tobago in 1976. Drilling in Venezuelan waters began in 1978 where several wells have outlined the prolific Patao area. The Patao-1 had a cumulative test rate of 86.0 MMcfpd from the three Miocene sandstones. A discovery was made on the northwest flank of the basin where Miocene-Pliocene sandstones pinch out against the Testigos platform. All of the gas discovered to date is rich in condensate. Government press releases provisionally credit the Patao area with reserves of 20,000 bcf. The region has good to excellent potential, primarily for gas, as shown by the current success ratio of 50 percent. Development has not yet commenced.

Eastern Caribbean

Geologic framework. The principal tectonic elements of the eastern Caribbean are: the Aves Ridge (a double magmatic arc), the Lesser Antilles (a volcanic arc that bifurcates north of Guadeloupe), and the nonvolcanic Barbados Ridge. On and between these positive features are six sedimentary areas: Aves Ridge, Grenada Basin, Saba Bank, Kallinago Depression, Tobago Basin, and Barbados Ridge. Aves Ridge and the Kallinago Depression are without merit as they are too small and the section is too thin. The other areas may locally have potential (Fig. 6).

Grenada Basin. This deep-water (2,800 m) basin lies between the Aves Ridge and the Lesser Antilles arc south of 16° N lat. Its southern end is the Margarita-Tobago continental slope. Basin fill increases from 1,000 m on the north to 7,000 m on the south, where seismic profiles indicate the presence of up to 4 km of flat-lying strata unconformably overlying a deeper folded section up to 3 km thick (Pinet and others, 1985). The disturbed sequence may correlate with Cretaceous–middle Eocene strata exposed in the southern Lesser Antilles (Westercamp and others, 1985). The northern part of the basin is unlikely to have petroleum deposits owing to the thin section and the probable high percentage of volcanic debris. On the south, however, much of the sediment load is probably derived from the continental shelf and mainland, so source and reservoir rocks are likely to be present buried deep enough for petroleum generation. The sedimentary sequence on the south continues up the continental slope to the shelf where discoveries have been made.

Saba Bank. The Saba Bank and the area east and south of it to the Lesser Antilles is underlain by an eastward-thickening wedge of sediments ranging in age from middle Eocene to Pliocene on severely deformed Cretaceous–early Eocene volcanogenic rocks. Eocene strata are both shallow-water limestones and volcaniclastics; the Oligocene is represented primarily by volcaniclastics; and reef buildup is Miocene-Holocene in age. Well data show that the sedimentary sequence is 2,800 m thick on the southwest side of the bank and thickens to 4,200 m at its northeast edge and to more than 6,000 m in the depression southwest of St. Eustatius. The section thins southward to less than 1,000 m at the cross-basin arch, which plunges southwest from Guadelupe and separates this basin from the Grenada Basin.

There is little apparent structure on Saba Bank; normal

faults mark its eastern edge. Short-period disharmonic folds and north-south faults characterize the southern part of the basin (Case and Holcombe, 1980).

Probably only the northeast portion of the region has potential for hydrocarbons, and it is only very poor to poor. Source and reservoir rocks are identified in the Saba Bank-2, and the top of the "oil window" maturation temperature was found at approximately 3,000 m.

Tobago Basin. This basin is a smaller and shallower replica of the Grenada Basin. A sedimentary wedge, up to 7,000 m thick at the south end, thins northward. Overlying acoustic basement are at least three seismic-stratigraphic units of upwardly decreasing structural complexity, believed to be middle Miocene and younger (Biju-Duval and others, 1982; Westbrook and others, 1984). This sequence, which is up to 4,000 m thick at the latitude of Barbados, onlaps both the east and west flanks and progrades northward.

Prospective petroleum areas are confined to the southern end of the basin beneath the continental slope of the Margarita-Tobago shelf and the eastern flank adjacent the Barbados Ridge. The potential for petroleum is suggested by oil deposits on Barbados and gas discoveries on the Margarita-Tobago shelf.

Barbados Ridge. This complex morphologic and structural feature is an uplifted, faulted, and folded pile of sediments several thousand meters thick, widely intruded by mud diapirs. The origin and tectogenesis of the ridge is the subject of numerous theories (Daviess, 1971; Speed and Larue, 1982; Speed, 1983; Morris and others, this volume, Ch. 17; and Pindell and Barrett, this volume).

Direct knowledge of stratigraphy is confined to wells and a window of pre-Quaternary sediments on Barbados, the apex of the range, and nine DSDP core holes at the base of the eastern flank. The sequence ranges in age from late Paleocene(?) through Holocene. The oldest formation (Pudsey and Reading, 1982) is the Joes River Formation, a dark, structureless, slickensided mudstone, generally oil saturated, believed to be late Paleocene–early Eocene (Larue and Speed, 1984), but also containing fragments of Cretaceous sediments (Senn, 1940, p. 1573). It is widely considered to be a mud diapir that has severely disturbed younger Tertiary rocks. Concentric cliffs and terraces of Pleistocene coral, rising from the coast to the top of the island, demonstrate episodic uplift (Poole and Barker, 1982). The chaotic structure precludes a reliable estimate of stratigraphic thickness.

Barbadian oil has been known for more than 360 years; since the late 1800s, shallow wells have produced small quantities of light oil from sandstones closely associated with the Joes River Formation. Reservoirs probably are small and discontinuous, as continuous drilling is required to maintain production to offset rapid well decline. In recent years, production has ranged from 500 to 1,800 bopd. Cumulative production through 1986 is estimated at 3.1 million bbl. Substantial discoveries are extremely unlikely, but the area could maintain its marginal production for one or more decades.

The petroleum potential of the flanks of the Barbados Ridge

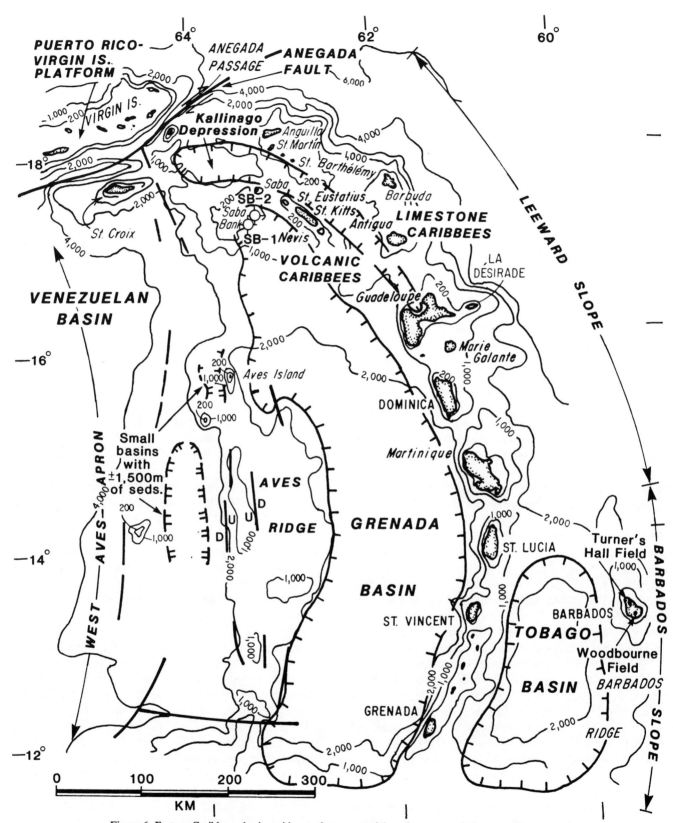

Figure 6. Eastern Caribbean: basins with petroleum potential; major structural elements. For sense of strike-slip motion on Anegada fault see Stephan and others, 1986.

probably is poor to very poor and limited to the southern end, but too little is known to do more than speculate.

Greater Antilles and southeastern North America

Geologic framework. The original Greater Antilles volcanic arc extended from the eastern end of the Puerto Rico–Virgin Islands platform westward through Hispaniola, the southern ranges of eastern Cuba, and the Cayman Ridge, a concept first propounded by Pardo (1966) and subsequently supported by Knipper and Cabrera (1974), Pardo (1975), and Millán and Somin (1981), although only Pardo (1975) specifically mentioned the Cayman Ridge. The volcanic arc and Bahamas platform were close to and parallel with one another east of Cuba. The Bahamas platform extended to north of Puerto Rico and the Virgin Islands until the end of early Pliocene time when it was tilted northward into the Puerto Rico Trench (Alonso and others, 1983; Meyerhoff and others, 1983a, 1983b). West of Hispaniola the volcanic arc was separated from the Bahamas platform by the Yucatán Basin and the Cuban volcanic arc (Morris and others, this volume, Ch. 17). The Cuban arc was the source of Cuban nappes west of the Cauto fault (Fig. 7).

The Bahamas carbonate platform was in existence by Callovian to Oxfordian time (Tator and Hatfield, 1975). The volcanic arcs on the south were formed by Hauterivian and Barremian times, or possibly earlier. From middle Cretaceous through middle Eocene time a series of nappes was emplaced northward onto the Bahamas platform. Earliest emplacement was in western and northern Cuba only; nappe ages become increasingly young eastward, but activity in the west continued throughout the period. In western Hispaniola, some thrusting continued during late Tertiary time (Morris and others, this volume, Ch. 17).

Petroleum prospects are limited mainly to the Bahamas platform, the overthrust belt closest to it, and some successor basins. In Cuba, most of the successor basins are on nappes emplaced during Campanian time and contain normal marine sequences of late Campanian through Miocene ages. East of the Cauto fault (Fig. 7), successor basins are mainly post-middle Eocene.

Basins of Puerto Rico. Sedimentary areas are present on and off the north and south coasts. The South Coast Tertiary basin occupies the continental shelf and upper slope and a small onshore fringe. From 1,500 to 2,000 m of middle Oligocene through lower Pliocene strata are present. Conglomerate and ill-sorted silt- and sandstone are characteristic, but Oligocene barrier reefs also are known. Normal faults, most reaching to the surface, are numerous except in the western part of the area, which appears less disturbed and has gentle rollover-type structures. Source rocks have not been identified; three wells onshore found no indications of hydrocarbons. Basin petroleum potential is poor to very poor.

The North Coast Tertiary basin, also known as the Arecibo, is mostly offshore from the Mona fault zone to the eastern Virgin Islands. From 1,000 to 1,800 m of Oligocene through Pliocene carbonates and subordinate terrigenous clastics overlie Late Cretaceous–early Eocene "economic basement" onshore. The section thickens seaward, and up to 1,500 m of older rocks underlies the sequence known onshore (Meyerhoff and others, 1983a, 1983b). The shallow-water sequences recognized onshore have been identified to the northern limit of the basin in waters 5,200 m and more deep (Fox and Heezen, 1975).

Basin structure is homoclinal, and regional dip is parallel approximately to the 4° continental slope, which commences at the shoreline. Offshore, north-dipping normal faults are common in the pre-Oligocene section. Some are listric and others show growth. Geochemical studies suggest the possibility of source rocks (Meyerhoff and others, 1983a, 1983b; Hayes and others, 1986). A single well onshore encountered potential sandstone reservoirs, which also are evident in outcrop. Carbonate reservoirs also are possible. Petroleum potential is probably only poor to very poor.

Basins of Hispaniola. Of the five sedimentary areas within this province, the San Cristóbal–Baní and the North Mona are offshore, and the Enriquillo (Cul de Sac), San Juan-Azua, and the Cibao are onshore.

The ovate San Cristóbal–Baní contains up to 3,000 m of Paleocene through Pliocene sediments on Late Cretaceous "economic basment." Water depths reach 1,200 m at the southern edge of the basin. On the narrow onshore fringe, sediments tend to grade from shallow-water to deep-water facies from east to west. On the west, severe structural deformation is oriented north-south. Offshore seismic data (Ladd and others, 1981) show that deformation dies out eastward, and there is gentle south dip of a sediment wedge that thickens to the southern boundary ridge. Oil seeps have been reported in the western part of the basin (Guerra-Peña, 1956; Ellis, 1982), and oil and gas shows in two wells indicate source rocks are present. Both carbonate and sandstones are potential reservoirs. Traps are more likely to be structural on the west and stratigraphic in the east. A total of four wells has been drilled onshore. Basin potential, at best, is poor.

The north Mona basin occupies approximately 15,000 km^2 of the continental slope between the Dominican Republic and Puerto Rico. It has stratigraphic and structural similarities to the North Coast Tertiary basin on the east. Up to 3,000 m of post–middle Eocene sediments is present in waters 400 to 800 m deep. Petroleum potential is poor.

The three onshore basins are sufficiently alike in stratigraphy and structure to warrant common treatment. All are long (225 to 300 km), narrow (20 to 25 km) depressions oriented approximately west-northwest. From 6,000 to 7,000 m of late Eocene-Pleistocene, predominantly marine strata are present. The older rocks tend to be of deeper water facies than the younger; evaporites are common in the Enriquillo basin. Thicknesses of individual stratigraphic units show a wide range; lateral facies changes are abrupt.

The basins generally are identified as grabens, but drilling and seismic data indicate they may be ramp valleys (Nemec, 1982). Folds are usually steep and show evidence of multiple compressive events.

The necessary conditions for oil and gas generation are pres-

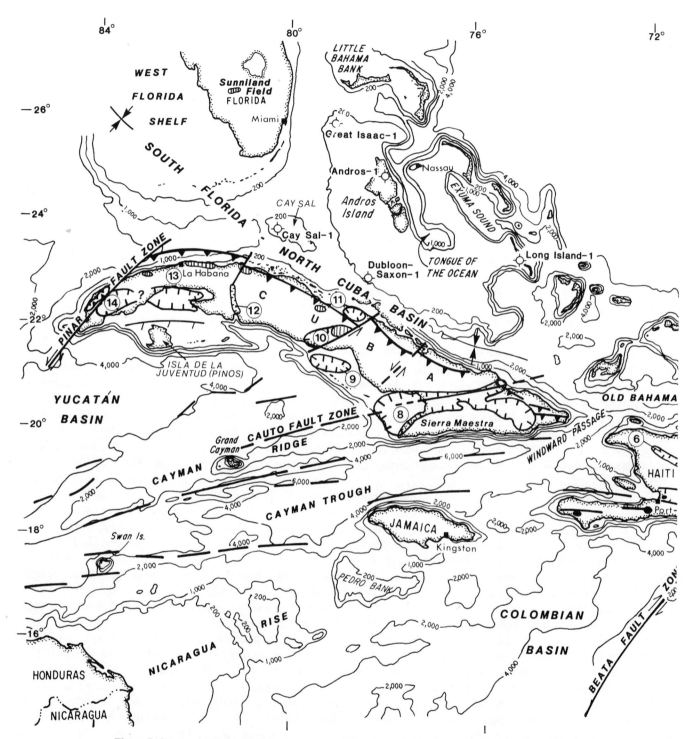

Figure 7. Greater Antilles and adjacent areas: petroleum-producing basins; petroleum-potential basins; petroleum-producing areas; major structural elements. For sense of strike-slip motion of Anegada fault see caption, Figure 6.

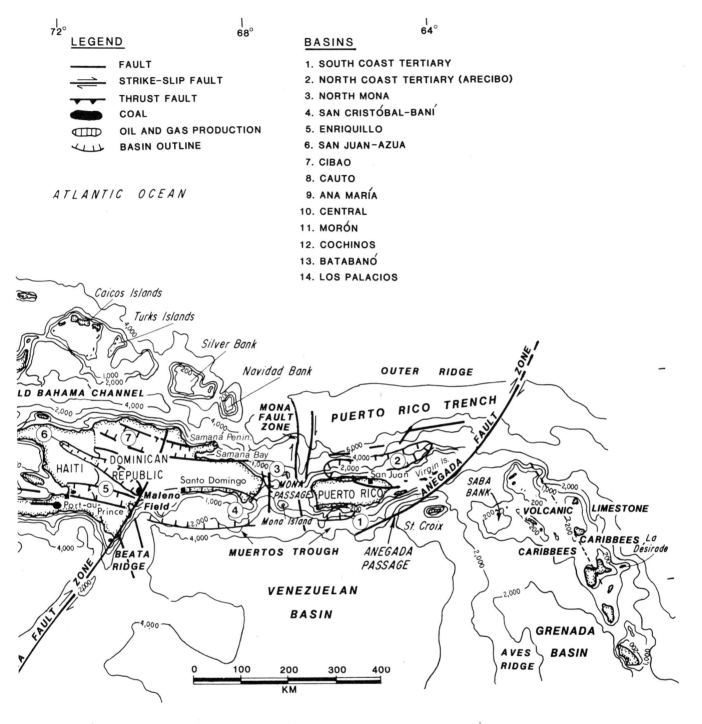

LEGEND

— FAULT
⇒ STRIKE-SLIP FAULT
▼▼ THRUST FAULT
◖◗ COAL
⊞⊞ OIL AND GAS PRODUCTION
⋀⋁ BASIN OUTLINE

ATLANTIC OCEAN

BASINS

1. SOUTH COAST TERTIARY
2. NORTH COAST TERTIARY (ARECIBO)
3. NORTH MONA
4. SAN CRISTÓBAL-BANÍ
5. ENRIQUILLO
6. SAN JUAN-AZUA
7. CIBAO
8. CAUTO
9. ANA MARÍA
10. CENTRAL
11. MORÓN
12. COCHINOS
13. BATABANÓ
14. LOS PALACIOS

ent in all the basins, as attested by numerous oil and gas seeps and asphaltic sandstones. The best oil indications have been from wells on and near the Maleno anticline, 90 km west of Santo Domingo. One well yielded 13,000 bbl from the interval 113 to 145 m (Ellis, 1982). A total of 45 wells has been drilled in the basins; 12 in the Enriquillo, 28 in the San Juan–Azua, and five in the Cibao.

Source rocks are established; adequate reservoirs are not, as Ellis (1982) found that many sandstones had porosities of 8 percent or less. Reef facies carbonates may have potential as reservoirs. The intensity of deformation precludes extensive reservoir continuity; there is poor potential for a few minor accumulations, none for major ones.

Successor basins of Cuba. Seven successor basins are perched on the Cuban nappes, but only four merit discussion: the Cauto, which contains only Tertiary rocks, and the Anna María, Central, and Los Palacios with Late Cretaceous and Tertiary sequences. All are associated with major faults. General references include Furrazola and others (1964), Iturralde-Vinent (1969, 1970, 1971, 1972), and Pardo (1975).

The Cauto basin of eastern Cuba straddles the Cauto fault. Approximately 3,000 m of marine to nonmarine, partly volcanogenic Paleocene and early Eocene beds are overlain by 1,000 m of marine middle Eocene to early Miocene and nonmarine middle Miocene to Pliocene strata; all are only mildly deformed. Source beds have not been identified, and the section is considered to be chemically immature. At least two dozen unsuccessful wells have been drilled.

The small, fault-bounded Central basin is underlain by up to 3,500 m of marine Campanian through Miocene terrigenous clastics, bank or reef limestone, and marl (Sánchez-Arango, 1977). Four small oil fields were found between 1954 and 1964. The reservoirs are fractured Lower Cretaceous tuffs, Campanian reefal limestone, and Maastrichtian reefs (Semenovich and Namestnikova, 1981). The established production confirms the presence of a petroleum environment, but the structural complexity and small size of the basin make it unlikely to contain any significant accumulations.

Little is known of the Anna María basin. The one well (2,957 m) found sediments ranging in age from Maastrichtian through Quaternary. The bottom 1,000 m (middle Eocene and older) consists of tuffaceous conglomerate, sandstone, siltstone, shale, and limestone. The overlying section, late Eocene and younger, is limestone with minor amounts of argillaceous limestone and dolomite (Furrazola-Bermúdez and others, 1964). The basin potential is probably poor to very poor.

The Los Palacios basin, which extends 100 km eastward from the Pinar fault, is up to 65 km wide and may be as deep as 3.5 km. Approximately 1,000 m of Late Cretaceous marine strata and 2,500 m of mixed terrigenous clastics and sandy limestones of Tertiary age are present. A petroleum environment has not been identified in this relatively unexplored basin (García-Sánchez, 1978).

Other successor basins of post–middle Eocene basins of little

or no petroleum potential include the Guantánamo, Morón, and Cochinos. Further information is available in Furrazola-Bermúdez and others (1964) and Meyerhoff and Hatten (1968).

South Florida–north Cuba basin. This vast area includes the Cuban overthrust belt (nappes) and the Bahamas platform from Navidad Bank to south Florida. The overthrust belt extends along the entire north coast of Cuba and continues into the Cordillera Septentrional of the northern Dominican Republic. The nappes, up to 6,000 m in thickness, override the depressed southern edge of the Bahamas platform.

Widespread manifestations of both solid and liquid petroleum have been known in Cuba since the sixteenth century. The surface occurrences of petroleum and most of the fields discovered to date are within the nappe belt. Since the first commercial discovery at Motembo, 90 km east of La Habana in 1881, 18 minor fields have been discovered. None are substantial as the extreme complexity of the overthrust sheets precludes reservoir continuity. Source rocks are deep-water limestones. Reservoirs, generally with fracture porosity, are serpentinites (shallowest fields), Campanian-Maastrichtian terrigenous-clastic synorogenic conglomerate and sandstone, and deep-water carbonates. The best production to date is derived from the deepest nappes with reservoirs of deep-water limestone. The complexity of the overthrust belt makes major oil fields unlikely; however, large deposits are possible in the autochthonous strata below the deepest nappe.

Beneath the overthrust belt and north of it is the vast carbonate-evaporite platform, which extends from Navidad Bank to south Florida and the west Florida shelf. Up to 11 km of sedimentary section is present, of which up to 7 km consists of Oxfordian through Miocene shallow-water bank limestones and dolomites with some salt and anhydrite beneath the Albian of the Bahamas and Aptian of Cuba (Meyerhoff and Hatten, 1974; Tator and Hatfield, 1975). This sequence is unconformable on red beds and volcanics of the Newark Group (Jacobs, 1977).

Despite the size and sedimentary volume of this region, many physical conditions severely limit its potential. Limited source rocks probably are deep-water limestones. The deep interbank channels and the eastern escarpment, which have existed since Early Cretaceous time (Schlager and others, 1984), have allowed sea-water invasion of most of the banks (Spencer, 1967). There may be some potential for small fields in the western Bahamas: the Great Isaac-1 had oil and gas shows in the Newark Group, and the Dubloon Saxon-1, abandoned in 1986 at 6,626 m, had an oil show in Lower Cretaceous strata (Wiman, 1987).

Oil production was established in south Florida in 1943. Through 1986 there were 14 small fields discovered along a northwest-southeast trend of the Sunniland Limestone. The potential of the shelf in general must be rated poor to possibly fair in the western part.

VERY HEAVY AND EXTRA-HEAVY CRUDE OILS

Until recently the terms "heavy oil" and "tar sand" were empirical definitions of high-density hydrocarbons. With the increasing awareness that the world's majority of reserves are in these categories, attempts have been made by Bestougeff and others (1984) and Khayan (1984) to develop more precise definitions. These classifications still are more empirical than precise owing to the immense compositional variety of crude oils. Three categories of heavy crude oil (HCO), based on density, viscosity, and composition, are identified as HCO-I, HCO-II (very heavy), and HCO-III (extra heavy; Table 4, Plate 14).

HCO-I and generally HCO-II oils are liquid at normal operating conditions. Many HCO-II and most HCO-III oils, including tar sands, require special extractive processes and unconventional storage and transportation. HCO-II and HCO-III are the principal focus of this section, as HCO-I oils are conventionally produced and account for 57 percent of Venezuela's cumulative production (Meyer and others, 1984).

Only Colombia, Venezuela, and Trinidad have appreciable volumes of heavy and extra-heavy oil. A deposit of 13.4° API oil at Xan, northern Guatemala, may become commercial in the future. Seeps of HCO-III oil and veins of solid bitumen abound in the nappes of Cuba and have been mined for many years for local use (Brodermann and others, 1945). Statistics concerning these and other minor occurrences are given in Table 5 (Plate 14).

Colombia

Two large deposits of heavy oil occur in the southern Middle Magdalena basin; Cocorna and Nare. The Cocorna oil occurs in shallow (700 m) Tertiary sandstone reservoirs on the west side of the basin. The field has produced 29 million bbl from its discovery in 1963 through 1986. Most of this production has been in the 1980s as a result of accelerated development drilling. Estimates of in-place oil range from 300 million to 4.0 billion bbl. Almost certainly the field will ultimately yield in excess of 100 million bbl, considering cumulative production and continuing development. The Nare deposit, much smaller, is in a pilot stage that commenced in 1981 and in 1986 was producing 250 to 350 bopd.

The Castilla field in the southern Llanos (14° API) is a possible indicator of a Colombian counterpart to the Orinoco Oil Belt.

Venezuela

The largest conterminous heavy-oil belt in the world is the Orinoco Oil Belt, which has been described by many, including Ayaleto-E. and Louder (1974), Young (1978), Fiorillo (1984a, 1984b), and Vega and de Rojas (1987). This belt, 90 km wide, parallels the Orinoco River on the north for 600 km. Approximately 1,200 billion bbl of oil in place underlies this 54,000 km^2 region, of which 267 billion bbl is considered recoverable with known technology at depths ranging from 300 to 1,000 m (Fiorillo, 1984b). The magnitude of 267 billion bbl can be grasped by the realization that it would take 411 years at Venezuela's 1986 production rate of 1.78 million bopd to deplete that volume.

The deposit is widely known as "tar sands" but, based on Table 4 (Plate 14), most of the oil is very heavy or extra heavy. Some true tar sands are found in the western end of the deposit. Oil gravities range from 4.7 to 17.4 degrees API and increase systematically from south to north. Remarkable reservoir characteristics account for part of the large volume: 27 to 34 percent porosity, 1 to 7 darcys permeability, and 65 to 90 percent oil saturation (de Rojas, 1987).

The reservoirs are principally stacked north-south–trending meander belts; point bars and channel fill account for 80 to 90 percent of reservoir volume. The reservoirs dip very gently northward; entrapment is accomplished by stratigraphic variations and an en echelon system of normal faults striking east-northeast.

Zamora and Zambrano (1984) estimate that an additional 134 billion bbl of 14° API oil or heavier is present in other basins: 80 billion bbl, associated with unconformities, in the Boscán, Urdaneta, and Bolívar Coastal fields of the Maracaibo basin, 10 billion bbl in middle Eocene sandstones in the Barinas basin, and 40 billion bbl in transgressive middle Miocene sandstones unconformable on Eocene beds in the Maturín basin. The reservoirs of these major accumulations all are found at shallow depths and have exceedingly high permeability (0.4–5.0 darcys) and porosity (18–32 percent).

Trinidad

The Great Pitch Lake in the southwest corner of the country is believed to have in-place reserves of 60 million bbl, of which nine is recoverable. Two nearby fields produce heavy and extra-heavy oils in the Point Fortin group of fields discovered in 1908 (Rambarran and Bertrand, 1984). Possibly 800 million bbl of HCO-II and HCO-III is recoverable from the Point Fortin area.

COAL, LIGNITE, AND PEAT

The only coal of any importance in Central America is in Costa Rica where three sizable deposits are known (Bohnenberger and Dengo, 1978). Development of the Talamanca field, near the Río Sixaola, began in 1984. A second, low-grade deposit is at San José, and the third is along the Río San Carlos.

Unevaluated thin coal seams are known in highly disturbed Jurassic beds in northern Honduras. Peat is mined in Jamaica (Robinson, 1976a, 1976b). Noncommercial lignite and peat deposits are reported from Trinidad, Barbados, Puerto Rico, Haiti, and Cuba.

Colombia

The largest coal reserves in the Caribbean region by far are in Colombia (Table 6, Plate 14). Proved and speculative reserves exceed 18,000 million mt. It is the only area with a mix of low-, medium-, and high-volatile coals suitable for large-scale export (UNIDO, 1979, p. 87). At least 33 percent of the reserve is anthracite and semianthracite; the balance is bituminous, 14 percent with medium and low volatiles and 53 percent with high volatiles (Suescún-Gómez, 1978; Table 7, Plate 14). Coal ages range from Maastriachtian to Miocene.

Despite a long history of coal development, it was only in 1984 that exports commenced with the start-up of the El Cerrejón field, northern César basin. The second year's production of four million mt more than doubled the country's annual production. Continued expansion is planned to reach a level of 15 milliom mt/yr from 1989 onward (Mellanby-Lee, 1986).

As many as 3,000 mines have been active, all relatively small producers. Coal is present around the margins of all the major ranges and in the Sabana de Bogotá (Fig. 3; Table 6, Plate 14). For additional details, see Durán and others (1978), Olive (1978), Suescún-Gómez (1978), and Carbocol (1983).

Venezuela

Coal has received relatively little attention, being overshadowed by the enormous oil reserves. Major deposits are found in the Sierra de Perijá, the Serranía del Interior, and the Orinoco Oil Belt (Fig. 3; Table 6, Plate 14).

Exploratory and development oil drilling near Ciudad Bolívar has delineated a 130-km east-west belt in which coal beds have an aggregate of 10 to 30 m thickness in a 200-m interval in Oligocene-Miocene sediments overlying the heavy oil reservoirs. This deposit has potential for the distant future.

Official reserves of 9,177 million mt of coal were released for the 27th World Geological Congress (1984), but this number is vague at best, as more than 97 percent of the figure is in the speculative category; hence, the imprecise statistics given in Table 6 (Plate 14).

OTHER ENERGY RESOURCES

Resources currently being exploited are hydropower, geothermal, biomass, wind, and solar. Potential resources include uranium-thorium, gas hydrates, and ocean thermal energy conversion (OTEC) systems.

Hydropower for electricity is widely used but, except for Costa Rica where it supplies 98 percent of electric power (Cunningham and others, 1984), is underdeveloped. Colombia, Venezuela, and northern Central America have the greatest potential. Colombia's potential is estimated at between 20,000 and 100,000 MW; utilization is 7,000 MW. Venezuela, very undeveloped, has a potential for 16,000 MW. Central America, mostly Guatemala and Costa Rica, has a potential for 27,000 MW (UNIDO, 1979).

Geothermal energy is utilized only in El Salvador where it provides 44 percent of electricity (Cunningham and others, 1984), and Colombia where a pilot plant near Nevado del Ruíz is operating. The volcanic areas of Central America and the eastern Caribbean have substantial potential.

Wind and solar power are employed sparingly. Solar opportunities are greatest on the south and west coasts of the Antillean islands as those areas are relatively cloud free. Opportunities for the use of wind lie in all the islands exposed to the trade winds, and currently this source is employed on the Guajira Peninsula where the trades are statistically the strongest and most persistent.

Biomass, especially firewood, is widely used, but not efficiently. Chinese-type biodigesters still are unknown in the Caribbean, and the expensive, Indian-designed ones are unaffordable. Commercial deposits of nuclear ores are unknown but are most likely in and near the Guayana Shield and in Nuclear Central America.

Ocean thermal energy conversion (OTEC) systems offer great promise for islands that have near-shore deep water. This system takes advantage of temperature differences between surface and deep water. A pilot system operating offshore Hawaii delivers both electricity and fresh water. OTEC systems are still experimental but offer great promise because of limitless resources.

Gas hydrates offer a distant future major supply of methane from the continental slopes of Guatemala, Panamá, Colombia, and Venezuela. The chemistry of hydrate formation provides for remarkable concentrations of methane within relatively small volumes of sediment. Krason and Ciesnik (1986) estimated that hydrate zones in the Panamá basin could contain 6,800 bcf per meter of saturated sediment with a possible maximum of 300 m. Finley and Krason (1986) projected a possible reserve of 12,000 to 5,800,000 bcf of methane in water between 900 and 4,000 m deep in the Colombian Basin. Evidence of gas hydrates has been found in the Barbados Ridge (Westbrook and Smith, 1983; Mauffret and others, 1984).

ACKNOWLEDGMENTS

We thank the following persons for supplying us with critical data, encouragement, and/or technical advice and "pep talks": Ramón Alonso-Harris, Chief Geologist, Commonwealth of Puerto Rico; Geologist Lolita Campos-Bejarano, RECOPE, San José, Costa Rica; Dr. James E. Case, U.S. Geological Survey, Menlo Park; Dr. Gabriel Dengo, consultant, Guatemala City; Hilda Díaz-Soltero, former Secretary of Natural Resources, San Juan, Puerto Rico; Dr. Herman Duque-Caro, Ingeominas, Bogotá, Colombia; Gregorio Escalante, consulting geologist, San José, Costa Rica; Giovanni J. Fiorillo, Petroven, Caracas, Venezuela; Larry Gordon, Pecten International Company, Houston; Dr. Manuel A. Iturralde-Vinent, Instituto de Geología y Paleontología, Academia de Ciencias, La Habana, Cuba; Dr. Rafael Picó, Banco Popular, San Juan, Puerto Rico; Dr. Peter Sprechmann, Universidad de Costa Rica, San José, Costa Rica; Ing. Leovigildo Vásquez, Corporacíon para el Desarrollo de Recursos Minerales (CODREMI), San Juan, Puerto Rico; and Henk Wories, Union Oil Company of California, Los Angeles. We also thank Mrs. Maria L. Morris, Miss Nancy Runge, and Miss Ernestine R. Voyles for typing, and Mrs. Kathryn L. Meyerhoff and Miss Zoe Rasmussen for drafting.

REFERENCES CITED

Alonso, R., Krieg, K. A., and Meyerhoff, A. A., 1983, Post-early Pliocene age of the Puerto Rico Trench [abs.], *in* Program and Abstracts of Papers, 10th Caribbean Geological Conference, Cartegena, 1983: Bogotá, Ingeominas, p. 17–18.

Alvarez, W., 1971, Fragmented Andean belt of northern Colombia, *in* Donnelly, T. W., ed., Caribbean geophysical, tectonic, and petrologic studies: Geological Society of America Memoir 130, p. 77–96.

Aubouin, J., Azéma, J., Carfantan, J.-Ch., Demant, A., Rangin, C., Tardy, M., and Tournon, J., 1982, The Middle America Trench in the geological framework of Central America, *in* Von Huene, R., Aubouin, J., and others, eds., Initial reports of the Deep Sea Drilling Project: Washington, D.C., U.S. Government Printing Office, v. 67, p. 747–755.

Ayaleto-E., M., and Louder, L. W., 1974, The geology and exploration potential of the heavy oil sands of Venezuela (the Orinoco Petroleum Belt): Canadian Society of Petroleum Geologists Memoir 3, p. 1–18.

Bane, S. C., and Chanpong, R. R., 1980, Geology and development of the Teak oil field, Trinidad, West Indies: American Association of Petroleum Geologists Memoir 30, p. 387–398.

Barr, K. W., Waite, S. T., and Wilson, C. C., 1958, The mode of oil occurrence in the Miocene of southern Trinidad, B. W. I., *in* Weeks, L. G., ed., Habitat of oil: American Association of Petroleum Geologists Symposium, p. 533–550.

Bestougeff, M., Burollet, P. F., and Byramjee, R. J., 1984, Heavy crude oils and their classification, *in* Meyer, R. F., Wynn, J. C., and Olson, J. C., eds., The Future of Heavy Crude and Tar Sands, 2nd International Conference, 7–17 February 1982, Caracas, Venezuela: New York, Coal Age Mining Information Services, McGraw-Hill, Incorporated, p. 12–16.

Biju-Duval, B., LeQuelle, P., Mascle, A., Renard, V., and Valery, P., 1982, Multibeam bathymetric survey and high resolution seismic investigations on the Barbados Ridge complex (eastern Caribbean); A key to the knowledge and interpretation of an accretionary wedge: Tectonophysics, v. 86, no. 1–3, p. 275–304.

Biju-Duval, B., Mascle, A., Rosales, H., and Young, G., 1983, Episutural Oligo-Miocene basins along the north Venezuelan margin: American Association of Petroleum Geologists Memoir 34, p. 347–358.

Bishop, W. F., 1980, Petroleum geology of northern Central America: Journal of Petroleum Geology, v. 3, no. 1, p. 3–59.

Bohnenberger, O. H., and Dengo, G., 1978, Coal resources in Central America: Geological Society of America Special Paper 179, p. 65–72.

Bolaños, K., 1983, Evaluación geológica de los depósitos carboníferos de Baja Talamanca para un estudio de prefactibilidad, Provincia de Limón, Costa Rica [Tesis]: San José, Universidad de Costa Rica, Escuela de Geología, 124 p.

Bonini, W. E., Hargraves, R. B., and Shagam, R., eds., 1984, The Caribbean–South American plate boundary and regional tectonics: Geological Society of America Memoir 162, 421 p.

Borger, H. D., 1952, Case history of Quiriquire field, Venezuela: American Association of Petroleum Geologists Bulletin, v. 36, p. 2291–2330.

Brodermann, J., Villoch, F., and Andreu, A., 1945, Yacimientos asfaltíferos de Cuba: La Habana, Dirección de Montes, Minas y Aguas, Boletín de Minas, núm. 19, 191 p.

Bueno S., R., 1970, The geology of Tubara region, Lower Magdalena basin, *in* Geological Field Trips Colombia 1959–1978: Bogotá, Colombia Society of Petroleum Geologists and Geophysicists, p. 299–324.

Bueno S., R., and Govea R., C., 1976, Potential for exploration and development of hydrocarbons in Atrato Valley and Pacific Coastal shelf basin of Colombia, *in* Halbouty, M. T., and others, eds., Circum–Pacific energy and mineral resources: American Association of Petroleum Geologists Memoir 25, p. 318–330.

Bürgl, H., 1967, The orogenesis of the Andean system of Colombia: Tectonophysics, v. 4, p. 429–443.

——, 1973, Precambrian to middle Cretaceous stratigraphy of Colombia: Bogotá, published privately by C. G. Allen and N. R. Rowlinson, 213 p.

Cáceres-Avila, F., Tappmeyer, D. M., Aves, H. S., Gillett, M., and Klenk, C. D., 1984, Recent studies of basins are encouraging for future exploration in Honduras: Oil and Gas Journal, v. 82, no. 38, p. 139–140, 143–144, 149.

Campbell, C. J., 1968, The Santa Marta wrench fault of Colombia and its regional setting, *in* Saunders, J. B., ed., Transactions, 4th Caribbean Geological Conference, Port-of-Spain, Trinidad, 1965: Arima, Caribbean Printers, p. 247–261.

Campbell, C. J., and Bürgl, H., 1965, Section through the eastern Cordillera of Colombia, South America: Geological Society of America Bulletin, v. 76, no. 5, p. 567–590.

Carbocol, 1983, Carbón en Colombia (unpublished report): Bogotá, Carbocol, 8 p.

Carmalt, S. W., and St. John, B., 1986, *in* Halbouty, M. T., ed., Future petroleum provinces of the world: American Association of Petroleum Geologists Memoir 40, p. 11–53.

Case, J. E., and Holcombe, T. L., 1980, Geologic-tectonic map of the Caribbean region: U.S. Geological Survey Miscellaneous Investigations Map I-1100, 3 sheets, scale 1:2,500,000.

Case, J. E., Holcombe, T. L., and Martin, R. G., 1984, Map of geologic provinces in the Caribbean region: Geological Society of America Memoir 162, p. 1–30.

Corrigan, H., 1967, The geology of the Upper Magdalena Valley (northern portion), *in* Geological Field Trips Colombia 1959–1978: Bogotá, Colombian Society of Petroleum Geologists and Geophysicists, p. 221–251.

Cunningham, C. G., Fary, R. W., Jr., Guffanti, D. L., Lee, M. P., Masters, C. D., Miller, R. L., Quiñones, F., Peebles, R. W., Reinemund, G. A., and Russ, D. P., 1984, Earth and water resources and hazards in Central America: U.S. Geological Survey Circular 925, 40 p.

Daviess, S. N., 1971, Barbados; A major submarine gravity slide: Geological Society of America Bulletin, v. 82, no. 9, p. 2593–2601.

Deal, C. S., 1983, Oil and gas developments in South America, Central America, Caribbean area, and Mexico in 1982: American Association of Petroleum Geologists Bulletin, v. 66, p. 1849–1883.

de Cizancourt, H., 1933, Tectonic structures of northern Andes in Colombia and Venezuela: American Association of Petroleum Geologists Bulletin, v. 17, no. 3, p. 211–228.

Dengo, G., 1962, Tectonic-igneous sequence in Costa Rica, *in* Engle, A.E.J., James, H. L., and Leonard, B. F., eds., Petrologic studies; A volume in honor of A. F. Buddington: Geological Society of America, p. 131–161.

——, 1969, Problems of tectonic relations between Central America and the Caribbean: Gulf Coast Association of Geological Societies Transactions, v. 19, p. 311–320.

de Rojas, I., 1987, Geological evaluation of San Diego Norte pilot project, Zuata area, Orinoco Oil Belt, Venezuela: American Association of Petroleum Geologists Bulletin, v. 71, no. 10, p. 1294–1303.

Dillon, W. P., and Vedder, J. C., 1973, Structure and development of the continental margin of British Honduras: Geological Society of America Bulletin, v. 84, no. 8, p. 2713–2732.

Duque-Caro, H., 1984, Structural style, diapirism, and accretionary episodes of the Sinú-San Jacinto terrane, southwestern Caribbean borderlands, *in* Bonini, W. E., Hargraves, R. B., and Shagam, R., eds., The Caribbean–South American plate boundary and regional tectonics: Geological Society of America Memoir 162, p. 303–316.

Durán, R., Mojica, P., Nigrinis, R., Granados, A., Mejía, L., and Gil, E., 1978, Carbón, *in* Recursos Minerales de Colombia, Publicación Geológica Especial: Bogotá, Ingeominas, p. 95–129.

Ellis, G. M., 1982, Aportes geológicos de la exploración petrolera en la República Dominicana, *in* Llinas, R., Gil-Gil, N., Seward, M., Travares, I., and Snow, W., eds., Transactions, 9th Caribbean Geological Conference, Santo Domingo, Dominican Republic, 1980: Santo Domingo, Amigo del Hogar, v. 1, p. 35–38.

Fahlquist, D. A., Antoine, J. W., Bryant, W. R., Bouma, A. H., and Pyle, P.,

1972, Seismic reflection profiles in the Yucatán Channel, *in* Petzall, C., ed., Transactions, 6th Caribbean Geological Conference, Isla de Margarita, Venezuela, 1971: Caracas, Cromotip, p. 367–371.

Feo-Codecido, G., Smith, F. D., Jr., Aboud, N., and Di Giacomo, E. de., 1984, Basement and Paleozoic rocks of the Venezuelan Llanos basins, *in* Bonini, W. E., Hargraves, R. B., and Shagam, R., eds., The Caribbean–South American plate boundary and regional tectonics: Geological Society of America Memoir 162, p. 175–187.

Finley, P., and Krazon, J., 1986, Geological evaluation and analysis of confirmed or suspected gas hydrate localities; v. 7, Basin analysis, formation, and stability of gas hydrates in Colombia basin: Morgantown, West Virginia, U.S. Department of Energy, Office of Fossil Energy, DOE/MC/21181–1950 (D 86006637), 134 p.

Fiorillo, G., 1984a, Exploration of the Orinoco Oil Belt; Review and general strategy, *in* Meyer, R. F., Wynn, J. C., and Olson, J. G., eds., The Future of Heavy Crude and Tar Sands, 2nd International Conference, 7–17 February 1982, Caracas, Venezuela: New York, Coal Age Mining Information Services, McGraw-Hill, Incorporated, p. 304–312.

——, 1984b, Exploration and evaluation of the Orinoco Oil Belt, *in* Meyer, R. F., Eardley, J. W., Barnea, J., and Johnson, R. L., convenors, Exploration for Heavy Crude Oil and Bitumen, AAPG Research Conference, October 28–November 2, 1984, Santa Maria, California: American Association of Petroleum Geologists, v. 1, 26 p.

Fox, P. J., and Heezen, B. C., 1975, Geology of the Caribbean crust, *in* Nairn, A.E.M., and Stehli, F. G., eds., The ocean basins and margins; v. 3, The Gulf of Mexico and the Caribbean: New York, Plenum Press, p. 421–466.

Frampton, J., and Birchwood, K. M., 1979, Historical and geological tour of Trinidad oil industry, *in* Carr-Brown, B., chairman, Field Guide, 4th Latin American Geological Congress, Port-of-Spain, Trinidad, 1979: Port-of-Spain, Key Caribbean Publications, p. 49–58.

Franco, A., 1975, Colombia's gas reserves climb: Oil and Gas Journal, v. 73, no. 45, p. 247.

Furrazola-Bermúdez, G., Judoley, C. M., Miljailóvskaya. M. S., Miroliúbov, Y. S., Novojatsky, I. P., Núñez-Jiménez, A., and Solsona, J. B., 1964, Geología de Cuba: La Habana, Instituto Cubano de Recursos Minerales, 239 p.

Gansser, A., 1973, Facts and theories on the Andes: Journal of the Geological Society of London, v. 129, pt. 2, p. 93–131.

García-Sánchez, R., 1978, Notas sobre la constitución geologo-estructural de la depressión Los Palacios: La Habana, La Minería en Cuba, v. 4, no. 3, p. 30–35.

González de Juana, C., Iturralde, J., and Picard, X., 1980, Geología de Venezuela y de sus cuencas petrolíferas: Caracas, Ediciones Fonives, 2 volumes, 1031 p.

Guariguata, P.R.C., and Richardson, J. A., 1960, Producción petrolífera del basamento en el oeste del Lago de Maracaibo, *in* Memoria, 3rd Congreso Geológico Venezolano: Venezuela Ministerio de Mines e Hidrocarburos, Boletin de Geología, Publicación Especial no. 3, v. 3, p. 985–1007.

Guerra-Peña, F., 1956, Las principales cuencas sedimentarias de la República Dominicana y sus posibilidades petrolíferas, *in* Symposium sobre yacimientos de petróleo y gas: Mexico D. F., 20th International Geological Congress Proceedings, v. 4, p. 141–159.

Hayes, J. A., Larue, D. K., Joyce, J., and Schellekens, J. H., 1986, Puerto Rico; Reconnaissance study of the maturation and source rock potential of an oceanic arc involved in a collision: Marine and Petroleum Geology, v. 3, no. 2, p. 126–138.

Hedberg, H. D., Sass, L. C., and Funkhouser, H. J., 1947, Oil fields of Greater Oficina area, central Anzoátegui, Venezuela: American Association of Petroleum Geologists Bulletin, v. 31, p. 2089–2169.

Hoylman, H. W., and Chilingar, G. V., 1965, Geología petrolera y exploración en Nicaragua: Asociación Mexicana de Geólogos Petroleros, Boletín, v. 17, p. 1–16.

Irving, E. M., 1975, Structural evolution of the northernmost Andes: U.S. Geological Survey Professional Paper 846, 47 p.

Iturralde-Vinent, M. A., 1969, Principal characteristics of Cuban Neogene stratigraphy: American Association of Petroleum Geologists Bulletin, v. 53, no. 9,

p. 1938–1955.

——, 1970, Neogene stratigraphy in western Cuba; New data: American Association of Petroleum Geologists Bulletin, v. 54, p. 658–661.

——, 1971, Correlación estratigrafica de los sedimentos del Neogeno de Cuba: La Habana, Revista Tecnológica, v. 9, p. 15–19.

——, 1972, Principal characteristics of Oligocene and lower Miocene stratigraphy of Cuba: American Association of Petroleum Geologists Bulletin, v. 56, p. 2369–2379.

Jacobs, C., 1977, Jurassic lithology in Great Isaac 1 well, Bahamas; Discussion: American Association of Petroleum Geologists Bulletin, v. 61, no. 3, p. 443.

Johnson, M. S., and Headington, E., 1971, Panama; Exploration history and petroleum potential: Oil and Gas Journal, v. 69, no. 15, p. 96–100.

Khayan, M., 1984, Proposed classification and definitions of heavy crude oils and tar sands, *in* Meyer, R. F., Wynn, J. C., and Olson, J. C., eds., The Future of Heavy Crude and Tar Sands, 2nd International Conference, 7–17 February 1982, Caracas, Venezuela: New York, Coal Age Mining Information Services, McGraw-Hill, Incorporated, p. 7–11.

Kellogg, J. N., 1984, Cenozoic tectonic history of the Sierra de Perijá, Venezuela–Colombia, and adjacent basins, *in* Bonini, W. E., Hargraves, R. B., and Shagam, R., eds., The Caribbean–South American plate boundary and regional tectonics: Geological Society of America Memoir 162, p. 239–261.

Knipper, A. L., and Cabrera, R., 1974, Tectónico y geología histórica de la zona de articulación entre el mio y eugeosinclinal y del cinturón hiperbásico de Cuba: La Habana, Academia de Ciencias de Cuba, Instituto de Geología y Paleontología, Publicación Especial no. 2, Contribución a la Geología de Cuba, p. 15–77.

Krason, J., and Ciesnik, M., 1986, Geological evaluation and analysis of confirmed or suspected gas hydrate localities; v. 6, Basin analysis, formation, and stability of gas hydrates in Panamá basin: Morgantown, West Virginia, U.S. Department of Energy, Office of Fossil Energy, DOE/MC/21181–1950 (DE 86006636), 85 p.

Krause, D. C., 1971, Bathymetry, geomagnetism, and tectonics, of the Caribbean Sea north of Colombia, *in* Donnelly, T. W., ed., Caribbean geophysical, tectonic, and petrologic studies: Geological Society of America Memoir 130, p. 35–54.

Kugler, H. G., 1956, Trinidad, *in* Jenks, W. F., ed., Handbook of South American geology: Geological Society of America Memoir 65, p. 355–365.

Ladd, J. W., Shih, Tai-Chang, and Tsai, C. J., 1981, Cenozoic tectonics of Central Hispaniola and adjacent Caribbean Sea: American Association of Petroleum Geologists Bulletin, v. 65, p. 466–489.

Larue, D. K., and Speed, R. C., 1984, Structure of the accretionary complex of Barbados; II, Bissex Hill: Geological Society of America Bulletin, v. 95, p. 1360–1372.

Leonard, R., 1983, Geology and hydrocarbon accumulations, Columbus basin, offshore Trinidad: American Association of Petroleum Geologists Bulletin, v. 67, no. 7, p. 1081–1093.

Liddle, R. A., 1946, The Geology of Venezuela and Trinidad (2nd edition): Ithaca, New York, Paleontological Research Institution, 890 p.

Lloyd, J. J., and Dengo, G., 1960, Continued drilling may uncover oil in Guatemala: Oil and Gas Journal, v. 58, no. 18, p. 208, 210, 212.

Lopez, V. M., Hedberg, H. D., and Kehrer, L., 1956, Venezuela, *in* Jenks, W. F., ed., Handbook of South American geology: Geological Society of America Memoir 65, p. 327–349.

Marrero, L., 1964, Venezuela y sus recursos: Caracas, Cultural Venezolana, S. A., 700 p.

Martinez, A. R., 1970, Giant fields of Venezuela, *in* Halbouty, M. T., ed., Geology of giant petroleum fields: American Association of Petroleum Geologists Memoir 14, p. 326–336.

Matveev, A. K., and 6 others, 1984, World resources of coals, *in* Energy Resources of the World: 27th International Geological Congress, Moscow, 1984, Reports, v. 2, Colloquium 02, p. 11–25.

Mauffret, A., Wesbrook, G. K., Truchan, M., and Ladd, J., 1984, The relief of oceanic basement and structure of the front of the accretionary complex in the region of Sites 541, 542, and 543, *in* Initial reports of the Deep Sea

Drilling Project: Washington, D.C., U.S. Government Printing Office, v. 78A, p. 49–62.

Maurrasse, F., Robert, J., Claude, J., and Loctamar, A., 1983, Geologic characteristics of the Massanga rock asphalt deposit, Southern Peninsula of Haiti [abs.], *in* Program and Abstracts of Papers, 10th Caribbean Geological Conference, Cartagena, 1983: Bogotá, Ingeominas, p. 52.

Mellanby-Lee, H., 1986, Coal, a mixed outlook for 1986: Engineering and Mining Journal, v. 187, no. 3, p. 28–29.

Mencher, E., Fichter, H. J., Wallis, W. E., Patterson, J. M., and Robie, R. H., 1953, Geology of Venezuela and its oil fields: American Association of Petroleum Geologists Bulletin, v. 37, no. 4, p. 690–777.

Meyer, R. F., Fulton, P. A., and Dietzman, W. D., 1984, A preliminary estimate of world heavy crude oil and bitumen resources, *in* Meyer, R. F., Wynn, J. C., and Olson, J. C., eds., The Future of Heavy Crude and Tar Sands, 2nd International Conference, 7–17 February 1982, Caracas, Venezuela: New York, Coal Age Mining Information Services, McGraw-Hill, Incorporated, p. 97–158.

Meyerhoff, A. A., 1967, Future hydrocarbon provinces of Gulf of Mexico–Caribbean regions: Gulf Coast Association of Geological Societies Transactions, v. 17, p. 217–260.

—— , 1973, Diapirlike features offshore Honduras; Implications regarding tectonic evolution of Cayman Trough in Central America; Discussion: Geological Society of America Bulletin, v. 84, p. 2147–2152.

Meyerhoff, A. A., and Hatten, C. W., 1968, Diapiric structures in central Cuba: American Association of Petroleum Geologists Memoir 8, p. 315–357.

—— , 1974, Bahamas salient of North America; Tectonic framework, stratigraphy, and petroleum potential: American Association of Petroleum Geologists Bulletin, v. 58, no. 6, pt. II, p. 1201–1239.

Meyerhoff, A. A., Krieg, E. A., Cloos, J. D., and Taner, I., 1983a, Petroleum potential of Puerto Rico: San Juan, CODREMI (Corporación para el Desarrollo de Recursos Minerales) and Departamento de Recursos Naturales, 174 p., 4 tables, 36 figures, and 39 plates.

—— , 1983b, Petroleum potential of Puerto Rico: Oil and Gas Journal, v. 81, no. 51, p. 113–120.

MIEM, 1982, Mapa de recursos minerales de Costa Rica: San José, Ministerio de Industria, Energía y Minas, Dirección de Geología y Minas, 1 sheet, scale 1:750,000.

Millán, G., and Somin, M. L., 1981, Litología, estratigrafía, tectónica, y metamorfismo del macizo de Escambray: La Habana, Editorial Academia, 104 p.

Miller, J. B., Edwards, K. L., Wolcott, P. P., Anisgard, H. W., Martin, R., and Anderegg, H., 1958, Habitat of oil in the Maracaibo basin, Venezuela, *in* Weeks, L. G., ed., Habitat of oil: American Association of Petroleum Geologists Symposium, p. 601–640.

Mills, R. A., and Hugh, K. E., 1974, Reconnaissance geologic map of Mosquitia region, Honduras and Nicaragua Caribbean coast: American Association of Petroleum Geologists Bulletin, v. 58, no. 2, p. 189–207.

Mills, R. A., Hugh, K. E., Feray, D. E., and Swolfs, H. S., 1967, Mesozoic stratigraphy of Honduras: American Association of Petroleum Geologists Bulletin, v. 51, no. 9, p. 1711–1786.

Morales, L. G., and Colombian Petroleum Industry, 1958, General geology and oil occurrences of Middle Magdalena Valley, Colombia, *in* Weeks, L. G., ed., Habitat of oil: American Association of Petroleum Geologists Symposium, p. 641–695.

Muessig, K. W., 1984, Structural and Cenozoic tectonics of the Falcón basin, Venezuela, and adjacent areas, *in* Bonini, W. E., Hargraves, R. B., and Shagam, R., eds., The Caribbean–South American plate boundary and regional tectonics: Geological Society of America Memoir 162, p. 217–230.

Nemec, M. C., 1982, A two phase model for the tectonic evolution of the Caribbean, *in* Llinas, R., Gil-Gil, N., Seward, M., Travares, I., and Snow, W., eds., Transactions, 9th Caribbean Geological Conference, Santo Domingo, Dominican Republic, 1980: Santo Domingo, Amigo del Hogar, p. 23–24.

Notestein, F. B., Hubman, C. W., and Bowler, J., 1944, Geology of the Barco Concession, Republic of Colombia, South America: Geological Society of

America Bulletin, v. 55, no. 10, p. 1165–1216.

Oil & Gas Journal, 1986, International briefs: v. 84, no. 49, p. 35.

—— , 1987, Big oil find fuels Lake Maracaibo exploration: v. 85, no. 34, p. 74.

Olive, W. W., 1978, Coal deposits of Latin America: Geological Society of America Special Paper 179, p. 57–64.

Olsson, A. A., 1956, Colombia, *in* Jenks, W. F., ed., Handbook of South American geology: Geological Society of America Memoir 65, p. 293–326.

Pardo, G., 1966, Stratigraphy and structure of central Cuba [abs.]: New Orleans Geological Society Log, v. 6, no. 12, p. 1, 3.

—— , 1975, Geology of Cuba, *in* Nairn, P.E.M. and Stehli, F. G., eds., The ocean basins and maragins; v. 3, The Gulf of Mexico and the Caribbean: New York, Plenum Press, p. 553–616.

Pedrazzini, C., Holguín, N., and Moreno, R., 1982, Evaluación geológico-geoquímica de la parte noroccidental del Golfo de Tehuantepec: Instituto Mexicano del Petróleo Revista, v. 14, no. 4, p. 6–26.

Pinet, B., Lajat, D., Le Quellec, P., and Bouysse, P., 1985, Strucure of Aves Ridge and Grenada Basin from multichannel seismic data, *in* Symposium sur la Géodynamique des Caraïbes, Paris, 5–8 Février 1985: Paris, Institut Française du Pétrole, 12 p. (preprint).

Pinet, P. R., 1972, Diapirlike features offshore Honduras; Implications regarding tectonic evolution of Cayman Trough and Central America: Geological Society of America Bulletin, v. 83, no. 7, p. 1911–1921.

Poole, E. G., and Barker, L. H., 1982, The geology of the Scotland District of Barbados, *in* Llinas, R., Gil-Gil, N., Seward, M., Travares, I., and Snow, W., eds., Transactions, 9th Caribbean Geological Conference, Santo Domingo, Dominican Republic, 1980: Santo Domingo, Amigo del Hogar, p. 641–656.

Preston, C. L., 1975, The geology of the Cúcuta area, Norte de Santander, *in* Geological Field Trips, Colombia 1959–1978; Bogotá, Colombian Society of Petroleum Geologists and Geophysicists, p. 433–451.

Pudsey, C. J., and Reading, H. G., 1982, Sedimentology and structure of the Scotland Group, Barbados, *in* Leggett, J. K., ed., Trench-forearc geology; Sedimentation and tectonics on modern and ancient active plate margins: The Geological Society of London Special Publication 10, p. 291–308.

Rambarran, H., and Bertrand, W. G., 1984, Significance of gravity segregation in heavy oil distribution, Forest A reservoir, Parrylands, Trinidad, West Indies, *in* Meyer, R. F., Eardley, J. W., Barnea, J., and Johnson, R. L., convenors, Exploration for Heavy Crude Oil and Bitumen, AAPG Research Conference, October 28–November 2, 1984, Santa Maria, California: American Association of Petroleum Geologists, v. 2, 12 p.

Renz, H. H., Alberding, H., Dallmus, K. F., Patterson, J. M., Robie, R. H., Weisbord, N. E., and Mas Vall, J., 1958, The eastern Venezuelan basin, *in* Weeks, L. G., ed., Habitat of oil: American Association of Petroleum Geologists Symposium, p. 551–600.

Roberts, J., Conley, D., and Millspaugh, K., 1959, The Barco concession, Santander del Norte, *in* Geological Field Trips, Colombia 1959–1978: Bogotá, Colombian Society of Petroleum Geologists and Geophysicists, p. 1–32.

Robinson, E., 1976a, Lignite in Jamaica with additional remarks on peat: Kingston, Ministry of Mines and Natural Resources, Mines and Geology Division, 63 p. and appendices.

—— , 1976b, Report on peat in Jamaica: Kingston, Ministry of Mines and Natural Resources, Mines and Geology Division, 30 p. and appendices.

Rod, E., 1956, Strike-slip faults of northern Venezuela: American Association of Petroleum Geologists Bulletin, v. 40, p. 457–476.

Rubio, F. E., 1961, Condiciones de las acumulaciones de petróleo en los campos costaneros del distrito Bolívar, Lago de Maracaibo, *in* Memoria, 3rd Congreso Geológico Venezolano: Caracas, Venezuela Ministerio de Minas e Hidrocarburos, Boletín de Geología, Publicación Especial no. 3, p. 1009–1023.

Sánchez-Arango, J. R., 1977, Estudio biostratigráfico del pozo Catalina no. 5 (cuenca Central): La Habana, La Minería en Cuba, v. 3, no. 4, p. 15–26.

Sawyer, J. H., 1975, Latin America after 1920, *in* Owen, E. W., Trek of the oil finders; A history of exploration for petroleum: American Association of Petroleum Geologists Memoir 6, p. 960–1251.

Schlager, W., Austin, J. A., Jr., Corso, W., McNulty, C. L., Fluegel, E., Renz, O., and Steinmetz, J. C., 1984, Early Cretaceous platform re-entrant and escarpment erosion in the Bahamas: Geology, v. 12, no. 3, p. 147–150.

Schuchert, C., 1935, Historical geology of the Antillean–Caribbean region *or* The lands bordering the Gulf of Mexico and the Caribbean Sea: New York, John Wiley and Sons, 811 p.

Seely, D. R., 1979, The evolution of structural highs bordering major forearc basins, *in* Watkins, J. S., Montadert, L., and Dickerson, P. W., eds., Geological and geophysical investigations of continental margins: American Association of Petroleum Geologists Memoir 29, p. 245–260.

Semenovich, V. V., and Namestnikova, Yu. G., eds., 1981, Oil and gas basins of the socialistic countries of Europe (NRB, VNR, GDR, PNR, SSR, SSSR, ChSSR, i SFRYu) i Republiki Kuba (and the Republic of Cuba): Moscow, Izdaterst'vo Otdel Upravelenniya Delami Sekretariata SEV, 400 p. (in Russian).

Senn, A., 1940, Paleocene of Barbados and its bearing on history and structure of Antillean–Caribbean region: American Association of Petroleum Geologists Bulletin, v. 24, p. 1548–1610.

Shagam, R., 1975, The northern termination of the Andes, *in* Nairn, A.E.M., and Stehli, F. G., eds., The ocean basins and margins; v. 3, The Gulf of Mexico and the Caribbean: New York, Plenum Press, p. 325–420.

Speed, R. C., 1983, Structure of the accretionary complex of Barbados; I, Chalky Mount: Geological Society of America Bulletin, v. 94, no. 1, p. 92–116.

Speed, R. C., and Larue, D. K., 1982, Barbados; Architecture and implications for accretion: Journal of Geophysical Research, v. 87, no. B5, p. 3633–3643.

Spencer, M., 1967, Bahamas deep test: American Association of Petroleum Geologists Bulletin, v. 51, no. 2, p. 263–268.

Staff of Caribbean Petroleum Company, 1948, Oil fields of Royal Dutch–Shell group in western Venezuela: American Association of Petroleum Geologists Bulletin, v. 32, no. 4, p. 517–628.

Stephan, J.-F., Beck, C., Bellizzia, A., and Blanchet, R., 1980, La chaîne caraïbe du Pacifique a l'Atlantique: Bureau de Recherches Géologiques et Minières Memoire 115, p. 38–59.

Stephan, J. F., Blanchet, R., and Mercier de Lepinay, B., 1986, Northern and southern Caribbean festoons (Panamá-Columbia-Venezuela and Hispaniola–Puerto Rico), interpreted as puesdosubduction induced by the east-west shortening of periCaribbean continental frame, *in* Wezel, F. C., ed., The origin of arcs: New York, Elsevier Publishing Company, Developments in geotectonics v. 21, p. 401–422.

Suescún-Gómez, D., 1978, Coal deposits in Colombia, *in* Kottlowski, F. E., Cross, A. T., and Meyerhoff, A. A., eds., Coal resources of the Americas; Selected papers: Geological Society of America Special Paper 179, p. 49–55.

Sutherland, J.A.F., 1972, Boscán field, western Venezuela, *in* King, R. E., ed., Stratigraphic oil and gas fields; Classification, exploration methods, and case histories: American Association of Petroleum Geologists Memoir 16, p. 559–567.

Sutton, F. A., 1946, Geology of Maracaibo basin, Venezuela: American Association of Petroleum Geologists Bulletin, v. 30, no. 10, p. 1621–1741.

Taborda, B., 1965, Guidebook to the geology of the De Mares Concession, *in* Geological Field Trips, Colombia 1959–1978: Bogotá, Colombian Society of Petroleum Geologists and Geophysicists, p. 119–159.

Tator, B. A., and Hatfield, L. E., 1975, Bahamas present complex geology: Oil and Gas Journal, v. 73, no. 43, p. 172–176; no. 44, p. 120–122.

UNIDO, 1979, Overview on energy and development in the Caribbean area (prepared for the UNEP/ECLA Caribbean Environment Project), English version: New York, United Nations Industrial Development Organization, id. 79–6307, 228 p.

Van Houten, F. B., and Travis, R. B., 1968, Cenozoic deposits, Upper Magdalena Valley, Colombia: American Association of Petroleum Geologists Bulletin, v. 52, p. 675–702.

Vásquez, E. E., 1975, Results of exploration in La Vela Bay, *in* Proceedings, 9th World Petroleum Congress, Tokyo, v. 3, p. 195–197.

Vega, A., and de Rojas, I., 1987, Exploration and evaluation of the Zuata area,

Orinoco Oil Belt, Venezuela: Journal of Petroleum Geology, v. 10, no. 2, p. 163–176.

Vierbuchen, R. C., 1984, The geology of the El Pilar fault zone and adjacent areas in northeastern Venezuela, *in* Bonini, W. E., Hargraves, R. B., and Shagam, R., eds., The Caribbean–South American plate boundary and regional tectonics: Geological Society of America Memoir 162, p. 189–212.

Viniegra-O., F., 1981, Great carbonate bank of Yucatán, southern Mexico: Journal of Petroleum Geology, v. 3, no. 3, p. 247–278.

Vinson, G. L., 1962, Upper Cretaceous and Tertiary stratigraphy of Guatemala: American Association of Petroleum Geologists Bulletin, v. 46, no. 4, p. 425–456.

Vinson, G. L., and Brineman, J. H., 1963, Nuclear Central America; Hub of Antillean transverse belt, *in* King, R. E., ed., Backbone of the Americas: American Association of Petroleum Geologists Memoir 2, p. 101–112.

Von Huene, R., Aubouin, J., Azéma, J., and others, 1980, Leg 67: The Deep Sea Drilling project Mid-America Trench transect off Guatemala: Geological Society of America Bulletin, v. 91, p. 421–432.

Von Huene, R., Miller, J., Taylor, D., and Blackman, D., 1985, A study of geophysical data along the Deep Sea Drilling Project active margin transect off Guatemala, *in* Initial reports of Deep Sea Drilling Project: Washington, D.C., U.S. Government Printing Office, v. 84, p. 895–909.

Weeks, L. G., 1947, Paleogeography of South America: American Association of Petroleum Geologists Bulletin, v. 31, no. 7, p. 1194–1241.

Westbrook, G. K., and Smith, M. J., 1983, Long décollements and mud volcanoes; Evidence from the Barbados Ridge complex for the role of high pore-fluid pressure in the development of an accretionary complex: Geology, v. 11, no. 5, p. 279–283.

Westbrook, G. K., Mascle, A., and Biju-Duval, B., 1984, Geophysics and the structure of the Lesser Antilles forearc, *in* Initial reports of the Deep Sea Drilling Project: Washington, D.C., U.S. Government Printing Office, v. 78, p. 23–38.

Westercamp, D., Andrieff, P., Bouysse, Ph., Mascle, A., and Baubron, J. C., 1985, The Grenadines, southern Lesser Antilles; Part 1, Stratigraphy and volcanostructural evolution, *in* Mascle, A., ed., Geodynamique de Caribes, Symposium, Paris, 5–8 Fevrier 1985: Paris, Editions Technip, p. 109–118.

Wilson, H. H., 1974, Cretaceous sedimentation and orogeny in Nuclear Central America: American Association of Petroleum Geologists Bulletin, v. 58, no. 7, p. 1348–1396.

Wiman, W. D., 1987, Oil and gas developments in South America, Central America, Caribbean area, and Mexico in 1986: American Association of Petroleum Geologists Bulletin, v. 71, no. 10B, p. 337–363.

Woodring, W. P., Brown, J. S., and Burbank, J. S., 1924, Geology of the Republic of Haiti: Port-au-Prince, Haiti, Department of Public Works, 631 p.

Young, G. A., 1978, Potential resources in the Eastern Venezuelan basin: Boletín Informativo, Asociación Venezolana de Geología, Minería y Petróleo, v. 20, nos. 1–3, p. 1–38.

Young, G. A., Bellizia, A., Renz, H. H., Johnson, F. W., Robie, R. H., and Mas Vall, J., 1956, Geología de las cuencas sedimentarias de Venezuela y de sus campos petrolíferos, *in* Symposium sobre Yacimientos de Petróleo y Gas, Tomo IV, América del Sur y Antillas: Mexico, 20th International Geological Congress, Mexico 1956, p. 161–322.

Zamora, L., and Zambrano, G., 1984, Occurrences of heavy and extra-heavy crude oil deposits in Venezuela, other than the Orinoco Oil Belt, *in* Meyer, R. F., Wynn, J. C., and Olson, J. C., eds., The Future of Heavy Crude and Tar Sands, 2nd International Conference, 7–17 February, 1982, Caracas, Venezuela: New York, Coal Age Mining Information Services, McGraw-Hill, Incorporated, p. 159–168.

Zenkovich, V. P., 1969, V dal'nem sinem more: Moscow, Izdatest'vo, Mysl', 264 p. (principally, p. 210–223) (in Russian).

MANUSCRIPT ACCEPTED BY THE SOCIETY JULY 12, 1988

Index

[Italic page numbers indicate major references]

Azuero Peninsula, 30, 204, *208*, 209, 210, *218*, 227, 323, 350, 415, 465
 anomalies, 26

Bagaces tuffs, 224
Bahama Bank, 94, 293, 295, 298, 299, 416
Bahama block, 444
Bahama Channel, 82, 421
Bahama-Florida Platform, 82
Bahama Platform, 31, 78, *82*, *92*, 112, 130, 348, *416*, 440, 441, *501*, 504
Bahamas, 1, 32, 233, 270, 426, 438, 481
Bahamas-Cuba intersection, 94
Bahía de Chiriqui, 214
Bahía Honda unit, Cuba, *79*, 464, 465
Bahoruco Mountains, *107*
Baie de Henne, 104
Baja Guajira Basin, *196*
Baja Verapaz, 45
Bálsamo Formation, 69, 383
Bananeras depression, *39*, 53
Banano Formation, 217
Banco Nuevo, 234
Baradel islet, 153
Baraderes, 110
Baraderes Formation, 107
Barahona Peninsula, 471
Barbados, 4, 5, *276*, *279*, 321, 329, *331*, 414, 433, 483, 499, 505
Barbados accretionary prism, *23*, 143, 162
Barbados Island, 23, 143
Barbados Ridge, *23*, 25, 276, *331*, 435, 444, *499*
Barbados Ridge Complex, *276*, *279*, 282
Barbados Ridge extension, 454
Barbados Ridge uplift, *277*, 285
Barbados Trough, 277
Barbecue River prospect, 471
Barbuda, 141, 144, *150*, 330
Barbudal Conglomerate Formation, *209*
Barbuito, 466
Barcelona area, 498
Barco Formation, 495
Barillas quadrangle, 45
Barinas-Apure basin, 196, 490
Barinas-Apure petroleum province, *497*
Barinas Basin, 324, 503
barite, 467, 469, 470
Barquisimeto area, 467
Barquisimeto depression, 170
Barquisimeto transverse zone, 446
Barquisimeto trough, 173
Barra Honda Formation, 212
Barracuda fracture zone, 377, 423
Barracuda Ridge, *146*, 276, 279, 283, 294, 296, *329*
Barranquitas quadrangle, 114
Barrial Group, 223
Bartlett Deep, 262

Barú Volcano, 224, 375, 377
Baruta area, 467
basal unit, 221
basalt, 26, 49, 52, 64, 68, 85, 88, 91, 102, 106, 110, 125, *127*, 148, *151*, *153*, 158, *160*, 168, 174, 192, 202, 207, 212, 214, 217, 235, 238, 244, 266, 269, 319, 328, *340*, 346, 348, *350*, 355, 363, *365*, 375, 380, 414, 466
 alkaline, 424
 flood, 441
 intrusion, 15
 mid-ocean ridge, 339
 ocean-island, 339
 oceanic, 50, 339
 olivine, 223, 224
 pillow, 49, 50, 61, 171, 208, 239, 266, 346, 347, 350, 354, 438
 tholeiitic, 381
basalt province, 351
basalt-rhyolite suite, 383
basanite, 106
basanitoid, 151
base-metal vein deposit, *469*
basement
 crystalline, 24
 magnetic, 82
 metamorphic, *42*
Basic Igneous Complex, 207
Basil Jones 1 well, 42
basins, *21*, *28*, *213*, *231*, *495*, *501*
 arc, *331*
 back-arc, 27, 440
 cratonic, 489
 fault-wedge, 315, 321
 fore-arc, 261, 277, 489
 intra-arc, 419
 molasse, 86
 oceanic, *397*, *402*
 pull-apart, 97, 102, *110*, 181, 197, 239, 294, 310, 311, 315, 319, 322, 333, 424
 ramp, 315
 rift, 242
 salt, 47, 438
 sedimentary, 210, *215*, 218, 221, 227, *277*, 315, 324, 385, 421, 440, 466, *484*
 strike-slip, 315
 successor, *504*
 See also specific basins
Basse-Terre de Guadeloupe, 141, 150, *158*
Bath-Dunrobin Formation, 127, 348
batholiths. *See specific batholiths*
bathymetry, 262
bauxite, *120*, 457, *472*
 mines, 470
Bay Islands, 30, 58, *59*, *236*, 318
Bayano Basin, 210, *219*
bayate, 466
Beata fault, 449
Beata fracture zone, 439, 444
Beata Ridge, 89, 22, 94, 105, 231, *241*, *244*, 270, 325, *332*, 351, 444, *445*, 448

Belen area, 470
Belize, 3, 30, 37, *39*, 43, *45*, *55*, 348, 476
Belize borderland, *484*
Belize Fan, 232, 234
Belmont Formation, 153
Beloc Formation, *108*
belts
 active volcanic, *375*
 deformed, 445
 magmatic, *414*
 metamorphic, 420
 mobile, *436*, 450
 See also specific belts
Benbow inlier, *123*
Benbow zone, 125
Benioff zone, 161, *301*, 302, 328, 330, 445
Bequia, 153
Bergje, 159
Bermeja Complex, *114*, *119*, *347*, 414, 423, 439, 465
Berriasin, *439*
bioherms, 65
biomass energy, 483, *506*
biomicrite, 65, 107, 215
biotite, 42, 44, 54, 89, 115, 468
bipartite, 42
Bisé area, rhyolite, 154
Bissex Hill, 281
Bissex Hill Formation, 281
bitumen, 505
bivalves, 64
Bladen Formation, 46
Bladen volcanics, 46
Blobotruncana contusa zone, 109
Blue Mountain belt, 120
Blue Mountain block, *122*
Blue Mountain inlier, 12, 359
Blue Mountains, 25, *120*, *125*, *348*
 southwestern, 269
blueschist, 78, 87, 91, 94, 98, 100, 122, 128, 192, 419
Bocas del Toro Basin, 210, *215*, 226, 227
Boconó fault zone, 179, 181, 272, 302, 303, 319, 322, *323*, *324*, 418, 424, 449, 490
Bogotá leg, 187
Bohío Formation, 218, *219*
Boiling Lake volcano, 156
Bolívar Coastal field, *495*, 505
Bolívar geosyncline, 490
Bonacca Ridge, 58
Bonaire, 448
Bonaire Basin, *273*, 424
Bonaire Island, 321, 351, 353, *354*, 414
Bonanza district, *470*
Booby Hill, 159
Boqueron volcano, 381, 384
Border Formation, 438
bornite, 471
Boscán field, 505
bottom currents, 242
Bouillante chain, *158*
brachiopods, 46
Bragman's Bluff Formation, *68*
Brasilito subunit, 349

Typeset by WESType Publishing Services, Inc., Boulder, Colorado
Printed in U.S.A. by Malloy Lithographing, Inc., Ann Arbor, Michigan